P9-CQC-669

# Customized Version of
# Human Anatomy

## Second Edition

Kenneth S. Saladin
*Georgia College and State University*

*with special contributor*
Robin K. McFarland
*Cabrillo College*

 **Learning Solutions**

Boston   Burr Ridge, IL   Dubuque, IA   New York   San Francisco   St. Louis
Bangkok   Bogotá   Caracas   Lisbon   London   Madrid
Mexico City   Milan   New Delhi   Seoul   Singapore   Sydney   Taipei   Toronto

The **McGraw-Hill** Companies

Customized Version of Human Anatomy
Second Edition

Copyright © 2008 by The McGraw-Hill Companies, Inc. All rights reserved. Printed in the United States of America. Except as permitted under the United States Copyright Act of 1976, no part of this publication may be reproduced or distributed in any form or by any means, or stored in a data base retrieval system, without prior written permission of the publisher.

This book is a McGraw-Hill Learning Solutions textbook and contains select material from *Human Anatomy*, Second Edition by Kenneth Saladin. Copyright © 2008 by The McGraw-Hill Companies, Inc. Reprinted with permission of the publisher. Many custom published texts are modified versions or adaptations of our best-selling textbooks. Some adaptations are printed in black and white to keep prices at a minimum, while others are in color.

2 3 4 5 6 7 8 9 0 DIG DIG 0 9

ISBN-13: 978-0-07-734129-9
ISBN-10: 0-07-734129-5

*Learning Solutions Specialist: James Doepke*
*Production Editor: Sue Culbertson*
*Printer/Binder: Digital Impressions*

**KEN SALADIN** is Distinguished Professor of Biology at Georgia College & State University, a public liberal arts university in Milledgeville, Georgia. He earned his B.S. in zoology at Michigan State University and his Ph.D. in parasitology at Florida State University. On the GCSU faculty since 1977, Ken has taught not only human anatomy and physiology, but also histology, parasitology, animal behavior, sociobiology, introductory biology at the majors and nonmajors levels, general zoology, biological etymology, and a study abroad course in the Galápagos Islands. He is a nine-time recipient of the Phi Kappa Phi Honor Professor Award, nominated by PKP student inductees who identified him as their most significant mentor. He was named Distinguished Professor in 2001.

Ken is a member of the Human Anatomy and Physiology Society, the Society for Integrative and Comparative Biology, the American Association of Anatomists, and the American Association for the Advancement of Science. He served for several years in the 1980s and '90s as a developmental reviewer and a supplement author for several other anatomy and physiology textbooks by the William C. Brown Co. before its acquisition by McGraw-Hill. In 1993, he began the first textbook of his own—*Anatomy and Physiology: The Unity of Form and Function,* now in its fourth edition and recipient of an Excellence in Research and Publication Award from his university. *Human Anatomy* is his second book.

Ken's avocational and philanthropic interests include the Charles Darwin Research Station in the Galápagos Islands and his local chapter of the Big Brothers/Big Sisters program for single-parent children, of which he was a founding board member and past president. He was also a founding board member and first treasurer of the National Center for Science Education, created for the defense of education in evolutionary biology.

Ken has been married for 27 years to Diane Saladin, a registered nurse. Their son, Emory, is a student in architectural design, and their daughter, Nicole, is a graduate student in marine environmental management.

· · · · ·

*This book is dedicated to my best friend, my life partner, she who sustains me and makes everything else worthwhile.*

DIANE

· · · · ·

**ROBIN MCFARLAND,** special contributor for this edition, teaches anatomy and physiology at Cabrillo College in Aptos, California. She earned her doctoral degree in physical anthropology from the University of Washington. She is a research associate at University of California, Santa Cruz, where she participates in studies of ape anatomy with Adrienne Zihlman. The research emphasizes comparison of apes and humans to better understand our adaptation and evolution. She and her husband, Jeff, have two children, Reid and Madeleine. In addition to spending time with her family, Robin also enjoys running, hiking, reading, and thinking about human biology.

# BRIEF CONTENTS

# TABLE OF CONTENTS

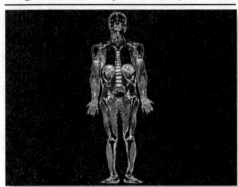
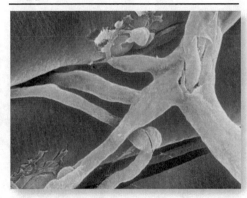

# PART FIVE

*Reproduction*

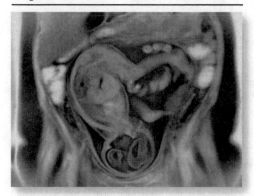

## • CHAPTER 26

My students come to human anatomy full of idealism, hoping to work in one of the health professions, from nursing or therapy to fitness training and health education. They quickly discover that it's a tremendous task just to master the prerequisites for the clinical phase of their training. One of the greatest challenges they face is to understand the structural complexity of the human body and its functional correlations.

My profession is to help them along the way by making this overwhelming amount of information manageable and stimulating. My students have always inspired me to spare no effort to present human form and function in a lucid, well organized, and interesting way in my classes. It has been a gratifying experience to bring that approach to the published page and reach students worldwide.

As enjoyable as this has been, I'm never fully satisfied with the book. Yet, dissatisfaction is better than complacency, because I'm always striving for a still more effective presentation. Perfection is an asymptote, a standard to be approached more and more closely but perhaps never quite attained. The ink never dries on a new edition before I'm already compiling a list of how the next one could be better. This is my latest attempt to reach that asymptote.

## Audience

*Human Anatomy* is intended primarily for a one-semester college course, usually taken in a student's first or second year in preparation for admission to programs in nursing, therapy, health education, or preprofessional health programs. The book has a minimal amount of physiology and pathology—only enough to lend sense to the anatomy and add a spark of interest to what would otherwise be a relatively dry discussion of structure only. An anatomy textbook should not be merely a recitation of structural appearances and names—form without function—yet neither is this meant as a physiology book that should explain such concepts as blood pressure regulation, immunology, and others suggested by occasional reviewers. Reviewers also differ in the overall level of detail desired, some wanting less than I present and some wanting more detail than given in anatomy books for postbaccalaureate readers. I seldom feel that such detail is warranted for readers in their first two years of college.

I realize that many anatomy students have taken no prior college biology or chemistry, since many institutions have no prerequisites for the course. Other students return to college to train for a health career after extended absences to raise families or try other careers, so even if a student has had biology or chemistry, I don't assume that he or she remembers it. Some chemistry is needed even for the study of human anatomy, but I introduce it infrequently, keep the chemical terminology as simple as I can, and define advanced chemical

terms (such as *glycoprotein*) where they are first introduced. Cell biology is another indispensable foundation for all anatomy. Chapter 2 provides all the basic concepts of cellular structure and function that a student needs in order to understand the subsequent chapters on the human organ systems.

*Human Anatomy* does much more than present the facts of human structure. I infuse the narrative with review activities such as a variety of self-testing questions at different cognitive levels; self-teaching prompts such as palpations and simple observations the reader can do at a desk; and learning aids such as pronunciation guides and insights into the roots and origins of medical terms. I try to conceive of enlightening ways to illustrate each major idea, often in ways that no other textbook has illustrated them before. To enliven the facts of science, I offer analogies, clinical insights, historical notes, biographical vignettes, and other seasoning that will make the book not only enjoyable to students, but rewarding even to experienced instructors who may have "heard it all before," yet may still get something new and interesting from these pages.

## What Sets This Book Apart?

When I was invited to write my first textbook in anatomy and physiology, I deliberated for several months before accepting. There were many good books already available, and I didn't want to simply write a "me too" book. I wanted to write only if I could offer something new to anatomy and physiology instructors—new perspectives or approaches not available in other books. These have been very well received in my other textbook, *Anatomy and Physiology*, and therefore used in *Human Anatomy* as well.

### Writing Style

Next to scientific accuracy, the most important quality of an effective textbook is writing style. Over my years of teaching from other college textbooks in various disciplines, I've seen styles to admire and emulate and others to avoid. Some are very correct and formal, but students find them aloof; such books do not "speak" to them, they say. Beginning college students get a stronger sense of engagement in the discipline from a more personal approach on the part of the author. Other college textbooks have such a chatty condescending tone that they appear a bit too cute and leave a student feeling patronized. I tend to emulate writers who take the middle course: a tone that is neither stuffy nor condescending; one that uses an occasional colloquialism without strained attempts to look "cool"; one that uses everyday events and innovative analogies to enable students to visualize and relate to a process; one that favors simple language and syntax over convoluted paragraphs and a needlessly multisyllabic, graduate school vocabulary. One of the nicest compliments I've received, not only from students in my own classroom but from students elsewhere who e-mail me, is that they say reading this book "feels as if you're sitting there talking to me about it." When I get feedback like that, I know I've hit my mark as a writer. However, I always feel that some passages deserve such compliments less than others, so my foremost effort in any revision is to work for ever-better ways of expressing anatomical concepts and strengthening the entire narrative style.

I'm well aware that many anatomy students, being early in their college careers, are still developing the intellectual skills and study habits necessary for success in a health science curriculum. I think of them as I choose my words and craft the structure of a sentence or paragraph. Mindful that many anatomy students learned English as a second language (and it is a tough language to learn!), I try to keep the prose free of unnecessary jargon and culturally narrow idioms, and as clear as any writing on this complex subject can be. Even words that seem ordinary to most of us who teach, such as *interdigitate,* can draw blank stares from a class of beginning students, so I define even such words as those when I use them in this book.

The task of conscientiously choosing the best textbook for one's students is never an easy one. I feel confident, however, in inviting my colleagues to select topics that students typically find most difficult, open this book to that topic alongside the comparable treatments in other books, and directly compare the presentations to determine which one will best serve their students.

> This text is the most easily understood treatment of the subjects compared to all other texts that I've reviewed. Students will find this text very interesting and understandable . . . I think they will enjoy the subject of anatomy when using this book.
> —Ronald Harris, Marymount College

> I think that Saladin's writing style contributes significantly to the readability of this text. Saladin has a fascinating story to tell the reader and it's his marvelous way of communicating that makes this book a joy to read! I cannot see how a student couldn't benefit from such a great experience.
> —William L. Trotter, Des Moines Area Community College

> There is absolutely no question that Saladin's text is one of the most readable I've yet encountered. His explanations are generally paragons of clarity and he provides interesting clinical and historical insights that make reading the book even more compelling.
> —Mark Birchette, Long Island University

> This text is wonderfully formatted and developed. After adopting this text, I have, for the first time in my career, had students positively comment on the layout and readability of the text. Without the minute details often included in anatomical texts, Saladin does an excellent job of presenting the information to the students in a concise, accurate and interesting manner. Overall, my students love this text!
> —Candi K. Heimgartner, University of Idaho

## Illustrations

What first attracted me to biology when I was an adolescent was the photography and artwork in the books I discovered. I've never forgotten the importance of the esthetics of science to stimulating and sustaining a student's interest, so another gratifying aspect of this project has been finding or commissioning excellent photographs and conceiving of innovative illustrative concepts. I am highly indebted to the medical illustrators and graphic artists who rendered the art for this book in such beautiful and captivating style. Reviewers, too, have been a great help in deciding on issues of size, color, labeling, and other aspects of attractive, informative, and effective art and photography. Here again, I think a side-by-side comparison of the art in this book with the corresponding figures in other anatomy textbooks will show this one to be second to none.

> The art program of this text is wonderful . . . very masterful and vibrant. The images jump off the page.
> —Pamela Byrd-Williams, Los Angeles Valley College

> Since anatomy is such a visual science, the art must be the best possible. The artwork in the Saladin text is easily some of the best that I've seen. In particular, the artwork for joints and muscles is superb.
> —David Dilkes, University of Wisconsin–Oshkosh

> The art program appears much superior to other texts. The illustrations are large and nicely labeled. The competition usually presents "postage stamp" art of anatomical structures, which is most unfortunate for the student. Good illustrations are essential. If the author continues to use the art in its present form, the textbook will stand out among the competition.
> —Victor P. Eroschenko, University of Idaho

## Vocabulary Aids

Among the greatest hurdles to studying human anatomy is its massive vocabulary and many students' unfamiliarity with biological word roots based heavily in Greek and Latin. Even as a graduate teaching assistant, I developed the habit of breaking words down into familiar roots in my lectures, and I have taught a course on biomedical etymology for many years. I am convinced that students find such terms as *pterygoid* and *extensor carpi radialis brevis* less forbidding and easier to pronounce, spell, and remember if they cultivate the habit of looking for familiar roots and affixes. I've brought this habit to *Human Anatomy.*

Chapter 1 has a section, unique among human anatomy textbooks at this level, titled "The Language of Anatomy." It aims to instill the habit of breaking words into familiar roots, intuiting the meaning of new terms from a familiarity with frequently used roots, and perceiving the relationship between singular and plural forms such as *corpus/corpora* and *digiti/digitorum;* noun and adjectival forms such as *brachium/brachii;* and positive, comparative, and superlative degrees such as *magnus/major/maximus.* It also explains the historic rationale for a medical language based in Greek and Latin, and the importance of precision and spelling in not confusing similar words such as *malleus/malleolus* or *ileum/ilium*.

Following up on this, every chapter has footnotes identifying the roots and origins of new vocabulary terms, and easily understood "pro-NUN-see-AY-shun" guides for terms whose pronunciations are not intuitively obvious. The most frequently used roots, prefixes, and suffixes are listed with their meanings and biomedical examples inside the back cover of the book.

## Thematic Approaches

Aside from the customary core information, this book has certain themes woven throughout the book. Like most human anatomy books, it includes numerous clinical Insight sidebars and other remarks that illuminate the relevance of normal structure by pointing out the consequences of abnormalities. Unlike other books, it also presents several evolutionary Insights into human structure and historical vignettes on the people and discoveries behind the science. The emphasis is on clinical applications (78 Insight essays), with relatively occasional evolutionary and historical essays (10 and 4 Insights, respectively).

### Evolutionary Medicine

No understanding of the human body can be complete without taking its evolutionary history into account; the human body today must be seen as reflecting adaptations to past environments. Since the mid-1990s, an increasing number of books on evolutionary medicine have appeared, along with many articles in medical journals exploring evolutionary interpretations of human structure, function, and disease. This trend shows no signs of abating; indeed, it is bound to be reinforced by the rapidly growing science of genomic medicine. *Gray's Anatomy* is now thoroughly evolutionary, with the first chapter devoted almost entirely to human evolution and numerous evolutionary interpretations of human anatomy throughout the book. Yet I've seen no other anatomy textbook for this audience incorporate evolutionary medicine into its perspective.

There is little room to delve very far into the subject, but the importance of evolution to human anatomy is introduced in a section of chapter 1, "The Evolution of Human Structure." It is then reinforced throughout the book by 10 "Evolutionary Medicine" Insight essays, which concern vestigial organs, mitochondrial DNA, morning sickness, homeobox genes, skin color, polythelia, the palate, limb musculature, erythrocytes, and the nephron loop. Shorter evolutionary comments are also dispersed throughout the main narrative. In spite of teaching somewhere pretty close to the "buckle of the Bible belt" and knowing that many of my students are preconditioned to reject evolutionary thought, this content has never generated any complaints in my classes, and many of my students have commented that they found these Insights quite fascinating.

### Medical History

Other books also say little, if anything, about the history and personalities behind the science of human anatomy. They seem to expect students to accept the information *ex cathedra* without asking, "Who says? How do they know that?" Again, introductory anatomy textbooks allow little room or luxury to discuss history at any great length, but I do provide a brief history of anatomy ("Early Anatomists") in chapter 1 and add historical remarks in four "Medical History" Insight essays, such as essays on the tragic mishaps that linked radiation to bone cancer (Insight 6.1) and linked brain trauma to a functional understanding of the prefrontal cortex (Insight 15.2). Historical comments are also found in the main narrative, such as Hippocrates' insight into brain function (chapter 15), Harvey's discoveries in blood circulation (chapter 21), and Beaumont's experiments in gastric function (chapter 24). I feel that such stories put the *human* in human anatomy, taking it beyond the realm of merely memorizing facts. My students often say they find these vignettes to be engaging and eye-opening reading even when I don't explicitly assign them.

### Developmental Biology

My reviewers had disparate opinions of how much embryology this book should contain. Some said they have no time to teach embryology and wanted none at all, while others regarded chapter 4 (Human Development) to be the most important chapter in the book and wanted much more depth. The modal response was that there should be a moderate amount of embryology on each organ system, but not very much detail. I have aimed at this middle ground.

Chapter 4 presents basic embryology and lays a foundation for understanding the more specialized embryology of individual organ systems. For each organ system, there is a developmental section near the end of the chapter that goes briefly into its further development from the basic primordia described in chapter 4. These sections are not encyclopedic treatments, but broad overviews and key examples. For instance, I let the eye and ear suffice for sense-organ embryology, and the pituitary, thyroid, and adrenal glands for the endocrine system. Neither space limitations nor, apparently, the interests of prospective users warrant a more comprehensive treatment of these organs or additional ones.

At the other end of the life span are the degenerative changes of old age. These are presented for each organ system in a section following prenatal development ("The Aging Vascular System," for example).

## *Human Anatomy* Evolves

A textbook that stands still is destined for extinction. *Human Anatomy* has evolved to adapt to the teaching environment and respond to the "selection pressure" of users and reviewers. Revising a book of this nature is certainly not a matter of simply putting the old book between new covers. It entails correction of errors, keeping the science up to date, devising better ways to describe or illustrate an idea, and weighing the sometimes contrasting advice of scores of reviewers and correspondents.

### Factual Accuracy

Textbook inaccuracies are an important source of frustration for instructors, students, and writers alike. We have taken several measures to avoid them in this book. Most of its content is based on my *Anatomy and Physiology,* which has now been through four very successful editions and has been reviewed by hundreds of instructors over the years. This book therefore reflects more than a decade of peer review and fact-checking, including many focus groups, innumerable e-mails from colleagues, and stimulating online discussions with other anatomy and physiology instructors through the listserv of the Human Anatomy and Physiology Society. Student e-mails also have been a significant help, as my efforts to answer their queries include looking up information, providing references, and arriving at new and clearer ways of explaining ideas at their level of understanding. The accuracy of this edition has benefited greatly from a special collaboration with Dr. Robin McFarland, whose role is described in the Acknowledgments (p. xxv).

A large part of the continual refinement of the factual content also comes from keeping up with the biological and medical journals that arrive in my mailbox almost daily, and bringing new editions of biomedical textbooks into my reference library. Some inconsistencies in the first edition arose from reliance on multiple, sometimes contradictory sources of information; as far as possible in this edition, I've conformed such things as nerves, muscle attachments and actions, and blood vessels to *Gray's Anatomy.* Through such means, this edition offers many new insights, corrects earlier errors, and abandons some widespread misconceptions not supported by the more expert and current literature.

## Updated Terminology

Even the terminology of anatomy changes with the years, challenging authors and students to keep up. I've updated several terms to agree with the international *Terminologia Anatomica* (TA). I've changed nearly all use of *dorsal* and *ventral* to *posterior* and *anterior,* except where the standard anatomical terms still demand *dorsal* and *ventral* (such as *dorsal root ganglion* and *ventral mesentery*). I've also deleted a number of terms and concepts that now seem obsolete—absent from the TA, *Gray's Anatomy,* and other authorities, or explicitly discredited by them: for example, dorsal and ventral body cavities, superficial versus deep fascia, glabrous skin, trichosiderin as the basis for red hair, series-elastic components in muscle, prolactin-releasing hormone, and suppressor T cells.

Eponymous and possessive terms, such as *crypts of Lieberkühn, fallopian tubes,* and *Alzheimer's disease,* are now discouraged by the TA, *Stedman's Medical Dictionary,* and the *AMA Manual of Style.* I have abandoned such usage as much as practical, although I give eponyms as parenthetical synonyms when terms such as *intestinal crypts* and *uterine tubes* are first introduced, and it remains unavoidable to use some eponyms as the primary or only term (*Golgi complex, Broca area*).

## Art Revisions

Compared to the first edition of *Human Anatomy,* almost every piece of line art has undergone at least some modification, and several have been entirely replaced. Some examples of the new art are shown in the Guided Tour following this preface. To view some of the major changes in the line art, see the plasma membrane (figs. 2.6 and 2.9), mitosis and meiosis (2.20 and 26.5), blastocyst implantation (4.3), muscle fiber and sarcomere structure (10.8 and 10.10), the neuromuscular junction (10.11), the muscle contraction cycle (10.14), pelvic floor muscles (11.17), the spinal cord and its meninges (14.1 and 14.2), the dorsal root ganglion (14.8), the brachial plexus (14.14), brainstem cross sections (15.7), cerebellar input and output (15.10), thalamic and hypothalamic nuclei (15.11), the accessory nerve (15.35), sympathetic nerve pathways (16.5), cerebral circulation (21.18 and 21.19), the azygos and celiac vascular systems (21.21 and 21.23), arteries and veins of the limbs (21.27–21.32), brainstem respiratory centers (23.14), and the anatomy and histology of the lymph nodes (22.11), teeth (24.7), salivary glands (24.9), liver (24.18), penis (26.10), ovary (26.12), and breast (26.22).

This edition also has some new illustrative concepts with no counterparts in the first edition: the hair growth cycle (fig. 5.8), inguinal hernia (11.18), muscle compartments and fasciae (12.1), the electrocardiogram (20.15) and cardiac cycle (20.16), actions of the respiratory muscles (23.13), a sectional view of the tongue (24.5), and a simpler schematic of the nephron (25.6).

## Content Changes

I can scarcely begin to itemize all the changes made in this edition—just listing them for my own record ran to 93 single-spaced pages—but the most important ones for each chapter are as follows, leaving aside the many changes in art and narrative style.

**Chapter 1 and Atlas A** – An amended explanation of hominid characteristics and classification, less detail on extinct hominids, and an updated discussion of bipedalism. Expanded explanation of the origins and comprehension of modern anatomical terminology.

**Chapter 2** – Updated terminology of transmembrane proteins; reorganized and clarified descriptions of membrane transport; improved descriptions of intercellular junctions (especially desmosomes), the cytoskeleton, and peroxisome functions. New notes on the nuclear cage and Golgi complex.

**Chapter 3** – Approximate magnifications added to the photo legends. Extensive rewrites on adipose tissue and bone. Expanded treatment of epithelial function and regenerative capacity, stem cells, and tissue necrosis. New essay on tissue engineering (Insight 3.4).

**Chapter 4** – Rewrites on sperm–egg fusion, polyspermy, neurulation, and teratogens. New essay on developmental genetics and homeobox genes (Insight 4.4).

**Chapter 5** – Corrections on the cross-sectional anatomy of hair and development of apocrine glands. New discussions of dendritic cells and the hair growth cycle. New essay on the evolution of skin color (Insight 5.2).

**Chapter 6** – Rewrites on the canal system of compact bone, ossification, bone growth, bone remodeling, and Wolff's law. Updated and condensed discussion of osteoporosis.

**Chapter 7** – Addition of a few bone features relevant to muscle attachments in chapters 11 and 12. New discussion of morphological changes in the mandible with age. New palpation exercises in the Before You Go On questions.

**Chapter 8** – New discussion of the biomechanical function of the interosseous membrane of the upper limb.

**Chapter 9** – Rewrites on classification of synovial joints, range of motion, and rheumatoid arthritis. Synovial joint movements redescribed in more kinesiologic terms and supported by new photographs. Updated information on joint prostheses.

**Chapter 10** – Enhanced explanation of the perimysium and endomysium, muscle fiber ultrastructure, and dystrophin. Redescription of indirect and direct muscle attachments, and new explanation of the ambiguity of origin and insertion terminology. Updated description of neuromuscular junctions and related terminology. New discussion of the Botox fad (Insight 10.2). Updated morphology of cardiac myocytes.

**Chapter 11** – All muscle tables replaced and content conformed as much as possible to *Gray's Anatomy*. Modified discussion of the suprahyoid, thyrohyoid, sternothyroid, sternocleidomastoid, and iliocostalis muscles, and the vocal roles of some orofacial muscles. Addition of the innermost intercostal, compressor urethrae, and deep transverse perineal muscles.

**Chapter 12** – All muscle tables replaced and standardized as in chapter 11. Enhanced explanation of muscle compartments and fasciae. New essay on the evolution of limb musculature (Insight 12.2). Modified discussion of the actions of the serratus anterior, triceps brachii, extensor pollicis longus, and quadriceps femoris muscles, and the innervations of some muscles. Some muscles listed in a new order to progress consistently from lateral to medial.

**Chapter 13** – Rewrites and updates on astrocyte functions, CNS versus PNS myelination, nerve regeneration, multiple sclerosis, embryonic origins of neurons, the fate of neural crest cells, and folic acid and spina bifida.

**Chapter 14** – New descriptions of the spinoreticular, tectospinal, and vestibulospinal tracts. Addition of sufficient information on the brainstem to make better sense of the terminations of the spinal cord tracts. New format for the tables of spinal nerve plexuses; deletion of some minor nerves rarely mentioned in other books, but expanded description of the tibial and common fibular nerves. Improved cross-referencing from the motor nerves here to the muscle tables of chapters 11 and 12. Updated discussion of shingles. Improved discussion of the vascular supply to peripheral nerves. Clearer distinction between nerve roots and rami.

**Chapter 15** – Rewrites on major brain landmarks, cranial meninges, the brainstem, thalamus, hypothalamus, special senses, and motor control. Expanded treatments of brain evolution and brain

imaging methods. New format for the cranial nerve tables, with correction of some details on the facial, vagus, and hypoglossal nerves.

**Chapter 16** – Clarified descriptions of the sympathetic chain, splanchnic nerve route, autonomic nerve plexuses, and autonomic neurotransmitters and their receptors. Shorter, simpler table of contrasting effects of sympathetic and parasympathetic divisions. New essay on megacolon and Hirschsprung disease (Insight 16.2).

**Chapter 17** – Improved discussions of receptive fields; lamellated corpuscles; pain, olfactory, and vestibular projection pathways; cerumen; inner-ear anatomy; the vascular layer of the eye; the pupillary dilator; vitreous body function; pathogenesis of cataracts and glaucoma; and autonomic innervation of the eye.

**Chapter 18** – Extensive reorganization of the hypothalamus, pituitary, and adrenal cortex to better integrate anatomy with the hormones and their roles. Expanded discussions of pituitary and thyroid cytology and pineal function. New or expanded coverage of enteric hormones and the endocrinology of adipose tissue, the liver, and the kidney. Less discussion of hormone synthesis, other endocrine physiology, and pathology.

**Chapter 19** – Rewritten Insights on the complete blood count and sickle-cell disease. Correction of ABO antigen chemistry. Distinction between specific and nonspecific WBC granules. Slightly expanded discussion of lymphocyte types. Bacterial phagocytosis added to platelet functions.

**Chapter 20** – Improved descriptions of heart valve function and the cardiac conduction system, with less reliance on physiological terms. Updated description of cardiocyte structure. New essay on normal and pathological electrocardiograms (Insight 20.3). Brief explanation and illustration of the cardiac cycle. Enhanced discussion of the closure of circulatory shunts in the neonate.

**Chapter 21** – Improved descriptions of blood vessel histology. Rewrite of pulmonary circulation. Extensive reorganization of the tables of blood vessels, with blood vessels now treated regionally (arteries and veins of the head, arteries and veins of the upper limb, and so forth). More descriptive table entries. Correction of some widespread textbook misconceptions of vascular anatomy, such as the number of radial, ulnar, brachial, tibial, and fibular veins. Expanded description of cerebral arteries and dural venous sinuses. Extensive redescription of the celiac and azygos systems. Less detail on metacarpal, metatarsal, and digital vessels. More recognition of male–female differences in pelvic circulation.

**Chapter 22** – Expanded description of the thymus. Inclusion of the three lines of defense.

**Chapter 23** – Redescription of the bronchial tree, with updated terminology. Expanded discussion of the respiratory muscles and brainstem respiratory centers. Improved essay on pulmonary collapse (Insight 23.2).

**Chapter 24** – More functional explanation of the muscularis mucosae, muscularis externa, intrinsic salivary glands, and Paneth cells. Correction of details on hepatic sinusoids and keratinization of the oral mucosa.

**Chapter 25** – New introduction to kidney functions. Updated detail on hormonal influences on the nephron. Expanded discussion of the juxtaglomerular apparatus and ureteric valves.

**Chapter 26** – New descriptions of spermatogenesis, descent of the testes, the zona pellucida, uterine tube histology, and histology of the cyclic uterine changes. Updates on semen composition and cervical cancer. Explanation of the unusual dorsal/ventral terminology for anatomy of the penis. Corrections regarding venous and lymphatic drainage of the testis and ovary, embryological terminology of the external genitalia, and ectopic pregnancy.

## Guided Tour

*Human Anatomy* contains not only information but also several pedagogical features designed to help the student understand and master it. Students and instructors can become acquainted with these and other key features of the book by browsing the Guided Tour in the following pages. This is a visual exposition of the book's art program and the pedagogical framework around which each chapter is organized.

## Suggestions Welcome!

Even though this book is now postpartum and dressed in hard covers, it is still very much a work in progress. It has benefited greatly from the many reviewers who provided critiques of the manuscript and art during its development, and from student users of the first edition who kindly e-mailed with their impressions and suggestions. Undoubtedly it will improve still more as I hear from additional students and colleagues who use it. I welcome any reader to send feedback to me at the following address, and I will be grateful for your contribution to the quality and accuracy of future editions.

**Ken Saladin**
Professor of Biology
Georgia College & State University
Milledgeville, GA 31061 (USA)
478-445-0816
Ken.Saladin@gcsu.edu

# New and Vivid Illustrations

Saladin's illustration program is unsurpassed among human anatomy texts! Dynamic illustrations harmonize with Saladin's clear and engaging writing style to create a textbook that is visually captivating and fun to read. Colorful, precise anatomical illustrations lend a realistic view of body structures, and three-dimensional details help students envision cellular-level structures.

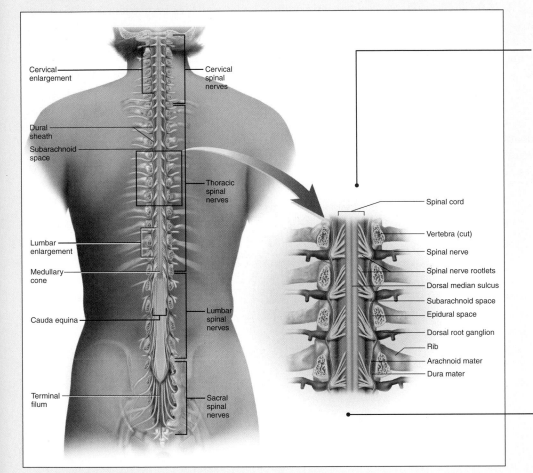

## Bright, Bold Colors

A bright color palette provides contrast for easy distinction of structures.

## Consistent Color Palette

Colors used to indicate specific structures are applied consistently for a cohesive art program from cover to cover.

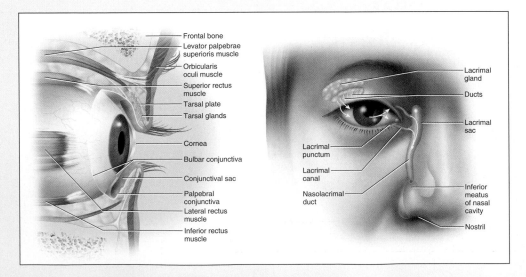

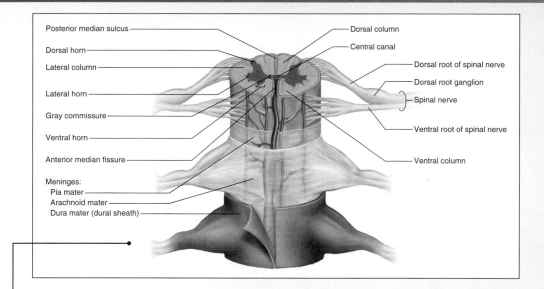

Posterior median sulcus
Dorsal horn
Lateral column
Lateral horn
Gray commissure
Ventral horn
Anterior median fissure

Dorsal column
Central canal
Dorsal root of spinal nerve
Dorsal root ganglion
Spinal nerve
Ventral root of spinal nerve
Ventral column

Meninges:
  Pia mater
  Arachnoid mater
  Dura mater (dural sheath)

## Three-Dimensional Detail

Rich textures and shading provide the visual depth and dimension that bring structures to life.

Internal jugular veins

Right jugular trunk
Right lymphatic duct
Right subclavian trunk
Right bronchio-mediastinal trunk
Azygos vein
Diaphragm
Cisterna chyli
Right lumbar trunk

Left jugular trunk
Thoracic duct
Left subclavian trunk
Left bronchiomediastinal trunk
Thoracic duct
Thoracic lymph nodes
Hemiazygos vein
Intestinal trunk
Left lumbar trunk

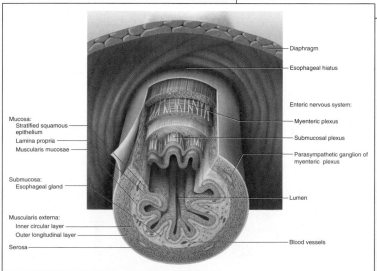

Mucosa:
  Stratified squamous epithelium
  Lamina propria
  Muscularis mucosae

Submucosa:
  Esophageal gland

Muscularis externa:
  Inner circular layer
  Outer longitudinal layer

Serosa

Diaphragm
Esophageal hiatus
Enteric nervous system:
  Myenteric plexus
  Submucosal plexus
Parasympathetic ganglion of myenteric plexus
Lumen
Blood vessels

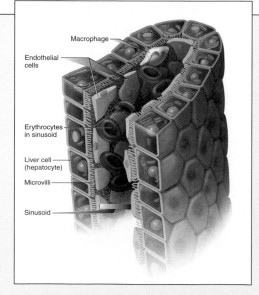

Macrophage
Endothelial cells
Erythrocytes in sinusoid
Liver cell (hepatocyte)
Microvilli
Sinusoid

# Message-Driven Layouts

Creating effective, educational artwork that conveys a clear message to students requires careful consideration of the relationship of the parts to the whole. Saladin's figures are organized in meaningful displays in which individual figure parts interact with one another to create big-picture explanations.

## Step-By-Step Process Figures

Numbered steps embedded in the artwork guide students through complex processes.

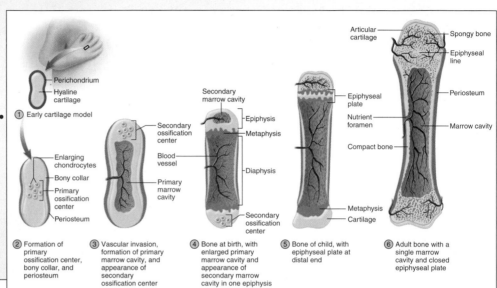

## Engaging Figure Presentations

Figures are arranged in cohesive layouts that emphasize relationships among figure parts.

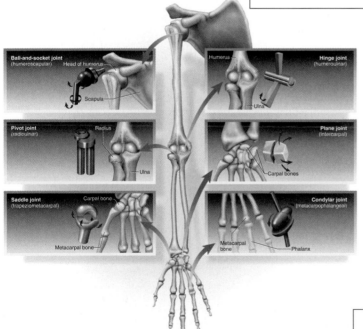

## Real-Life Context

Framing new material within familiar contexts makes learning relevant to life. Many figures incorporate visual cues that relate anatomical concepts to the student's everyday experience. This artistic technique is paralleled throughout the book by Saladin's analogy-rich writing style.

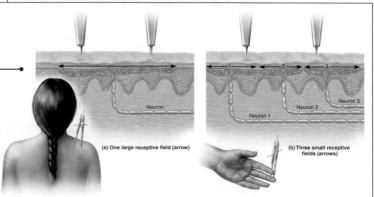

# Information-Rich Visuals

Interpreting anatomical views can be difficult, so Saladin's figures have been designed with students in mind. Special aids like view indicators, orientation icons, and clear figure navigation paths make the focus of each figure readily apparent. Descriptive information previously confined to figure legends has been embedded directly into the artwork to make figures understandable at first glance.

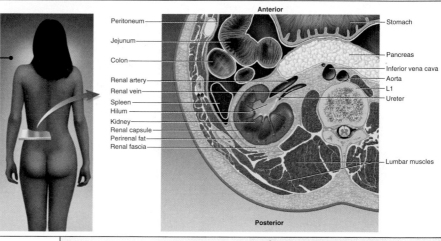

## Orientation Icons

Reference diagrams clarify the view or plane an illustration represents.

## View Indicators

Helpful labels indicating figure views facilitate easy interpretation of what is shown.

## Macroscopic to Microscopic Progression

Saladin's figures guide students fluidly from the intuitive level of gross anatomy to the functional foundations revealed by microscopic anatomy.

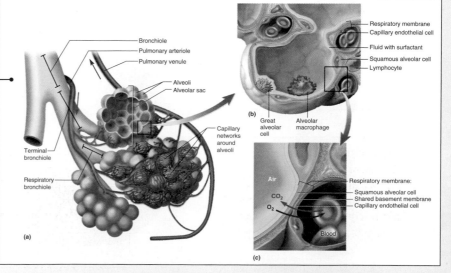

# Atlas-Quality Photographs

Photographs capture the truest appearance of gross and microscopic anatomy, and familiarize students with actual structures they may encounter in laboratory activities. Saladin's stunning collection of cadaver dissection images and light, TEM, and SEM photomicrographs balances the simplified clarity of illustrations with the realism of photos.

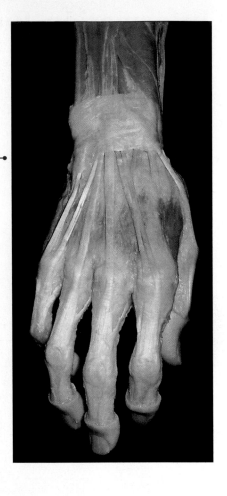

### Cadaver Dissections

High-quality photographs of expertly dissected cadaver specimens capture the texture and detail of real human structures, and emphasize their anatomical relationships.

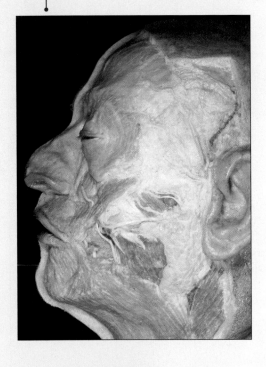

Renal capsule
Renal cortex
Renal medulla
Renal papilla
Renal sinus
Adipose tissue in renal sinus
Renal pelvis
Major calyx
Minor calyx
Renal column
Renal pyramid
Ureter
Renal blood vessels

(a)  (b)

### Complementary Views

Drawings paired with photographs enhance visualization of structures. Labeling of art and photo mirror each other whenever possible, making it easy to correlate structures between views.

## Micrographs

A carefully researched collection of LM, SEM, and TEM photomicrographs reveals the intricate detail of microscopic structures.

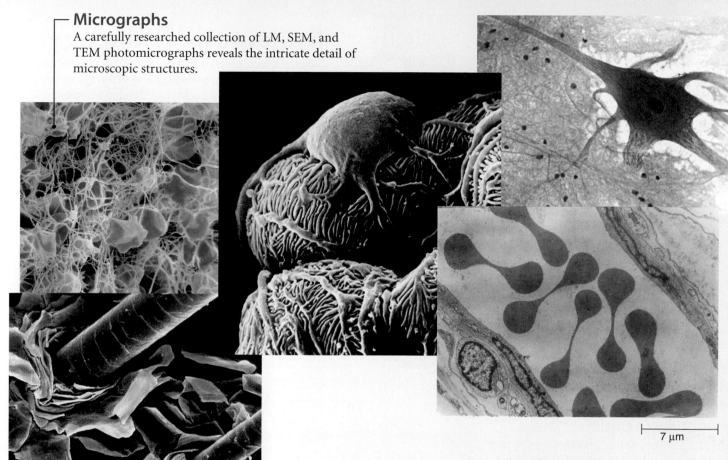

7 μm

0.1 mm

## Scale Bars

Scale bars are used whenever possible to provide a reference point for estimating the sizes of structures shown in micrographs.

## Photomicrographs Correlated with Illustrations

Photomicrographs are often paired with illustrations to give students the best of both perspectives: the realism of photos and the explanatory clarity of drawings.

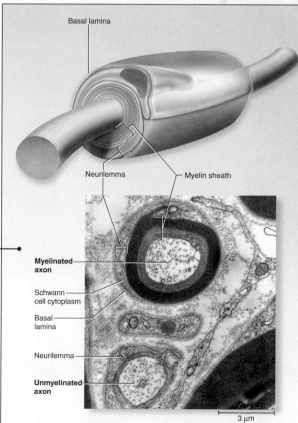

Basal lamina

Neurilemma

Myelin sheath

**Myelinated axon**

Schwann cell cytoplasm

Basal lamina

Neurilemma

**Unmyelinated axon**

3 μm

*xix*

# Systematic Pedagogy

Saladin structures each chapter around a standardized framework of unique pedagogical devices. Whatever the subject matter of a chapter, students can develop a consistent learning strategy. Orienting features such as chapter outlines and learning objectives help students organize study time and set goals, and self-testing questions in various formats and difficulty levels challenge students to recall terms and facts, to describe concepts, to analyze and apply ideas, and to relate concepts across chapters. Each chapter is seasoned with boxed discussions of clinical or scientific relevance that demonstrate application of concepts and add interest.

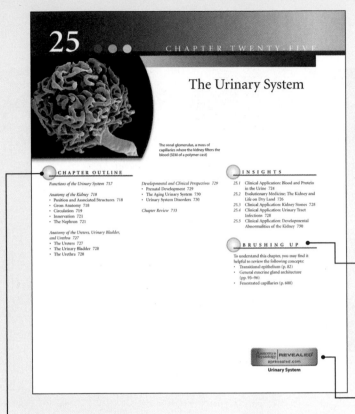

## Brushing Up

Each chapter-opening page lists concepts in earlier chapters that a student should understand before beginning the new chapter. This reinforces the interrelationships of different organ systems and helps when an instructor covers chapters in a different order than the book does.

## *Anatomy & Physiology Revealed*

Chapters covering systems presented in McGraw-Hill's *Anatomy & Physiology Revealed* include an icon indicating which area of this program coincides with the chapter.

## Chapter Outline

A chapter outline provides a quick overview of the chapter contents and organization.

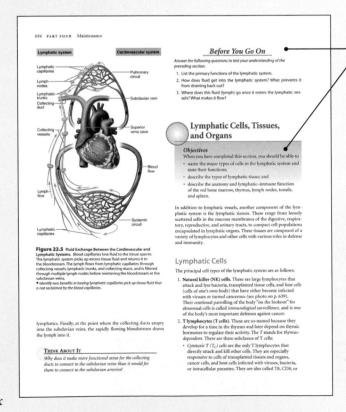

## Learning Objectives and Before You Go On

Saladin divides each chapter typically into five or six short, digestible segments of just a few pages each, with a list of learning objectives at the beginning and a list of Before You Go On content review questions at the end of each one. This enables students to set tangible goals for short study periods and to assess their progress before moving on.

## Vocabulary Aids

Anatomy students must assimilate a large working vocabulary. This is far easier and more meaningful if they can pronounce words correctly and if they understand the roots that compose them.

Pronunciation guides are given parenthetically when new words are introduced, using a "pro-NUN-see-AY-shun" format that is easy to interpret.

New terms are accompanied by footnotes that identify their roots and origins, and a lexicon of about 400 most commonly used word roots and affixes is printed on the inside back cover.

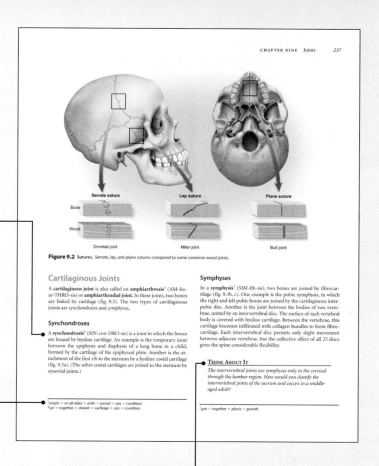

**Figure 9.2** Sutures. Serrate, lap, and plane sutures compared to some common wood joints.

### Cartilaginous Joints

A **cartilaginous joint** is also called an **amphiarthrosis**[1] (AM-fee-ar-THRO-sis) or **amphiarthrodial joint**. In these joints, two bones are linked by cartilage (fig. 9.3). The two types of cartilaginous joints are *synchondroses* and *symphyses*.

#### Synchondroses

A **synchondrosis**[2] (SIN-con-DRO-sis) is a joint in which the bones are bound by hyaline cartilage. An example is the temporary joint between the epiphysis and diaphysis of a long bone in a child, formed by the cartilage of the epiphyseal plate. Another is the attachment of the first rib to the sternum by a hyaline costal cartilage (fig. 9.3a). (The other costal cartilages are joined to the sternum by synovial joints.)

#### Symphyses

In a **symphysis**[3] (SIM-fih-sis), two bones are joined by fibrocartilage (fig. 9.3b, c). One example is the pubic symphysis, in which the right and left pubic bones are joined by the cartilaginous interpubic disc. Another is the joint between the bodies of two vertebrae, united by an intervertebral disc. The surface of each vertebral body is covered with hyaline cartilage. Between the vertebrae, this cartilage becomes infiltrated with collagen bundles to form fibrocartilage. Each intervertebral disc permits only slight movement between adjacent vertebrae, but the collective effect of all 23 discs gives the spine considerable flexibility.

> **THINK ABOUT IT**
> *The intervertebral joints are symphyses only in the cervical through the lumbar region. How would you classify the intervertebral joints of the sacrum and coccyx in a middle-aged adult?*

[1]*amphi* = on all sides + *arthr* = joined + *osis* = condition
[2]*syn* = together + *chondr* = cartilage + *osis* = condition

[3]*sym* = together + *physis* = growth

## Think About It

Success in human anatomy requires far more than memorization. More important is students' insight and ability to apply what they remember to new cases and problems. Strategically distributed throughout each chapter, Think About It questions encourage stopping and thinking more deeply about the meaning or broader significance of a concept.

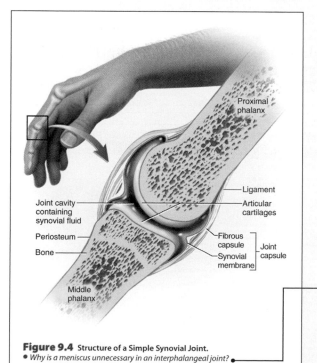

**Figure 9.4** Structure of a Simple Synovial Joint.
• *Why is a meniscus unnecessary in an interphalangeal joint?*

## Figure Questions

On average, five figures per chapter include a thought question beneath the figure legend. These questions trigger students to analyze the artwork and make connections between what they've read in the text and what they see in the figures. Answers are provided in the Appendix.

# Clinical Relevance

Most students who study from this book will be interested in clinical careers, and clinical insights show how the basic biology of the body is relevant to those interests. The importance of bone collagen, for example, becomes obvious when reading about osteogenesis imperfecta (Insight 3.3). Similarly, the warming and humidifying function of the nasal cavity becomes especially apparent when it is bypassed by tracheostomy (Insight 23.1). Each organ system chapter also ends with a section on developmental and clinical perspectives.

## Disorders Tables

For each organ system, Saladin presents a table that briefly describes several well-known pathologies and provides page references to other disorders of that system.

| TABLE 12.10 | Muscle Injuries |
|---|---|
| Baseball finger | Tears in the extensor tendons of the fingers resulting from the impact of a baseball with the extended fingertip |
| Blocker's arm | Abnormal calcification in the lateral margin of the forearm as a result of repeated impact such as occurs in football |
| Pitcher's arm | Inflammation at the origin of the wrist flexors resulting from hard wrist flexion in releasing a baseball |
| Pulled groin | Strain in the adductor muscles of the thigh; common in gymnasts and dancers who perform splits and high kicks |
| Pulled hamstrings | Strained hamstring muscles or a partial tear in the tendinous origin, often with a hematoma (blood clot) in the fascia lata; frequently caused by repetitive kicking (as in football and soccer) or long, hard running |
| Rider's bones | Calcification in the tendons of the thigh adductors; results from prolonged abduction of the thighs when riding horses |
| Shinsplints | General term for several kinds of injury with pain in the crural region—tendinitis of the tibialis posterior, inflammation of the tibial periosteum, and anterior compartment syndrome. May result from unaccustomed jogging, walk-a-thons, walking on snowshoes, or any vigorous activity of the legs after a period of inactivity |
| Tennis elbow | Inflammation at the origin of the extensor carpi muscles on the lateral epicondyle of the humerus occurs when these muscles are repeatedly tensed during backhand strokes and then strained by sudden impact with the tennis ball. Any activity that requires rotary movements of the forearm and a firm grip of the hand (for example, using a screwdriver) can cause the symptoms of tennis elbow. |
| Tennis leg | Partial tear in the lateral origin of the gastrocnemius; results from repeated strains put on the muscle while supporting the body weight on the toes |

**Disorders Described Elsewhere**

Back injuries 317
Carpal tunnel syndrome 338
Compartment syndrome 325

Hamstring injuries 347
Hernias 320
Rotator cuff injury 331

Hamstring injuries 347
Hernias 320
Rotator cuff injury 331

## Concept Connections

Awareness of how chapter topics relate to other sciences gives students a more holistic view of the study of anatomy. Saladin's informative Insight sidebars offer clinical, historical, and evolutionary perspectives tied to the chapter content.

## Clinical Applications

Each chapter has three to five Insight boxes, over 80% of which are clinical in nature. These essays illuminate the clinical relevance of a concept and give insight on disease as it relates to normal structure and function.

## Medical History

Inspiring historical and biographical vignettes give students a more humanistic perspective of the field and a chance to consider chapter topics in other contexts.

## Evolutionary Medicine

Considering the evolutionary adaptations highlighted in these Insight sidebars gives students a sense of how and why the human body came to be as it is.

### INSIGHT 11.3
#### Clinical Application

**Hernias**

A hernia is any condition in which the viscera protrude through a weak point in the muscular wall of the abdominopelvic cavity. The most common type to require treatment is an *inguinal hernia* (fig. 11.18). In the male fetus, each testis descends from the pelvic cavity into the scrotum by way of a passage called the *inguinal canal* through the muscles of the groin. This canal remains a weak point in the pelvic floor, especially in infants and children. When pressure rises in the abdominal cavity, it can force part of the intestine or bladder into this canal or even into the scrotum. This also sometimes occurs in men who hold their breath while lifting heavy weights. When the diaphragm and abdominal muscles contract, pressure in the abdominal cavity can soar to 1,500 pounds per square inch—more than 100 times the normal pressure and quite sufficient to produce an inguinal hernia, or "rupture." Inguinal hernias rarely occur in women.

Two other sites of hernia are the diaphragm and navel. A *hiatal hernia* is a condition in which part of the stomach protrudes through the diaphragm into the thoracic cavity. This is most common in overweight people over 40. It may cause heartburn due to the regurgitation of stomach acid into the esophagus, but most cases go undetected. In an *umbilical hernia*, abdominal viscera protrude through the navel.

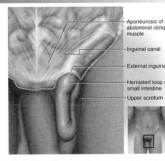

**Figure 11.18 Inguinal Hernia.** A loop of small intestine has protruded through the inguinal canal into a space beneath the skin.

### INSIGHT 15.2
#### Medical History

**An Accidental Lobotomy**

Accidental but nonfatal destruction of parts of the brain has afforded many clues to the function of various regions. One of the most famous incidents occurred in 1848 to Phineas Gage, a laborer on a railroad construction project in Vermont. Gage was packing blasting powder into a hole with a 3 1/2 ft tamping iron when the powder prematurely exploded. The tamping rod was blown out of the hole and passed through Gage's maxilla, orbit, and the frontal lobe of his brain before emerging [...] the hairline and landing 50 ft away (fig. 15.21). [...]ons, but later sat up and conversed with his [...] him to a physician in an oxcart. On arrival, he [...]nd told the physician, "Doctor, here is business [...]or, John Harlow, reported that he could insert [...] into Gage's wound. Yet 2 months later, Gage [...]h carrying on his normal business.

[...], the Phineas Gage people had known. Before [...]e ventromedial region of both frontal lobes [...] the competent, responsible, financially prudent [...]ociates. In an 1868 publication on the incident, [...]ng the accident, Gage was "fitful, irreverent, [...] grossest profanity." He became irresponsible, [...] while as a circus sideshow attraction, and died

[...]alysis of Gage's skull indicated that the brain [...]he ventromedial region of both frontal lobes. [...]s were reluctant to attribute social behavior [...]any region of the brain. These functions were [...]religion and ethics and were considered inac-[...]ysis. Based partly on Phineas Gage and other [...]him, neuroscientists today recognize that plan-[...]d emotional control are among the functions

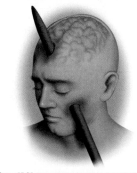

**Figure 15.21 Phineas Gage's 1848 Accident.** Gage suffered frontal lobe damage when a tamping bar flew upward, entered his maxilla, passed through the orbit and between the two frontal lobes, and exited the top of his head near the hairline. The accident resulted in permanent personality changes that helped to define some functions of the frontal lobes.

### INSIGHT 25.2
#### Evolutionary Medicine

**The Kidney and Life on Dry Land**

Physiologists first suspected that the nephron loop plays a role in water conservation because of their studies of a variety of animal species. Animals that must conserve water have longer, more numerous nephron loops than animals with little need to conserve it. Fish and amphibians lack nephron loops and produce urine that is isotonic to their blood plasma. Aquatic mammals such as beavers have short nephron loops and only slightly hypertonic urine.

But the kangaroo rat, a desert rodent, provides an instructive contrast. It lives on seeds and other dry foods and can live without drinking any water at all. The water produced by its aerobic respiration is enough to meet its needs because its kidneys are extraordinarily efficient at conserving it. They have extremely long nephron loops and produce urine that is 10 to 14 times as concentrated as their blood plasma (compared with about 4 times, at most, in humans).

Comparative studies thus suggested a hypothesis for the function of the nephron loop that was confirmed through a long line of ensuing research. This shows how comparative anatomy provides suggestions and insights into function and why physiologists do not study human function in isolation from other species.

# End-of-Chapter Review

A carefully devised set of learning aids at the end of each chapter helps students review the chapter content, evaluate their grasp of key concepts, and utilize what they have learned. Reading the chapter summary and completing the exercises are great ways to assess learning.

## Review of Key Concepts
Each chapter concludes with a brief restatement of key points, with page references back to major sections.

## Testing Your Recall
Multiple choice and short answer questions allow students to check their knowledge.

## True or False
True or False questions require students to explain why the false statements are untrue, thus challenging them to think more deeply into the material and to appreciate and express subtle points.

## Testing Your Comprehension
These questions go beyond memorization to require a deeper level of analysis and clinical application.

## Online Resources
Each chapter ends with a reminder to visit *Anatomy & Physiology Revealed* and the Saladin ARIS website for additional study help.

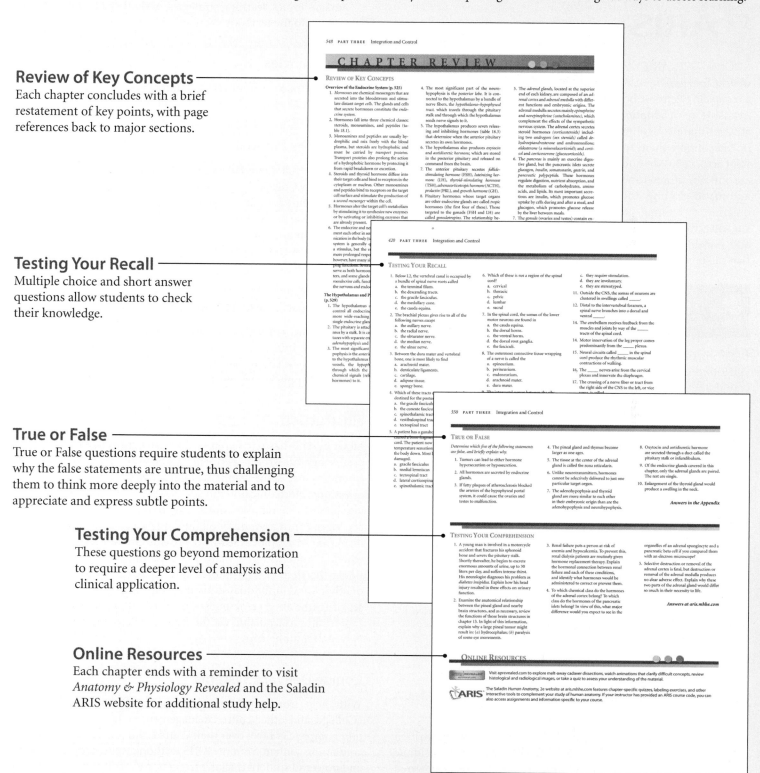

# Teaching and Learning Supplements

## Instructor Supplements

Instructors can obtain teaching aids to accompany this textbook by visiting www.mhhe.com, calling 800-338-3987, or contacting a McGraw-Hill sales representative.

McGraw-Hill's ARIS (Assessment, Review, and Instruction System) website for *Human Anatomy,* 2nd edition, found at aris.mhhe.com, is a complete electronic homework and course management system. Available upon adoption of *Human Anatomy,* instructors can create and share course materials and assignments with colleagues or disseminate them to students with a few clicks of the mouse. Instructors can edit questions, import their own content, and create announcements and due dates for assignments. ARIS features automatic grading and reporting of easy-to-assign homework, quizzing, and testing. Once a student is registered in the course, all student activity within McGraw-Hill's ARIS is automatically recorded and available to the instructor through a fully integrated grade book that can be downloaded to Excel.

*Build instructional materials where-ever, when-ever, and how-ever you want!* ARIS Presentation Center is an online digital library containing assets such as illustrations, photographs, animations, PowerPoints, and other media files that can be used to create customized lectures, visually enhanced tests and quizzes, compelling course websites, or attractive printed support materials.

*Access to your book, access to all books!* The Presentation Center library includes thousands of assets from many McGraw-Hill titles. This ever-growing resource gives instructors the power to utilize assets specific to an adopted textbook as well as content from all other books in the library.

*Nothing could be easier!* Accessed from the instructor side of your textbook's ARIS website, Presentation Center's dynamic search engine allows you to explore by discipline, course, textbook chapter, asset type, or keyword. Simply browse, select, and download the files you need to build engaging course materials. All assets are copyright McGraw-Hill Higher Education but can be used by instructors for classroom purposes.

## Instructor's Testing and Resource CD-ROM

This cross-platform CD delivers the following supplemental materials.

- **Test Bank**—A comprehensive bank of test questions written by Robin McFarland, Cabrillo College, is provided as simple Word files, and also within a computerized test bank powered by McGraw-Hill's flexible EZ Test program. EZ Test allows in-structors to search for questions by topic, format, or difficulty level; edit existing questions or add new ones; and create multiple versions of a test. Any test can be exported for use with course management systems such as WebCT, BlackBoard, or PageOut. EZ Test Online is a new service that offers a place to easily administer EZ Test exams and quizzes online.
- **Instructor's Manual**—This handy guide prepared by Robin McFarland, Cabrillo College, includes chapter overviews, discussion topics, learning strategies, and other helpful materials specific to the textbook.

## Transparencies

A set of 600 transparency overheads includes most illustrations from the book. Unlabeled versions of key anatomical views are included.

## Laboratory Manual

The *Human Anatomy Laboratory Manual,* by Eric Wise of Santa Barbara City College, is expressly written to coincide with the chapters of Saladin's *Human Anatomy.* It contains a variety of laboratory exercises designed to provide a comprehensive overview of the human body, and is appropriate for laboratory courses using cats or cadavers as dissection specimens. An instructor's manual containing answers to laboratory reports is available.

## Clinical Applications Manual

This manual, written by Michael Hendrix, Southwest Missouri State University, expands on *Human Anatomy*'s clinical themes and introduces new clinical topics and case studies to develop students' abilities to apply knowledge to realistic situations.

## eInstruction

McGraw-Hill has partnered with eInstruction to bring the revolutionary Classroom Performance System (CPS) to the classroom. An instructor using this interactive system can administer questions electronically during class while students respond via hand-held remote-control keypads. Individual responses are logged into a grade book, and aggregated responses can be displayed in graphical form to provide immediate feedback on whether students understand a lecture topic or if more clarification is needed. CPS promotes student participation, class productivity, and individual student accountability. A downloadable set of textbook-specific questions, formatted for both CPS and PowerPoint, is available via the ARIS for Saladin's *Human Anatomy* at aris.mhhe.com

## Course Delivery Systems

With help from our partners WebCT, Blackboard, Top-Class, eCollege, and other course management systems, professors can take complete control over their course content. Course cartridges containing content from the ARIS textbook website, online testing, and powerful student tracking features are readily available for use within these platforms.

## Student Supplements

Students can order supplemental study materials by calling 800-262-4729 or contacting their campus bookstore.

### Anatomy & Physiology Revealed

This amazing multimedia tool is designed to help students learn and review human anatomy using cadaver specimens. Detailed cadaver photographs blended together with a state-of-the-art layering technique provide a uniquely interactive dissection experience. The newly updated online version features the following sections:

- **Dissection**—Peel away layers of the human body to reveal structures beneath the surface. Structures can be pinned and labeled, just like in a real dissection lab. Each labeled structure is accompanied by detailed information and an audio pronunciation. Dissection images can be captured and saved.
- **Animation**—Compelling animations demonstrate muscle actions, clarify anatomical relationships, or explain difficult concepts.
- **Histology**—Labeled light micrographs presented with each body system allow students to study tissues at their own pace.
- **Imaging**—Labeled X-ray, MRI, and CT images familiarize students with the appearance of key anatomical structures as seen through different medical imaging techniques.
- **Self-Test**—Challenging exercises let students test their ability to identify anatomical structures in a timed practical exam format or traditional multiple choice. A results page provides analysis of test scores plus links back to all incorrectly identified structures for review.
- **Anatomy Terms**—This visual glossary of general terms includes directional and regional terms, as well as planes and terms of movement.

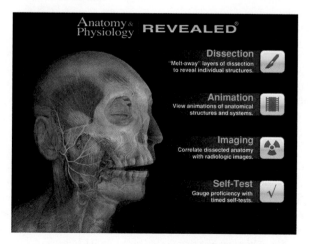

### Textbook Website

McGraw-Hill's ARIS (Assessment, Review, and Instruction System) for *Human Anatomy* at aris.mhhe.com offers students access to a vast array of online content to fortify the learning experience.

- **Text-Specific Study Tools**—The Saladin ARIS site features quizzes, interactive learning games, and study tools tailored to coincide with each chapter of the text.

- **Course Assignments and Announcements**—Students of instructors choosing to utilize McGraw-Hill's ARIS tools for course administration will receive a course code to log into their specific course for assignments.

### Virtual Anatomy Dissection Review

This multimedia program created by John Waters of Pennsylvania State University, and Melissa Janssen and Donna White of Collin County Community College, contains vivid, high-quality, labeled cat dissection photographs. Available online or on CD, the program helps students easily identify and compare cat structures with the corresponding human structures.

## Acknowledgments

As every textbook author knows, a book on this scale is never the work of only one person or even a few, but the product of a large and well-orchestrated team.

I've been especially fortunate to partner once again with Developmental Editor Kristine Queck on this edition. This book has benefited tremendously from her enthusiastic interest and keen understanding of the scientific content, her sharp eye for detail, her vision for excellence, and her uncompromising commitment to quality in art, photography, and design. Kris's standard of quality has been an inspiration to me and has been a key factor in bringing out the best in my own work. I've been delightfully surprised, over and over, at how informed and perceptive Kris is about the slightest issues of anatomical accuracy, especially in the art. Although it is rumored that she has produced some other terrific textbooks and multimedia supplements as well, Kris devoted so much time and attention to this book that I could almost believe I was McGraw-Hill's only author. One could not ask for a better editor.

A close second has been my colleague and new collaborator Robin McFarland, comparative primate anatomist at Cabrillo College. Robin meticulously reviewed the first edition and worked closely with me throughout this project, making many valuable suggestions for simplifying and clarifying the narrative, improving the scientific content, and enhancing the illustrations. As one who taught from the first edition of this book, Robin provided a valuable perspective on how best to meet the needs of students in anatomy-only courses. Several passages in this edition and some of the new Insight sidebars are largely her writing or our joint writing. Robin was also deeply engaged in the editing and proofreading stages of the project and contributed greatly to the accuracy of both the text and art.

I am grateful to my Publisher, Michelle Watnick, and Sponsoring Editor, Colin Wheatley, for their unflagging encouragement and support and for providing the resources to produce this book. The appearance of the book owes a great deal to Designer David Hash, Photo Coordinator John Leland, Photo Researcher Mary Reeg, and Medical Illustrator Joanne Brummett and the team of illustrators at Precision Graphics (Champaign, Illinois). Jane DeShaw copyedited the manuscript and spared me from countless little errors and inconsistencies. Lead Project Manager Mary Powers coordinated us all and kept the project running according to schedule. The resources brought to bear in each edition hinge on the success of previous editions, and for that I am indebted to Marketing Manager Lynn Breithaupt and the legions of sales managers and sales representatives who creatively promoted the first edition.

Finally, the scientific content and accuracy of the book have gained immeasurably from scores of colleagues who have provided a wealth of suggestions, corrections, and information. These include the reviewers, advisors, and focus group participants listed in the following pages; my colleagues in the Human Anatomy and Physiology Society with whom I have enjoyed so many fruitful discussions on the HAPS-L listserv; and many who wrote to me spontaneously with suggestions for improvement. Their specialized knowledge of individual organ systems and concepts was an important complement to my broader, generalist perspective. Also immeasurably valuable to me have been the many students around the world who have written, phoned, or dropped into my office with their observations, compliments, corrections, and suggestions for better ways to describe or illustrate a concept. I think of them, above all, as I strive for more effective ways of expressing ideas for the student reader and for increasingly lucid and dynamic illustrative concepts.

As always, I welcome further input from any readers—students and colleagues alike—who care to point out not only what they like about the treatment in these pages, but also how future editions can be made still better. I can be contacted at

Ken.Saladin@gcsu.edu
478-445-0816

# Reviewers and Advisors

## Textbook Reviewers

Jonathan H. Anning
*Slippery Rock University*

W. Sue Ball
*Southwestern Oklahoma State University*

Mary Lou Bareither
*University of Illinois at Chicago*

Steven Bassett
*Southeast Community College*

Mary Tracy Bee
*University of Detroit Mercy*

Mark G. Birchette
*Long Island University*

Moges Bizuneh
*Ivy Tech State College*

Leann Blem
*Virginia Commonwealth University*

Joel A. Bloom
*University of Houston*

Mary Bracken
*Trinity Valley Community College*

Elaine L. Bukowski
*The Richard Stockton College of New Jersey*

Anne Bullerjahn
*Owens Community College*

Alphonse R. Burdi
*University of Michigan Medical School*

Jett S. Chinn
*San Francisco State University*

David R. Chong
*Kapi'olani Community College and University of Utah*

Warren Darling
*University of Iowa*

Inez Devlin-Kelly
*Bakersfield College*

Charles J. Dick
*Pasco-Hernando Community College*

Alan Dietsche
*University of Rochester*

David Dilkes
*University of Wisconsin–Oshkosh*

John C. Duncan
*Pacific Union College*

Victor P. Eroschenko
*University of Idaho*

Gibril O. Fadika
*Hampton University*

David K. Ferris
*University of South Carolina–Spartanburg*

Don Lowell Fisher
*University of Michigan*

Allan Forsman
*East Tennessee State University*

Michael L. Foster
*Eastern Kentucky University*

Pamela Fouche
*Walters State Community College*

Ron Gaines
*Cameron University*

Kindra A. Girard
*Glendale Community College*

Kimberly A. Gray
*Southern Illinois University–Carbondale*

David L. Hammerman
*Long Island University*

Cindy Handley
*Seward County Community College*

Wanda G. Hargroder
*Louisiana State University*

Ronald T. Harris
*Marymount College*

Ralph E. Hatcher
*Butler University*

Jackie Hedgpeth
*Everett Community College*

Candi K. Heimgartner
*University of Idaho*

Ruth Heisler
*University of Colorado–Boulder*

E. Michael Hendrix
*Southwest Missouri State University*

Phyllis C. Hirsch
*East Los Angeles College*

James J. Hoffmann
*Diablo Valley College*

Leland Norman Holland Jr.
*Southeastern College*

Pavla Hoyer
*Los Angeles Valley College*

Trey Hoyt
*Central Missouri State University*

Steven L. Keffer
*James Madison University*

Theodore I. King II
*University of Wisconsin–Milwaukee*

Christine Kisiel
*Mount Wachusett Community College*

Jeanne Kowalczyk
*University of South Carolina–Spartanburg*

Winston C. Lancaster
*California State University, Sacramento*

John H. Langdon
*University of Indianapolis*

John E. Leffert
*Lock Haven University of Pennsylvania*

James E. Leone
*Southern Illinois University*

Lanny W. Leroy
*Benedictine College*

Theresa Martin
*College of San Mateo*

Michele Monlux
*Modesto Junior College*

Qian F. Moss
*Des Moines Area Community College*

Virginia L. Naples
*Northern Illinois University*

Daniel R. Olson
*Northern Illinois University*

Anthony T. Paganini
*Michigan State University*

Mark Paternostro
*Pennsylvania College of Technology*

John Pellegrini
*College of St. Catherine*

Catrin Pittack
*University of Washington–Seattle*

Melissa Presch
*California State University, Fullerton*

Danielle M. Purdy
*Santa Rosa Junior College*

David J. Saxon
*Morehead State University*

Judith L. Schotland
*Boston University*

Heather C. Scott
*Bastyr University*

Michael J. Shaughnessy Jr.
*University of Central Oklahoma*

Tracy L. Soltesz
*Pikeville College*

Michael Stark
*Brigham Young University*

Bruce J. Stephen
*Southeast Community College*

Suzanne G. Strait
*Marshall University*

William J. Swartz
*Louisiana State University*

Ernest F. Talarico
*Indiana University*

Mark F. Teaford
*Johns Hopkins University*

Richard D. Torres
*Ohio Northern University*

William Trotter
*Des Moines Area Community College*

Leticia Vostros
*Ozarks Technical Community College*

Peggie L. Williamson
*Central Texas College*

Carola Z. Wright
*Mount San Antonio College*

Glenn Yoshida
*Los Angeles Southwest College*

## Class Testers

Susan C. Baldi-Edelstein
*Santa Rosa Junior College*

Linda Banta
*Sierra College*

Ty Bryan
*Bossier Parish Community College*

Robert Droual
*Modesto Junior College*

David Ferris
*University of South Carolina–Spartanburg*

David Hammerman
*Long Island University*

Felicia Harvey
*Eastern New Mexico University*

Ken Hebert
*Carl Albert Junior College*

Phyllis Hirsch
*East Los Angeles College*

Judy Jiang
*Triton College*

Allison Jones
*Samford University*

Irina A. Koretsky
*Howard University*

Malinda McMurry
*Morehead State University*

Ernest Mellas
*Monroe Community College*

Virginia Pascoe
*Mount San Antonio College*

John Pellegrini
*College of St. Catherine*

W. Todd Pierson
*Southern Illinois University*

Wayne H. Preston
*College of Sequoias*

Elliott S. Stern
*Everett Community College*

Rodney Brent Thomas
*University of South Carolina–Spartanburg*

Ned Williams
*Minnesota State University–Mankato*

Carola Z. Wright
*Mount San Antonio College*

Kelly A. Young
*California State University, Long Beach*

Gilbert L. Zink
*University of the Sciences in Philadelphia*

## Focus Group Participants

Sharon Babcock
*James Madison University*

Fredric Bassett
*Rose State College*

Mary Bracken
*Trinity Valley Community College*

David R. Garris
*University of Missouri–Kansas City*

Wanda Hargroder
*Louisiana State University*

Cynthia Herbrandson
*Kellogg Community College*

Gavin C. O'Connor
*Ozarks Technical Community College*

Regina Rector
*William Rainey Harper College*

Marci Smith
*University of Wyoming*

Michael Sneary
*San Jose State University*

Ned Williams
*Minnesota State University–Mankato*

Gilbert L. Zink
*University of the Sciences in Philadelphia*

1

# The Study of Human Anatomy

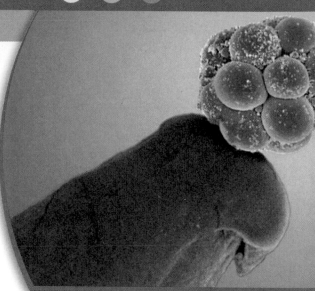

A new life begins—a human embryo
on the point of a pin (scanning
electron micrograph)

PART ONE

This book is an introduction to the structure of the human body. It is meant primarily to provide a foundation for advanced study in fields related to health and fitness. Beyond that purpose, however, the study of anatomy can also provide a satisfying sense of self-understanding. Even as children, we are curious about what's inside the body. Dried skeletons, museum exhibits, and beautifully illustrated atlases of the body have long elicited special fascination.

This chapter lays a foundation for our study of anatomy by considering some broad themes—What does this science encompass? What methods are used to study anatomy? How did our understanding of human anatomy develop? What aspects of human anatomy differentiate us from other animals and define us as humans? How did the human body come to be as it is? How can a beginner more easily master the complex language of anatomy?

# The Scope of Human Anatomy

### Objectives

When you have completed this section, you should be able to

- define *anatomy* and some of its subdisciplines;
- name and describe some approaches to studying anatomy;
- describe some methods of medical imaging;
- discuss the variability of human anatomy; and
- state the levels of human structure from organismal to subatomic.

**Human anatomy** is the study of the structure of the human body. It provides an essential foundation for the understanding of **physiology,** the study of function; anatomy and physiology together are the bedrock of the health sciences. You can study human anatomy from an atlas; yet as beautiful, fascinating, and valuable as many anatomy atlases are, they teach almost nothing but the locations, shapes, and names of structures. This book is much different; it deals with what biologists call **functional morphology**[1]—not just the structure of organs, but the functional reasons behind that structure.

Anatomy and physiology are complementary to each other; each makes sense of the other, and each molds the other in the course of human development and evolution. We cannot delve into the details of physiology in this book, but enough will be said of function to help you make sense of human structure and to more deeply appreciate the beauty of human form.

## The Anatomical Sciences

Anatomy embraces several subdisciplines that study human structure from different perspectives. **Gross anatomy** is the study of structure visible to the naked eye, using methods such as surface observation, dissection, X-rays, and MRI scans. **Surface anatomy** is the external structure of the body, and is especially important in conducting a physical examination of a patient. **Radiologic anatomy** is the study of internal structure, using X-rays and other medical imaging techniques described in the next section. In many cases, such as MRI scans, this entails examination of a two-dimensional image of a thin "slice" through the body. **Systemic anatomy** is the study of one organ system at a time and is the approach taken by most introductory textbooks such as this one. **Regional anatomy** is the study of multiple organ systems at once in a given region of the body, such as the head or chest. Medical schools typically teach anatomy from this perspective, because it is more logical to dissect all structures of the head and neck, the chest, or a limb, than it would be to try to dissect the entire digestive system, then the cardiovascular system, and so forth. Dissecting one system almost invariably destroys organs of another system that stand in the way. Furthermore, as surgeons operate on a particular area of the body, they must think from a regional perspective and attend to the interrelationships of all structures in that area.

Ultimately, the structure and function of the body result from its individual cells. To see those, we usually take tissue specimens, thinly slice and stain them, and observe them under the microscope. This approach is called **microscopic anatomy (histology)**. **Histopathology**[2] is the microscopic examination of tissues for signs of disease. **Cytology**[3] is the study of the structure and function of individual cells. **Ultrastructure** refers to fine detail, down to the molecular level, revealed by the electron microscope.

Anatomy, of course, is not limited to the study of humans, but extends to all living organisms. Even students of human structure benefit from **comparative anatomy**—the study of more than one species in order to examine structural similarities and differences and analyze evolutionary trends. Anatomy students often begin by dissecting other animals with which we share a common ancestry and many structural similarities. Indeed, many of the reasons for human structure become apparent only when we look at the structure of other animals. In chapter 25, for example, you will see that physiologists had little idea of the purpose of certain tubular loops in the kidney *(nephron loops)* until they compared human kidneys with those of desert and aquatic animals, which have greater and lesser needs to conserve water. The greater an animal's need to conserve water (the drier its habitat), the longer these loops are. Thus, comparative anatomy hinted at the function of the nephron loop. Such are the insights that can be gained by comparing different species with each other.

## Methods of Study

There are several ways to examine the structure of the human body. The simplest is **inspection**—simply looking at the body's appearance, as in performing a physical examination or making a clinical diagnosis from surface appearance. Physical examinations involve

---

[1] *morpho* = form, structure + *logy* = study of

[2] *histo* = tissue + *patho* = disease + *logy* = study of
[3] *cyto* = cell + *logy* = study of

not only looking at the body for signs of normalcy or disease, but also touching and listening to it. **Palpation**[4] means feeling a structure with the hands, such as palpating a swollen lymph node or taking a pulse. **Auscultation**[5] (AWS-cul-TAY-shun) is listening to the natural sounds made by the body, such as heart and lung sounds. In **percussion,** the examiner taps on the body, feels for abnormal resistance, and listens to the emitted sound for signs of abnormalities such as pockets of fluid or air.

A deeper understanding of the body depends on **dissection**—the careful cutting and separation of tissues to reveal their relationships. The very words *anatomy*[6] and *dissection*[7] both mean "cutting apart"; until the nineteenth century, dissection was called "anatomizing." In many schools of health science, one of the first steps in the training of students is dissection of the **cadaver,**[8] a dead human body (fig. 1.1).

Dissection, of course, is not the method of choice when studying a living person! It was once common to diagnose disorders through **exploratory surgery**—opening the body and taking a look inside to see what was wrong and what could be done about it. Any breach of the body cavities is risky, however, and most exploratory surgery has now been replaced by **medical imaging** techniques—methods of viewing the inside of the body without surgery. The branch of medicine concerned with imaging is called **radiology.** Imaging methods are called *noninvasive* if they do not involve any penetration of the skin or body orifices. *Invasive* imaging techniques may entail inserting ultrasound probes into the esophagus, vagina, or rectum to get closer to the organ to be imaged, or injecting substances into the bloodstream or body passages to enhance image formation.

Any anatomy student today must be acquainted with the basic techniques of radiology and their respective advantages and limitations. Many of the images printed in this book have been produced by the following techniques.

## Radiography

**Radiography** is the process of photographing internal structures with X-rays, a form of high-energy radiation. Until the 1960s, this was the only imaging method that was widely available, and even today, it accounts for more than 50% of all clinical imaging. X-rays penetrate soft tissues of the body and darken photographic film on the other side. They are absorbed, however, by dense tissues such as bones, teeth, tumors, and tuberculosis nodules, which leave the film lighter in these areas (fig. 1.2a). The term *X-ray* also applies to a photograph (*radiograph*) made by this method. Radiography is commonly used in dentistry, mammography, diagnosis of fractures, and examination of the chest. Hollow organs can be visualized by filling them with a *radiopaque* substance that absorbs X-rays. Barium sulfate, for example, is given orally for examination of the esophagus, stomach, and small intestine, or by enema for examination of the large intestine. Other substances are given by in-

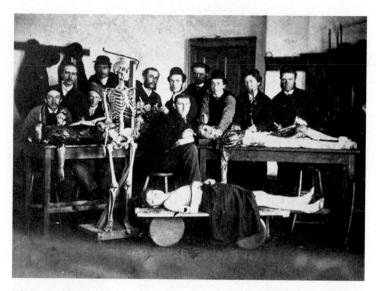

**Figure 1.1** **Early Medical Students in the Gross Anatomy Laboratory with Three Cadavers.** Students of the health sciences have long begun their professional training by dissecting cadavers.

jection for *angiography*, the examination of blood vessels (fig. 1.2b). Some disadvantages of radiography are that images of overlapping organs can be confusing and slight differences in tissue density are not easily detected. In addition, X-rays can trigger cancer and therefore cannot be used indiscriminately. However, the benefits of periodic mammograms, dental X-rays, and so forth substantially outweigh the small cancer risk.

## Computed Tomography

**Computed tomography** (a **CT scan**), formerly called a *computerized axial tomographic*[9] *(CAT) scan,* is a more sophisticated application of X-rays developed in 1972. The patient is moved through a ring-shaped machine that emits low-intensity X-rays on one side and receives them with a detector on the opposite side. A computer analyzes signals from the detector and produces an image of a "slice" of the body about as thin as a coin (fig. 1.2c). The computer can "stack" a series of these images to construct a three-dimensional image of the body. CT scanning has the advantage of imaging thin sections of the body, so there is little organ overlap and the image is much sharper than a conventional X-ray. It requires extensive knowledge of cross-sectional anatomy to interpret the images. CT scanning is useful for identifying tumors, aneurysms, cerebral hemorrhages, kidney stones, and other abnormalities. It has replaced most exploratory surgery.

## Magnetic Resonance Imaging

**Magnetic resonance imaging** (**MRI**) was conceived as a technique superior to CT for visualizing soft tissues. The patient lies in a chamber surrounded by a large electromagnet that creates a magnetic field

---

[4]*palp* = touch, feel + *ation* = process
[5]*auscult* = listen + *ation* = process
[6]*ana* = apart + *tom* = cut
[7]*dis* = apart + *sect* = cut
[8]from *cadere* = to fall down or die

[9]*tomo* = section, cut, slice + *graphic* = pertaining to a recording

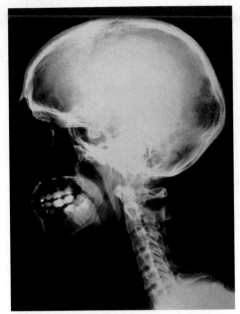

**(a) X-ray (radiograph)**

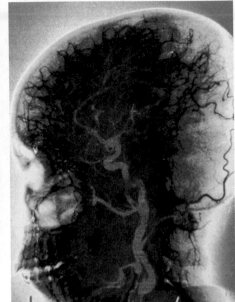

**(b) Cerebral angiogram**

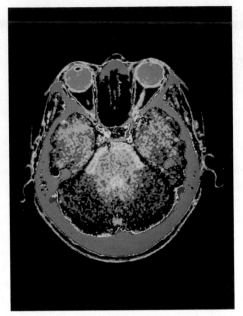

**(c) Computed tomographic (CT) scan**

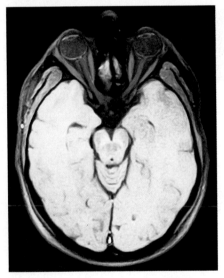

**(d) Magnetic resonance image (MRI)**

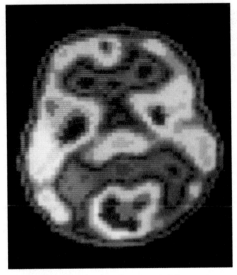

**(e) Positron emission tomographic (PET) scan**

**Figure 1.2** Radiologic Images of the Head. (a) X-ray (radiograph) showing the bones and teeth. (b) An angiogram of the cerebral blood vessels. The arteries are enhanced with false color. (c) A CT scan. The eyes and skin are shown in blue, bone in pink, and the brain in green. (d) An MRI scan at the level of the eyes. The optic nerves appear in red, and the muscles that move the eyes appear in green. (e) A PET scan of the brain of an unmedicated schizophrenic patient. Red areas indicate regions of high metabolic rate. In this patient, the visual center of the brain at the rear of the head (bottom of photo) was especially active during the scan.
● *What structures are seen better by MRI than by X-ray? What structures are seen better by X-ray than by PET?*

3,000 to 60,000 times as strong as the earth's. Hydrogen atoms in the tissues align themselves with the magnetic field. The radiologic technologist then turns on a field of radio waves, causing the hydrogen atoms to absorb additional energy and align in a different direction. When the radio waves are turned off, the hydrogen atoms abruptly realign to the magnetic field, giving off their excess energy at rates that depend on the type of tissue. A computer analyzes the emitted energy to produce an image of the body. MRI can "see" clearly through the skull and vertebral column to produce images of the nervous tissue (fig. 1.2d). Moreover, it is better than CT for distinguishing between soft tissues such as the white and gray matter of the nervous system. It also avoids the harmful effects of X-rays. *Functional MRI (fMRI)* is a form of MRI that visualizes moment-to-moment changes in tissue function; fMRI scans of the brain, for example, show shifting patterns of activity as the brain applies itself to a specific task.

## THINK ABOUT IT

*The concept of MRI was conceived in 1948 but was not put into clinical practice until the 1970s. Speculate on a possible reason for this delay.*

## Positron Emission Tomography

**Positron emission tomography** (a **PET scan**), developed in the 1970s, is used to assess the metabolic state of a tissue and to distinguish which tissues are most active at a given moment (fig. 1.2e). The procedure begins with an injection of radioactively labeled glucose, which emits positrons (electron-like particles with a positive charge). When a positron and electron meet, they annihilate each other and give off gamma rays that can be detected by sensors and analyzed by computer. The result is a color image that shows which tissues were using the most glucose at the moment. In cardiology, PET scans can show the extent of damaged heart tissue. Since damaged tissue consumes little or no glucose, it appears dark. In neuroscience, PET scans are used, like fMRI, to show which regions of the brain are most active when a person performs a specific task. The PET scan is an example of **nuclear medicine**—the use of radioisotopes to treat disease or form diagnostic images of the body.

## Sonography

**Sonography**[10] is the second oldest and second most widely used method of imaging. It is an outgrowth of sonar technology developed in World War II. A handheld device held firmly against the skin produces high-frequency ultrasound waves and receives the signals reflected back from internal organs. Sonography avoids the harmful effects of X-rays, and the equipment is inexpensive and portable. Its primary disadvantage is that it does not produce a very sharp image (fig. 1.3). Although sonography was first used medically in the 1950s, images of significant clinical value had to wait until computer technology had developed enough to analyze differences in the way tissues reflect ultrasound. Sonography is not very useful for examining bones or lungs, but it is the method of choice in obstetrics, where the image *(sonogram)* can be used to locate the placenta and evaluate fetal age, position, and development. *Echocardiography* is the sonographic examination of the beating heart.

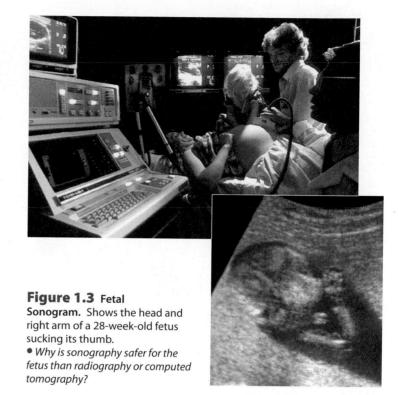

**Figure 1.3** Fetal Sonogram. Shows the head and right arm of a 28-week-old fetus sucking its thumb.
● *Why is sonography safer for the fetus than radiography or computed tomography?*

# Variation in Human Structure

A quick look around any classroom is enough to show that no two humans look exactly alike; on close inspection, even identical twins exhibit differences. Anatomy atlases and textbooks can easily give you the impression that everyone's internal anatomy is the same, but this simply is not true. Books such as this one can teach you only the most common structure—the anatomy seen in approximately 70% or more of people. Someone who thinks that all human bodies are the same internally would make a very confused medical student or an incompetent surgeon.

Some people completely lack certain organs. For example, most of us have a *palmaris longus* muscle in the forearm and a *plantaris* muscle in the leg, but not everyone has them. Most of us have five lumbar vertebrae (bones of the lower spine), but some have four and some have six. Most of us have one spleen, but some people have two. Most have two kidneys, but some have only one. Most kidneys are supplied by a single *renal artery* and drained by one *ureter*, but in some people, a single kidney has two renal arteries or ureters. Figure 1.4 shows some common variations in human anatomy, and Insight 1.1 describes a particularly dramatic variation.

### THINK ABOUT IT

*People who are allergic to penicillin or aspirin often wear Medic Alert bracelets or necklaces that note this fact in case they need emergency treatment and cannot communicate. Why would it be important for a person with situs inversus (see Insight 1.1) to have this noted on a Medic Alert bracelet?*

---

[10]*sono* = sound + *graphy* = recording process

## INSIGHT 1.1

### Clinical Application

## Situs Inversus and Other Unusual Anatomy

In most people, the heart tilts toward the left, the spleen and sigmoid colon are on the left, the liver and gallbladder lie mainly on the right, the appendix is on the right, and so forth. This normal arrangement of the viscera is called *situs* (SITE-us) *solitus.* About 1 in 8,000 people are born, however, with a striking developmental abnormality called *situs inversus*—the organs of the thoracic and abdominal cavities are reversed between right and left. A selective left–right reversal of the heart is called *dextrocardia.* In *situs perversus,* a single organ occupies an atypical position, not necessarily a left–right reversal—for example, a kidney located low in the pelvic cavity instead of high in the abdominal cavity.

Some conditions, such as dextrocardia in the absence of complete situs inversus, can cause serious medical problems. Complete situs inversus, however, usually causes no functional problems because all of the viscera, though reversed, maintain their normal relationships to each other. Situs inversus is often diagnosed prenatally by sonography, but many people remain unaware of their condition for several decades until it is discovered by medical imaging, on physical examination, or in surgery. However, you can easily imagine the importance of such conditions in diagnosing appendicitis, performing gallbladder surgery, interpreting an X-ray, auscultating the heart valves, or recording an electrocardiogram.

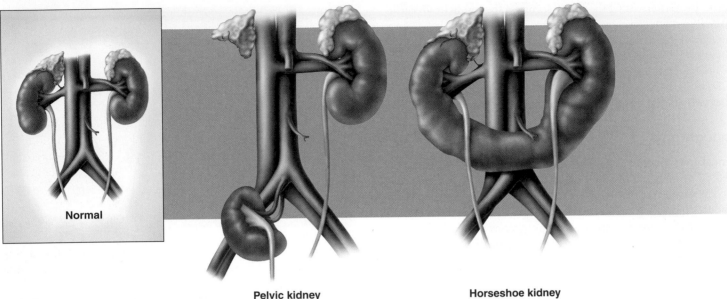

**Normal**

**Pelvic kidney**

**Horseshoe kidney**

**Normal**

**Variations in branches of the aorta**

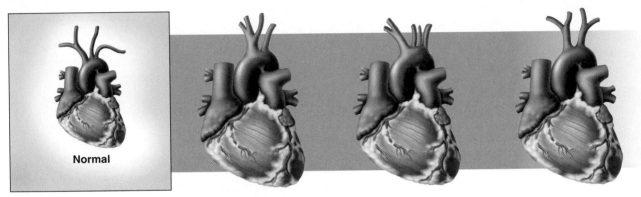

**Figure 1.4** Variations in Anatomy of the Kidneys and Major Arteries Near the Heart.
● *Why is it important for medical students to study multiple cadavers and not learn anatomy from only one?*

## Levels of Human Structure

Although this book is concerned mainly with gross anatomy, the study of human structure spans all levels from the organismal to the subatomic. Consider for a moment an analogy to human structure: The English language, like the human body, is very complex, yet an endless array of ideas can be conveyed with a limited number of words. All words in the English language are, in turn, composed of various combinations of just 26 letters. Between an essay and the alphabet are successively simpler levels of organization: paragraphs, sentences, words, and syllables. Language has a hierarchy of complexity, with letters, syllables, words, and so forth being successive levels of the hierarchy. Humans have an analogous hierarchy of complexity (fig. 1.5), as follows:

The organism is composed of organ systems,

organ systems are composed of organs,

organs are composed of tissues,

tissues are composed (in part) of cells,

cells are composed (in part) of organelles,

organelles are composed of molecules,

molecules are composed of atoms, and

atoms are composed of subatomic particles.

The **organism** is a single, complete individual.

An **organ system** is a group of organs that carry out a basic function of the organism such as circulation, respiration, or di-

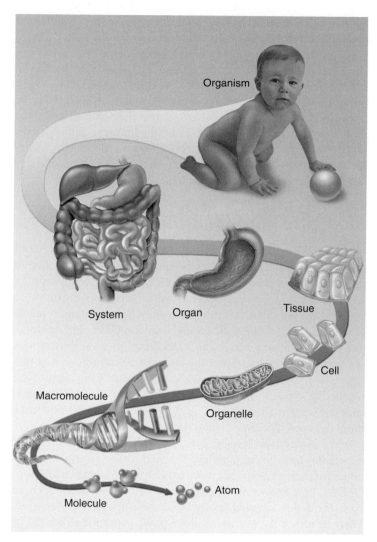

**Figure 1.5** **The Body's Structural Hierarchy.** Each level depends on the structure and function of the level below it.

Labels in figure: Organism, System, Organ, Tissue, Macromolecule, Cell, Organelle, Molecule, Atom

gestion. The human body has 11 organ systems, defined and illustrated in atlas A following this chapter: the integumentary, skeletal, muscular, nervous, endocrine, circulatory, lymphatic, respiratory, urinary, digestive, and reproductive systems. Usually, the organs of a system are physically interconnected, such as the kidneys, ureters, urinary bladder, and urethra that compose the urinary system. The endocrine system, however, is a group of hormone-secreting glands and tissues that, for the most part, have no physical connection to each other.

An **organ** is a structure composed of two or more tissue types that work together to carry out a particular function. Organs have definite anatomical boundaries and are visibly distinguishable from adjacent structures. A single organ can belong to two organ systems. For example, the pancreas belongs to both the endocrine and digestive systems. Most organs and higher levels

of structure are within the domain of gross anatomy. However, there are organs within organs—the large organs visible to the naked eye often contain smaller organs visible only with the microscope. The skin, for example, is the body's largest organ. Included within it are thousands of smaller organs: each hair follicle, nail, sweat gland, nerve, and blood vessel of the skin is an organ in itself.

A **tissue** is a mass of similar cells and cell products that forms a discrete region of an organ and performs a specific function. The body is composed of only four primary classes of tissue—epithelial, connective, nervous, and muscular tissues. *Histology,* the study of tissues, is the subject of chapter 3.

**Cells** are the smallest units of an organism that carry out all the basic functions of life; nothing simpler than a cell is considered alive. A cell is enclosed in a *plasma membrane* composed of lipids and protein. Most cells have one *nucleus,* an organelle that contains most of its DNA. *Cytology,* the study of cells and organelles, is the subject of chapter 2.

**Organelles**[11] are microscopic structures in a cell that carry out its individual functions. Examples include mitochondria, centrioles, and lysosomes.

Organelles and other cellular components are composed of **molecules.** The largest molecules, such as proteins, fats, and DNA, are called *macromolecules.* A molecule is a particle composed of at least two **atoms,** and an atom is composed of **subatomic particles**—protons, neutrons, and electrons.

## THINK ABOUT IT

*Architect Louis Henri Sullivan coined the phrase, "Form ever follows function." What do you think he meant by this? Discuss how this idea could be applied to the human body and cite a specific example of human anatomy to support it. Identify some exceptions to this rule.*

## *Before You Go On*

Answer the following questions to test your understanding of the preceding section:

1. How does functional morphology differ from the sort of anatomy taught by a photographic atlas of the body?

2. Why would regional anatomy be a better learning approach than systemic anatomy for a cadaver dissection course?

3. What is the difference between radiology and radiography?

4. What are some reasons that sonography would be unsuitable for examining the size and location of a brain tumor?

5. Put the following list in order from the largest and most complex to the smallest and least complex components of the human body: cells, molecules, organelles, organs, organ systems, tissues.

[11]*elle* = little

# Early Anatomists

## Objectives

When you have completed this section, you should be able to

- describe the major contributions of ancient Greece and Rome to anatomy;
- identify some contributors to medicine in the Middle Ages;
- describe the change that anatomy underwent in the Renaissance; and
- discuss the origin and importance of microscopic anatomy.

Any science is more enjoyable if we consider not just the current state of knowledge, but how it compares to past understandings of the subject and how our current knowledge was gained. Of all sciences, medicine has one of the most fascinating histories. Medical science has progressed far more in the last 50 years than in the 2,500 years before that, but the field did not spring up overnight. It is built upon centuries of thought and controversy, triumph and defeat. We cannot fully understand its present state without understanding people who had the curiosity to try new things, the vision to look at human form and function in new ways, and the courage to question authority.

## The Greek and Roman Legacy

Anatomy is an ancient human interest, undoubtedly older than any written language we know. We can only guess when people began deliberately cutting into human bodies out of curiosity, simply to know what was inside. The Greek philosopher **Aristotle** (384–322 BCE) was one of the earliest to write about anatomy. In his book *Of the Parts of Animals*, he tried to identify unifying themes in anatomy and argued that complex structures are built from a smaller variety of simple components—as we have seen in our look at the hierarchy of human structure. Aristotle believed that diseases and other natural events could have either supernatural causes, which he called *theologi*, or natural ones, which he called *physici* or *physiologi*. We derive such terms as *physician* and *physiology* from the latter. Until the nineteenth century, physicians were called "doctors of physic."

**Herophilus** (c. 335–280 BCE) was the most experienced anatomist of antiquity. A Greek working at Alexandria, Egypt, he dissected hundreds of cadavers and gave public demonstrations of anatomy. He named the duodenum; wrote good descriptions of the retina, optic nerve, ovaries, uterus, prostate gland, liver, and pancreas; and distinguished between cranial and spinal nerves, sensory and motor nerves, and arteries and veins. His work remained the highest achievement in human anatomy until the Renaissance.

But **Claudius Galen** (129–c. 199 CE), Greek-born physician to the Roman gladiators, was more influential. His medical textbook was worshipped to excess by European medical professors for centuries to follow. Cadaver dissection was banned in Galen's time because of some horrid excesses that preceded him, including public dissections of living slaves and prisoners. Aside from what he could learn by treating the gladiators' wounds, Galen was therefore limited to dissecting pigs, monkeys, and other animals. Because he was not permitted to dissect cadavers, he had to guess at much of human anatomy and made some incorrect deductions from animal dissections. He described the human liver, for example, as having five fingerlike lobes, somewhat like a baseball glove, because that is what he had seen in baboons. But Galen saw science as a method of discovery, not as a body of fact to be taken on faith. He knew that he might be wrong, and he advised his followers to trust their own observations more than they trusted any book, including his own. Unfortunately, his advice was not heeded. For nearly 1,500 years, medical professors dogmatically taught what they read in Aristotle and Galen, and few dared to question the authority of these "ancient masters."

## Medicine in the Middle Ages

In the Middle Ages, the state of medical science varied greatly from one religious culture to another. Science was severely repressed in the Christian culture of Europe until about the sixteenth century, although some of the most famous medical schools of Europe were founded during this era. Their professors, however, taught medicine primarily as a dogmatic commentary on Galen and Aristotle, not as a field of original research. Medieval medical illustrations were crude representations of the body intended more to decorate a page than to depict the body realistically. Some were astrological charts that showed which sign of the zodiac was thought to influence each organ of the body (fig. 1.6). From such pseudoscience came the word *influenza,* Italian for *influence.*

Free inquiry was less inhibited in Jewish and Muslim culture during this time. Jewish physicians were the most esteemed practitioners of their art, and none more famous than **Moses ben Maimon** (1135–1204), known in Christendom as **Maimonides.** Born in Spain, he fled to Egypt at age 24 to escape antisemitic persecution. There he served the rest of his life as physician to the eldest son of the sultan Saladin. A highly admired rabbi, Maimonides wrote voluminously on Jewish law and theology, but also wrote 10 influential medical books and numerous treatises on specific diseases.

Probably the most influential Muslim physician was **Ibn-Sina,** known in Europe as **Avicenna** (980–1037), court physician to the vizier of southern Persia. He wrote 16 medical treatises, most famously the *Canon of Medicine*—a five-volume, million-word encyclopedia of medical knowledge up to that time. The *Canon* was widely translated and became a leading reference for over 500 years in European medical schools, where Avicenna was nicknamed "the Galen of Islam."

**Ibn an-Nafis** (1210–88) was the personal physician of the sultan of Egypt. He discovered the pulmonary circuit and coronary circulation and corrected many of the errors of Galen and Avicenna. His work remained largely unknown in Europe for 300 years, but after his books were rediscovered and translated to Latin in 1547, they strongly influenced leading European anatomists including Vesalius, discussed next.

## The Birth of Modern Anatomy

**Andreas Vesalius** (1514–64) is commonly regarded as the pioneer of modern anatomy. He was a Flemish physician who taught in Italy. In his time, cadaver dissection had resumed for legal purposes

the first to publish accurate anatomical illustrations (fig. 1.7). When others began to plagiarize them, Vesalius published the first atlas of anatomy, *De Humani Corporis Fabrica (On the Structure of the Human Body)*, in 1543. This book began a rich tradition of medical illustration that has been handed down through the vividly illustrated atlases and textbooks of today.

## The Discovery of Microscopic Anatomy

Modern anatomy also owes an enormous debt to two inventors from this era, Robert Hooke and Antony van Leeuwenhoek, who extended the vision of biologists to the cellular level.

**Robert Hooke** (1635–1703), an Englishman, designed scientific instruments of various kinds and made many improvements in the compound microscope. This is a tube with a lens at each end (fig. 1.8a)—an *objective lens* near the specimen, which produces an initial magnified image, and an *ocular lens (eyepiece)* near the observer's eye, which magnifies the first image still further. Although crude compound microscopes had existed since 1595, Hooke improved the optics and invented several of the helpful features found in microscopes today—a stage to hold the specimen, an illuminator,

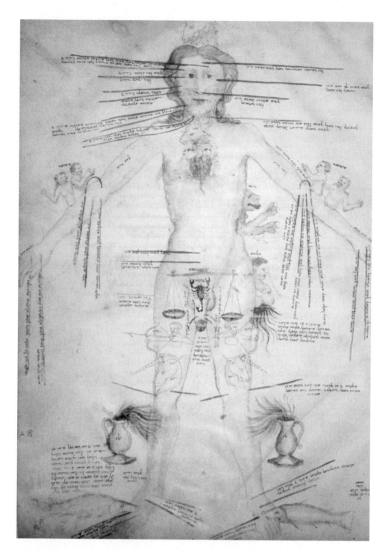

**Figure 1.6 Zodiacal Man.** This illustration from a fifteenth-century medical manuscript reflects the medieval belief in the influence of astrology on parts of the body.

(autopsies) and gradually found its way into the training of medical students throughout Europe. Furthermore, the Italian Renaissance created an environment more friendly to creative scholarship within Christendom. Dissection was an unpleasant business, however, and most professors considered it beneath their dignity. In those days before refrigeration or embalming, the odor from the decaying cadaver was unbearable. Dissections were often conducted outdoors in a nonstop 4-day race against decay. Bleary medical students had to fight the urge to vomit, lest they offend their overbearing professor. The professor typically sat in an elevated chair, the *cathedra,* reading dryly from Galen or Aristotle while a lower-ranking *barber-surgeon* removed putrefying organs from the cadaver and held them up for the students to see. Barbering and surgery were considered to be "kindred arts of the knife"; today's barber poles date from this era, their red and white stripes symbolizing blood and bandages.

Vesalius broke with tradition by coming down from the cathedra and doing the dissections himself. He was quick to point out that Galen's books were wrong on many points, and he was

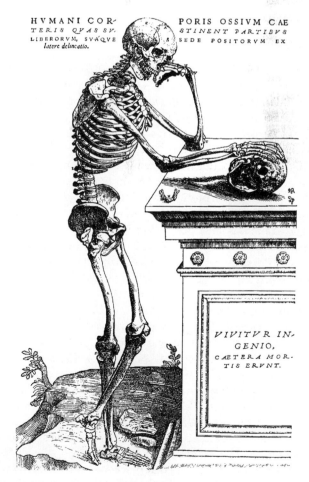

**Figure 1.7 The Art of Vesalius.** Andreas Vesalius revolutionized medical illustration with the realistic art commissioned for his 1543 book, *De Humani Corporis Fabrica.*

and coarse- and fine-focus controls. His microscopes magnified only about 30 times, but with them, he was the first to see and name cells. In 1663, he observed thin shavings of cork and observed that they "consisted of a great many little boxes," which he called *cellulae* (little cells) after the cubicles of a monastery (fig. 1.8b). He later observed thin slices of fresh wood and saw living cells "filled with juices." Hooke became particularly interested in microscopic examination of such material as insects, plant tissues, and animal parts. He published the first comprehensive book of microscopy, *Micrographia,* in 1665.

**Antony van Leeuwenhoek** (an-TOE-nee vahn LAY-wen-hook) (1632–1723), a Dutch textile merchant, invented a *simple* (single-lens) *microscope,* originally for the purpose of examining the weave of fabrics. His microscope was a beadlike lens mounted in a metal plate equipped with a movable specimen clip. Owing to Leeuwenhoek's superior lens-grinding skill, his microscopes magnified about 200 times. Out of curiosity, he examined a drop of lake water and was astonished to find a variety of microorganisms—"little animalcules," he called them, "very prettily a-swimming." He went on to observe practically everything he could get his hands on, including blood cells, blood capillaries, sperm, muscular tissue, and bacteria from tooth scrapings. Leeuwenhoek began submitting his observations to the Royal Society of London in 1673. He was praised at first, and his observations were eagerly read by scientists, but enthusiasm for the microscope did not last. By the end of the seventeenth century, it was treated as a mere toy for the upper classes, as amusing and meaningless as a kaleidoscope. Leeuwenhoek and Hooke had even become the brunt of satire. But probably no one in history had looked at nature in such a revolutionary way. By taking biology to the cellular level, the two men had laid an entirely new foundation for the modern medicine to follow centuries later.

The Hooke and Leeuwenhoek microscopes produced poor images with blurry edges (*spherical aberration*) and rainbow-colored distortions (*chromatic aberration*). These problems had to be solved before the microscope could be widely used as a biological tool. In nineteenth-century Germany, optician **Carl Zeiss** (1816–88) and his business partner, physicist **Ernst Abbe** (1840–1905), greatly improved the compound microscope, adding the condenser and developing superior optics. With improved microscopes, biologists began eagerly examining a wider variety of specimens. By 1839, botanist **Matthias Schleiden** (1804–81) and zoologist **Theodor Schwann** (1810–82) concluded that all organisms were composed of cells. Although it took another century for this idea to be generally accepted, it became the first tenet of the **cell theory,** added to by later biologists and summarized in chapter 2. The cell theory was perhaps the most important breakthrough in biomedical history; all functions of the body are now interpreted as the effects of cellular activity.

Although the philosophical foundation for modern medicine was largely established by the time of Leeuwenhoek and Hooke, clinical practice was still in a dismal state. Only a few doctors attended medical school or received any formal education in basic science or human anatomy. Physicians tended to be ignorant, ineffective, and pompous. Their practice was heavily based on expelling imaginary toxins from the body by bleeding their patients or inducing vomiting, sweating, or diarrhea. They performed operations with filthy hands and instruments, spreading lethal infections from one patient to another and refusing, in their vanity, to believe that they themselves were the carriers of disease. Countless women in childbirth died from infections acquired from their obstetricians. Fractured limbs often became gangrenous and had to be amputated, and there was no anesthesia to lessen the pain. Disease was still widely attributed to demons and witches, and many people felt they would be interfering with God's will if they tried to cure an illness.

The twentieth century saw vast improvements in medical education and the application of scientific observations to clinical practices. Modern medicine now progresses hand in hand with scientific research and changes as new information becomes available.

**(a)**                    **(b)**

**Figure 1.8** Hooke's Compound Microscope.  (a) The compound microscope had a lens at each end of a tubular body. (b) Hooke's drawing of cork cells, showing the thick cell walls characteristic of plants.

## Before You Go On

*Answer the following questions to test your understanding of the preceding section:*

6. In what way did the followers of Galen disregard his advice? How does Galen's advice apply to you?

7. Why did medical science develop more freely in Muslim countries than in Christian culture in the Middle Ages?

8. Describe two ways in which Vesalius improved medical education and set standards that remain relevant today.

9. How is our concept of human form and function today affected by the inventions of Leeuwenhoek and Hooke?

# The Nature of Human Life

## Objectives

When you have completed this section, you should be able to

- state the characteristics that distinguish living organisms from nonliving objects;
- outline the classification of humans within the animal kingdom; and
- describe the anatomical features that define "human" and distinguish humans from other animals.

This book is a study of human life, so before we go much further, we should consider what we mean by the expression, "human life." This is really two questions: What is life? and What is a human?

## What Is Life?

Why do we consider a growing child to be alive, but not a growing crystal? Is abortion the taking of a human life? If so, what about a contraceptive foam that kills only sperm? As a patient is dying, at what point does it become ethical to disconnect life-support equipment and remove organs for donation? If these organs are alive, as they must be to serve someone else, then why isn't the donor considered alive? Such questions have no easy answers, but they demand a concept of what life is—a concept that may differ with one's biological, medical, religious, or legal perspective.

From a biological viewpoint, life is not a single property. It is a collection of properties that help to distinguish living from nonliving things:

- **Organization.** Living things exhibit a far higher level of organization than the nonliving world around them. They expend a great deal of energy to maintain order, and a breakdown in this order is accompanied by disease and often death.
- **Cellular composition.** Living matter is always compartmentalized into one or more cells.
- **Biochemical unity.** All living things have a universal chemical composition that includes DNA, proteins, lipids, and carbohydrates. Such compounds are not found in anything of nonbiological origin.
- **Metabolism.**[12] Living things take in molecules from the environment and chemically change them into molecules that form their own structures, control their physiology, or provide energy. **Metabolism** is the sum of all this internal chemical change. It consists of two classes of reactions: *anabolism,*[13] in which relatively complex molecules are synthesized from simpler ones (for example, protein synthesis), and *catabolism,*[14] in which relatively complex molecules are broken down into simpler ones (for example, protein digestion). There is a constant turnover of molecules in the body;

although you sense a continuity of personality and experience from your childhood to the present, nearly every molecule of your body has been replaced within the past year.

- **Excitability.** The ability of organisms to sense and react to *stimuli* (changes in their environment) is called *excitability, irritability,* or *responsiveness.* It occurs at all levels from the single cell to the entire body, and it characterizes all living things from bacteria to humans. Responsiveness is especially obvious in animals because of nerve and muscle cells that exhibit high sensitivity to environmental stimuli, rapid transmission of information, and quick reactions.
- **Homeostasis.**[15] **Homeostasis** is the tendency for the internal conditions of the body to remain stable in spite of changes in the environment around the organism. Homeostasis is the purpose of nearly all normal physiology. There are hormonal and neural mechanisms, for example, for maintaining a stable body temperature, blood pressure, and blood glucose concentration. As a case in point, if your body temperature drops, blood vessels of the skin constrict to minimize heat loss, and you may shiver to generate more heat. If the body becomes too warm, blood vessels of the skin dilate and you may sweat to enhance heat loss.
- **Growth.** Some nonliving things grow, but not in the way your body does. When a saturated sugar solution evaporates, crystals grow from it, but not through a change in the composition of the sugar. They merely add more sugar molecules from the solution to the crystal surface. The growth of the body, by contrast, occurs through chemical change; for the most part, the body is not composed of the molecules one eats, but of molecules made by chemically altering the food.
- **Development.** Development is any change in form or function over the lifetime of the organism. It includes not only growth, but also *differentiation*—the transformation of cells and tissues with no specialized function into ones that are committed to a particular task. For example, a single embryonic, unspecialized tissue called mesoderm differentiates into muscle, bone, cartilage, blood, and several other specialized tissues.
- **Reproduction.** Living organisms produce copies of themselves at some point in their life cycles, thus passing their genes on to new, younger "containers"—their offspring.
- **Evolution.** All living species exhibit genetic change from generation to generation, and therefore evolve. This occurs because *mutations* (changes in the genes) are inevitable and environmental conditions favor some individuals over others, thus perpetuating some genes and eliminating others from the population. Unlike the other characteristics of life, evolution is a characteristic seen only in the population as a whole. No single individual evolves over the course of its life.

Clinical and legal criteria of life differ from these biological criteria. A person who has shown no brain waves for 24 hours and has no reflexes, respiration, or heartbeat other than what is provided

---

[12]*metabol* = change + *ism* = process
[13]*anabol* = buildup + *ism* = process
[14]*catabol* = cast down + *ism* = process

[15]*homeo* = the same + *stasis* = stability

by artificial life support can be declared legally dead. At such time, however, most of the body is still biologically alive, and its organs may be useful for transplant.

## What Is a Human?

Our second question was What is a human? We belong to the animal kingdom—as opposed to plants, fungi, protists, or bacteria—but what distinguishes us from other animals? To answer this, it helps to begin with an outline of our classification within the kingdom Animalia. We belong to each of the following progressively smaller groups:

Phylum Chordata

Subphylum Vertebrata

Class Mammalia

Order Primates

Family Hominidae

Genus *Homo*

Species *Homo sapiens*

(A species name is always a two-word name that includes the genus.)

### Our Chordate Characteristics

What identifies us as chordates? During the course of human embryonic development, we exhibit the following structures:

- *Pharyngeal arches,* a series of bulges that develop in the pharyngeal (throat) region (fig. 1.9). *Pharyngeal pouches* between these open and form gill slits in fish and amphibians, but not in humans.
- A *tail* that extends beyond the anus. The small bones of the *coccyx* ("tailbone") remain after birth as a remnant of this.
- A *notochord,* a dorsal, flexible rod found only in the embryo.
- A dorsal hollow *nerve cord,* a column of nervous tissue that passes along the dorsal (upper) side of the body and has a central canal filled with fluid.

The first three of these features are found only in the embryo and fetus; only the nerve cord persists through life, as the spinal cord and brain.

These four features identify humans as members of the phylum *Chordata.* They distinguish us from nonchordates such as clams, worms, and insects, but not from fellow chordates such as fish, lizards, and birds. They only begin to narrow down our concept of what it means, anatomically, to be human.

### Our Vertebrate Characteristics

The following human features are shared by all *Vertebrata*[16]—a subphylum that includes fish, amphibians, reptiles, birds, and mammals:

- A well-developed brain and sense organs.
- An internal skeleton.
- A jointed *vertebral column* (spine).
- A protective, usually bony enclosure for the brain, called the *cranium.*

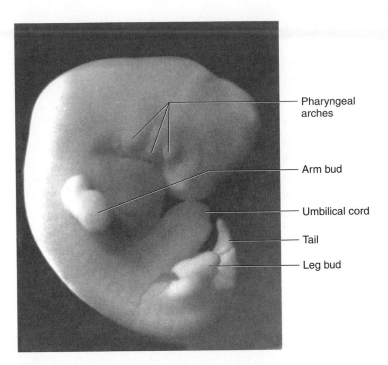

**Figure 1.9** **Primitive Chordate Characteristics in Humans.** This 38-day human embryo shows the tail and pharyngeal arches that characterize all Chordata at some point in their development.
● *What does the embryonic tail suggest about the evolutionary history of Homo sapiens?*

Labels: Pharyngeal arches / Arm bud / Umbilical cord / Tail / Leg bud

### Our Mammalian Characteristics

To narrow things down further, humans are members of the class *Mammalia.*[17] Mammals share the following characteristics:

- *Mammary glands* for nourishing the young with milk.
- Hair, which serves in most mammals to retain body heat.
- *Endothermy,*[18] the ability to generate most body heat by metabolic means instead of having to warm up by basking in the sun or seeking other warm places.
- *Heterodonty,*[19] the possession of varied types of teeth (incisors, canines, premolars, and molars) specialized to puncture, cut, and grind food. These varied teeth break food into small pieces, making chemical digestion faster. Rapid digestion is necessary to support the high metabolic rate needed to maintain endothermic animals.
- A single lower jawbone (mandible).
- Three middle-ear bones (known colloquially as the *hammer, anvil,* and *stirrup*).

Fewer than 0.2% of the known animal species are mammals. Thus, we have narrowed down the classification of humans quite a lot, but still have not distinguished ourselves from rats, horses, dogs, or monkeys, which also have the characteristics listed so far.

---

[16]*vertebr* = backbone + *ata* = possessing
[17]*mamma* = breast + *alia* = possessing
[18]*endo* = within + *therm* = heat
[19]*hetero* = different, varied + *odont* = teeth

## Our Primate and Hominid Characteristics

Mammals are divided into as many as 26 orders. Humans belong to the *Primates,* an order that contains about 4% of the mammals including not just humans but also apes, monkeys, lemurs, and a few other species. We and most other primates have the following characteristics:

- Four upper and four lower incisors, the front cutting teeth.
- A pair of functional *clavicles* (collarbones).
- Only two mammary glands.
- Forward-facing eyes with stereoscopic vision.
- Flat *nails* in place of claws.
- *Opposable thumbs* that can touch the fingertips, enabling the hand to encircle and grasp objects (fig. 1.10).

Humans are in the family **Hominidae** (ho-MIN-ih-dee). Over the course of their evolutionary history, members of this family have shown a trend toward exceptionally large brains, complex symbolic speech, and sophisticated tool making. However, the clearest distinction between hominids and other primates is *bipedalism,*[20] the habit of walking on two legs. Authorities have several contrasting definitions of *hominid,* but for present purposes, we will consider them to be the bipedal primates.

Numerous fossil hominids span the last 6 million years. Most of them are classified in the early genus *Australopithecus* (aus-TRAL-oh-PITH-eh-cus) or the more recent genus *Homo. Homo sapiens* is the only surviving species. There is no unanimously accepted definition of *human.* Some authorities treat all Hominidae as humans; some restrict the word *human* to the genus *Homo;* and some go even further and limit it to *Homo sapiens.*

---

[20]*bi* = two + *ped* = foot

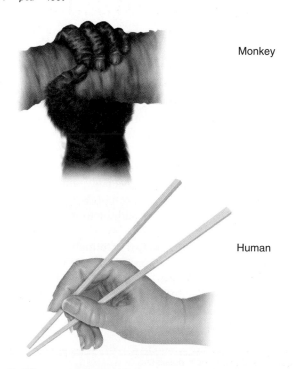

Monkey

Human

**Figure 1.10** **Primate Hands.** The opposable thumb makes the primate hand prehensile, able to encircle and grasp objects.

### *Before You Go On*

*Answer the following questions to test your understanding of the preceding section:*

10. List four biological criteria of life and one clinical criterion. Explain how a person could be considered clinically dead but biologically alive.

11. Explain why humans are classified as vertebrates, why they are classified as mammals, and why they are classified as primates.

12. What are the defining characteristics of hominids? Why is *Homo sapiens* considered to be in the family Hominidae?

# The Evolution of Human Structure

### *Objectives*
When you have completed this section, you should be able to

- define *evolution, natural selection,* and *adaptation;*
- explain the relevance of evolution to medical science;
- explain how the tree-dwelling habits of early primates account for certain aspects of modern human anatomy; and
- describe some human characteristics that evolved in connection with upright walking.

If any two theories have the broadest implications for understanding the human body, they are probably the cell theory and the theory of natural selection. *Natural selection,* an explanation of how species originate and change through time, was the brainchild primarily of **Charles Darwin** (1809–82)—probably the most influential biologist who ever lived. His book *On the Origin of Species by Means of Natural Selection* (1859) has been called "the book that shook the world." In presenting the first well-supported theory of evolution, the *Origin of Species* not only caused the restructuring of all of biology, but also profoundly changed the prevailing view of our origin, nature, and place in the universe.

While the *Origin of Species* scarcely touched upon human biology, its unmistakable implications for humans created an intense storm of controversy that continues even today. In *The Descent of Man* (1871), Darwin directly addressed the issue of human evolution and emphasized features of anatomy and behavior that reveal our relationship to other animals. More recent studies of fossils, comparative anatomy, and genetics have confirmed Darwin's original insights and provided rich details about human evolution. No understanding of human form and function is complete without an understanding of our evolutionary history.

## Evolution, Selection, and Adaptation

**Evolution** simply means change in the genetic composition of a population of organisms. Examples include the evolution of bacterial resistance to antibiotics, the appearance of new strains of the AIDS virus, and the emergence of new species of organisms.

**Natural selection,** the principal theory of how evolution works, is essentially this: Some individuals within a species have hereditary advantages over their competitors—for example, better camouflage, disease resistance, or ability to attract mates—that enable them to produce more offspring. They pass these advantages on to their offspring, and such characteristics therefore become more and more common in successive generations. This brings about the genetic change in a population that constitutes evolution.

Natural forces that favor some individuals over others are called **selection pressures.** They include such things as climate, predators, disease, competition, and the availability of food. **Adaptations** are features of a species' anatomy, physiology, and behavior that have evolved in response to selection pressures and enable the organism to cope with the challenges of its environment. We will consider shortly some selection pressures and adaptations that were important to human evolution.

Several aspects of our anatomy make little sense without an awareness that the human body has a history (see Insight 1.2). Our evolutionary relationship to other species is also important in choosing animals for biomedical research. If there were no issues of cost, availability, or ethics, we might test drugs on our close living relatives, the chimpanzees, before approving them for human use. Their genetics, anatomy, and physiology are most similar to ours, and their reactions to drugs therefore afford the best prediction of how the human body would react. On the other hand, if we had no kinship with any other species, the selection of a test species would be arbitrary; we might as well use frogs or snails. In reality, we compromise. Rats and mice are used extensively for research because they are fellow mammals with a physiology similar to ours, but present fewer of the aforementioned issues than chimpanzees or other mammals do. An animal species or strain selected for research on a particular problem is called a **model**—for example, a mouse model for leukemia.

### THINK ABOUT IT

*The human species may yet undergo evolutionary change, but it is impossible for any one person to do so. Explain why.*

## Life in the Trees

As we have already seen, humans belong to the order Primates, which also includes the monkeys and apes. Primates originated 55 to 60 million years ago, when certain squirrel-sized, insect-eating mammals (insectivores) took up life in the trees. This **arboreal**[21] (treetop) habitat probably afforded greater safety from predators, less competition, and a rich food supply of leaves, fruits, insects, and lizards. But the forest canopy is a challenging world, with dim and dappled sunlight, swaying branches, and prey darting about in the dense foliage. Any new feature that enabled arboreal animals to move about more easily in the treetops would have been strongly favored by natural selection. Thus, the shoulder became more mobile, enabling primates to reach out in any direction (even

### INSIGHT 1.2

#### Evolutionary Medicine

### Vestiges of Human Evolution

One of the classic lines of evidence for evolution, debated even before Darwin was born, is *vestigial organs.* These structures are the reduced remnants of organs that apparently were more functional in the ancestors of a species. They now serve little or no purpose or, in some cases, have been converted to new functions.

Our bodies, for example, are covered with millions of hairs, each equipped with a useless little muscle called a *piloerector.* In other mammals, these muscles fluff the hair and conserve heat. In humans, they merely produce goosebumps. Above each ear, we have three *auricularis* muscles. In other mammals, they move the ears to receive sounds better or to repel flies and other pests, but most people cannot contract them at all. As Darwin said, it makes no sense that humans would have such structures were it not for the fact that we came from nonhuman ancestors in which they were functional.

overhead, which other mammals cannot do). The thumbs became opposable and thus made the hands **prehensile**[22]—able to grasp objects by encircling them with the thumb and fingers (fig. 1.10). The thumb is so important to us that it receives highest priority in the repair of hand injuries. If the thumb can be saved, the hand can be reasonably functional; if it is lost, hand functions are severely diminished.

The eyes of primates moved to a more forward-facing position (fig. 1.11), allowing for **stereoscopic**[23] **vision** (depth perception). This adaptation allows better hand–eye coordination in catching and manipulating prey, with the added advantage of making it easier to judge distances accurately in leaping from tree to tree. Color vision, rare among mammals, is also a primate hallmark. Primates eat mainly fruit and leaves. The ability to distinguish subtle shades of orange and red enables them to distinguish ripe, sugary fruits from unripe ones. Distinguishing subtle shades of green helps them to differentiate between tender young leaves and tough, more toxic older foliage.

Various fruits ripen at different times and widely separated places in the tropical forest. This requires a good memory of what will be available, when it will be available, and how to get to it. Larger brains may have evolved in response to the challenge of efficient food finding and, in turn, laid the foundation for more sophisticated social organization.

None of this is meant to imply that humans evolved from monkeys or modern apes—a common misconception about evolution that no biologist believes. Monkeys, apes, and humans do, however, share common ancestors. Our relationship is not like parent and child, but more like cousins who have the same grandparents.

---

[21]*arbor* = tree + *eal* = pertaining to

[22]*prehens* = to seize
[23]*stereo* = solid + *scop* = vision

**Figure 1.11** **Primitive Tool Use in a Chimpanzee.** Chimpanzees exhibit the prehensile hands and forward-facing eyes typical of most primates. Such traits endow primates with stereoscopic vision and good hand–eye coordination, two supremely important factors in human evolution.

| TABLE 1.1 | Brain Volumes of the Hominidae | |
|---|---|---|
| **Genus or Species** | **Time of Origin (millions of years ago)** | **Brain Volume (cc)** |
| *Australopithecus* | 3–4 | 400 |
| Early *Homo* | 2.5 | 650 |
| *Homo erectus* | 2.0 | 1,100 |
| *Homo sapiens* | 0.2 | 1,350 |

Observations of monkeys and apes provide insight into how primates have adapted to the arboreal habitat, and therefore into how certain aspects of human anatomy probably originated.

## Walking Upright

About 4 to 5 million years ago, parts of Africa became hotter and drier, and much of the forest was replaced by savanna (grassland). Some primates adapted to living on the savanna, but this was a dangerous place with more predators and less protection. Just as squirrels stand briefly on their hind legs to look around for danger, so would these early ground-dwelling primates. Being able to stand up not only helps an animal stay alert, but also frees the forelimbs for purposes other than walking. Chimpanzees sometimes walk upright to carry food, infants, or weapons (sticks and rocks), and it is reasonable to suppose that our early ancestors did so too. Fossil evidence suggests that bipedalism was firmly established more than 4 million years ago; footprints of bipedal hominids have been preserved in volcanic ash in Tanzania dated to 3.6 million years ago.

Scientists have proposed several hypotheses to explain the evolution of bipedalism, including the ability to walk efficiently for long distances between food patches; to look for predators in tall grass; and to use the forelimbs for carrying offspring, food, or weapons. Probably a combination of advantages led to the transition to the form of locomotion that is now unique to hominids. These benefits were so great they favored musculoskeletal modifications that made bipedalism easier—changes in the pelvis, femur, knee, great toe, foot arches, spinal column, skull, arms, and many muscles.

Changes in pelvic shape included narrowing of the outlet through which an infant's head passes during birth. Meanwhile, brain volume increased dramatically (table 1.1). It must have become increasingly difficult for a fully developed, large-brained infant to pass through the mother's pelvic outlet at birth. This may explain why humans are born in a relatively immature, helpless state compared to other mammals, before their nervous systems have matured and the bones of the skull have fused. The relative helplessness of human young and their extended dependence on parental care may explain why human family ties are exceptionally strong.

Most of the oldest bipedal primates are classified in the genus *Australopithecus*. About 2.5 million years ago, hominids appeared with taller stature, greater brain volumes, simple stone tools, and probably articulate speech. These are the earliest members of the genus *Homo*. By at least 1.8 million years ago, *Homo erectus* migrated from Africa to parts of Asia. *Homo sapiens* originated in Africa about 200,000 years ago (fig. 1.12) and is the sole surviving hominid species.

This brief account barely begins to explain how human anatomy, physiology, and behavior have been shaped by ancient selection pressures. Later chapters further demonstrate that the evolutionary perspective provides a meaningful understanding of why humans are the way we are. Evolution is the basis for comparative anatomy and physiology, which have been so fruitful for the understanding of human biology. The emerging science of **evolutionary (darwinian) medicine** traces some of our diseases and imperfections to our evolutionary past.

## *Before You Go On*

Answer the following questions to test your understanding of the preceding section:

13. Define *adaptation* and *selection pressure*. Why are these concepts important in understanding human anatomy?

14. Select any two human characteristics and explain how they may have originated in primate adaptations to an arboreal habitat.

15. Select two other human characteristics and explain how they may have resulted from adaptation to a savanna habitat.

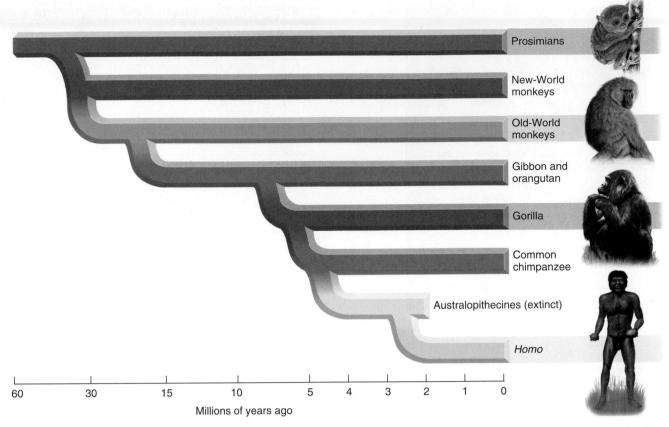

**Figure 1.12 The Place of Humans in Primate Evolution.** Figures at the right show representative primates. The branch points in this "family tree" show approximate times that different lines diverged from a common ancestor. Note that the timescale is not uniform; recent events are expanded for clarity.
● *Which is more closely related to* Homo sapiens—*a gorilla or a monkey? How long ago did the last common ancestor of chimpanzees and humans exist?*

# The Language of Anatomy

### Objectives
When you have completed this section, you should be able to

- explain why modern anatomical terminology is so heavily based on Greek and Latin;

- recognize eponyms when you see them;

- describe the efforts to achieve an internationally uniform anatomical terminology;

- discuss the Greek, Latin, or other derivations of medical terms;

- state some reasons why the literal meaning of a word may not lend insight into its definition;

- relate singular noun forms to their plural forms; and

- discuss why precise spelling is important to anatomical communication.

One of the greatest challenges faced by students of anatomy and physiology is the vocabulary. In this book, you will encounter such Latin terms as *corpus callosum* (a brain structure), *ligamentum arteriosum* (a small fibrous band near the heart), and *extensor carpi radialis longus* (a forearm muscle). You may wonder why structures aren't named in "just plain English," and how you will ever remember such formidable names. This section will give you some answers to these questions and some useful tips on mastering anatomical terminology.

## The History of Anatomical Terminology

The major features of human gross anatomy have standard international names prescribed by a book titled the *Terminologia Anatomica* (TA). The TA was codified in 1998 by an international body of anatomists, the Federated Committee on Anatomical Terminology, and approved by professional associations of anatomists in more than 50 countries.

About 90% of today's medical terms are formed primarily from about 1,200 Greek and Latin roots. Scientific investigation began in ancient Greece and soon spread to Rome. The ancient Greeks and Romans coined many of the words still used in human anatomy today: *duodenum, uterus, prostate, cerebellum, diaphragm, sacrum, amnion,* and others. In the Renaissance, the fast pace of anatomical discovery required a profusion of new terms to describe things. Anatomists in different countries began giving different names to the same structures. Adding to the confusion, they often named new structures and diseases in honor of their esteemed teachers and predecessors, giving us such nondescript terms as the *fallopian tube* and *duct of Santorini*. Terms coined from the names of people, called **eponyms,**[24] afford little clue as to what a structure or condition is.

In hopes of resolving this growing confusion, anatomists began meeting as early as 1895 to try to devise a uniform international terminology. After several false starts, a list of terms titled the *Nomina Anatomica* (NA) was agreed upon. The NA rejected all eponyms as unofficial and gave each structure a unique Latin name to be used worldwide. Even if you were to look at an anatomy atlas in Japanese or Arabic, the illustrations would be labeled with the same Latin terms as in an English-language atlas. The NA served for many decades until recently replaced by the TA, which prescribes both Latin names and accepted English equivalents. The terminology in this book conforms to the TA except where undue confusion would result from abandoning widely used, yet unofficial, terms.

## Analyzing Medical Terms

The task of learning anatomical terminology seems overwhelming at first, but there is a simple trick to becoming more comfortable with the technical language of medicine. People who find scientific terms confusing and difficult to pronounce, spell, and remember usually feel more confident once they realize the logic of how terms are composed. A term such as *hyponatremia* is less forbidding once we recognize that it is composed of three common word elements: *hypo-* (below normal), *natr-* (sodium), and *-emia* (blood condition). Thus, hyponatremia is a deficiency of sodium in the blood. Those three word elements appear over and over in many other medical terms: *hypothermia, natriuretic, anemia,* and so on. Once you learn the meanings of *hypo-, natri-,* and *-emia,* you already have the tools at least to partially understand hundreds of other biomedical terms. Inside the back cover, you will find a lexicon of the 400 word elements most commonly footnoted in this book.

Scientific terms are typically composed of one or more of the following elements:

- At least one *root (stem)* that bears the core meaning of the word. In *cardiology,* for example, the root is *cardi-* (heart). Many words have two or more roots. In *adipocyte,* the roots are *adip-* (fat) and *cyte* (cell).

- *Combining vowels,* which are often inserted to join roots and make the word easier to pronounce. The letter *o* is the most common combining vowel (as in *adipocyte*), but all vowels are used in this way, such as *a* in *ligament, e* in *vitreous,* the first *i* in *spermicidal, u* in *ovulation,* and *y* in *tachycardia.* Some words have no combining vowels. A combination of a root and combining vowel is called a *combining form:* for example, *odont* (tooth) + *o* (the combining vowel) make the combining form *odonto-,* as in *odontoblast* (a cell that produces the dentin of a tooth).

- A *prefix* may be present to modify the core meaning of the word. For example, *gastric* (pertaining to the stomach or to the belly of a muscle) takes on a wide variety of new meanings when prefixes are added to it: *epigastric* (above the stomach), *hypogastric* (below the stomach), *endogastric* (within the stomach), and *digastric* (a muscle with two bellies).

- A *suffix* may be added to the end of a word to modify its core meaning. For example, *microscope, microscopy, microscopic,* and *microscopist* have different meanings because of their suffixes alone. Often two or more suffixes, or a root and suffix, occur together so often that they are treated jointly as a *compound suffix;* for example, *log* (study) + *y* (process) form the compound suffix *-logy* (the study of).

To summarize these basic principles, consider the word *gastroenterology,* a branch of medicine dealing with the stomach and small intestine. It breaks down into

gastro/entero/logy

*gastro* = a combining form meaning "stomach"
*entero* = a combining form meaning "small intestine"
*logy* = a compound suffix meaning "the study of"

"Dissecting" words in this way and paying attention to the word-origin footnotes throughout this book will help make you more comfortable with the language of anatomy. Knowing how a word breaks down and knowing the meaning of its elements make it far easier to pronounce a word, spell it, and remember its definition.

There are a few unfortunate exceptions, however. The path from original meaning to current usage has often become obscured by history (see Insight 1.3). The foregoing approach also is no help with eponyms or **acronyms**—words composed of the first letter, or first few letters, of a series of words. For example, *calmodulin,* a calcium-binding protein found in many cells, is cobbled together from a few letters of the three words, *cal*cium *modul*ating prote*in.*

## INSIGHT 1.3

### Medical History

## Obscure Word Origins

The literal translation of a word doesn't always provide great insight into its modern meaning. The history of language is full of twists and turns that are fascinating in their own right and say much about the history of the whole of human culture, but they can create confusion for students.

For example, the *amnion* is a transparent sac that forms around the developing fetus. The word is derived from *amnos,* from the Greek for "lamb." From this origin, *amnos* came to mean a bowl for catching the blood of sacrificial lambs, and from there the word found its way into biomedical usage for the membrane that emerges (quite bloody) as part of the afterbirth. The *acetabulum,* the socket of the hip joint, literally means "vinegar cup." Apparently the hip socket reminded an anatomist of the little cups used to serve vinegar as a condiment on dining tables in ancient Rome. The word *testicles* literally means "little witnesses." The history of medical language has several amusing conjectures as to why this word was chosen to name the male gonads.

---

[24]*epo* = after, related to + *nym* = name

## Plural, Adjectival, and Possessive Forms

A point of confusion for many beginning students is how to recognize the plural forms of medical terms. Few people would fail to recognize that *ovaries* is the plural of *ovary*, but the connection is harder to make in other cases: For example, the plural of *cortex* is *cortices* (COR-ti-sees), the plural of *corpus* is *corpora*, and the plural of *epididymis* is *epididymides* (EP-ih-DID-ih-MID-eze). Table 1.2 will help you make the connection between common singular and plural noun terminals.

In some cases, what appers to the beginner to be two completely different words may be only the noun and adjectival forms of the same word. For example, *brachium* denotes the arm, and *brachii* (as in the muscle name *biceps brachii*) means "of the arm." *Carpus* denotes the wrist, and *carpi*, a word used in several muscle names, means "of the wrist." Adjectives can also take different forms for the singular and plural and for different degrees of comparison. The *digits* are the fingers and toes. The word *digiti* in a muscle name means "of a single finger (or toe)," whereas *digitorum* is the plural, meaning "of multiple fingers (or toes)." Thus, the *extensor digiti minimi* muscle extends only the little finger, whereas the *extensor digitorum* muscle extends all fingers except the thumb.

The English words *large*, *larger*, and *largest* are examples of the positive, comparative, and superlative degrees of comparison. In Latin, these are *magnus*, *major* (from *maior*), and *maximus*. We find these in the muscle names *adductor magnus* (a *large* muscle of the thigh), the *pectoralis major* (the *larger* of the two *pectoralis* muscles of the chest), and *gluteus maximus* (the *largest* of the three gluteal muscles of the buttock).

Some noun variations indicate the possessive, such as the *rectus abdominis*, a straight (*rectus*) muscle of the abdomen (*abdominis*, "of the abdomen"), and the *erector spinae*, a muscle that straightens (*erector*) the spinal column (*spinae*, "of the spine").

Anatomical terminology also frequently follows the Greek and Latin practice of placing the adjective after the noun. Thus, we have such names as the *stratum lucidum* for a clear (*lucidum*) layer (*stratum*) of the epidermis, the *foramen magnum* for a large (*magnum*) hole (*foramen*) in the skull, and the aforementioned *pectoralis major* muscle of the chest.

This is not to say that you must be conversant in Latin or Greek grammar to proceed with your study of anatomy. These few examples, however, may alert you to some patterns to watch for in the terminology you study, and ideally, will make your enccounters with anatomical terminology less confusing.

## The Importance of Precision

A final word of advice for your study of anatomy: Be precise in your use of anatomical terms. It may seem trivial if you misspell *trapezius* as *trapezium*, but in doing so, you would be changing the name of a back muscle to the name of a wrist bone. Similarly, changing *occipitalis* to *occipital* or *zygomaticus* to *zygomatic* changes other muscle names to bone names. A "little" error such as misspelling *ileum* as *ilium* changes the name of the final portion of the small intestine to the name of the hip bone. Changing *malleus* to *malleolus* changes the name of a middle-ear bone to the name of a bony protuberance of the ankle. *Elephantiasis* is a disease that produces an elephant-like thickening of the limbs and skin. Many people misspell this *elephantitis*; if such a word existed, it would mean inflammation of an elephant.

The health professions demand the utmost attention to detail and precision—people's lives may one day be in your hands. The habit of carefulness must extend to your use of language as well. Many patients die because of miscommunication in the hospital.

| TABLE 1.2 | Singular and Plural Forms of Some Noun Terminals | |
|---|---|---|
| **Singular Ending** | **Plural Ending** | **Examples** |
| -a | -ae | axilla, axillae |
| -ax | -aces | thorax, thoraces |
| -en | -ina | lumen, lumina |
| -ex | -ices | cortex, cortices |
| -is | -es | diagnosis, diagnoses |
| -is | -ides | epididymis, epididymides |
| -ix | -ices | appendix, appendices |
| -ma | -mata | carcinoma, carcinomata |
| -on | -a | ganglion, ganglia |
| -um | -a | septum, septa |
| -us | -era | viscus, viscera |
| -us | -i | villus, villi |
| -us | -ora | corpus, corpora |
| -x | -ges | phalanx, phalanges |
| -y | -ies | ovary, ovaries |
| -yx | -ices | calyx, calices |

### *Before You Go On*

*Answer the following questions to test your understanding of the preceding section:*

16. Explain why modern anatomical terminology is so heavily based on Greek and Latin.

17. Distinguish between an eponym and an acronym, and explain why both of these present difficulties for interpreting anatomical terms.

18. Break each of the following words down into its roots and affixes and state their meanings, following the example of *gastroenterology* analyzed earlier: *pericardium, appendectomy, subcutaneous, arteriosclerosis, hypercalcemia.* Consult the list of word elements inside the back cover of the book for help.

19. Write the singular form of each of the following words: *pleurae, gyri, foramina, ganglia, fissures.* Write the plural form of each of the following: *villus, tibia, encephalitis, cervix, stoma.*

# CHAPTER REVIEW

## REVIEW OF KEY CONCEPTS

### The Scope of Human Anatomy (p. 2)

1. *Functional morphology* is the study of anatomy not merely from the standpoint of the appearances and names of structures, but how structure relates to function.

2. Approaches to the study of anatomy include *gross, surface, radiologic, systemic, regional,* and *comparative anatomy. Microscopic anatomy (histology), cytology, histopathology,* and *ultrastructure* are studies of structure at the tissue to cellular level.

3. Methods of study include *inspection, palpation, auscultation, percussion,* and *dissection.*

4. The internal anatomy of a living person can be examined by such imaging methods as *radiography, computed tomography (CT), magnetic resonance imaging (MRI), positron emission tomography (PET),* and *sonography.*

5. Introductory textbooks teach the most typical anatomy of a given organ or system, but organs vary not only in appearance but also in number and location from one person to another.

6. The human body exhibits a hierarchy of structural complexity. From the largest and most complex, to the smallest and simplest, the principal levels of human structure are the *organism, organ systems, organs, tissues, cells, organelles, molecules,* and *atoms.*

### Early Anatomists (p. 8)

1. Some of the most innovative and influential anatomists of ancient Greece and Rome were *Aristotle, Herophilus,* and *Galen.*

2. In the Middle Ages, science and medicine developed little within Christian culture, but significant advances were made in Jewish culture by the physician *Maimonides* and in Muslim culture by such physician-scientists as *Ibn-Sina (Avicenna)* and *Ibn an-Nafis.*

3. Gross anatomy was modernized by Renaissance physician and professor *Andreas Vesalius,* who commissioned the first accurate anatomical art.

4. In the seventeenth to eighteenth centuries, *Robert Hooke* and *Antony van Leeuwenhoek* developed microscopes that extended the study of anatomy to the cellular level. *Carl Zeiss* and *Ernst Abbe* greatly improved microscopes in the early nineteenth century.

5. With such instruments, *Mathias Schleiden* and *Theodor Schwann* examined a broad range of plant and animal tissues and concluded that all organisms are composed of cells. The *cell theory* is one of the major foundations of modern anatomy, physiology, and medicine.

### The Nature of Human Life (p. 11)

1. Life is not a single, easily defined property. Rather, living organisms are distinguished from nonliving matter by a combination of characteristics: a high degree of organization, cellular composition, biochemical unity, metabolism, responsiveness, homeostasis, growth, development, reproduction, and evolution.

2. Clinical criteria of death typically include an absence of reflexes, respiration, heartbeat, and brain waves.

3. Within the animal kingdom, humans belong to the phylum *Chordata,* whose members have pharyngeal arches, a postanal tail, a notochord, and a dorsal hollow nerve cord.

4. Within the Chordata, humans belong to the subphylum *Vertebrata,* characterized by a well-developed brain and sense organs, internal skeleton, jointed vertebral column, and cranium.

5. Within the Vertebrata, humans belong to the class *Mammalia,* defined by mammary glands, hair, endothermy, heterodonty (varied types of teeth), a single mandible, and three middle-ear bones.

6. Within the Mammalia, humans belong to the order *Primates,* which also includes monkeys and apes. Primates are characterized by four upper and four lower incisors, a pair of functional clavicles, only two mammary glands, forward-facing eyes, flat nails, and opposable thumbs.

7. The family *Hominidae* contains the bipedal primates—those that habitually walk on two legs. In addition to bipedalism, hominids evolved larger brains, complex symbolic speech, and sophisticated tool making.

### The Evolution of Human Structure (p. 13)

1. Human anatomy is most fully understood from the standpoint of how it evolved.

2. *Natural selection* is a theory of evolution that says that populations evolve because some individuals have hereditary advantages over their competitors and pass those advantages to more offspring than their competitors do.

3. Environmental factors called *selection pressures*—such as climate, food, disease, and predation—shape the evolution of *adaptations* that promote survival and reproductive success.

4. The mobile shoulder, opposable thumbs, prehensile hands, stereoscopic vision, and color vision of humans are common to most primates, and probably first evolved as adaptations to selection pressures in the arboreal habitat of early primates.

5. Bipedalism, which entailed extensive remodeling of the skeleton, evolved later as an adaptation to the African savanna. Bipedalism, in turn, was probably a factor in the evolution of early childbirth and strong family ties of humans.

6. Humans belong to the species *Homo sapiens.* The genus *Homo* evolved from early bipedal primates in the genus *Australopithecus.*

7. Evolutionary medicine is a branch of medical science that interprets some human dysfunctions and diseases in terms of the evolutionary history of *Homo sapiens.*

### The Language of Anatomy (p. 16)

1. Anatomical and medical terminology, most of it derived from Latin and Greek, can be an obstacle to the beginning anatomy student. Insight into word derivations, however, can make it significantly easier to understand, remember, spell, and pronounce biomedical terms. This goal is supported by word derivation footnotes throughout this book.

2. Anatomists began by 1895 to standardize international anatomical terminology. Official international terms are now codified in the *Terminologia Anatomica* (TA) of 1998.

3. The TA rejects eponyms (anatomical terms based on the names of people) and provides preferred Latin and English terms for most human structures in gross anatomy.

4. Scientific words can typically be broken down into one or more word *roots (stems)* and *affixes* (prefixes and suffixes), often joined by *combining vowels.*

5. About 90% of medical terms are composed of various combinations of only 1,200 roots and affixes. Therefore a relatively modest vocabulary of roots and affixes can give one insight into the meanings of most medical terms.

6. It is easier to become comfortable with anatomical terminology as one recognizes that many word variations are merely singular, plural, adjectival, and possessive forms of one another.

7. Precision is extremely important in medical communication. Minor changes in spelling can radically change the meaning of a word—for example, a one-letter difference changing the name of part of the intestine to the name of a hip bone. Similarly "minor" errors can make life-and-death differences in the hospital, and it is therefore crucial to cultivate the habit of precision early in one's studies.

## TESTING YOUR RECALL

1. Structure that can be observed with the naked eye is called
   a. gross anatomy.
   b. ultrastructure.
   c. microscopic anatomy.
   d. macroscopic anatomy.
   e. cytology.

2. Which of the following techniques requires an injection of radioisotopes into a patient's bloodstream?
   a. sonography
   b. a PET scan
   c. radiography
   d. a CT scan
   e. an MRI scan

3. The simplest structures considered to be alive are
   a. organs.
   b. tissues.
   c. cells.
   d. organelles.
   e. proteins.

4. Which of the following people revolutionized the teaching of gross anatomy?
   a. Vesalius
   b. Aristotle
   c. Hippocrates
   d. Leeuwenhoek
   e. Avicenna

5. Which of the following characteristics do humans *not* share with all other chordates?
   a. pharyngeal arches
   b. a hollow nerve cord
   c. a tail extending beyond the anus
   d. a notochord
   e. a vertebral column

6. Which of the following men argued that all living organisms are composed of cells?
   a. Hippocrates
   b. an-Nafis
   c. Schwann
   d. Leeuwenhoek
   e. Avicenna

7. When a person's blood sugar (glucose) level rises, insulin is secreted. This stimulates cells to absorb glucose and thus brings the glucose level back to normal. This is an example of
   a. homeostasis.
   b. differentiation.
   c. organization.
   d. anabolism.
   e. catabolism.

8. The word root *histo-* means
   a. visible.
   b. diseased.
   c. cellular.
   d. tissue.
   e. microscopic.

9. The word root *patho-* means
   a. doctor.
   b. medicine.
   c. disease.
   d. organ.
   e. health.

10. The prefix *hetero-* means
    a. same.
    b. different.
    c. both.
    d. solid.
    e. below.

11. Cutting and separating tissues to reveal their structural relationships is called _____.

12. _____ invented many components of the compound microscope and named the cell.

13. The term for all chemical change in the body is _____.

14. Most physiology serves the purpose of _____, maintaining a stable internal environment in the body.

15. _____ is a science that doesn't merely describe bodily structure but interprets structure in terms of its function.

16. When a doctor presses on the upper abdomen to feel the size and texture of the liver, he or she is using a technique of physical examination called _____.

17. _____ is a method of medical imaging that uses X-rays and a computer to generate images of thin slices of the body.

18. A/an _____ is the simplest body structure to be composed of two or more types of tissue.

19. Depth perception, or the ability to form three-dimensional images, is called _____ vision.

20. Our hands are said to be _____ because they can encircle an object such as a branch or tool. The presence of a/an _____ thumb is important to this ability.

***Answers in the Appendix***

## TRUE OR FALSE

*Determine which five of the following statements are false, and briefly explain why.*

1. Regional anatomy is a variation of gross anatomy.

2. The inventions of Carl Zeiss and Ernst Abbe are necessary to the work of a modern histopathologist.

3. Abnormal skin color or dryness could be one piece of diagnostic information gained by auscultation.

4. Radiology refers only to those medical imaging methods that use radioisotopes.

5. It is more harmful to have only the heart reversed from left to right than to have all of the thoracic and abdominal organs reversed.

6. There are more cells than organelles in the body.

7. Leeuwenhoek was a biologist who invented the microscope in order to study cells.

8. All Vertebrata have a notochord, but not all of them are endothermic.

9. Human stereoscopic vision probably evolved in response to the demands of the savanna habitat of the first hominids.

10. The word *scuba,* derived from the words *self-contained underwater breathing apparatus,* is an acronym.

*Answers in the Appendix*

## TESTING YOUR COMPREHENSION

1. Classify each of the following radiologic techniques as invasive or noninvasive and explain your reasoning for each: angiography, sonography, CT, MRI, and PET.

2. Beginning medical students are always told to examine multiple cadavers and not confine their study to just one. Other than the obvious purpose of studying both male and female anatomy, why is this instruction so important to medical education?

3. Which characteristics of living things are possessed by an automobile? What bearing does this have on our definition of life?

4. Why is a monkey not classified as human? Why is a horse not classified as a primate? (*Hint:* What characteristics must an animal have to be a human or a primate, and which of these are monkeys or horses lacking?)

5. Why do you think the writers of the *Terminologia Anatomica* decided to reject eponyms? Do you agree with that decision? Why do you think they decided to name structures in Latin? Do you agree with that decision? Explain your reasons for agreeing or disagreeing with each.

*Answers at aris.mhhe.com*

## ONLINE RESOURCES

Visit aprevealed.com to explore melt-away cadaver dissections, watch animations that clarify difficult concepts, review histological and radiological images, or take a quiz to assess your understanding of the material.

The Saladin *Human Anatomy,* 2e website at aris.mhhe.com features chapter-specific quizzes, labeling exercises, and other interactive tools to complement your study of human anatomy. If your instructor has provided an ARIS course code, you can also access assignments and information specific to your course.

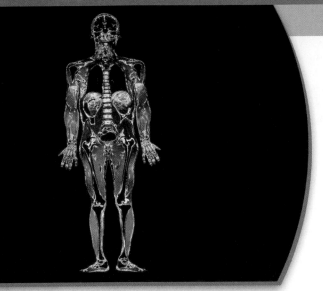

# Survey of the Human Body

A full-body colorized MRI scan

Anatomy & Physiology **REVEALED**
aprevealed.com

**Anatomy Terms**

# General Anatomical Terminology

## Anatomical Position

**Anatomical position** is a stance in which a person stands erect with the feet flat on the floor, arms at the sides, and the palms, face, and eyes facing forward (fig. A.1). This position provides a precise and standard frame of reference for anatomical description and dissection. Without such a frame of reference, to say that a structure such as the sternum, thymus, or aorta is "above the heart" would be vague, since it would depend on whether the subject was standing, lying face down, or lying face up. From the perspective of anatomical position, however, we can describe the thymus as *superior* to the heart, the sternum as *anterior* or *ventral* to it, and the aorta as *posterior* or *dorsal* to it. These descriptions remain valid regardless of the subject's position.

Unless stated otherwise, assume that all anatomical descriptions refer to anatomical position. Bear in mind that if a subject is facing you in anatomical position, the subject's left will be on your right, and vice versa. In most anatomical illustrations, for example, the left atrium of the heart appears toward the right side of the page, and although the appendix is located in the right lower quadrant of the abdomen, it appears on the left side of most illustrations.

The forearm is said to be **supinated** when the palms face up or anteriorly and **pronated** when they face down or posteriorly (fig. A.2). The difference is particularly important in descriptions of anatomy of this region. In the supinated position, the two forearm bones (radius and ulna) are parallel and the radius is lateral to the ulna. In the pronated position, the radius and ulna cross; the radius is lateral to the ulna at the elbow but medial to it at the wrist. Descriptions of nerves, muscles, blood vessels, and other structures of the arm assume that the arm is supinated.

## Anatomical Planes

Many views of the body are based on real or imaginary "slices" called sections or planes. *Section* implies an actual cut or slice to reveal internal anatomy, whereas *plane* implies an imaginary flat surface passing through the body. The three major anatomical planes are *sagittal*, *frontal*, and *transverse* (fig. A.3).

**Figure A.1 Anatomical Position.** The feet are flat on the floor and close together, the arms are held downward and supine, and the face is directed forward.

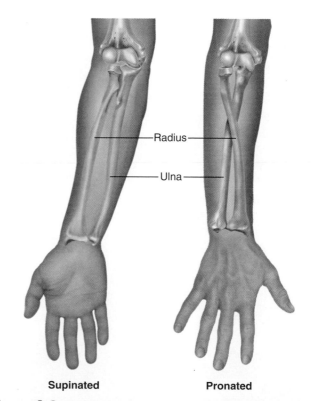

Radius

Ulna

**Supinated**  **Pronated**

**Figure A.2 Positions of the Forearm.** When the forearm is supinated, the palm faces anteriorly; when pronated, it faces posteriorly. Note the differences in the relationship of the radius to the ulna.

A **sagittal**[1] (SADJ-ih-tul) **plane** extends vertically and divides the body or an organ into right and left portions. The **median (midsagittal) plane** passes through the midline of the body and divides it into *equal* right and left halves. Other sagittal planes parallel to this (off center) divide the body into unequal right and left portions. The head and pelvic organs are commonly illustrated in median views (fig. A.4a).

A **frontal (coronal) plane** also extends vertically, but it is perpendicular to the sagittal plane and divides the body into anterior (front) and posterior (back) portions. A frontal section of the head, for example, would divide it into one portion bearing the face and another bearing the back of the head. Contents of the thoracic and abdominal cavities are most commonly shown in frontal section (fig. A.4b).

A **transverse (horizontal) plane** passes across the body or an organ perpendicular to its long axis (fig. A.4c); it divides the body into superior (upper) and inferior (lower) portions. CT scans are typically transverse sections (see fig. 1.2c, p. 4).

## Directional Terms

Table A.1 summarizes frequently used terms that describe the position of one structure relative to another. Intermediate directions are often indicated by combinations of these terms. For example, one structure may be described as *dorsolateral* to another (toward the back and side). The dorsal surface of a structure is also called the **dorsum**; for example, the dorsum of your hand is what most people call the "back" of the hand. The dorsum of the foot is its upper surface (see fig. A.5b). The dorsal surface of the hand or foot is the surface that bears the nails.

Because of the bipedal, upright stance of humans, some directional terms have different meanings for humans than they do for other animals. *Anterior,* for example, denotes the region of the body that leads the way in normal locomotion. For a four-legged animal such as a cat, this is the head end of the body; for a human, however, it is the front of the chest and abdomen. Thus, *anterior* has the same meaning as *ventral* for a human but not for a cat. *Posterior* denotes the region of the body that comes last in normal locomotion—the tail end of a cat but the dorsal side (back) of a human. These differences must be kept in mind when dissecting other animals for comparison to human anatomy.

---

[1]*sagitta* = arrow

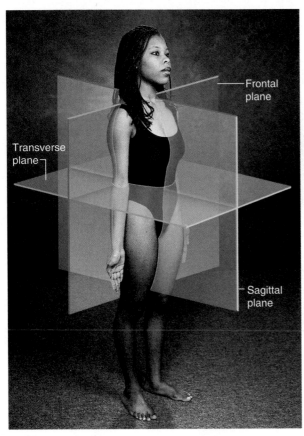

**Figure A.3** Anatomical Planes of Reference.
● *What is another name for the particular sagittal plane shown here?*

## Body Regions

Knowledge of the external anatomy and landmarks of the body is important in performing a physical examination and many other clinical procedures. For purposes of study, the body is divided into two major regions called the *axial* and *appendicular regions*. Smaller areas within the major regions are described in the following paragraphs and illustrated in figure A.5.

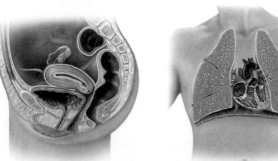

**(a) Sagittal section**

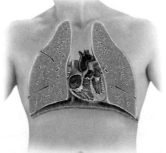

**(b) Frontal section**

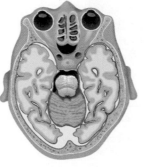

**(c) Transverse section**

**Figure A.4** Views of the Body in the Three Primary Anatomical Planes.
(a) Sagittal section of the pelvic region.
(b) Frontal section of the thoracic region.
(c) Transverse section of the head at the level of the eyes.
● *Other than the transverse section in part (c), what other type of section could show both eyes at once?*

| TABLE A.1 | Directional Terms in Human Anatomy | |
|---|---|---|
| **Term** | **Meaning** | **Examples of Usage** |
| Ventral | Toward the front* or belly | The aorta is *ventral* to the vertebral column. |
| Dorsal | Toward the back or spine | The vertebral column is *dorsal* to the aorta. |
| Anterior | Toward the ventral side* | The sternum is *anterior* to the heart. |
| Posterior | Toward the dorsal side* | The esophagus is *posterior* to the trachea. |
| Cephalic | Toward the head or superior end | The *cephalic* end of the embryonic neural tube develops into the brain. |
| Rostral | Toward the forehead or nose | The forebrain is *rostral* to the brainstem. |
| Caudal | Toward the tail or inferior end | The spinal cord is *caudal* to the brain. |
| Superior | Above | The heart is *superior* to the diaphragm. |
| Inferior | Below | The liver is *inferior* to the diaphragm. |
| Medial | Toward the midsagittal plane | The heart is *medial* to the lungs. |
| Lateral | Away from the midsagittal plane | The eyes are *lateral* to the nose. |
| Proximal | Closer to the point of attachment or origin | The elbow is *proximal* to the wrist. |
| Distal | Farther from the point of attachment or origin | The fingernails are at the *distal* ends of the fingers. |
| Superficial | Closer to the body surface | The skin is *superficial* to the muscles. |
| Deep | Farther from the body surface | The bones are *deep* to the muscles. |

*In humans only; definition differs for other animals.

## Axial Region

The **axial region** consists of the **head, neck (cervical[2] region)**, and **trunk.** The trunk is further divided into the **thoracic region** above the diaphragm and the **abdominal region** below it.

One way of referring to the locations of abdominal structures is to divide the region into quadrants. Two perpendicular lines intersecting at the umbilicus (navel) divide the abdomen into a **right upper quadrant (RUQ), right lower quadrant (RLQ), left upper quadrant (LUQ),** and **left lower quadrant (LLQ)** (fig. A.6a, b). The quadrant scheme is often used to describe the site of an abdominal pain or abnormality.

The abdomen also can be divided into nine regions defined by four lines that intersect like a tic-tac-toe grid (fig. A.6c, d). Each vertical line is called a *midclavicular line* because it passes through the midpoint of the clavicle (collarbone). The superior horizontal line is called the *subcostal[3] line* because it connects the inferior borders of the lowest costal cartilages (cartilage connecting the tenth rib on each side to the inferior end of the sternum). The inferior horizontal line is called the *intertubercular[4] line* because it passes from left to right between the tubercles *(anterior superior spines)* of the pelvis—two points of bone located about where the front pockets open on most pants. The three lateral regions of this grid, from upper to lower, are the **hypochondriac,[5] lateral (lumbar),** and **inguinal[6] (iliac) regions.** The three medial regions from upper to lower are the **epigastric,[7] umbilical,** and **hypogastric (pubic)** regions.

## Appendicular Region

The **appendicular** (AP-en-DIC-you-lur) **region** of the body consists of the **upper limbs** and **lower limbs** (also called *appendages* or *extremities*). The upper limb includes the **arm (brachium,** BRAY-kee-um), **forearm (antebrachium,[8]** AN-teh-BRAY-kee-um), **wrist (carpus), hand (manus),** and **fingers (digits).** The lower limb includes the **thigh, leg (crus), ankle (tarsus), foot (pes),** and **toes (digits).** In strict anatomical terms, *arm* refers only to that part of the upper limb between the shoulder and elbow. *Leg* refers only to that part of the lower limb between the knee and ankle.

# Body Cavities and Membranes

The body wall encloses several **body cavities,** each lined by a membrane and containing internal organs called the **viscera** (VISS-er-uh) (singular, *viscus[9]*) (fig. A.7, table A.2).

## The Cranial Cavity and Vertebral Canal

The **cranial** (CRAY-nee-ul) **cavity** is enclosed by the cranium (braincase) and contains the brain. The **vertebral canal** is enclosed by the vertebral column (backbone) and contains the spinal cord. The two are continuous with each other and lined by three membrane layers called the **meninges** (meh-NIN-jeez). Among other functions, the meninges protect the delicate nervous tissue from the hard protective bone that encloses it, and anchor the spinal cord to the vertebral column and limit its movement.

---

[2]*cervic* = neck
[3]*sub* = below + *cost* = rib
[4]*inter* = between + *tubercul* = little swelling
[5]*hypo* = below + *chondr* = cartilage
[6]*inguin* = groin
[7]*epi* = above, over + *gastr* = stomach

---

[8]*ante* = fore, before + *brachi* = arm
[9]*viscus* = body organ

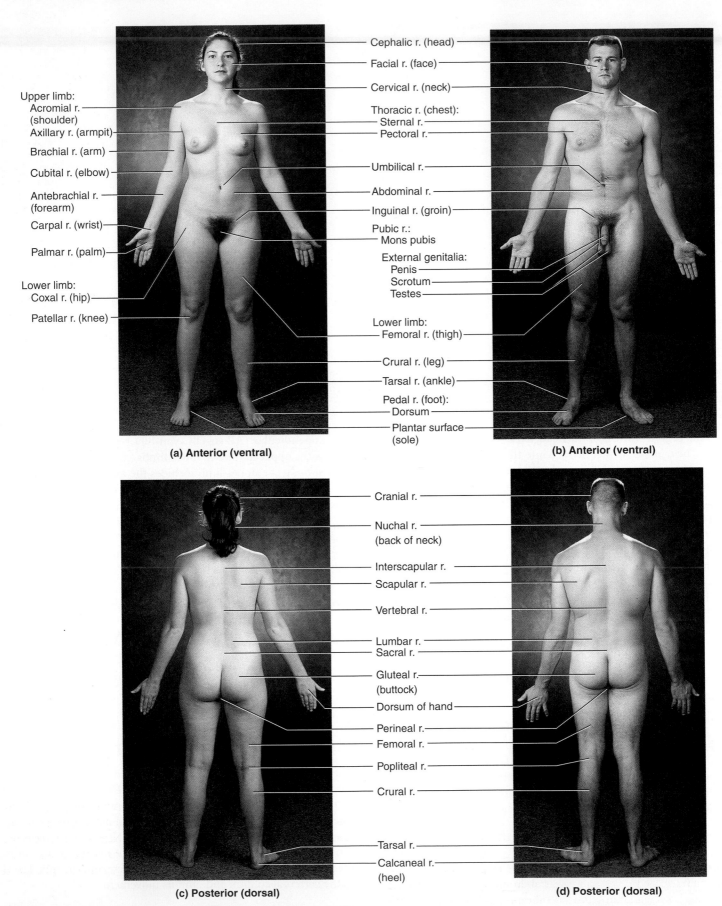

Cephalic r. (head)
Facial r. (face)
Cervical r. (neck)
Thoracic r. (chest):
Sternal r.
Pectoral r.
Umbilical r.
Abdominal r.
Inguinal r. (groin)
Pubic r.:
Mons pubis
External genitalia:
Penis
Scrotum
Testes
Lower limb:
Femoral r. (thigh)
Crural r. (leg)
Tarsal r. (ankle)
Pedal r. (foot):
Dorsum
Plantar surface
(sole)

Upper limb:
Acromial r.
(shoulder)
Axillary r. (armpit)
Brachial r. (arm)
Cubital r. (elbow)
Antebrachial r.
(forearm)
Carpal r. (wrist)
Palmar r. (palm)
Lower limb:
Coxal r. (hip)
Patellar r. (knee)

**(a) Anterior (ventral)**

**(b) Anterior (ventral)**

Cranial r.
Nuchal r.
(back of neck)
Interscapular r.
Scapular r.
Vertebral r.
Lumbar r.
Sacral r.
Gluteal r.
(buttock)
Dorsum of hand
Perineal r.
Femoral r.
Popliteal r.
Crural r.
Tarsal r.
Calcaneal r.
(heel)

**(c) Posterior (dorsal)**

**(d) Posterior (dorsal)**

**Figure A.5**  The Adult Female and Male Bodies.  (*r.* = region)

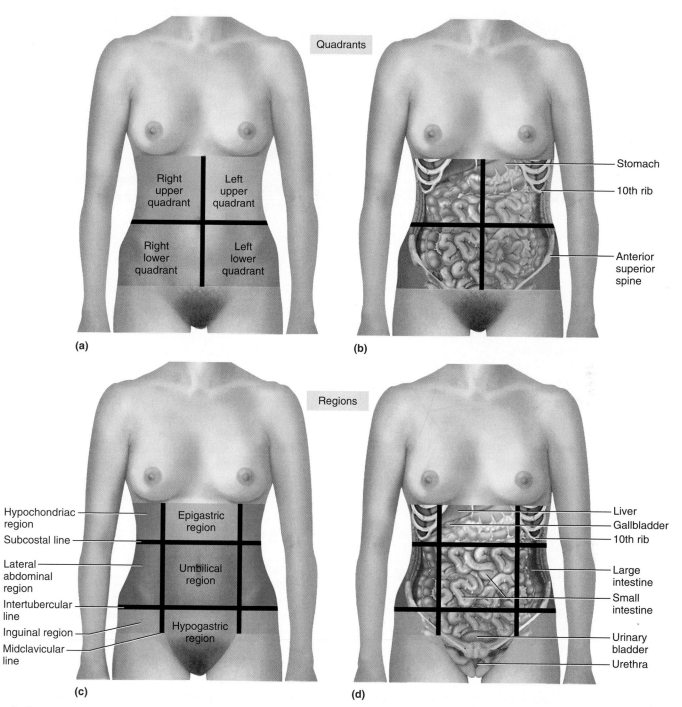

Quadrants

**Right upper quadrant** **Left upper quadrant** **Right lower quadrant** **Left lower quadrant**

(a)

Stomach
10th rib
Anterior superior spine

(b)

Regions

Hypochondriac region
Subcostal line
Lateral abdominal region
Intertubercular line
Inguinal region
Midclavicular line

**Epigastric region** **Umbilical region** **Hypogastric region**

(c)

Liver
Gallbladder
10th rib
Large intestine
Small intestine
Urinary bladder
Urethra

(d)

**Figure A.6** **Four Quadrants and Nine Regions of the Abdomen.** (a) External division into four quadrants. (b) Internal anatomy correlated with the four quadrants. (c) External division into nine regions. (d) Internal anatomy correlated with the nine regions.
● *In which quadrant of the abdomen would you expect a person to feel pain from the gallbladder?*

## The Thoracic Cavity

During embryonic development, a space called the **coelom** (SEE-loam) forms ventrally within the trunk (see fig. 4.5c, p. 111). It subsequently becomes partitioned by a muscular sheet, the **diaphragm,** into a superior **thoracic cavity** and an inferior **abdominopelvic cavity.** Both cavities are lined with thin **serous membranes,** which secrete a lubricating film of moisture similar to blood serum (hence their name).

The thoracic cavity is divided by a thick partition called the **mediastinum**[10] (ME-dee-ah-STY-num) (fig. A.7). This is the region between the lungs, extending from the base of the neck to the diaphragm, occupied by the heart, the major blood vessels connected to it, the esophagus, the trachea and bronchi, and a gland called the *thymus.*

---

[10]*mediastinum* = in the middle

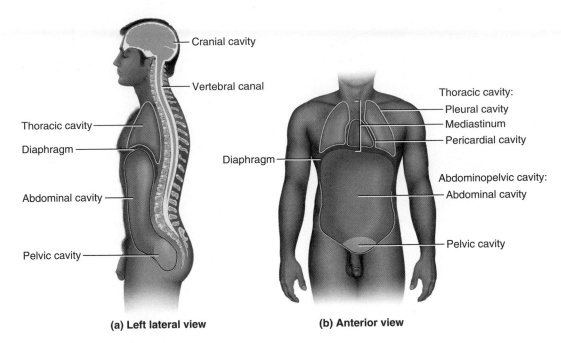

(a) Left lateral view          (b) Anterior view

**Figure A.7**  The Major Body Cavities.

| TABLE A.2 | Body Cavities and Membranes | |
|---|---|---|
| **Name of Cavity** | **Associated Viscera** | **Membranous Lining** |
| Cranial cavity | Brain | Meninges |
| Vertebral canal | Spinal cord | Meninges |
| Thoracic cavity | | |
|   Pleural cavities (2) | Lungs | Pleurae |
|   Pericardial cavity | Heart | Pericardium |
| Abdominopelvic cavity | | |
|   Abdominal cavity | Digestive organs, spleen, kidneys | Peritoneum |
|   Pelvic cavity | Bladder, rectum, reproductive organs | Peritoneum |

The heart is enclosed by a two-layered serous membrane called the **pericardium.**[11] The inner layer of the pericardium forms the surface of the heart itself and is called the **visceral** (VISS-er-ul) **pericardium (epicardium).** The outer layer is called the **parietal**[12] (pa-RY-eh-tul) **pericardium (pericardial sac).** It is separated from the visceral pericardium by a space called the **pericardial cavity** (fig. A.8a). This space is lubricated by **pericardial fluid.**

The right and left sides of the thoracic cavity contain the lungs. Each is lined by a serous membrane called the **pleura**[13] (PLOOR-uh) (fig. A.8b). Like the pericardium, the pleura has visceral (inner) and parietal (outer) layers. The **visceral pleura** forms the external surface of the lung, and the **parietal pleura** lines the inside of the rib cage. The narrow space between them is called the **pleural cavity** (see fig. A.19). It is lubricated by slippery **pleural fluid.**

Note that in both the pericardium and pleura, the visceral layer of the membrane *covers* the surface of an organ and the parietal layer *lines* the inside of a body cavity. We will see this pattern repeated elsewhere, including the abdominopelvic cavity.

## The Abdominopelvic Cavity

The abdominopelvic cavity consists of the **abdominal cavity** superiorly and the **pelvic cavity** inferiorly. These are separated by a bony landmark called the *brim* of the pelvis (see fig. A.16 and 8.6). The abdominal cavity, above the brim, contains most of the digestive organs as well as the kidneys and ureters. The pelvic cavity, below the brim, is markedly narrower and tilts posteriorly (see fig. A.7a). It contains the rectum, urinary bladder, urethra, and the reproductive organs.

The abdominopelvic cavity contains a two-layered serous membrane called the **peritoneum**[14] (PERR-ih-toe-NEE-um). The **parietal peritoneum** lines the cavity wall. The **visceral peritoneum** turns inward from the body wall, wraps around the abdominal viscera, binds them to the body wall or suspends them from it, and holds them in their proper place. The **peritoneal cavity** is the space between the parietal and visceral layers. It is lubricated by **peritoneal fluid.**

Some organs of the abdominal cavity lie against the posterior body wall and are covered by peritoneum only on the side facing the peritoneal cavity. They are said to have a **retroperitoneal**[15]

---

[11]*peri* = around + *cardi* = heart
[12]*pariet* = wall
[13]*pleur* = rib, side

[14]*peri* = around + *tone* = stretched
[15]*retro* = behind

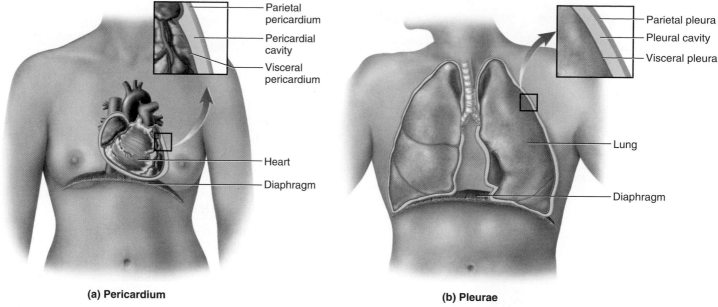

**Figure A.8** Parietal and Visceral Layers of Double-Walled Membranes.

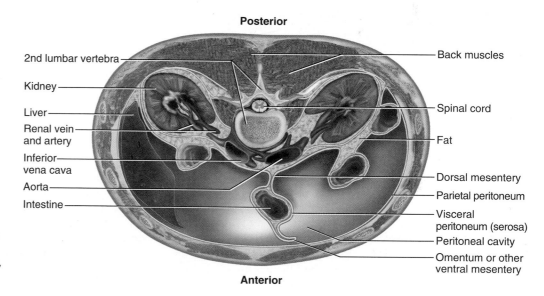

**Figure A.9** Transverse Section Through the Abdomen. Shows the peritoneum, peritoneal cavity (with most viscera omitted), and some retroperitoneal organs.

position (fig. A.9). These include the kidneys, ureters, adrenal glands, most of the pancreas, and abdominal portions of two major blood vessels—the aorta and inferior vena cava (see fig. A.15). Organs that are encircled by peritoneum and connected to the posterior body wall by peritoneal sheets are described as **intraperitoneal.**[16]

The intestines are suspended from the posterior (dorsal) abdominal wall by a translucent membrane called the **dorsal mesentery**[17] (MEZ-en-tare-ee), an infolding of the peritoneum. The dorsal mesentery of the large intestine is called the **mesocolon.** In some places, after wrapping around the intestines or other viscera, the mesentery continues toward the anterior body wall as the **ventral mesentery.** The most significant example of this is a fatty membrane called the **greater omentum,**[18] which hangs like an apron from the inferolateral margin of the stomach and overlies the intestines (figs. A.10 and A.13). It is unattached at its inferior border and can be lifted to reveal the intestines. A smaller **lesser omentum** extends from the superomedial border of the stomach to the liver.

---

[16]*intra* = within
[17]*mes* = in the middle + *enter* = intestine

[18]*omentum* = covering

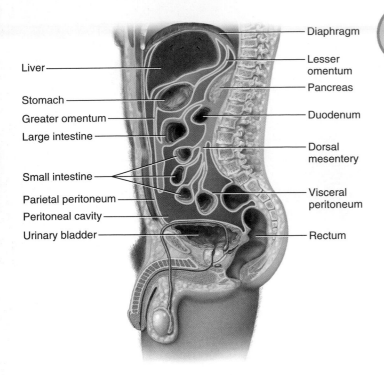

Figure A.10 labels:
- Liver
- Stomach
- Greater omentum
- Large intestine
- Small intestine
- Parietal peritoneum
- Peritoneal cavity
- Urinary bladder
- Diaphragm
- Lesser omentum
- Pancreas
- Duodenum
- Dorsal mesentery
- Visceral peritoneum
- Rectum

**Figure A.10** **Serous Membranes of the Abdominal Cavity.** Sagittal section, left lateral view.
● *Is the urinary bladder in the peritoneal cavity?*

Where the visceral peritoneum meets an organ such as the stomach or small intestine, it divides and wraps around it, forming an outer layer of the organ called the **serosa** (seer-OH-sa) (fig. A.10). The visceral peritoneum thus consists of the mesenteries and serosae.

## Potential Spaces

Some of the spaces between body membranes are considered to be **potential spaces,** so named because under normal conditions, the membranes are pressed firmly together and there is no actual space between them. The membranes are not physically attached, however, and under unusual conditions, they may separate and create a space filled with fluid or other matter. Thus, there is only a potential for the membranes to separate and create a space.

The pleural cavity is one example. Normally, the parietal and visceral pleurae are pressed together without a gap between them, but under pathological conditions, air or serous fluid can accumulate between the membranes and open up a space. Another example is the internal cavity *(lumen)* of the uterus. In a nonpregnant uterus, the mucous membranes of the opposite walls are pressed together, so there is little or no open space in the organ. In pregnancy, of course, a growing fetus occupies this space and pushes the mucous membranes apart.

# Organ Systems

The human body has 11 organ systems (fig. A.11) and an immune system, which is better described as a population of cells than as an organ system. These systems are classified in the following list by their principal functions, but this is an unavoidably flawed classification. Some organs belong to two or more systems—for example, the male urethra is part of both the urinary and reproductive systems; the pharynx is part of the respiratory and digestive systems; and the mammary glands can be considered part of the integumentary and female reproductive systems.

> **Protection, Support, and Movement**
>> Integumentary system
>> Skeletal system
>> Muscular system
>
> **Internal Communication and Integration**
>> Nervous system
>> Endocrine system
>
> **Fluid Transport**
>> Circulatory system
>> Lymphatic system
>
> **Defense**
>> Immune system
>
> **Input and Output**
>> Respiratory system
>> Urinary system
>> Digestive system
>
> **Reproduction**
>> Reproductive system

Some medical terms combine the names of two systems—for example, the *musculoskeletal system, cardiopulmonary system,* and *urogenital (genitourinary) system.* These terms serve to call attention to the close anatomical or physiological relationships between two systems, but these are not literally individual organ systems.

# A Visual Survey of the Body

Figures A.12 through A.16 provide an overview of the anatomy of the trunk and internal organs of the thoracic and abdominopelvic cavities. Figures A.17 through A.22 are photographs of the cadaver showing the major organs of the body cavities.

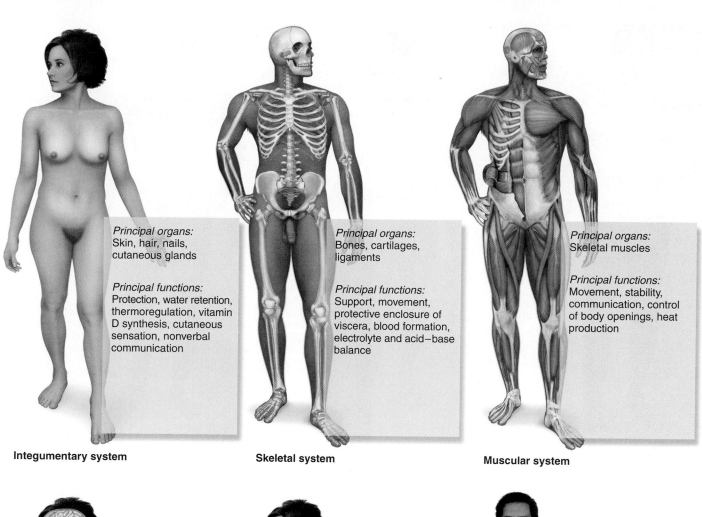

**Integumentary system**

*Principal organs:*
Skin, hair, nails, cutaneous glands

*Principal functions:*
Protection, water retention, thermoregulation, vitamin D synthesis, cutaneous sensation, nonverbal communication

**Skeletal system**

*Principal organs:*
Bones, cartilages, ligaments

*Principal functions:*
Support, movement, protective enclosure of viscera, blood formation, electrolyte and acid–base balance

**Muscular system**

*Principal organs:*
Skeletal muscles

*Principal functions:*
Movement, stability, communication, control of body openings, heat production

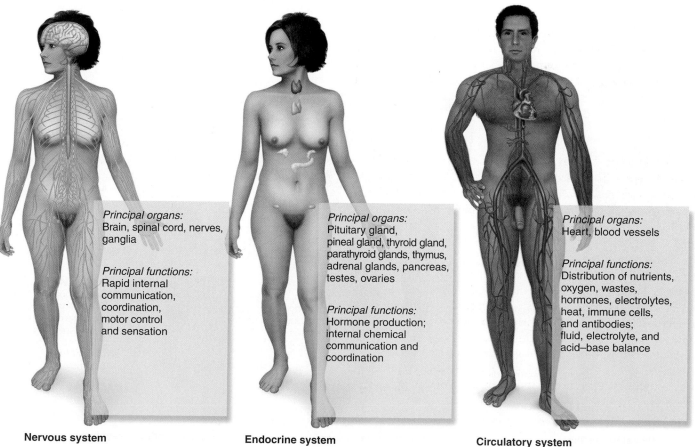

**Nervous system**

*Principal organs:*
Brain, spinal cord, nerves, ganglia

*Principal functions:*
Rapid internal communication, coordination, motor control and sensation

**Endocrine system**

*Principal organs:*
Pituitary gland, pineal gland, thyroid gland, parathyroid glands, thymus, adrenal glands, pancreas, testes, ovaries

*Principal functions:*
Hormone production; internal chemical communication and coordination

**Circulatory system**

*Principal organs:*
Heart, blood vessels

*Principal functions:*
Distribution of nutrients, oxygen, wastes, hormones, electrolytes, heat, immune cells, and antibodies; fluid, electrolyte, and acid–base balance

**Figure A.11** The Human Organ Systems.

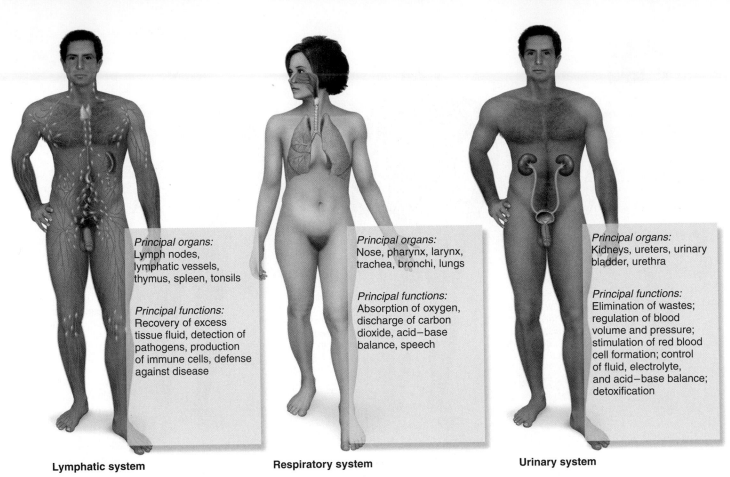

**Principal organs:**
Lymph nodes, lymphatic vessels, thymus, spleen, tonsils

**Principal functions:**
Recovery of excess tissue fluid, detection of pathogens, production of immune cells, defense against disease

**Lymphatic system**

**Principal organs:**
Nose, pharynx, larynx, trachea, bronchi, lungs

**Principal functions:**
Absorption of oxygen, discharge of carbon dioxide, acid–base balance, speech

**Respiratory system**

**Principal organs:**
Kidneys, ureters, urinary bladder, urethra

**Principal functions:**
Elimination of wastes; regulation of blood volume and pressure; stimulation of red blood cell formation; control of fluid, electrolyte, and acid–base balance; detoxification

**Urinary system**

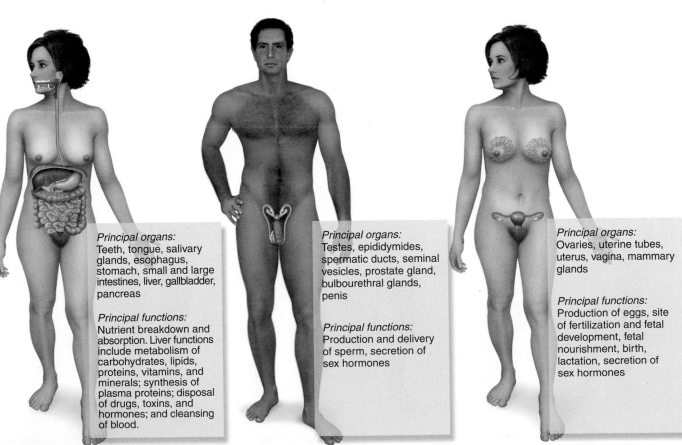

**Principal organs:**
Teeth, tongue, salivary glands, esophagus, stomach, small and large intestines, liver, gallbladder, pancreas

**Principal functions:**
Nutrient breakdown and absorption. Liver functions include metabolism of carbohydrates, lipids, proteins, vitamins, and minerals; synthesis of plasma proteins; disposal of drugs, toxins, and hormones; and cleansing of blood.

**Digestive system**

**Principal organs:**
Testes, epididymides, spermatic ducts, seminal vesicles, prostate gland, bulbourethral glands, penis

**Principal functions:**
Production and delivery of sperm, secretion of sex hormones

**Male reproductive system**

**Principal organs:**
Ovaries, uterine tubes, uterus, vagina, mammary glands

**Principal functions:**
Production of eggs, site of fertilization and fetal development, fetal nourishment, birth, lactation, secretion of sex hormones

**Female reproductive system**

**Figure A.11** The Human Organ Systems. (continued)

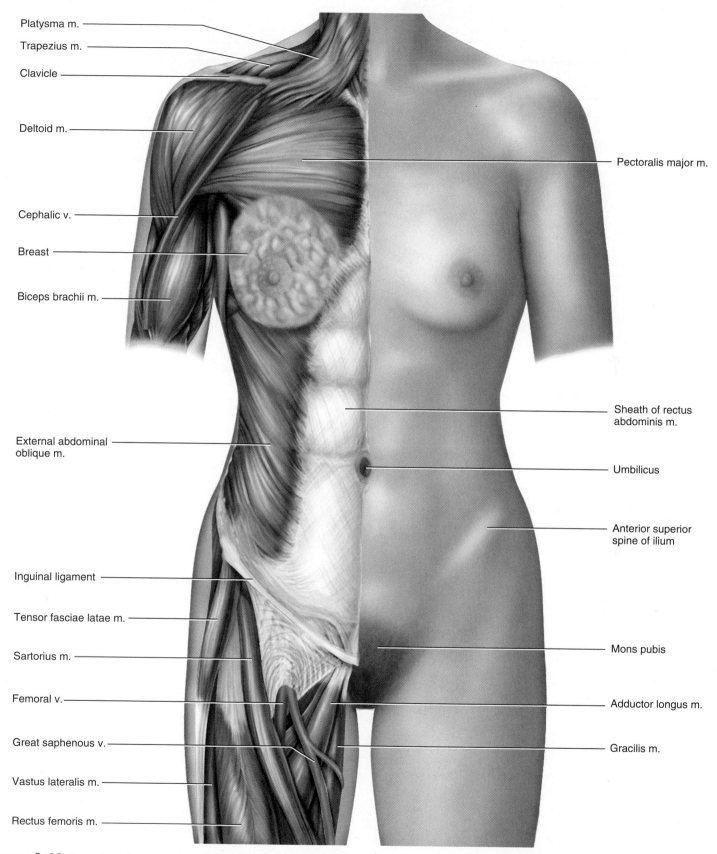

Platysma m.
Trapezius m.
Clavicle
Deltoid m.
Cephalic v.
Breast
Biceps brachii m.
External abdominal oblique m.
Inguinal ligament
Tensor fasciae latae m.
Sartorius m.
Femoral v.
Great saphenous v.
Vastus lateralis m.
Rectus femoris m.

Pectoralis major m.
Sheath of rectus abdominis m.
Umbilicus
Anterior superior spine of ilium
Mons pubis
Adductor longus m.
Gracilis m.

**Figure A.12 Superficial Anatomy of the Trunk (Female).** Surface anatomy is shown on the anatomical left, and structures immediately deep to the skin on the right (*m.* = muscle; *v.* = vein).

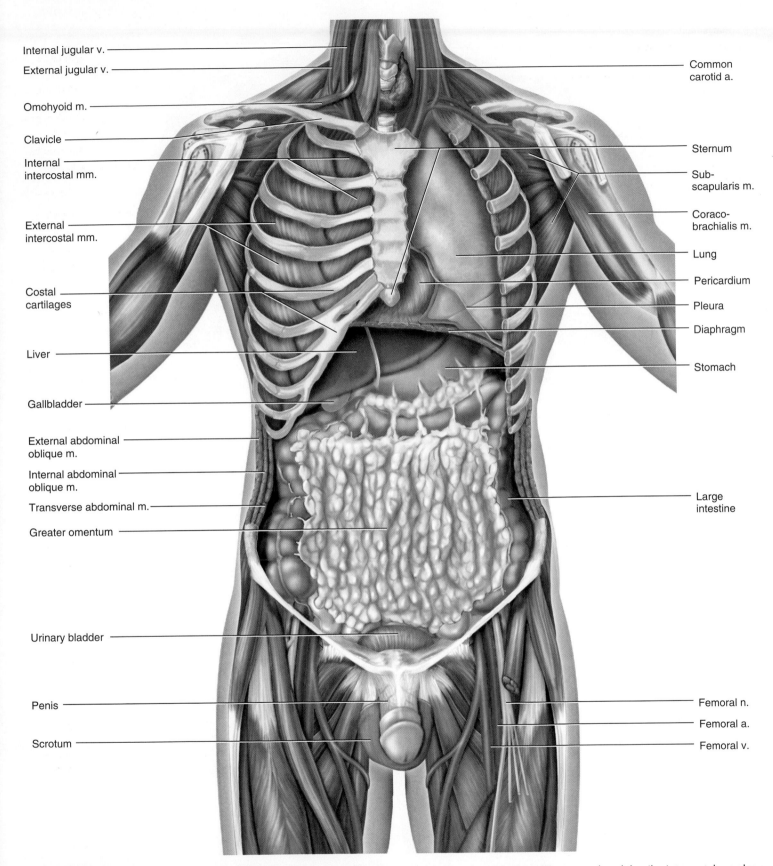

Internal jugular v.

External jugular v.

Omohyoid m.

Clavicle

Internal intercostal mm.

External intercostal mm.

Costal cartilages

Liver

Gallbladder

External abdominal oblique m.

Internal abdominal oblique m.

Transverse abdominal m.

Greater omentum

Urinary bladder

Penis

Scrotum

Common carotid a.

Sternum

Sub-scapularis m.

Coraco-brachialis m.

Lung

Pericardium

Pleura

Diaphragm

Stomach

Large intestine

Femoral n.

Femoral a.

Femoral v.

**Figure A.13** **Anatomy at the Level of the Rib Cage and Greater Omentum (Male).** The ventral body wall is removed, and the ribs, intercostal muscles, and pleura are removed from the anatomical left (*a.* = artery; *v.* = vein; *m.* = muscle; *mm.* = muscles; *n.* = nerve).
- *Name a muscle that is deep to the internal abdominal oblique. Name a muscle that is superficial to it.*

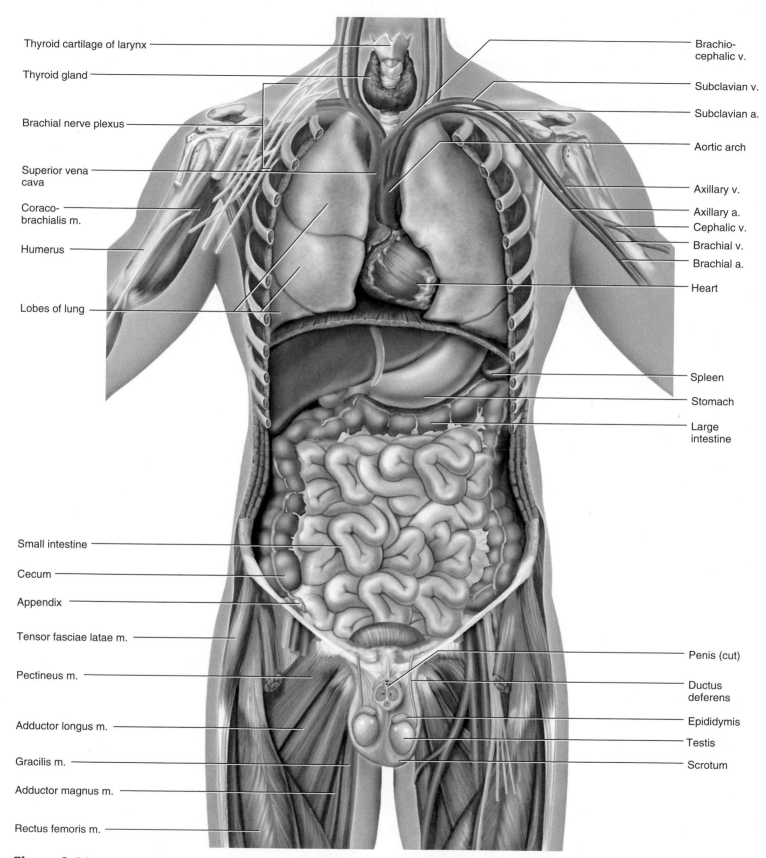

Thyroid cartilage of larynx

Thyroid gland

Brachial nerve plexus

Superior vena cava

Coraco-brachialis m.

Humerus

Lobes of lung

Small intestine

Cecum

Appendix

Tensor fasciae latae m.

Pectineus m.

Adductor longus m.

Gracilis m.

Adductor magnus m.

Rectus femoris m.

Brachio-cephalic v.

Subclavian v.

Subclavian a.

Aortic arch

Axillary v.

Axillary a.

Cephalic v.

Brachial v.

Brachial a.

Heart

Spleen

Stomach

Large intestine

Penis (cut)

Ductus deferens

Epididymis

Testis

Scrotum

**Figure A.14** **Anatomy at the Level of the Lungs and Intestines (Male).** The sternum, ribs, and greater omentum are removed (*a.* = artery; *v.* = vein; *m.* = muscle).

• *Name several viscera that are protected by the rib cage.*

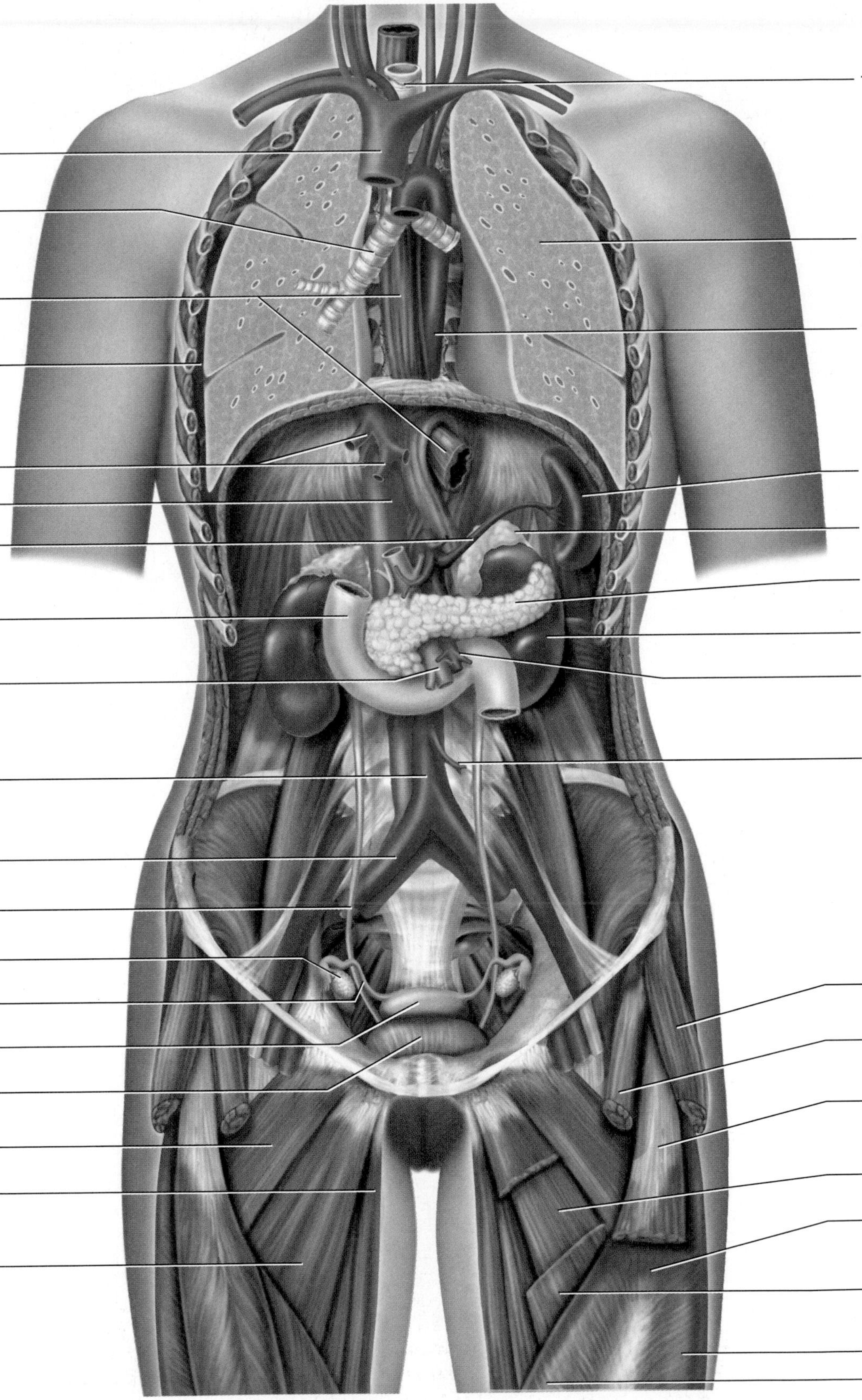

Trachea

Superior vena cava

Bronchus

Esophagus

Lung (sectioned)

Pleural cavity

Thoracic aorta

Hepatic vv.

Spleen

Inferior vena cava

Adrenal gland

Splenic a.

Pancreas

Duodenum

Kidney

Superior mesenteric v.

Superior mesenteric a.

Inferior mesenteric a.

Abdominal aorta

Common iliac a.

Ureter

Ovary

Uterine tube

Tensor fasciae latae m. (cut)

Sartorius m. (cut)

Uterus

Urinary bladder

Rectus femoris m. (cut)

Pectineus m.

Adductor brevis m.

Gracilis m.

Vastus intermedius m.

Adductor longus m.

Adductor longus m. (cut)

Vastus lateralis m.

Vastus medialis m.

**Figure A.15** **Anatomy at the Level of the Retroperitoneal Viscera (Female).** The heart is removed, the lungs are frontally sectioned, and the viscera of the peritoneal cavity and the peritoneum itself are removed (*a.* = artery; *v.* = vein; *vv.* = veins; *m.* = muscle).

• *Name an organ in this figure that is medial to the lungs. Name one that is superior to the kidneys.*

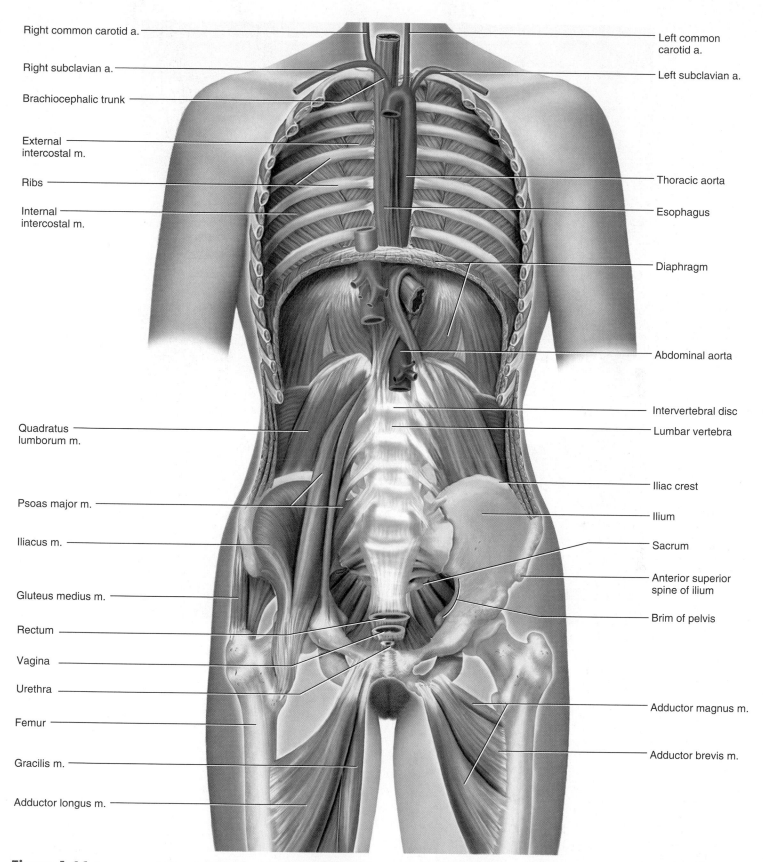

Right common carotid a.

Right subclavian a.

Brachiocephalic trunk

External
intercostal m.

Ribs

Internal
intercostal m.

Quadratus
lumborum m.

Psoas major m.

Iliacus m.

Gluteus medius m.

Rectum

Vagina

Urethra

Femur

Gracilis m.

Adductor longus m.

Left common
carotid a.

Left subclavian a.

Thoracic aorta

Esophagus

Diaphragm

Abdominal aorta

Intervertebral disc

Lumbar vertebra

Iliac crest

Ilium

Sacrum

Anterior superior
spine of ilium

Brim of pelvis

Adductor magnus m.

Adductor brevis m.

**Figure A.16** **Anatomy at the Level of the Dorsal Body Wall (Female).** The lungs and retroperitoneal viscera are removed (*a.* = artery; *m.* = muscle).
● *What directional term describes the position of the thoracic aorta relative to the diaphragm? What term describes the position of the iliacus muscle relative to the psoas major muscle?*

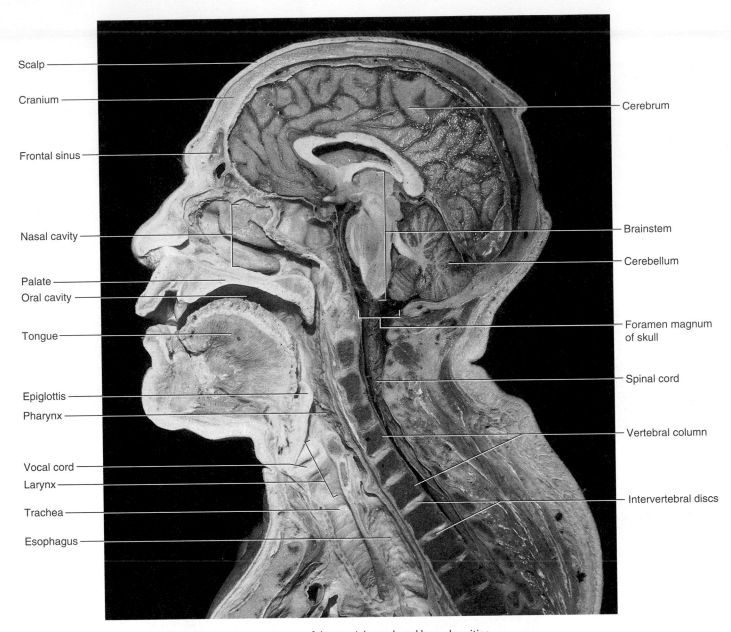

Scalp

Cranium

Frontal sinus

Nasal cavity

Palate

Oral cavity

Tongue

Epiglottis

Pharynx

Vocal cord

Larynx

Trachea

Esophagus

Cerebrum

Brainstem

Cerebellum

Foramen magnum
of skull

Spinal cord

Vertebral column

Intervertebral discs

**Figure A.17** **Median Section of the Head.** Shows contents of the cranial, nasal, and buccal cavities.
● *What directional term describes the postion of the esophagus relative to the trachea? What term describes the position of the palate relative to the tongue?*

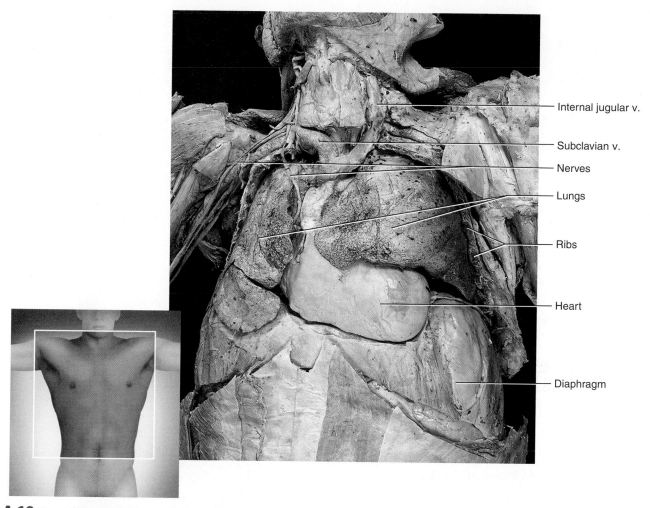

**Figure A.18** **Frontal View of the Thoracic Cavity.** (*v.* = vein)
● *Aside from the thoracic cavity, what are two other body cavities that can be seen in this photograph?*

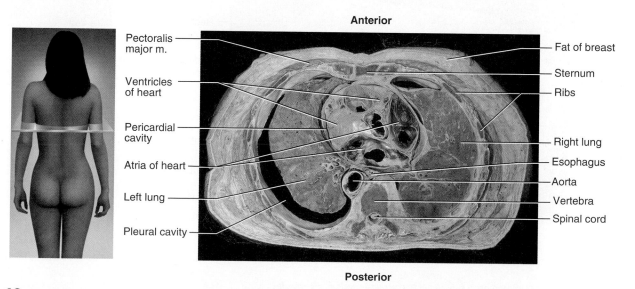

**Figure A.19** **Transverse Section of the Thorax.** Section taken at the level shown by the inset and oriented the same as the reader's body. (*m.* = muscle)
● *In this section, which term best describes the position of the aorta relative to the heart: posterior, lateral, inferior, or proximal?*

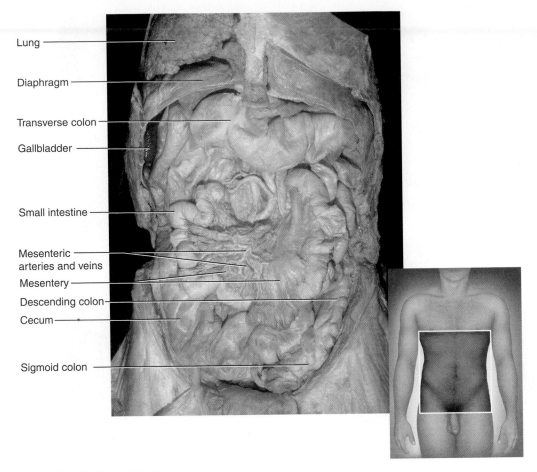

Lung

Diaphragm

Transverse colon

Gallbladder

Small intestine

Mesenteric
arteries and veins

Mesentery

Descending colon

Cecum

Sigmoid colon

**Figure A.20** Frontal View of the Abdominal Cavity.

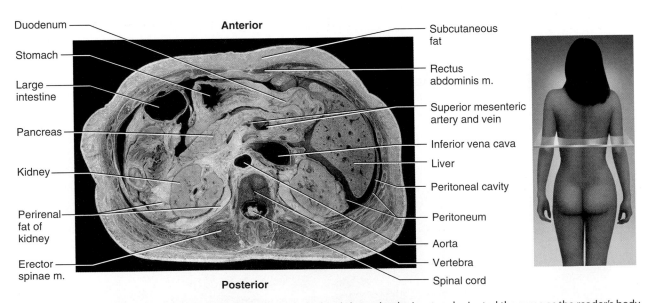

Duodenum

Stomach

Large
intestine

Pancreas

Kidney

Perirenal
fat of
kidney

Erector
spinae m.

**Anterior**

**Posterior**

Subcutaneous
fat

Rectus
abdominis m.

Superior mesenteric
artery and vein

Inferior vena cava

Liver

Peritoneal cavity

Peritoneum

Aorta

Vertebra

Spinal cord

**Figure A.21** Transverse Section of the Abdomen.  Section taken at the level shown by the inset and oriented the same as the reader's body.
(*m.* = muscle
• *What tissue in this photograph is immediately superficial to the rectus abdominis muscle?*

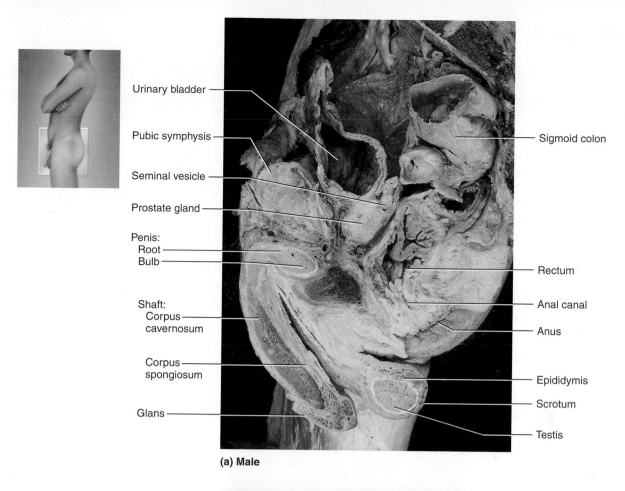

Urinary bladder

Pubic symphysis

Seminal vesicle

Prostate gland

Penis:
Root
Bulb

Shaft:
Corpus
cavernosum

Corpus
spongiosum

Glans

Sigmoid colon

Rectum

Anal canal

Anus

Epididymis

Scrotum

Testis

**(a) Male**

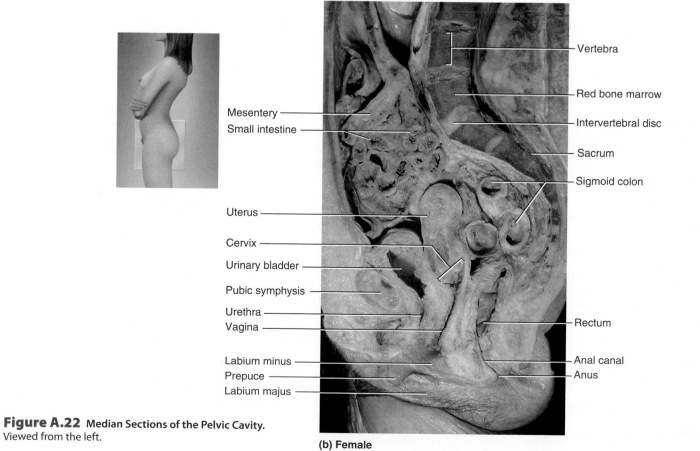

Mesentery
Small intestine

Uterus

Cervix

Urinary bladder

Pubic symphysis

Urethra
Vagina

Labium minus
Prepuce
Labium majus

Vertebra

Red bone marrow

Intervertebral disc

Sacrum

Sigmoid colon

Rectum

Anal canal
Anus

**Figure A.22** **Median Sections of the Pelvic Cavity.**
Viewed from the left.

**(b) Female**

# ATLAS REVIEW

## REVIEW OF KEY CONCEPTS

### General Anatomical Terminology (p. 23)

1. *Anatomical position* provides a standard frame of reference so that directional terms remain consistent regardless of the orientation of the subject's body relative to the observer.

2. In anatomical position, the forearm is held *supine* (palms forward) rather than *prone* (palms rearward). The feet are close together and flat on the floor, arms to the sides, and the head and eyes directed forward.

3. Three mutually perpendicular planes through the body are the *sagittal, frontal,* and *transverse planes.* The sagittal plane that divides the body or an organ into equal halves is called the *median plane.*

4. The positions of structures relative to each other are described by standard directional terms defined in table A.1. Some of these definitions are different for a human than for four-legged animals. Such differences must be kept in mind when doing laboratory animal dissections for comparison to humans.

### Body Regions (p. 24)

1. The *axial region* of the body consists of the head, neck, and trunk. The trunk is divided into the *thoracic* and *abdominal regions,* separated by the diaphragm.

2. The abdomen can be divided into four quadrants (right and left, upper and lower) or nine smaller regions (the *hypochondriac, lateral,* and *inguinal regions* on each side, and the *epigastric, umbilical,* and *hypogastric regions* medially). These divisions are useful for anatomical and clinical descriptions of the locations of organs, pain, or other abnormalities.

3. The *appendicular regions* are the upper and lower limbs. From proximal to distal, the upper limb is divided into the arm proper (*brachium*), forearm (*antebrachium*), wrist (*carpus*), hand (*manus*), and fingers (*digits*). The lower limb is divided, from proximal to distal, into the thigh (*femoral region*), leg proper (*crus*), ankle (*tarsus*), foot (*pes*), and toes (*digits*).

### Body Cavities and Membranes (p. 25)

1. The major body cavities are the cranial cavity, vertebral canal, thoracic cavity, and abdominopelvic cavity. Each is lined by a membrane and contains organs collectively called the *viscera.*

2. The *cranial cavity* is enclosed in the cranium and contains the brain. The *vertebral canal* is enclosed by the vertebral column and contains the spinal cord. These cavities are lined by three membranes called the *meninges.*

3. The thoracic cavity develops from the embryonic *coelom* and lies superior to the diaphragm. Its median portion, from the base of the neck to the diaphragm, is the *mediastinum,* which contains the heart, some major blood vessels, and the esophagus, trachea, bronchi, and thymus.

4. The heart is enclosed in a double-walled serous membrane, the *pericardium.* Its inner layer, the *visceral pericardium,* forms the heart surface. This is separated from the outer layer, the *parietal pericardium,* by the *pericardial cavity.* The cavity is lubricated by *pericardial fluid.*

5. Each lung is enclosed in a double-walled serous membrane, the *pleura.* The *visceral pleura* forms the lung surface, and the *parietal pleura* lines the inside of the rib cage. The *pleural cavity* between these layers is lubricated by *pleural fluid.*

6. The *abdominopelvic cavity* consists of the abdominal cavity above the pelvic brim and the pelvic cavity below it. It is lined by a serous membrane called the *peritoneum.* The *parietal peritoneum* forms the inner lining of the body wall, and the *visceral peritoneum* wraps around the abdominal viscera, suspends them from the wall, and holds them in place. The cavity is lubricated by *peritoneal fluid.*

7. *Retroperitoneal* organs lie against the dorsal body wall and are covered by peritoneum on only one side. *Intraperitoneal* organs lie more loosely within the abdominal cavity. They are encircled on all sides by peritoneum and are suspended from the body wall by peritoneal sheets.

8. The *dorsal mesentery* is a peritoneal sheet that turns inward from the posterior body walls and extends to the abdominal viscera. The dorsal mesentery of the colon is the *mesocolon.* The *ventral mesentery* continues beyond the viscera toward the ventral body wall. The major ventral mesenteries are the *greater* and *lesser omentum.*

9. Where it wraps around viscera such as the stomach and intestines, the peritoneum forms the outer surface of the organ, called the *serosa.*

10. Some body membranes are pressed closely together and enclose only a *potential space* between them. Potential spaces can open up and create actual spaces when air, liquid, or other matter accumulates in them. The pleural cavity and lumen of the uterus are examples of potential spaces.

### Organ Systems (p. 30)

1. The body has 11 organ systems (fig. A.11). Some organs play roles in two or more of these systems.

2. The *integumentary, skeletal,* and *muscular systems* provide protection, support, and movement.

3. The *nervous* and *endocrine systems* provide internal communication and integration.

4. The *circulatory* and *lymphatic systems* provide fluid transport.

5. The *respiratory, urinary,* and *digestive systems* provide for the input of gases and nutrients and the output of metabolic wastes.

6. The *reproductive system* produces offspring and thus serves for continuity of the species.

7. The *immune system* is not an organ system but a population of cells that colonize many of the organ systems and provide defense against pathogens.

## TESTING YOUR RECALL

1. Which of the following is *not* an essential part of anatomical position?
   a. eyes facing forward
   b. feet flat on the floor
   c. forearms supine
   d. mouth closed
   e. arms down to the sides

2. A ring-shaped section of the small intestine would be a _____ section.
   a. posterior
   b. midsagittal
   c. transverse
   d. frontal
   e. median

3. The tarsal region is _____ to the popliteal region.
   a. medial
   b. superficial
   c. superior
   d. dorsal
   e. distal

4. The greater omentum is _____ to the small intestine.
   a. posterior
   b. parietal
   c. deep
   d. superficial
   e. proximal

5. A _____ line passes through the sternum, umbilicus, and mons pubis.
   a. central
   b. proximal
   c. midclavicular
   d. midsagittal
   e. intertubercular

6. The _____ region is immediately medial to the coxal region.
   a. inguinal
   b. hypochondriac
   c. umbilical
   d. popliteal
   e. antecubital

7. Which of the following regions is *not* part of the upper limb?
   a. plantar
   b. carpal
   c. antecubital
   d. brachial
   e. palmar

8. Which of these organs is intraperitoneal?
   a. urinary bladder
   b. kidneys
   c. heart
   d. small intestine
   e. brain

9. In which area do you think pain from the gallbladder would be felt?
   a. umbilical region
   b. right upper quadrant
   c. hypogastric region
   d. left hypochondriac region
   e. left lower quadrant

10. Which of the following is *not* an organ system?
    a. muscular system
    b. integumentary system
    c. endocrine system
    d. lymphatic system
    e. immune system

11. The forearm is said to be _____ when the palms are facing forward.

12. The more superficial layer of the pleura is called the _____ pleura.

13. The right and left pleural cavities are separated by a thick region called the _____.

14. The back of the head is called the _____ region, and the back of the neck is the _____ region.

15. The manus is more commonly known as the _____, and the pes is more commonly known as the _____.

16. The cranial cavity is lined by membranes called the _____.

17. Abdominal organs that lie against the posterior abdominal wall and are covered with peritoneum only on the anterior side are said to have a/an _____ position.

18. The sternal region is _____ to the pectoral region.

19. The pelvic cavity can be described as _____ to the abdominal cavity in position.

20. The anterior pit of the elbow is the _____ region, and the corresponding (but posterior) pit of the knee is the _____ fossa.

***Answers in the Appendix***

## TRUE OR FALSE

*Determine which five of the following statements are false, and briefly explain why.*

1. A single sagittal section of the body can pass through one lung but not through both.

2. It would be possible to see both eyes in one frontal section of the head.

3. The knee is both superior and proximal to the tarsal region.

4. The diaphragm is ventral to the lungs.

5. Each lung is contained between the parietal pleura and visceral pleura.

6. The liver is in the lateral abdominal region.

7. The heart is in the mediastinum.

8. Both kidneys could be shown in a single coronal section of the body.

9. The peritoneum lines the inside of the stomach and intestines.

10. The sigmoid colon is in the lower right quadrant of the abdomen.

***Answers in the Appendix***

## TESTING YOUR COMPREHENSION

1. Identify which anatomical plane—sagittal, frontal, or transverse—is the only one that could *not* show (*a*) both the brain and tongue, (*b*) both eyes, (*c*) both the hypogastric and gluteal regions, (*d*) both kidneys, (*e*) both the sternum and vertebral column, and (*f*) both the heart and uterus.

2. Laypeople often misunderstand anatomical terminology. What do you think people really mean when they say they have "planter's warts"?

3. Name one structure or anatomical feature that could be found in each of the following locations relative to the ribs: medial, lateral, superior, inferior, deep, superficial, posterior, and anterior. Try not to use the same example twice.

4. Based on the illustrations in this atlas, identify an internal organ that is (*a*) in the upper left quadrant and retroperitoneal, (*b*) in the lower right quadrant of the peritoneal cavity, (*c*) in the hypogastric region, (*d*) in the right hypochondriac region, and (*e*) in the pectoral region.

5. Why do you think people with imaginary illnesses came to be called hypochondriacs?

*Answers at aris.mhhe.com*

## ONLINE RESOURCES

Visit aprevealed.com to explore melt-away cadaver dissections, watch animations that clarify difficult concepts, review histological and radiological images, or take a quiz to assess your understanding of the material.

The Saladin *Human Anatomy,* 2e website at aris.mhhe.com features chapter-specific quizzes, labeling exercises, and other interactive tools to complement your study of human anatomy. If your instructor has provided an ARIS course code, you can also access assignments and information specific to your course.

# Bone Tissue

Spongy bone of the human femur

## CHAPTER OUTLINE

## INSIGHTS

## BRUSHING UP

To understand this chapter, you may find it helpful to review the following concepts:
- Hyaline cartilage (p. 90)
- Introduction to bone histology (p. 91)

Anatomy & Physiology REVEALED®
aprevealed.com

**Skeletal System**

In art and history, nothing has symbolized death so much as a skull or skeleton.[1] Bones and teeth are the most durable remains of a once-living body and the most vivid reminder of the impermanence of life.

The dry bones presented for laboratory study may wrongly suggest that the skeleton is a nonliving scaffold for the body, like the steel girders of a building. Seeing it in such a sanitized form makes it easy to forget that the living skeleton is made of dynamic tissues, full of cells—that it continually remodels itself and interacts physiologically with all of the other organ systems. The skeleton is permeated with nerves and blood vessels, evidence of its sensitivity and metabolic activity.

Bone is the subject of chapters 6 through 8. In this chapter, we study bone as a tissue—its composition, development, and growth. This will provide a basis for understanding the skeleton, joints, and muscles in the chapters that follow.

# Tissues and Organs of the Skeletal System

## Objectives
When you have completed this section, you should be able to
- name the tissues and organs that compose the skeletal system;
- state several functions of the skeletal system;
- distinguish between bone as a tissue and as an organ;
- describe how bones are classified by shape; and
- describe the general features of a long bone.

The **skeletal system** consists of bones, cartilages, and ligaments tightly joined to form a strong, flexible framework for the body. Cartilage, the embryonic forerunner of most bones, covers many joint surfaces in the mature skeleton. Ligaments hold bones together at the joints and are discussed in chapter 9. Tendons are structurally similar to ligaments but attach muscles to bones; they are discussed with the muscular system in chapters 11 and 12.

## Functions of the Skeleton

The skeleton obviously provides the body with physical support, but it plays many other roles that go unnoticed by most people. Its functions include:

- **Support.** Bones of the legs, pelvis, and vertebral column hold up the body; the jaw bones support the teeth; and nearly all bones provide support for muscles.
- **Movement.** Skeletal muscles would serve little purpose if not for their attachment to the bones and ability to move them.

- **Protection.** Bones enclose and protect such delicate organs and tissues as the brain, spinal cord, lungs, heart, pelvic viscera, and bone marrow.
- **Blood formation.** Red bone marrow is the major producer of blood cells, including most cells of the immune system.
- **Electrolyte balance.** The skeleton is the body's main reservoir of calcium and phosphate. It stores these minerals and releases them when needed for other purposes.
- **Acid–base balance.** Bone buffers the blood against excessive pH changes by absorbing or releasing alkaline salts such as calcium phosphate.
- **Detoxification.** Bone tissue removes heavy metals and other foreign elements from the blood and thus reduces their toxic effects on other tissues. It can later release these contaminants more slowly for excretion. The tendency of bone to absorb foreign elements can, however, have terrible consequences (see Insight 6.1).

## Bones and Osseous Tissue

The study of **bone,** or **osseous**[2] **tissue,** is called **osteology.**[3] Bone is a connective tissue in which the matrix is hardened by the deposition of calcium phosphate and other minerals. The hardening process

## INSIGHT 6.1
### Medical History
### Radioactivity and Bone Cancer

Radioactivity captured the public imagination when Marie and Pierre Curie and Henri Becquerel shared the 1903 Nobel Prize for its discovery. Not for several decades, however, did anyone realize its dangers. Factories employed women to paint luminous numbers on watch and clock dials with radium paint. As they moistened the paint brushes with their tongues to keep them finely pointed, the women ingested radium. Their bones readily absorbed it and many of the women developed *osteosarcoma,* the most common and deadly form of bone cancer.

Even more horrific, in the wisdom of hindsight, was a deadly health fad in which people drank "tonics" made of radium-enriched water. One famous enthusiast was the champion golfer and millionaire playboy Eben Byers, who drank several bottles of radium tonic each day and praised its virtues as a wonder drug and aphrodisiac. Like the factory women, Byers contracted osteosarcoma. By the time of his death, holes had formed in his skull and doctors had removed his entire upper jaw and most of his mandible in an effort to halt the spreading cancer. Byers's bones and teeth were so radioactive they could expose photographic film in complete darkness. Brain damage left him unable to speak, but he remained mentally alert to the bitter end. His tragic decline and death in 1932 shocked the world and put an end to the radium tonic fad.

---

[1]*skelet* = dried up

[2]*os, osse, oste* = bone
[3]*osteo* = bone + *logy* = study of

is called **mineralization** or **calcification.** Osseous tissue, however, is only one of the components of a bone. Also present are blood, bone marrow, cartilage, adipose tissue, nervous tissue, and fibrous connective tissue. The word *bone* can denote an organ composed of all these components, or it can denote just the osseous tissue.

## The Shapes of Bones

Bones are classified into four groups according to their shapes and corresponding functions (fig. 6.1):

1. **Long bones** are roughly cylindrical in shape and significantly longer than wide. Like crowbars, they serve as rigid levers that are acted upon by the skeletal muscles to produce body movements. Long bones include the humerus of the arm, the radius and ulna of the forearm, the metacarpals and phalanges of the hand, the femur of the thigh, the tibia and fibula of the leg, and the metatarsals and phalanges of the feet.

2. **Short bones** are more nearly equal in length and width. They include the carpal (wrist) and tarsal (ankle) bones. They have limited motion and merely glide across one another, enabling the ankles and wrists to flex in multiple directions.

3. **Flat bones** enclose and protect soft organs and provide broad surfaces for muscle attachment. They include most cranial bones, the ribs, the sternum (breastbone), the scapula (shoulder blade), and the ossa coxae (hipbones).

4. **Irregular bones** have elaborate shapes that do not fit into any of the preceding categories. They include the vertebrae and some skull bones, such as the sphenoid and ethmoid bones.

## General Features of Bones

Bones have an outer shell of dense white osseous tissue called **compact (dense) bone,** usually enclosing a more loosely organized form of osseous tissue called **spongy (cancellous) bone** (figs. 6.2 and 6.5). The skeleton is about three-quarters compact bone and one-quarter spongy bone by weight. Compact and spongy bone are described later in more detail.

Figure 6.2 shows a longitudinal section through a long bone. The principal features of a long bone are its shaft, called the **diaphysis**[4] (dy-AF-ih-sis), and an expanded head at each end, called the **epiphysis**[5] (eh-PIF-ih-sis). The diaphysis consists largely of a cylinder of compact bone enclosing a space called the **medullary**[6] (MED-you-lerr-ee) **cavity.** The epiphysis is filled with spongy bone. Bone marrow occupies the medullary cavity and the spaces amid the spongy bone of the epiphysis. The diaphysis of a long bone provides leverage, whereas the epiphysis is enlarged to strengthen the joint and provide added surface area for the attachment of tendons and ligaments.

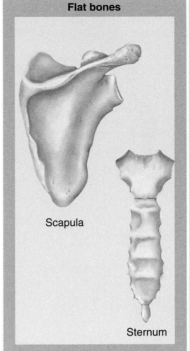

**Flat bones**

Scapula

Sternum

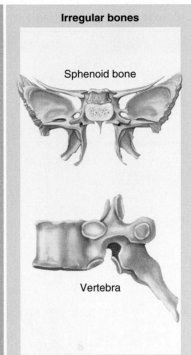

**Irregular bones**

Sphenoid bone

Vertebra

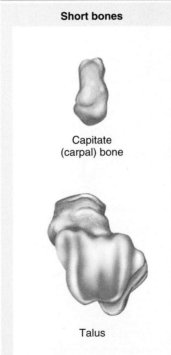

**Short bones**

Capitate
(carpal) bone

Talus

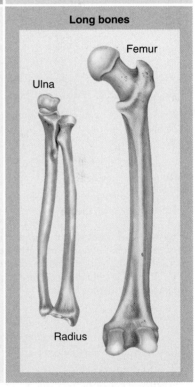

**Long bones**

Femur

Ulna

Radius

**Figure 6.1** **Classification of Bones by Shape.** The light-blue areas are articular cartilages.

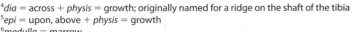

[4]*dia* = across + *physis* = growth; originally named for a ridge on the shaft of the tibia
[5]*epi* = upon, above + *physis* = growth
[6]*medulla* = marrow

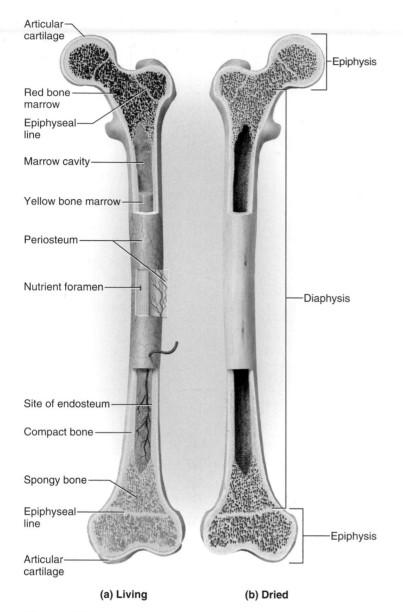

**Figure 6.2** Anatomy of a Long Bone. (a) The femur, with its soft tissues including bone marrow, articular cartilage, blood vessels, and periosteum. (b) A dried femur in longitudinal section.
● *What is the functional significance of a long bone being wider at the epiphyses than at the diaphysis?*

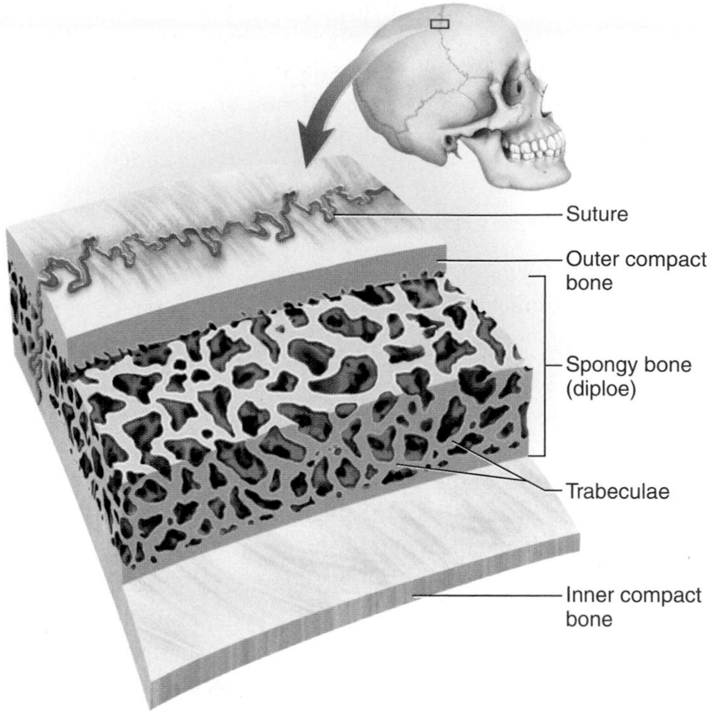

**Figure 6.3** Anatomy of a Flat Bone.

In children and adolescents, an **epiphyseal** (EP-ih-FIZZ-ee-ul) **plate** of hyaline cartilage separates the marrow spaces of the epiphysis and diaphysis. On X-rays, it appears as a transparent line at the end of a long bone (see fig. 6.11). The epiphyseal plate is a zone where the bones grow in length. In adults, the plate is depleted and the bones can grow no longer, but an *epiphyseal line* on the bone surface marks its former location.

Externally, most of the bone is covered with a sheath called the **periosteum.**[7] This has a tough, outer *fibrous layer* of collagen and an inner *osteogenic layer* of bone-forming cells. Some collagen fi-

bers of the outer layer are continuous with the tendons that bind muscle to bone, and some penetrate into the bone matrix as **perforating (Sharpey**[8]**) fibers.** The periosteum thus provides strong attachment and continuity from muscle to tendon to bone. The osteogenic layer is important to the growth of bone and healing of fractures. Blood vessels of the periosteum penetrate into the bone through minute holes called **nutrient foramina** (for-AM-ih-nuh); we will trace where they go when we consider bone histology. The internal surface of a bone is lined with **endosteum,**[9] a thin layer of reticular connective tissue with cells that deposit osseous tissue and others that dissolve it.

At most joints, the ends of the adjoining bones have no periosteum but rather a thin layer of hyaline cartilage, the **articular**[10] **cartilage.** Together with a lubricating fluid secreted between the bones, this cartilage enables a joint to move far more easily than it would if one bone rubbed directly against the other.

Flat bones have a sandwichlike construction, with two layers of compact bone enclosing a middle layer of spongy bone (fig. 6.3). In the skull, the spongy layer is called the **diploe**[11] (DIP-lo-ee). A moderate blow to the skull can fracture the outer layer of compact bone, but the diploe can sometimes absorb the impact and leave the inner layer of compact bone unharmed.

---

[7]*peri* = around + *oste* = bone

[8]William Sharpey (1802–80), Scottish histologist
[9]*endo* = within + *oste* = bone
[10]*artic* = joint
[11]*diplo* = double

## *Before You Go On*

*Answer the following questions to test your understanding of the preceding section:*

1. Name five tissues found in a bone.
2. List three or more functions of the skeletal system other than supporting the body and protecting some of the internal organs.
3. Name the four bone shapes and give an example of each.
4. Explain the difference between compact and spongy bone, and describe their spatial relationship to each other.
5. State the anatomical terms for the shaft, head, growth zone, and fibrous covering of a long bone.

# Histology of Osseous Tissue

### *Objectives*

When you have completed this section, you should be able to
- list and describe the cells, fibers, and ground substance of bone tissue;
- state the functional importance of each constituent of bone tissue;
- compare the histology of the two types of bone tissue; and
- distinguish between two types of bone marrow.

## Cells

Like any other connective tissue, bone consists of cells, fibers, and ground substance. There are four types of bone cells (fig. 6.4):

1. **Osteogenic**[12] (**osteoprogenitor**) **cells** are stem cells found in the endosteum, the inner layer of the periosteum, and within the *central canals,* to be described shortly. They arise from embryonic fibroblasts. Osteogenic cells multiply continually, and some of them differentiate into the *osteoblasts* described next.

2. **Osteoblasts**[13] are bone-forming cells that synthesize the organic matter of the matrix and help to mineralize the bone. They line up in rows in the endosteum and inner layer of periosteum and resemble a cuboidal epithelium on the bone surface (see fig. 6.9). Osteoblasts are nonmitotic, so the only source of new osteoblasts is the osteogenic cells. Stress and fractures stimulate accelerated mitosis of those cells and therefore a rapid rise in the number of osteoblasts, which then reinforce or rebuild the bone.

---

[12]*osteo* = bone + *genic* = producing
[13]*osteo* = bone + *blast* = form, produce

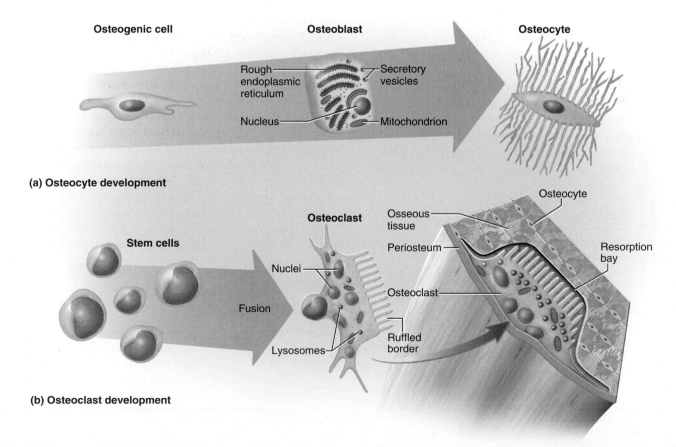

**Figure 6.4  Bone Cells and Their Development.**  (a) Osteogenic cells give rise to osteoblasts, which deposit matrix around themselves and transform into osteocytes. (b) Bone marrow stem cells fuse to form osteoclasts.

3. **Osteocytes** are former osteoblasts that have become trapped in the matrix they deposited. They live in tiny cavities called **lacunae,**[14] which are connected to each other by slender channels called **canaliculi**[15] (CAN-uh-LIC-you-lye). Each osteocyte has delicate cytoplasmic processes that reach into the canaliculi to meet the processes of neighboring osteocytes. Adjacent osteocytes are joined by gap junctions at the tip of these processes. These junctions allow osteocytes to pass nutrients and chemical signals to each other and to transfer wastes to the nearest blood vessels for disposal. Osteocytes also communicate by gap junctions with the osteoblasts on the bone surface.

   Osteocytes have multiple functions. Some resorb bone matrix and others deposit it, so they contribute to the homeostatic maintenance of both bone density and blood concentrations of calcium and phosphate ions. Perhaps even more importantly, they are strain sensors. When a load is applied to a bone, it produces a flow in the extracellular fluid of the lacunae and canaliculi. This stimulates the osteocytes to secrete biochemical signals that may regulate bone remodeling—adjustments in shape and bone density to adapt to stress.

4. **Osteoclasts**[16] are bone-dissolving macrophages found on bone surfaces. They develop from the same stem cells that produce monocytes of the blood. Several stem cells fuse with each other to form an osteoclast; thus, osteoclasts are unusually large (up to 150 μm in diameter) and typically have 3 or 4 nuclei, but sometimes up to 50. The side of the osteoclast facing the bone has a *ruffled border* with many deep infoldings of the plasma membrane, increasing its surface area. Hydrogen pumps in the ruffled border secrete hydrogen ions ($H^+$) into the extracellular fluid, and chloride ions ($Cl^-$) follow by electrical attraction; thus, the space between the osteoclast and the bone becomes filled with hydrochloric acid (HCl). The HCl, with a pH of about 4, dissolves the minerals of the adjacent bone. Lysosomes of the osteoclast then release enzymes that digest the organic component. Osteoclasts often reside in little pits called *resorption bays (Howship*[17] *lacunae)* that they have etched into the bone surface.

### THINK ABOUT IT

*Considering the function of osteoblasts, what organelles do you think are especially abundant in their cytoplasm?*

## Matrix

The matrix of osseous tissue is, by dry weight, about one-third organic and two-thirds inorganic matter. The organic matter includes collagen and various large protein–carbohydrate complexes called glycosaminoglycans, proteoglycans, and glycoproteins. The

[14]*lac* = lake, hollow + *una* = little
[15]*canal* = canal, channel + *icul* = little
[16]*osteo* = bone + *clast* = destroy, break down
[17]J. Howship (1781–1841), English surgeon

# INSIGHT 6.2

## Clinical Application

### Polymers, Ceramics, and Bones

The physical properties of bone can be understood by analogy to some principles of engineering. Engineers use four kinds of construction materials: metals, ceramics (stone, glass, cement), polymers (rubber, plastic, cellulose), and composites (mixtures of two or more of the other classes). Bone is a composite of polymer (protein) and ceramic (mineral). The protein gives it flexibility and resistance to tension, while the mineral gives it resistance to compression. Owing to the mineral component, a bone can support the weight of the body without sagging, and owing to the protein component, it can bend a little when subjected to stress.

Bone is somewhat like a fiberglass fishing rod, which is made of a ceramic (glass fibers) embedded in a polymer (resin). The fibers alone would be too flexible and limp to serve the purpose of a fishing rod, while the resin alone would be too brittle and would easily break. The combination of the two, however, gives the rod strength and flexibility. Unlike fiberglass, however, the ratio of ceramic to polymer in a bone varies from one location to another, adapting osseous tissue to different amounts of tension and compression exerted on different parts of the skeleton.

inorganic matter is about 85% **hydroxyapatite,** a crystallized calcium phosphate salt $[Ca_{10}(PO_4)_6(OH)_2]$, 10% calcium carbonate $(CaCO_3)$, and lesser amounts of magnesium, sodium, potassium, fluoride, sulfate, carbonate, and hydroxide ions.

The minerals and collagen form a composite that gives bones a combination of flexibility and strength similar to fiberglass (see Insight 6.2). The minerals resist compression (crumbling or sagging when weight is applied). When bones are deficient in calcium salts, they become soft and bend easily. Soft bones are characteristic of a childhood disease called **rickets,** which occurs when a child is deficient in vitamin D and therefore cannot absorb enough dietary calcium to adequately harden the bones. The legs become bowed outward by the weight of the body.

The collagen fibers of bone give it the ability to resist tension, so the bone can bend slightly without snapping. Without collagen, the bones become very brittle, as in brittle bone disease (see Insight 3.3, p. 89). Without collagen, a jogger's bones would shatter under the impact of running.

## Compact Bone

The histological study of compact bone usually uses slices that have been dried, cut with a saw, and ground to translucent thinness. This procedure destroys the cells and much of the other organic content but reveals fine details of the inorganic matrix (fig. 6.5d). Such sections show onionlike **concentric lamellae**—layers of matrix concentrically arranged around a **central (haversian**[18] or **osteonic) canal.**

[18]Clopton Havers (1650–1702), English anatomist

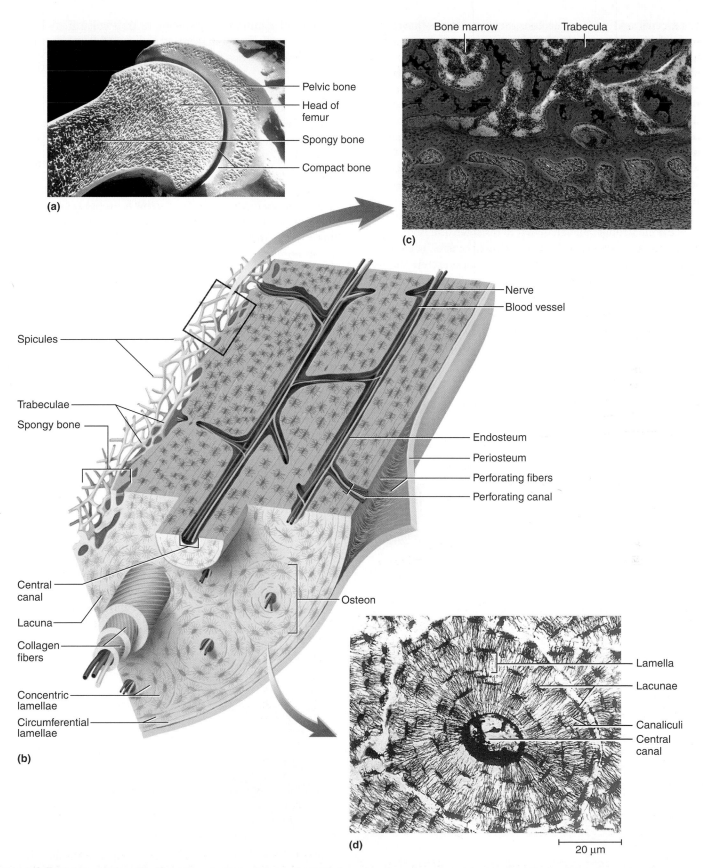

**Figure 6.5** **The Histology of Osseous Tissue.** (a) Compact and spongy bone in a frontal section of the hip joint. (b) The three-dimensional structure of compact bone. Lamellae of the uppermost osteon are telescoped to show their alternating arrangement of collagen fibers. (c) Microscopic appearance of a cross section of compact bone. (d) Microscopic appearance of spongy bone.

● *Which type of osseous tissue has more surface area exposed to osteoclast action?*

A central canal and its lamellae constitute an **osteon (haversian system)**—the basic structural unit of compact bone. In longitudinal views and three-dimensional reconstructions, we find that an osteon is a cylinder of tissue surrounding a central canal. Along their length, central canals are joined by transverse or diagonal passages called **perforating (Volkmann**[19]**) canals.** The central and perforating canals contain blood vessels and nerves. Lacunae lie between adjacent layers of matrix and are connected with each other by canaliculi. Canaliculi of the innermost lacunae open into the central canal.

In each lamella, the collagen fibers "corkscrew" down the matrix in a helical pattern like the threads of a screw. The helices coil in one direction in one lamella and in the opposite direction in the next lamella. Like alternating layers of a sheet of plywood, this makes the bone stronger and enables it to resist tension in multiple directions. In areas where the bone must resist tension (bending), the helix is loosely coiled like the threads on a wood screw and the fibers are more stretched out on the longitudinal axis of the bone. In weight-bearing areas, where the bone must resist compression, the helix is more tightly coiled like the closely spaced threads on a bolt, and the fibers are more nearly transverse.

The skeleton receives about half a liter of blood per minute. Blood vessels, along with nerves, enter the bone tissue through nutrient foramina on the surface. These open into perforating canals that cross the matrix and lead to the central canals. The innermost osteocytes around each central canal receive nutrients from these blood vessels and pass them along through their gap junctions to neighboring osteocytes. They also receive wastes from their neighbors and convey them to the central canal for removal by the bloodstream. Thus, the cytoplasmic processes of the osteocytes maintain a two-way flow of nutrients and wastes between the central canal and the outermost cells of the osteon.

Not all of the matrix is organized into osteons. The inner and outer boundaries of dense bone are arranged in *circumferential lamellae* that run parallel to the bone surface. Between osteons, we can find irregular patches of *interstitial lamellae*, the remains of old osteons that broke down as the bone grew and remodeled itself.

## Spongy Bone

Spongy bone consists of a lattice of delicate-looking slivers of bone called **spicules**[20] (rods or spines, as in the photo on p. 153) and **trabeculae**[21] (thin plates as in fig. 6.5c). Although calcified and hard, spongy bone is named for its spongelike appearance; it is permeated by spaces filled with bone marrow. The matrix is arranged in lamellae like those of compact bone, but they are not arranged in concentric layers, and there are few osteons. Central canals are not needed here because no osteocyte is very far from the blood supply in the marrow. Spongy bone is well designed to impart strength to a bone with a minimum of weight. Its trabeculae are not randomly arranged as they might seem at a glance, but develop along the bone's lines of stress (fig. 6.6).

## Bone Marrow

**Bone marrow** is a general term for the soft material that occupies the medullary cavity of a long bone, the spaces amid the trabeculae of spongy bone, and the larger central canals. In a child, the medullary cavity of nearly every bone is filled with **red bone marrow,** which gets its color from an abundance of red blood cells. Although it is called *myeloid tissue,* red bone marrow is probably best regarded as an organ. Chapter 22 (p. 647) describes the microscopic structure that justifies that assessment. Red bone marrow is also described as (or more accurately, it includes) *hemopoietic*[22] (HE-mo-poy-ET-ic), or blood-forming tissue. All types of blood cells are produced here, although some types are also produced in hemopoietic tissues elsewhere, such as the lymph nodes and thymus.

With age, the red bone marrow is gradually replaced by fatty **yellow bone marrow,** like the fat at the center of a ham bone. By early adulthood, red bone marrow is limited to the skull, vertebrae, sternum, ribs, part of the pelvic (hip) girdle, and the proximal heads of the humerus and femur, while the rest of the skeleton contains yellow marrow (fig. 6.7). Yellow bone marrow no longer produces blood, although in the event of severe or chronic anemia, it can transform back into red marrow and resume that role.

[22]*hemo* = blood + *poietic* = forming

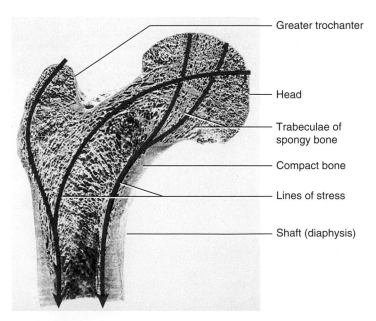

**Figure 6.6 Spongy Bone Structure in Relation to Mechanical Stress.** In this frontal section of the femur, the trabeculae of spongy bone can be seen oriented along lines of mechanical stress applied by the weight of the body.

*Greater trochanter*

*Head*

*Trabeculae of spongy bone*

*Compact bone*

*Lines of stress*

*Shaft (diaphysis)*

[19]Alfred Volkmann (1800–77), German physiologist
[20]*spicul* = dart, little point
[21]*trabe* = plate + *cul* = little

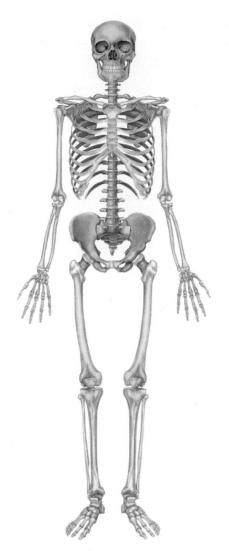

**Figure 6.7** **Distribution of Red and Yellow Bone Marrow.** In an adult, red bone marrow occupies the medullary cavities in the regions colored red. Yellow bone marrow occurs in the long bones of the limbs.
• *Suppose red bone marrow were needed for transfusion to a patient. On the basis of this illustration, suggest one or more optimal anatomical sites for drawing red bone marrow from a donor.*

## Before You Go On

*Answer the following questions to test your understanding of the preceding section:*

6. Suppose you had unlabeled electron micrographs of the four kinds of bone cells and their neighboring tissues. Name each of the four cells and explain how you could visually distinguish each one from the other three.
7. Name three organic components of the bone matrix.
8. What are the mineral crystals of bone called, and what are they made of?
9. Sketch a cross section of an osteon and label its major parts.
10. What are the two kinds of bone marrow? What does *hemopoietic tissue* mean? Which type of bone marrow fits this description?

# Bone Development

### Objectives
When you have completed this section, you should be able to
• describe two mechanisms of bone formation;
• explain how a child grows in height; and
• explain how mature bone continues to grow and remodel itself.

The formation of bone is called **ossification** (OSS-ih-fih-CAY-shun), or **osteogenesis.** There are two methods of ossification—*intramembranous* and *endochondral.*

## Intramembranous Ossification

**Intramembranous**[23] (IN-tra-MEM-bruh-nus) **ossification** produces the flat bones of the skull and most of the clavicle (collarbone). Such bones develop within a fibrous sheet similar to the dermis of the skin, so they are sometimes called *dermal bones.* Figure 6.8 shows the stages of the process.

1. An area of the embryonic connective tissue (mesenchyme) condenses into a layer of soft tissue with a dense supply of blood capillaries. The mesenchymal cells enlarge and differentiate into osteogenic cells, and regions of mesenchyme become a network of soft sheets called trabeculae.

2. Osteogenic cells gather on these trabeculae and differentiate into osteoblasts. These cells deposit an organic matrix called **osteoid**[24] **tissue**—soft collagenous tissue similar to bone except for a lack of minerals (fig. 6.9). As the trabeculae grow thicker, calcium phosphate is deposited in the matrix. Some osteoblasts become trapped in the matrix and are now osteocytes. Mesenchyme close to the surface of a trabecula remains uncalcified, but becomes denser and more fibrous, forming a periosteum.

3. Osteoblasts continue to deposit minerals, producing a honeycomb of bony trabeculae. Some trabeculae persist as permanent spongy bone, while osteoclasts resorb and remodel others to form a marrow cavity in the middle of the bone.

4. Trabeculae at the surface continue to calcify until the spaces between them are filled in, converting the spongy bone to compact bone. This process gives rise to the sandwichlike arrangement typical of mature flat bones.

---

[23]*intra* = within + *membran* = membrane
[24]*oste* = bone + *oid* = like, resembling

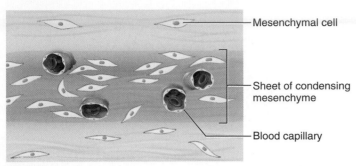

① Condensation of mesenchyme into soft sheet permeated with blood capillaries

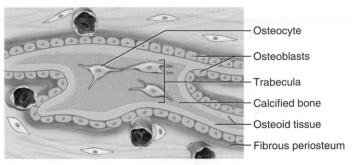

② Deposition of osteoid tissue by osteoblasts on mesenchymal surface; entrapment of first osteocytes; formation of periosteum

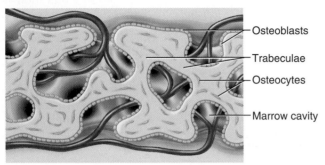

③ Honeycomb of bony trabeculae formed by continued mineral deposition; creation of spongy bone

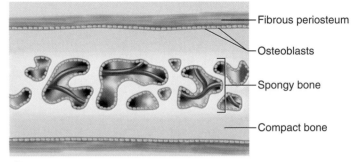

④ Surface bone filled in by bone deposition, converting spongy bone to compact bone. Persistence of spongy bone in the middle layer.

**Figure 6.8 Stages of Intramembranous Ossification.** Developing cranial bones of the human fetus. Note the layers of osteoid tissue, osteoblasts, and fibrous periosteum on both sides of the bone.
● *With the aid of chapter 7, name at least two specific bones that would form by this process.*

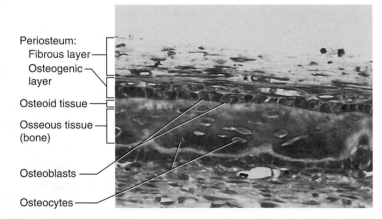

**Figure 6.9 Intramembranous Ossification of a Cranial Bone of the Human Fetus.** Note the layers of osteoid tissue, osteoblasts, and fibrous periosteum on both sides of the bone.

## Endochondral Ossification

**Endochondral**[25] (EN-doe-CON-drul) **ossification** is a process in which a bone develops from a preexisting model composed of hyaline cartilage. It begins around the sixth week of fetal development

and continues into a person's 20s. Most bones of the body, including the vertebrae, ribs, sternum, scapula, pelvis, and bones of the limbs, develop in this way. Figure 6.10 shows the following steps in endochondral ossification, using the example of a *metacarpal bone* in the palmar region of the hand.

① Mesenchyme develops into a body of hyaline cartilage, covered with a fibrous perichondrium, in the location of a future bone. For a time, the perichondrium produces chondrocytes and the cartilage model grows in thickness.

② Eventually, the perichondrium stops producing chondrocytes and begins producing osteoblasts. These deposit a thin collar of bone around the middle of the cartilage model, encircling it like a napkin ring and providing physical reinforcement. The former perichondrium is now considered to be a periosteum. Meanwhile, chondrocytes in the middle of the model enlarge and the matrix between their lacunae is reduced to thin walls. This region of chondrocyte enlargement is called the **primary ossification center.** The walls of matrix between the lacunae calcify and block nutrients from reaching the chondrocytes. The cells die and their lacunae merge into a single cavity in the middle of the model.

[25]*endo* = within + *chondr* = cartilage

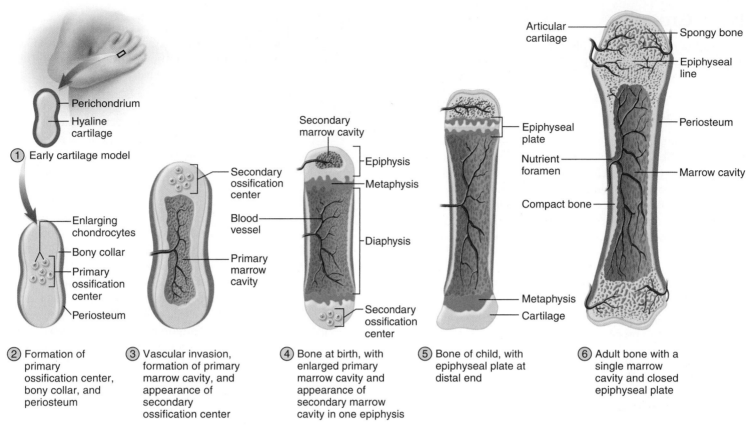

**Figure 6.10** Stages of Endochondral Ossification. A metacarpal bone of the hand.
● *With the aid of chapter 8, name at least two specific bones that would have two epiphyseal plates (proximal and distal) at stage 5.*

③ Blood vessels penetrate the bony collar and invade the primary ossification center. As the center of the model is hollowed out and filled with blood and stem cells, it becomes the **primary marrow cavity.** Various stem cells introduced with the blood give rise to osteoblasts and osteoclasts. Osteoblasts line the cavity, begin depositing osteoid tissue, and calcify it to form a temporary network of bony trabeculae. As the bony collar under the periosteum thickens and elongates, a wave of cartilage death progresses toward the ends of the bone. Osteoclasts in the marrow cavity follow this wave, dissolving calcified cartilage remnants and enlarging the marrow cavity of the diaphysis. The region of transition from cartilage to bone at each end of the primary marrow cavity is called a **metaphysis** (meh-TAF-ih-sis).

Soon, chondrocyte enlargement and death occur in the epiphysis of the model as well, creating a **secondary ossification center.** In the metacarpal bones, as illustrated in figure 6.10, this occurs in only one epiphysis. In longer bones of the arms, forearms, legs, and thighs, it occurs at both ends.

④ The secondary ossification center becomes hollowed out by the same process as the diaphysis, generating a **secondary marrow cavity** in the epiphysis. This cavity expands outward from the center, in all directions. At the time of birth, the bone typically looks like step 4 in figure 6.10. In bones with two secondary ossification centers, one center lags behind the other in development, so at birth there is a secondary marrow cavity at one end, but chondrocyte growth has just begun at the other. The joints of the limbs are still cartilaginous at birth, much as they are in the 12-week fetus in figure 7.30, p. 230.

⑤ During infancy and childhood, the epiphyses fill with spongy bone. Cartilage is then limited to the articular cartilage covering each joint surface and to the epiphyseal plate of cartilage separating the primary and secondary marrow cavities at one or both ends of the bone. The plate persists through childhood and adolescence and serves as a growth zone for bone elongation. This growth process is described in the next section.

⑥ By the late teens to early twenties, all remaining cartilage in the epiphyseal plate is generally consumed, and the gap between the epiphysis and diaphysis closes. The primary and secondary marrow cavities then unite into a single cavity, and the bone can no longer grow in length.

# Bone Growth

Ossification does not end at birth, but continues throughout life with the growth and remodeling of bones. Bones grow in two directions: length and width.

## Bone Elongation

To understand growth in length, we must return to the epiphyseal plates mentioned earlier. On an X-ray, the plate appears as a translucent line across the end of a bone, since it is not yet ossified (fig. 6.11; compare the X-ray of an adult hand in figure 8.5, p. 216). It consists of a band of typical hyaline cartilage in the middle and a metaphysis on each side. In figure 6.10, steps 4 and 5, the cartilage is the blue region and each metaphysis is violet. Even if one end of a bone lacks an epiphyseal plate, it has a metaphysis—the transitional zone between the epiphyseal cartilage and diaphyseal osseous tissue.

At the metaphysis, the cartilage thickens through cell division and enlargement and then undergoes replacement by bone. Figure 6.12 shows the histological structure of the metaphysis and the following steps in this process.

1. **Zone of reserve cartilage.** This region, farthest from the marrow cavity, consists of typical resting hyaline cartilage.

2. **Zone of cell proliferation.** A little closer to the marrow cavity, chondrocytes multiply and arrange themselves into longitudinal columns of flattened lacunae.

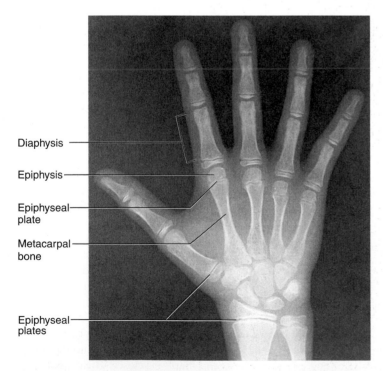

Diaphysis

Epiphysis

Epiphyseal plate

Metacarpal bone

Epiphyseal plates

**Figure 6.11   X-ray of a Child's Hand.** The cartilaginous epiphyseal plates are evident at the ends of the long bones. These will disappear and the epiphyses will fuse with the diaphyses by adulthood. Long bones of the hand and fingers develop only one epiphyseal plate.

3. **Zone of cell hypertrophy.** Next, the chondrocytes cease to multiply and begin to hypertrophy (enlarge), much like they do in the primary ossification center of the fetus. The walls of matrix between lacunae become very thin.

4. **Zone of calcification.** Minerals are deposited in the matrix between the columns of lacunae and calcify the cartilage. These are not the permanent mineral deposits of bone, but only a temporary support for the cartilage that would otherwise soon be weakened by the breakdown of the enlarged lacunae.

5. **Zone of bone deposition.** Within each column, the walls between the lacunae break down and the chondrocytes die. This converts each column into a longitudinal channel (white spaces in the figure), which is immediately invaded by blood vessels and marrow from the marrow cavity. Osteoblasts line up along the walls of these channels and begin depositing concentric lamellae of matrix, while osteoclasts dissolve the temporarily calcified cartilage.

The process of bone deposition in zone 5 creates a region of spongy bone at the end of the marrow cavity facing the metaphysis. This spongy bone remains for life, although with extensive lifelong remodeling. But around the perimeter of the marrow cavity, continuing ossification converts this spongy bone to compact bone. Osteoblasts lining the aforementioned channels deposit layer after layer of bone matrix, so the channel grows narrower and narrower. These layers become the concentric lamellae of an osteon. Finally only a slender channel persists, the central canal of a new osteon. As usual, osteoblasts trapped in the matrix become osteocytes.

### THINK ABOUT IT

*In a given osteon, which lamellae are the oldest—those immediately adjacent to the central canal or those around the perimeter of the osteon? Explain your answer.*

How does a child or adolescent grow in height? Chondrocyte multiplication in zone 2 and hypertrophy in zone 3 continually push the zone of reserve cartilage (1) toward the ends of the bone, so the bone elongates. In the lower limbs, this process causes a person to grow in height, while bones of the upper limbs grow proportionately.

Thus, bone elongation is really a result of cartilage growth. Cartilage growth from within, by the multiplication of chondrocytes and deposition of new matrix in the interior, is called **interstitial growth.**[26] The most common form of dwarfism results from a failure of cartilage growth in the long bones (see Insight 6.3).

In the late teens to early twenties, all the cartilage of the epiphyseal plate is depleted. The primary and secondary marrow cavities now unite into one cavity. The junctional region where they meet

---

[26]*inter* = between + *stit* = to place, stand

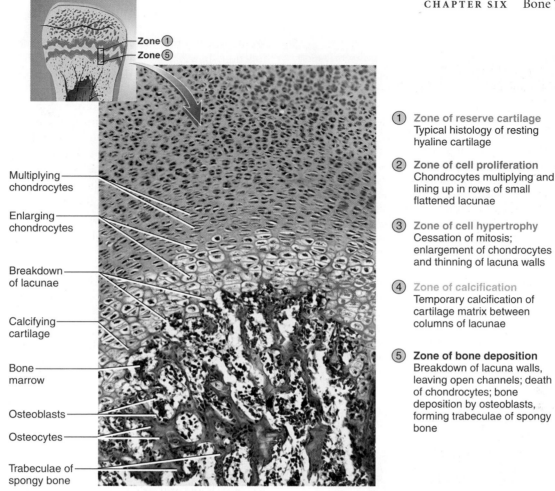

Zone ①
Zone ⑤

Multiplying chondrocytes

Enlarging chondrocytes

Breakdown of lacunae

Calcifying cartilage

Bone marrow

Osteoblasts

Osteocytes

Trabeculae of spongy bone

① **Zone of reserve cartilage**
Typical histology of resting hyaline cartilage

② **Zone of cell proliferation**
Chondrocytes multiplying and lining up in rows of small flattened lacunae

③ **Zone of cell hypertrophy**
Cessation of mitosis; enlargement of chondrocytes and thinning of lacuna walls

④ **Zone of calcification**
Temporary calcification of cartilage matrix between columns of lacunae

⑤ **Zone of bone deposition**
Breakdown of lacuna walls, leaving open channels; death of chondrocytes; bone deposition by osteoblasts, forming trabeculae of spongy bone

**Figure 6.12 Zones of the Metaphysis.** This micrograph shows the replacement of cartilage with bone in the growth zone of a long bone.
● *Which two zones in this figure account for the growth of a child in height?*

is filled with spongy bone, and the site of the original epiphyseal plate is marked with a line of slightly denser spongy bone called the **epiphyseal line** (see figs. 6.2 and 6.10, step 6). Often a delicate ridge on the bone surface marks the location of this line. When the epiphyseal plate is depleted, we say that the epiphyses have "closed" because no gap between the epiphysis and diaphysis is visible on an X-ray. Once the epiphyses have all closed in the lower limbs, a person can grow no taller. The epiphyseal plates close at different ages in different bones and in different regions of the same bone. The state of closure in various bones is often used in forensic science to estimate the age at death of a subadult skeleton.

## Bone Widening and Thickening

Bones also grow throughout life in diameter and thickness. This involves a process called **appositional growth,**[27] the deposition of new tissue at the surface. Cartilages can enlarge by both interstitial and appositional growth, but osseous tissue is limited to the appositional method. Embedded in a calcified matrix, the osteocytes have little room to spare for the deposition of more matrix internally.

Appositional growth is similar to intramembranous ossification. Osteoblasts in the inner layer of periosteum deposit osteoid tissue on the bone surface, calcify it, and become trapped in it as osteocytes—much like the process in figure 6.9. They lay down matrix in layers parallel to the surface, not in cylindrical osteons like those deeper in the bone. This process produces the surface layers of bone called *circumferential lamellae,* described earlier. As a bone increases in diameter, its marrow cavity also widens. This is achieved by osteoclasts of the endosteum dissolving tissue on the inner bone surface.

## Bone Remodeling

In addition to their growth, bones are continually remodeled throughout life by the absorption of old bone and deposition of new. This process replaces about 10% of the skeletal tissue per year. It repairs microfractures, releases minerals into the blood, and reshapes bones in response to use and disuse. **Wolff's**[28] **law of bone** states that the architecture of a bone is determined by the mechanical stresses placed upon it, and the bone thereby adapts to withstand those stresses.

[27] *ap = ad* = to, near + *posit* = to place

[28] Julius Wolff (1836–1902), German anatomist and surgeon

## Achondroplastic Dwarfism

*Achondroplastic*[29] (ah-con-dro-PLAS-tic) *dwarfism* is a condition in which the long bones of the limbs stop growing in childhood, while the growth of other bones is unaffected. As a result, a person has a short stature but a normal-sized head and trunk (fig. 6.13). As its name implies, achondroplastic dwarfism results from a failure of cartilage growth—specifically, failure of the chondrocytes in zones 2 and 3 of the metaphysis to multiply and enlarge. This is different from *pituitary dwarfism*, in which a deficiency of growth hormone stunts the growth of all of the bones and a person has short stature but normal proportions throughout the skeletal system.

Achondroplastic dwarfism results from a spontaneous mutation that can arise any time DNA is replicated. Two people of normal height with no family history of dwarfism can therefore have a child with achondroplastic dwarfism. The mutant allele is dominant, so the children of a heterozygous achondroplastic dwarf have at least a 50% chance of exhibiting dwarfism, depending on the genotype of the other parent.

**Figure 6.13** **Achondroplastic Dwarfism.** The student on the right, pictured with her roommate of normal height, is an achondroplastic dwarf with a height of about 122 cm (48 in.). Her parents were of normal height. Note the normal proportion of head to trunk but shortening of the limbs.

[29]*a* = without + *chondro* = cartilage + *plast* = growth

Wolff's law is a fine example of the complementarity of form and function, showing that the form of a bone is shaped by its functional experience. It is admirably demonstrated by figure 6.6, in which we see that the trabeculae of spongy bone have developed along the lines of stress placed on the femur. Wolff observed that these stress lines were very similar to the ones that engineers saw in mechanical cranes.

Bone remodeling comes about through the collaborative action of osteoblasts and osteoclasts. If a bone is little used, osteoclasts remove matrix and get rid of unnecessary mass. If a bone is heavily used or a stress is consistently applied to a particular region of a bone, osteoblasts deposit new osseous tissue and thicken the bone. Consequently, the comparatively smooth bones of an infant or toddler develop a variety of surface bumps, ridges, and spines (described in chapter 7) as the child begins to walk. The greater trochanter of the femur, for example (see figs. 6.8 and 8.10; p. 162 and p. 222, respectively), is a massive outgrowth of bone stimulated by the pull of tendons from several powerful hip muscles employed in walking.

On average, bones have greater density and mass in athletes and people engaged in heavy manual labor than they do in sedentary people. Anthropologists who study ancient skeletal remains use evidence of this sort to help distinguish between members of different social classes, such as distinguishing royalty from laborers. Even in studying modern skeletal remains, as in investigating a suspicious death, Wolff's law comes into play as the bones give evidence of a person's sex, race, height, weight, work or exercise habits, nutritional status, and medical history.

The orderly remodeling of bone depends on a precise balance between deposition and resorption, between osteoblasts and osteoclasts. If one process outpaces the other, or both processes occur too rapidly, various bone deformities, developmental abnormalities, and other disorders occur, such as *osteitis deformans* (Paget disease), *osteogenesis imperfecta* (brittle bone disease), and *osteoporosis* (see table 6.2; Insight 3.3, p. 89; and p. 169, respectively).

## Nutritional and Hormonal Factors

The balance between bone deposition and resorption is influenced by nearly two dozen nutrients, hormones, and growth factors. The most important factors that promote bone deposition are as follows.

- **Calcium** and **phosphate** are needed as raw materials for the calcified ground substance of bone.
- **Vitamin A** promotes synthesis of the glycosaminoglycans (GAGs) of the bone matrix.
- **Vitamin C (ascorbic acid)** promotes the cross-linking of collagen molecules in bone and other connective tissues.
- **Vitamin D (calcitriol)** is necessary for calcium absorption by the small intestine, and it reduces the urinary loss of calcium and phosphate. Vitamin D is synthesized by one's own body. The process begins when the ultraviolet radiation in sunlight acts on a cholesterol derivative (7-dehydrocholesterol) in the keratinocytes of the epidermis. The product is picked up by the bloodstream, and the liver and kidneys complete its conversion to vitamin D.

- **Calcitonin,** a hormone secreted by the thyroid gland, stimulates osteoblast activity. It functions chiefly in children and pregnant women; it seems to be of little significance in nonpregnant adults.
- **Growth hormone** promotes intestinal absorption of calcium, the proliferation of cartilage at the epiphyseal plates, and the elongation of bones.
- **Sex steroids** (estrogen and testosterone) stimulate osteoblasts and promote the growth of long bones, especially in adolescence.

Bone deposition is also promoted by thyroid hormone, insulin, and local *growth factors* produced within the bone itself. Bone resorption is stimulated mainly by one hormone:

- **Parathyroid hormone (PTH)** is produced by four small *parathyroid glands,* which adhere to the back of the thyroid gland in the neck. The parathyroid glands secrete PTH in response to a drop in blood calcium level. PTH stimulates osteoblasts, which then secrete an *osteoclast-stimulating factor* that promotes bone resorption by the osteoclasts. The principal purpose of this response is not to maintain bone composition but to maintain an appropriate level of blood calcium, without which a person can suffer fatal muscle spasms. PTH also reduces urinary calcium losses and promotes calcitriol synthesis.

## The Aging Skeletal System

The predominant effect of aging on the skeleton is a loss of bone mass and strength. After age 35 or 40, osteoblasts become less active than osteoclasts. The imbalance between deposition and resorption leads to **osteopenia,**[30] the loss of bone; when the loss is severe enough to compromise physical activity and health, it is called *osteoporosis* (discussed in the next section). After age 40, women lose about 8% of their bone mass per decade, and men lose about 3%. Bone loss from the jaws is a contributing factor in tooth loss. Not only does bone density decline with age, but the bones become more brittle as the osteoblasts synthesize less protein. Fractures occur more easily and heal more slowly. Arthritis, a family of joint disorders associated with aging, is discussed in chapter 9.

### *Before You Go On*

*Answer the following questions to test your understanding of the preceding section:*

11. Describe the stages of intramembranous ossification. Name a bone that is formed in this way.
12. Describe the five zones of a metaphysis and the major distinctions between them.

[30]*osteo* = bone + *penia* = lack, deficiency

13. How does Wolff's law explain some of the structural differences between the bones of a young child and the bones of a young adult?
14. Identify the nutrients most important to bone growth.
15. Identify the principal hormones that stimulate bone growth.

# Structural Disorders of Bone

### *Objectives*
When you have completed this section, you should be able to
- name and describe the types of fractures;
- explain how a fracture is repaired;
- discuss the causes and effects of osteoporosis; and
- briefly describe a few other structural defects of the skeleton.

Fractures are probably the most familiar disorder of the skeletal system, although the most common structural defect is *osteoporosis.* This section describes both of these defects and briefly defines a few others.

## Fractures

There are multiple ways of classifying bone fractures. A **stress fracture** is a break caused by abnormal trauma to a bone, such as fractures incurred in falls, athletics, and military combat. A **pathologic fracture** is a break in a bone weakened by some other disease, such as bone cancer or osteoporosis, usually due to a stress that would not normally fracture a bone. Fractures are also classified according to the direction of the fracture line, whether or not the skin is broken, and whether a bone is merely cracked or is broken into separate pieces (table 6.1; fig. 6.14).

Most fractures are set by *closed reduction,* a procedure in which the bone fragments are manipulated into their normal positions without surgery. *Open reduction* involves the surgical exposure of the bone and the use of plates, screws, or pins to realign the fragments (fig. 6.15b). To stabilize the bone during healing, fractures are often set in fiberglass casts. *Traction* is used to treat fractures of the femur in children. It aids in the alignment of the bone fragments by overriding the force of the strong thigh muscles. Traction is rarely used for elderly patients, however, because the risks from long-term confinement to bed outweigh the benefits. Hip fractures are usually pinned, and early ambulation (walking) is encouraged because it promotes blood circulation and healing.

An uncomplicated fracture heals in 8 to 12 weeks, but complex fractures take longer, and all fractures heal more slowly in older people. Figure 6.16 shows the healing process. Usually, a healed fracture leaves a slight thickening of the bone visible by X-ray, but in some cases, healing is so complete that no trace of the fracture can be found.

| TABLE 6.1 | Classification of Fractures |
| --- | --- |
| **Type** | **Description** |
| Closed | Skin is not broken (formerly called a *simple* fracture) |
| Open | Skin is broken; bone protrudes through skin or wound extends to fractured bone (formerly called a *compound* fracture) |
| Complete | Bone is broken into two or more pieces |
| Incomplete | Partial fracture that extends only partway across bone; pieces remain joined |
| Greenstick | Bone is bent on one side and has incomplete fracture on opposite side |
| Hairline | Fine crack in which sections of bone remain aligned; common in skull |
| Comminuted | Bone is broken into three or more pieces |
| Displaced | The portions of a fractured bone are out of anatomical alignment |
| Nondisplaced | The portions of bone are still in correct anatomical alignment |
| Impacted | One bone fragment is driven into the medullary space or spongy bone of the other |
| Depressed | Broken portion of bone forms a concavity, as in skull fractures |
| Linear | Fracture parallel to long axis of bone |
| Transverse | Fracture perpendicular to long axis of bone |
| Oblique | Diagonal fracture, between linear and transverse |
| Spiral | Fracture spirals around axis of long bone, the result of a twisting stress, often produced when an abusive adult roughly picks a child up by the arm |

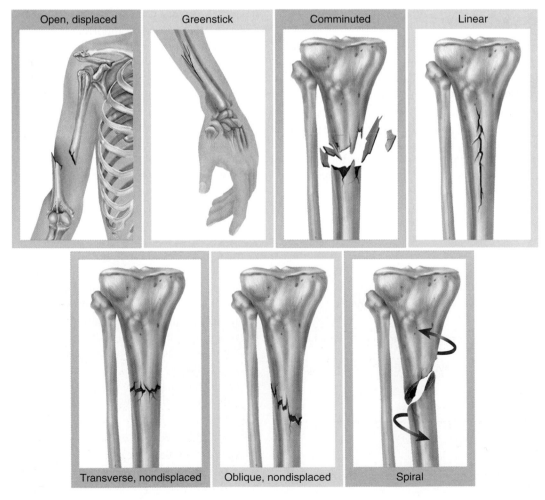

**Figure 6.14** Some Types of Bone Fractures.

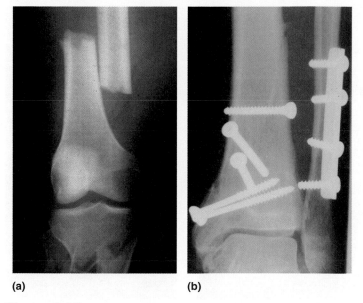

**(a)**  **(b)**

**Figure 6.15 X-rays of Bone Fractures.** (a) A displaced fracture of the femur. (b) An ankle fracture involving both the tibia and fibula. This fracture has been set by open reduction, a process of surgically exposing the bone and realigning the fragments with plates and screws.

# INSIGHT 6.4
## Clinical Application

### When *Not* to Eat Your Spinach

Many a child has been exhorted to "Eat your spinach! It's good for you." There is one time, however, when it may not be healthy. People with healing bone fractures are sometimes advised not to eat it. Why? Spinach is rich in oxalate, an organic compound that binds calcium and magnesium in the digestive tract and interferes with their absorption. Consequently, the oxalate can deprive a fractured bone of the free calcium that it needs in order to heal. There are about 571 milligrams of oxalate per 100 grams of spinach. Some other foods high in oxalate are cocoa (623 mg), rhubarb (447 mg), and beets (109 mg).

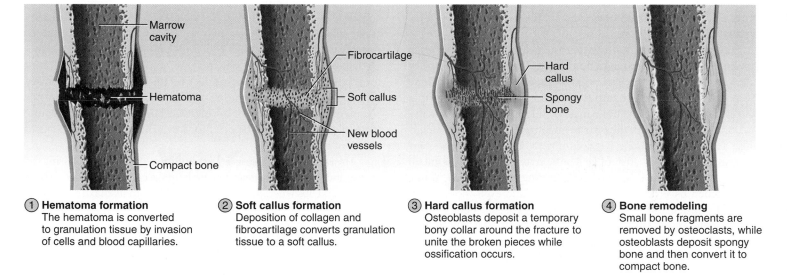

**① Hematoma formation**
The hematoma is converted to granulation tissue by invasion of cells and blood capillaries.

**② Soft callus formation**
Deposition of collagen and fibrocartilage converts granulation tissue to a soft callus.

**③ Hard callus formation**
Osteoblasts deposit a temporary bony collar around the fracture to unite the broken pieces while ossification occurs.

**④ Bone remodeling**
Small bone fragments are removed by osteoclasts, while osteoblasts deposit spongy bone and then convert it to compact bone.

**Figure 6.16 The Healing of a Bone Fracture.**

## Osteoporosis

**Osteoporosis**[31] (OSS-tee-oh-pore-OH-sis) is a disease in which bone density declines to the extent that the bones become brittle and subject to pathologic fractures. It involves the loss of proportionate amounts of organic matrix and minerals, especially from the spongy bone, since this is the most metabolically active osseous tissue and has the greatest surface area exposed to osteoclast action. The bone that remains is histologically normal, but insufficient in quantity to support the body's weight (fig. 6.17a).

People with osteoporosis are especially subject to fractures of the hip, wrist, and vertebral column. Their bones may break under stresses as slight as sitting down too quickly. Among the elderly, slowly healing hip fractures can impose prolonged immobility which, in turn, may lead to fatal complications such as pneumonia. Those who survive often face a long, costly recovery. Spinal deformity is also common consequence of osteoporosis. As the bodies of the vertebrae lose spongy bone, they become compressed by body weight (fig. 6.17b). People commonly lose height after middle age because of this, but those with osteoporosis often develop a more noticeable spinal deformity called

---

[31]*osteo* = bone + *por* = porous + *osis* = condition

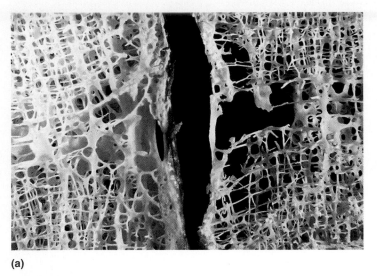

(a)

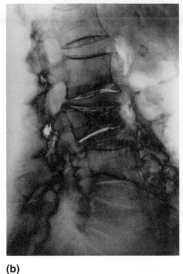

(b)

(c)

**Figure 6.17** Spinal Osteoporosis. (a) Spongy bone in the body of a vertebra in good health (left) and with osteoporosis (right). (b) Colorized X-ray of lumbar vertebrae severely damaged by osteoporosis. (c) Abnormal thoracic spinal curvature (kyphosis) due to compression of thoracic vertebrae with osteoporosis.

kyphosis,[32] an exaggerated thoracic curvature ("widow's hump" or "dowager's hump") (fig. 6.17c).

Those at greatest risk for osteoporosis are postmenopausal white women, especially those of light body build. Compared to men, they have less initial bone mass and begin to lose it at an earlier age. Bone loss accelerates after menopause, when the estrogen level declines sharply. Estrogen supports bone mass by inhibiting osteoclast activity (bone resorption), but the ovaries no longer secrete it after menopause and the rate of bone resorption rises. By age 70, the average white woman has lost 30% of her bone mass, and some as much as 50%. Osteoporosis is less common among black women. Young black women have denser bone on average, and even though they too lose bone density after menopause, the loss usually doesn't reach the threshold for osteoporosis and pathologic fractures. About 20% of osteoporosis sufferers are men. Men produce estrogen in both the adrenal glands and testes. By age 70, 50% of men have estrogen levels below the threshold needed to maintain bone density. Osteoporosis also occurs among young female runners, dancers, and gymnasts in spite of their vigorous exercise. Their percentage of body fat is so low that they may stop ovulating, and their ovaries secrete unusually low levels of estrogen. Other risk factors for osteoporosis include dietary deficiencies of calcium, vitamin D, and protein; inadequate exercise; smoking; and diabetes mellitus.

Osteoporosis is now diagnosed with *dual-energy X-ray absorptiometry (DEXA)*, which uses low-dose X-rays to measure bone density. DEXA has allowed for earlier diagnosis and more effective drug treatment. However, the severity of osteoporosis depends not on bone density alone, but also on the degree of connectivity between the spongy bone trabeculae, which is lost as trabeculae deteriorate. Neither DEXA nor any other diagnostic method yet available can detect this.

Treatment of osteoporosis is aimed at slowing the rate of bone resorption. Estrogen-replacement therapy has fallen out of favor because it raises the risk of breast cancer, stroke, and coronary artery disease. One of the current preferred treatments is a family of osteoclast-destroying drugs called *bis-phosphonates* (trade names Fosamax, Actonel). They can increase bone mass and cut the risk of fractures in half, but their safety is still being evaluated. Pulsed doses of parathyroid hormone or derivatives such as teriparatide (trade name Forteo) can also increase bone mass by stimulating osteoblasts, but cannot be used for longer than 2 years because of a risk of bone cancer.

The risk of osteoporosis is best minimized by weight-bearing exercise and ample calcium and protein intake early in life, especially in the 20s and 30s when the skeleton is building to its maximum mass.

## Other Structural Disorders

Several additional bone disorders are summarized in table 6.2. **Orthopedics**[33] is the branch of medicine that deals with the prevention and correction of injuries and disorders of the bones, joints, and muscles. As the word suggests, this field originated as the treatment of skeletal deformities in children, but it is now much more extensive. It includes the design of artificial joints and limbs and the treatment of athletic injuries.

### *Before You Go On*

*Answer the following questions to test your understanding of the preceding section:*

16. Name and describe any five types of bone fractures.
17. What is a callus? How does it contribute to fracture repair?
18. List the major risk factors for osteoporosis and describe some ways of preventing it.

---

[32]*kypho* = bent, humpbacked + *osis* = condition

[33]*ortho* = straight + *ped* = child, foot

| TABLE 6.2 | Structural Disorders of Bone |
|---|---|
| **Acromegaly**[34] | A result of adult growth hormone hypersecretion, resulting in thickening of the bones and soft tissues, especially noticeable in the face, hands, and feet. |
| **Osteitis deformans (Paget**[35] **disease)** | Excessive osteoclast proliferation and bone resorption, with osteoblasts attempting to compensate by depositing extra bone. This results in rapid, disorderly bone remodeling and weak, deformed bones. Osteitis deformans usually passes unnoticed, but in some cases it causes pain, disfiguration, and fractures. It is most common in males over the age of 50. |
| **Osteomalacia** | Adult form of rickets, most common in poorly nourished women who have had multiple pregnancies. Bones become softened, deformed, and more susceptible to fractures. |
| **Rickets** | Defective mineralization of bone in children, usually as a result of insufficient sunlight or vitamin D, sometimes due to a dietary deficiency of calcium or phosphate or to liver or kidney diseases that interfere with calcitriol synthesis. Causes bone softening and deformity, especially in the weight-bearing bones of the lower limbs. |

**Disorders Described Elsewhere**

Achondroplastic dwarfism 166

Brittle bone disease 89

Fractures 167

Osteopenia 167

Osteoporosis 169

---

[34]*acro*= extremity + *megaly* = abnormal enlargement

[35]Sir James Paget (1814–99), English surgeon

# CHAPTER REVIEW   ● ● ●

## REVIEW OF KEY CONCEPTS

### Tissues and Organs of the Skeletal System (p. 154)

1. The *skeletal system* is a framework composed of bones, cartilages, and ligaments. The study of this system is called *osteology.*
2. The functions of this system include support, movement, protection of soft tissues, blood formation, electrolyte balance, acid–base balance, and detoxification.
3. *Osseous tissue* (bone) is a connective tissue in which the matrix is hardened by calcium phosphate and other minerals. Other tissues found in a bone include blood, bone marrow, cartilage, adipose tissue, nervous tissue, and fibrous connective tissue.
4. Bones are classified into four categories by shape: *long, short, flat,* and *irregular* bones.
5. A bone has an outer shell of *compact bone,* which usually encloses more loosely organized *spongy bone.*
6. A long bone has a relatively narrow, long *diaphysis* (shaft) with an expanded *epiphysis* (head) at each end. The epiphysis is filled with spongy bone. Bone marrow occupies the diaphysis and the spaces amid the spongy bone of the epiphysis.
7. A cartilaginous *epiphyseal plate* separates the marrow spaces of the epiphysis and diaphysis in children and adolescents. It is the site of bone elongation.
8. A bone is externally covered with a fibrous *periosteum,* which is bound to the bone by collagenous *perforating fibers.* The medullary cavity is lined with a fibrous *endosteum.*
9. At most joints, the ends of a bone have no periosteum but are covered with hyaline *articular cartilage.*
10. Flat bones consist of a sandwichlike arrangement of spongy bone enclosed between two layers of compact bone. The spongy bone layer of the skull is called the *diploe.*

### Histology of Osseous Tissue (p. 157)

1. Osseous tissue has four kinds of cells: osteogenic cells, osteoblasts, osteocytes, and osteoclasts.
2. *Osteogenic cells* are stem cells found in the endosteum, periosteum, and central canals. They give rise to osteoblasts.
3. *Osteoblasts* are bone-depositing cells found on the bone surfaces. They produce the organic components of the bone matrix and promote its mineralization.
4. *Osteocytes* are bone cells found within the *lacunae* and surrounded by bone matrix.

They communicate with each other and with surface osteoblasts by way of cytoplasmic processes in the *canaliculi* of the matrix. They both deposit and absorb bone matrix, and function as strain detectors that stimulate osteoblasts to deposit bone.

5. *Osteoclasts* are bone-dissolving cells found on the bone surfaces. They secrete hydrochloric acid, which dissolves the inorganic salts of the bone matrix, and enzymes that digest the organic components.
6. The matrix of bone is about one-third organic and two-thirds inorganic matter by dry weight.
7. The inorganic part of the matrix is about 85% hydroxyapatite (crystalline calcium phosphate), 10% calcium carbonate, and 5% other minerals.
8. The organic part of the matrix consists of collagen and large protein–carbohydrate complexes called glycosaminoglycans, proteoglycans, and glycoproteins.
9. The mineral component of the bone renders it resistant to compression, so it does not crumble under the body's weight, while the protein component renders it resistant to tension, so it can bend slightly without breaking.
10. Compact bone is composed largely of cylindrical units called *osteons,* in which the matrix is arranged in concentric *lamellae* around a central canal. Osteocytes in their lacunae lie between the lamellae of matrix, and their canaliculi cross from one lamella to the next.
11. Collagen fibers wind helically along the length of each lamella, with the helices coiling in alternating directions in adjacent lamellae to give the matrix added strength.
12. Blood vessels enter the bone matrix through *nutrient foramina* on the surface and pass by way of *perforating canals* to reach the central canals.
13. In addition to the concentric lamellae of osteons, compact bone exhibits circumferential lamellae that travel parallel to the inner and outer bone surfaces, and *interstitial lamellae* located between osteons, representing the remains of older osteons that have partially broken down.
14. Spongy bone consists of thin *trabeculae* of osseous tissue, with spaces between the trabeculae occupied by bone marrow. The matrix is arranged in lamellae but shows few osteons. Spongy bone provides a bone with

maximal strength in proportion to its light weight.
15. There are two kinds of bone marrow: blood-forming (hemopoietic) *red marrow* and fatty *yellow marrow.* Red marrow occupies the medullary spaces of nearly all bones in children and adolescents. By adulthood, red marrow is limited to the skull, vertebrae, ribs, sternum, parts of the pelvic girdle, and proximal heads of the humerus and femur; it is replaced by yellow marrow elsewhere.

### Bone Development (p. 161)

1. Bones are produced by two developmental processes: *intramembranous ossification,* which produces mainly flat bones, and *endochondral ossification,* which produces most of the skeleton.
2. Intramembranous ossification begins when mesenchyme condenses into a sheet of soft tissue populated with osteogenic cells. Osteogenic cells gather along soft trabeculae of mesenchyme and differentiate into osteoblasts. The osteoblasts deposit soft osteoid tissue and then calcify it. Calcified trabeculae become spongy bone, while compact surface bone is formed by filling in the spaces between trabeculae with osseous tissue.
3. Endochondral ossification is a process in which a hyaline cartilage model is replaced by bone. It begins when chondrocytes in the middle of the cartilage model enlarge and form a *primary ossification center.* As the cartilage lacunae break down, they merge into a *primary marrow cavity* and the chondrocytes die.
4. Stem cells enter the primary marrow cavity by way of blood vessels and differentiate into osteoblasts and osteoclasts. Osteoblasts deposit osteoid tissue and then calcify it to form temporary bony trabeculae. Osteoclasts dissolve cartilage remnants and enlarge the marrow cavity, which grows toward the ends of the bone.
5. Near the time of birth, a *secondary ossification center* appears in the middle of the epiphysis. Ossification proceeds from here outward, creating a *secondary marrow cavity* and leaving a layer of articular cartilage over the end of the bone. The primary and secondary marrow cavities remain separated for a time by a cartilaginous *epiphyseal plate.*
6. Long bones increase in length by the *interstitial growth* of cartilage in a transitional zone

called the *metaphysis,* which lies between the primary marrow cavity and the cartilage of an epiphysis or epiphyseal plate.

7. The metaphysis has five zones: the *zone of reserve cartilage* farthest from the marrow space; the *zone of cell proliferation,* where chondrocytes multiply and form longitudinal columns of cells; the *zone of cell hypertrophy,* where these chondrocytes enlarge; the *zone of calcification,* where the matrix becomes temporarily calcified; and nearest the marrow space, the *zone of bone deposition,* where lacunae break down, chondrocytes die, and bone is deposited.

8. Bones grow in thickness and width by *appositional growth,* the depostion of new osseous tissue on the bone surface by a process similar to intramembraneous ossification.

9. Bones are remodeled throughout life to accommodate bodily growth and changes in force applied to the skeleton. According to *Wolff's law of bone,* osteoblasts and osteoclasts reshape bones throughout life to adapt to the stresses placed on them.

10. Some nutrients required for bone development include calcium, phosphate, and vitamins A, C, and D. Hormones that stimulate bone growth include calcitonin, growth hormone, estrogen, testosterone, thyroid hormone, and insulin. Parathyroid hormone promotes bone resorption by osteoclasts.

11. With age, osteoblast activity begins to lag behind osteoclast activity, resulting in a loss of bone mass *(osteopenia).* This can lead to tooth loss and bone brittleness, and if severe enough, to osteoporosis.

**Structural Disorders of Bone (p. 167)**

1. The prevention and treatment of bone, joint, and muscle disorders is called *orthopedics.*

2. Bones can break because of trauma *(stress fracture)* or diseases that weaken a bone and make it unable to withstand normal levels of stress *(pathologic fracture).* Table 6.1 defines the various types of fractures. Fractures are set by either *closed reduction,* which does not involve surgical exposure of the bone, or *open reduction,* which involves the surgical use of plates, screws, or pins to align bone fragments.

3. The most common bone disease is *osteoporosis,* a loss of bone mass (especially spongy bone) causing increasing susceptibility to pathologic fractures. Fractures of the vertebrae, wrist, and hip, and a spinal deformity called *kyphosis* (exaggerated thoracic curvature) commonly result from osteoporosis.

4. Osteoporosis can occur in either sex, any race, and a wide range of ages, but risk factors that increase its incidence include being white, female, of light build, and of postmenopausal age, as well as inadequate exercise, low calcium intake, smoking, vitamin C deficiency, and diabetes mellitus.

## TESTING YOUR RECALL

1. Which cells have a ruffled border and secrete hydrochloric acid?
   a. chondrocytes
   b. osteocytes
   c. osteogenic cells
   d. osteoblasts
   e. osteoclasts

2. The medullary cavity of a child's bone may contain
   a. red bone marrow.
   b. hyaline cartilage.
   c. periosteum.
   d. osteocytes.
   e. articular cartilages.

3. The long bones of the limbs grow in length by cell proliferation and hypertrophy in
   a. the epiphysis.
   b. the epiphyseal line.
   c. the dense bone.
   d. the metaphysis.
   e. the spongy bone.

4. Osteoclasts are most closely related, by common descent, to
   a. osteocytes.
   b. osteogenic cells.
   c. monocytes.
   d. fibroblasts.
   e. osteoblasts.

5. The walls between cartilage lacunae break down in the zone of
   a. cell proliferation.
   b. calcification.
   c. reserve cartilage.
   d. bone deposition.
   e. cell hypertrophy.

6. Which of these does *not* promote bone deposition?
   a. dietary calcium
   b. vitamin D
   c. parathyroid hormone
   d. calcitonin
   e. testosterone

7. A child jumps to the ground from the top of a playground "jungle gym." His leg bones do not shatter mainly because they contain
   a. an abundance of glycosaminoglycans.
   b. young, resilient osteocytes.
   c. an abundance of calcium phosphate.
   d. collagen fibers.
   e. hydroxyapatite crystals.

8. One long bone meets another at its
   a. diaphysis.
   b. epiphyseal plate.
   c. periosteum.
   d. metaphysis.
   e. epiphysis.

9. Calcitriol is made from
   a. calcitonin.
   b. 7-dehydrocholesterol.
   c. hydroxyapatite.
   d. estrogen.
   e. PTH.

10. One sign of osteoporosis is
    a. osteitis deformans.
    b. osteomalacia.
    c. a stress fracture.
    d. kyphosis.
    e. a calcium deficiency.

11. Calcium phosphate crystallizes in bone as a mineral called _____.

12. Osteocytes contact each other through channels called _____ in the bone matrix.

13. A bone increases in diameter only by _____ growth, the addition of new surface lamellae.

14. Most compact bone is organized in cylindrical units called _____, composed of lamellae encircling a central canal.

15. The _____ glands secrete a hormone that stimulates cells to resorb bone and return its minerals to the blood.

16. The ends of a bone are covered with a layer of hyaline cartilage called the _____.

17. The cells that deposit new bone matrix are called _____.

18. The most common bone disease is _____.

19. The transitional region between epiphyseal cartilage and the primary marrow cavity of a young bone is called the _____.

20. The cranial bones develop from a flat sheet of condensed mesenchyme in a process called _____.

*Answers in the Appendix*

## TRUE OR FALSE

*Determine which five of the following statements are false, and briefly explain why.*

1. Spongy bone is normally covered by compact bone.

2. Most bones develop from hyaline cartilage.

3. Fractures are the most common bone disorder.

4. The growth zone of the long bones of adolescents is the articular cartilage.

5. Osteoclasts develop from osteoblasts.

6. Osteocytes develop from osteoblasts.

7. The protein of the bone matrix is called hydroxyapatite.

8. Blood vessels travel through the central canals of compact bone.

9. Yellow bone marrow has a hemopoietic function.

10. Parathyroid hormone promotes bone resorption and raises blood calcium concentration.

***Answers in the Appendix***

## TESTING YOUR COMPREHENSION

1. Most osteocytes of an osteon are far removed from blood vessels, but still receive blood-borne oxygen and nutrients. Explain how this is possible.

2. Predict what symptoms a person might experience if he or she suffered a degenerative disease in which the articular cartilages were worn away and the fluid between the bones dried up.

3. One of the more common fractures in children and adolescents is an *epiphyseal fracture*, in which the epiphysis of a long bone separates from the diaphysis. Explain why this would be more common in children than in adults.

4. Describe how the arrangement of trabeculae in spongy bone demonstrates the complementarity of form and function.

5. Identify two bone diseases you would expect to see if the epidermis were a completely effective barrier to UV radiation and a person took no dietary supplements to compensate for this. Explain your answer.

***Answers at aris.mhhe.com***

## ONLINE RESOURCES

Visit aprevealed.com to explore melt-away cadaver dissections, watch animations that clarify difficult concepts, review histological and radiological images, or take a quiz to assess your understanding of the material.

The Saladin *Human Anatomy,* 2e website at aris.mhhe.com features chapter-specific quizzes, labeling exercises, and other interactive tools to complement your study of human anatomy. If your instructor has provided an ARIS course code, you can also access assignments and information specific to your course.

# The Axial Skeleton

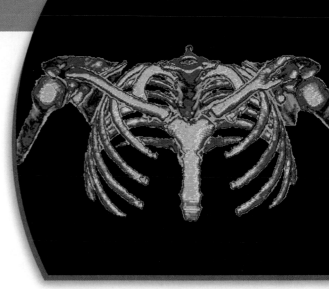

Anterosuperior view of the
thoracic cage and pectoral girdle
(colorized CT scan)

## CHAPTER OUTLINE

## INSIGHTS

## BRUSHING UP

To understand this chapter, you may find it
helpful to review the following concepts:
- Directional terms (p. 24)
- The axial and appendicular body regions
  (p. 25)
- Embryonic folding and organogenesis
  (p. 111)
- General features of bones (p. 155)
- Intramembranous and endochondral
  ossification (pp. 161–163)

**Skeletal System**

A knowledge of skeletal anatomy will be useful as you study later chapters. It provides a point of reference for studying the gross anatomy of other organ systems because many organs are named for their relationships to nearby bones. The subclavian artery and vein, for example, are located beneath the clavicles; the temporalis muscle is attached to the temporal bone; the ulnar nerve and radial artery travel beside the ulna and radius of the forearm; and the frontal, parietal, temporal, and occipital lobes of the brain are named for adjacent bones of the cranium. An understanding of how the muscles produce body movements also depends on knowledge of skeletal anatomy. In addition, the positions, shapes, and processes of bones can serve as landmarks for a clinician in determining where to give an injection or record a pulse, what to look for in an X-ray, or how to perform physical therapy and other medical procedures.

# Overview of the Skeleton

### Objectives

When you have completed this section, you should be able to

- state the approximate number of bones in the adult body;
- explain why this number varies with age and from one person to another; and
- define several terms that denote surface features of bones.

The skeleton (fig. 7.1) is divided into two regions: axial and appendicular. The **axial skeleton,** studied in this chapter, forms the central supporting axis of the body and includes the skull, vertebral column, and thoracic cage (ribs and sternum). The **appendicular skeleton,** studied in chapter 8, includes the bones of the upper limb and pectoral girdle, and bones of the lower limb and pelvic girdle.

## Bones of the Skeletal System

It is often stated that there are 206 bones in the skeleton, but this is only a typical adult count. At birth, there are about 270, and even more bones form during childhood. With age, however, the number decreases as separate bones fuse. For example, each half of the pelvis is a single *hip bone* in adults, but in children, it consists of three bones—the ilium, ischium, and pubis. The fusion of several bones, completed by late adolescence to the mid-20s,

brings about the average adult number of 206. These bones are listed in table 7.1

The number varies even among adults. One reason is the development of **sesamoid**[1] **bones**—bones that form within certain tendons in response to stress. The patella (kneecap) is the largest of these; most of the others are small, rounded bones in such locations as the knuckles. Another reason for adult variation is that some people have extra bones in the skull called **sutural** (SOO-chure-ul), or **wormian,**[2] **bones** (see fig. 7.6).

## Anatomical Features of Bones

A bone may exhibit a variety of ridges, spines, bumps, depressions, canals, pores, slits, cavities, and articular surfaces, often called *bone markings.* It is important to know the names of these features because later descriptions of joints, muscle attachments, and the routes traveled by nerves and blood vessels are based on this terminology. The terms for the most common of these features are listed in table 7.2, and several of them are illustrated in figure 7.2.

As you study the skeleton, use yourself as a model. You can easily palpate (feel) many of the bones and some of their details through the skin. Rotate your forearm, cross your legs, palpate your skull and wrist, and think about what is happening beneath the surface or what you can feel through the skin. You will gain the most from this chapter (and indeed, the entire book) if you are conscious of your own body in relation to what you are studying.

### *Before You Go On*

*Answer the following questions to test your understanding of the preceding section:*

1. Name the major components of the axial skeleton. Name those of the appendicular skeleton.

2. Explain why an adult does not have as many bones as a child does. Explain why one adult may have more bones than another adult of the same age.

3. Briefly describe each of the following bone features: condyle, epicondyle, process, tubercle, fossa, sulcus, and foramen.

---

[1]*sesam* = sesame seed + *oid* = resembling
[2]Ole Worm (1588–1654), Danish physician

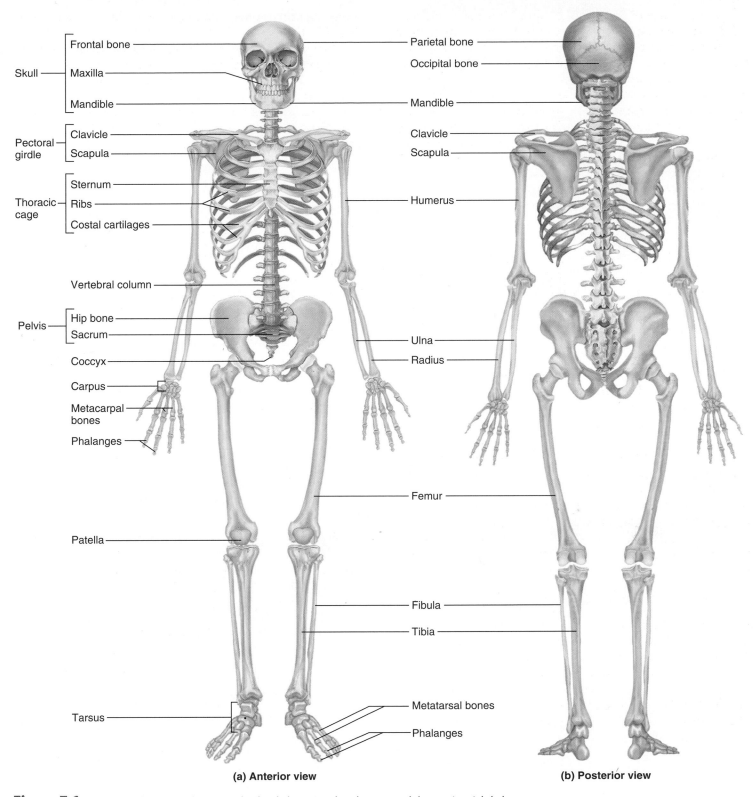

Skull
- Frontal bone
- Maxilla
- Mandible

Pectoral girdle
- Clavicle
- Scapula

Thoracic cage
- Sternum
- Ribs
- Costal cartilages

Vertebral column

Pelvis
- Hip bone
- Sacrum

Coccyx

Carpus

Metacarpal bones

Phalanges

Patella

Tarsus

Parietal bone

Occipital bone

Mandible

Clavicle

Scapula

Humerus

Ulna

Radius

Femur

Fibula

Tibia

Metatarsal bones

Phalanges

**(a) Anterior view**

**(b) Posterior view**

**Figure 7.1** **The Adult Skeleton.** The appendicular skeleton is colored green, and the rest is axial skeleton.

## TABLE 7.1 — Bones of the Adult Skeletal System

### Axial Skeleton

**Skull** — Total 22

- Cranial bones
  - Frontal bone (1)
  - Parietal bones (2)
  - Occipital bone (1)
  - Temporal bones (2)
  - Sphenoid bone (1)
  - Ethmoid bone (1)
- Facial bones
  - Maxillae (2)
  - Palatine bones (2)
  - Zygomatic bones (2)
  - Lacrimal bones (2)
  - Nasal bones (2)
  - Vomer (1)
  - Inferior nasal conchae (2)
  - Mandible (1)

**Auditory Ossicles** — Total 6

- Malleus (2)
- Incus (2)
- Stapes (2)

**Hyoid Bone (1)** — Total 1

**Vertebral Column** — Total 26

- Cervical vertebrae (7)
- Thoracic vertebrae (12)
- Lumbar vertebrae (5)
- Sacrum (1)
- Coccyx (1)

**Thoracic Cage** — Total 25

- Ribs (24)
- Sternum (1)

### Appendicular Skeleton

**Pectoral Girdle** — Total 4

- Scapulae (2)
- Clavicles (2)

**Upper Limbs** — Total 60

- Humerus (2)
- Radius (2)
- Ulna (2)
- Carpals (16)
- Metacarpals (10)
- Phalanges (28)

**Pelvic Girdle** — Total 2

- Hip bones (2)

**Lower Limbs** — Total 60

- Femur (2)
- Patella (2)
- Tibia (2)
- Fibula (2)
- Tarsals (14)
- Metatarsals (10)
- Phalanges (28)

**Grand Total: 206**

## TABLE 7.2 — Surface Features (Markings) of Bones

| Term | Description and Example |
| --- | --- |
| **Articulations** | |
| Condyle | A rounded knob (occipital condyles of the skull) |
| Facet | A smooth, flat, slightly concave or convex articular surface (articular facets of the vertebrae) |
| Head | The prominent expanded end of a bone, sometimes rounded (head of the femur) |
| **Extensions and Projections** | |
| Crest | A narrow ridge (iliac crest of the pelvis) |
| Epicondyle | A projection superior to a condyle (medial epicondyle of the femur) |
| Line | A slightly raised, elongated ridge (nuchal lines of the skull) |
| Process | Any bony prominence (mastoid process of the skull) |
| Protuberance | A bony outgrowth or protruding part (mental protuberance of the chin) |
| Spine | A sharp, slender, or narrow process (spine of the scapula) |
| Trochanter | Two massive processes unique to the femur |
| Tubercle | A small, rounded process (greater tubercle of the humerus) |
| Tuberosity | A rough surface (tibial tuberosity) |
| **Depressions** | |
| Alveolus | A pit or socket (tooth socket) |
| Fossa | A shallow, broad, or elongated basin (mandibular fossa) |
| Fovea | A small pit (fovea capitis of the femur) |
| Sulcus | A groove for a tendon, nerve, or blood vessel (intertubercular sulcus of the humerus) |
| **Passages and Cavities** | |
| Canal | A tubular passage or tunnel in a bone (condylar canal of the skull) |
| Fissure | A slit through a bone (orbital fissures behind the eye) |
| Foramen | A hole through a bone, usually round (foramen magnum of the skull) |
| Meatus | An opening into a canal (acoustic meatus of the ear) |
| Sinus | An air-filled space in a bone (frontal sinus of the forehead) |

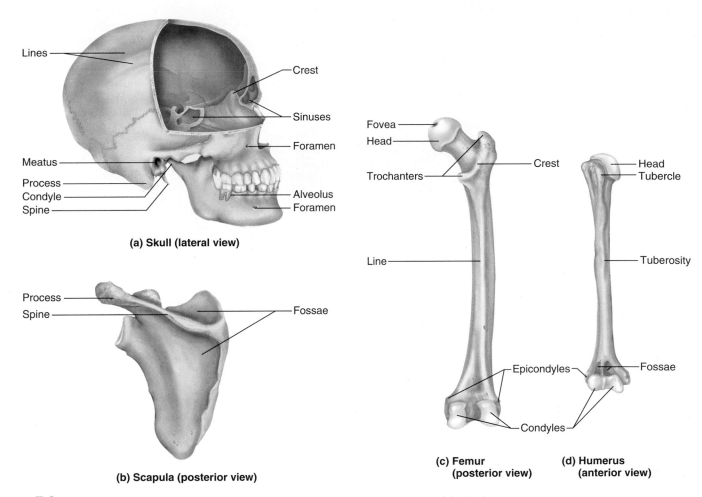

**Figure 7.2** **Anatomical Features of Bones.**  Most of these also occur on many other bones of the body.

# The Skull

## Objectives

When you have completed this section, you should be able to

- name the bones of the skull and their anatomical features;
- identify the cavities within the skull and in some of its individual bones;
- name the principle sutures that join bones of the skull;
- describe some bones that are closely associated with the skull; and
- describe some adaptations of the skull for upright locomotion.

The skull is the most complex part of the skeleton. Figures 7.3 to 7.6 present an overview of its general anatomy. Although the skull may seem to consist only of the mandible (lower jaw) and "the rest," it is composed of 22 bones and sometimes more. Most of them are rigidly joined by **sutures** (SOO-chures), joints that appear as seams on the cranial surface (fig. 7.4). These are important landmarks in the descriptions that follow.

The skull contains several prominent cavities (fig. 7.7). The largest, with an adult volume of about 1,300 mL, is the **cranial cavity,** which encloses the brain. Other cavities include the **orbits** (eye sockets), **nasal cavity, oral cavity** (mouth or buccal cavity), **middle-** and **inner-ear cavities,** and **paranasal sinuses.** The paranasal sinuses are named for the bones in which they occur (fig. 7.8)—the **frontal, ethmoid, sphenoid,** and **maxillary sinuses.** These cavities are connected with the nasal cavity, lined by a mucous membrane, and filled with air. They lighten the anterior portion of the skull and act as chambers that add resonance to the voice.

Bones of the skull have especially conspicuous **foramina**— singular, *foramen* (fo-RAY-men)—holes that allow passage for nerves and blood vessels. The major foramina are summarized in table 7.3. The details of this table will mean more to you when you study cranial nerves and blood vessels in later chapters.

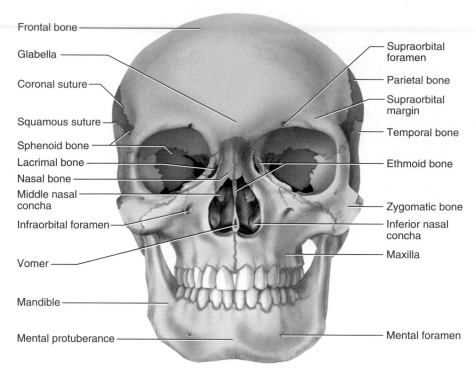

**Figure 7.3** The Skull, Anterior View.

## Cranial Bones

The cranial cavity is enclosed by the **cranium**[3] (braincase), which protects the brain and associated sensory organs. The cranium is composed of eight bones called the **cranial bones:**

| | |
|---|---|
| 1 frontal bone | 1 occipital bone |
| 2 parietal bones | 1 sphenoid bone |
| 2 temporal bones | 1 ethmoid bone |

The delicate brain tissue does not directly touch the cranial bones but is separated from them by three membranes, the *meninges* (meh-NIN-jeez) (see chapter 13). The thickest and toughest of these, the *dura mater* (DUE-rah MAH-tur), is essentially the periosteum of the cranial bones. It lies loosely against the cranium in most places but is attached to it at a few points.

The cranium consists of two major parts—the calvaria and the base. The **calvaria**[4] (skullcap) forms the roof and walls (see fig. 7.6). In study skulls, it is often sawed so that the top can be lifted off for examination of the interior. This reveals the **base** (floor) of the cranial cavity (see fig. 7.5b), which is divided into three basins called **cranial fossae.** The fossae correspond to the contour of the inferior surface of the brain (fig. 7.9). The relatively shallow *anterior cra-*

*nial fossa* is crescent-shaped and accommodates the frontal lobes of the brain. The *middle cranial fossa*, which drops abruptly deeper, is shaped like a pair of outstretched bird's wings and accommodates the temporal lobes. The *posterior cranial fossa* is deepest and houses a large posterior division of the brain called the cerebellum.

We now consider the eight cranial bones and their distinguishing features.

### Frontal Bone

The **frontal bone** extends from the forehead back to a prominent *coronal suture,* which crosses the crown of the head from right to left and joins the frontal bone to the parietal bones (see figs. 7.3 and 7.4). The frontal bone forms the anterior wall and about one-third of the roof of the cranial cavity, and it turns inward to form nearly all of the anterior cranial fossa and the roof of the orbit. Deep to the eyebrows it has a ridge called the **supraorbital margin.** The center of each margin is perforated by a single **supraorbital foramen** (see figs. 7.3 and 7.14), which provides passage for a nerve, artery, and vein. In some people, the edge of this foramen breaks through the margin of the orbit and forms a *supraorbital notch.* The frontal bone also contains the frontal sinus. You may not see this on all study skulls. It is absent from some people, and on some skulls, the calvaria is cut too high to show the sinus. Along the cut edge of the calvaria, you can see the diploe—the layer of spongy bone in the middle of the cranial bones (see fig. 7.5b).

[3]*crani* = helmet
[4]*calvar* = bald, skull

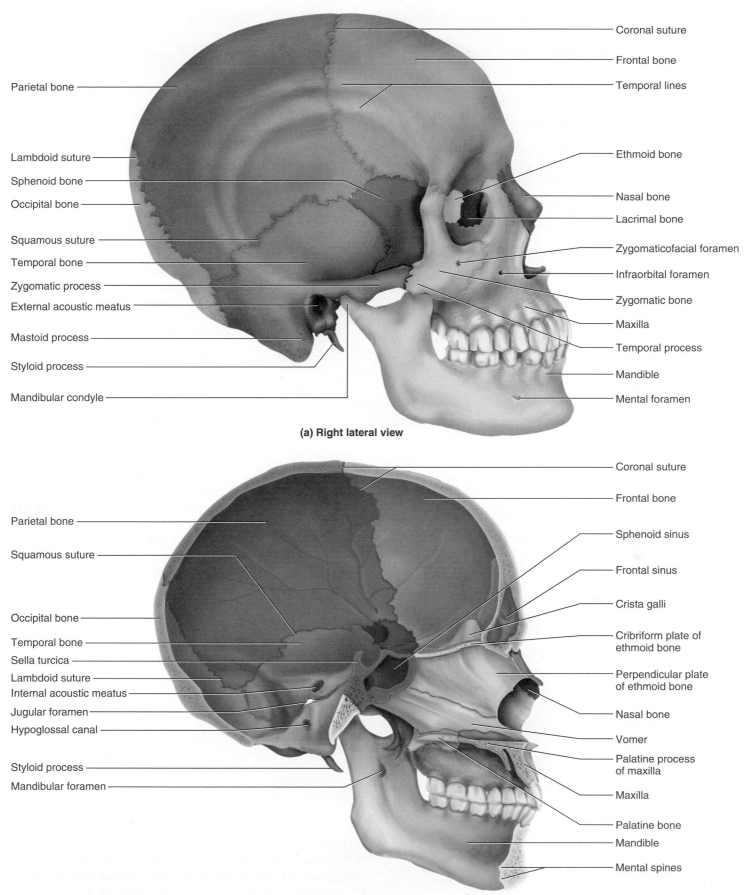

**(a) Right lateral view**

**(b) Median section**

**Figure 7.4** The Skull, Lateral Views (External and Internal).

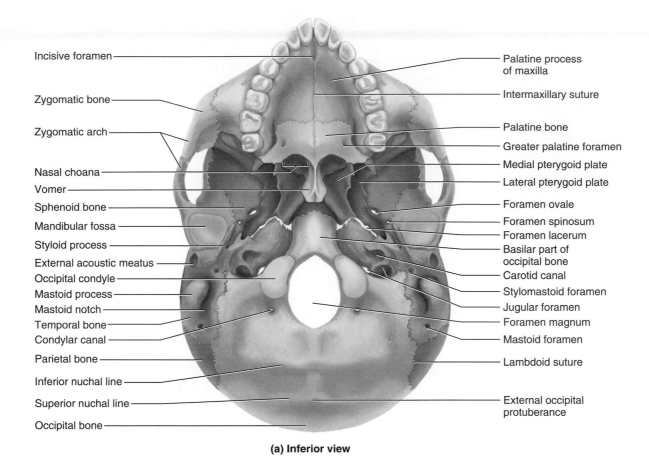

Incisive foramen

Zygomatic bone

Zygomatic arch

Nasal choana

Vomer

Sphenoid bone

Mandibular fossa

Styloid process

External acoustic meatus

Occipital condyle

Mastoid process

Mastoid notch

Temporal bone

Condylar canal

Parietal bone

Inferior nuchal line

Superior nuchal line

Occipital bone

Palatine process of maxilla

Intermaxillary suture

Palatine bone

Greater palatine foramen

Medial pterygoid plate

Lateral pterygoid plate

Foramen ovale

Foramen spinosum

Foramen lacerum

Basilar part of occipital bone

Carotid canal

Stylomastoid foramen

Jugular foramen

Foramen magnum

Mastoid foramen

Lambdoid suture

External occipital protuberance

**(a) Inferior view**

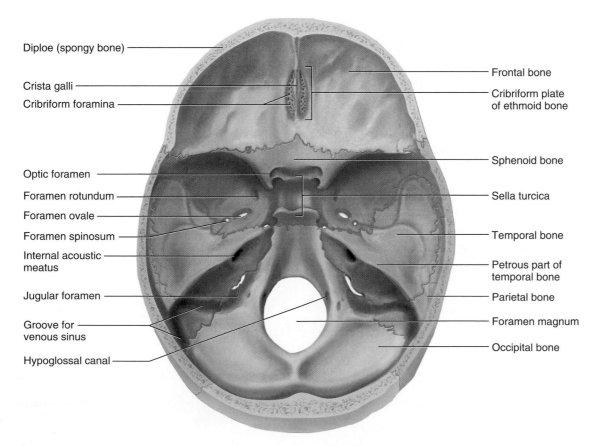

Diploe (spongy bone)

Crista galli

Cribriform foramina

Optic foramen

Foramen rotundum

Foramen ovale

Foramen spinosum

Internal acoustic meatus

Jugular foramen

Groove for venous sinus

Hypoglossal canal

Frontal bone

Cribriform plate of ethmoid bone

Sphenoid bone

Sella turcica

Temporal bone

Petrous part of temporal bone

Parietal bone

Foramen magnum

Occipital bone

**Figure 7.5** The Base of the Skull.

**(b) Superior view of cranial floor**

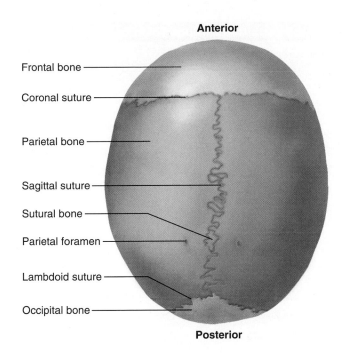

**Anterior**

Frontal bone

Coronal suture

Parietal bone

Sagittal suture

Sutural bone

Parietal foramen

Lambdoid suture

Occipital bone

**Posterior**

**Figure 7.6** The Calvaria (Skullcap), Superior View.

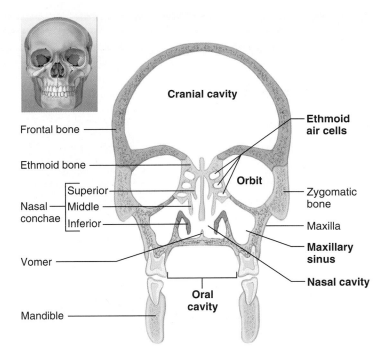

Cranial cavity

Frontal bone

Ethmoid bone

Nasal conchae — Superior, Middle, Inferior

Vomer

Mandible

**Ethmoid air cells**

**Orbit**

Zygomatic bone

Maxilla

**Maxillary sinus**

**Nasal cavity**

**Oral cavity**

**Figure 7.7** Major Cavities of the Skull, Frontal Section.
● *What is the function of the nasal conchae?*

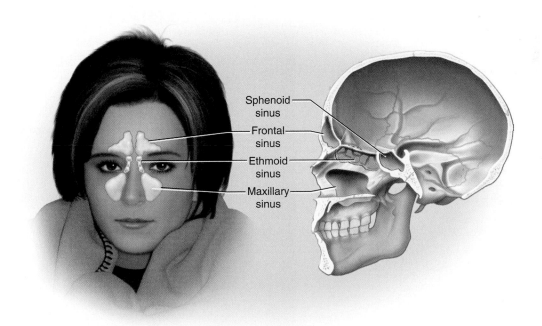

Sphenoid sinus

Frontal sinus

Ethmoid sinus

Maxillary sinus

**Figure 7.8** The Paranasal Sinuses.
● *If these sinuses did not exist, it would require significantly more effort to hold the head erect. Explain.*

| TABLE 7.3 | Foramina of the Skull and the Nerves and Blood Vessels Transmitted Through Them | |
|---|---|---|
| **Bones** | **Foramina\*** | **Structures Transmitted** |
| Frontal bone | Supraorbital foramen or notch | Supraorbital nerve, artery, and vein; ophthalmic nerve |
| Parietal bone | Parietal foramen | Emissary vein of superior longitudinal sinus |
| Temporal bone | Carotid canal | Internal carotid artery |
| | External acoustic meatus | Sound waves to eardrum |
| | Internal acoustic meatus | Vestibulocochlear and facial nerves; internal auditory vessels |
| | Stylomastoid foramen | Facial nerve |
| | Mastoid foramen | Meningeal artery; vein from sigmoid sinus |
| Temporal–occipital region | Jugular foramen | Internal jugular vein; glossopharyngeal, vagus, and accessory nerves |
| Temporal–occipital–sphenoid region | Foramen lacerum | No major nerves or vessels; closed by cartilage |
| Occipital bone | Foramen magnum | Spinal cord; accessory nerve; vertebral arteries |
| | Hypoglossal canal | Hypoglossal nerve to muscles of tongue |
| | Condylar canal | Vein from transverse sinus |
| Sphenoid bone | Foramen ovale | Mandibular division of trigeminal nerve; accessory meningeal artery |
| | Foramen rotundum | Maxillary division of trigeminal nerve |
| | Foramen spinosum | Middle meningeal artery; spinosal nerve; part of trigeminal nerve |
| | Optic foramen | Optic nerve; ophthalmic artery |
| | Superior orbital fissure | Oculomotor, trochlear, and abducens nerves; ophthalmic division of trigeminal nerve; ophthalmic veins |
| Ethmoid bone | Olfactory foramina | Olfactory nerves |
| Maxilla | Infraorbital foramen | Infraorbital nerve and vessels; maxillary division of trigeminal nerve |
| | Incisive foramen | Nasopalatine nerves |
| Maxilla–sphenoid region | Inferior orbital fissure | Infraorbital nerve; zygomatic nerve; infraorbital vessels |
| Lacrimal bone | Lacrimal foramen | Tear duct leading to nasal cavity |
| Palatine bone | Greater palatine foramen | Palatine nerves |
| Zygomatic bone | Zygomaticofacial foramen | Zygomaticofacial nerve |
| | Zygomaticotemporal foramen | Zygomaticotemporal nerve |
| Mandible | Mental foramen | Mental nerve and vessels |
| | Mandibular foramen | Inferior alveolar nerves and vessels to the lower teeth |

\*When two or more bones are listed together (for example, temporal–occipital), it indicates that the foramen passes between them.

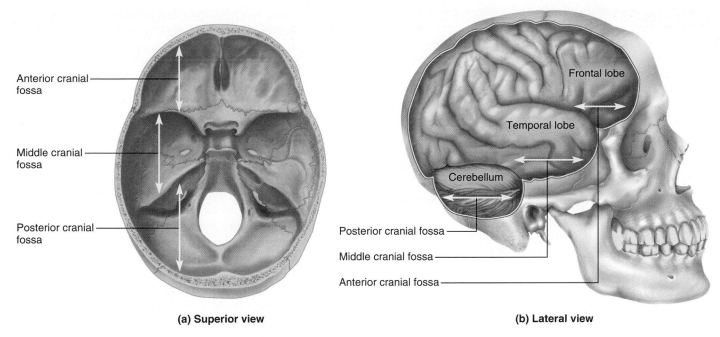

**(a) Superior view**

Anterior cranial fossa

Middle cranial fossa

Posterior cranial fossa

**(b) Lateral view**

Frontal lobe

Temporal lobe

Cerebellum

Posterior cranial fossa

Middle cranial fossa

Anterior cranial fossa

**Figure 7.9** Cranial Fossae. The three fossae conform to the contours of the base of the brain.
● *Which of these three brain regions is not named for an adjacent cranial bone?*

## Parietal Bones

The right and left **parietal** (pa-RYE-eh-tul) **bones** form most of the cranial roof and part of its walls (see figs. 7.4 and 7.6). Each is bordered by four sutures that join it to the neighboring bones: (1) the **sagittal suture** between the parietal bones; (2) the **coronal**[5] **suture** at the anterior margin; the **lambdoid**[6] (LAM-doyd) **suture** at the posterior margin; and (4) the **squamous suture** laterally. Small sutural (wormian) bones are often seen along the sagittal and lambdoid sutures, like little islands of bone with the suture lines passing around them. Internally, the parietal and frontal bones have markings that look a bit like aerial photographs of river tributaries (see fig. 7.4b). These represent places where the bone has been molded around blood vessels of the meninges.

Externally, the parietal bones have few features. A **parietal foramen** sometimes occurs near the corner of the lambdoid and sagittal sutures (see fig. 7.6). A pair of slight thickenings, the superior and inferior **temporal lines,** form an arc across the parietal and frontal bones (see fig. 7.4a). They mark the attachment of the large, fan-shaped *temporalis* muscle, a chewing muscle that inserts on the mandible.

## Temporal Bones

If you palpate your skull just above and anterior to the ear—that is, the temporal region—you can feel the **temporal bone,** which forms the lower wall and part of the floor of the cranial cavity (fig. 7.10). The temporal bone derives its name from the fact that people often

develop their first gray hairs on the temples with the passage of time.[7] The relatively complex shape of the temporal bone is best understood by dividing it into four parts:

1. The **squamous**[8] **part** (which you just palpated) is relatively flat and vertical. It is encircled by the squamous suture. It bears two prominent features: (1) the **zygomatic process,** which extends anteriorly to form part of the **zygomatic arch** (cheekbone), and (2) the **mandibular fossa,** a depression where the mandible articulates with the cranium.

2. The **tympanic**[9] **part** is a small plate of bone that borders the **external acoustic meatus** (me-AY-tus), the opening into the ear canal. It has a pointed spine on its inferior surface, the **styloid process,** named for its resemblance to the stylus used by ancient Greeks and Romans to write on wax tablets. The styloid process provides attachment for muscles of the tongue, pharynx, and hyoid bone.

3. The **mastoid**[10] **part** lies posterior to the tympanic part. It bears a heavy **mastoid process,** which you can palpate as a prominent lump behind the earlobe. It is filled with small air sinuses that communicate with the middle-ear cavity. These sinuses are subject to infection and inflammation (mastoiditis), which can erode the bone and spread to the brain. Inferiorly, there is a groove called the **mastoid notch** medial to the mastoid process (see fig. 7.5a). It is the origin

---

[5]*corona* = crown
[6]*lambd* = the Greek letter lambda (λ) + *oid* = resembling

[7]*tempor* = time
[8]*squam* = flat + *ous* = characterized by
[9]*tympan* = drum (eardrum) + *ic* = pertaining to
[10]*mast* = breast + *oid* = resembling

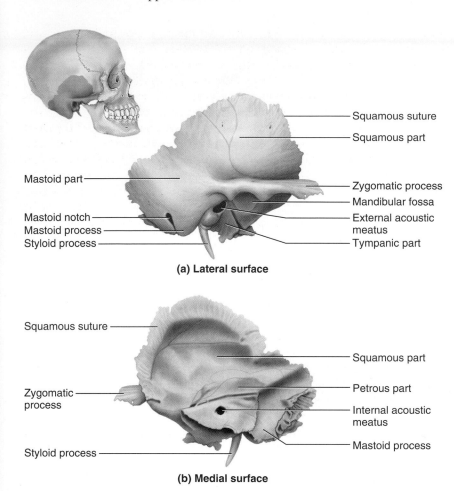

**(a) Lateral surface**

Squamous suture
Squamous part
Mastoid part
Zygomatic process
Mandibular fossa
Mastoid notch
Mastoid process
Styloid process
External acoustic meatus
Tympanic part

**(b) Medial surface**

Squamous suture
Squamous part
Zygomatic process
Petrous part
Internal acoustic meatus
Styloid process
Mastoid process

**Figure 7.10** **The Right Temporal Bone.** The lateral surface faces the scalp and external ear; the medial surface faces the brain.
● List five bones that articulate with the temporal bone.

of the *digastric muscle,* a muscle that opens the mouth. The notch is perforated by the **stylomastoid foramen** at its anterior end and the **mastoid foramen** at its posterior end.

4. The **petrous**[11] **part** can be seen in the cranial floor, where it resembles a little mountain range separating the middle cranial fossa from the posterior fossa (fig. 7.10b). It houses the middle- and inner-ear cavities. The **internal acoustic meatus,** an opening on its posteromedial surface, allows passage of the vestibulocochlear (vess-TIB-you-lo-COC-lee-ur) nerve, which carries sensations of hearing and balance from the inner ear to the brain. On the inferior surface of the petrous part are two prominent foramina named for the major blood vessels that pass through them (see fig. 7.5a): (1) The **carotid canal** is a passage for the internal carotid artery, a major blood supply to the brain. This artery is so close to the inner ear that you can sometimes hear the pulsing of its blood when your ear is resting on a pillow or your heart is beating hard. (2) The **jugular foramen** is a large, irregular opening just medial to the styloid process, between the temporal and occipital bones.

Blood from the brain drains through this foramen into the internal jugular vein of the neck. Three cranial nerves also pass through this foramen.

## Occipital Bone

The **occipital** (oc-SIP-ih-tul) **bone** forms the rear of the skull *(occiput)* and much of its base (see fig. 7.5). Its most conspicuous feature is a large opening, the **foramen magnum** (literally "big hole"), which admits the spinal cord to the cranial cavity and provides a point of attachment for the dura mater. An important consideration in treatment of head injuries is swelling of the brain. Since the cranium cannot enlarge, swelling puts pressure on the brain and results in even more tissue damage. Severe swelling may squeeze the brainstem out through the foramen magnum, usually with fatal consequences.

The occipital bone continues anterior to the foramen magnum as a thick median plate, the **basilar part.** On each side of the foramen magnum is a smooth knob called the **occipital condyle** (CON-dile), where the skull rests on the vertebral column. At the anterolateral edge of each condyle is a **hypoglossal**[12] **canal,** named for the hypoglossal nerve that passes through it to supply the muscles of the tongue. In some people, a **condylar** (CON-dih-lur) **canal** occurs posterior to each occipital condyle.

Internally, the occipital bone displays impressions left by large venous sinuses that drain blood from the brain (see fig. 7.5b). One of these grooves travels along the midsagittal line. Just before reaching the foramen magnum, it branches into right and left grooves that wrap around the occipital bone like outstretched arms before terminating at the jugular foramina. The sinuses that occupy these grooves are described in chapter 21.

Other features of the occipital bone can be palpated on the back of your head. One is a prominent median bump called the **external occipital protuberance**—the attachment for the **nuchal**[13] (NEW-kul) **ligament,** which binds the skull to the vertebral column. A ridge, the **superior nuchal line,** can be traced horizontally from the protuberance toward the mastoid process (see fig. 7.5a). It defines the superior limit of the neck and provides attachment for several neck and back muscles to the skull. By pulling down on the occipital bone, some of these muscles help to keep the head erect. The **inferior nuchal line** provides attachment for some of the deep neck muscles. This inconspicuous ridge cannot be palpated on the living body but is visible on an isolated skull.

## Sphenoid Bone

The **sphenoid**[14] (SFEE-noyd) **bone** has a complex shape with a thick median **body** and outstretched **greater** and **lesser wings,** which give the bone as a whole a somewhat ragged mothlike shape. Most

[11]*petr* = stone, rock + *ous* = like

[12]*hypo* = below + *gloss* = tongue
[13]*nucha* = back of the neck
[14]*sphen* = wedge + *oid* = resembling

of it is best seen from the superior perspective (fig. 7.11a). In this view, the lesser wings form the posterior margin of the anterior cranial fossa and end at a sharp bony crest, where the sphenoid drops abruptly to the greater wings. The greater wings form about half of the middle cranial fossa (the temporal bone forming the rest) and are perforated by several foramina to be discussed shortly.

The greater wing forms part of the lateral surface of the cranium just anterior to the temporal bone (see fig. 7.4a). The lesser wing forms the posterior wall of the orbit and contains the **optic foramen,** which permits passage of the optic nerve and ophthalmic artery (see fig. 7.14). Superiorly, a pair of bony spines of the lesser wing called the **anterior clinoid processes** appear to guard the optic foramina. A gash in the posterior wall of the orbit, the **superior orbital fissure,** angles upward lateral to the optic foramen. It serves as a passage for nerves that supply the muscles of eye movement.

The body of the sphenoid has a saddlelike feature named the **sella turcica**[15] (SEL-la TUR-sih-ca). It consists of a deep pit called the *hypophyseal fossa,* which houses the pituitary gland (hypophysis); a raised anterior margin called the *tuberculum sellae* (too-BUR-cu-lum SEL-lee); and a posterior margin called the *dorsum sellae.* In life, a fibrous membrane stretches over the sella turcica and attaches to the anterior clinoid processes. A stalk penetrates the membrane to connect the pituitary gland to the floor of the brain.

Lateral to the sella turcica, the sphenoid is perforated by several foramina (see fig. 7.5). The **foramen rotundum** and **foramen ovale** (oh-VAY-lee) are passages for two branches of the trigeminal nerve. The **foramen spinosum,** about the diameter of a pencil lead,

provides passage for an artery of the meninges. An irregular gash called the **foramen lacerum**[16] (LASS-eh-rum) occurs at the junction of the sphenoid, temporal, and occipital bones. It is filled with cartilage in life and transmits no major vessels or nerves.

In an inferior view of the skull, the sphenoid can be seen just anterior to the basilar part of the occipital bone (see fig. 7.5a). The internal openings of the nasal cavity seen here are called the **nasal choanae**[17] (co-AH-nee), or **internal nares.** Lateral to each choana, the sphenoid bone exhibits a pair of parallel plates—the **medial pterygoid**[18] (TERR-ih-goyd) **plate** and **lateral pterygoid plate.** Each plate has a narrow inferior extension called the *pterygoid process* (see fig. 7.5a). The plates provide attachment for some of the jaw muscles. The sphenoid sinus occurs within the body of the sphenoid bone.

## Ethmoid Bone

The **ethmoid**[19] (ETH-moyd) **bone** is located between the orbital cavities and forms the roof of the nasal cavity (fig. 7.12). An inferior projection of the ethmoid, called the **perpendicular plate,** forms the superior part of the **nasal septum,** which divides the nasal cavity into right and left **nasal fossae** (FOSS-ee). Three curled, scroll-like **nasal conchae**[20] (CON-kee) project into each fossa from the lateral wall (fig. 7.13; see also fig 7.7). The superior and middle

---

[15]*sella* = saddle + *turcica* = Turkish

[16]*lacerum* = torn, lacerated
[17]*choana* = funnel
[18]*pterygo* = wing
[19]*ethmo* = sieve, strainer + *oid* = resembling
[20]*conchae* = conchs (large marine snails)

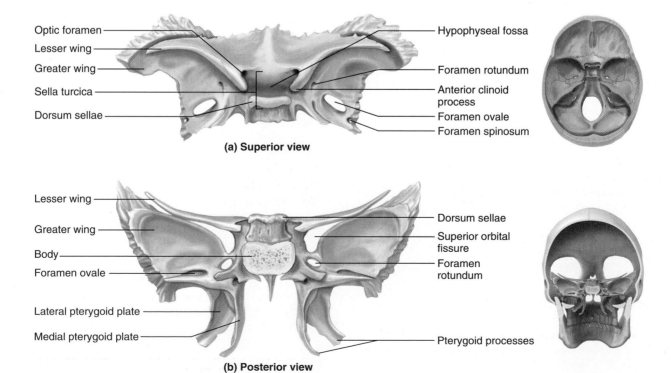

**(a) Superior view**

**(b) Posterior view**

**Figure 7.11** The Sphenoid Bone.

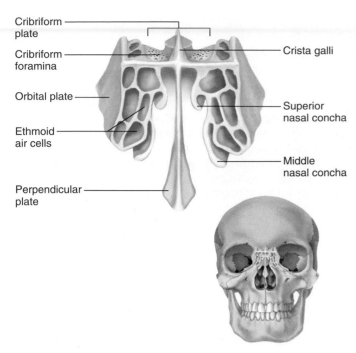

Cribriform plate
Cribriform foramina
Orbital plate
Ethmoid air cells
Perpendicular plate
Crista galli
Superior nasal concha
Middle nasal concha

**Figure 7.12** The Ethmoid Bone, Anterior View.
● *List five bones that articulate with the ethmoid bone.*

conchae are extensions of the ethmoid bone. The inferior concha—a separate bone—is included in the discussion of facial bones in the next section. The conchae are covered with the mucous membrane of the nasal cavity. The three of them together occupy most of the space in the nasal cavity. By filling space and creating turbulence in the inhaled air, they ensure that the air contacts the mucous mem-

branes that cover these bones. This cleanses, humidifies, and warms the inhaled air before it reaches the lungs. The superior concha and the adjacent region of the nasal septum also bear the receptor cells for the sense of smell (olfactory sense). The ethmoid bone includes a large, delicate mass on each side of the perpendicular plate, honeycombed with chambers called **ethmoid air cells;** collectively, these constitute the ethmoid sinus.

From the interior of the skull, one can see only a small superior part of the ethmoid bone. It exhibits a median crest called the **crista galli**[21] (GAL-eye), a point of attachment for the meninges (see figs. 7.4b and 7.5b). On each side of the crista is a horizontal **cribriform**[22] (CRIB-rih-form) **plate** marked by numerous perforations, the **cribriform (olfactory) foramina.** These foramina allow nerve fibers for the sense of smell to pass from the nasal cavity to the brain.

## Facial Bones

The **facial bones** are those that have no direct contact with the brain or meninges. They support the teeth, give shape and individuality to the face, form part of the orbital and nasal cavities, and provide attachment for the muscles of facial expression and mastication. There are 14 facial bones:

| | |
|---|---|
| 2 maxillae | 2 nasal bones |
| 2 palatine bones | 2 inferior nasal conchae |
| 2 zygomatic bones | 1 vomer |
| 2 lacrimal bones | 1 mandible |

[21]*crista* = crest + *galli* = of a rooster
[22]*cribri* = sieve + *form* = in the shape of

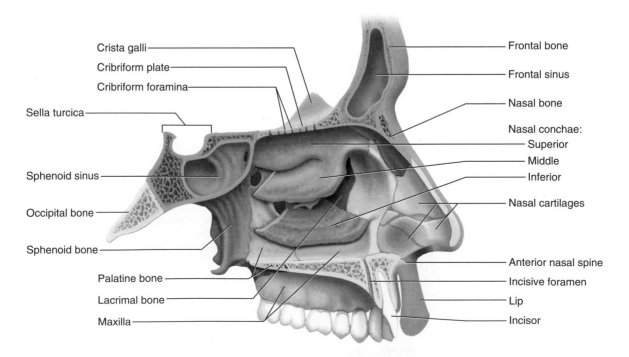

Crista galli
Cribriform plate
Cribriform foramina
Sella turcica
Sphenoid sinus
Occipital bone
Sphenoid bone
Palatine bone
Lacrimal bone
Maxilla
Frontal bone
Frontal sinus
Nasal bone
Nasal conchae:
Superior
Middle
Inferior
Nasal cartilages
Anterior nasal spine
Incisive foramen
Lip
Incisor

**Figure 7.13** The Left Nasal Fossa, Sagittal Section.
● *What bone(s), or parts of bone(s), in figure 7.4b would have to be removed to see the structures in this figure?*

## Clinical Application

### Injury to the Ethmoid Bone

The ethmoid bone is very delicate and easily injured by a sharp upward blow to the nose, such as a person might suffer by striking an automobile dashboard in a collision. The force of a blow can drive bone fragments through the cribriform plate into the meninges or brain tissue. Such injuries are often evidenced by leakage of cerebrospinal fluid into the nasal cavity, and may be followed by the spread of infection from the nasal cavity to the brain. Blows to the head can also shear off the olfactory nerves that pass through the ethmoid bone and cause *anosmia,* an irreversible loss of the sense of smell and a great reduction in the sense of taste (most of which depends on smell). This not only deprives life of some of its pleasures, but can also be dangerous, as when a person fails to smell smoke, gas, or spoiled food.

### Maxillae

The **maxillae** (mac-SILL-ee) are the largest facial bones. They form the upper jaw and meet each other at a median **intermaxillary suture** (see figs. 7.3 and 7.4a). Small points of maxillary bone called **alveolar processes** grow into the spaces between the bases of the teeth. The root of each tooth is inserted into a deep socket, or **alveolus.** Even though the teeth are preserved with the skull, they are not bones. They are discussed in detail in chapter 24.

Each maxilla extends from the teeth upward to the inferomedial wall of the orbit. Just below the orbit, it exhibits an **infraorbital foramen,** which provides passage for a blood vessel to the face and a nerve that receives sensations from the nasal region and cheek. This

## Evolutionary Medicine

### Evolutionary Significance of the Palate

In most vertebrates, the nasal passages open into the oral cavity. Mammals, by contrast, have a palate that separates the nasal and oral cavities. In order to maintain our high metabolic rate, we must digest our food rapidly; in order to do this, we chew it thoroughly to break it up into small, easily digested particles before swallowing it. We would be unable to breathe freely during this prolonged chewing if we lacked a palate to separate the airflow from the oral cavity.

nerve emerges through the foramen rotundum into the cranial cavity. The maxilla forms part of the floor of the orbit, where it exhibits a gash called the **inferior orbital fissure** that angles downward and medially (fig. 7.14). The inferior and superior orbital fissures form a sideways V whose apex lies near the optic foramen. The inferior orbital fissure is a passage for blood vessels and sensory nerves from the face.

The **palate** forms the roof of the mouth and floor of the nasal cavity. It consists of a bony **hard palate** in front and a fleshy **soft palate** in the rear. Most of the hard palate is formed by horizontal extensions of the maxilla called **palatine** (PAL-uh-tine) **processes** (see fig. 7.5a). Near the anterior margin of each palatine process, just behind the incisors, is an **incisive foramen.** The palatine processes normally meet at the intermaxillary suture at about 12 weeks of fetal development. Failure to join causes cleft palate (see table 7.7, p. 206).

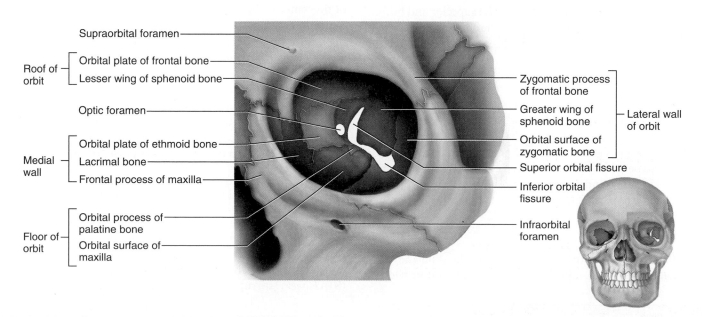

Supraorbital foramen

Roof of orbit
— Orbital plate of frontal bone
— Lesser wing of sphenoid bone

Optic foramen

Medial wall
— Orbital plate of ethmoid bone
— Lacrimal bone
— Frontal process of maxilla

Floor of orbit
— Orbital process of palatine bone
— Orbital surface of maxilla

Zygomatic process of frontal bone

Greater wing of sphenoid bone

Orbital surface of zygomatic bone

Lateral wall of orbit

Superior orbital fissure

Inferior orbital fissure

Infraorbital foramen

**Figure 7.14** The Left Orbit, Anterior View.

## Palatine Bones

The **palatine bones** form the rest of the hard palate, part of the wall of the nasal cavity, and part of the floor of the orbit (see figs. 7.5a and 7.13). At the posterolateral corners of the hard palate are the two large **greater palatine foramina.**

## Zygomatic Bones

The **zygomatic**[23] **bones** form the angles of the cheeks inferolateral to the eyes and form part of the lateral wall of each orbit; they extend about halfway to the ear (see figs. 7.4a and 7.5a). Each zygomatic bone has an inverted T shape and usually a small **zygomaticofacial** (ZY-go-MAT-ih-co-FAY-shul) **foramen** near the intersection of the stem and crossbar of the T. The prominent zygomatic arch that flares from each side of the skull is formed by the union of the zygomatic and temporal bones.

## Lacrimal Bones

The **lacrimal**[24] (LACK-rih-mul) **bones** form part of the medial wall of each orbit (fig. 7.14). These are the smallest bones of the skull, about the size of a fingernail. A depression called the **lacrimal fossa** houses a membranous *lacrimal sac* in life. Tears from the eye collect in this sac and drain into the nasal cavity.

## Nasal Bones

Two small rectangular **nasal bones** form the bridge of the nose (see fig. 7.3) and support cartilages that shape the lower portion of the nose. They are only slightly larger than the lacrimal bones. If you palpate the bridge, you can easily feel where the nasal bones end and the cartilages begin. The nasal bones are often fractured by blows to the nose.

## Inferior Nasal Conchae

There are three conchae in the nasal cavity. The superior and middle conchae, as discussed earlier, are parts of the ethmoid bone. The **inferior nasal concha**—the largest of the three—is a separate bone (see fig. 7.13).

## Vomer

The **vomer** forms the inferior portion of the nasal septum (see figs. 7.3 and 7.4b). Its name literally means "plowshare," which refers to its resemblance to the blade of a plow. The superior half of the nasal septum is formed by the perpendicular plate of the ethmoid bone, as mentioned earlier. The vomer and perpendicular plate support a wall of *septal cartilage* that forms most of the anterior part of the nasal septum.

## Mandible

The **mandible** (fig. 7.15) is the strongest bone of the skull and the only one that can move. It supports the lower teeth and provides

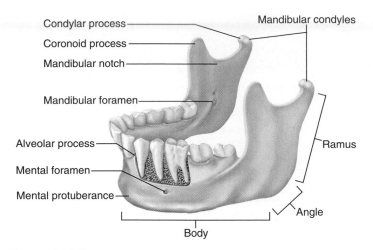

**Figure 7.15** The Mandible.

attachment for muscles of mastication and facial expression. The horizontal portion is called the **body;** the vertical-to-oblique posterior portion is the **ramus** (RAY-mus)—plural, *rami* (RAY-my); and these two portions meet at a corner called the **angle.** The point of the chin is the **mental protuberance.** The inner (posterior) surface of the mandible in this region has a pair of small points, the **mental spines,** which serve for attachment of certain chin muscles (see fig. 7.4b). On the anterolateral surface of the body, the **mental foramen** permits the passage of nerves and blood vessels of the chin. The inner surface of the body has a number of shallow depressions and ridges to accommodate muscles and salivary glands. The angle of the mandible has a rough lateral surface for insertion of the *masseter,* a muscle of mastication. Like the maxilla, the mandible has pointed alveolar processes between the teeth.

The ramus is somewhat Y-shaped. Its posterior branch, called the **condylar** (CON-dih-lur) **process,** bears the **mandibular condyle**—an oval knob that articulates with the mandibular fossa of the temporal bone. The hinge of the mandible is the **temporomandibular joint (TMJ).** The anterior branch of the ramus, called the **coronoid process,** is the point of insertion for the temporalis muscle, which pulls the mandible upward when you bite. The U-shaped arch between the two processes is called the **mandibular notch.** Just below the notch, on the medial surface of the ramus, is the **mandibular foramen,** a passage for the nerve and blood vessels that supply the lower teeth (see fig. 7.4b). Dentists inject anesthetic near here to deaden sensation from the lower teeth, and near the foramen rotundum to deaden sensation from the upper teeth.

## Bones Associated with the Skull

Seven bones are closely associated with the skull but not considered part of it. These are the three auditory ossicles in each middle-ear cavity and the hyoid bone beneath the chin. The **auditory ossicles**[25]—named the **malleus** (hammer), **incus** (anvil), and **stapes** (STAY-peez) (stirrup)—are discussed in connection with hearing in

---

[23]*zygo* = to join, unite
[24]*lacrim* = tear, to cry

[25]*os* = bone + *icle* = little

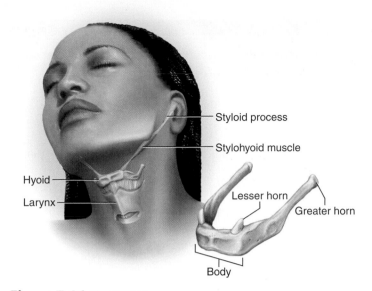

**Figure 7.16** **The Hyoid Bone.**
● *Why would a fractured hyoid bone be a common finding in strangulation cases?*

chapter 17. The **hyoid**[26] **bone** is a slender U-shaped bone between the chin and larynx (fig. 7.16). It is one of the few bones that does not articulate with any other. The hyoid is suspended from the styloid processes of the skull, somewhat like a hammock, by the small *stylohyoid muscles* and *stylohyoid ligaments.* The medial **body** of the hyoid is flanked on either side by projections called the **greater** and **lesser horns.** The hyoid bone serves for attachment of several muscles that control the mandible, tongue, and larynx. Forensic pathologists look for a fractured hyoid as evidence of strangulation.

## Adaptations of the Skull for Bipedalism

Some mammals can stand, hop, or walk briefly on their hind legs, but humans are the only mammals that are habitually bipedal. Chapter 1 explored some possible reasons why upright locomotion originally evolved in the Hominidae. Efficient bipedal locomotion is possible only because of several adaptations of the feet, legs, vertebral column, and skull.

The human head is balanced on the vertebral column with the gaze directed forward. This was made possible in part by an evolutionary remodeling of the skull. The foramen magnum moved to a more inferior location in the course of human evolution, and the face is much flatter than an ape's face, so there is less weight anterior to the occipital condyles (fig. 7.17). Being balanced on the spine, the head does not require strong muscles to hold it erect. Apes have prominent supraorbital ridges for the attachment of muscles that pull back on the skull. In humans, these ridges are much lighter and the muscles of the forehead serve only for facial expression, not to hold the head up.

Table 7.4 summarizes the bones of the skull.

[26]*hy* = the letter *U* + *oid* = resembling

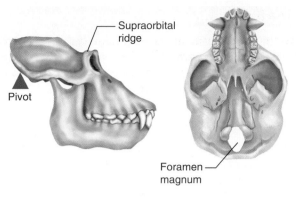

**Chimpanzee**

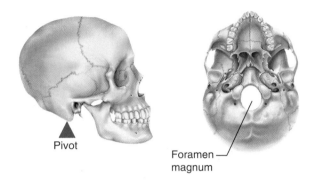

**Human**

**Figure 7.17** **Adaptations of the Skull for Bipedalism.** Comparison of chimpanzee and human skulls. The foramen magnum is shifted rostrally and the face is flatter in humans. Thus, the skull is balanced on the vertebral column and the gaze is directed forward when a person is standing.
● *Why do apes need a stronger supraorbital ridge than humans do?*

## *Before You Go On*

*Answer the following questions to test your understanding of the preceding section:*

4. Name the paranasal sinuses and state their locations. Name any four other cavities in the skull.

5. Explain the difference between a cranial bone and a facial bone. Give four examples of each.

6. Draw an oval representing a superior view of the calvaria. Draw lines representing the coronal, lambdoid, and sagittal sutures. Label the four bones separated by these sutures.

7. State which bone has each of these features: a squamous part, hypoglossal foramen, greater horn, greater wing, condylar process, and cribriform plate.

8. Palpate as many of the following structures as possible, and identify which ones cannot normally be palpated on a living person: the mastoid process, crista galli, superior orbital fissure, palatine processes, zygomatic bone, mental protuberance, and stapes.

| TABLE 7.4 | Anatomical Checklist for the Skull and Associated Bones |
|---|---|

## Cranial Bones

**Frontal Bone (figs. 7.3 to 7.7)**

Supraorbital margin
Supraorbital foramen or notch
Frontal sinus

**Parietal Bones (figs. 7.4 and 7.6)**

Temporal lines
Parietal foramen

**Temporal Bones (figs. 7.4, 7.5, and 7.10)**

Squamous part
  Zygomatic process
  Mandibular fossa
Tympanic part
  External acoustic meatus
  Styloid process
Mastoid part
  Mastoid process
  Mastoid notch
  Mastoid foramen
  Stylomastoid foramen
Petrous part
  Internal acoustic meatus
  Carotid canal
  Jugular foramen

**Occipital Bone (figs. 7.4, 7.5, and 7.6)**

Foramen magnum
Basilar part
Occipital condyles
Hypoglossal canal

**Occipital Bone (continued)**

Condylar canal
External occipital protuberance
Superior nuchal line
Inferior nuchal line

**Sphenoid Bone (figs. 7.4, 7.5, and 7.11)**

Body
Lesser wing
  Optic foramen
  Anterior clinoid process
  Superior orbital fissure
Greater wing
  Foramen ovale
  Foramen rotundum
  Foramen spinosum
  Foramen lacerum
Medial and lateral pterygoid plates
Pterygoid processes
Nasal choanae
Sphenoid sinus
Sella turcica
Dorsum sellae

**Ethmoid Bone (figs. 7.4, 7.7, and 7.12)**

Perpendicular plate
Superior nasal concha
Middle nasal concha
Ethmoid sinus (air cells)
Crista galli
Cribriform plate

## Facial Bones

**Maxilla (figs. 7.3, 7.4, and 7.5a)**

Alveoli
Alveolar processes
Infraorbital foramen
Inferior orbital fissure
Palatine processes
Incisive foramen
Maxillary sinus

**Palatine Bones (figs. 7.4b, 7.5a, and 7.13)**

Greater palatine foramen

**Zygomatic Bones (figs. 7.4a and 7.5a)**

Zygomaticofacial foramen

**Lacrimal Bones (figs. 7.3 and 7.14)**

Lacrimal fossa

**Nasal Bones (figs. 7.3 and 7.13)**

**Inferior Nasal Concha (fig. 7.13)**

**Vomer (figs. 7.3 and 7.4b)**

**Mandible (figs. 7.3 and 7.15)**

Body
  Mental protuberance
  Mental foramen
Angle
Ramus
  Condylar process
  Mandibular condyle
  Coronoid process
  Mandibular notch
  Mandibular foramen

## Bones Associated with the Skull

**Auditory Ossicles**

Malleus (hammer)
Incus (anvil)
Stapes (stirrup)

**Hyoid Bone (fig. 7.16)**

Body
Greater horn
Lesser horn

# The Vertebral Column and Thoracic Cage

## Objectives

When you have completed this section, you should be able to

- describe the general features of the vertebral column and those of a typical vertebra;
- describe the special features of vertebrae in different regions of the vertebral column, and discuss the functional significance of the regional differences;
- relate the shape of the vertebral column to upright locomotion; and
- describe the anatomy of the sternum and ribs and how the ribs articulate with the thoracic vertebrae.

## General Features of the Vertebral Column

The **vertebral column** (spine) physically supports the skull and trunk, allows for their movement, protects the spinal cord, and absorbs stresses produced by walking, running, and lifting. It also provides attachment for the limbs, thoracic cage, and postural muscles. Although commonly called the backbone, it does not consist of a single bone but a chain of 33 **vertebrae** with **intervertebral discs** of fibrocartilage between most of them. The adult vertebral column averages about 71 cm (28 in.) long, with the 23 intervertebral discs accounting for about one-quarter of the length. Most people are about 1% shorter when they go to bed at night than when first rising in the morning. This is because during the day, the weight of the body compresses the intervertebral discs and squeezes water out of them. When one is sleeping, with the weight off the spine, the discs reabsorb water and swell.

As shown in figure 7.18, the vertebrae are divided into five groups: 7 *cervical* (SUR-vih-cul) *vertebrae* in the neck, 12 *thoracic vertebrae* in the chest, 5 *lumbar vertebrae* in the lower back, 5 *sacral vertebrae* at the base of the spine, and 4 tiny *coccygeal* (coc-SIDJ-ee-ul) *vertebrae*. To help remember the numbers of cervical, thoracic, and lumbar vertebrae—7, 12, and 5—you might think of a typical work day: go to work at 7, have lunch at 12, and go home at 5.

Variations in this arrangement occur in about 1 person in 20. For example, the last lumbar vertebra is sometimes incorporated into the sacrum, producing 4 lumbar and 6 sacral vertebrae. In other cases, the first sacral vertebra fails to fuse with the second, producing 6 lumbar and 4 sacral vertebrae. The cervical and thoracic vertebrae are more constant in number.

Beyond the age of 3 years, the vertebral column is slightly S-shaped, with four bends called the **cervical, thoracic, lumbar,** and **pelvic curvatures** (fig. 7.19). The thoracic and pelvic curvatures are called *primary curvatures* because they are present at birth, when the spine has a single C-shaped curvature. The cervical and lumbar curvatures are called *secondary curvatures* because they develop later, in the child's first few years of crawling and walking, as described later in this chapter. The resulting S shape makes sustained bipedal walking possible because the trunk of the body does not lean forward as

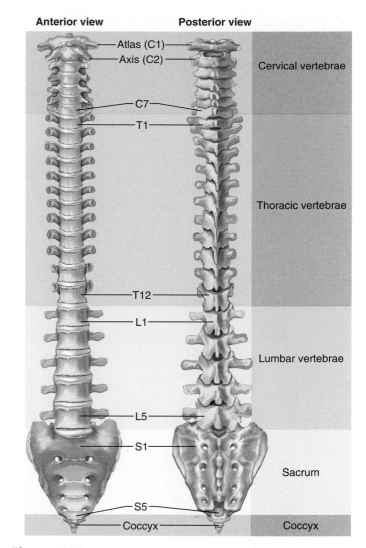

**Figure 7.18** The Vertebral Column.

it does in primates such as a chimpanzee; the head is balanced over the body's center of gravity; and the eyes are directed straight forward (fig. 7.20). Abnormal lateral or anterior–posterior spinal curvatures are among the most common back problems (see Insight 7.3).

## General Structure of a Vertebra

A representative vertebra and intervertebral disc are shown in figure 7.22. The most obvious feature of a vertebra is the **body,** or **centrum**—a mass of spongy bone and red bone marrow covered with a thin layer of compact bone. This is the weight-bearing portion of the vertebra. Its rough superior and inferior surfaces provide firm attachment for the intervertebral discs.

### THINK ABOUT IT

*The lower we look on the vertebral column, the larger the vertebral bodies and intervertebral discs are. What is the functional significance of this trend?*

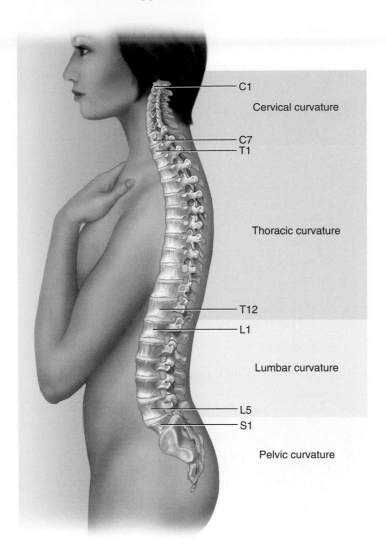

**Figure 7.19** Curvatures of the Adult Vertebral Column.

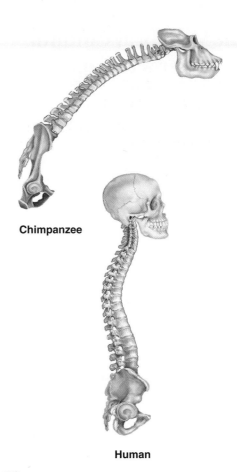

**Figure 7.20** **Comparison of Chimpanzee and Human Vertebral Columns.** The S-shaped human vertebral column is an adaptation for bipedal locomotion.

Posterior to the body of each vertebra is an ovoid to triangular canal called the **vertebral foramen.** Collectively, these foramina form the **vertebral canal,** a passage for the spinal cord. The foramen is bordered by a bony **vertebral arch** composed of two parts, a pillarlike **pedicle**[27] and platelike **lamina,**[28] on each side. Extending from the apex of the arch, a projection called the **spinous process** is directed toward the rear and downward. You can see and feel the spinous processes as a row of bumps along the spine. A **transverse process** extends laterally from the point where the pedicle and lamina meet. The spinous and transverse processes provide points of attachment for spinal muscles and ligaments.

A pair of **superior articular processes** project upward from one vertebra and meet a similar pair of **inferior articular processes** that project downward from the vertebra just above (fig. 7.23a). Each process has a flat articular surface (facet) facing that of the adjacent vertebra. These processes restrict twisting of the vertebral column, which could otherwise severely damage the spinal cord.

Where two vertebrae are joined, they exhibit an opening between their pedicles called the **intervertebral foramen.** This allows passage for spinal nerves that connect with the spinal cord at regular intervals. Each foramen is formed by an **inferior vertebral notch** in the pedicle of the superior vertebra and a **superior vertebral notch** in the pedicle of the one just below it (fig. 7.23b).

## Intervertebral Discs

An **intervertebral disc** is a pad consisting of an inner gelatinous **nucleus pulposus** surrounded by a ring of fibrocartilage called the **anulus fibrosus** (see fig. 7.22). The discs bind adjacent vertebrae together, enhance spinal flexibility, support the weight of the body, and absorb shock. Under stress—for example, when you lift a heavy weight—the discs bulge laterally. Excessive stress can cause a *herniated disc* (see p. 207).

## Regional Characteristics of Vertebrae

We are now prepared to consider how vertebrae differ from one region of the vertebral column to another and from the generalized anatomy just described. Knowing these variations will enable you

[27]*ped* = foot + *icle* = little
[28]*lamina* = layer, plate

## INSIGHT 7.3

### Clinical Application

## Abnormal Spinal Curvatures

Abnormal spinal curvatures (fig. 7.21) can result from disease, weakness, or paralysis of the trunk muscles, poor posture, or congenital defects in vertebral anatomy. The most common deformity is an abnormal lateral curvature called *scoliosis*. It occurs most often in the thoracic region, particularly among adolescent girls. It sometimes results from a developmental abnormality in which the body and arch of a vertebra fail to develop on one side. If the person's skeletal growth is not yet complete, scoliosis can be corrected with a back brace.

An exaggerated thoracic curvature is called *kyphosis* (hunchback, in lay language). It is usually a result of osteoporosis, but it also occurs in people with osteomalacia or spinal tuberculosis and in adolescents who engage heavily in such sports as wrestling and weightlifting. An exaggerated lumbar curvature is called *lordosis* (swayback). It can have the same causes as kyphosis, or it can result from added abdominal weight in pregnancy or obesity.

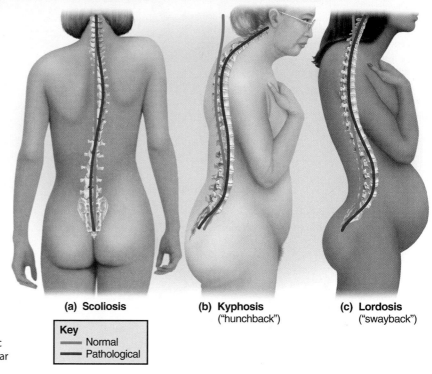

**(a) Scoliosis**    **(b) Kyphosis** ("hunchback")    **(c) Lordosis** ("swayback")

Key
— Normal
— Pathological

**Figure 7.21** **Abnormal Spinal Curvatures.** (a) Scoliosis, an abnormal lateral deviation. (b) Kyphosis, an exaggerated thoracic curvature common in old age. (c) Lordosis, an exaggerated lumbar curvature common in pregnancy and obesity.

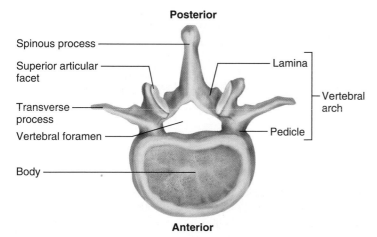

Posterior

Spinous process

Superior articular facet

Transverse process

Vertebral foramen

Body

Lamina

Vertebral arch

Pedicle

Anterior

**(a) 2nd lumbar vertebra (L2)**

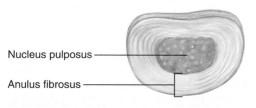

Nucleus pulposus

Anulus fibrosus

**(b) Intervertebral disc**

to identify the region of the spine from which an isolated vertebra was taken. More importantly, these modifications in form reflect functional differences among the vertebrae.

## Cervical Vertebrae

The **cervical vertebrae (C1–C7)** are the smallest and lightest. The first two (C1 and C2) have unique structures that allow for head movements (fig. 7.24). Vertebra C1 is called the **atlas** because it supports the head in a manner reminiscent of the Titan of Greek mythology who was condemned by Zeus to carry the world on his shoulders. It scarcely resembles the typical vertebra; it has no body and is little more than a delicate ring surrounding a large vertebral foramen. On each side is a **lateral mass** with a deeply concave **superior articular facet,** which articulates with the occipital condyle of the skull. In nodding motions of the skull, as in gesturing "yes," the

**Figure 7.22** **A Representative Vertebra and Intervertebral Disc, Superior Views.** (a) A typical vertebra. (b) An intervertebral disc oriented the same way as the vertebral body in part (a) for comparison. (See fig. 7.25 for lateral views.)

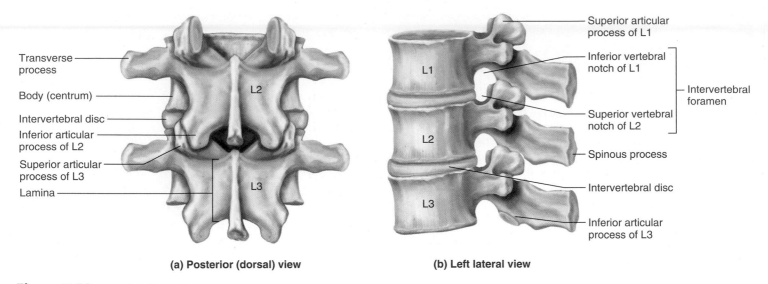

**(a) Posterior (dorsal) view**

Transverse process
Body (centrum)
Intervertebral disc
Inferior articular process of L2
Superior articular process of L3
Lamina
L2
L3

**(b) Left lateral view**

Superior articular process of L1
Inferior vertebral notch of L1
Intervertebral foramen
Superior vertebral notch of L2
Spinous process
Intervertebral disc
Inferior articular process of L3
L1
L2
L3

**Figure 7.23** Articulated Vertebrae.
● *What is the function of the intervertebral foramina?*

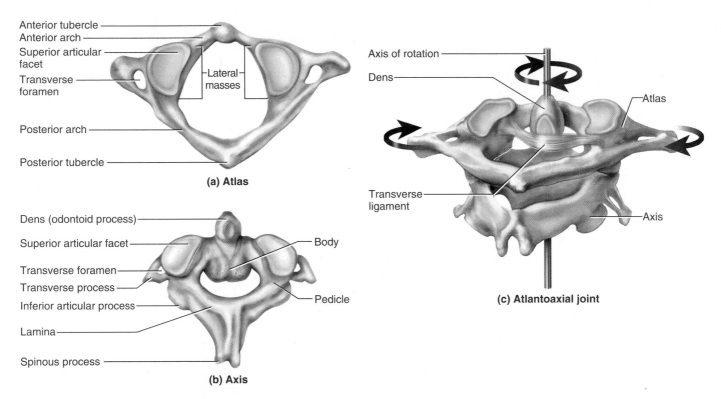

**(a) Atlas**

Anterior tubercle
Anterior arch
Superior articular facet
Transverse foramen
Posterior arch
Posterior tubercle
Lateral masses

**(b) Axis**

Dens (odontoid process)
Superior articular facet
Transverse foramen
Transverse process
Inferior articular process
Lamina
Spinous process
Body
Pedicle

**(c) Atlantoaxial joint**

Axis of rotation
Dens
Transverse ligament
Atlas
Axis

**Figure 7.24** The Atlas and Axis, Cervical Vertebrae C1 and C2.   (a) The atlas, superior view. (b) The axis, posterosuperior view. (c) Articulation of the atlas and axis and rotation of the atlas. This movement turns the head from side to side, as in gesturing "no." Note the transverse ligament holding the dens of the axis in place.
● *What serious consequence could result from a ruptured transverse ligament?*

occipital condyles rock back and forth on these facets. The **inferior articular facets,** which are comparatively flat or only slightly concave, articulate with C2. The lateral masses are connected by an **anterior arch** and a **posterior arch,** which bear slight protuberances called the **anterior** and **posterior tubercle,** respectively.

Vertebra C2, the **axis,** allows rotation of the head, as in gesturing "no." Its most distinctive feature is a prominent knob called the

**dens** (pronounced "denz"), or **odontoid**[29] **process,** on its anterosuperior side. No other vertebra has a dens. It begins to form as an independent ossification center during the first year of life and fuses with the axis by the age of 3 to 6 years. It projects into the vertebral foramen of the atlas, where it is nestled in a facet and held in place

[29]*dens = odont = tooth + oid = resembling*

by a **transverse ligament** (fig. 7.24c). A heavy blow to the top of the head can cause a fatal injury in which the dens is driven through the foramen magnum into the brainstem. The articulation between the atlas and the cranium is called the **atlanto–occipital joint;** the one between the atlas and axis is called the **atlantoaxial joint.**

The axis is the first vertebra that exhibits a spinous process. In vertebrae C2 to C6, the process is forked, or *bifid*,[30] at its tip (fig. 7.25a). This fork provides attachment for the *nuchal ligament* of the back of the neck. All seven cervical vertebrae have a prominent round **transverse foramen** in each transverse process. These foramina provide passage and protection for the *vertebral arteries,* which supply blood to the brain, and *vertebral veins,* which drain blood from various neck structures. Transverse foramina occur in no other vertebrae and thus provide an easy means of recognizing a cervical vertebra.

### THINK ABOUT IT

*How would head movements be affected if vertebrae C1 and C2 had the same structure as C3? What is the functional advantage of the lack of a spinous process in C1?*

Cervical vertebrae C3 to C6 are similar to the typical vertebra described earlier, with the addition of the transverse foramina and bifid spinous processes. Vertebra C7 is a little different—its spinous process is not bifid, but it is especially long and forms a prominent bump on the lower back of the neck. C7 is sometimes called the *vertebra prominens* because of this especially conspicuous spinous process. This feature is a convenient landmark for counting vertebrae.

---

[30]*bifid* = cleft into two parts

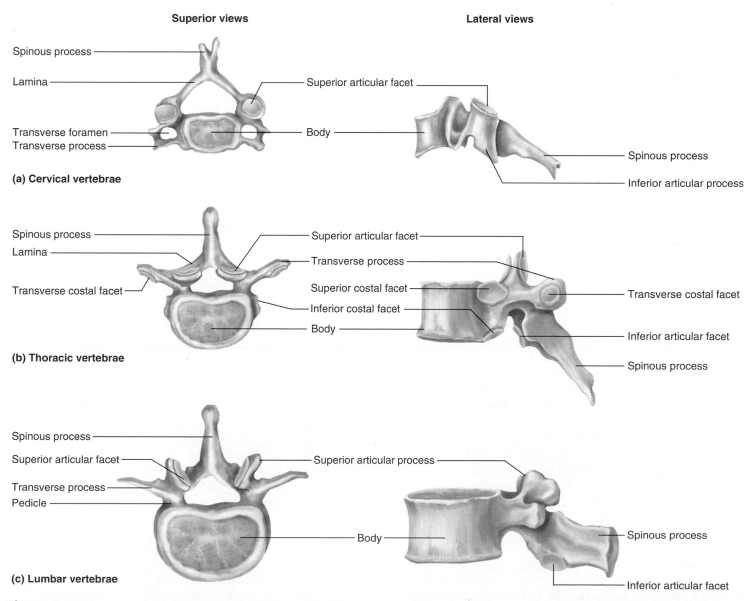

**Superior views**     **Lateral views**

**(a) Cervical vertebrae**

- Spinous process
- Lamina
- Transverse foramen
- Transverse process
- Superior articular facet
- Body
- Spinous process
- Inferior articular process

**(b) Thoracic vertebrae**

- Spinous process
- Lamina
- Transverse costal facet
- Superior articular facet
- Transverse process
- Superior costal facet
- Inferior costal facet
- Body
- Transverse costal facet
- Inferior articular facet
- Spinous process

**(c) Lumbar vertebrae**

- Spinous process
- Superior articular facet
- Transverse process
- Pedicle
- Superior articular process
- Body
- Spinous process
- Inferior articular facet

**Figure 7.25** **Typical Cervical, Thoracic, and Lumbar Vertebrae.** The left-hand figures are superior views, and the right-hand figures are left lateral views.

## Thoracic Vertebrae

There are 12 **thoracic vertebrae (T1–T12),** corresponding to the 12 pairs of ribs attached to them. They lack the transverse foramina and bifid processes that distinguish the cervicals, but possess the following distinctive features of their own (fig. 7.25b):

- The spinous processes are relatively pointed and angle sharply downward.
- The body is somewhat heart-shaped and more massive than in the cervical vertebrae, but less than in the lumbar vertebrae.
- The body has small, smooth, slightly concave spots called *costal facets* (to be described shortly) for attachment of the ribs.
- Vertebrae T1 to T10 have a shallow, cuplike **transverse costal**[31] **facet** at the end of each transverse process. These provide a second point of articulation for ribs 1 to 10. There are no transverse costal facets on T11 and T12, and ribs 11 and 12 attach only to the bodies of the vertebrae.

No other vertebrae have ribs articulating with them. Thoracic vertebrae vary among themselves mainly in the mode of articulation with the ribs. In most cases, a rib inserts between two vertebrae, so each vertebra contributes one-half of the articular surface—the rib articulates with the **inferior costal facet** of the upper vertebra and the **superior costal facet** of the vertebra below that. This terminology may be a little confusing, but note that the facets are named for their position on the vertebral body, not for which part of the rib's articulation they provide. Vertebrae T1 and T10 to T12, however, have complete costal facets on the bodies for ribs 1 and 10 to 12, which articulate on the vertebral body instead of between vertebrae. Vertebrae T11 and T12, as noted, have no transverse costal facets. These variations will be more functionally

understandable after you have studied the anatomy of the ribs, so we will return then to the details of these articular surfaces.

Vertebra T12 differs in its articular processes from those above it. Its superior articular processes face posteriorly to meet the anteriorly-facing inferior processes of T11, but the inferior articular processes of T12 face laterally like those of the lumbar vertebrae, described next. T12 thus represents a transition between the thoracic and lumbar pattern.

## Lumbar Vertebrae

There are five **lumbar vertebrae (L1–L5).** Their most distinctive features are a thick, stout body and a blunt, squarish spinous process (fig. 7.25c). In addition, their articular processes are oriented differently than those of other vertebrae. In thoracic vertebrae, the superior processes face posteriorly and the inferior processes face anteriorly. In lumbar vertebrae, the superior processes face medially (like the palms of your hands about to clap), and the inferior processes face laterally, toward the superior processes of the next vertebra. This arrangement makes the lumbar region of the spine especially resistant to twisting. These differences are best observed on an articulated (assembled) skeleton.

## Sacrum

The **sacrum** (SACK-rum or SAY-krum) is a bony plate that forms the posterior wall of the pelvic cavity (fig. 7.26). It is named for the fact that it was once considered the seat of the soul.[32] In children, there are five separate **sacral vertebrae (S1–S5).** They begin to fuse around age 16 and are fully fused by age 26.

The anterior surface of the sacrum is relatively smooth and concave and has four transverse lines that indicate where the five vertebrae

---

[31]*costa* = rib + *al* = pertaining to

[32]*sacr* = sacred

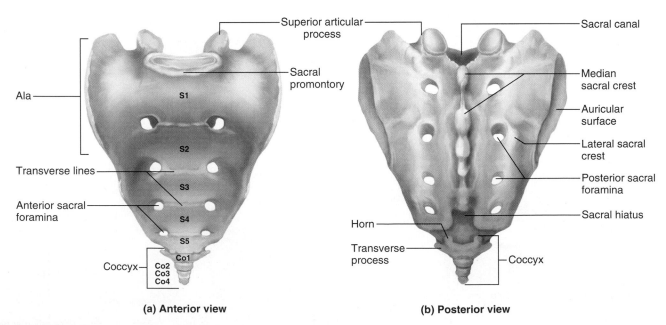

**(a) Anterior view**　　　　**(b) Posterior view**

**Figure 7.26 The Sacrum and Coccyx.** (a) The anterior surface, which faces the viscera of the pelvic cavity. (b) The posterior surface, whose surface features can be palpated in the sacral region.

have fused. This surface exhibits four pairs of large **anterior sacral (pelvic) foramina,** which allow for the passage of nerves and arteries to the pelvic organs. The posterior surface of the sacrum is very rough. The spinous processes of the vertebrae fuse into a posterior ridge called the **median sacral crest.** The transverse processes fuse into a less prominent **lateral sacral crest** on each side of the median crest. Again on the posterior side of the sacrum, there are four pairs of openings for spinal nerves, the **posterior sacral foramina.** The nerves that emerge here supply the gluteal region and lower limb.

A **sacral canal** runs through the sacrum and ends in an inferior opening called the **sacral hiatus** (hy-AY-tus). This canal contains spinal nerve roots in life. On each side of the sacrum is an ear-shaped region called the **auricular**[33] (aw-RIC-you-lur) **surface.** This articulates with a similarly shaped surface on the hip bone and forms the strong, nearly immovable **sacroiliac** (SAY-cro-ILL-ee-ac) **(SI) joint.** The body of vertebra S1 juts anteriorly to form a **sacral promontory,** which supports the body of vertebra L5. Lateral to the median sacral crest, S1 also has a pair of **superior articular processes** that articulate with L5. Lateral to these are a pair of large, rough, winglike extensions called the **alae**[34] (AIL-ee).

### Coccyx

The **coccyx**[35] (fig. 7.26) usually consists of four (sometimes five) small vertebrae, **Co1** to **Co4,** which fuse by the age of 20 to 30 into a single

[33]*auri* = ear + *cul* = little + *ar* = pertaining to
[34]*alae* = wings
[35]*coccyx* = cuckoo (named for resemblance to a cuckoo's beak)

triangular bone. Vertebra Co1 has a pair of **horns (cornua),** which serve as attachment points for ligaments that bind the coccyx to the sacrum. The coccyx can be fractured by a difficult childbirth or a hard fall on the buttocks. Although it is the vestige of a tail, it is not entirely useless; it provides attachment for muscles of the pelvic floor.

## The Thoracic Cage

The **thoracic cage** (fig. 7.27) consists of the thoracic vertebrae, sternum, and ribs. It forms a more or less conical enclosure for the lungs and heart and provides attachment for the pectoral girdle and upper limb. It has a broad base and a somewhat narrower superior apex; it is rhythmically expanded by the respiratory muscles to create a vacuum that draws air into the lungs. The inferior border of the thoracic cage is formed by a downward arc of the ribs called the **costal margin.** The cage protects not only the thoracic organs but also the spleen, most of the liver, and to some extent the kidneys.

### Sternum

The **sternum** (breastbone) is a bony plate anterior to the heart (fig. 7.27). It is subdivided into three regions: the *manubrium*, *body*, and *xiphoid process*. The **manubrium**[36] (ma-NOO-bree-um) is the broad superior portion. It has a median **suprasternal notch (jugular notch),** which you can easily palpate between your clavicles (collarbones), and right and left **clavicular notches** where it articulates

[36]*manubrium* = handle

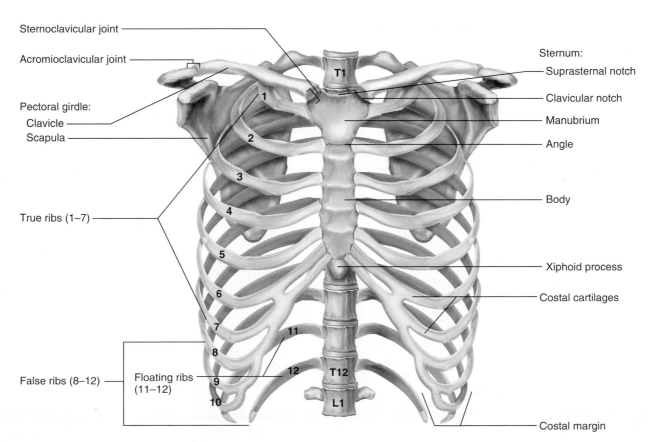

**Figure 7.27** **The Thoracic Cage and Pectoral Girdle, Anterior View.**

with the clavicles. The **body,** or **gladiolus,**[37] is the longest part of the sternum. It joins the manubrium at the **sternal angle,** which can be palpated as a transverse ridge at the point where the sternum projects farthest forward. In some people, however, the angle is rounded or concave. The second rib attaches here, making the sternal angle a useful landmark for counting ribs in a physical examination. The manubrium and body have scalloped lateral margins where cartilages of the ribs are attached. At the inferior end of the sternum is a small, pointed **xiphoid**[38] (ZIF-oyd) **process** that provides attachment for some of the abdominal muscles. In cardiopulmonary resuscitation, improperly performed chest compression can drive the xiphoid process into the liver and cause a fatal hemorrhage.

## Ribs

There are 12 pairs of **ribs,** with no difference between the sexes. Each is attached at its posterior (proximal) end to the vertebral column, and most of them are also attached at the anterior (distal) end to the sternum. The anterior attachment is by way of a long strip of hyaline cartilage called the **costal cartilage.**

As a general rule, the ribs increase in length from 1 through 7 and become progressively smaller again through rib 12. They are increasingly oblique (slanted) in orientation from 1 through 9, then less so from 10 through 12. They also differ in their individual structure and attachments at different levels of the thoracic cage, so we will examine them in order as we descend the torso, taking note of their universal characteristics as well as their individual variations.

Rib 1 is peculiar. On an articulated skeleton, you must look for its vertebral attachement just below the base of the neck; much of this rib lies above the level of the clavicle (see fig. 7.27). It is a short, flat, C-shaped plate of bone (fig. 7.28a). At the vertebral end, it exhibits a knobby **head** that articulates with the body of vertebra T1. On an isolated vertebra, you can find a smooth costal facet for the attachment on the middle of the body. Immediately distal to the head, the rib narrows to a **neck** and then widens again to form a rough area called the **tubercle.** This is its point of attachment to the transverse costal facet of the same vertebra. Beyond the tubercle, the rib flattens and widens into a gently sloping bladelike **shaft.** The shaft ends distally in a squared-off, rough area. In the living individual, the costal cartilage begins here and spans the rest of the distance to the upper sternum.

Ribs 2 through 7 present a more typical appearance (fig. 7.28b). At the proximal end, each exhibits a head, neck, and tubercle. The head is wedge-shaped and inserts between two vertebrae. Each margin of the wedge has a smooth surface called an *articular facet.* The **superior articular facet** joins the inferior costal facet of the vertebra above; the **inferior articular facet** joins the superior costal facet of vertebra below. The tubercle of the rib articulates with the transverse costal facet of each same-numbered vertebra. Figure 7.29 details the three rib–vertebra attachments typical of this region of the rib cage. Beyond the tubercle, each rib makes a sharp curve around the side of the torso and then progresses anteriorly to

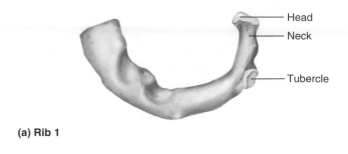

**(a) Rib 1**

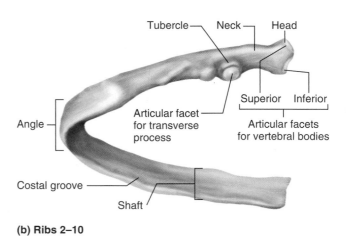

**(b) Ribs 2–10**

**(c) Ribs 11–12**

**Figure 7.28** **Anatomy of the Ribs.** (a) Rib 1 is an atypical flat plate. (b) Typical features of ribs 2 to 10. (c) Appearance of the floating ribs, 11 and 12.

approach the sternum (see fig. 7.27). The curve is called the **angle** of the rib and the rest of the bony blade distal to it is called the shaft. The inferior margin of the shaft has a **costal groove** that marks the path of the intercostal blood vessels and nerve. Each of these ribs, like rib 1, ends in a blunt, rough area where the costal cartilage begins. Each has its own costal cartilage connecting it to the sternum; because of this feature, ribs 1 through 7 are called **true ribs.**

Ribs 8 through 12 are called **false ribs** because they lack independent cartilaginous connections to the sternum. In 8 through 10, the costal cartilages sweep upward and end on the costal cartilage of rib 7 (see fig. 7.27). Rib 10 also differs from 2 through 9 in that it attaches to the body of a single vertebra (T10) rather than between vertebrae. Thus, vertebra T10 has a small superior costal facet that helps to anchor rib 9 above it, plus a complete costal facet on its body for rib 10.

Ribs 11 and 12 are again quite unusual (fig. 7.28c). Posteriorly, they articulate with the bodies of vertebrae T11 and T12, but they do not have tubercles and do not attach to the transverse processes of the vertebrae. Those two vertebrae therefore have no transverse costal facets. At the distal end, these two relatively small, delicate ribs taper

---

[37]*gladiolus* = sword
[38]*xipho* = sword + *oid* = resembling

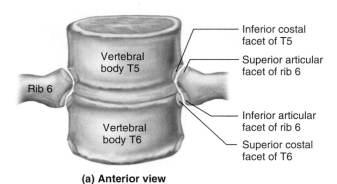

**(a) Anterior view**

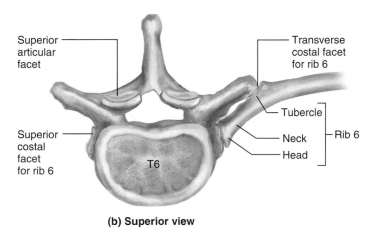

**(b) Superior view**

**Figure 7.29** **Articulation of Rib 6 with Vertebrae T5 and T6.** (a) Anterior view. Note the relationship of the articular facets of the rib with the costal facets of the two vertebrae. (b) Superior view. Note that the rib articulates with a vertebra at two points: the costal facet of the vertebral body and the transverse costal facet on the transverse process.

to a point and are capped by a small cartilaginous tip, but there is no cartilaginous connection to the sternum or to any of the higher costal cartilages. The ribs are merely embedded in lumbar muscle at this end. Consequently, 11 and 12 are also called **floating ribs.** Among the Japanese and some other people, rib 10 is also usually floating.

Table 7.5 summarizes these variations in rib anatomy and their vertebral and sternal attachments. Table 7.6 provides a checklist that you can use to review your knowledge of the vertebral column and thoracic cage.

## *Before You Go On*

*Answer the following questions to test your understanding of the preceding section:*

9. Discuss the contributions of the intervertebral discs to the length and flexibility of the spine.

10. Make a table with three columns headed "cervical," "thoracic," and "lumbar." In each column, list the identifying characteristics of each type of vertebra.

11. Describe how rib 5 articulates with the spine. How do ribs 1 and 12 differ from this and from each other in their modes of articulation?

12. Distinguish between true, false, and floating ribs. State which ribs fall into each category.

13. Palpate as many of the following structures as possible, and identify which ones cannot normally be palpated on a living person: the dens; the spinous process of vertebra C7; the transverse process of vertebra T12; the median sacral crest; the coccyx; the manubrium; the xiphoid process; and the costal cartilage of rib 5.

| TABLE 7.5 | Articulations of the Ribs | | | | |
|---|---|---|---|---|---|
| Rib | Type | Costal Cartilage | Articulating Vertebral Bodies | Articulating with a Transverse Costal Facet? | Rib Tubercle |
| 1 | True | Individual | T1 | Yes | Present |
| 2 | True | Individual | T1 and T2 | Yes | Present |
| 3 | True | Individual | T2 and T3 | Yes | Present |
| 4 | True | Individual | T3 and T4 | Yes | Present |
| 5 | True | Individual | T4 and T5 | Yes | Present |
| 6 | True | Individual | T5 and T6 | Yes | Present |
| 7 | True | Individual | T6 and T7 | Yes | Present |
| 8 | False | Shared with rib 7 | T7 and T8 | Yes | Present |
| 9 | False | Shared with rib 7 | T8 and T9 | Yes | Present |
| 10 | False | Shared with rib 7 | T10 | Yes | Present |
| 11 | False, floating | None | T11 | No | Absent |
| 12 | False, floating | None | T12 | No | Absent |

| TABLE 7.6 | Anatomical Checklist for the Vertebral Column and Thoracic Cage |
|---|---|

**Vertebral Column**

**Spinal Curvatures (fig. 7.19)**

Cervical curvature
Thoracic curvature
Lumbar curvature
Pelvic curvature

**General Vertebral Structure (figs. 7.22 and 7.23)**

Body (centrum)
Vertebral foramen
Vertebral canal
Vertebral arch
   Pedicle
   Lamina
Spinous process
Transverse process
Superior articular process
Inferior articular process
Intervertebral foramen
   Inferior vertebral notch
   Superior vertebral notch

**Intervertebral Discs (fig. 7.22)**

Anulus fibrosus
Nucleus pulposus

**Cervical Vertebrae (figs. 7.24 and 7.25a)**

Transverse foramina
Bifid spinous process
Atlas
   Anterior arch
   Anterior tubercle

**Cervical Vertebrae (continued)**

   Posterior arch
   Posterior tubercle
   Lateral mass
   Superior articular facet
   Inferior articular facet
   Transverse ligament
Axis
   Dens (odontoid process)

**Thoracic Vertebrae (fig. 7.25b)**

Superior costal facet
Inferior costal facet
Transverse costal facet

**Lumbar Vertebrae (figs. 7.23 and 7.25c)**

**Sacral Vertebrae (fig. 7.26)**

Sacrum
Anterior sacral foramina
Posterior sacral foramina
Median sacral crest
Lateral sacral crest
Sacral canal
Sacral hiatus
Auricular surface
Superior articular process
Ala

**Coccygeal Vertebrae (fig. 7.26)**

Coccyx
Cornu

**Thoracic Cage**

**Sternum (fig. 7.27)**

Manubrium
   Suprasternal notch
   Clavicular notch
   Sternal angle
Body (gladiolus)
Xiphoid process

**Ribs (figs. 7.27 to 7.29)**

True ribs (ribs 1–7)
False ribs (ribs 8–12)
Floating ribs (ribs 11–12)

**Ribs (continued)**

Head
Superior articular facet
Inferior articular facet
Neck
Tubercle
Angle
Shaft
Costal groove
Costal cartilage

# Developmental and Clinical Perspectives

### Objectives

When you have completed this section, you should be able to

- describe the prenatal development of the axial skeleton; and
- describe some common disorders of the axial skeleton.

## Development of the Axial Skeleton

The axial skeleton develops primarily by endochondral ossification. This is a two-step process: (1) **chondrification,** in which embryonic mesenchyme condenses and differentiates into hyaline cartilage, and (2) **ossification,** in which the cartilage is replaced by bone, as described in chapter 6. Significant parts of the skull develop by intramembranous ossification, with no cartilage precursor. Bones that form by this mode are called *membranous bones.*

## The Skull

Development of the skull is extremely complex, and we will take only a broad overview of the process here. We can view the skull as developing in three major parts: the base, the calvaria, and the facial bones. The base and calvaria are collectively called the **neurocranium** because they enclose the brain; the facial skeleton is called the **viscerocranium** because it develops from the pharyngeal (visceral) arches. (These arches are described in chapter 4.) Both the neurocranium and viscerocranium have regions of cartilaginous and membranous origin. The cartilaginous neurocranium is also called the **chondrocranuim.**

The base of the cranium develops from several pairs of cartilaginous plates inferior to the brain. These plates undergo endochondral ossification and give rise to most parts of the sphenoid, ethmoid, temporal, and occipital bones. The flat bones of the calvaria form, in contrast, by the intramembranous method. They begin to ossify in week 9, slightly later than the cranial base. As a membranous bone ossifies, trabeculae and spicules of osseous tissue first appear in the center and then spread toward the edges (fig. 7.30).

Facial bones develop mainly from the first two pharyngeal arches. Although these arches are initially supported by cartilage, the cartilages do not transform into bone. They become surrounded by developing membranous bone, and while some of the cartilages become middle-ear bones and part of the hyoid bone, others simply degenerate and disappear. Thus, the facial bones are built *around* cartilages but develop by the intramembranous process.

The skull therefore develops from a multitude of separate pieces. These pieces undergo considerable fusion by the time of birth, but their fusion is by no means complete then. At birth, the frontal bone is still paired. The right and left halves usually fuse by the age of 5 or 6 years, but in some people a *metopic*[39] *suture* persists between them. Traces of this suture are evident in some adult skulls.

The cranial bones are separated at birth by gaps called **fontanels,**[40] bridged by fibrous membranes (fig. 7.31). The term refers to the fact that pulsation of the infant's blood can be felt there. Fontanels permit the bones to shift and the skull to deform during the birth passage. This shifting may deform the infant's head, but the head usually assumes a normal shape within a few days after birth. Four of the fontanels are especially prominent and regular in location: the **anterior, posterior, sphenoid,** and **mastoid fontanels.** The fontanels close by intramembranous ossification. Most are fully ossified by 12 months of age, but the largest one, the anterior fontanel, does not close for 18 to 24 months. A "soft spot" can still be palpated in the corner formed by the frontal and parietal bones up to that age.

---

[39]*met* = beyond + *op* = the eyes
[40]*fontan* = fountain + *el* = little

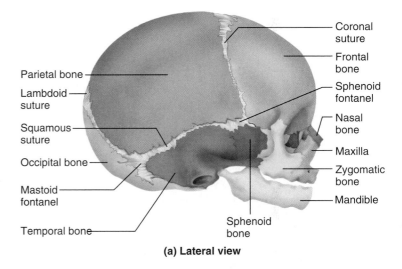

**(a) Lateral view**

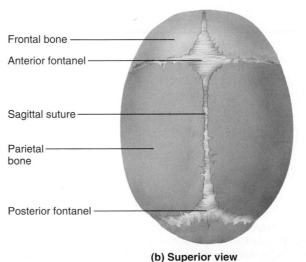

**(b) Superior view**

**Figure 7.31** The Fetal Skull Near the Time of Birth.
• *At what approximate age will all of these fontanels first be closed?*

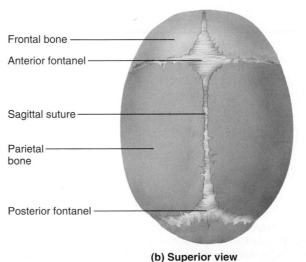

**Figure 7.30** The Fetal Skeleton at 12 Weeks. The red-stained regions are ossified at this age, whereas the elbow, wrist, knee, and ankle joints appear translucent because they are still cartilaginous. The cranial bones are still widely separated.
• *Why are the joints of an infant weaker than those of an older child?*

The mandible undergoes marked changes with age. At birth, it consists of separate right and left bones joined medially by the *mental symphysis,* a zone of cartilage and fibrous connective tissue. The halves begin to fuse in the first year and become fully united into a single bone within the third year. The body of the mandible is very slender at birth, and the ramus is not strongly developed (see fig. 7.31). In early childhood, the mandible grows in a generally downward and forward direction, making the ramus longer and the chin more pronounced. The deciduous ("baby") teeth begin to erupt at about 7 months and continue through the second year, as the body of the mandible widens to accommodate their roots. The deciduous teeth are replaced with permanent teeth mostly between 6 and 13 years, although the third molar, if it emerges at all, may come as late as age 25 (see fig. 24.6, p. 691). If teeth are lost in old age, the alveoli are resorbed and the body of the mandible becomes narrower, much as it was in infancy.

### THINK ABOUT IT

*Suppose you were studying a skull with some teeth missing. How could you tell whether the teeth had been lost after the person's death or years before it?*

The face of a newborn is flat and small compared to the large cranium. It enlarges as the mandible, teeth, and paranasal sinuses develop. To accommodate the growing brain, a child's skull grows more rapidly than the rest of the skeleton. It reaches about half its adult size by 9 months of age, three-quarters by age 2, and nearly final size by 8 or 9 years. The heads of babies and young children are therefore much larger in proportion to the trunk than the heads of adults—an attribute thoroughly exploited by cartoonists and advertisers who draw big-headed characters to give them a more endearing or immature appearance. In humans and other animals, the large rounded heads of the young are thought to promote survival by stimulating parental caregiving instincts.

## The Vertebral Column

One of the universal characteristics of all chordate animals, including humans, is the **notochord,** a flexible, middorsal rod of mesodermal tissue. In humans, the notochord is evident inferior to the neural tube in the third week of development. Segments of embryonic mesoderm called *somites* lie on either side of the notochord and neural tube (see p. 112, p. 114, and fig. 4.8). In the fourth week, part of each somite becomes a sclerotome. This gives rise to vertebral cartilage, which is replaced by bone in the process of endochondral ossification. The sclerotomes are temporarily separated by zones of looser mesenchyme (fig. 7.32a). As shown in figure 7.32b, each vertebral body arises from portions of two adjacent sclerotomes and the loose mesenchyme between them. The midportion of each sclerotome gives rise to the anulus fibrosus of the intervertebral disc. The notochord degenerates and disappears in the regions of the developing vertebral bodies, but persists and expands between the vertebrae to form the nucleus pulposus of the intervertebral discs.

Meanwhile, mesenchyme surrounding the neural tube condenses and forms the vertebral arches of the vertebrae. Approaching the end of the embryonic phase, the mesenchyme of the sclerotomes forms the cartilaginous forerunners of the vertebral bodies. The two halves of the vertebral arch fuse with each other and with the body, and the spinous and transverse processes grow outward from the arch. Thus, a complete cartilaginous vertebral column is established.

Ossification of the vertebrae begins during the embryonic period and is not completed until age 25. Each vertebra develops three primary ossification centers: one in the body and one in each half of the vertebral arch. At birth, these three bony parts of the vertebra are still connected by hyaline cartilage (fig. 7.33). The bony halves of the vertebral arch finish ossifying and fuse around 3 to 5 years of age, beginning in the lumbar region and progressing rostrally. The attachments of the arch to the body remain cartilaginous for a time in order to

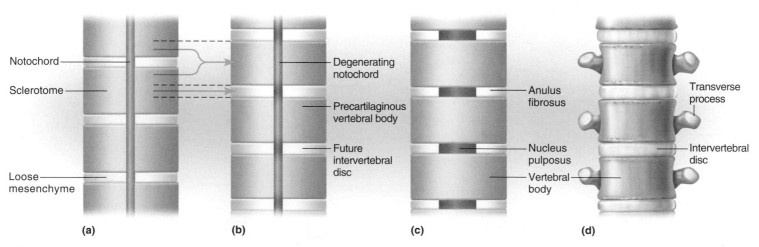

**Figure 7.32** **Development of the Vertebrae and Intervertebral Discs.** (a) The notochord is flanked by sclerotomes, which are separated by zones of loose mesenchyme. (b) Each vertebral body forms by the condensation of parts of two sclerotomes and the loose mesenchyme between them. The midregion of each sclerotome remains less condensed and forms the anulus fibrosus of the intervertebral disc. The notochord degenerates in the regions of condensing mesenchyme but persists between vertebral bodies as the nucleus pulposus. Dashed lines indicate which regions of the sclerotomes in part (a) give rise to the vertebral body and intervertebral disc in part (b). (c) Further condensation of the vertebral bodies. The notochord has now disappeared except at the nucleus pulposus of each disc. (d) Chondrification and ossification give rise to the fully developed vertebral bodies.

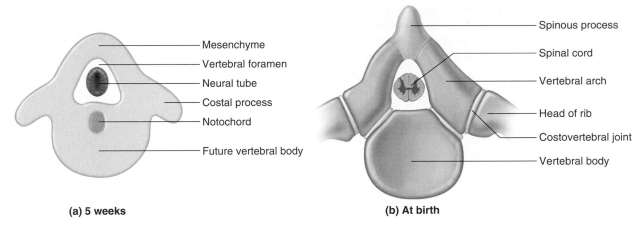

**(a) 5 weeks**

Mesenchyme
Vertebral foramen
Neural tube
Costal process
Notochord
Future vertebral body

**(b) At birth**

Spinous process
Spinal cord
Vertebral arch
Head of rib
Costovertebral joint
Vertebral body

**Figure 7.33** **Development of a Thoracic Vertebra.** (a) At 5 weeks. (b) At birth. In part (a), the vertebra is composed of mesenchyme surrounding the neural tube. The notochord is still present. The costal process is the forerunner of the rib. In part (b), the vertebra shows three centers of ossification at birth—the body and the two vertebral arches. Hyaline cartilage (blue) still composes the spinous process, the joints between the vertebral arches and the body, and the joints between the ribs and the vertebra.

allow for growth of the spinal cord. These attachments ossify at an age of 3 to 6 years. Secondary ossification centers form in puberty at the tips of the spinous and transverse processes and in a ring encircling the body. They unite with the rest of the vertebra by age 25.

At birth, the vertebral column exhibits one continuous C-shaped curve (fig. 7.34), as it does in monkeys, apes, and most other four-legged animals. As an infant begins to crawl and lift its head, the cervical curvature forms, enabling an infant on its belly to look forward. The lumbar curvature begins to develop as a toddler begins walking.

### The Ribs and Sternum

At 5 weeks, a developing thoracic vertebra consists of a body of mesenchyme with a vertebral body, vertebral foramen, and a pair of winglike lateral extensions called the **costal processes** (see fig. 7.33a), which soon give rise to the ribs. At 6 weeks, a chondrification center develops at the base of each process. At 7 weeks, these centers begin to undergo endochondral ossification. A *costovertebral joint* now appears at the base of the process, separating it from the vertebral body (see fig. 7.33b). By this time, the first seven ribs (true ribs) connect to the sternum by way of costal cartilages. An ossification center soon appears at the angle of the rib, and endochondral ossification proceeds from there to the distal end of the shaft. Secondary ossification centers appear in the tubercle and head of the rib during adolescence.

The sternum begins as a pair of longitudinal strips of condensed mesenchyme called the **sternal bars.** These form initially in the ventrolateral body wall and migrate medially during chondrification. The right and left sternal bars begin to fuse in week 7 as the most cranial pairs of ribs contact them. Fusion of the sternal bars progresses caudally, ending with the formation of the xiphoid process in week 9. The sternal bones form by endochondral ossification beginning rostrally and progressing caudally. Ossification begins in month 5 and is completed shortly after birth. In some cases, the sternal bars fail to fuse completely at the caudal end, so the infant xiphoid process is forked or perforated.

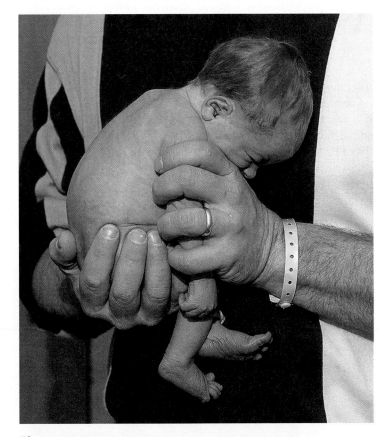

**Figure 7.34** **Spinal Curvature of the Newborn Infant.** At this age, the spine forms a single C-shaped curve.

## Pathology of the Axial Skeleton

Disorders that affect all parts of the skeleton are discussed in chapter 6, especially fractures and osteoporosis. Table 7.7 lists some disorders that affect especially the axial skeleton. We will consider in slightly more depth skull fractures, vertebral fractures and dislocations, and herniated intervertebral discs.

| **TABLE 7.7** | **Disorders of the Axial Skeleton** |
|---|---|
| **Cleft palate** | Failure of the palatine processes of the maxilla to fuse during fetal development, resulting in a fissure connecting the oral and nasal cavities; often accompanied by cleft lip. Causes difficulty for an infant in nursing. Can be surgically corrected with good cosmetic results. |
| **Craniosynostosis** | Premature closure of the cranial sutures within the first two years after birth, resulting in skull asymmetry, deformity, and sometimes mental retardation. Cause is unknown. Surgery can limit brain damage and improve appearance. |
| **Spinal stenosis** | Abnormal narrowing of the vertebral canal or intervertebral foramina caused by hypertrophy of the vertebral bone. Most common in middle-aged and older people. May compress spinal nerves and cause low back pain or muscle weakness. |
| **Spondylosis** | A defect of the laminae of the lumbar vertebrae. Defective vertebrae may shift anteriorly, especially at the L5 to S1 level. Stress on the bone may cause microfractures in the laminae and eventual dissolution of the laminae. May be treated by nonsurgical manipulation or by surgery, depending on severity. |

**Disorders Described Elsewhere**

## Skull Fractures

The domed shape of the skull distributes the force of most blows and tends to minimize their effects. Hard blows can nevertheless fracture the calvaria (fig. 7.35a). Most cranial fractures are *linear fractures* (elongated cracks), which can radiate away from the point of impact. In a *depressed fracture,* the cranium caves inward and may compress and damage underlying brain tissue. If a blow occurs in an area where the calvaria is especially thick, as in the occipital region, the bone may bend inward at the point of impact without breaking, but as the force is distributed through the cranium it can fracture it some distance away, even on the opposite side of the skull (a *contrafissura fracture*). In addition to damaging brain tissue, skull fractures can damage cranial nerves and meningeal blood vessels. A break in a blood vessel may cause a hematoma (mass of clotted blood) that compresses the brain tissue, potentially leading to death within a few hours.

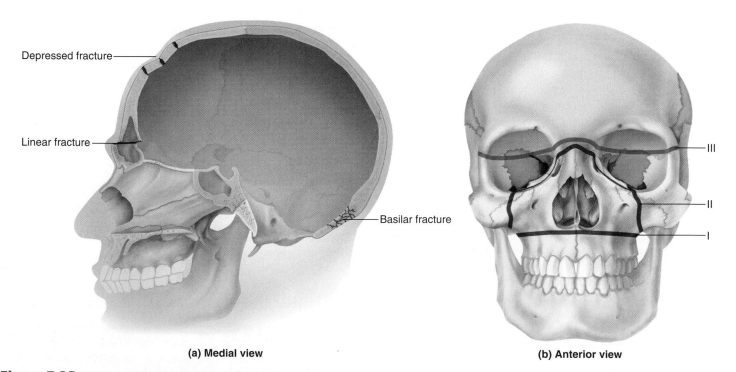

**(a) Medial view**  **(b) Anterior view**

**Figure 7.35 Skull Fractures.** (a) Medial view showing linear and depressed fractures of the frontal bone and a basilar fracture of the occipital bone. (b) The three types of Le Fort fractures of the facial bones.

Facial trauma can produce linear *Le Fort*[41] *fractures,* which predictably follow lines of weakness in the facial bones. The three typical Le Fort fractures are shown in figure 7.35b. The type II Le Fort fracture separates the entire central region of the face from the rest of the skull.

### THINK ABOUT IT

*Describe two accidents or other incidents in a person's life that could result in a depressed fracture of the calvaria, and two that could result in a Le Fort facial fracture.*

## Vertebral Fractures and Dislocations

Injury to the cervical vertebrae (a "broken neck") often results from violent blows to the head, as in diving, motorcycle, and equestrian accidents, and sudden flexion or extension of the neck, as in automobile accidents. Such injuries often crush the body or arches of a vertebra or cause one vertebra to slip forward relative to the one below it. The dislocation of one vertebra relative to the next can cause irreparable damage to the spinal cord. "Whiplash" often results from rear-end automobile collisions causing violent hyperextension of the neck (backward jerking of the head). This stretches or tears the *anterior longitudinal ligament* that courses anteriorly along the vertebral bodies, and it may fracture the vertebral body (fig. 7.36a). Dislocations are relatively rare in the thoracic and lumbar regions because of the way the vertebrae are tightly interlocked. When fractures occur in these regions ("broken back"), they most often involve vertebra T11 or T12, at the transition from the thoracic to lumbar spine.

## Herniated Discs

A **herniated** ("slipped" or "ruptured") **disc** is cracking of the anulus fibrosis of an intervertebral disc under strain, often caused by violent flexion of the vertebral column or by lifting heavy weights. Cracking of the anulus allows the gelatinous nucleus pulposus to ooze out, sometimes putting pressure on a spinal nerve root or the spinal cord (fig. 7.36b). Pressure on the spinal cord can be relieved by *laminectomy,* a surgery in which the vertebrae laminae are cut and sometimes the laminae and spinous process are removed. Back pain results from both pressure on the nervous tissue and inflammation stimulated by the nucleus pulposus. About 95% of disc herniations occur at levels L4/L5 and L5/S1. The nucleus pulposus usually escapes in a posterolateral direction, where the anulus is thinnest. Herniated discs rarely occur in young people because their discs are well hydrated and absorb pressure well. As people get older, the discs become dehydrated and they degenerate and grow thinner, becoming more susceptible to herniation. After middle age, however, the anulus fibrosus becomes thicker and tougher, and the nucleus pulposus is smaller, so disc herniations again become less common.

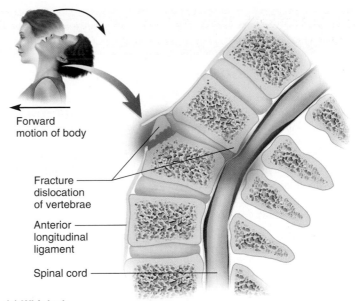

**Forward motion of body**

Fracture dislocation of vertebrae

Anterior longitudinal ligament

Spinal cord

**(a) Whiplash**

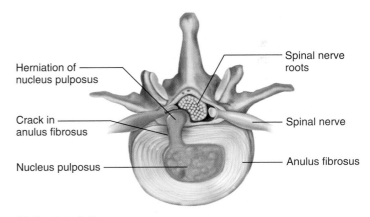

Herniation of nucleus pulposus

Crack in anulus fibrosus

Nucleus pulposus

Spinal nerve roots

Spinal nerve

Anulus fibrosus

**(b) Herniated disc**

**Figure 7.36  Injuries to the Vertebral Column.**  (a) Whiplash injury. Violent hyperextension of the neck has torn the anterior longitudinal ligament and fractured the vertebral body. (b) Herniated intervertebral disc. The nucleus pulposus is oozing into the vertebral canal and compressing a bundle of spinal nerve roots that passes through the lumbar vertebrae.
● *Herniated discs are more common in the lumbar region than in the cervical region. Explain.*

## *Before You Go On*

Answer the following questions to test your understanding of the preceding section:

14. Define *chondrocranium* and *viscerocranium,* and explain why each of them is named that.

15. What is the functional significance of fontanels? When does the last fontanel close?

16. What structure in the adult is a remnant of the embryonic notochord?

17. What is a Le Fort fracture? What is whiplash?

18. Explain why a herniated disc can cause nerve pain (neuralgia).

---

[41]Léon C. Le Fort (1829–93), French surgeon and gynecologist

# CHAPTER REVIEW

## REVIEW OF KEY CONCEPTS

### Overview of the Skeleton (p. 176)

1. The skeleton is divided into the *axial skeleton* (skull, vertebral column, and thoracic cage) and *appendicular skeleton* (limbs, pectoral girdle, and pelvic girdle).

2. There are typically about 270 bones at birth. Additional bones form during childhood, but then certain bones begin to fuse and the number drops to an average of 206 by adulthood.

3. The number of adult bones varies, especially the number of *sesamoid* and *sutural bones.*

4. Bones have a variety of surface features that provide muscle attachments, articular surfaces, and passages for nerves and blood vessels. The terminology of these features (table 7.2) is important in skeletal anatomy.

### The Skull (p. 179)

1. The skull consists of 22 bones (and sometimes additional sutural bones), most of which are rigidly joined by *sutures.*

2. Cavities in the skull include the *cranial cavity, orbits, nasal cavity, oral cavity, middle-* and *inner-ear cavities,* and the *frontal, ethmoid, sphenoid,* and *maxillary sinuses.*

3. The skull has numerous *foramina* that provide passage for nerves and blood vessels (table 7.3).

4. Eight of the skull bones are called *cranial bones* because they form the cranial cavity: the *frontal, parietal, temporal, occipital, sphenoid,* and *ethmoid bones.* The parietal and temporal bones are paired and the others are single.

5. The brain is separated from these bones by membranes called meninges. One of these, the *dura mater,* is the periosteum of the cranial bones.

6. The roof of the cranial cavity is called the *calvaria* and its floor is the *base.* The base exhibits *anterior, middle,* and *posterior cranial fossae* that conform to the contours of the base of the brain.

7. Fourteen of the skull bones are called *facial bones;* they do not contribute to the cranial cavity but are located anteriorly on the skull and shape the face. These are the *maxillae, inferior nasal conchae, vomer, mandible,* and the *palatine, zygomatic, lacrimal,* and *nasal bones.* The vomer and mandible are single and the others are paired.

8. The anatomical features of the 22 skull bones are summarized in table 7.4.

9. Seven other bones are closely associated with the skull: three *auditory ossicles (malleus,*

*incus,* and *stapes)* in each ear and a single *hyoid bone* just below the chin. The auditory ossicles transfer sound to the inner ear, and the hyoid bone provides attachment for muscles of the mandible, tongue, and larynx.

10. The inferior location of the foramen magnum, relative flatness of the face, and lack of prominent supraorbital ridges reflect adaptations of the human skull for bipedal locomotion.

### The Vertebral Column and Thoracic Cage (p. 193)

1. The vertebral column normally consists of 33 *vertebrae* and 23 cartilaginous *intervertebral discs.* The vertebrae are divided into five groups: 7 *cervical vertebrae* in the neck; 12 *thoracic vertebrae* in the chest, with ribs attached to them; 5 *lumbar vertebrae* in the lower back; 5 *sacral vertebrae* fused in a single adult bone, the *sacrum;* and a "tailbone" *(coccyx)* of 4 fused coccygeal vertebrae. The numbers differ in about 5% of adults, especially in the lumbar to sacral area.

2. The vertebral column is C-shaped at birth. Beyond the age of 3 years, it has four bends called the *cervical, thoracic, lumbar,* and *pelvic curvatures.*

3. Some major features of a vertebra are the *body* or *centrum;* a *vertebral arch* composed of two *pedicles* and two *laminae;* a posterior *spinous process* arising where the two laminae meet; and a pair of lateral *transverse processes.*

4. The vertebral arch encloses a space called the *vertebral foramen;* collectively, the vertebral foramina form the *vertebral canal,* which houses the spinal cord.

5. Each vertebra joins the one above it through its *superior articular processes* and the one below it through its *inferior articular processes.*

6. Between two adjacent vertebrae, there is a gap called the *intervertebral foramen,* which allows for the passage of a spinal nerve.

7. An intervertebral disc consists of a fibrous ring, the *anulus fibrosus,* enclosing a gelatinous center, the *nucleus pulposus.* The discs bind adjacent vertebrae together, add flexibility to the vertebral column, support the body weight, and absorb shock.

8. Cervical vertebrae (C1–C7) are relatively small. All are characterized by a *transverse foramen* in each transverse process, through which the vertebral arteries and veins travel. C2 through C6 typically exhibit a forked spinous process. C1, the *atlas,* is a relatively

simple ring of bone with a pair of *lateral masses* joined by an *anterior* and *posterior arch,* but with no body. C2, the *axis,* has a unique superior process called the *dens.*

9. Thoracic vertebrae (T1–T12) are specialized for rib attachment. They all exhibit *costal facets* on the body, and T1 through T10 also have *transverse costal facets* at the ends of the transverse processes. Ribs 1 through 10 attach to their respective vertebrae at two points, the vertebral body and transverse process; ribs 11 and 12 attach to the body only.

10. The lumbar vertebrae (L1–L5) have no unique features, but have especially heavy bodies and stout, squarish spinous processes. Their articular facets meet each other in a lateral-to-medial direction (instead of dorsoventrally like those of other vertebrae), except at the T12-L1 joint and the L5-S1 joint.

11. The adult sacrum is a triangular plate of bone formed by the fusion of five sacral vertebrae (S1–S5). Fusion of their spinous processes forms a posterior *median sacral crest,* and fusion of their transverse processes produces a *lateral sacral crest* on each side. The intervertebral foramina are represented by the *anterior* and *posterior sacral foramina.* The sacrum and hip bone have complementary *auricular surfaces* where they meet at the *sacroiliac joint.*

12. The coccyx is a small pointed "tailbone" formed by the fusion of usually four *coccygeal vertebrae* (Co1–Co4).

13. The *thoracic cage* is a bony enclosure for the lungs and heart and is composed of the thoracic vertebrae, ribs, and sternum.

14. The sternum (breastbone) consists of a superior *manubrium,* a long middle *body,* and a small, pointed *xiphoid process* at the inferior end. Its margins are scalloped where they receive the *costal cartilages* of the ribs, and the superolateral corners of the manubrium exhibit *clavicular notches* for articulation with the clavicles.

15. There are 12 pairs of ribs. Most of them exhibit a *head* where they articulate with the body of a vertebra; a narrow *neck;* a rough *tubercle* where they articulate with the transverse process of a vertebra; and a flat blade-like *shaft.* In most, the shaft has a squared end where it meets a *costal cartilage,* which connects the rib to the sternum.

16. Ribs 1 through 7 are called *true ribs* because they each connect to the sternum by their own costal cartilage. Ribs 8 through 12 are called *false ribs* because they do not have in-

dependent attachments to the sternum. The costal cartilages of ribs 8 through 10 connect to the cartilage of rib 7. Ribs 11 and 12 have no costal cartilages and do not attach to the sternum at all; thus, they are also called *floating ribs*. They attach only to the bodies of vertebrae T11 and T12 and have no tubercles.

### Developmental and Clinical Perspectives (p. 202)

1. Parts of the skull develop by intramembranous ossification. The rest of the skull and most of the rest of the skeleton develop by endochondral ossification. In the latter case, bone development begins when mesenchyme condenses and differentiates into hyaline cartilage, a process called *chondrification*. The cartilage is then replaced by bone in the process of endochondral ossification.

2. The base of the skull develops primarily by the endochondral ossification of several cartilaginous plates inferior to the brain. The calvaria develops mainly by intramembranous ossification. The base and calvaria are collectively called the *neurocranium* because they enclose the cranial cavity and surround the brain. The portion arising by endochondral ossification is also called the *chondrocranium*.

3. The facial skeleton is called the *viscerocranium* because it develops from the pharyngeal (visceral) arches. The facial bones form primarily by intramembranous ossification.

4. The infant skull exhibits gaps (*fontanels*) between the cranial bones where the bones have not yet fused; the *anterior* and *posterior fontanels* are located at the anterior and posterior ends of the sagittal suture. The *sphenoid* and *mastoid fontanels* are paired and laterally situated anterior and posterior to the temporal bone on each side.

5. The frontal bone and mandible are each represented by separate right and left bones in the newborn infant. The halves fuse in early childhood. The skull reaches nearly adult size by 8 or 9 years of age.

6. The vertebral column is preceded by a dorsal rod, the *notochord,* formed around day 22 to 24. Most of the notochord later degenerates as the *sclerotomes* of mesoderm produce the vertebral bodies and intervertebral discs, but notochordal tissue persists as the nucleus pulposus of the intervertebral discs.

7. The vertebral column develops at first by chondrification of the mesenchyme of the sclerotomes, creating a cartilaginous fetal vertebral column. Vertebral ossification begins during the embryonic period but is not completed until 25 years after birth. The vertebral column acquires its cervical and lumbar curvatures in infancy and early childhood, in association with lifting of the head and walking.

8. The ribs develop as lateral extensions of the vertebrae called *costal processes.* The processes chondrify and then ossify and separate from the vertebral body. Secondary ossification centers do not appear in the ribs until adolescence.

9. The sternum begins as a pair of longitudinal *sternal bars* of mesenchyme. These migrate medially and fuse as the ribs attach to them. Ossification is by the endochondral method, beginning in month 5 and concluding soon after birth.

10. Skull fractures may be *linear* (elongated cracks) or *depressed* (indentations of the bone). They can damage cranial nerves, meningeal blood vessels, and brain tissue, and may result in hematomas (blood clots) that fatally compress the brain. Blows to the face may produce Le Fort fractures along lines of weakness that separate regions of the face from the rest of the skull.

11. The cervical vertebrae are often fractured, displaced, or both by violent blows to the head or extreme flexion or extension of the neck. Such injuries can cause irreparable damage to the spinal cord. Fractures lower in the vertebral column are most often at vertebra T11 or T12.

12. A herniated disc is the cracking of the anulus fibrosus and oozing of the nucleus pulposus through the crack. This triggers inflammation and puts pressure on the spinal cord and spinal nerves, causing back pain. Some cases require a *laminectomy* to relieve pressure on the spinal cord.

## TESTING YOUR RECALL

1. Which of these is *not* a paranasal sinus?
   a. frontal
   b. temporal
   c. sphenoid
   d. ethmoid
   e. maxillary

2. Which of these is a facial bone?
   a. frontal
   b. ethmoid
   c. occipital
   d. temporal
   e. lacrimal

3. What occupies the transverse foramina seen in certain vertebrae?
   a. vertebral arteries
   b. nucleus pulposus
   c. spinal nerves
   d. the spinal cord
   e. internal jugular veins

4. All of the following are groups of vertebrae *except* for _____, which is a spinal curvature.
   a. thoracic
   b. cervical
   c. lumbar
   d. pelvic
   e. sacral

5. Thoracic vertebrae do *not* have
   a. transverse foramina.
   b. costal facets.
   c. transverse costal facets.
   d. transverse processes.
   e. pedicles.

6. Which of these bones forms by intramembranous ossification?
   a. a vertebra
   b. a parietal bone
   c. the occipital bone
   d. the sternum
   e. a rib

7. The viscerocranium includes
   a. the maxilla.
   b. the parietal bones.
   c. the occipital bone.
   d. the temporal bone.
   e. the atlas.

8. Which of these is *not* a suture?
   a. parietal
   b. coronal
   c. lambdoid
   d. sagittal
   e. squamous

9. The sella turcica contains
   a. the pituitary gland.
   b. the auditory ossicles.
   c. air cells.
   d. the foramen lacerum.
   e. the lacrimal sac.

10. The nasal septum is composed partly of the same bone as
    a. the zygomatic arch.
    b. the hard palate.
    c. the cribriform plate.
    d. the nasal concha.
    e. the centrum.

11. Gaps between the cranial bones of an infant are called _____.

12. The external acoustic meatus is an opening in the _____ bone.

13. Bones of the skull are joined along lines called _____.

14. The _____ bone has greater and lesser wings and protects the pituitary gland.

15. A herniated disc occurs when a ring called the _____ cracks.

16. The transverse ligament of the atlas holds the _____ of the axis in place.

17. The sacroiliac joint is formed where the _____ surface of the sacrum articulates with that of the ilium.

18. We have five pairs of _____ ribs and two pairs of _____ ribs.

19. Ribs 1 to 10 are joined to the sternum by way of strips of connective tissue called _____.

20. The point at the inferior end of the sternum is the _____.

*Answers in the Appendix*

## TRUE OR FALSE

*Determine which five of the following statements are false, and briefly explain why.*

1. The bodies of the vertebrae are derived from the notochord of the embryo.

2. Adults have more bones than children do.

3. A smooth round knob on a bone is called a condyle.

4. The zygomatic arch consists entirely of the zygomatic bone.

5. The dura mater adheres tightly to the entire inner surface of the cranial cavity.

6. The sphenoid bone forms part of the orbit.

7. The nasal septum is not entirely bony.

8. Not everyone has a frontal sinus.

9. The anterior surface of the sacrum is smoother than the posterior surface.

10. The lumbar vertebrae do not articulate with any ribs and therefore do not have transverse processes.

*Answers in the Appendix*

## TESTING YOUR COMPREHENSION

1. A child was involved in an automobile collision. She was not wearing a safety restraint, and her chin struck the dashboard hard. When the physician looked into her auditory canal, he could see into her throat. What do you infer from this about the nature of her injury?

2. Chapter 1 noted that there are significant variations in the internal anatomy of different people (p. 5). Give some examples from this chapter other than pathological cases (such as cleft palate) and normal age-related differences.

3. Vertebrae T12 and L1 look superficially similar and are easily confused. Explain how to tell the two apart.

4. What effect would you predict if an ossification disorder completely closed off the superior and inferior orbital fissures?

5. For each of the following bones, name all the other bones with which it articulates: parietal, zygomatic, temporal, and ethmoid bones.

*Answers at aris.mhhe.com*

## ONLINE RESOURCES

Visit aprevealed.com to explore melt-away cadaver dissections, watch animations that clarify difficult concepts, review histological and radiological images, or take a quiz to assess your understanding of the material.

The Saladin *Human Anatomy,* 2e website at aris.mhhe.com features chapter-specific quizzes, labeling exercises, and other interactive tools to complement your study of human anatomy. If your instructor has provided an ARIS course code, you can also access assignments and information specific to your course.

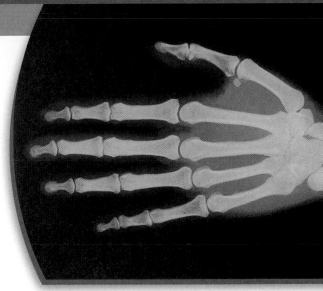

## CHAPTER EIGHT

# The Appendicular Skeleton

X-ray of an adult hand

## CHAPTER OUTLINE

## INSIGHTS

## BRUSHING UP

To understand this chapter, you may find it helpful to review the following concepts:
- Evolution of bipedal locomotion in humans (p. 15)
- Terminology of the appendicular region (p. 25)
- General features of bones (p. 155)
- Intramembranous and endochondral ossification (pp. 161–163)

**Skeletal System**

In this chapter, we turn our attention to the *appendicular skeleton*—the bones of the upper and lower limbs and the pectoral and pelvic girdles that attach them to the axial skeleton. We depend so heavily on the limbs for mobility and the ability to manipulate objects that deformities and injuries to the appendicular skeleton are more disabling than most disorders of the axial skeleton. Hand injuries, especially, can disable a person far more than a comparable amount of tissue injury elsewhere on the body. Injuries to the appendicular skeleton are especially common in athletics, recreation, and the workplace. A knowledge of the anatomy of the appendicular skeleton is therefore especially important to such professionals as athletic trainers, physical therapists, and other health-care providers.

# The Pectoral Girdle and Upper Limb

## Objectives
When you have completed this section, you should be able to
- identify and describe the features of the clavicle, scapula, humerus, radius, ulna, and bones of the wrist and hand; and
- describe the evolutionary innovations of the human forelimb.

## Pectoral Girdle

The **pectoral**[1] **girdle** (shoulder girdle) supports the arm. It consists of two bones on each side of the body: the *clavicle* (collarbone) and the *scapula* (shoulder blade). The medial end of the clavicle articulates with the sternum at the **sternoclavicular joint,** and its lateral end articulates with the scapula at the **acromioclavicular**[2] **joint** (see fig. 7.27, p. 199). The scapula also articulates with the humerus at the **glenohumeral**[3] **(shoulder) joint.** These are loose attachments that result in a shoulder far more flexible than that of most other mammals, but they also make the shoulder joint easy to dislocate.

### THINK ABOUT IT
*How is the unusual flexibility of the human shoulder joint related to the habitat of our primate ancestors?*

## Clavicle

The **clavicle**[4] (fig. 8.1) is a slightly S-shaped bone, somewhat flattened dorsoventrally and easily seen and palpated on the upper thorax (see fig. B.1b, p. 362). The superior surface is relatively smooth,

[1] *pect* = chest + *oral* = pertaining to
[2] *acr* = extremity, peak + *omo* = shoulder
[3] *gleno* = socket
[4] *clav* = hammer, club + *icle* = little

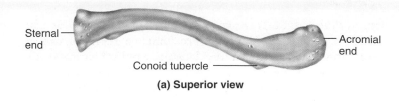

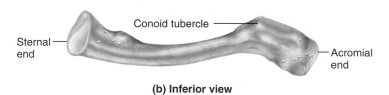

**Figure 8.1**  The Right Clavicle (Collarbone).
● *The clavicle is broken more often than any other bone in the body. State some reasons why.*

whereas the inferior surface is marked by grooves and ridges for muscle attachment. The medial **sternal end** has a rounded, hammerlike head, and the lateral **acromial end** is markedly flattened. Near the acromial end is a rough tuberosity called the **conoid**[5] **tubercle**—a ligament attachment that faces posteriorly and slightly downward.

The clavicle braces the shoulder, keeping the upper limb away from the midline of the body. It is thickened in people who do heavy manual labor, and because most people are right-handed, the right clavicle is usually stronger and shorter than the left. Without the clavicles, the pectoralis major muscles would pull the shoulders forward and medially—which indeed happens when a clavicle is fractured (see Insight 8.1).

# INSIGHT 8.1
## Clinical Application

### Fractured Clavicle

The clavicle is the most frequently broken bone of the body. It can break when one falls directly on the shoulder or thrusts out an arm to break a fall and the force of the fall is transmitted through the limb to the pectoral girdle. Fractures most often occur at a weak point about one-third of the way from the lateral end. When the clavicle is broken, the shoulder tends to drop, the sternocleidomastoid muscle of the neck elevates the medial fragment, and the pectoralis major muscle of the chest may pull the lateral fragment toward the sternum. The clavicle sometimes fractures during birth in wide-shouldered infants, but these neonatal fractures heal quickly. In children, clavicular fractures are often of the greenstick type (see fig. 6.14, p. 169).

[5] *con* = cone + *oid* = shaped

## Scapula

The **scapula**[6] (fig. 8.2) is a triangular plate that overlies ribs 2 to 7. The three sides of the triangle are called the **superior, medial (vertebral),** and **lateral (axillary) borders,** and its three angles are the **superior, inferior,** and **lateral angles.** A conspicuous **suprascapular notch** in the superior border provides passage for a nerve. The broad anterior surface of the scapula, called the **subscapular fossa,** is slightly concave and relatively featureless. The posterior surface has a transverse shelflike ridge called the **spine,** a deep indentation superior to the spine called the **supraspinous fossa,** and a broad surface inferior to it called the **infraspinous fossa.**[7]

The most complex region of the scapula is the lateral angle, which has three main features:

1. The **acromion** (ah-CRO-me-on) is a platelike extension of the scapular spine that forms the apex of the shoulder. It articulates with the clavicle—the sole point of attachment of the scapula and upper limb to the axial skeleton.

2. The **coracoid**[8] (COR-uh-coyd) **process** is shaped like a bent finger but named for a vague resemblance to a crow's beak; it provides attachment for tendons of the biceps brachii and other muscles of the arm.

3. The **glenoid** (GLEN-oyd) **cavity** is a shallow socket that articulates with the head of the humerus, forming the glenohumeral joint.

---

[6]*scap* = spade, shovel + *ula* = little
[7]*supra* = above; *infra* = below
[8]*corac* = crow + *oid* = shaped, resembling

**THINK ABOUT IT**

*What part of the scapula do you think is most commonly fractured? Why?*

## Upper Limb

The upper limb is divided into 4 regions containing a total of 30 bones per limb:

1. The **brachium**[9] (BRAY-kee-um), or arm proper, extends from shoulder to elbow. It contains only one bone, the *humerus.*

2. The **antebrachium,**[10] or forearm, extends from elbow to wrist and contains two bones—the *radius* and *ulna.* In anatomical position, these bones are parallel, and the radius is lateral to the ulna.

3. The **carpus,**[11] or wrist, contains eight small bones arranged in two rows.

4. The **manus,**[12] or hand, contains 19 bones in two groups—5 *metacarpals* in the palm and 14 *phalanges* in the digits.

### Humerus

The **humerus** has a hemispherical **head** that articulates with the glenoid cavity of the scapula (fig. 8.3). The smooth surface of

---

[9]*brachi* = arm
[10]*ante* = before
[11]*carp* = wrist
[12]*man* = hand

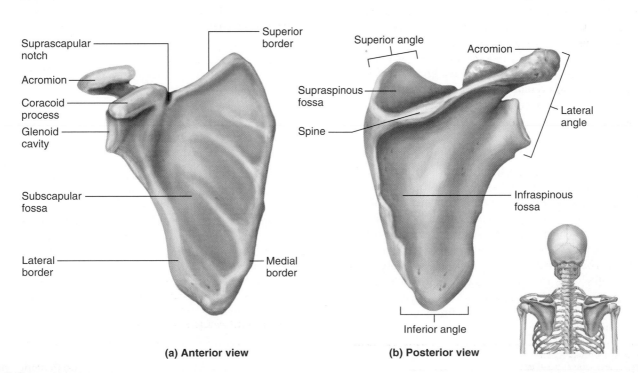

**(a) Anterior view**                    **(b) Posterior view**

**Figure 8.2** The Right Scapula.
● *Identify the two points where this bone is attached to the rest of the skeleton.*

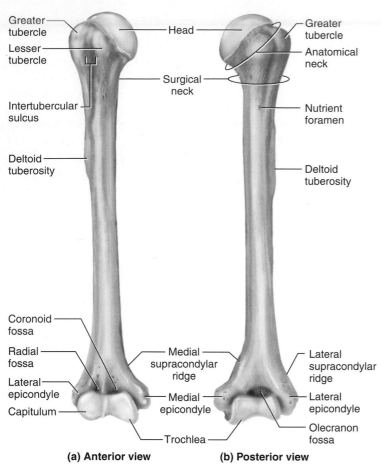

**(a) Anterior view**     **(b) Posterior view**

**Figure 8.3** The Right Humerus.

the head (covered with articular cartilage in life) is bordered by a groove called the **anatomical neck.** Other prominent features of the proximal end are muscle attachments called the **greater** and **lesser tubercles** and an **intertubercular sulcus (groove)** between them that accommodates a tendon of the biceps muscle. The **surgical neck,** a common fracture site, is a narrowing of the bone just distal to the tubercles, at the transition from the head to the shaft. The shaft has a rough area called the **deltoid tuberosity** on its lateral surface. This is an insertion for the deltoid muscle of the shoulder.

The distal end of the humerus has two smooth condyles. The lateral one, called the **capitulum**[13] (ca-PIT-you-lum), is shaped somewhat like a fat wheel and articulates with the radius. The medial one, called the **trochlea**[14] (TROCK-lee-uh), is pulleylike and articulates with the ulna. Immediately proximal to these condyles, the humerus flares out to form two bony processes, the **lateral** and **medial epicondyles.** The medial epicondyle protects the ulnar nerve, which passes close to the surface across the back of the elbow. This epicondyle is popularly known as the "funny bone" because a sharp blow to the elbow at this point stimulates the ulnar nerve

---

[13]*capit* = head + *ulum* = little
[14]*troch* = wheel, pulley

and produces an intense tingling sensation. Proximal to the epicondyles, the margins of the humerus are sharply angular and form the **lateral** and **medial supracondylar ridges.** These are attachments for certain forearm muscles.

The distal end of the humerus also shows three deep pits—two anterior and one posterior. The posterior pit, called the **olecranon**[15] (oh-LEC-ruh-non) **fossa,** accommodates the olecranon of the ulna when the elbow is extended. On the anterior surface, a medial pit called the **coronoid**[16] **fossa** accommodates the coronoid process of the ulna when the elbow is flexed. The lateral pit is the **radial fossa,** named for the nearby head of the radius.

## Radius

The **radius** has a distinctive disc-shaped **head** at its proximal end (fig. 8.4). When the forearm is rotated so the palm turns forward and back, the circular superior surface of this disc spins on the capitulum of the humerus, and the edge of the disc spins on the radial notch of the ulna. Immediately distal to the head, the radius has a narrower **neck** and then widens to a rough prominence, the **radial tuberosity,** on its medial surface. The tendon of the biceps muscle terminates on this tuberosity.

---

[15]*olecranon* = elbow
[16]*coron* = something curved + *oid* = shaped

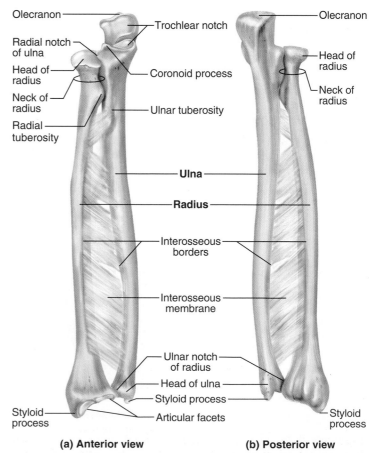

**(a) Anterior view**     **(b) Posterior view**

**Figure 8.4** The Right Radius and Ulna.

The distal end of the radius has the following features, from lateral to medial:

1. A bony point, the **styloid**[17] **process,** can be palpated proximal to the thumb.
2. Two shallow depressions (articular facets) articulate with the scaphoid and lunate bones of the wrist.
3. The **ulnar notch** articulates with the end of the ulna.

## Ulna

At the proximal end of the **ulna**[18] (fig. 8.4) is a deep, C-shaped **trochlear notch** that wraps around the trochlea of the humerus. The posterior side of this notch is formed by a prominent **olecranon**—the bony point where you rest your elbow on a table. The anterior side is formed by a less prominent **coronoid process.** Laterally, the head of the ulna has a less conspicuous **radial notch,** which accommodates the head of the radius. At the distal end of the ulna is a medial **styloid process.** The bony lumps you can palpate on each side of your wrist are the styloid processes of the radius and ulna.

The radius and ulna are attached along their shafts by a ligament called the **interosseous**[19] (IN-tur-OSS-ee-us) **membrane**

(IM), which is attached to an angular ridge called the **interosseous border** on the facing margins of each bone. Most fibers of the IM are oriented obliquely, slanting upward from the ulna to the radius. If you lean forward on a table supporting your weight on your hands, about 80% of the force is borne by the radius. This tenses the IM, which pulls the ulna upward and transfers some of this force through the ulna to the humerus. The IM therefore enables the two elbow joints (between humerus and radius, and humerus and ulna) to share the load and reduces the wear and tear that one joint would otherwise have to bear alone. The IM also serves as an attachment for several forearm muscles.

## Carpal Bones

The **carpal bones,** which form the wrist, are arranged in two rows of four bones each (fig. 8.5). These short bones allow movements of the wrist from side to side and forward and back (in anatomical position). The carpal bones of the proximal row, starting at the lateral (thumb) side, are the **scaphoid, lunate, triquetrum (tri-QUEE-trum),** and **pisiform** (PY-sih-form)—Latin for boat-, moon-, triangle-, and pea-shaped, respectively. Unlike the other carpal bones, the pisiform is a sesamoid bone; it is not present at birth but develops around the age of 9 to 12 years within the tendon of the *flexor carpi ulnaris muscle.*

---

[17]*styl* = pillar + *oid* = shaped
[18]*ulna* = elbow
[19]*inter* = between + *osse* = bones

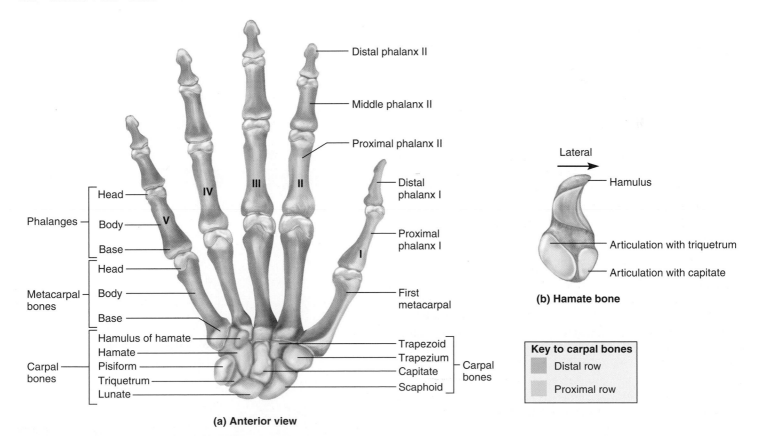

**(a) Anterior view**

**Lateral**

**(b) Hamate bone**

**Key to carpal bones**
Distal row
Proximal row

**Figure 8.5   The Right Wrist and Hand, Anterior (Palmar) View.**   (a) Some people remember the names of the carpal bones with the mnemonic, "Sally left the party to take Charlie home." The first letters of these words correspond to the first letters of the carpal bones, from lateral to medial, proximal row first. (b) The right hamate bone, viewed from the proximal side of the wrist to show its distinctive hook. This unique bone is a useful landmark for locating the others when studying the skeleton.

The bones of the distal row, again starting on the lateral side, are the **trapezium,**[20] **trapezoid, capitate,**[21] and **hamate.**[22] The hamate can be recognized by a prominent hook, or **hamulus,** on the palmar side.

## Metacarpal Bones

Bones of the palm are called **metacarpals.**[23] Metacarpal I is located proximal to the thumb and metacarpal V is proximal to the little finger (fig. 8.5). On a skeleton, the metacarpals look like extensions of the fingers, so the fingers seem much longer than they really are. The proximal end of a metacarpal bone is called the **base,** the shaft is called the **body,** and the distal end is called the **head.** The heads of the metacarpals form the knuckles when you clench your fist.

## Phalanges

The bones of the fingers are called **phalanges** (fah-LAN-jeez); in the singular, *phalanx*[24] (FAY-lanks). There are two phalanges in the **pollex** (thumb) and three in each of the other digits (fig. 8.5). Phalanges are identified by Roman numerals preceded by *proximal, middle,* and *distal.* For example, proximal phalanx I is in the basal segment of the thumb (the first segment beyond the web between the thumb and palm); the left proximal phalanx IV is where people usually wear wedding rings; and distal phalanx V forms the tip of the little finger. The three parts of a phalanx are the same as in a metacarpal: *base, body,* and *head.* The ventral surface of a phalanx is slightly concave from end to end and flattened from side to side; the dorsal surface is rounder and slightly convex from end to end.

Table 8.1 summarizes the bones of the pectoral girdle and upper limb.

## Evolution of the Forelimb

Elsewhere in chapters 7 and 8, we examine how the evolution of bipedal locomotion in humans has affected the skull, vertebral column, and lower limb. The effects of bipedalism on the upper limb are less immediately obvious, but nevertheless substantial. In apes, all four limbs are adapted primarily for walking and climbing, and the forelimbs are longer than the hindlimbs. Thus, the shoulders are higher than the hips when the animal walks. When some apes such as orangutans and gibbons walk bipedally, they typically hold

---

[20]*trapez* = table, grinding surface
[21]*capit* = head + *ate* = possessing
[22]*ham* = hook + *ate* = possessing
[23]*meta* = beyond + *carp* = wrist
[24]*phalanx* = line of soldiers, closely knit row

---

| TABLE 8.1 | Anatomical Checklist for the Pectoral Girdle and Upper Limb | | |
|---|---|---|---|
| **Pectoral Girdle** | | | |

| | | |
|---|---|---|
| **Clavicle (fig. 8.1)** | **Scapula (continued)** | **Scapula (continued)** |
| Sternal end | Lateral (axillary) border | Fossae |
| Acromial end | Angles | Subscapular fossa |
| Conoid tubercle | Superior angle | Supraspinous fossa |
| | Inferior angle | Infraspinous fossa |
| **Scapula (fig. 8.2)** | Lateral angle | Acromion |
| Borders | Suprascapular notch | Coracoid process |
| Superior border | Spine | Glenoid cavity |
| Medial (vertebral) border | | |

| **Upper Limb** | | |
|---|---|---|
| **Humerus (fig. 8.3)** | **Radius (fig. 8.4)** | **Carpal Bones (continued)** |
| Proximal end | Head | Triquetrum |
| Head | Neck | Pisiform |
| Anatomical neck | Radial tuberosity | Distal group |
| Surgical neck | Styloid process | Trapezium |
| Greater tubercle | Articular facets | Trapezoid |
| Lesser tubercle | Ulnar notch | Capitate |
| Intertubercular sulcus | | Hamate |
| Shaft | **Ulna (fig. 8.4)** | Hamulus |
| Deltoid tuberosity | Trochlear notch | |
| Distal end | Olecranon | **Bones of the Hand (fig. 8.5)** |
| Capitulum | Coronoid process | |
| Trochlea | Radial notch | Metacarpal bones I–V |
| Lateral epicondyle | Styloid process | Base |
| Medial epicondyle | Interosseous border | Body |
| Lateral supracondylar ridge | Interosseous membrane | Head |
| Medial supracondylar ridge | | Phalanges I–V |
| Olecranon fossa | **Carpal Bones (fig. 8.5)** | Proximal phalanx |
| Coronoid fossa | Proximal group | Middle phalanx |
| Radial fossa | Scaphoid | Distal phalanx |
| | Lunate | |

their long forelimbs over their heads to prevent them from dragging on the ground. By contrast, the human forelimbs are adapted primarily for reaching out, exploring the environment, and manipulating objects. They are shorter than the hindlimbs and far less muscular than the forelimbs of apes. No longer needed for locomotion, our forelimbs, especially the hands, have become better adapted for carrying objects, holding things closer to the eyes, and manipulating them more precisely. Although the forelimbs have the same basic bone and muscle pattern as the hindlimbs, the joints of the shoulder and hands, especially, give the forelimbs far greater mobility.

## *Before You Go On*

*Answer the following questions to test your understanding of the preceding section:*

1. Describe how to distinguish the medial and lateral ends of the clavicle from each other and how to distinguish its superior and inferior surfaces.

2. Name the three fossae of the scapula and describe the location of each.

3. What three bones meet at the elbow? Identify the fossae, articular surfaces, and processes of this joint and state to which bone each of these features belongs.

4. Name the four bones of the proximal row of the carpus from lateral to medial, and then the four bones of the distal row in the same order.

5. Name the four bones from the tip of the little finger to the base of the hand on that side.

6. Palpate as many of the following structures as possible, and identify which ones cannot normally be palpated on a living person: the inferior angle of the scapula, the subscapular fossa, the acromion, the epicondyles of the humerus, the olecranon, and the interosseous membrane of the forearm.

# The Pelvic Girdle and Lower Limb

## *Objectives*
When you have completed this section, you should be able to

• identify and describe the features of the pelvic girdle, femur, patella, tibia, fibula, and bones of the foot;

• compare the anatomy of the male and female pelvis and explain the functional significance of the differences; and

• describe the evolutionary adaptations of the pelvis and hindlimb for bipedal locomotion.

## Pelvic Girdle

The **pelvic girdle** is composed of two **hip bones,** formerly known as the *ossa coxae*[25] (OS-sa COC-see). They are still sometimes called the *innominate*[26] bones—arguably the most self-contradictory term in human anatomy ("the bones with no name"). The pelvic girdle and sacrum together constitute the **pelvis**[27] (fig. 8.6). The pelvis supports the trunk on the lower limbs and provides a protective enclosure for the viscera of the pelvic cavity—mainly the lower colon, urinary bladder, and internal reproductive organs.

Each hip bone is joined to the vertebral column at one point, the **sacroiliac (SI) joint,** where its **auricular**[28] **surface** matches the auricular surface of the sacrum. The two hip bones articulate with each other on the anterior side of the pelvis, where they are joined by a pad of fibrocartilage called the **interpubic disc.** The interpubic disc and the adjacent region of pubic bone on each side constitute the **pubic symphysis,**[29] which can be palpated as a hard prominence immediately above the genitalia.

The pelvis has a bowl-like shape with the broad **greater (false) pelvis** between the flare of the hips and the narrow **lesser (true) pelvis** below (fig. 8.6b). The two are separated by a somewhat round margin called the **pelvic brim.** The opening circumscribed by the brim is called the **pelvic inlet**—an entry into the lesser pelvis through which an infant's head passes during birth. The lower margin of the lesser pelvis is called the **pelvic outlet.**

The hip bones have three distinctive features that will serve as landmarks for further description. These are the **iliac**[30] **crest** (superior crest of the hip); **acetabulum**[31] (ASS-eh-TAB-you-lum) (the hip socket—named for its resemblance to vinegar cups used on ancient Roman dining tables); and **obturator**[32] **foramen** (a large round-to-triangular hole below the acetabulum, closed in life by a ligament called the *obturator membrane*).

The adult hip bone forms by the fusion of three childhood bones called the *ilium* (ILL-ee-um), *ischium* (ISS-kee-um), and *pubis* (PEW-biss), identified by color in figure 8.7. The largest of these is the **ilium,** which extends from the iliac crest to the center of the acetabulum. The iliac crest extends from an anterior point or angle called the **anterior superior iliac spine** to a sharp posterior angle called the **posterior superior iliac spine.** In a lean person, the anterior spines form visible anterior protrusions, and the posterior spines are sometimes marked by dimples above the buttocks where connective tissue attached to the spines pulls inward on the skin (see fig. B.4, p. 365).

Below the superior spines are the **anterior** and **posterior inferior iliac spines.** Below the latter is a deep **greater sciatic**[33] (sy-AT-ic) **notch,** named for the sciatic nerve that passes through it and continues down the posterior side of the thigh.

---

[25]*os, ossa* = bone, bones + *coxae* = of the hip(s)
[26]*in* = without + *nomin* = name + *ate* = possessing
[27]*pelvis* = basin, bowl
[28]*aur* = ear + *icul* = little + *ar* = like
[29]*sym* = together + *physis* = growth
[30]*ili* = flank, loin + *ac* = pertaining to
[31]*acetabulum* = vinegar cup
[32]*obtur* = to close, stop up + *ator* = that which
[33]*sciat* = hip or ischium + *ic* = pertaining to

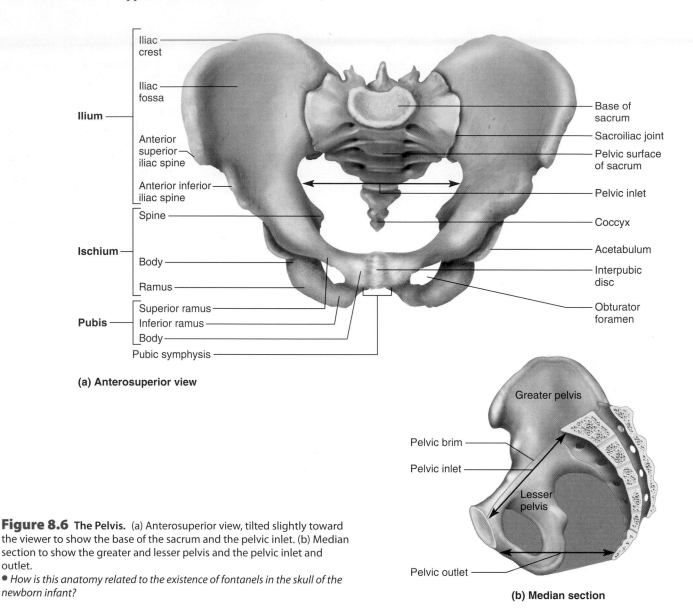

**(a) Anterosuperior view**

**Figure 8.6** **The Pelvis.** (a) Anterosuperior view, tilted slightly toward the viewer to show the base of the sacrum and the pelvic inlet. (b) Median section to show the greater and lesser pelvis and the pelvic inlet and outlet.

● *How is this anatomy related to the existence of fontanels in the skull of the newborn infant?*

**(b) Median section**

The posterolateral surface of the ilium is relatively rough-textured because it serves for attachment of several muscles of the buttocks and thighs. The anteromedial surface, by contrast, is the smooth, slightly concave **iliac fossa,** covered in life by the broad *iliacus* muscle. Medially, the ilium exhibits an auricular surface that matches the one on the sacrum, so the two bones form the sacroiliac joint.

The **ischium**[34] forms the inferoposterior portion of the hip bone. Its heavy **body** is marked with a prominent **spine.** Inferior to the spine is a slight indentation, the **lesser sciatic notch,** and then the thick, rough-surfaced **ischial tuberosity,** which supports your body when you are sitting. The tuberosity can be palpated by sitting on your fingers. The **ramus** of the ischium joins the inferior ramus of the pubis anteriorly.

The **pubis (pubic bone)** is the most anterior portion of the hip bone. It has a **superior** and **inferior ramus** and a triangular **body.** The body of one pubis meets the body of the other at the pubic symphysis. The pubis and ischium encircle the obturator foramen. The pubis is often fractured when the pelvis is subjected to violent anteroposterior compression, as in seat-belt injuries.

Human pelvic anatomy is a compromise between two requirements—bipedalism and childbirth. In apes and other qua-drupedal (four-legged) mammals, the abdominal viscera are supported by the muscular wall of the abdomen. In humans, however, the viscera bear down on the floor of the pelvic cavity, and a bowl-shaped pelvis helps to support their weight. This has resulted in a narrower pelvic outlet—a condition that creates pain and difficulty in giving birth to such large-brained infants. Humans must be born before the cranial bones fuse so that the head can squeeze through the outlet. This is thought to be the reason why our infants are born in such an immature state compared to those of other primates.

[34]*ischium* = hip

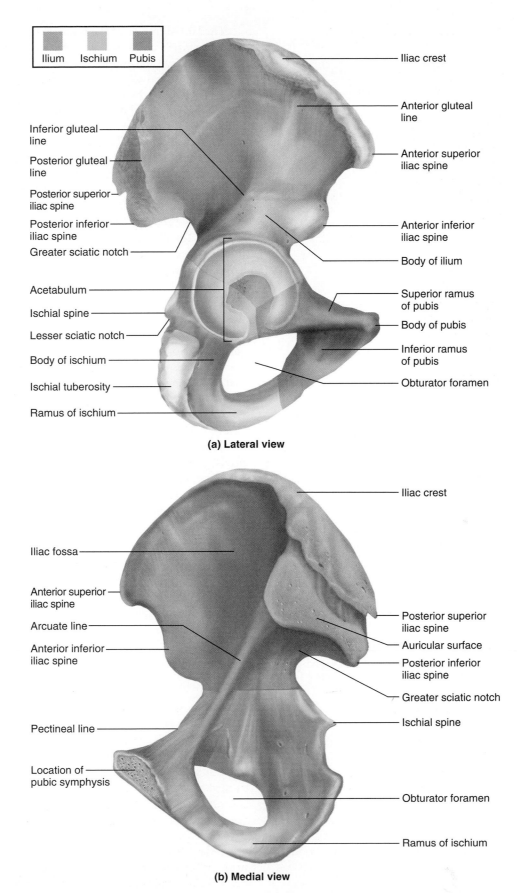

Ilium   Ischium   Pubis

Iliac crest

Anterior gluteal line

Anterior superior iliac spine

Inferior gluteal line

Posterior gluteal line

Posterior superior iliac spine

Posterior inferior iliac spine

Greater sciatic notch

Anterior inferior iliac spine

Body of ilium

Acetabulum

Ischial spine

Lesser sciatic notch

Body of ischium

Ischial tuberosity

Ramus of ischium

Superior ramus of pubis

Body of pubis

Inferior ramus of pubis

Obturator foramen

**(a) Lateral view**

Iliac crest

Iliac fossa

Anterior superior iliac spine

Arcuate line

Anterior inferior iliac spine

Posterior superior iliac spine

Auricular surface

Posterior inferior iliac spine

Greater sciatic notch

Ischial spine

Pectineal line

Location of pubic symphysis

Obturator foramen

Ramus of ischium

**(b) Medial view**

**Figure 8.7**  **The Right Hip Bone.**  The three childhood bones that fuse to form the adult hip bone are identified by color.

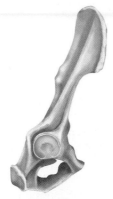

**Chimpanzee**

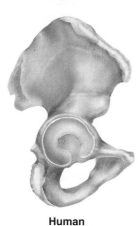

**Human**

**Figure 8.8  Chimpanzee and Human Hip Bones.**  The human ilium forms a more bowl-like greater pelvis and is expanded posteriorly (page left) so that the gluteus maximus muscle produces an effective backswing of the thigh during the stride.

The largest muscle of the buttock, the *gluteus maximus,* serves in chimpanzees and other apes primarily as an abductor of the thigh—that is, it moves the lower limb laterally. In humans, however, the ilium has expanded posteriorly, so the gluteus maximus originates behind the hip joint. This changes the function of the muscle—instead of abducting the thigh, it pulls it back in the second half of a stride (pulling back on your right thigh, for example, when your left foot is off the ground and swinging forward). When one is standing, the gluteus maximus also pulls the pelvis posteriorly so that the body's weight is better balanced on the lower limbs. This helps us to stand upright without expending a great deal of energy to keep from falling forward. The posterior growth of the ilium is the reason the greater sciatic notch is so deeply concave (fig. 8.8). The ilium also curves farther anteriorly in humans than in apes. This positions other gluteal muscles (the *gluteus medius* and *minimus*) in front of the hip joint, where they rotate and balance the trunk so we do not sway from side to side like chimpanzees do when they walk bipedally. These evolutionary changes in the pelvis and associated muscles account for the smooth, efficient stride of a human as compared to the awkward, shuffling gait of a chimpanzee or gorilla when it walks upright.

The pelvis is the most *sexually dimorphic* part of the skeleton—that is, the one whose anatomy most differs between the sexes. In identifying the sex of skeletal remains, forensic scientists focus especially on the pelvis. The average male pelvis is more robust (heavier and thicker) than the female's owing to the forces exerted on the bone by stronger muscles. The female pelvis is adapted to the needs of pregnancy and childbirth. It is wider and shallower and has a larger pelvic inlet and outlet for passage of the infant's head. Table 8.2 and figure 8.9 summarize the most useful features of the pelvis in sex identification.

| TABLE 8.2 | Comparison of the Male and Female Pelvis | |
|---|---|---|
| **Feature** | **Male** | **Female** |
| General appearance | More massive; rougher; heavier processes | Less massive; smoother; more delicate processes |
| Tilt | Upper end of pelvis relatively vertical | Upper end of pelvis tilted forward |
| Ilium | Deeper; projects farther above sacroiliac joint | Shallower; does not project as far above sacroiliac joint |
| Sacrum | Narrower and deeper | Wider and shallower |
| Coccyx | Less movable; more vertical | More movable; tilted posteriorly |
| Width of greater pelvis | Anterior superior spines closer together; hips less flared | Anterior superior spines farther apart; hips more flared |
| Pelvic inlet | Heart-shaped | Round or oval |
| Pelvic outlet | Smaller | Larger |
| Pubic symphysis | Taller | Shorter |
| Greater sciatic notch | Narrower | Wider |
| Obturator foramen | Round | Triangular to oval |
| Acetabulum | Larger, faces more laterally | Smaller, faces slightly ventrally |
| Pubic arch | Usually 90° or less | Usually greater than 100° |

## Lower Limb

The number and arrangement of bones in the lower limb are similar to those of the upper limb. In the lower limb, however, they are adapted for weight-bearing and locomotion and are therefore shaped and articulated differently. The lower limb is divided into four regions containing a total of 30 bones per limb:

1. The **femoral region,** or thigh, extends from hip to knee and contains the *femur* (the longest bone in the body). The *patella* (kneecap) is a sesamoid bone at the junction of the femoral and crural regions.

2. The **crural** (CROO-rul) **region,** or leg proper, extends from knee to ankle and contains two bones, the medial *tibia* and lateral *fibula.*

3. The **tarsal region (tarsus),** or ankle, is the union of the crural region with the foot. The tarsal bones are treated as part of the foot.

4. The **pedal region (pes),** or foot, is composed of 7 *tarsal bones,* 5 *metatarsals,* and 14 *phalanges* in the toes.

### Femur

The **femur** (FEE-mur) is the longest and strongest bone of the body (fig. 8.10). It has a nearly spherical head that articulates with the acetabulum of the pelvis, forming a quintessential *ball-and-socket joint.* A ligament extends from the acetabulum to a pit, the **fovea capitis**[35] (FOE-vee-uh CAP-ih-tiss), in the head of the femur. Distal to the head is a constricted **neck,** a common site of femoral fractures (see Insight 8.2 and fig. 8.11). Just beyond the

neck are two massive, rough processes called the **greater** and **lesser trochanters**[36] (tro-CAN-turs), which are insertions for the powerful muscles of the hip. The trochanters are connected on the posterior side by a thick oblique ridge of bone, the **intertrochanteric crest,** and on the anterior side by a more delicate **intertrochanteric line.**

The primary feature of the shaft is a posterior ridge called the **linea aspera**[37] (LIN-ee-uh ASS-peh-ruh). At its upper end, the linea aspera forks into a medial **spiral line** and a lateral **gluteal tuberosity.** The gluteal tuberosity is a rough ridge (sometimes a depression) that serves for attachment of the gluteus maximus muscle. At its lower end, the linea aspera forks into **medial** and **lateral supracondylar lines,** which continue down to the respective epicondyles.

The distal end of the femur flares into **medial** and **lateral epicondyles,** the widest points of the femur at the knee. These and the supracondylar lines are attachments for certain thigh and leg muscles and knee ligaments. Distal to these are two smooth round surfaces of the knee joint, the **medial** and **lateral condyles,** separated by a groove called the **intercondylar** (IN-tur-CON-dih-lur) **fossa.** On the anterior side of the femur, a smooth medial depression called the **patellar surface** articulates with the patella. On the posterior side is a flat or slightly depressed area called the **popliteal surface.**

Although the femurs of apes are nearly vertical, in humans they angle medially from the hip to the knee (fig. 8.12). This places our knees closer together, beneath the body's center of gravity. We lock our knees when standing (see chapter 9, p. 256), allowing us to maintain an erect posture with little muscular effort. Apes cannot do this, and they cannot stand on two legs for very long without tiring—much as you would if you tried to maintain an erect posture with your knees slightly bent.

---

[35]*fovea* = pit + *capitis* = of the head

[36]*trochanter* = to run
[37]*linea* = line + *asper* = rough

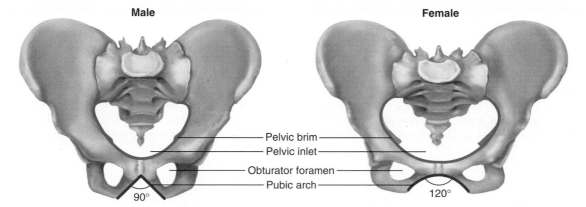

**Male**          **Female**

Pelvic brim
Pelvic inlet
Obturator foramen
Pubic arch

90°          120°

**Figure 8.9** **Comparison of the Male and Female Pelves.** The pelvic brim is the margin highlighted in blue; the pubic arch is highlighted in red. Compare with table 8.2.

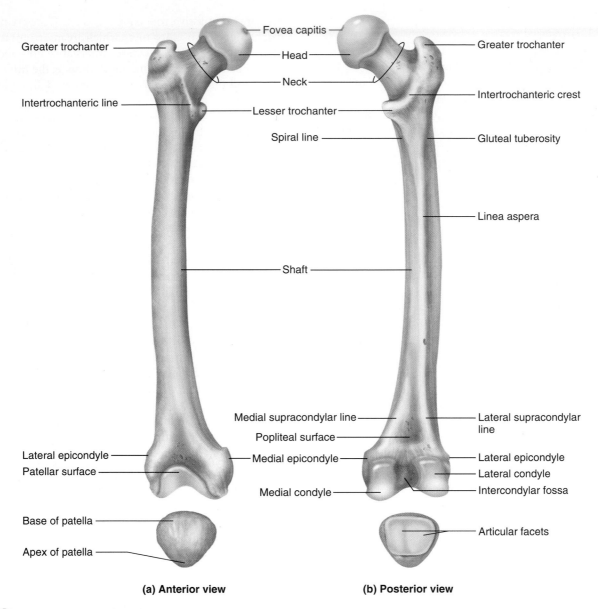

**Figure 8.10**  The Right Femur and Patella.
● *How many articular surfaces can you identify on the femur? Where are they?*

## Patella

The **patella,**[38] or kneecap (see fig. 8.10), is a roughly triangular sesamoid bone embeded in the tendon of the knee. It is cartilaginous at birth and ossifies at 3 to 6 years of age. It has a broad superior **base,** a pointed inferior **apex,** and a pair of shallow **articular facets** on its posterior surface where it articulates with the femur. The lateral facet is usually larger than the medial. The *quadriceps femoris tendon* extends from the anterior quadriceps femoris muscle of the thigh to the patella, then continues as the *patellar ligament* from the patella to the tibia. This is a change in terminology more than a change in structure or function, as a tendon connects muscle to bone and a ligament connects bone to bone.

[38]*pat* = pan + *ella* = little

INSIGHT 8.2

## Clinical Application

### Femoral Fractures

The femur is a very strong bone, well guarded by the thigh muscles, and it is not often fractured. Nevertheless, it can break in high-impact trauma suffered in automobile and equestrian accidents, figure skating falls, and so forth. If a person in an automobile collision has the feet braced against the floor or brake pedal with the knees locked, the force of impact is transmitted up the shaft and may fracture the shaft or neck of the femur (fig. 8.11). Comminuted and spiral fractures of the shaft can take up to a year to heal.

A "broken hip" is usually a fracture of the femoral neck, the weakest part of the femur. Elderly people often break the femoral neck when they stumble or are knocked down—especially women whose femurs are weakened by osteoporosis. Fractures of the femoral neck heal poorly because this is an anatomically unstable site and it has an especially thin periosteum with limited potential for ossification. In addition, fractures in this site often break blood vessels and cut off blood flow, resulting in degeneration of the head (*posttraumatic avascular necrosis*).

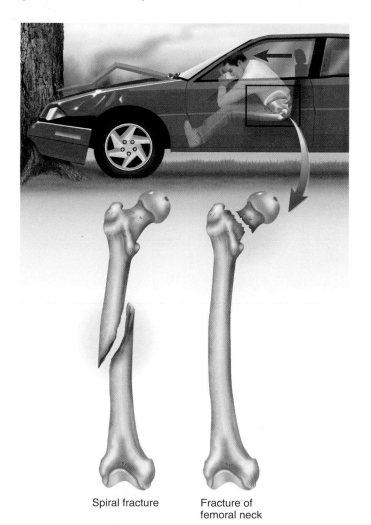

Spiral fracture    Fracture of femoral neck

**Figure 8.11**  **Fractures of the Femur.**  Violent trauma, as in automobile accidents, may cause spiral fractures of the femoral shaft. The femoral neck often fractures in elderly people as a result (or cause) of falls.

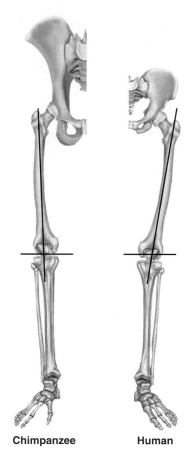

**Chimpanzee**    **Human**

**Figure 8.12**  **Adaptation of the Lower Limb for Bipedalism.**  In contrast to chimpanzees, which are quadrupedal, humans have the femurs angled medially so the knees are more nearly below the body's center of gravity.

## Tibia

The leg has two bones—a thick strong tibia (TIB-ee-uh) on the medial side and a slender fibula (FIB-you-luh) on the lateral side (fig. 8.13). The **tibia**[39] is the only weight-bearing bone of the crural region. Its broad superior head has two fairly flat articular surfaces, the **medial** and **lateral condyles,** separated by a ridge called the **intercondylar eminence.** The condyles of the tibia articulate with those of the femur. The rough anterior surface of the tibia, the **tibial tuberosity,** can be palpated just below the patella. This is where the patellar ligament inserts and the quadriceps muscle exerts its pull when it extends the leg. Distal to this, the shaft has a sharply angular **anterior crest,** which can be palpated in the shin region. At the ankle, just above the rim of a standard dress shoe, you can palpate a prominent bony knob on each side. These are the **medial** and **lateral malleoli**[40] (MAL-ee-OH-lie). The medial malleolus is part of the tibia, and the lateral malleolus is part of the fibula.

---

[39]*tibia* = shinbone
[40]*malle* = hammer + *olus* = little

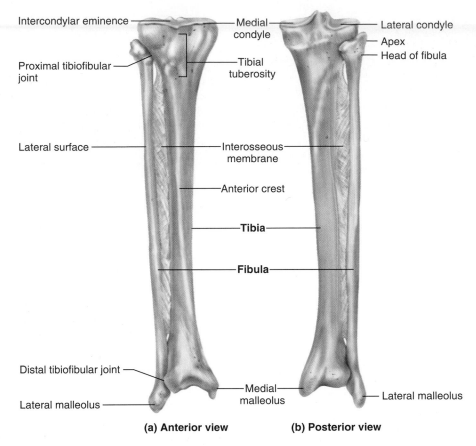

Intercondylar eminence

Proximal tibiofibular joint

Lateral surface

Anterior crest

**Tibia**

**Fibula**

Distal tibiofibular joint

Lateral malleolus

Medial condyle

Tibial tuberosity

Interosseous membrane

Medial malleolus

Lateral condyle

Apex

Head of fibula

Lateral malleolus

**(a) Anterior view**     **(b) Posterior view**

**Figure 8.13** The Right Tibia and Fibula.

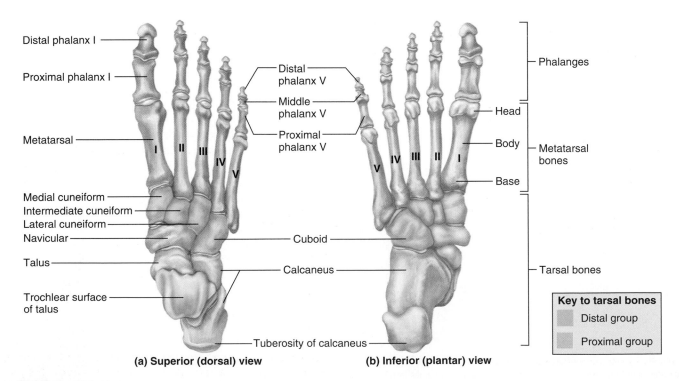

Distal phalanx I

Proximal phalanx I

Metatarsal

Medial cuneiform
Intermediate cuneiform
Lateral cuneiform
Navicular

Talus

Trochlear surface of talus

Tuberosity of calcaneus

Distal phalanx V

Middle phalanx V

Proximal phalanx V

Cuboid

Calcaneus

Phalanges

Head

Body

Base

Metatarsal bones

Tarsal bones

**Key to tarsal bones**
Distal group
Proximal group

**(a) Superior (dorsal) view**     **(b) Inferior (plantar) view**

**Figure 8.14** The Right Foot.

## Fibula

The **fibula**[41] (fig. 8.13) is a slender lateral strut that helps to stabilize the ankle. It does not bear any of the body's weight; indeed, orthopedic surgeons sometimes remove part of the fibula and use it to replace damaged or missing bone elsewhere in the body. The fibula is somewhat thicker and broader at its proximal end, the **head,** than at the distal end. The point of the head is called the **apex.** The distal expansion is the lateral malleolus. The fibula is joined to the tibia by a ligament called the *interosseous membrane,* similar to the one that joins the ulna and radius.

## The Ankle and Foot

The **tarsal bones** of the ankle are arranged in proximal and distal groups somewhat like the carpal bones of the wrist (fig. 8.14). Because of the load-bearing role of the ankle, however, their shapes and arrangement are conspicuously different from those of the carpal bones, and they are thoroughly integrated into the structure of the foot. The largest tarsal bone is the **calcaneus**[42] (cal-CAY-nee-us), which forms the heel. Its posterior end is the point of attachment for the **calcaneal (Achilles) tendon** from the calf muscles. The second-largest tarsal bone, and the most superior, is the **talus.**[43] It has three articular surfaces: an inferoposterior one that articulates with the calcaneus, a superior **trochlear**[44] **surface** that articulates with the tibia, and an anterior surface that articulates with a short, wide tarsal bone called the **navicular.**[45] The talus, calcaneus, and navicular are considered the proximal row of tarsal bones.

The distal group forms a row of four bones. Proceeding from medial side to lateral, these are the **medial, intermediate,** and **lateral cuneiforms**[46] (cue-NEE-ih-forms) and the **cuboid.**[47] The cuboid is the largest.

The remaining bones of the foot are similar in arrangement and name to those of the hand. The proximal **metatarsals**[48] are similar to the metacarpals. They are **metatarsals I** to **V** from medial to lateral, metatarsal I being proximal to the great toe. Note that Roman numeral I represents the *medial* group of bones in the foot but the *lateral* group in the hand. In both cases, however, Roman numeral I refers to the largest digit of the limb (see Insight 8.3). Metatarsals I to III articulate with the three cuneiforms; metatarsals IV and V articulate with the cuboid.

Bones of the toes, like those of the fingers, are called phalanges. The great toe is the **hallux** and contains only two bones, the proximal and distal phalanx I. The other toes each contain a proximal, middle, and distal phalanx. The metatarsal and phalangeal bones each have a base, body, and head, like the bones of the hand. All of them, especially the phalanges, are slightly concave on the inferior (plantar) side.

As important as the hand has been to human evolution, the foot may be an even more significant adaptation. Unlike other mammals, humans support their entire body weight on two feet. The tarsal bones are tightly articulated with each other, and the calcaneus is strongly developed. The hallux is not opposable as it is in most Old World monkeys and apes (fig. 8.15), but it is highly developed so that it provides the "toe-off" that pushes the body forward in the last phase of the stride. For this reason, loss of the hallux has a more crippling effect than the loss of any other toe.

Although apes are flat-footed, humans have strong, springy foot arches that absorb shock as the body jostles up and down during walking and running (fig. 8.16). The **medial longitudinal arch,** which essentially extends from heel to hallux, is formed from the calcaneus, talus, navicular, cuneiforms, and metatarsals I to III. The **lateral longitudinal arch** extends from heel to little toe and includes the calcaneus, cuboid, and metatarsals IV and V. The **transverse arch** includes the cuboid, cuneiforms, and proximal heads of the metatarsals. These arches are held together by short, strong ligaments. Excessive weight, repetitive stress, or congenital weakness of these ligaments can stretch them, resulting in *pes planus* (commonly called flat feet or fallen arches). This condition makes a person less tolerant of prolonged standing and walking.

Table 8.3 summarizes the pelvic girdle and lower limb.

## INSIGHT 8.3

### Medical History

## Anatomical Position—Clinical and Biological Perspectives

It may seem puzzling that we count metacarpal bones I to V from lateral to medial, but count metatarsal bones I to V from medial to lateral. This minor point of confusion is the legacy of a committee of anatomists who met in the early 1900s to define anatomical position. A controversy arose as to whether the arms should be presented with the palms forward or facing the rear in anatomical position. Veterinary anatomists argued that palms to the rear (forearms pronated) would be a more natural position comparable to forelimb orientation in other animals. It is more comfortable to stand with the forearms pronated, and when a child crawls on all fours, he or she does so with the palms on the floor, in the pronated position. In this animal-like stance, the largest digits (thumbs and great toes) are medial on all four limbs. Human clinical anatomists, however, argued that if you ask patients to "show me your arms" or "show me your hands," most present the palms forward or upward—that is, supinated. The clinical anatomists won the debate, forcing us, the heirs to this terminology, to number the hand and foot bones in a biologically less rational order.

A few other anatomical terms also reflect less than perfect logic. The *dorsum* of the foot is its superior surface—it does not face dorsally—and the dorsal artery and nerve of the penis lie along the surface that faces anteriorly (ventrally) (see fig. 26.10, p. 747). In a cat, dog, or other quadrupedal mammal, however, the dorsum of the foot and the dorsal artery and nerve of the penis do face dorsally (upward). However illogical some of these terms may seem, we inherit them from comparative anatomy and the habit of naming human structures after the corresponding structures in other species.

---

[41]*fib* = pin + *ula* = little
[42]*calc* = stone, chalk
[43]*talus* = ankle
[44]*trochlear* = like a pully
[45]*nav* = boat + *icul* = little + *ar* = like
[46]*cunei* = wedge + *form* = in the shape of
[47]*cub* = cube + *oid* = shaped
[48]*meta* = beyond + *tars* = ankle

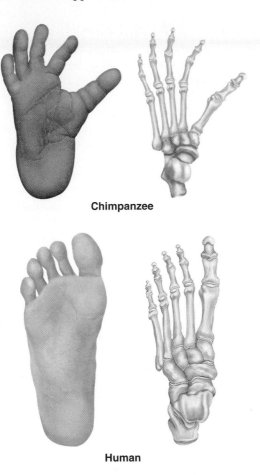

**Chimpanzee**

**Human**

**Figure 8.15** **Some Adaptations of the Foot for Bipedalism.** In contrast to the prehensile great toe (hallux) of the chimp, the human great toe is nonprehensile but is more robust and is adapted for the toe-off part of the stride.

## Before You Go On

*Answer the following questions to test your understanding of the preceding section:*

7. Name the bones of the adult pelvic girdle. What three bones of a child fuse to form the hip bone of an adult?

8. Name any four structures of the pelvis that you can palpate, and describe where to palpate them.

9. Describe several ways in which the male and female pelvis differ.

10. What parts of the femur are involved in the hip joint? What parts are involved in the knee joint?

11. Name the prominent knobs on each side of your ankle. What bones contribute to these structures?

12. Name all the bones that articulate with the talus and describe the location of each.

13. Describe several ways in which the human and ape pelvis and hindlimb differ, and the functional reason for the differences.

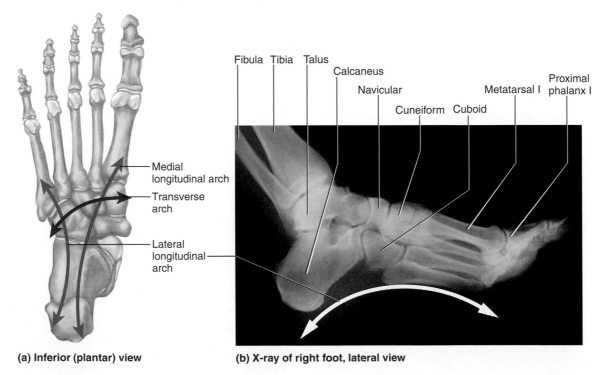

Fibula  Tibia  Talus  Calcaneus  Navicular  Cuneiform  Cuboid  Metatarsal I  Proximal phalanx I

Medial longitudinal arch

Transverse arch

Lateral longitudinal arch

**(a) Inferior (plantar) view**

**(b) X-ray of right foot, lateral view**

**Figure 8.16** Arches of the Foot.

| **TABLE 8.3** | **Anatomical Checklist for the Pelvic Girdle and Lower Limb** |
|---|---|

## Pelvic Girdle

### Hip Bone (figs. 8.6–8.9)

Pubic symphysis
Interpubic disc
Greater (false) pelvis
Lesser (true) pelvis
Pelvic brim
Pelvic inlet
Pelvic outlet
Acetabulum
Obturator foramen
Ilium
  Iliac crest
  Anterior superior spine
  Anterior inferior spine
  Posterior superior spine
  Posterior inferior spine

### Hip Bone (continued)

  Greater sciatic notch
  Iliac fossa
  Auricular surface
Ischium
  Body
  Ischial spine
  Lesser sciatic notch
  Ischial tuberosity
  Ramus
Pubis
  Superior ramus
  Inferior ramus
  Body

## Lower Limb

### Femur (fig. 8.10)

Proximal end
  Head
  Fovea capitis
  Neck
  Greater trochanter
  Lesser trochanter
  Intertrochanteric crest
  Intertrochanteric line
Shaft
  Linea aspera
Distal end
  Medial condyle
  Lateral condyle
  Intercondylar fossa
  Medial epicondyle
  Lateral epicondyle
  Patellar surface

### Patella (fig. 8.10)

Base
Apex
Articular facets

### Tibia (fig. 8.13)

Medial condyle
Lateral condyle
Intercondylar eminence
Tibial tuberosity
Anterior crest
Medial malleolus

### Fibula (fig. 8.13)

Head
Apex (styloid process)
Lateral malleolus

### Tarsal Bones (fig. 8.14)

Proximal group
  Calcaneus
  Talus
  Navicular
Distal group
  Medial cuneiform
  Intermediate cuneiform
  Lateral cuneiform
  Cuboid

### Bones of the Foot (figs. 8.14–8.16)

Metatarsal bones I–V
Phalanges
  Proximal phalanx
  Middle phalanx
  Distal phalanx
Arches of the foot
  Medial longitudinal arch
  Lateral longitudinal arch
  Transverse arch

# Developmental and Clinical Perspectives

## Objectives

When you have completed this section, you should be able to

- describe the pre- and postnatal development of the appendicular skeleton; and
- describe some common disorders of the appendicular skeleton.

## Development of the Appendicular Skeleton

With few exceptions, the bones of the limbs and their girdles form by endochondral ossification. The process begins when mesenchyme condenses and differentiates into hyaline cartilage (chondrification) and continues as the cartilage is replaced by osseous tissue (ossification). Exceptions include the clavicle, which forms primarily by intramembranous ossification, and sesamoid bones (the pisiform and patella). Although limb and limb girdle ossification is well under way at the time of birth, it is not completed until a person is in his or her twenties.

The first sign of limb development is the appearance of upper **limb buds** around day 26 to 27 and lower limb buds 1 or 2 days later. A limb bud consists of a core of mesenchyme covered with ectoderm. The limb buds elongate as the mesenchyme proliferates. The distal ends of the limb buds flatten into paddlelike **hand** and **foot plates.** By day 38 in the hand and day 44 in the foot, these plates show parallel ridges called **digital rays,** the future fingers and toes. The mesenchyme between the digital rays breaks down by apoptosis, forming notches between the rays which deepen until, at the end of week 8, the digits are well separated.

Condensed mesenchymal models of the future limb bones begin to appear during week 5. Chondrification is apparent by the end of that week, and by the end of week 6, a complete cartilaginous limb skeleton is present. The long bones begin to ossify in the following week, in the manner described in chapter 6 (see fig. 6.10, p. 163). The humerus, radius, ulna, femur, and tibia develop primary ossification centers in weeks 7 to 8; the scapula and ilium in week 9; the metacarpals, metatarsals, and phalanges over the next 3 weeks; and the ischium and pubis in weeks 15 and 20, respectively. The clavicle ossifies intramembranously beginning early in week 7.

The carpal bones are still cartilaginous at birth. Some of them ossify as early as 2 months of age (the capitate) and some as late as 9 years (the pisiform). Among the tarsal bones, the calcaneus and talus begin to ossify prenatally at 3 and 6 months, respectively; the cuboid begins to ossify just before or after birth; and the cuneiforms do not ossify until 1 to 3 years of age. The patella ossifies at 3 to 6 years. The epiphyses of the long bones are cartilaginous at birth, with their secondary ossification centers just beginning to form. The epiphyseal plates persist until about age 20, at which time the epiphysis and diaphysis fuse and bone elongation ceases. The ilium, ischium, and pubis are not fully fused into a single hip bone until the age of 25.

It may seem curious that the largest digits (the thumb and great toe) are lateral in the hand but medial in the foot, and that the elbows and knees flex in opposite directions. This results from a rotation of the limbs that occurs in week 7. Early that week, the limbs extend anteriorly from the body, the hand plate shows the first traces of separation of the finger buds, and the foot is still a relatively undifferentiated foot plate (fig. 8.17a). The future thumb and great toe are both directed superiorly, and the future palms and soles face each other medially. But then the limbs rotate about 90° in opposite directions. The upper limb rotates laterally. To visualize this, hold your hands straight out in front of you with the palms facing each other as if you were about to clap. Then rotate your forearms so the thumbs face away from each other (laterally) and the palms face upward. The lower limbs rotate in the opposite direction, medially, so that the soles face downward and the great toes become medial. Thus, the thumb and great toe end up on opposite sides of the hand and foot (fig. 8.17b). This rotation also explains why the elbow and knee flex in opposite directions, and why (as you will see in chapter 12) the muscles that flex the elbow are on the anterior side of the arm, but those that flex the knee are on the posterior side of the thigh.

## Pathology of the Appendicular Skeleton

The appendicular skeleton is subject to several developmental abnormalities, occurring in as many as 2 out of 1,000 live births. The most striking is **amelia,**[49] a complete absence of one or more limbs. The partial absence of a limb is called **meromelia.**[50] Meromelia typically entails an absence of the long bones, with rudimentary hands or feet attached directly to the trunk (see fig. 4.15, p. 123). Such defects are often accompanied by deformities of the heart, urogenital system, or craniofacial skeleton. These abnormalities are usually hereditary, but they can be induced by teratogenic chemicals such as thalidomide. The limbs are most vulnerable to teratogens in the fourth and fifth weeks of development.

Another class of developmental limb disorders includes **polydactyly,**[51] the presence of extra fingers or toes (fig. 8.18a), and **syndactyly,**[52] the fusion of two or more digits. The latter results from a failure of the digital rays to separate. *Cutaneous syndactyly,* most common in the foot, is the persistence of a skin web between the digits, and is relatively easy to correct surgically. *Osseous syndactyly* is fusion of the bones of the digits, owing to failure of the notches to form between the embryonic digital rays. Polydactyly and syndactyly are usually hereditary, but can also be induced by teratogens.

**Clubfoot,** or **talipes**[53] (TAL-ih-peez) is a congenital deformity in which the feet are adducted and plantar flexed (defined in chapter 9), with the soles turned medially (fig. 8.18b). This is a relatively

---

[49]*a* = without + *melia* = limb
[50]*mero* = part + *melia* = limb
[51]*poly* = many + *dactyl* = finger
[52]*syn* = together + *dactyl* = finger
[53]*tali* = heel + *pes* = foot

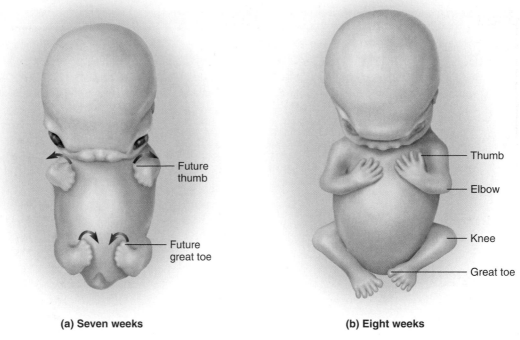

**(a) Seven weeks**                                    **(b) Eight weeks**

**Figure 8.17  Embryonic Limb Rotation.**  In the seventh week of development, the forelimbs and hindlimbs of the embryo rotate about 90° in opposite directions. This explains why the largest digits (digit I) are on opposite sides of the hand and foot, and why the elbow and knee flex in opposite directions.

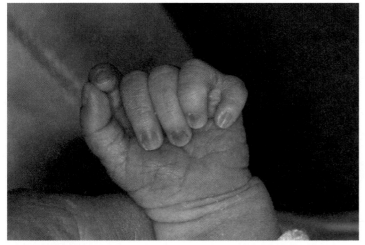

**(a) Polydactyly**

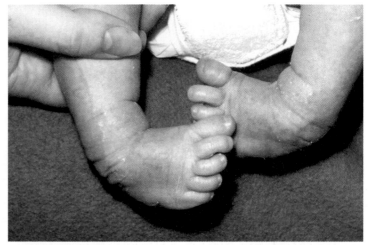

**(b) Talipes (clubfoot)**

**Figure 8.18  Congenital Deformities of the Hands and Feet.**

common birth defect, present in about 1 out of 1,000 live births, but the cause remains obscure. It is sometimes hereditary, and some think it may also result from malposition of the fetus in the uterus, but the latter hypothesis remains unproven. Children with talipes cannot support their weight on their feet and tend to walk on their ankles. In some cases, talipes requires that the foot be manipulated and set in a new cast every week beginning in the neonatal nursery and lasting 4 to 6 months. Some cases require surgery at 6 to 9 months to release tight ligaments and tendons and realign the foot.

The most common noncongenital disorders of the appendicular skeleton are osteoporosis, fractures, dislocations, and arthritis. Even though these disorders can affect the axial skeleton as well, they are more common and more often disabling in the appendicular skeleton. The general classification of bone fractures is discussed in chapter 6, and some fractures specific to the appendicular skeleton are discussed in Insights 8.1 and 8.2 of this chapter. Arthritis, dislocation, and other joint disorders are described in chapter 9. Table 8.4 describes some other disorders of the appendicular skeleton.

| TABLE 8.4 | Disorders of the Appendicular Skeleton |
|---|---|
| **Avulsion** | A fracture in which a body part, such as a finger, is completely torn from the body, as in many accidents with farm and factory machinery. The term can also refer to nonosseous structures such as the avulsion of an ear. |
| **Calcaneal (heel) spurs** | Abnormal outgrowths of the calcaneus. Often results from high-impact exercise such as aerobics and running, especially if done with inappropriate footwear. Stress on the plantar aponeurosis (a connective tissue sheet in the sole of the foot) stimulates exostosis, or growth of a bony spur, and can cause severe foot pain. |
| **Colles[54] fracture** | Pathologic fracture at the distal end of the radius and ulna, often occurring when stress is placed on the wrist (as in pushing oneself up from an armchair) and the bones have been weakened by osteoporosis. |
| **Epiphyseal fracture** | Separation of the epiphysis from the diaphysis of a long bone. Common in children and adolescents because of their cartilaginous epiphyseal plates. May present a threat to normal completion of bone growth. |
| **Pes planus[55]** | "Flat feet" or "fallen arches" (absence of visible arches) in adolescents and adults. Caused by stretching of plantar ligaments due to prolonged standing or excess weight. |
| **Pott[56] fracture** | Fracture of the distal end of the tibia, fibula, or both; a sports injury common in football, soccer, and snow skiing. |

**Disorders Described Elsewhere**

Fracture of the clavicle 212          Fracture of the femur 223

## *Before You Go On*

*Answer the following questions to test your understanding of the preceding section:*

14. Describe the progression from a limb bud to a hand with fully formed and separated fingers.

15. Name some appendicular bones that do not ossify until a person is at least a few years old.

16. Distinguish between amelia and meromelia, and between polydactyly and syndactyly.

---

[54]Abraham Colles (1773–1843), Irish surgeon
[55]*pes* = foot + *planus* = flat
[56]Sir Percivall Pott (1713–88), British surgeon

# CHAPTER REVIEW

## REVIEW OF KEY CONCEPTS

### The Pectoral Girdle and Upper Limb (p. 212)

1. The *pectoral girdle* supports the upper limb. It consists of a clavicle and scapula on each side of the body. The *clavicle* articulates with the sternum medially and the scapula laterally. The *scapula* also articulates with the humerus of the arm at the *glenohumeral joint.* The anatomical features of the clavicle and scapula are summarized in table 8.1.

2. The upper limb has 30 bones divided into 4 regions: the *brachium* (arm), containing the *humerus;* the *antebrachium* (forearm) containing the *radius* and *ulna;* the *carpus* (wrist), containing 2 rows of 4 *carpal bones* each; and the *manus* (hand) containing 5 *metacarpal bones* in the palmar region and 14 *phalanges* in the digits. The anatomical features of these bones are summarized in table 8.1.

3. The evolution of bipedal locomotion is reflected in the anatomy of the upper limb, whose function has changed from locomotion to reaching and grasping. Its adaptations include a shorter length, lighter musculature, and increased mobility of the joints of the shoulder and hand.

### The Pelvic Girdle and Lower Limb (p. 217)

1. The adult *pelvic girdle* supports the trunk on the lower limbs and encloses and protects viscera of the pelvic cavity. It consists of two *hip bones.* With the sacrum, they form the *pelvis.*

2. Each hip bone articulates with the vertebral column at the *sacroiliac joint.* The hip bones articulate anteriorly with each other at the *pubic symphysis,* where a fibrocartilage *interpubic disc* separates the two bones. Each hip bone has a deep socket, the *acetabulum,* where it articulates with the femur.

3. The pelvis is bowl-like, with a broad *greater pelvis* superiorly, a narrow *lesser pelvis* inferiorly, and a *pelvic brim* marking the boundary between them. In childbirth, an infant's head descends from the greater pelvis, through the *pelvic inlet* surrounded by the brim, into the lesser pelvis, and then out the *pelvic outlet.*

4. The adult hip bone forms by fusion of three childhood bones, the *ilium, ischium,* and *pubis.*

5. The anatomy of the pelvis exhibits adaptations to bipedalism in both sexes and to childbirth in women. This is the most sexually dimorphic region of human skeletal anatomy (table 8.2).

6. The anatomical features of the pelvis are summarized in table 8.3.

7. The lower limb has 30 bones divided into 4 regions: the *femoral region* (thigh) containing the *femur* and *patella;* the *crural region* (leg) containing the *tibia* and *fibula;* the *tarsal region* (ankle), whose bones are regarded as part of the foot; and the *pes* (foot) containing 7 *tarsal bones,* 5 *metatarsal bones,* and 14 *phalanges.* Anatomical features of the lower limb bones are summarized in table 8.3.

8. Adaptations of the lower limb to bipedalism include medially angled femurs, locking knees, a great toe strengthened for the toe-off part of the stride, and foot arches.

### Developmental and Clinical Perspectives (p. 228)

1. The clavicle forms mainly by intramembranous ossification and the other limb and girdle bones by endochondral ossification. The latter process proceeds through chondrification (condensation of mesenchyme into cartilage) and then ossification (replacement of the cartilage with bone).

2. The limbs begin as *limb buds,* which elongate and form paddlelike *hand* and *foot plates.* Ridges called *digital rays* appear in each plate, and the tissue between the rays breaks down by apoptosis, separating the fingers and toes by the end of the embryonic stage (8 weeks). The limb bones begin to ossify at various times from 7 weeks of embryonic development to 9 years after birth, and some bones do not complete their ossification until a person is 25 years old.

3. Developmental abnormalities of the appendicular skeleton include the complete absence of one or more limbs *(amelia),* partial absence *(meromelia),* excess fingers or toes *(polydactyly),* failure of toes or fingers to separate *(syndactyly),* and clubfoot *(talipes).*

4. The most common disorders appearing after birth are osteoporosis, fractures, joint dislocations, and arthritis.

## TESTING YOUR RECALL

1. The hip bone is attached to the axial skeleton through its
   a. auricular surface.
   b. articular cartilage.
   c. pubic symphysis.
   d. conoid tubercle.
   e. coronoid process.

2. Which of these bones supports the most body weight?
   a. ilium
   b. pubis
   c. femur
   d. tibia
   e. talus

3. Which of these structures can be most easily palpated on a living person?
   a. the deltoid tuberosity
   b. the greater sciatic notch
   c. the medial malleolus
   d. the coracoid process of the scapula
   e. the glenoid cavity

4. Compared to the male pelvis, the pelvis of a female
   a. has a less movable coccyx.
   b. has a rounder pelvic inlet.
   c. is narrower between the iliac crests.
   d. has a narrower pubic arch.
   e. has a narrower sacrum.

5. The lateral and medial malleoli are most similar to
   a. the radial and ulnar styloid processes.
   b. the humeral capitulum and trochlea.
   c. the acromion and coracoid process.
   d. the base and head of a metacarpal bone.
   e. the anterior and posterior superior iliac spines.

6. When you rest your hands on your hips, you are resting them on
   a. the pelvic inlet.
   b. the pelvic outlet.
   c. the pelvic brim.
   d. the iliac crests.
   e. the auricular surfaces.

7. The disc-shaped head of the radius articulates with the _____ of the humerus.
   a. radial tuberosity
   b. trochlea
   c. capitulum
   d. olecranon process
   e. glenoid cavity

8. All of the following are carpal bones *except* the _____, which is a tarsal bone.
   a. trapezium
   b. cuboid
   c. trapezoid
   d. triquetrum
   e. pisiform

9. The bone that supports your body weight when you are sitting down is
   a. the acetabulum.
   b. the pubis.
   c. the ilium.
   d. the coccyx.
   e. the ischium.

10. Which of these is the bone of the heel?
    a. cuboid
    b. calcaneus
    c. navicular
    d. trochlear
    e. talus

11. The Latin anatomical name for the thumb is _____, and the name for the great toe is _____.

12. The acromion and coracoid process are parts of what bone?

13. How many phalanges, total, does the human body have?

14. The bony prominences on each side of your elbow are the lateral and medial _____ of the humerus.

15. One of the wrist bones, the _____, is characterized by a prominent hook.

16. The fibrocartilage pad that holds the pelvic girdle together anteriorly is called the _____.

17. The leg proper, between the knee and ankle, is called the _____ region.

18. The _____ processes of the radius and ulna form bony protuberances on each side of the wrist.

19. Two massive protuberances unique to the proximal end of the femur are the greater and lesser _____.

20. The _____ arch of the foot extends from the heel to the great toe.

*Answers in the Appendix*

## TRUE OR FALSE

*Determine which five of the following statements are false, and briefly explain why.*

1. There are more carpal bones than tarsal bones.

2. The hands have more phalanges than the feet.

3. The upper limb is attached to the axial skeleton at only one point, the acromioclavicular joint.

4. On a living person, it would be possible to palpate the muscles in the infraspinous fossa but not those of the subscapular fossa.

5. In strict anatomical terminology, the words *arm* and *leg* both refer to regions with only one bone.

6. If you rest your chin on your hands with your elbows on a table, the olecranon of the ulna rests on the table.

7. The most frequently broken bone in humans is the humerus.

8. The proximal end of the radius articulates with both the humerus and ulna.

9. The pisiform bone and patella are both sesamoid bones.

10. The pelvic outlet is the opening in the floor of the greater pelvis leading into the lesser pelvis.

*Answers in the Appendix*

## TESTING YOUR COMPREHENSION

1. In adolescents, trauma sometimes separates the head of the femur from the neck. Why do you think this is more common in adolescents than in adults?

2. By palpating the hind leg of a cat or dog or examining a laboratory skeleton, you can see that cats and dogs stand on the heads of their metatarsal bones; the calcaneus does not touch the ground. How is this similar to the stance of a woman wearing high-heeled shoes? How is it different?

3. A deer hunter discovers a human skeleton in the woods and notifies authorities. A news report on the finding describes it as the body of an unidentified male between 17 and 20 years of age. What skeletal features would have been most useful for determining the sex and approximate age of the individual?

4. A surgeon has removed 8 cm of Joan's radius because of osteosarcoma, a bone cancer, and replaced it with a graft taken from one of the bones of Joan's lower limb. What bone do you think would most likely be used as the source of the graft? Explain your answer.

5. Andy, a 55-year-old, 75-kg (165-lb) roofer, is shingling the steeply pitched roof of a new house when he loses his footing and slides down the roof and over the edge, feet first. He braces himself for the fall, and when he hits the ground, he cries out and doubles up in excruciating pain. Emergency medical technicians called to the scene tell him he has broken his hips. Describe, more specifically, where his fractures most likely occurred. On the way to the hospital, Andy says, "You know it's funny, when I was a kid, I used to jump off roofs that high, and I never got hurt." Why do you think Andy was more at risk of a fracture as an adult than he was as a boy?

*Answers at aris.mhhe.com*

## ONLINE RESOURCES

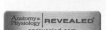 Visit aprevealed.com to explore melt-away cadaver dissections, watch animations that clarify difficult concepts, review histological and radiological images, or take a quiz to assess your understanding of the material.

 The Saladin *Human Anatomy,* 2e website at aris.mhhe.com features chapter-specific quizzes, labeling exercises, and other interactive tools to complement your study of human anatomy. If your instructor has provided an ARIS course code, you can also access assignments and information specific to your course.

# Joints

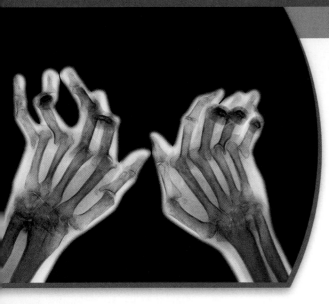

X-ray of hands with severe rheumatoid arthritis

## CHAPTER OUTLINE

## INSIGHTS

## BRUSHING UP

To understand this chapter, you may find it helpful to review the following concepts:
- Anatomical planes (p. 23)
- The distinction between hyaline cartilage and fibrocartilage (p. 89)
- Anatomy of the skeletal system (chapters 7 and 8)

Anatomy & Physiology **REVEALED**®
aprevealed.com

**Skeletal System**

Joints, or articulations, link the bones of the skeletal system into a functional whole—a system that supports the body, permits effective movement, and protects the softer organs. Joints such as the shoulder, elbow, and knee are remarkable specimens of biological design—self-lubricating, almost frictionless, and able to bear heavy loads and withstand compression while executing smooth and precise movements. Yet, it is equally important that other joints be less movable or even immobile. Such joints are better able to support the body and protect delicate organs. The vertebral column, for example, is only moderately movable, for it must allow for flexibility of the torso and yet protect the delicate spinal cord and support much of the body's weight. Bones of the cranium must protect the brain and sense organs, but need not allow for movement (except during birth); thus, they are locked together by immobile joints, the sutures studied in chapter 7.

In everyday life, we take the greatest notice of the most freely movable joints of the limbs, and it is here that people feel most severely compromised by such disabling diseases as arthritis. Much of the work of physical therapists focuses on limb mobility. In this chapter, we will survey all types of joints, from the utterly immobile to the most movable, but with an emphasis on the latter. This survey of joint anatomy and movements will provide a foundation for the study of muscle actions in chapters 11 and 12.

## Joints and Their Classification

### Objectives
When you have completed this section, you should be able to

- explain what joints are, how they are named, and what functions they serve;
- name and describe the four major classes of joints;
- name some joints that become solidly fused by bone as they age;
- describe the three types of fibrous joints and give an example of each;
- distinguish between the three types of sutures; and
- describe the two types of cartilaginous joints and give an example of each.

Any point where two bones meet is called a **joint (articulation)**, whether or not the bones are movable at that interface. The science of joint structure, function, and dysfunction is called **arthrology.** The study of musculoskeletal movement is **kinesiology** (kih-NEE-see-OL-oh-jee). This is a branch of **biomechanics,** which deals with a broad variety of movements and mechanical processes in the body, including the physics of blood circulation, respiration, and hearing.

The name of a joint is typically derived from the names of the bones involved. For example, the *atlanto–occipital joint* is where the occipital condyles meet the atlas, the *glenohumeral joint* is where the humerus meets the glenoid cavity of the scapula, and the *radio-ulnar joint* is where the radius meets the ulna.

Joints are classified according to the manner in which the adjacent bones are bound to each other, with corresponding differences in how freely the bones can move. Authorities differ in their classification schemes, but one common view places the joints in four major categories: *bony, fibrous, cartilaginous,* and *synovial joints.* This section will describe the first three of these and the subclasses of each. The remainder of the chapter will then be concerned primarily with synovial joints.

## Bony Joints

A **bony joint,** or **synostosis**[1] (SIN-oss-TOE-sis), is an immobile joint formed when the gap between two bones ossifies and they become, in effect, a single bone. Bony joints can form by ossification of either fibrous or cartilaginous joints. An infant is born with right and left frontal and mandibular bones, for example, but these soon fuse seamlessly to form single bones. In old age, some cranial sutures become obliterated by ossification, and the adjacent cranial bones, such as the parietal bones, fuse. The epiphyses and diaphyses of the long bones are joined by cartilaginous joints in childhood and adolescence, and these become synostoses in early adulthood. The attachment of the first rib to the sternum also becomes a synostosis with age.

## Fibrous Joints

A **fibrous joint** is also called a **synarthrosis**[2] (SIN-ar-THRO-sis) or **synarthrodial joint.** It is a point at which adjacent bones are bound by collagen fibers that emerge from the matrix of one bone, cross the space between them, and penetrate into the matrix of the other (fig. 9.1). There are three kinds of fibrous joints: *sutures, gomphoses,* and *syndesmoses.* In sutures and gomphoses, the fibers are very short and allow for little or no movement. In syndesmoses, the fibers are longer and the attached bones are more movable.

### Sutures

**Sutures** are immobile fibrous joints that closely bind the bones of the skull to each other; they occur nowhere else. In chapter 7, we did not take much notice of the differences between one suture and another, but some differences may have caught your attention as you studied the diagrams in that chapter or examined laboratory specimens. Sutures can be classified as *serrate, lap,* and *plane sutures.* Readers with some knowledge of woodworking may recognize that the structures and functional properties of these sutures have something in common with basic types of carpentry joints (fig. 9.2).

A **serrate suture** is one in which the adjoining bones firmly interlock by their serrated margins, like pieces of a jigsaw puzzle. It is analogous to a dovetail wood joint. On the surface, it appears as a wavy line between the two bones, as we see in the coronal, sagittal, and lambdoid sutures that border the parietal bones.

---

[1]*syn* = together + *ost* = bone + *osis* = condition
[2]*syn* = together + *arthr* = joined + *osis* = condition

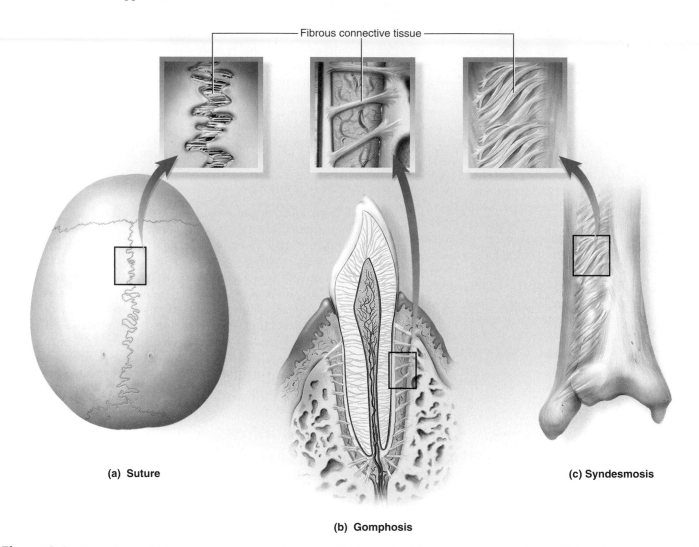

Fibrous connective tissue

**(a) Suture**

**(b) Gomphosis**

**(c) Syndesmosis**

**Figure 9.1** **Fibrous Joints.** (a) A suture between the parietal bones. (b) A gomphosis between a tooth and the jaw. (c) A syndesmosis between the tibia and fibula.

● *Which of these is* not *a joint between two bones?*

A **lap (squamous) suture** is one in which the adjacent bones have overlapping beveled edges, like a miter joint in carpentry. An example is the squamous suture that encircles most of the temporal bone. The beveled edge of this bone can be seen in figure 7.10b (p. 186). On the surface, a lap suture appears as a relatively smooth (nonserrated) line.

A **plane (butt) suture** is one in which the adjacent bones have straight nonoverlapping edges. The two bones merely border each other, like two boards glued together in a butt joint. An example is seen between the palatine processes of the maxillae in the roof of the mouth.

## Gomphoses

Even though the teeth are not bones, the attachment of a tooth to its socket is classified as a joint called a **gomphosis** (gom-FOE-sis). The term refers to its similarity to a nail hammered into wood.[3] The tooth is held firmly in place by a fibrous **periodontal ligament,** which consists of collagen fibers that extend from the bone matrix of the jaw into the dental tissue (see fig. 9.1b). The periodontal ligament allows the tooth to move or give a little under the stress of chewing. This allows us to sense how hard we are biting and to sense a particle of food stuck between the teeth.

## Syndesmoses

A **syndesmosis**[4] (SIN-dez-MO-sis) is a fibrous joint at which two bones are bound by relatively long collagenous fibers. The separation between the bones and length of the fibers gives these joints more mobility than a suture or gomphosis. An especially movable syndesmosis exists between the shafts of the radius and ulna, which are joined by a broad fibrous *interosseous membrane.* This syndesmosis permits such movements as pronation and supination of the forearm. A less mobile syndesmosis is the one that binds the distal ends of the tibia and fibula together, side by side (see fig. 9.1c).

---

[3]*gomph* = nail, bolt + *osis* = condition

[4]*syn* = together + *desm* = band + *osis* = condition

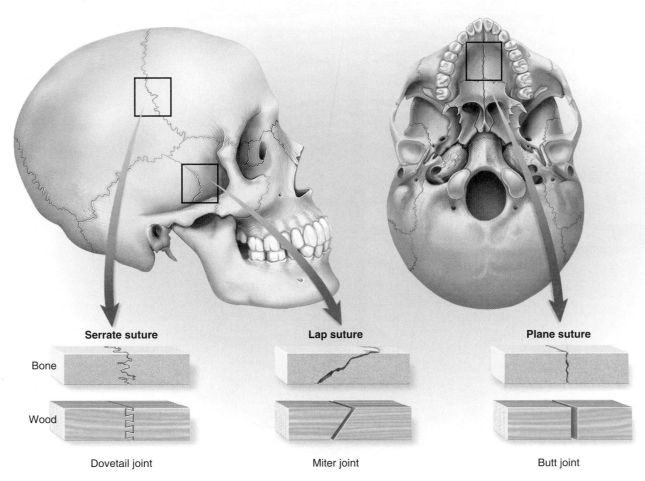

**Serrate suture**

Bone

Wood

Dovetail joint

**Lap suture**

Miter joint

**Plane suture**

Butt joint

**Figure 9.2** **Sutures.** Serrate, lap, and plane sutures compared to some common wood joints.

## Cartilaginous Joints

A **cartilaginous joint** is also called an **amphiarthrosis**[5] (AM-fee-ar-THRO-sis) or **amphiarthrodial joint.** In these joints, two bones are linked by cartilage (fig. 9.3). The two types of cartilaginous joints are *synchondroses* and *symphyses*.

### Synchondroses

A **synchondrosis**[6] (SIN-con-DRO-sis) is a joint in which the bones are bound by hyaline cartilage. An example is the temporary joint between the epiphysis and diaphysis of a long bone in a child, formed by the cartilage of the epiphyseal plate. Another is the attachment of the first rib to the sternum by a hyaline costal cartilage (fig. 9.3a). (The other costal cartilages are joined to the sternum by synovial joints.)

### Symphyses

In a **symphysis**[7] (SIM-fih-sis), two bones are joined by fibrocartilage (fig. 9.3b, c). One example is the pubic symphysis, in which the right and left pubic bones are joined by the cartilaginous interpubic disc. Another is the joint between the bodies of two vertebrae, united by an intervertebral disc. The surface of each vertebral body is covered with hyaline cartilage. Between the vertebrae, this cartilage becomes infiltrated with collagen bundles to form fibrocartilage. Each intervertebral disc permits only slight movement between adjacent vertebrae, but the collective effect of all 23 discs gives the spine considerable flexibility.

### THINK ABOUT IT

*The intervertebral joints are symphyses only in the cervical through the lumbar region. How would you classify the intervertebral joints of the sacrum and coccyx in a middle-aged adult?*

---

[5]*amphi* = on all sides + *arthr* = joined + *osis* = condition
[6]*syn* = together + *chondr* = cartilage + *osis* = condition

[7]*sym* = together + *physis* = growth

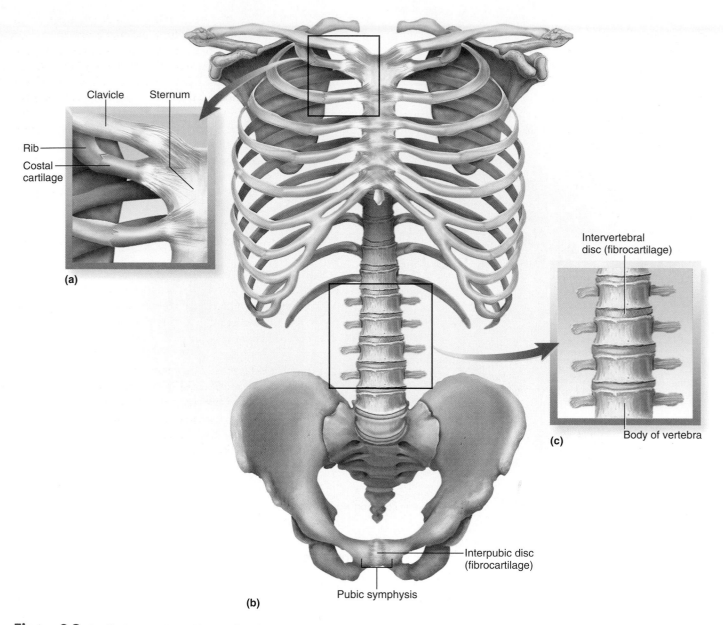

**Figure 9.3** **Cartilaginous Joints.** (a) A synchondrosis, represented by the costal cartilage joining rib 1 to the sternum. (b) The pubic symphysis. (c) Intervertebral discs, which join adjacent vertebrae to each other by symphyses.
● *What is the difference between the pubic symphysis and the interpubic disc?*

## *Before You Go On*

*Answer the following questions to test your understanding of the preceding section:*

1. What is the difference between arthrology and kinesiology?

2. Explain the distinction between a synostosis, amphiarthrosis, and synarthrosis.

3. Give some examples of joints that become synostoses with age.

4. Define *suture, gomphosis,* and *syndesmosis,* and explain what these three joints have in common.

5. Name the three types of sutures and describe how they differ.

6. Name two synchondroses and two symphyses.

## Synovial Joints

### *Objectives*

When you have completed this section, you should be able to

- describe the anatomy of a synovial joint and its associated structures;

- describe the six types of synovial joints;

- list and demonstrate the types of movements that occur at diarthroses; and

- discuss the factors that affect the range of motion of a joint.

The most familiar type of joint is the **synovial** (sih-NO-vee-ul) **joint,** also called a **diarthrosis**[8] (DY-ar-THRO-sis) or **diarthrodial joint.** Ask most people to point out any joint in the body, and they are likely to point to a synovial joint such as the elbow, knee, or knuckles. Many synovial joints, like these examples, are freely movable. Others, such as the joints between the wrist and ankle bones and between the articular processes of the vertebrae, have more limited mobility. Synovial joints are the most structurally complex type of joint and are the most likely to develop uncomfortable and crippling dysfunctions.

## General Anatomy

In synovial joints, the facing surfaces of the two bones are covered with **articular cartilage,** a layer of hyaline cartilage usually about 2 or 3 mm thick. These surfaces are separated by a narrow space, the **joint (articular) cavity,** containing a slippery lubricant called **synovial fluid** (fig. 9.4). This fluid, for which the joint is named, is rich in albumin and hyaluronic acid, which give it a viscous, slippery texture similar to raw egg white.[9] It nourishes the articular cartilages, removes their wastes, and makes movements at synovial joints almost friction-free. A connective tissue **joint (articular) capsule** encloses the cavity and retains the fluid. It has an outer **fibrous capsule** continuous with the periosteum of the adjoining bones, and an inner, cellular **synovial membrane.** The synovial membrane is composed

mainly of fibroblast-like cells that secrete the fluid, and is populated by macrophages that remove debris from the joint cavity.

In a few synovial joints, fibrocartilage grows inward from the joint capsule and forms a pad between the articulating bones. In the jaw (temporomandibular) and distal radioulnar joints, and at both ends of the clavicle (sternoclavicular and acromioclavicular joints), the pad crosses the entire joint capsule and is called an **articular disc** (see fig. 9.18c). In the knee, two cartilages extend inward from the left and right but do not entirely cross the joint (see fig. 9.23d). Each is called a **meniscus**[10] because of its crescent shape. These cartilages absorb shock and pressure, guide the bones across each other, improve the fit between the bones, and stabilize the joint, reducing the chance of dislocation.

Accessory structures associated with a synovial joint include tendons, ligaments, and bursae. A **tendon** is a strip or sheet of tough collagenous connective tissue that attaches a muscle to a bone. Tendons are often the most important structures in stabilizing a joint. A **ligament** is a similar tissue that attaches one bone to another. Several ligaments are named and illustrated in our later discussion of individual joints, and tendons are more fully considered in chapters 10 through 12 along with the gross anatomy of muscles.

A **bursa**[11] is a fibrous sac filled with synovial fluid, located between adjacent muscles or where a tendon passes over a bone (see fig. 9.19). Bursae cushion muscles, help tendons slide more easily over the joints, and sometimes enhance the mechanical effect of a muscle by modifying the direction in which its tendon pulls. Bursae called **tendon sheaths** are elongated cylinders wrapped around a tendon. These are especially numerous in the hand and

---

[8]*dia* = separate, apart + *arthr* = joint + *osis* = condition
[9]*ovi* = egg

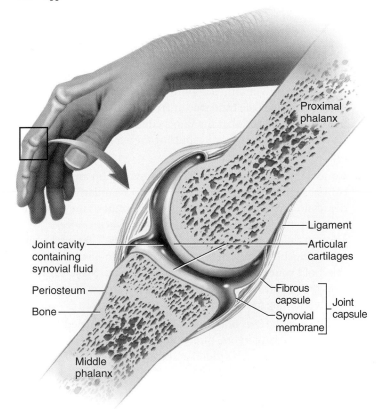

**Figure 9.4** Structure of a Simple Synovial Joint.
• *Why is a meniscus unnecessary in an interphalangeal joint?*

Proximal phalanx

Ligament

Articular cartilages

Fibrous capsule ⎤
Synovial membrane ⎦ Joint capsule

Joint cavity containing synovial fluid

Periosteum

Bone

Middle phalanx

---

# INSIGHT 9.1

## Clinical Application

### Exercise and Articular Cartilage

When synovial fluid is warmed by exercise, it becomes thinner (less viscous) and more easily absorbed by the articular cartilage. The cartilage then swells and provides a more effective cushion against compression. For this reason, a warm-up period before vigorous exercise helps protect the articular cartilage from undue wear and tear.

Because cartilage is nonvascular, its repetitive compression during exercise is important to its nutrition and waste removal. Each time a cartilage is compressed, fluid and metabolic wastes are squeezed out of it. When weight is taken off the joint, the cartilage absorbs synovial fluid like a sponge, and the fluid carries oxygen and nutrients to the chondrocytes. Lack of exercise causes the articular cartilages to deteriorate more rapidly from lack of nutrition, oxygenation, and waste removal.

Weight-bearing exercise builds bone mass and strengthens the muscles that stabilize many of the joints, thus reducing the risk of joint dislocations. Excessive joint stress, however, can hasten the progression of osteoarthritis (p. 258) by damaging the articular cartilage. Swimming is a good way of exercising the joints with minimal damage.

---

[10]*men* = moon, crescent + *iscus* = little
[11]*burs* = purse

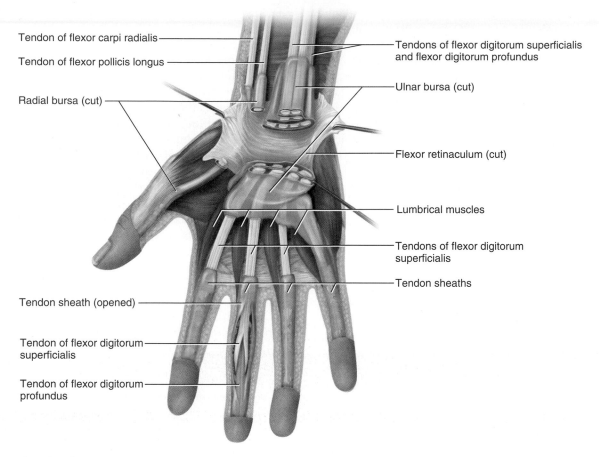

Tendon of flexor carpi radialis

Tendon of flexor pollicis longus

Radial bursa (cut)

Tendons of flexor digitorum superficialis and flexor digitorum profundus

Ulnar bursa (cut)

Flexor retinaculum (cut)

Lumbrical muscles

Tendons of flexor digitorum superficialis

Tendon sheaths

Tendon sheath (opened)

Tendon of flexor digitorum superficialis

Tendon of flexor digitorum profundus

**Figure 9.5** Tendon Sheaths and Other Bursae in the Hand and Wrist.

foot (fig. 9.5). **Bursitis** is inflammation of a bursa, usually due to overexertion of a joint. **Tendinitis** is a form of bursitis in which a tendon sheath is inflamed.

## Classes of Synovial Joints

There are six fundamental classes of synovial joints, distinguished by patterns of motion determined by the shapes of the articular surfaces of the bones. The upper limb contains examples of all six (fig. 9.6; table 9.1).

The movement of these joints can be described with reference to three mutually perpendicular planes in space (*x, y,* and *z*). If a bone can move in any of these planes, the joint is said to be **multiaxial;** if it can move in only two planes, the joint is **biaxial;** and if it moves in only one plane, the joint is **monaxial.** Here we survey examples of each, in descending order of mobility: one multiaxial type (ball-and-socket joints), three biaxial types (condylar, saddle, and plane joints), and two monaxial types (hinge and pivot joints).

1. **Ball-and-socket joints.** These are the shoulder and hip joints—the only multiaxial joints in the body. In both cases, one bone (the humerus or femur) has a smooth hemispherical head that fits into a cuplike socket on the other (the glenoid cavity of the scapula or the acetabulum of the hip bone).

2. **Condylar (ellipsoid) joints.** These joints exhibit an oval convex surface on one bone that fits into a similarly shaped depression on the other. The radiocarpal joint of the wrist and metacarpophalangeal (MET-uh-CAR-po-fah-LAN-jee-ul) joints at the bases of the fingers are examples. They are biaxial joints, capable of movement in two planes. To demonstrate this, hold your hand with the palm facing you. Make a fist, and these joints flex in the sagittal plane. Fan your fingers apart, and they move in the frontal plane.

3. **Saddle joints.** Here, both bones have a saddle-shaped surface—concave in one direction (like the front to rear curvature of a horse's saddle) and convex in the other (like

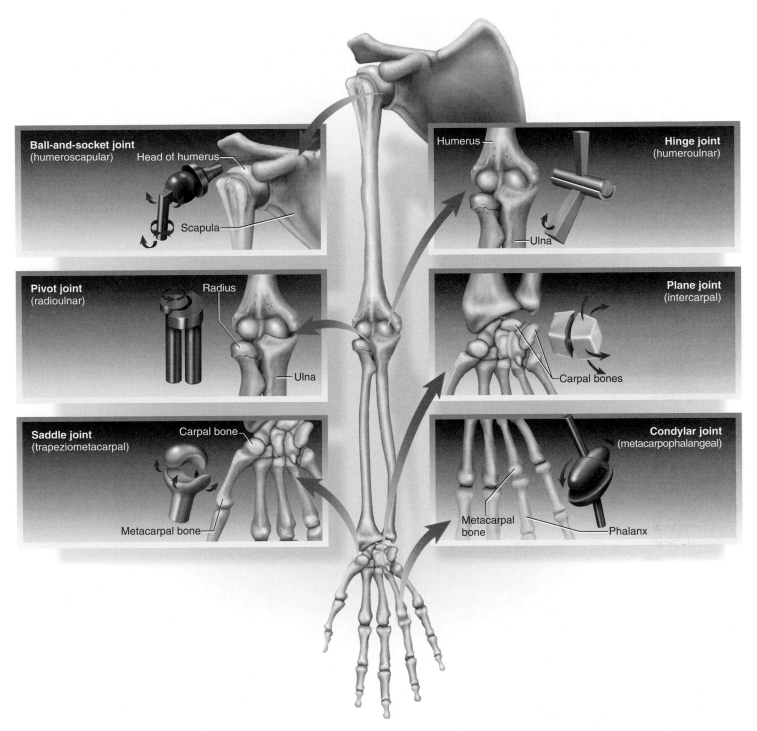

**Figure 9.6  The Six Types of Synovial Joints.** All six have representatives in the forelimb. Mechanical models show the types of motion possible at each joint.

the left to right curvature of a saddle). The clearest example of this is the trapeziometacarpal joint at the base of the thumb. Saddle joints are biaxial. The thumb, for example, moves in a frontal plane when you spread the fingers apart, and in a sagittal plane when you move it as if to grasp a tool such as a hammer. This range of motion gives us and other primates that anatomical hallmark, the opposable thumb. Another

saddle joint is the sternoclavicular joint, where the clavicle articulates with the sternum. The clavicle moves vertically in the frontal plane at this joint when you lift a suitcase, and moves horizontally in the transverse plane when you reach forward to push open a door.

4. **Plane (gliding) joints.** Here the bone surfaces are flat or only slightly concave and convex. The adjacent bones slide

over each other and have relatively limited movement. Plane joints are found between the carpal bones of the wrist, the tarsal bones of the ankle, and the articular processes of the vertebrae. Their movements, although slight, are complex. They are usually biaxial. For example, when the head is tilted forward and back, the articular facets of the vertebrae slide anteriorly and posteriorly; when the head is tilted from side to side, the facets slide laterally. Although any one joint moves only slightly, the combined action of the many joints in the wrist, ankle, and vertebral column allows for a significant amount of overall movement.

5. **Hinge joints.** These are essentially monaxial joints, moving freely in one plane with very little movement in any other. Examples include the elbow, knee, and interphalangeal (finger and toe) joints. In these cases, one bone has a convex (but not hemispherical) surface, such as the trochlea of the humerus and the condyles of the femur. This fits into a concave depression on the other bone, such as the trochlear notch of the ulna and the condyles of the tibia.

6. **Pivot joints.** These are monaxial joints in which a bone spins on its longitudinal axis. There are two principal examples: the atlantoaxial joint between the first two vertebrae and the radioulnar joint at the elbow. At the atlantoaxial joint, the dens of the axis projects into the vertebral foramen of the atlas and is held against its anterior arch by the transverse ligament (see fig. 7.24, p. 196). As the head rotates left and right, the skull and atlas pivot around the dens. At the radioulnar joint, the anular ligament of the ulna wraps around the neck of the radius. During pronation and supination of the forearm, the disclike radial head pivots like a wheel turning on its axle. The edge of the wheel spins against the radial notch of the ulna like a car tire spinning in snow.

Some joints cannot be easily classified into any one of these six categories. The temporomandibular joint, for example, has some aspects of condylar, hinge, and plane joints. It clearly has an elongated condyle where it meets the temporal bone of the cranium, but it moves in a hingelike fashion when the mandible moves up and down in speaking, biting, and chewing; it glides slightly for-

| TABLE 9.1 | Anatomical Classification of the Joints |
|---|---|
| **Joint** | **Characteristics and Examples** |
| **Bony joint (synostosis)** | Former fibrous or cartilaginous joint in which adjacent bones have become fused by ossification. Examples: midsagittal line of frontal bone; fusion of epiphysis and diaphysis of an adult long bone; and fusion of ilium, ischium, and pubis to form hip bone |
| **Fibrous joint (synarthrosis)** | Adjacent bones bound by collagen fibers extending from the matrix of one into the matrix of the other |
| Suture (figs. 9.1a, 9.2) | Immobile fibrous joint between cranial or facial bones |
| Serrate suture | Bones joined by a wavy line formed by interlocking teeth along the margins. Examples: coronal, sagittal, and lambdoid sutures |
| Lap suture | Bones beveled to overlap each other; superficial appearance is a smooth line. Example: squamous suture around temporal bone |
| Plane suture | Bones butted against each other without overlapping or interlocking. Example: palatine suture |
| Gomphosis (fig. 9.1b) | Insertion of a tooth into a socket, held in place by collagen fibers of periodontal ligament |
| Syndesmosis (fig. 9.1c) | Slightly movable joint held together by ligaments or interosseous membranes. Examples: tibiofibular joint and radioulnar joint |
| **Cartilaginous joint (amphiarthrosis)** | Adjacent bones bound by cartilage |
| Synchondrosis (fig. 9.3a) | Bones held together by hyaline cartilage. Examples: articulation of rib 1 with sternum, and epiphyseal plate uniting the epiphysis and diaphysis of a long bone of a child |
| Symphysis (fig. 9.3b, c) | Slightly movable joint held together by fibrocartilage. Examples: intervertebral discs and pubic symphysis |
| **Synovial joint (diarthrosis) (figs. 9.4 and 9.6)** | Adjacent bones covered with hyaline articular cartilage, separated by lubricating synovial fluid and enclosed in a fibrous joint capsule |
| Ball-and-socket | Multiaxial diarthrosis in which a smooth hemispherical head of one bone fits into a cuplike depression of another. Examples: shoulder and hip joints |
| Condylar (ellipsoid) | Biaxial diarthrosis in which an oval convex surface of one bone articulates with an elliptical depression of another. Examples: radiocarpal and metacarpophalangeal joints |
| Saddle | Joint in which each bone surface is saddle-shaped (concave on one axis and convex on the perpendicular axis). Examples: trapeziometacarpal and sternoclavicular joints |
| Plane | Usually biaxial diarthroses with slightly concave or convex bone surfaces that slide across each other. Examples: intercarpal and intertarsal joints; joints between the articular processes of the vertebrae |
| Hinge | Monaxial diarthrosis, able to flex and extend in only one plane. Examples: elbow, knee, and interphalangeal joints |
| Pivot | Joint in which a projection of one bone fits into a ringlike ligament of another, allowing one bone to rotate on its longitudinal axis. Examples: atlantoaxial joint and proximal radioulnar joint |

ward when the jaw juts (protracts) to take a bite; and it glides from side to side to grind food between the molars. The knee is a classic hinge joint, but has an element of the pivot type; when we lock our knees to stand more effortlessly, the femur pivots slightly on the tibia. The humeroradial joint (between humerus and radius) acts as a hinge joint when the elbow flexes and a pivot joint when the forearm pronates.

## Movements of Synovial Joints

Kinesiology, physical therapy, and other medical and scientific fields have a specific vocabulary for the movements of synovial joints. The following terms form a basis for describing the muscle actions in chapters 11 and 12 and may also be indispensible to your advanced coursework or intended career. This section introduces the terms for joint movements, many of which are presented in pairs or groups with opposite or contrasting meanings. This section relies on familiarity with the three cardinal anatomical planes and the directional terms in atlas A. All directional terms used here refer to a person in standard anatomical position. When one is in anatomical position, each joint is said to be in its **zero position.** Joint movements can be described as deviation from the zero position or returning to it.

### Flexion and Extension

**Flexion** (fig. 9.7) is a movement that decreases a joint angle, usually in the sagittal plane. This is particularly common at hinge joints—for example, bending of the elbow or knee—but it occurs in other types of joints as well. For example, if you hold out your hands with the palms up, flexion of the wrist tips your palms toward you. The meaning of *flexion* is perhaps least obvious in the ball-and-socket joints of the shoulder and hip. At the shoulder, it means to raise your arm as if pointing at something directly in front of you or to continue in that arc and point toward the sky. At the hip, it means to raise the thigh, for example to place your foot on the next higher step when ascending a flight of stairs.

**Extension** is a movement that straightens a joint and generally returns a body part to the zero position—for example, straightening the elbow, wrist, or knee, or returning the arm or thigh back to zero position. In stair climbing, both the hip and knee extend when lifting the body to the next higher step.

Extreme extension of a joint, beyond the zero position, is called **hyperextension.**[12] For example, if you hold your hand in front of you with the palm down, then raise the back of your hand as if you were admiring a new ring, you hyperextend the wrist. Hyperextension of the upper or lower limb means to move the limb to a position behind the frontal plane of the trunk, as in reaching around with your arm to scratch your back. Each backswing of the lower limb when you walk hyperextends the hip.

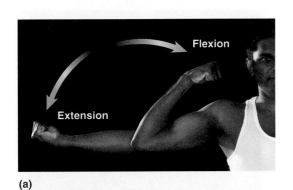

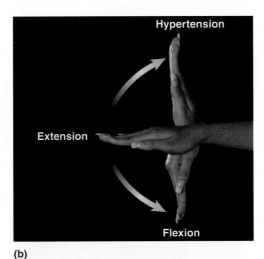

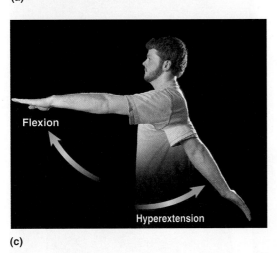

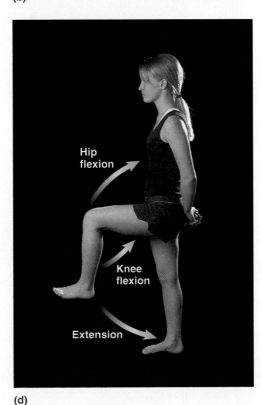

**Figure 9.7** **Flexion and Extension.** (a) Flexion and extension of the elbow. (b) Flexion, extension, and hyperextension of the wrist. (c) Flexion and hyperextension of the shoulder. (d) Flexion and extension of the hip and knee.

(a)   (b)   (c)   (d)

---

[12]*hyper* = excessive, beyond normal

Flexion and extension occur at nearly all diarthroses, but hyperextension is limited to only a few. At most diarthroses, ligaments or bone structure prevents hyperextension.

### THINK ABOUT IT

*Some synovial joints have articular surfaces or ligaments that prevent them from being hyperextended. Try hyperextending some of your synovial joints and list a few for which this is impossible.*

### Abduction and Adduction

**Abduction**[13] (ab-DUC-shun) (fig. 9.8a) is the movement of a body part in the frontal plane away from the midline of the body—for

example, moving the feet apart to stand spread-legged, or raising an arm to one side of the body. **Adduction**[14] (fig. 9.8b) is movement in the frontal plane back toward the midline. Some joints can be **hyperadducted,** as when you stand with your ankles crossed, cross your fingers, or hyperadduct the shoulder to stand with your elbows straight and your hands clasped below your waist. You **hyperabduct** the arm if you raise it high enough to cross slightly over the front or back of your head.

### Elevation and Depression

**Elevation** (fig. 9.9a) is a movement that raises a body part vertically in the frontal plane. **Depression** (fig. 9.9b) lowers a body part in the same plane. For example, to lift a heavy suitcase from the floor, you elevate your scapula; in setting it down again, you depress the scapula.

---

[13]*ab* = away + *duc* = to lead or carry

[14]*ad* = toward + *duc* = to lead or carry

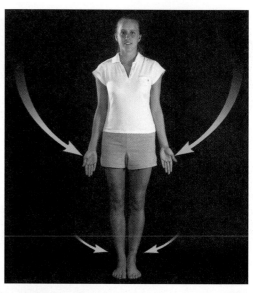

**Figure 9.8** Abduction and Adduction.

**(a) Abduction**

**(b) Adduction**

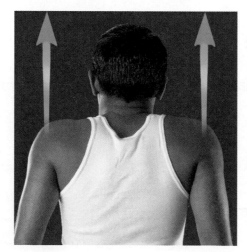

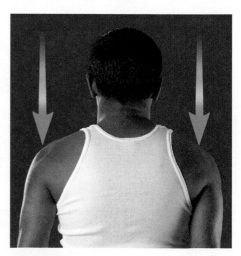

**Figure 9.9** Elevation and Depression.
● *In addition to the scapulae, what bone(s) undergo elevation and depression in the motion illustrated here? Identify a locality other than the shoulder where elevation and depression occur.*

**(a) Elevation**

**(b) Depression**

(a) Protraction       (b) Retraction

**Figure 9.10**  Protraction and Retraction.

**Figure 9.11**  Circumduction.

## Protraction and Retraction

**Protraction**[15] (fig. 9.10a) is the anterior movement of a body part in the transverse (horizontal) plane, and **retraction**[16] (fig. 9.10b) is posterior movement. Your shoulder protracts, for example, when you reach in front of you to push a door open. It retracts when you return it to the resting (zero) position or pull the shoulders back to stand at military attention. Such exercises as rowing a boat, bench presses, and push-ups involve repeated protraction and retraction of the shoulders.

## Circumduction

In **circumduction**[17] (fig. 9.11), one end of an appendage remains fairly stationary while the other end makes a circular motion. If an artist standing at an easel reaches forward and draws a circle on a canvas, she circumducts the upper limb; the shoulder remains stationary while the hand moves in a circle. A baseball player winding up for the pitch circumducts the upper limb in a more extreme "windmill" fashion. One can also circumduct an individual finger, the hand, the thigh, the foot, the trunk, and the head.

> **THINK ABOUT IT**
>
> *Choose any example of circumduction and explain why this motion is actually a sequence of flexion, abduction, extension, and adduction.*

## Rotation

In one sense, the term *rotation* applies to any bone turning around a fixed axis, as described earlier. But in the terminology of specific joint movements, **rotation** (fig. 9.12) is a movement in which a bone spins on its longitudinal axis. For example, if you stand with bent elbow and move your forearm to place your palm against your abdomen, your humerus spins in a motion called **medial (internal) rotation**. If you make the opposite action, so the forearm points away from the trunk, your humerus undergoes **lateral (external) rotation**. If you turn your right foot so your toes are pointing away from your left foot, and then turn it so your toes are pointing toward your left foot, your femur undergoes lateral and medial rotation, respectively. Other examples are given in the ensuing discussions of forearm and head movements.

## Supination and Pronation

Supination and pronation (fig. 9.13) are known primarily as forearm movements, but see also the later discussion of foot movements. **Supination**[18] (SOO-pih-NAY-shun) of the forearm is a movement that turns the palm to face anteriorly or upward; in anatomical position, the forearm is supinated and the radius is parallel to the ulna. **Pronation**[19] is the opposite movement, causing the palm to face posteriorly or downward and the radius to cross the ulna like an X. During these movements, the concave end of the disc-shaped head of the radius spins on the capitulum of the humerus, and the edge of the disc spins in the radial notch of the ulna. The ulna remains relatively stationary.

As an aid to remembering these terms, think of it this way: You are *prone* to stand in the most comfortable position, which is with the forearm *pronated*. But if you were holding a bowl of *soup* in your palm, you would need to *supinate* the forearm to keep from spilling it.

---

[15]*pro* = forward + *trac* = to pull or draw
[16]*re* = back + *trac* = to pull or draw
[17]*circum* = around + *duc* = to carry, lead

[18]*supin* = to lay back
[19]*pron* = to bend forward

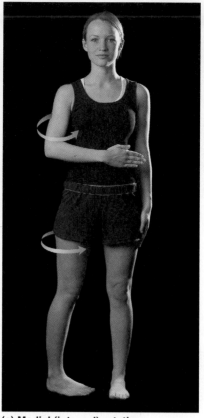

**(a) Medial (internal) rotation**

**(b) Lateral (external) rotation**

**Figure 9.12** **Medial (Internal) and Lateral (External) Rotation.** Shows rotation of both the humerus and the femur.

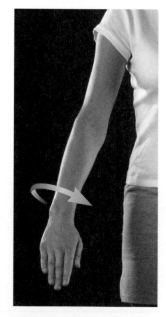

**(a) Supination**

**(b) Pronation**

**Figure 9.13** **Supination and Pronation.**

Chapter 12 describes the muscles that perform these actions. Of these, the *supinator* is the most powerful. Supination is the type of movement you would usually make with your right hand to turn a doorknob clockwise or to drive a screw into a piece of wood. The threads of screws and bolts are designed with the relative strength of the supinator in mind, so the greatest power can be applied when driving them with a screwdriver in the right hand.

We will now consider a few body regions that combine the foregoing motions or have unique movements and terminology.

## Special Movements of the Head and Trunk

*Flexion* of the vertebral column produces forward-bending movements, as in tilting the head forward or bending at the waist in a toe-touching exercise (fig. 9.14a). *Extension* of the vertebral column straightens the trunk or neck, as in standing up or returning the head to a forward-looking zero position. *Hyperextension* is employed in looking up toward the sky or bending over backward (fig. 9.14b).

**Lateral flexion** is tilting the head or the trunk to the right or left of the midline (fig. 9.14c). Twisting at the waist or turning the head is called **right rotation** or **left rotation** when the chest or the face turns to the right or left of the forward-facing zero position (fig. 9.14d, e). Powerful right and left rotation at the waist is important in baseball pitching, discus throwing, and other sports.

## Special Movements of the Mandible

Movements of the mandible are concerned especially with biting and chewing (fig. 9.15). Imagine taking a bite of raw carrot. Most people have some degree of overbite; at rest, the upper incisors (front teeth) overhang the lower ones. For effective biting, however, the chisel-like edges of the incisors must meet. In preparation to bite, we therefore *protract* the mandible to bring the lower incisors forward. After the bite is taken, we *retract* it. To actually take the bite, we must *depress* the mandible to open the mouth, then *elevate* it so the incisors can cut off the piece of food.

Next, to chew the food, we do not simply raise and lower the mandible as if hammering away at the food between the teeth; rather, we exercise a grinding action that shreds the food between the broad, bumpy surfaces of the premolars and molars. This entails a side-to-side movement of the mandible called **lateral excursion** (movement to the left or right of the zero position) and **medial excursion** (movement back to the median, zero position).

## Special Movements of the Hand and Fingers

The hand moves anteriorly and posteriorly by flexion and extension of the wrist. It can also move in the frontal plane. **Radial flexion**

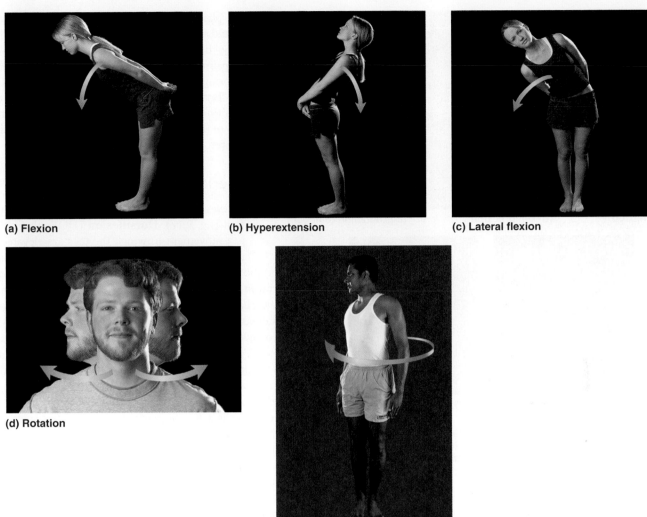

**Figure 9.14** Movements of the Head and Trunk.
● *In rotation of the head (d), what bone spins on its axis?*

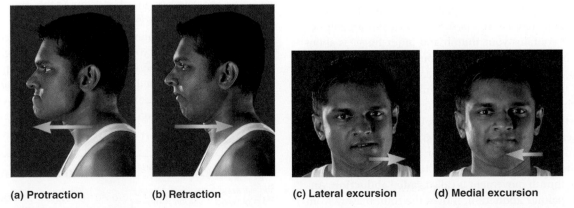

**Figure 9.15** Movements of the Mandible.

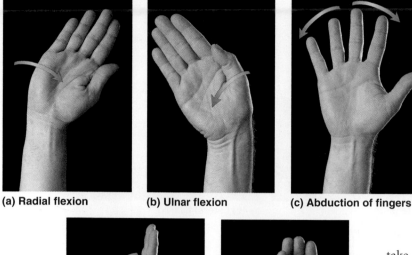

| (a) Radial flexion | (b) Ulnar flexion | (c) Abduction of fingers |

**(d) Palmar abduction of thumb**   **(e) Opposition of thumb**

**Figure 9.16** **Movements of the Hand and Fingers.** (a) Radial flexion of the wrist. (b) Ulnar flexion of the wrist. (c) Abduction of the fingers. The thumb position in this figure is called *radial abduction*. Parts (a) and (b) show adduction of the fingers. (d) Palmar abduction of the thumb. (e) Opposition of the thumb (reposition is shown in parts [a] and [b]).

tilts the hand toward the thumb, and **ulnar flexion** tilts it toward the little finger (fig. 9.16a, b). We often use such motions when waving hello to someone with a side-to-side wave of the hand or when washing windows or polishing furniture.

Movements of the fingers are more varied, especially those of the thumb (fig. 9.16c–e). *Flexion* of the fingers is curling them; *extension* is straightening them. Most people cannot hyperextend their fingers. Spreading the fingers apart is *abduction,* and bringing them together again so they touch along their surfaces is *adduction.*

The thumb is different, however, because in embryonic development it rotates nearly 90° from the rest of the hand. If you hold your hand in a completely relaxed position, you will probably see that the plane that contains your thumb and index finger is about 90° to the plane that contains the index through little fingers. Much of the terminology of thumb movement therefore differs from that of the other four fingers. *Flexion* of the thumb is bending the joints so the tip of the thumb is directed toward the palm, and *extension* is straightening it. If your place the palm of your hand on a table top with all five fingers parallel and touching, the thumb is extended. Keeping your hand there, if you move your thumb away from the index finger so they form a 90° angle (but both are in the plane of the table top), the thumb movement is called **radial abduction.** Another movement, **palmar abduction,** moves the thumb away from

the plane of the hand so it points anteriorly, as you would do if you were about to wrap your hand around a tool handle (fig. 9.16d). From either position—radial or palmar abduction—*adduction* of the thumb means to bring it back to touch the base of the index finger.

Two additional terms are unique to the thumb: **Opposition**[20] means to move the thumb to touch the tip of any of the other four fingers (fig. 9.16e). **Reposition**[21] is the return to zero position.

## Special Movements of the Foot

A few additional movement terms are unique to the foot (fig. 9.17). **Dorsiflexion** (DOR-sih-FLEC-shun) is a movement in which the toes are elevated, as one might do in applying toenail polish. In each step you take, the foot dorsiflexes as it comes forward. This prevents you from scraping your toes on the ground and results in the characteristic *heel strike* of human locomotion when the foot touches down in front of you. **Plantar flexion** is movement of the foot so the toes point downward, as in pressing the gas pedal of a car or standing on tiptoes. This motion also produces the *toe-off* in each step you take, as the heel of the foot behind you lifts off the ground. Plantar flexion can be a very powerful motion, epitomized by high jumpers and the jump shots of basketball players.

**Inversion**[22] is a foot movement that tips the soles medially, somewhat facing each other, and **eversion**[23] is a movement that tips them laterally, away from each other. These movements are common in fast sports such as tennis and football, and sometimes cause ankle sprains. These terms also refer to congenital deformities of the feet, which are often corrected by orthopedic shoes or braces.

*Pronation* and *supination,* while used mainly for forearm movements, also apply to the feet but refer here to a more complex combination of movements. Pronation of the foot is a combination of dorsiflexion, eversion, and abduction—that is, the toes are elevated and turned away from the other foot and the sole is tilted away. Supination of the foot is a combination of plantar flexion, inversion, and adduction—the toes are lowered and turned toward the other foot and the sole is tilted toward it. These may seem a little difficult to visualize and perform, but they are ordinary motions during walking, running, and crossing uneven surfaces such as stepping stones.

You can perhaps understand why these terms apply to the feet if you place the palms of your hands on a table and pretend they are your soles. Tilt your hands so the inner edge (thumb side) of each is raised from the table. This is like raising the medial edge of your foot from the ground, and as you can see, it involves a slight supination of your forearms. Resting your hands palms down on a table, your forearms are already pronated; but if you raise the outer edges of your hands (the little finger side), like pronating the feet, you will see that it involves a continuation of the pronation movement of the forearm.

---

[20]*op* = against + *posit* = to place
[21]*re* = back + *posit* = to place
[22]*in* = inward + *version* = turning
[23]*e* = outward + *version* = turning

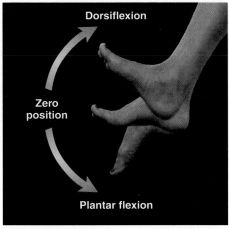

(b) Inversion

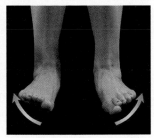

(c) Eversion

(a) Flexion of ankle

**Figure 9.17** Movements of the Foot.
● *Identify some common activities in which inversion and eversion of the foot would be important.*

## Range of Motion

A joint's **range of motion (ROM)** is the number of degrees through which one bone can move relative to another at that joint. For example, the ankle has a ROM of about 74°, the first knuckle about 90°, and the knee about 130° to 140°. ROM obviously affects a person's functional independence and quality of life. It is also an important consideration in training for athletics or dance, in clinical diagnosis, and in monitoring the progress of rehabilitation. Several factors affect the ROM and stability of a joint:

- **Structure of the articular surfaces of the bones.** In many cases, joint movement is limited by the shapes of the bone surfaces. For example, you cannot straighten your elbow beyond 180° or so because, as it straightens, the olecranon of the ulna swings into the olecranon fossa of the humerus and cannot move farther.

- **Strength and tautness of ligaments and joint capsules.** Some bone surfaces impose little if any limitation on joint movement. The articulations of the phalanges are an example; as one can see by examining a dry skeleton, an interphalangeal joint can bend through a broad arc. In life, however, these bones are joined by ligaments that limit their movement. As you flex one of your knuckles, ligaments on the anterior (palmar) side of the joint go slack, but ligaments on the posterior (dorsal) side tighten and prevent the joint from flexing beyond 90° or so. The knee is another case in point. In kicking a football, the knee rapidly extends to about 180°, but it can go no farther. Its motion is limited in part by a *cruciate ligament* and other knee ligaments described later. Gymnasts, dancers, and acrobats increase the ROM of their synovial joints by gradually stretching their ligaments during training. "Double-jointed" people have unusually large ROMs at some joints, not because the joint is actually double or fundamentally different from normal in its anatomy, but because the ligaments are unusually long or slack.

- **Action of the muscles and tendons.** Extension of the knee is also limited by the *hamstring muscles* on the posterior side of the thigh. In many other joints, too, pairs of muscles oppose each other and moderate the speed and range of joint motion. Even a resting muscle maintains a state of tension called *muscle tone*, which serves in many cases to stabilize a joint. One of the major factors preventing dislocation of the shoulder joint, for example, is tension in the *biceps brachii* muscle, whose tendons cross the joint, insert on the scapula, and hold the head of the humerus against the glenoid cavity. The nervous system continually monitors and adjusts joint angles and muscle tone to maintain joint stability and limit unwanted movements.

### *Before You Go On*

*Answer the following questions to test your understanding of the preceding section:*

7. What are the two components of a joint capsule? What is the function of each?

8. Give at least one example each of a monaxial, biaxial, and multiaxial joint, and explain the reason for its classification.

9. Name the joints that would be involved if you reached directly overhead and screwed a light bulb into a ceiling fixture. Describe the joint actions that would occur.

## Anatomy of Selected Synovial Joints

### *Objectives*

When you have completed this section, you should be able to

- identify the major anatomical features of the jaw, shoulder, elbow, hip, knee, and ankle joints; and

- explain how the anatomical differences between these joints are related to differences in function.

We now examine the gross anatomy of certain diarthroses. It is beyond the scope of this book to discuss all of them, but the ones selected here most often require medical attention and many of them have a strong bearing on athletic performance.

## The Jaw Joint

The **temporomandibular joint** (**TMJ**) is the articulation of the condyle of the mandible with the mandibular fossa of the temporal bone (fig. 9.18). You can feel its action by pressing your fingertips against the jaw immediately anterior to the ear while opening and closing your mouth. This joint combines elements of condylar, hinge, and plane joints. It functions in a hingelike fashion when the mandible is elevated and depressed, it glides slightly forward when the jaw is protracted to take a bite, and it glides from side to side to grind food between the molars.

The synovial cavity of the TMJ is divided into superior and inferior chambers by an articular disc, which permits lateral and medial excursion of the mandible. Two ligaments support the joint. The **lateral ligament** prevents posterior displacement of the mandible. If the jaw receives a hard blow, this ligament normally

INSIGHT 9.2    ●●●

### Clinical Application

## TMJ Syndrome

Temporomandibular joint (TMJ) syndrome has received medical recognition only recently, although it may affect as many as 75 million Americans. It can cause moderate intermittent facial pain, clicking sounds in the jaw, limitation of jaw movement, and in some people, more serious symptoms—severe headaches, vertigo (dizziness), tinnitus (ringing in the ears), and pain radiating from the jaw down the neck, shoulders, and back. It seems to be caused by a combination of psychological tension and malocclusion (misalignment of the teeth). Treatment may involve psychological management, physical therapy, analgesic and anti-inflammatory drugs, and sometimes corrective dental appliances to align the teeth properly.

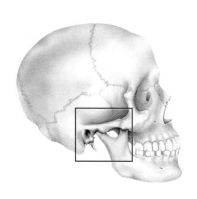

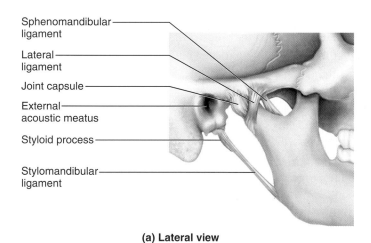

Sphenomandibular ligament

Lateral ligament

Joint capsule

External acoustic meatus

Styloid process

Stylomandibular ligament

**(a) Lateral view**

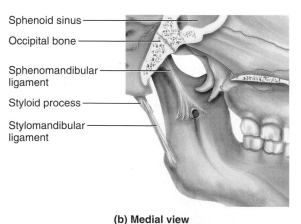

Sphenoid sinus

Occipital bone

Sphenomandibular ligament

Styloid process

Stylomandibular ligament

**(b) Medial view**

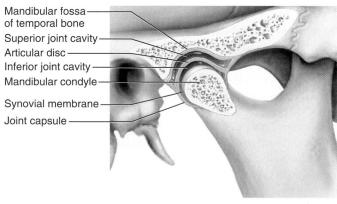

Mandibular fossa of temporal bone

Superior joint cavity

Articular disc

Inferior joint cavity

Mandibular condyle

Synovial membrane

Joint capsule

**(c) Sagittal section**

**Figure 9.18** The Temporomandibular Joint (TMJ).

prevents the condylar process from being driven upward and fracturing the base of the skull. The **sphenomandibular ligament** on the medial side of the joint extends from the sphenoid bone to the ramus of the mandible. A *stylomandibular ligament* extends from the styloid process to the angle of the mandible but is not part of the TMJ proper.

A deep yawn or other strenuous depression of the mandible can dislocate the TMJ by making the condyle pop out of the fossa and slip forward. The joint can be relocated by pressing down on the molars while pushing the jaw backward.

# The Shoulder Joint

The shoulder joint is called the **glenohumeral (humeroscapular) joint** (fig. 9.19). It is the most freely movable joint of the body but also one of the most commonly injured. The shallowness of the glenoid cavity and looseness of the joint capsule sacrifice joint stability for freedom of movement. The cavity, however, has a ring of fibrocartilage called the **glenoid labrum**[24] around its margin, which makes it somewhat deeper than it appears on a dried skeleton.

---

[24]*labrum* = lip

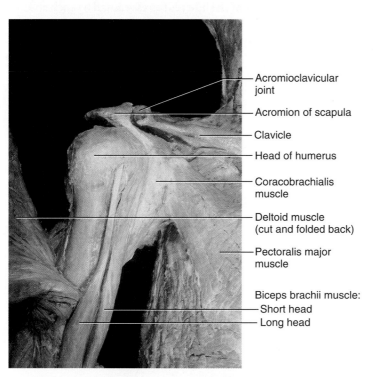

**(a) Anterior dissection**

Labels:
- Acromioclavicular joint
- Acromion of scapula
- Clavicle
- Head of humerus
- Coracobrachialis muscle
- Deltoid muscle (cut and folded back)
- Pectoralis major muscle
- Biceps brachii muscle:
- Short head
- Long head

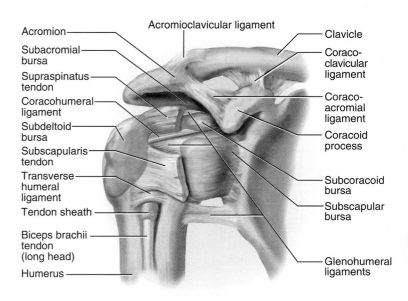

**(b) Anterior view**

Labels:
- Acromion
- Subacromial bursa
- Supraspinatus tendon
- Coracohumeral ligament
- Subdeltoid bursa
- Subscapularis tendon
- Transverse humeral ligament
- Tendon sheath
- Biceps brachii tendon (long head)
- Humerus
- Acromioclavicular ligament
- Clavicle
- Coraco-clavicular ligament
- Coraco-acromial ligament
- Coracoid process
- Subcoracoid bursa
- Subscapular bursa
- Glenohumeral ligaments

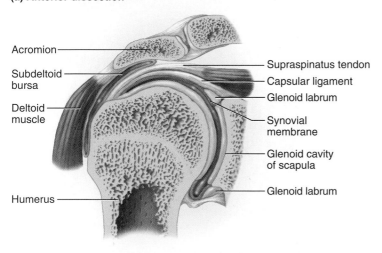

**(c) Frontal section**

Labels:
- Acromion
- Subdeltoid bursa
- Deltoid muscle
- Humerus
- Supraspinatus tendon
- Capsular ligament
- Glenoid labrum
- Synovial membrane
- Glenoid cavity of scapula
- Glenoid labrum

**(d) Lateral view, humerus removed**

Labels:
- Acromion
- Supraspinatus tendon
- Subdeltoid bursa
- Infraspinatus tendon
- Glenoid cavity (articular cartilage)
- Teres minor tendon
- Synovial membrane (cut)
- Coracoid process
- Coracohumeral ligament
- Superior glenohumeral ligament
- Biceps brachii tendon (long head)
- Subscapular bursa
- Subscapularis tendon
- Middle glenohumeral ligament
- Inferior glenohumeral ligament

**Figure 9.19** The Glenohumeral (Shoulder) Joint.
● *The socket of the shoulder joint is a little deeper in life than it appears on a dried skeleton. What structure makes it so?*

Five principal ligaments support this joint. The **coracohumeral ligament** extends from the coracoid process of the scapula to the greater tubercle of the humerus, and the **transverse humeral ligament** extends from the greater to the lesser tubercle of the humerus, creating a tunnel, the intertubercular sulcus, through which a tendon of the biceps brachii passes. The other three ligaments, called **glenohumeral ligaments,** are relatively weak and sometimes absent.

A tendon of the biceps brachii muscle is the most important stabilizer of the shoulder. It originates on the margin of the glenoid cavity, passes through the joint capsule, and emerges into the intertubercular sulcus, where it is held by the transverse humeral ligament. Inferior to the sulcus, it merges into the biceps brachii. Thus, the tendon functions as a taut, adjustable strap that holds the humerus against the glenoid cavity.

In addition to the biceps brachii, four muscles important in stabilizing the glenohumeral joint are the *subscapularis, supraspinatus,* *infraspinatus,* and *teres minor.* The tendons of these four muscles form the *rotator cuff,* which is fused to the joint capsule on all sides except inferiorly. The rotator cuff is discussed more fully on page 331.

Shoulder dislocations are very painful and can result in permanent damage. The most common dislocation is downward displacement of the humerus, because (1) the rotator cuff protects the joint in all directions except inferiorly, and (2) the joint is protected from above by the coracoid process, acromion process, and clavicle. Dislocations most often occur when the arm is abducted and then receives a blow from above—for example, when the outstretched arm is struck by heavy objects falling off a shelf. They also occur in children who are jerked off the ground by one arm or forced to follow by a hard tug on the arm. Children are especially prone to such injury not only because of the inherent stress caused by such abuse, but also because a child's shoulder is not fully ossified and the rotator cuff is not strong enough to withstand such stress. Because this

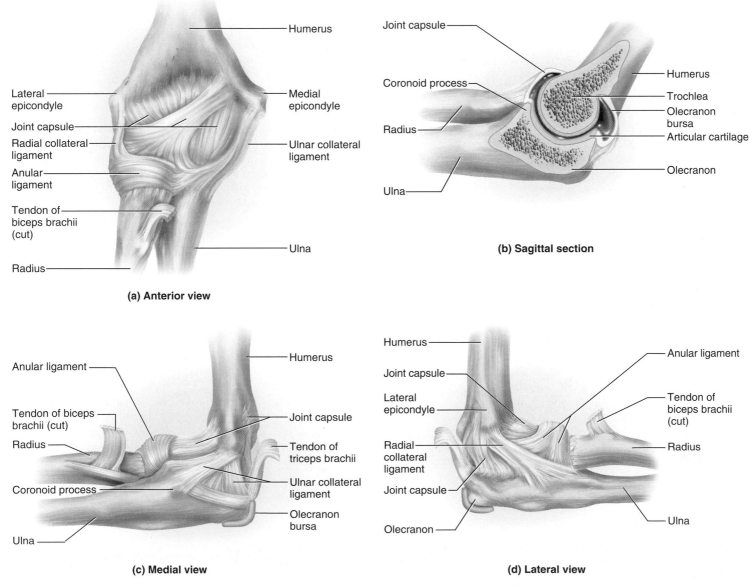

**Figure 9.20** The Elbow Joint.

joint is so easily dislocated, you should never attempt to move an immobilized person by pulling on his or her arm.

Four bursae are associated with the shoulder joint. Their names describe their locations—the **subdeltoid, subacromial, subcoracoid,** and **subscapular bursae.**

## The Elbow Joint

The elbow is a hinge joint composed of two articulations—the **humeroulnar joint,** where the trochlea of the humerus joins the trochlear notch of the ulna, and the **humeroradial joint,** where the capitulum of the humerus meets the head of the radius (fig. 9.20). Both are enclosed in a single joint capsule. On the posterior side of the elbow, there is a prominent **olecranon bursa** to ease the movement of tendons over the elbow. Side-to-side motions of the elbow joint are restricted by a pair of ligaments, the **radial (lateral) collateral ligament** and **ulnar (medial) collateral ligament.**

Another joint occurs in the elbow region, the **proximal radioulnar joint,** but it is not involved in the hinge. At this joint, the disclike head of the radius fits into the radial notch of the ulna and is held in place by the **anular ligament,** which encircles the head of the radius and attaches at each end to the ulna.

## The Hip Joint

The **coxal** (hip) **joint** is the point where the head of the femur inserts into the acetabulum of the hip bone (fig. 9.22). Because the coxal joints bear much of the body's weight, they have deep sockets and are much more stable than the shoulder joint. The depth of the socket is somewhat greater than you see on dried bones because a horseshoe-shaped ring of fibrocartilage, the **acetabular labrum,** is attached to its rim. A **transverse acetabular ligament** bridges a gap in the inferior margin of the acetabular labrum. Dislocations of the hip are rare, but some infants suffer congenital dislocations because the acetabulum is

# INSIGHT 9.3

## Clinical Application

### Pulled Elbow

The immature skeletons of children and adolescents are especially vulnerable to injury. Pulled elbow (dislocation of the radius), a common injury in preschool children (especially girls), typically occurs when an adult lifts or jerks a child up by one arm when the arm was pronated, as in lifting a child into a high chair or shopping cart (fig. 9.21). This tears the anular ligament from the head of the radius, and the radius pulls

partially or entirely out of the ligament. The proximal part of the torn ligament is then painfully pinched between the radial head and the capitulum of the humerus. Radial dislocation is treated by supinating the forearm with the elbow flexed and then putting the arm in a sling for about 2 weeks—time enough for the anular ligament to heal.

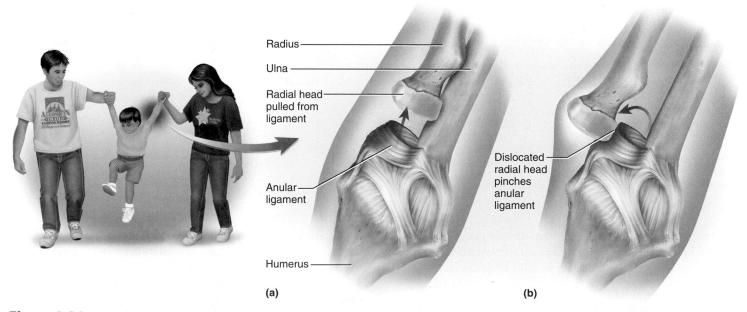

(a)    (b)

**Figure 9.21** **Pulled Elbow.** Lifting a child by the arm can dislocate the radius. (a) The anular ligament tears, and the radial head is pulled from the ligament. (b) Muscle contraction pulls the radius upward. The head of the radius produces a lump on the lateral side of the elbow and may painfully pinch the anular ligament.

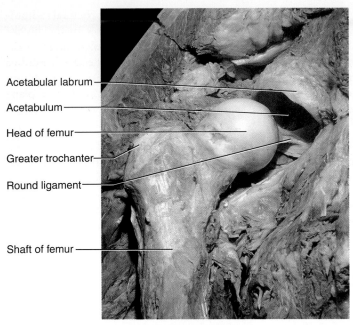

**(a) Anterior dissection**

Acetabular labrum
Acetabulum
Head of femur
Greater trochanter
Round ligament
Shaft of femur

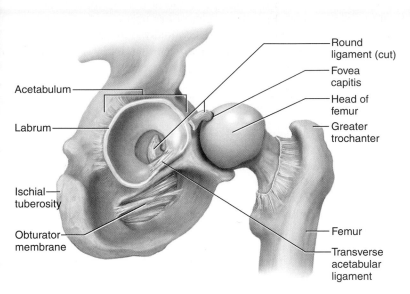

**(b) Lateral view, femur retracted**

Acetabulum
Labrum
Ischial tuberosity
Obturator membrane
Round ligament (cut)
Fovea capitis
Head of femur
Greater trochanter
Femur
Transverse acetabular ligament

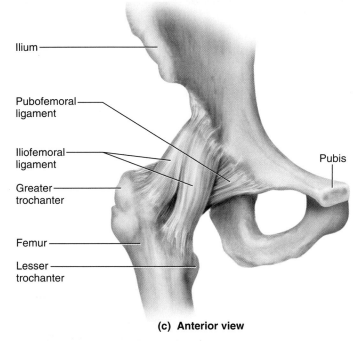

**(c) Anterior view**

Ilium
Pubofemoral ligament
Iliofemoral ligament
Greater trochanter
Femur
Lesser trochanter
Pubis

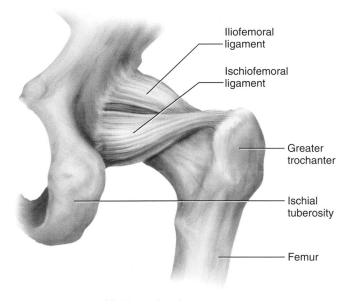

**(d) Posterior view**

Iliofemoral ligament
Ischiofemoral ligament
Greater trochanter
Ischial tuberosity
Femur

**Figure 9.22** The Coxal (Hip) Joint.
● *True or false? The round ligament holds the head of the femur tightly in the acetabulum. Explain.*

not deep enough to hold the head of the femur in place. This condition can be treated by placing the infant in traction until the acetabulum develops enough strength to support the body's weight.

### THINK ABOUT IT

*Where else in the body is there a structure similar to the acetabular labrum? What do those two locations have in common?*

Ligaments that support the coxal joint include the **iliofemoral** (ILL-ee-oh-FEM-oh-rul) and **pubofemoral** (PYU-bo-FEM-or-ul) **ligaments** on the anterior side and the **ischiofemoral** (ISS-kee-oh-FEM-or-ul) **ligament** on the posterior side. The name of each ligament refers to the bones to which it attaches—the femur and the ilium, pubis, or ischium. When you stand up, these ligaments become twisted and pull the head of the femur tightly into the acetabulum. The head of the femur has a conspicuous pit called the *fovea capitis*. The **round ligament**, or **ligamentum** teres[25] (TERR-eez), arises here and attaches to the lower margin of the acetabulum. This is a relatively slack ligament, so it is questionable whether it plays a significant role in holding the femur in its socket. It does, however, contain an artery that supplies blood to the head of the femur.

[25]*teres* = round

## The Knee Joint

The **tibiofemoral** (knee) **joint** is the largest and most complex diarthrosis of the body (figs. 9.23 and 9.24). It is primarily a hinge joint, but when the knee is flexed it is also capable of slight rotation and lateral gliding. The patella and its ligament also form a plane **patellofemoral joint** with the femur.

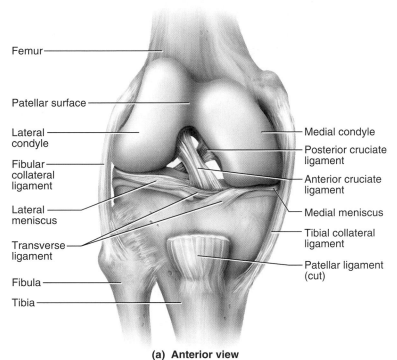

(a)  Anterior view

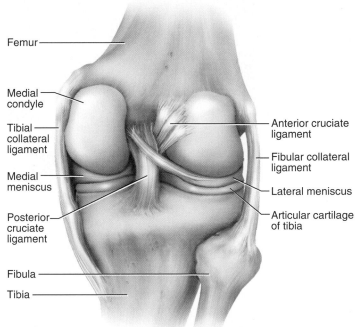

(b)  Posterior view

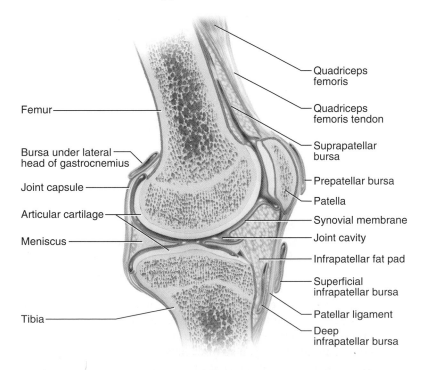

(c)  Sagittal section

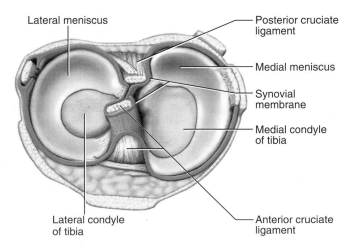

(d)  Superior view of tibia and menisci

**Figure 9.23** The Right Tibiofemoral (Knee) Joint.

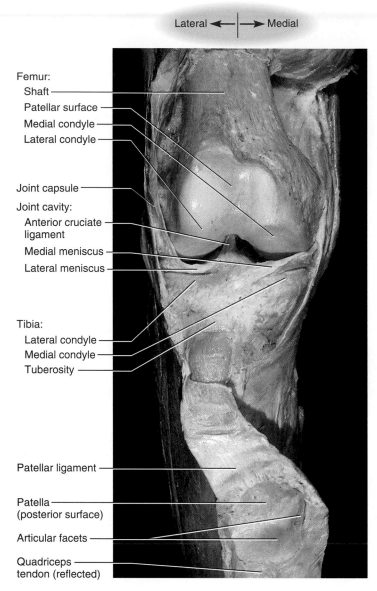

Lateral ←—|—→ Medial

Femur:
Shaft
Patellar surface
Medial condyle
Lateral condyle

Joint capsule

Joint cavity:
Anterior cruciate ligament
Medial meniscus
Lateral meniscus

Tibia:
Lateral condyle
Medial condyle
Tuberosity

Patellar ligament

Patella (posterior surface)

Articular facets

Quadriceps tendon (reflected)

**Figure 9.24** **The Right Knee, Anterior Dissection.** The quadriceps tendon has been cut and folded (reflected) downward to expose the joint cavity and the posterior surface of the patella.

The joint capsule encloses only the lateral and posterior sides of the knee joint, not the anterior. The anterior side is covered by the patellar ligament and the **lateral** and **medial patellar retinacula** (not illustrated). These are extensions of the tendon of the *quadriceps femoris* muscle, the large anterior muscle of the thigh. The knee is stabilized mainly by the quadriceps tendon in front and the tendon of the *semimembranosus* muscle on the rear of the thigh. Developing strength in these muscles therefore reduces the risk of knee injury.

The joint cavity contains two C-shaped cartilages called the **lateral meniscus** and **medial meniscus,** joined by a **transverse ligament.** They absorb the shock of the body weight jostling up and down on the knee and prevent the femur from rocking from side to side on the tibia. The posterior side of the knee, the **popliteal** (pop-LIT-ee-ul) **region,** is supported by a complex array of **intracapsular ligaments** within the joint capsule and **extracapsu-**lar ligaments external to it. The extracapsular ligaments are the **oblique popliteal ligament** (an extension of the semimembranosus tendon), **arcuate** (AR-cue-et) **popliteal ligament, fibular (lateral) collateral ligament,** and **tibial (medial) collateral ligament.** Only the two collateral ligaments are illustrated; they prevent the knee from rotating when the joint is extended.

There are two intracapsular ligaments deep within the joint cavity. The synovial membrane folds around them, however, so that they are excluded from the fluid-filled synovial cavity. These ligaments cross each other in the form of an X; hence, they are called the **anterior cruciate**[26] (CROO-she-ate) **ligament (ACL)** and **posterior cruciate ligament (PCL).** These are named according to whether they attach to the anterior or posterior side of the tibia, not for their attachments to the femur. When the knee is extended, the ACL is pulled tight and prevents hyperextension. The PCL prevents the femur from sliding off the front of the tibia and prevents the tibia from being displaced backward. The ACL is one of the commonest sites of knee injury (fig. 9.25).

An important aspect of human bipedalism is the ability to "lock" the knees and stand erect without tiring the extensor muscles of the thigh. When the knee is extended to the fullest degree allowed by the ACL, the femur rotates medially on the tibia. This action locks the knee, and in this state, all the major knee ligaments are twisted and taut. To unlock the knee, the *popliteus* muscle rotates the femur laterally, causing the ligaments to untwist.

The knee joint has at least 13 bursae. Four of these are anterior—the **superficial infrapatellar, suprapatellar, prepatellar,** and **deep infrapatellar.** Located in the popliteal region are the **popliteal bursa** and **semimembranosus bursa** (not illustrated). At least seven more bursae are found on the lateral and medial sides of the knee joint. From figure 9.23a, your knowledge of the relevant word elements (*infra-, supra-, pre-*), and the terms *superficial* and *deep,* you should be able to work out the reasoning behind most of these names and develop a system for remembering the locations of these bursae.

## The Ankle Joint

The **talocrural**[27] (ankle) **joint** includes two articulations—a medial joint between the tibia and talus and a lateral joint between the fibula and talus, both enclosed in one joint capsule (fig. 9.26). The malleoli of the tibia and fibula overhang the talus on each side like a cap and prevent most side-to-side motion. The ankle therefore has a more restricted range of motion than the wrist.

The ligaments of the ankle include (1) **anterior** and **posterior tibiofibular ligaments,** which bind the tibia to the fibula; (2) a multipart **medial (deltoid) ligament,** which binds the tibia to the foot on the medial side; and (3) a multipart **lateral collateral ligament,** which binds the fibula to the foot on the lateral side. The **calcaneal (Achilles) tendon** extends from the calf muscles to the calcaneus. It plantarflexes the foot and limits dorsiflexion. Plantar flexion is limited by extensor tendons on the anterior side of the ankle and by the anterior part of the joint capsule.

[26]*cruci* = cross + *ate* = characterized by
[27]*talo* = ankle + *crural* = pertaining to the leg

## Knee Injuries and Arthroscopic Surgery

Although the knee can bear a lot of weight, it is highly vulnerable to rotational and horizontal stress, especially when the knee is flexed (as in skiing or running) and receives a blow from behind or from the side (fig. 9.25). The most common injuries are to a meniscus or the anterior cruciate ligament (ACL). Knee injuries heal slowly because ligaments and tendons have a very scanty blood supply and cartilage usually has no blood vessels at all.

The diagnosis and surgical treatment of knee injuries has been greatly improved by *arthroscopy,* a procedure in which the interior of a joint is viewed with a pencil-thin instrument, the *arthroscope,* inserted through a small incision. The arthroscope has a light source, a lens, and fiber optics that allow a viewer to see into the cavity, take photographs or videotapes of the joint, and withdraw samples of synovial fluid. Saline is often introduced through another incision to expand the joint and provide a clearer view of its structures. If surgery is required, additional small incisions can be made for the surgical instruments and the procedures can be observed through the arthroscope or on a monitor. Arthroscopic surgery produces much less tissue damage than conventional surgery and enables patients to recover more quickly.

Orthopedic surgeons often replace a damaged ACL with a graft from the patellar ligament. The surgeon "harvests" a strip from the middle one-third of the patient's patellar ligament, drills a hole into the femur and tibia within the joint cavity, threads the ligament through the holes, and fastens it with screws. The grafted ligament is more taut and "competent" than the damaged ACL. It becomes ingrown with blood vessels and serves as a substrate for the deposition of more collagen, which further strengthens it in time. Following arthroscopic ACL reconstruction, a patient typically must use crutches for 7 to 10 days and undergo supervised physical therapy for 6 to 10 weeks, followed by self-directed exercise therapy. Healing is completed in about 9 months.

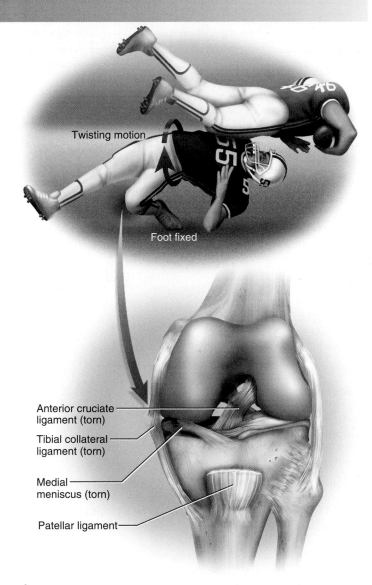

Twisting motion

Foot fixed

Anterior cruciate ligament (torn)

Tibial collateral ligament (torn)

Medial meniscus (torn)

Patellar ligament

**Figure 9.25**  Knee Injuries.

Sprains (torn ligaments and tendons) are common at the ankle, especially when the foot is suddenly inverted or everted to excess. They are painful and usually accompanied by immediate swelling. They are best treated by immobilizing the joint and reducing swelling with an ice pack, but in extreme cases may require a cast or surgery.

The synovial joints described in this section are summarized in table 9.2.

## *Before You Go On*

Answer the following questions to test your understanding of the preceding section:

10. What keeps the mandibular condyle from slipping out of its fossa in a posterior direction?

11. List at least three ways that the shoulder joint is stabilized.

12. What keeps the femur from slipping backward off the tibia?

13. What keeps the tibia from slipping sideways off the talus?

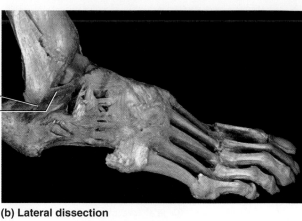

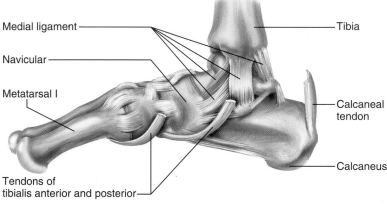

**(a) Lateral view**

Fibula
Tibia
Anterior and posterior tibiofibular ligaments
Lateral ligament:
Posterior talofibular ligament
Calcaneofibular ligament
Anterior talofibular ligament
Calcaneal tendon
Calcaneus
Tendons of fibularis longus and brevis
Metatarsal V

**(b) Lateral dissection**

**(c) Medial view**

Medial ligament
Navicular
Metatarsal I
Tendons of tibialis anterior and posterior
Tibia
Calcaneal tendon
Calcaneus

**(d) Posterior view**

Tibia
Fibula
Interosseous membrane
Medial malleolus
Calcaneus
Posterior tibiofibular ligament
Lateral malleolus
Posterior talofibular ligament
Calcaneofibular ligament

**Figure 9.26** The Talocrural (Ankle) Joint and Ligaments of the Right Foot.

# Clinical Perspectives

### *Objectives*

When you have completed this section, you should be able to

- define *rheumatism* and describe the profession of rheumatology;
- define *arthritis* and describe its forms and causes;
- discuss the design and application of artificial joints; and
- identify several joint diseases other than arthritis.

Our quality of life depends greatly on mobility, and mobility depends on proper functioning of the diarthroses. Not surprisingly, therefore, joint dysfunctions are among the most common medical complaints. **Rheumatism** is a broad term for any pain in the supportive and locomotory organs of the body, including bones, ligaments, tendons, and muscles. Physicians who deal with the study, diagnosis, and treatment of joint disorders are called **rheumatologists.**

## Arthritis

The most widespread crippling disorder in the United States is **arthritis,**[28] a broad term that embraces more than a hundred diseases of largely obscure or unknown causes. In general, arthritis means inflammation of a joint. Nearly everyone develops arthritis to some degree after middle age and sometimes earlier.

The most common form of arthritis is **osteoarthritis (OA),** also called "wear-and-tear arthritis" because it is apparently a normal consequence of years of wear on the joints. As joints age, the

---

[28]*arthr* = joint + *itis* = inflammation

| TABLE 9.2 | Review of the Principal Diarthroses |
|-----------|-------------------------------------|
| **Joint** | **Major Anatomical Features and Actions** |
| Temporomandibular joint (fig. 9.18) | *Type:* condylar, hinge, and plane<br>*Movements:* elevation, depression, protraction, retraction, lateral and medial excursion<br>*Articulation:* condyle of mandible, mandibular fossa of temporal bone<br>*Ligaments:* lateral, sphenomandibular<br>*Cartilage:* articular disc |
| Glenohumeral joint (fig. 9.19) | *Type:* ball-and-socket<br>*Movements:* adduction, abduction, flexion, extension, circumduction, medial and lateral rotation<br>*Articulation:* head of humerus, glenoid fossa of scapula<br>*Ligaments:* coracohumeral, transverse humeral, three glenohumerals<br>*Tendons:* rotator cuff (tendons of subscapularis, supraspinatus, infraspinatus, teres minor), tendon of biceps brachii<br>*Bursae:* subdeltoid, subacromial, subcoracoid, subscapular<br>*Cartilage:* glenoid labrum |
| Elbow (fig. 9.20) | *Type:* hinge and pivot<br>*Movements:* flexion, extension, pronation, supination, rotation<br>*Articulation:* humeroulnar—trochlea of humerus, trochlear notch of ulna; humeroradial—capitulum of humerus, head of radius; radioulnar—head of radius, radial notch of ulna<br>*Ligaments:* radial collateral, ulnar collateral, anular<br>*Bursa:* olecranon |
| Coxal joint (fig. 9.22) | *Type:* ball-and-socket<br>*Movements:* adduction, abduction, flexion, extension, circumduction, medial and lateral rotation<br>*Articulation:* head of femur, acetabulum of hip bone<br>*Ligaments:* iliofemoral, pubofemoral, ischiofemoral, ligamentum teres, transverse acetabular<br>*Cartilage:* acetabular labrum |
| Knee joint (fig. 9.23) | *Type:* primarily hinge<br>*Movements:* flexion, extension, slight rotation<br>*Articulation:* tibiofemoral, patellofemoral<br>*Ligaments:* anterior—lateral patellar retinaculum, medial patellar retinaculum; popliteal intracapsular—anterior cruciate, posterior cruciate; popliteal extracapsular—oblique popliteal, arcuate popliteal, lateral collateral, medial collateral<br>*Bursae:* anterior—superficial infrapatellar, suprapatellar, prepatellar, deep infrapatellar; popliteal—popliteal, semimembranosus; medial and lateral—seven other bursae not named in this chapter<br>*Cartilages:* lateral meniscus, medial meniscus (connected by transverse ligament) |
| Ankle joint (fig. 9.26) | *Type:* hinge<br>*Movements:* dorsiflexion, plantar flexion, extension<br>*Articulation:* tibia–talus, fibula–talus, tibia–fibula<br>*Ligaments:* anterior and posterior tibiofibular, deltoid, lateral collateral<br>*Tendon:* calcaneal (Achilles) |

articular cartilage softens and degenerates. As the cartilage becomes roughened by wear, joint movement may be accompanied by crunching or crackling sounds called *crepitus.* OA affects especially the fingers, intervertebral joints, hips, and knees. As the articular cartilage wears away, exposed bone tissue often develops spurs that grow into the joint cavity, restrict movement, and cause pain. OA rarely occurs before age 40, but it affects about 85% of people older than 70. It usually does not cripple, but in severe cases it can immobilize the hip.

**Rheumatoid arthritis (RA),** which is far more severe, results from an autoimmune attack against the joint tissues. Like other autoimmune diseases, RA is caused by an *autoantibody*—a misguided antibody that attacks the body's own tissues instead of limiting its attack to foreign matter. In RA, an autoantibody called *rheumatoid factor* attacks the synovial membranes. Inflammatory cells accumulate in the synovial fluid and produce enzymes that degrade the articular cartilage. The synovial membrane thickens and adheres to the articular cartilage, fluid accumulates in the joint capsule, and the capsule is invaded by fibrous connective tissue. As articular cartilage degenerates, the joint begins to ossify, and sometimes the bones become solidly fused and immobilized, a condition called **ankylosis**[29] (fig. 9.27). The disease tends to develop symmetrically—if the right wrist or hip develops RA, so does the left.

RA tends to flare up and subside (go into remission) periodically.[30] It affects women far more than men and typically begins between the ages of 30 and 40. There is no cure, but joint damage

[29]*ankyl* = bent, crooked + *osis* = condition
[30]*rheumat* = tending to change

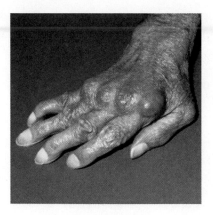

**Figure 9.27** **Rheumatoid Arthritis (RA).** A severe case with ankylosis of the joints. Compare the X-ray on page 234.

can be slowed with hydrocortisone or other steroids. Because long-term use of steroids weakens the bone, however, aspirin is the treatment of first choice to control the inflammation. Physical therapy is also used to preserve the joint's range of motion and the patient's functional ability.

Several common pathologies of the joints are briefly described in table 9.3.

## Joint Prostheses

**Arthroplasty,**[31] a treatment of last resort, is the replacement of a diseased joint with an artificial device called a **joint prosthesis.**[32] Joint prostheses were first developed to treat war injuries in World War II and the Korean War. Total hip replacement (THR), first performed in 1963 by English orthopedic surgeon Sir John Charnley, is now the most common orthopedic procedure for the elderly. The first knee replacements were performed in the 1970s. Joint prostheses are now available for finger, shoulder, and elbow joints, as well as for hip and knee joints. Arthroplasty is performed on over 250,000 patients per year in the United States, primarily to relieve pain and restore function in elderly people with OA or RA.

Arthroplasty presents ongoing challenges for biomedical engineering. An effective prosthesis must be strong, nontoxic, and corrosion-resistant. In addition, it must bond firmly to the patient's bones and enable a normal range of motion with a minimum of friction. The heads of long bones are usually replaced with prostheses made of a metal alloy such as cobalt-chrome, titanium alloy, or stainless steel. Joint sockets are made of polyethylene (fig. 9.28). Prostheses are bonded to the patient's bone with screws or bone cement.

Over 90% of artificial knees last 10 years, 85% for 15 years, and 75% for 20 years. The most common form of failure is detachment of the prosthesis from the bone. This problem has been reduced by using *porous-coated prostheses,* which become infiltrated by the patient's own bone and create a firmer bond. A prosthesis is not as strong as a natural joint, however, and is not an option for many young, active patients.

---

[31]*arthro* = joint + *plasty* = surgical repair
[32]*prosthe* = something added

## *Before You Go On*

Answer the following questions to test your understanding of the preceding section:

14. Define *arthritis.* How do the causes of osteoarthritis and rheumatoid arthritis differ? Which type is more common?

15. What are the major engineering problems in the design of joint prostheses? What is the most common cause of failure of a prosthesis?

| TABLE 9.3 | Disorders of the Joints |
|---|---|
| Dislocation (luxation) | Displacement of a bone from its normal position at a joint, usually accompanied by a sprain of the adjoining connective tissues. Most common at the fingers, thumb, shoulder, and knee. |
| Gout | A hereditary disease, most common in men, in which uric acid crystals accumulate in the joints and irritate the articular cartilage and synovial membrane. Causes *gouty arthritis,* with swelling, pain, tissue degeneration, and sometimes fusion of the joint. Most commonly affects the great toe. |
| Strain | Painful overstretching of a tendon or muscle without serious tissue damage. Often results from inadequate warm-up before exercise. |
| Subluxation | Partial dislocation in which two bones maintain contact between their articular surfaces. |
| Synovitis | Inflammation of a joint capsule, often as a complication of a sprain. |

### Disorders Described Elsewhere

| | | |
|---|---|---|
| Ankle sprains 257 | Dislocation of the shoulder 252 | Rotator cuff injury 331 |
| Bursitis 239 | Knee injuries 257 | Tendinitis 240 |
| Congenital hip dislocation 253 | Osteoarthritis 258 | TMJ syndrome 250 |
| Dislocation of the elbow 253 | Rheumatoid arthritis 259 | |

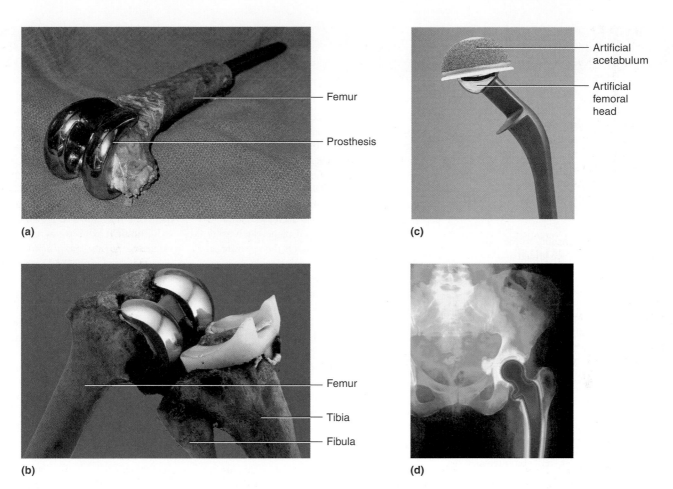

**Figure 9.28** Joint Prostheses. (a) Artificial femoral condyles affixed to the distal end of the femur. (b) An artificial knee joint bonded to a natural femur and tibia. (c) A porous-coated hip prosthesis. The caplike portion replaces the acetabulum of the hip bone, and the ball and shaft below it are bonded to the proximal end of the femur. (d) X-ray of a patient with a total hip replacement.

# CHAPTER REVIEW

## REVIEW OF KEY CONCEPTS

### Joints and Their Classification (p. 235)

1. A *joint (articulation)* is any point at which two bones meet. Not all joints are movable.

2. The sciences dealing with joints include arthrology, kinesiology, and biomechanics.

3. Joints are typically named after the bones or articular surfaces involved, such as the glenohumeral joint.

4. Joints are classified according to the manner in which the bones are joined and corresponding differences in how freely the bones can move.

5. *Bony joints (synostoses)* are joints at which the original gap between two bones becomes ossified and adjacent bones become, in effect, a single bone—for example, union of the two frontal bones into a single bone.

6. *Fibrous joints (synarthroses)* are joints at which two bones are united by collagenous fibers. The three types of fibrous joints are *sutures* (which are of *serrate, lap,* and *plane* types), *gomphoses* (teeth in their sockets), and *syndesmoses* (exemplified by long bones joined along their shafts by interosseous membranes).

7. *Cartilaginous joints (amphiarthroses)* are joints at which two bones are united by cartilage. In *synchondroses,* the cartilage is hyaline (as in the epiphyseal plates of juvenile bones), and in *symphyses,* it is fibrocartilage (as in the intervertebral discs and pubic symphysis).

### Synovial Joints (p. 238)

1. A *synovial joint (diarthrosis)* is a joint at which two bones are separated by a *joint cavity,* which contains lubricating *synovial fluid.* The ends of the adjacent bones are covered with hyaline *articular cartilages.* The cavity is enclosed by a *joint capsule,* which is composed of an outer *fibrous capsule* and inner *synovial membrane.* The synovial membrane secretes the synovial fluid. Most synovial joints are highly movable.

2. Some synovial joints contain a fibrocartilage *articular disc* or (in the knee) a pair of *menisci,* which absorb shock and pressure, guide bone movements, improve the fit between the bones, and stabilize the joint.

3. Accessory structures of a synovial joint include *tendons* (from muscle to bone), *ligaments* (from bone to bone), and *bursae.* Bursae are fibrous sacs continuous with the joint cavity and filled with synovial fluid. Some bursae are elongated cylinders called *tendon sheaths.*

4. Synovial joints are described as *monaxial, biaxial,* or *multiaxial* based on the number of geometric planes (one to three) along which a bone can move.

5. The six categories of synovial joints are *ball-and-socket, condylar, saddle, plane, hinge,* and *pivot joints* (fig. 9.6).

6. *Flexion* is a movement that decreases a joint angle, usually in a sagittal plane, such as flexing the elbow. *Extension* is the opposite movement; it increases a joint angle, as in straightening the elbow. Some joints such as the wrist are also capable of *hyperextension,* which increases the joint angle beyond the *zero position.*

7. *Abduction* is the movement of a body part away from the median plane, as in spreading the fingers or raising the arm to one's side. *Adduction* is the opposite movement, moving a body part toward the median plane. Some joints can be *hyperadducted* or *hyperabducted* by moving a limb segment to and beyond the median plane.

8. *Elevation* is a movement that raises a bone vertically, as in shrugging the shoulders or biting, and *depression* is the lowering of a bone, as in dropping the shoulders or opening the mouth.

9. *Protraction* is movement of a bone anteriorly, and *retraction* is the movement of a bone posteriorly, exemplified by the shoulder movements in rowing a boat.

10. *Circumduction* is a movement in which the attached end of an appendage remains relatively stationary while the free end describes a circle.

11. *Rotation* is the turning of a bone such as the humerus on its longitudinal axis. In *medial rotation,* a bone spins toward the median plane of the body, and in *lateral rotation,* it spins away.

12. *Supination* of the forearm turns the palm forward or upward; *pronation* turns it rearward or downward.

13. *Flexion* of the vertebral column is forward-bending movement, *extension* is straightening the spine, and *hyperextension* is bending it posteriorly. Lateral flexion is bending it to one side. Rotation is twisting the spine to turn the head or the torso to the left or right.

14. The mandible is capable of *elevation* and *depression* (up and down biting movements), *protraction* and *retraction* (forward and back movements), and *lateral* and *medial excursion* (side-to-side grinding movements).

15. The wrist is capable of *flexion* and *extension* anteriorly and posteriorly, and *ulnar* and *radial flexion* from side to side in the frontal plane. The fingers are capable of flexion, extension, abduction, and adduction. The thumb is a special case because of its embryonic rotation into a plane perpendicular to the palm and the mobility of the saddle joint. It exhibits not only flexion and extension, but also *radial abduction, palmar abduction, opposition,* and *reposition.*

16. *Dorsiflexion* is an ankle movement that raises the toes, and *plantar flexion* is an ankle movement that lowers them. *Inversion* of the feet turns the soles medially, facing each other; *eversion* turns them laterally, away from each other. *Pronation* of the foot is a complex movement that combines dorsiflexion, eversion, and abduction; *supination* of the foot combines plantar flexion, inversion, and adduction.

17. The *range of motion (ROM)* of a joint is the number of degrees through which one bone moves relative to the other. It depends on the structure of the articular surfaces of the bones, structure and tautness of the ligaments and joint capsule, and the action of muscles and tendons.

### Anatomy of Selected Synovial Joints (p. 249)

1. This chapter describes six synovial joints or joint groups: the temporomandibular joint (TMJ), glenohumeral (shoulder) joint, the elbow (a complex of three joints), the coxal (hip) joint, the tibiofemoral (knee) joint, and the talocrural (ankle) joint. The principal structures and types of movement at each joint are summarized in table 9.2.

2. The *temporomandibular joint* is involved in biting and chewing and has an articular disc to absorb the pressure produced in such actions. Two common disorders of this joint are dislocation and TMJ syndrome.

3. The *glenohumeral joint* is notable for its great mobility and shallow socket (glenoid cavity), making it very susceptible to dislocation. Rotator cuff injuries are also common at this joint.

4. The elbow contains three joints—*humeroulnar, humeroradial,* and *proximal radioulnar.* It allows for hingelike movements of the forearm and for rotation of the radius on the ulna when the forearm is pronated and supinated.

5. The *coxal joint* is an important weight-bearing ball-and-socket joint and therefore

has an especially deep socket, the acetabulum of the hip bone. When a person stands, some of the ligaments at this joint twist and pull the head of the femur more tightly into the acetabulum.

6. The *tibiofemoral joint* is the most complex diarthrosis of the body. It has numerous ligaments and bursae. The most important stabilizing structures within the joint cavity are the *anterior* and *posterior cruciate ligaments* and the *lateral* and *medial menisci*. Injuries to these ligaments and cartilages are common.

7. At the *talocrural joint,* the tibia and fibula articulate with each other, and each articu-

lates with the talus. Numerous ligaments support this joint. Ankle sprains are tearing of these ligaments and adjacent tendons.

## Clinical Perspectives (p. 258)

1. *Rheumatism* is a broad term for pain in the bones, joints, ligaments, tendons, or muscles. Physicians who specialize in joint disorders are called *rheumatologists.*

2. *Arthritis* is a general term for more than 100 inflammatory joint diseases. The most common form of arthritis is *osteoarthritis (OA),* which occurs to some degree in almost everyone as a result of years of wear

and tear on the joints. It is marked especially by erosion of the articular cartilages.

3. *Rheumatoid arthritis (RA)* is a more severe autoimmune joint disease caused by an antibody called *rheumatoid factor* that damages synovial membranes. RA can be severely crippling, sometimes causing a fusion of the bones called *ankylosis.*

4. *Arthroplasty* is the replacement of a diseased joint with an artificial joint, or *joint prosthesis.* It was first developed for hip and knee joints but is now also performed at finger, shoulder, and elbow joints.

# TESTING YOUR RECALL

1. Lateral and medial excursion are movements unique to
   a. the ankle.
   b. the thumb.
   c. the mandible.
   d. the knee.
   e. the clavicle.

2. Which of the following is the least movable?
   a. a diarthrosis
   b. a synostosis
   c. a symphysis
   d. a syndesmosis
   e. a condylar joint

3. Which of the following movements are unique to the foot?
   a. dorsiflexion and inversion
   b. elevation and depression
   c. circumduction and rotation
   d. abduction and adduction
   e. opposition and reposition

4. Which of the following joints cannot be circumducted?
   a. trapeziometacarpal
   b. metacarpophalangeal
   c. glenohumeral
   d. coxal
   e. interphalangeal

5. Which of the following terms denotes a general condition that includes the other four?
   a. gout
   b. arthritis
   c. rheumatism
   d. osteoarthritis
   e. rheumatoid arthritis

6. In the adult, the ischium and pubis are united by
   a. a synchondrosis.
   b. a diarthrosis.
   c. a synostosis.
   d. an amphiarthrosis.
   e. a symphysis.

7. Articular discs are found only in certain
   a. synostoses.
   b. symphyses.
   c. diarthroses.
   d. synchondroses.
   e. amphiarthroses.

8. Which of the following joints has anterior and posterior cruciate ligaments?
   a. the shoulder
   b. the elbow
   c. the hip
   d. the knee
   e. the ankle

9. To bend backward at the waist involves _____ of the vertebral column.
   a. rotation
   b. hyperextension
   c. dorsiflexion
   d. abduction
   e. flexion

10. If you sit on a sofa and then raise your left arm to rest it on the back of the sofa, your left shoulder joint undergoes primarily
    a. lateral excursion.
    b. abduction.
    c. elevation.
    d. adduction.
    e. extension.

11. The lubricant of a diarthrosis is _____.

12. A fluid-filled sac that eases the movement of a tendon over a bone is called a/an _____.

13. A/an _____ joint allows one bone to swivel on another.

14. _____ is the science of movement.

15. The joint between a tooth and the mandible is called a/an _____.

16. In a/an _____ suture, the articulating bones have interlocking wavy margins, somewhat like a dovetail joint in carpentry.

17. In kicking a football, what type of action does the knee joint exhibit?

18. The angle through which a joint can move is called its _____.

19. A person with a degenerative joint disorder would most likely be treated by a physician called a/an _____.

20. The femur is prevented from slipping sideways off the tibia in part by a pair of cartilages called the lateral and medial _____.

***Answers in the Appendix***

## TRUE OR FALSE

*Determine which five of the following statements are false, and briefly explain why.*

1. More people get rheumatoid arthritis than osteoarthritis.

2. A doctor who treats arthritis is called a kinesiologist.

3. Synovial joints are also known as synarthroses.

4. Most ligaments, but not all, connect one bone to another.

5. Reaching behind you to take something out of your hip pocket involves hyperextension of the elbow.

6. The anterior cruciate ligament normally prevents hyperextension of the knee.

7. There is no meniscus in the elbow joint.

8. The knuckles are diarthroses.

9. Synovial fluid is secreted by the bursae.

10. Most condylar joints can move in more planes than a hinge joint.

***Answers in the Appendix***

## TESTING YOUR COMPREHENSION

1. Why are there menisci in the knee joint but not in the elbow, the corresponding joint of the upper limb? Why is there an articular disc in the temporomandibular joint?

2. What ligaments would most likely be torn if you slipped and your foot were suddenly forced into an excessively inverted position: (*a*) the posterior talofibular and calcaneofibular ligaments, or (*b*) the deltoid ligament? Explain. What would the resulting condition of the ankle be called?

3. In order of occurrence, list the joint actions (flexion, pronation, etc.) and the joints where they would occur as you (*a*) sit down at a table, (*b*) reach out and pick up an apple, (*c*) take a bite, and (*d*) chew it. Assume that you start in anatomical position.

4. What structure in the elbow joint serves the same purpose as the anterior cruciate ligament (ACL) of the knee?

5. List the six types of synovial joints and for each one, if possible, identify a joint in the upper limb and a joint in the lower limb that falls into each category. Which of these six joints have no examples in the lower limb?

***Answers at aris.mhhe.com***

## ONLINE RESOURCES

Visit aprevealed.com to explore melt-away cadaver dissections, watch animations that clarify difficult concepts, review histological and radiological images, or take a quiz to assess your understanding of the material.

The Saladin *Human Anatomy,* 2e website at aris.mhhe.com features chapter-specific quizzes, labeling exercises, and other interactive tools to complement your study of human anatomy. If your instructor has provided an ARIS course code, you can also access assignments and information specific to your course.

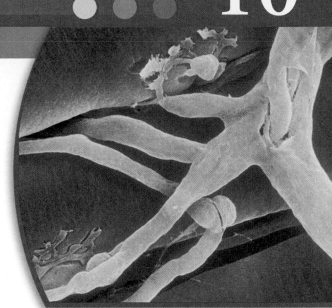

**10**

# The Muscular System— Introduction

Neuromuscular junctions (SEM). Muscle fibers are shown in blue and nerve fibers in yellow.

## CHAPTER OUTLINE

## INSIGHTS

## BRUSHING UP

To understand this chapter, you may find it helpful to review the following concepts:
- Proteins of the plasma membrane (p. 51)
- Components of a neuron (p. 92)
- The three types of muscle (p. 93)
- Embryonic mesoderm, somites, and myotomes (p. 112)
- Skeletal anatomy (chapters 7 and 8)

Anatomy & Physiology | REVEALED®
aprevealed.com

**Muscular System**

Muscles constitute nearly half of the body's weight and occupy a place of central interest in several fields of health care and fitness. Physical and occupational therapists must be well acquainted with the muscular system to design and carry out rehabilitation programs. Athletes and trainers, dancers and acrobats, and amateur fitness enthusiasts follow programs of resistance training to strengthen individual muscle groups through movement regimens based on exact knowledge of muscle, bone, and joint anatomy. Nurses employ their knowledge of the muscular system to give intramuscular injections correctly and to safely and effectively move patients who are physically incapacitated. Gerontological nurses are keenly aware of how deeply a person's muscular condition affects the quality of life in old age. The muscular system is highly important to biomedical disciplines even beyond the scope of the movement sciences. It is the primary source of body heat in the moving individual, and through its absorption, storage, and use of glucose, it is a major factor in control of blood glucose levels. Indeed, loss of muscle mass is often a significant factor in the onset of diabetes mellitus.

The next three chapters focus on the muscular system—the functional anatomy of muscular tissue in this chapter, muscles of the axial region of the body (head and trunk) in chapter 11, and muscles of the appendicular region (limbs and limb girdles) in chapter 12. These chapters draw on what we have covered in the preceding chapters—bone and joint structure—to flesh out our comprehension of body posture and movement. The current chapter also considers cardiac and smooth muscle and how they compare with skeletal muscle.

# Muscle Types and Functions

## Objectives
When you have completed this section, you should be able to
- describe the distinctions between the three types of muscular tissue; and
- list the functions of muscular tissue and the properties it must have to carry out these functions.

As we saw in chapter 3, there are three kinds of muscular tissue in the human body—skeletal, cardiac, and smooth. All types, however, are specialized for one fundamental purpose: to convert the chemical energy of ATP into the mechanical energy of motion. Muscle cells exert a useful force on other cells or tissues—either to produce desirable movements or to prevent undesirable ones.

Although we examine all three muscle types in this chapter, most of our attention will focus on the **muscular system,** composed of the skeletal muscles only. The study of the skeletal muscles is called **myology.**[1]

---

[1]*myo* = muscle + *logy* = study of

## Types of Muscle

**Skeletal muscle** may be defined as voluntary striated muscle that is usually attached to one or more bones. It is called *voluntary* because it is usually subject to one's voluntary control; we can decide when to contract a skeletal muscle. It is called *striated* because it exhibits a microscopic pattern of alternating light and dark bands, or **striations,** which result from the overlapping arrangement of the contractile proteins within each cell (fig. 10.1). A typical skeletal muscle cell is about 100 μm in diameter and 3 cm (30,000 μm) long; some are as thick as 500 μm and as long as 30 cm. Because of their extraordinary length, skeletal muscle cells are usually called **muscle fibers** or **myofibers.**

**Cardiac muscle** is also striated, but it is **involuntary**—not normally under conscious control. Its cells are not fibrous in shape, but relatively short and stumpy, somewhat like logs with notched ends. Thus, they are called **cardiocytes** or **myocytes** rather than fibers. Cardiocytes are commonly about 80 μm long × 15 μm wide.

**Smooth muscle** is also involuntary, and unlike skeletal and cardiac muscle, it lacks striations; hence the description *smooth.* It contains the same contractile proteins as the other muscle types, but they are not arranged in a regularly overlapping way, so there are no striations. Its cells, also called myocytes, are fusiform in shape—thick in the middle and tapered at the ends. They average about 200 μm long × 5 μm wide at the thickest part, but they can be as short as 20 μm in small blood vessels or as long as 500 μm in the pregnant uterus.

## Functions of Muscle

The functions of muscular tissue are as follows:

- **Movement.** Muscles enable us to move from place to place and to move individual body parts. Muscular contractions also move body contents in the course of breathing, blood circulation, feeding and digestion, defecation, urination, and childbirth. Muscular movements also serve varied roles in communication: speech, writing, and nonverbal body language such as facial expressions.

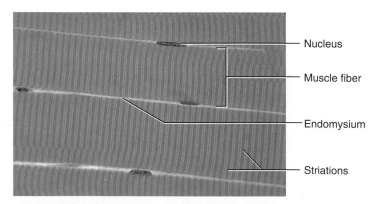

Nucleus

Muscle fiber

Endomysium

Striations

**Figure 10.1** Skeletal Muscle Fibers.
● *What tissue characteristics evident in this photo distinguish this from cardiac and smooth muscle?*

- **Stability.** Muscles maintain posture by preventing unwanted movements. Some are called *antigravity muscles* because, at least part of the time, they resist the pull of gravity and prevent us from falling or slumping over. Many muscles also stabilize the joints by maintaining tension on tendons and bones.

- **Control of body openings and passages.** Muscles encircling the mouth serve not only for speech but also for food intake and retention of food while chewing. In the eyelid and pupil, they regulate the admission of light to the eye. Internal muscular rings control the movement of food, bile, blood, and other materials within the body. Muscles encircling the urethra and anus control the elimination of waste. (Some of these muscles are called *sphincters,* and others are not; this is discussed later.)

- **Heat production.** The skeletal muscles produce as much as 85% of one's body heat, which is vital to the functioning of enzymes and therefore to all metabolism.

## Properties of Muscle

To carry out the foregoing functions, muscle cells must have the following properties:

- **Excitability (responsiveness).** This is a property of all living cells, but it is developed to the highest degree in muscle and nerve cells. When stimulated by chemical signals, stretch, and other stimuli, muscle cells exhibit electrical and mechanical responses.

- **Conductivity.** The local electrical excitation produced at the point of muscle stimulation is conducted throughout the entire plasma membrane, stimulating all regions of the muscle cell and initiating the events that lead to contraction.

- **Contractility.** Muscle fibers are unique in their ability to shorten substantially when stimulated. This enables them to pull on bones and other tissues and organs to create movement.

- **Extensibility.** Most cells rupture if they are stretched even a little, but skeletal muscle fibers are unusually extensible; they can stretch to as much as three times their contracted length without harm. If it were not for this property, the muscle on one side of a joint would resist the action of a muscle on the other side. An elbow flexor such as the *biceps brachii,* for example, would resist elbow extension by the *triceps brachii* (see fig. 10.4).

- **Elasticity.** When a muscle cell is stretched and then the tension is released, it recoils to its original length. (Elasticity refers to the tendency to recoil, not the ability to stretch.) If it were not for this property, resting muscles would be very flabby.

From this point on, this chapter concerns skeletal muscles unless otherwise stated.

*Before You Go On*

*Answer the following questions to test your understanding of the preceding section:*

1. What general function of muscular tissue distinguishes it from other tissue types?
2. What are the basic structural differences between skeletal, cardiac, and smooth muscle?
3. State four functions of the muscular system.
4. State five special properties of muscular tissue that enable it to perform its functions.

# General Anatomy of Muscles

## *Objectives*
When you have completed this section, you should be able to

- describe the connective tissues and associated structural organization of a muscle;
- explain how muscles are classified by the arrangement of their fiber bundles (fascicles);
- describe the parts of a typical muscle;
- describe the types of muscle–bone attachments;
- describe the way that muscles are arranged in groups with complementary actions at a joint;
- explain what intrinsic and extrinsic muscles are; and
- describe three types of musculoskeletal levers and their respective advantages.

## Connective Tissues and Fascicles

A skeletal muscle is more than muscular tissue. It also contains connective tissue, nervous tissue, and blood vessels. In this section, we will examine the connective tissue components. From the smallest to largest and from deep to superficial, these are as follows (fig. 10.2):

- **Endomysium**[2] (EN-doe-MIZ-ee-um). This is a thin sleeve of loose connective tissue that surrounds each muscle fiber. It creates room for blood capillaries and nerve fibers to reach every muscle fiber, ensuring that no muscle cell is without stimulation and nourishment. The endomysium also provides the extracellular chemical environment for the muscle fiber and its associated nerve ending. Excitation of a muscle fiber is based on the exchange of calcium, sodium, and potassium ions between the endomysial tissue fluid and the nerve and muscle fibers.

---

[2]*endo* = within + *mys* = muscle

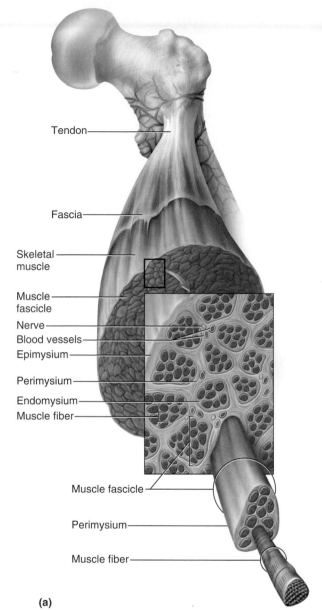

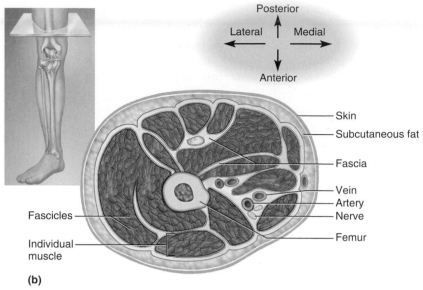

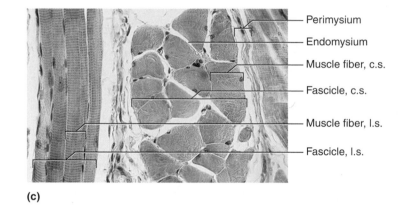

**Figure 10.2** **The Connective Tissues of a Skeletal Muscle.** (a) The muscle–bone attachment. There is a continuity of connective tissue from endomysium around the muscle fibers to the perimysium, epimysium, fascia, and tendon, grading into the periosteum and finally the matrix of the bone. (b) A cross section of the thigh showing the relationship of neighboring muscles to fascia and bone. (c) Muscle fascicles in the tongue. Vertical fascicles passing between the dorsal and ventral surfaces of the tongue are seen alternating with cross-sectioned horizontal fascicles that pass from the tip to the rear of the tongue. A fibrous perimysium can be seen between the fascicles, and endomysium can be seen between individual muscle fibers within each fascicle. (c.s. = cross section; l.s. = longitudinal section)

- **Perimysium.**[3] This is a thicker connective tissue sheath that wraps muscle fibers together in bundles called **fascicles**[4] (FASS-ih-culs). Fascicles are visible to the naked eye as parallel strands—the "grain" in a cut of meat; tender roast beef is easily pulled apart along its fascicles. The perimysium carries the larger nerves and blood vessels as well as stretch receptors called muscle spindles (see p. 488).

- **Epimysium.**[5] This is a fibrous sheath that surrounds the entire muscle. On its outer surface, the epimysium grades into the fascia, and on its inner surface, it issues projections between the fascicles to form the perimysium.

- **Fascia** (FASH-ee-uh). This is a sheet of connective tissue that separates neighboring muscles or muscle groups from each other and from the subcutaneous tissue. As we will see in chapter 12, muscles of the limbs, especially, are grouped in *compartments* separated from each other by fascia.

## Fascicles and Muscle Shapes

The strength of a muscle and the direction of its pull are determined partly by the orientation of its fascicles. Muscles can be classified according to fascicle orientation as follows (fig. 10.3):

[3]*peri* = around
[4]*fasc* = bundle + *icle* = little
[5]*epi* = upon, above

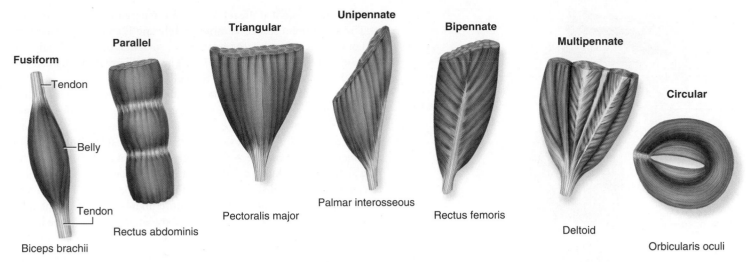

**Figure 10.3** **Classification of Muscles According to Fascicle Orientation.** The fascicles are the "grain" visible in each illustration.
● *Why could some parallel muscles be stronger than some pennate muscles?*

- **Fusiform**[6] **muscles** are thick in the middle and tapered at each end. The *biceps brachii* of the arm and *gastrocnemius* of the calf are examples of this type. Having a greater number of muscle fibers than a parallel muscle of similar mass, a fusiform muscle can generate more force.

- **Parallel muscles** have a fairly uniform width and parallel fascicles. Some of these are elongated straps, such as the *rectus abdominis* of the abdomen, *sartorius* of the thigh, and *zygomaticus major* of the face (see fig. 11.1, p. 296). Others are more squarish and are called *quadrilateral* (four-sided) muscles, such as the *thyrohyoid* in the neck. Parallel muscles can span long distances, such as from hip to knee, and they shorten more than other muscle types, but they produce relatively limited force.

- **Triangular (convergent) muscles** are fan-shaped—broad at the origin and converging toward a narrower insertion. Examples include the *pectoralis major* in the chest and the *temporalis* on the side of the head. Despite their small localized insertions on a bone, these muscles are relatively strong because they contain a large number of fibers in the wider part of the muscle.

- **Pennate**[7] **muscles** are feather-shaped. Their fascicles insert obliquely on a tendon that runs the length of the muscle, like the shaft of a feather. There are three types of pennate muscles: *unipennate,* in which all fascicles approach the tendon from one side (for example, the *palmar interosseous muscles* of the hand and *semimembranosus* of the thigh); *bipennate,* in which fascicles approach the tendon from both sides (for example, the *rectus femoris* of the thigh); and *multipennate,* shaped like a bunch of feathers with their quills converging on a single point (for example, the *deltoid* of the shoulder). These muscles generate more force than the preceding types because they fit more muscle fibers into a given length of muscle.

- **Circular muscles (sphincters)** form rings around certain body openings. When they contract, they constrict the opening and tend to prevent the passage of material through it. Examples include the *orbicularis oculi* of the eyelids and the *external urethral* and *anal* sphincters. Smooth muscle can also form sphincters—for example, the pyloric valve at the passage from the stomach to the small intestine and the internal urethral and anal sphincters.

## Muscle Attachments

Skeletal muscles are attached to bones through extensions of their connective tissue components. There are two forms of attachment—*indirect* and *direct.*

In an **indirect attachment,** the muscle ends conspicuously short of its bony destination, and the gap is bridged by a fibrous band or sheet called a **tendon.** See, for example, the two ends of the biceps brachii in figure 10.4 and the photographs in figures 12.10b (p. 339) and 12.16 (p. 348). You can easily palpate tendons and feel their texture just above the heel (your *calcaneal* or *Achilles tendon*) and on the anterior side of the wrist (tendons of the *palmaris longus* and *flexor carpi radialis* muscles). Collagen fibers of the muscle (the endo-, peri-, and epimysium) continue into the tendon and from there into the periosteum and matrix of the bone, creating very strong structural continuity from muscle to bone.

In some cases, the tendon is a broad sheet called an **aponeurosis**[8] (AP-oh-new-RO-sis). This term originally referred to the tendon located beneath the scalp, but now it also refers to similar tendons associated with certain abdominal, lumbar, hand, and foot muscles. For example, the palmaris longus tendon passes through the wrist and then expands into a fanlike *palmar aponeurosis* beneath the skin of the palm (see fig. 12.8a, p. 335).

---

[6]*fusi* = spindle + *form* = shape
[7]*penna* = feather + *ate* = characterized by

[8]*apo* = upon, above + *neuro* = nerve, nervous tissue

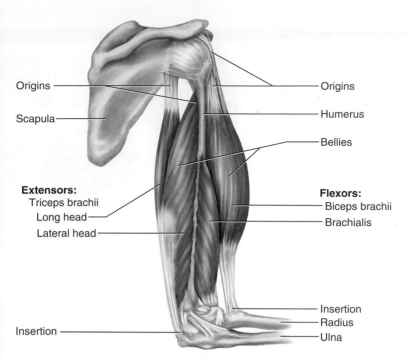

**Figure 10.4** **Muscle Groups Acting on the Elbow.** The biceps brachii and brachialis are synergists in elbow flexion. The brachialis is the prime mover in flexion. The triceps brachii is an antagonist of these two muscles and is the prime mover in elbow extension.

● *Which of these muscles have direct attachments to the bones, and which have indirect attachments?*

In a **direct (fleshy) attachment,** there is so little separation between muscle and bone that to the naked eye, the red muscular tissue seems to emerge directly from the bone—for example, along the margins of the *brachialis* and lateral head of the *triceps brachii* in figure 10.4. At a microscopic level, however, the muscle fibers stop slightly short of the bone, and the gap between muscle and bone is spanned by collagen fibers.

Some muscles insert not on bone but on the fascia or tendon of another muscle or on collagen fibers of the dermis of the skin. The distal tendon of the biceps brachii, for example, inserts partly on the fascia of the forearm. Many facial muscles insert in the skin, enabling them to produce facial expressions such as a smile.

Some authorities contend that the tendons and other collagenous tissues stretch and recoil significantly during muscle action and contribute to the power output and efficiency of a muscle. When you are running, for example, recoil of the calcaneal tendon may help to lift the heel and produce some of the thrust as your toes push off from the ground. (Such recoil contributes significantly to the long, energy-efficient leaping of kangaroos.) Others feel the elasticity of these components is negligible in humans and that the recoil is produced entirely by components within the muscle fibers.

## Muscle Origins and Insertions

Most skeletal muscles are attached to a different bone at each end, so either the muscle or its tendon spans at least one joint. When the muscle contracts, it moves one bone relative to the other. The bony site of attachment at the relatively stationary end is called its **origin.** The attachment site at its more mobile end is called the **insertion.** For the biceps brachii, for example, the origin is the scapula and the insertion is the radius (fig. 10.4). The middle region between the origin and insertion is called the **belly.**

The terminology of origins and insertions, however, is imperfect and sometimes misleading. One end of a muscle might function as its stationary origin during one action, but as its moving insertion during a different action. For example, consider the *quadriceps femoris* muscle on the anterior side of the thigh. It is a powerful extensor of the knee, connected at its proximal end mainly to the femur and at its distal end to the tibia, just below the knee. If you kick a soccer ball, the tibia moves more than the femur, so the tibia would be considered the insertion of the quadriceps and the femur would be considered its origin. But as you sit down in a chair, the tibia remains stationary and the femur moves, with the quadriceps acting as a brake so you don't sit down too abruptly and hard. By the foregoing definitions, the tibia would now be considered the origin of the quadriceps and the femur would be its insertion.

There are many other cases in which the moving and nonmoving ends of the muscle are reversed when different actions are performed. Consider the difference, for example, in the relative movements of the humerus and ulna when flexing the elbow to lift dumbbells as compared with flexing the elbow to perform chin-ups or scale a climbing wall. For such reasons, some anatomists are abandoning origin and insertion terminology and speaking instead of a muscle's proximal and distal or superior and inferior attachments, especially in the limbs. Nevertheless, this book uses the traditional, admittedly imperfect descriptions.

## Functional Groups of Muscles

The effect produced by a muscle, whether it is to produce or prevent a movement, is called its **action.** Skeletal muscles seldom act independently; instead, they function in groups whose combined actions produce the coordinated motion of a joint. Muscles can be classified into at least four categories according to their actions, but it must be stressed that a particular muscle can act in a certain way during one joint action and in a different way during other actions of the same joint. The following examples are illustrated in figure 10.4:

1. The **prime mover (agonist)** is the muscle that produces most of the force during a particular joint action. In flexing the elbow, for example, the prime mover is the *brachialis.*

2. A **synergist**[9] (SIN-ur-jist) is a muscle that aids the prime mover. Several synergists acting on a joint can produce more power than a single larger muscle. The *biceps brachii,* for example, overlies the brachialis and works with it as a synergist to flex the elbow. The actions of a prime mover and its synergist are not necessarily identical and redundant. If the prime mover worked alone at a joint, it might cause rotation or other undesirable movements of a bone. A synergist may

---

[9]*syn* = together + *erg* = work

stabilize a joint and restrict these movements, or modify the direction of a movement so that the action of the prime mover is more coordinated and specific.

3. An **antagonist**[10] is a muscle that opposes the prime mover. In some cases, it relaxes to give the prime mover almost complete control over an action. More often, however, the antagonist maintains some tension on a joint and thus limits the speed or range of the prime mover, preventing excessive movement, joint injury, or inappropriate actions. If you extend your arm to reach out and pick up a cup of tea, for example, your *triceps brachii* serves as the prime mover of elbow extension, and your brachialis acts as an antagonist to slow the extension and stop it at the appropriate point. If you extend your arm rapidly to throw a dart, however, the brachialis must be quite relaxed. The brachialis and triceps represent an **antagonistic pair** of muscles that act on opposite sides of a joint. We need antagonistic pairs at a joint because a muscle can only pull, not push—for example, a single muscle cannot flex *and* extend the elbow. Which member of the pair acts as the agonist depends on the motion under consideration. In flexion of the elbow, the brachialis is the agonist and the triceps is the antagonist; when the elbow is extended, their roles are reversed.

4. A **fixator** is a muscle that prevents a bone from moving. To *fix* a bone means to hold it steady, allowing another muscle attached to it to pull on something else. For example, consider again the flexion of the elbow by the biceps brachii. The biceps originates on the scapula, and inserts on the radius. The scapula is loosely attached to the axial skeleton, so when the biceps contracts, it seems that it would pull the scapula laterally. However, there are fixator muscles that attach the scapula to the vertebral column. They contract at the same time as the biceps, holding the scapula firmly in place and ensuring that the force generated by the biceps moves the radius rather than the scapula.

## Intrinsic and Extrinsic Muscles

In places such as the tongue, larynx, back, hand, and foot, anatomists distinguish between intrinsic and extrinsic muscles. An **intrinsic muscle** is entirely contained within a particular region, having both its origin and insertion there. An **extrinsic muscle** acts upon a designated region but has its origin elsewhere. For example, some movements of the fingers are produced by extrinsic muscles in the forearm, whose long tendons reach to the phalanges; other finger movements are produced by the intrinsic muscles located between the metacarpal bones of the hand.

## Muscles, Bones, and Levers

Many bones, especially the long bones, act as levers on which the muscles exert their force. A **lever** is any elongated, rigid object that rotates around a fixed point called the **fulcrum** (fig. 10.5). Familiar examples include a seesaw and a crowbar. Rotation occurs when

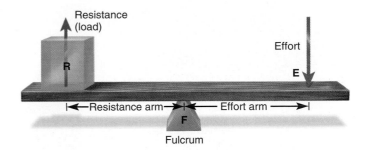

**Figure 10.5** Basic Components of a Lever.
● *Is this a first-, second-, or third-class lever? How do you know?*

an **effort** applied to one point on the lever overcomes a **resistance** (**load**) located at some other point. The part of a lever from the fulcrum to the point of effort is called the **effort arm,** and the part from the fulcrum to the point of resistance is the **resistance arm.** In the body, a long bone acts as a lever, a joint serves as the fulcrum, and the effort is generated by a muscle attached to the bone.

The function of a lever is to produce a gain in the speed, distance, or force of a motion—either to exert more force against a resisting object than the force applied to the lever (for example, in moving a heavy boulder with a crowbar) or to move the resisting object farther or faster than the effort arm is moved (as in rowing a boat). A single lever cannot confer both advantages. There is a trade-off between force on one hand and speed or distance on the other—as one increases, the other decreases.

The **mechanical advantage (MA)** of a lever is the ratio of its output force to its input force. It is equal to the length of the effort arm, $L_E$, divided by the length of the resistance arm, $L_R$; that is, MA $= L_E/L_R$. If MA is greater than 1.0, the lever produces more force, but less speed or distance, than the force exerted on it. If MA is less than 1.0, the lever produces more speed or distance, but less force, than the input. Consider the elbow joint, for example (fig. 10.6a). The resistance arm of the ulna is longer than the effort arm, so we know

# INSIGHT 10.1

## Clinical Application

### Muscle-Bound

Any well-planned program of resistance (strength) training or body-building must include exercises aimed at proportional development of the different members of a muscle group, such as flexors and extensors of the arm. Otherwise, the muscles on one side of a joint may develop out of proportion to their antagonists and restrict the joint's range of motion (ROM). If the biceps brachii is heavily developed without proportionate attention to the triceps brachii, for example, the stronger biceps will cause the elbow to be somewhat flexed constantly, and the ROM of the elbow will be restricted. The joint is then said to be "muscle-bound." People with muscle-bound joints move awkwardly and are poor at activities that require agility, such as dance and ball games.

---

[10]*ant* = against + *agonist* = actor, competitor

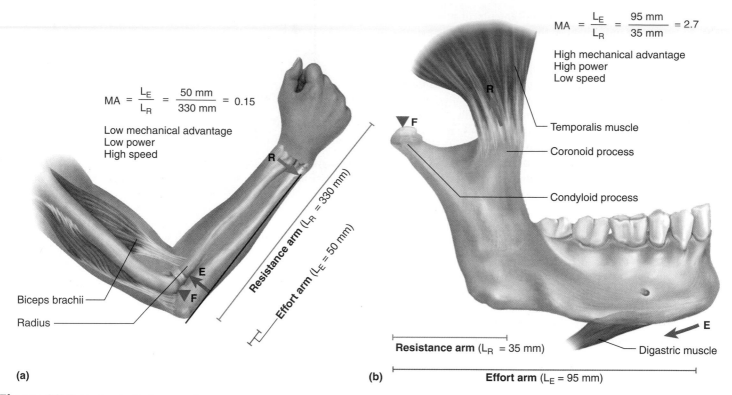

$$MA = \frac{L_E}{L_R} = \frac{50 \text{ mm}}{330 \text{ mm}} = 0.15$$

Low mechanical advantage
Low power
High speed

Resistance arm ($L_R$ = 330 mm)

Effort arm ($L_E$ = 50 mm)

R

E

F

Biceps brachii

Radius

(a)

$$MA = \frac{L_E}{L_R} = \frac{95 \text{ mm}}{35 \text{ mm}} = 2.7$$

High mechanical advantage
High power
Low speed

R

F

Temporalis muscle

Coronoid process

Condyloid process

E

Digastric muscle

Resistance arm ($L_R$ = 35 mm)

(b)

Effort arm ($L_E$ = 95 mm)

**Figure 10.6** **Mechanical Advantage (MA).** MA is calculated as the length of the effort arm divided by the length of the resistance arm. (a) The forearm acts as a third-class lever during flexion of the elbow. (b) The mandible acts as a second-class lever when the jaw is forcibly opened. The digastric muscle and others provide the effort, while tension in the temporalis muscle and others provides the resistance.

from the preceding formula that the mechanical advantage is less than 1.0. The figure shows some representative values for $L_E$ and $L_R$ that yield MA = 0.15. The biceps brachii muscle puts more power into the lever than we get out of it, but the hand moves farther and faster than the insertion of the biceps tendon. By contrast, when the digastric muscle depresses the mandible, the MA is about 2.7. The coronoid process of the mandible moves with greater force, but a shorter distance, than the insertion of the digastric (fig. 10.6b).

As we have already seen, some joints have two or more muscles acting on them that seemingly produce the same effect, such as elbow flexion. At first, you might consider this arrangement redundant, but it makes sense if the tendinous insertions of the muscles are at slightly different places and produce different mechanical advantages. A runner taking off from the starting line, for example, uses "low-gear" (high-MA) muscles that do not generate much speed but have the power to overcome the inertia of the body. A runner then "shifts into high gear" by using muscles with different insertions that have a lower mechanical advantage but produce more speed at the feet. This is analogous to the way an automobile transmission works to get a car to move and then cruise at high speed.

There are three classes of levers that differ with respect to which component is in the middle—the fulcrum (F), effort (E), or resistance (R). A **first-class lever** (fig. 10.7a) is one with the fulcrum in the middle (EFR), such as a seesaw. An anatomical example is the atlanto–occipital joint of the neck, where the muscles of the back

of the neck pull down on the occipital bone of the skull and oppose the tendency of the head to tip forward. Loss of muscle tone here can be embarrassing if you nod off in class.

A **second-class lever** (fig. 10.7b) is one in which the resistance is in the middle (FRE). Lifting the handles of a wheelbarrow, for example, makes it pivot on its wheel at the opposite end and lift a load in the middle. The mandible acts as a second-class lever when the *digastric muscle* pulls down on the chin to open the mouth. The fulcrum is the temporomandibular joint, the effort is applied to the chin by the digastric muscle, and the resistance is the tension of muscles such as the *temporalis,* which is used to bite and to hold the mouth closed. (This arrangement is upside down relative to a wheelbarrow, but the mechanics remain the same.)

In a **third-class lever** (fig. 10.7c), the effort is applied between the fulcrum and resistance (FER). For example, in paddling a canoe, the relatively stationary grip at the upper end of the paddle is the fulcrum, the effort is applied to the middle of the shaft, and the resistance is produced by the water against the blade. Most levers in the human body are third-class levers. At the elbow, the fulcrum is the joint between the ulna and humerus; the effort is applied by the brachialis and biceps brachii muscles, and the resistance can be provided by any weight in the hand or the weight of the forearm itself. The mandible acts as a third-class lever when you close your mouth to bite off a piece of food. Again, the temporomandibular joint is the fulcrum, but now the temporalis muscle exerts the effort, while the resistance is supplied by the item of food being bitten.

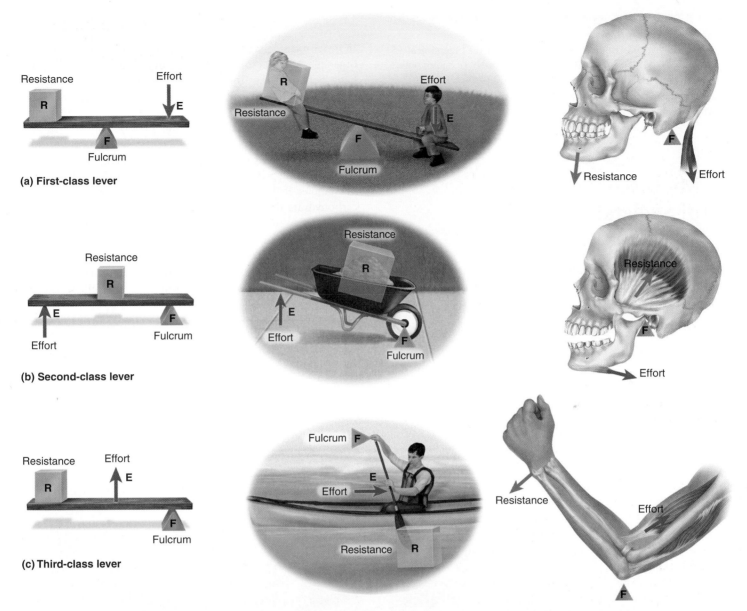

**Figure 10.7** **The Three Classes of Levers.** *Left:* The lever classes defined by the relative positions of the resistance (load), fulcrum, and effort. *Center:* Mechanical examples. *Right:* Anatomical examples. (a) Muscles at the back of the neck pull down on the occipital bone to oppose the tendency of the head to tip forward. The fulcrum is the occipital condyles. (b) To open the mouth, the digastric muscle pulls down on the chin. It is resisted by the temporalis muscle on the side of the head. The fulcrum is the temporomandibular joint. (c) In flexing the elbow, the biceps brachii exerts an effort on the radius. Resistance is provided by the weight of the forearm or anything held in the hand. The fulcrum is the elbow joint.

## THINK ABOUT IT

*Sit on the edge of a desk with your feet off the floor. Plantarflex your foot. Where is the effort? Where is the fulcrum? (Name the specific joint, based on chapter 9.) Where is the resistance? Which class of lever does the foot represent in plantar flexion?*

## Before You Go On

*Answer the following questions to test your understanding of the preceding section:*

5. Name the connective tissue layers of a muscle beginning with the individual muscle fiber and ending with the tissue that separates the muscles from the skin.

6. Sketch the fascicle arrangements that define a fusiform, parallel, convergent, pennate, and circular muscle.

7. Define the *origin, insertion,* and *action* of a muscle.

8. Distinguish between a prime mover, synergist, antagonist, and fixator.

9. What is the difference between intrinsic and extrinsic muscles that control the fingers?

10. What is the principal benefit of a joint action with a mechanical advantage less than 1.0? What is the principal benefit of a joint action with a mechanical advantage greater than 1.0?

11. Define a first-, second-, and third-class lever and give an example of each in the musculoskeletal system.

# Microscopic Anatomy of Skeletal Muscle

### Objectives
When you have completed this section, you should be able to

- describe the ultrastructure of a muscle fiber and its myofilaments;

- explain what accounts for the striations of skeletal muscle;

- describe the relationship of a nerve fiber to a muscle fiber;

- define a *motor unit* and discuss its functional significance; and

- describe the blood vessels of a skeletal muscle.

## Ultrastructure of Muscle Fibers

In order to understand muscle function, you must know how the organelles and macromolecules of a muscle fiber are arranged. Perhaps more than any other cell, a muscle fiber exemplifies the adage, form follows function. It has a complex, tightly organized internal structure in which even the spatial arrangement of protein molecules is closely tied to its contractile function (fig. 10.8).

The plasma membrane is called the **sarcolemma,**[11] and the cytoplasm is called the **sarcoplasm.** The sarcoplasm is occupied mainly by long protein bundles called **myofibrils,** each about 1 μm in diameter. It also contains an abundance of **glycogen,** a starchlike carbohydrate that provides energy for the cell during periods of heightened exercise, and the red pigment **myoglobin,** which stores oxygen until needed for muscular activity.

Muscle fibers have numerous flattened or sausage-shaped nuclei pressed against the inside of the sarcolemma. This unusual multinucleate condition results from the embryonic development

---

[11]*sarco* = flesh, muscle + *lemma* = husk

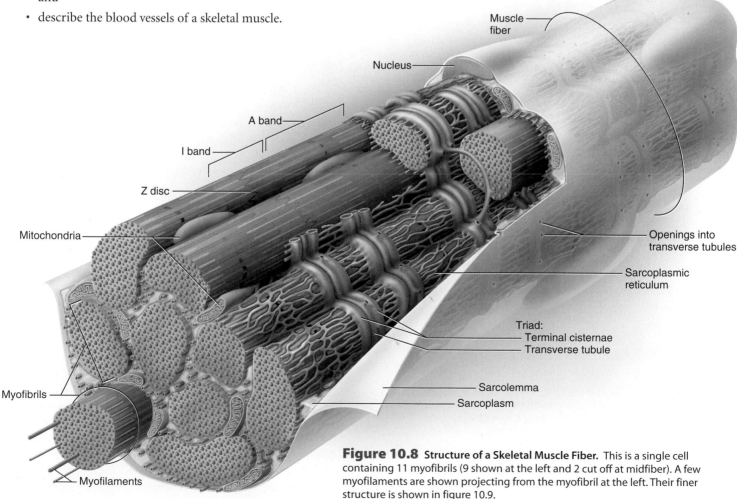

**Figure 10.8 Structure of a Skeletal Muscle Fiber.** This is a single cell containing 11 myofibrils (9 shown at the left and 2 cut off at midfiber). A few myofilaments are shown projecting from the myofibril at the left. Their finer structure is shown in figure 10.9.

● *Why is it important for the transverse tubule to be so closely associated with the terminal cisternae?*

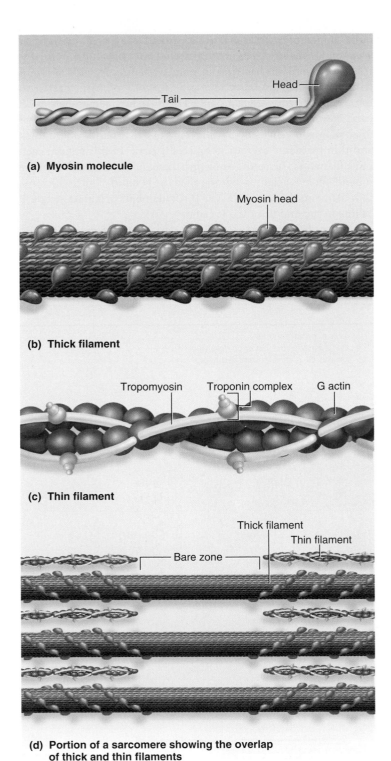

**(a)  Myosin molecule**

**(b)  Thick filament**

**(c)  Thin filament**

**(d)  Portion of a sarcomere showing the overlap
of thick and thin filaments**

**Figure 10.9**  **Molecular Structure of Thick and Thin Filaments.**  (a) A single myosin molecule consists of two intertwined proteins forming a filamentous tail and a double globular head. (b) A thick filament consists of 200 to 500 myosin molecules bundled together with the heads projecting outward in a helical array. (c) A thin filament consists of two intertwined chains of G actin molecules, smaller filamentous tropomyosin molecules, and a calcium-binding protein called troponin associated with the tropomyosin. (d) A region of overlap between the thick and thin myofilaments.

of the muscle fiber, as we will see near the end of this chapter. Most other organelles of the cell, such as mitochondria, are packed into the spaces between the myofibrils. The smooth endoplasmic reticulum, here called the **sarcoplasmic reticulum (SR),** forms a network around each myofibril. It periodically exhibits dilated end-sacs called **terminal cisternae,** which cross the muscle fiber from one side to the other. The sarcolemma turns inward at many points to form tunnels called **transverse (T) tubules,** which penetrate through the cell and emerge on the other side. Each T tubule is intimately associated with two terminal cisternae, which run alongside it on each side. A T tubule and the two terminal cisternae associated with it constitute a *triad*. The T tubule carries electrical signals from the cell surface into the interior and induces gates in the SR membrane to open. The SR contains a reservoir of calcium ions ($Ca^{2+}$). On command, it opens the gates and releases a flood of $Ca^{2+}$ into the cytosol, and the $Ca^{2+}$ activates muscle contraction.

## Myofilaments

Most of the muscle fiber is filled with myofibrils. Each myofibril is composed of parallel protein microfilaments called **myofilaments.** The key to muscle contraction lies in the arrangement and action of these myofilaments, so we must examine these at a molecular level. There are three kinds of myofilaments:

1. **Thick filaments** (fig. 10.9a, b) are about 15 nm in diameter. Each is made of several hundred molecules of a protein called **myosin.** A myosin molecule is shaped like a golf club, with two chains that intertwine to form a shaftlike *tail* and a double globular *head* projecting from it at an angle. A thick filament may be likened to a bundle of 200 to 500 such "golf clubs," with their heads directed outward in a helical array around the bundle. The heads on one half of the thick filament angle to the left, and the heads on the other half angle to the right; in the middle is a *bare zone* with no heads.

2. **Thin filaments** (fig. 10.9c, d), 7 nm in diameter, are composed primarily of two intertwined strands of a protein called **fibrous (F) actin.** Each F actin is like a bead necklace, consisting of a string of subunits called **globular (G) actin.** Each G actin has an **active site** that can bind to the head of a myosin molecule (see fig. 10.14).

   A thin filament also has 40 to 60 molecules of yet another protein called **tropomyosin.** When a muscle fiber is relaxed, tropomyosin blocks the active sites of actin and prevents myosin from binding to them. Each tropomyosin molecule, in turn, has a smaller calcium-binding protein called **troponin** bound to it.

3. **Elastic filaments** (fig. 10.10b), 1 nm in diameter, are made of a huge springy protein called **titin**[12] (**connectin**). They flank each thick filament and anchor it to a structure called the *Z disc*. This helps to stabilize the thick filament, center it between the thin filaments, and prevent overstretching.

   Myosin and actin are called the **contractile proteins** of muscle because they do the work of shortening the muscle fiber. Tropomyosin

---

[12]*tit* = giant + *in* = protein

and troponin are called the **regulatory proteins** because they act like a switch to determine when it can contract and when it cannot.

At least seven other accessory proteins occur in the thick and thin filaments or are associated with them. They anchor the myofilaments, regulate their length, and keep them aligned with each other for optimal contractile effectiveness. The most clinically important of these is **dystrophin,** an enormous protein located just under the sarcolemma in the vicinity of each I band of the striations described in the next section. It links the actin filaments to transmembrane proteins in the sarcolemma. These, in turn, are linked to proteins immediately external to the muscle fiber and ultimately to the endomysium. Thus, it is dystrophin that links the shortening of components within the fiber to a mechanical pull on the connective tissue external to the muscle fiber. Genetic defects in dystrophin are responsible for the disabling disease, muscular dystrophy (see p. 288).

## Striations and Sarcomeres

Myosin and actin are not unique to muscle; these proteins occur in all cells, where they function in cellular motility, mitosis, and transport of intracellular materials. In skeletal and cardiac muscle they are espe-

cially abundant, however, and are organized into a precise array that accounts for the striations of these two muscle types (fig. 10.10).

Striated muscle has dark **A bands** alternating with lighter **I bands.** (*A* stands for *anisotropic* and *I* for *isotropic,* which refers to the way these bands affect polarized light. To help remember which band is which, think "d**A**rk" and "l**I**ght.") Each A band consists of thick filaments lying side by side. Part of the A band, where thick and thin filaments overlap, is especially dark. In this region, each thick filament is surrounded by thin filaments. In the middle of the A band, there is a lighter region called the **H band,**[13] into which the thin filaments do not reach. The thick filaments originate at a dark **M line** in the middle of the H band.

Each light I band is bisected by a dark narrow **Z disc**[14] (**Z line**), which provides anchorage for the thin filaments and elastic filaments. Each segment of a myofibril from one Z disc to the next is called a **sarcomere**[15] (SAR-co-meer), the functional contractile unit of the muscle fiber.

---

[13]H = *helle* = bright (German)
[14]Z = *Zwischenscheibe* = between disc (German)
[15]*sarco* = muscle + *mere* = part, segment

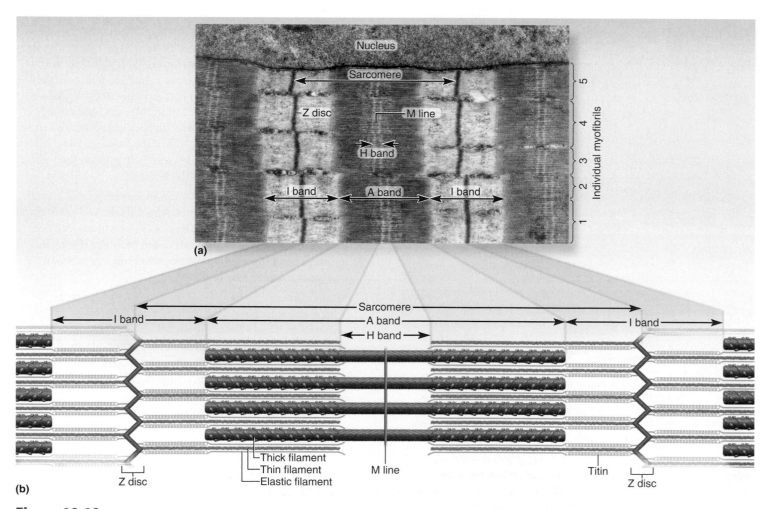

**(a)**

**(b)**

**Figure 10.10  Muscle Striations and Their Molecular Basis.** (a) Five myofibrils of a single muscle fiber, showing the striations in the relaxed state (TEM). (b) The overlapping pattern of thick and thin myofilaments that accounts for the striations seen in part (a).

The terminology of muscle fiber structure is reviewed in table 10.1.

## The Nerve–Muscle Relationship

Skeletal muscle never contracts unless it is stimulated by a nerve (or artificially with electrodes). If its nerve connections are severed or poisoned, a muscle is paralyzed. Thus, muscle contraction cannot be understood without first understanding the relationship between nerve and muscle cells. Any point where a nerve fiber meets and stimulates another cell is called a **synapse** (SIN-aps). The other cell can be another neuron, a gland cell, a muscle cell, or other type of cell. The heart of the nerve–muscle relationship is the synapse formed by a nerve cell and a skeletal muscle fiber.

### Motor Neurons

Skeletal muscles are innervated by *somatic motor neurons* (see fig. 3.24, p. 93). The cell bodies of these neurons lie in the brainstem and spinal cord and their axons, called **somatic motor fibers,** lead

| TABLE 10.1 | Structural Components of a Muscle Fiber |
|---|---|
| **Term** | **Definition** |
| **General Structure and Contents of the Muscle Fiber** | |
| Sarcolemma | The plasma membrane of a muscle fiber |
| Sarcoplasm | The cytoplasm of a muscle fiber |
| Glycogen | An energy-storage polysaccharide abundant in muscle |
| Myoglobin | An oxygen-storing red pigment of muscle |
| T tubule | A tunnel-like extension of the sarcolemma extending from one side of the muscle fiber to the other; conveys electrical signals from the cell surface to its interior |
| Sarcoplasmic reticulum | The smooth ER of a muscle fiber; a $Ca^{2+}$ reservoir |
| Terminal cisternae | The dilated ends of sarcoplasmic reticulum adjacent to a T tubule |
| **Myofibrils** | |
| Myofibril | A bundle of protein microfilaments (myofilaments) |
| Myofilament | A threadlike complex of several hundred contractile protein molecules |
| Thick filament | A myofilament about 11 nm in diameter composed of bundled myosin molecules |
| Elastic filament | A myofilament about 1 nm in diameter composed of a giant protein, titin, that flanks a thick filament and anchors it to a Z disc; stabilizes and centers the thick filament and prevents overstretching. |
| Thin filament | A myofilament about 5 to 6 nm in diameter composed of actin, troponin, and tropomyosin |
| Myosin | A protein with a long shaftlike tail and a globular head; constitutes the thick myofilament |
| F actin | A fibrous protein made of a long chain of G actin molecules twisted into a helix; main protein of the thin myofilament |
| G actin | A globular subunit of F actin with an active site for binding a myosin head |
| Regulatory proteins | Troponin and tropomyosin, proteins that do not directly engage in the sliding filament process of muscle contraction, but regulate myosin–actin binding |
| Tropomyosin | A regulatory protein that lies in the groove of F actin and, in relaxed muscle, blocks the myosin-binding active sites |
| Troponin | A regulatory protein associated with tropomyosin that acts as a calcium receptor |
| Titin | A springy protein that forms the elastic filaments and anchors the thick filaments to the Z discs |
| Dystrophin | A large protein that links thin filaments to transmembrane proteins, which, in turn, are linked to extracellular proteins; transfers the force of sarcomere contraction to the fibrous connective tissues of a muscle |
| **Striations and Sarcomeres** | |
| Striations | Alternating light and dark transverse bands across a myofibril |
| A band | Dark band formed by parallel thick filaments that partly overlap the thin filaments |
| H band | A lighter region in the middle of an A band that contains thick filaments only; thin filaments do not reach this far into the A band in relaxed muscle |
| M line | A dark line in the middle of an H band marking the origin of the thick filaments |
| I band | A light band composed of thin filaments only |
| Z disc | A disc of protein to which thin and elastic filaments are anchored at each end of a sarcomere; appears as a narrow dark line in the middle of the I band, and is often called the Z line |
| Sarcomere | A segment from one Z disc to the next; the contractile unit of a muscle fiber |

to the skeletal muscles. At its distal end, each somatic motor fiber branches out to innervate a number of muscle fibers, but any given muscle fiber is supplied by only one motor neuron.

## The Neuromuscular Junction

As a nerve fiber approaches an individual muscle fiber, it branches again to establish several points of contact within an ovoid region called the **neuromuscular junction (NMJ),** or **motor end plate** (fig. 10.11). Each terminal branch of the nerve fiber within the NMJ forms a synapse with the muscle fiber. The sarcolemma of the NMJ is irregularly indented, a little like a handprint pressed into soft clay. If you imagine the nerve fiber to be like your forearm and your hand to be spread out in this handprint, the individual synapses would be like the points where your fingertips contact the clay. Thus, one nerve fiber stimulates the muscle fiber at several points within each NMJ.

At each synapse, the nerve fiber ends with a bulbous swelling called a **synaptic** (sih-NAP-tic) **knob.** The knob doesn't directly touch the muscle fiber, but is separated from it by a narrow space called the **synaptic cleft,** about 60 to 100 nm wide (scarcely any wider than the thickness of one plasma membrane). A third cell, called a *Schwann cell,* envelops the entire junction and isolates it from the surrounding tissue fluid.

The synaptic knob contains spheroid organelles called **synaptic vesicles,** which are filled with a chemical called **acetylcholine (ACh)** (ASS-eh-till-CO-leen). When a nerve signal arrives at the synaptic knob, some of these vesicles release their ACh by exocytosis. ACh diffuses across the synaptic cleft and binds to membrane proteins called **ACh receptors** on the sarcolemma. These receptors respond to ACh by initiating electrical events that lead to muscle contraction. The sarcolemma has infoldings called **junctional folds** that increase the membrane surface area and allow for more ACh receptors, and thus more sensitivity of the muscle fiber to nervous stimulation.

The entire muscle fiber is surrounded by a *basal lamina,* a thin layer composed partly of collagen and glycoproteins, which separates it from the surrounding connective tissue. The basal lamina passes through the synaptic cleft and virtually fills it, and covers the Schwann cell of the neuromuscular junction. An enzyme called **acetylcholinesterase (AChE)** (ASS-eh-till-CO-lin-ESS-ter-ase) is found in both the sarcolemma and basal lamina. It breaks down ACh after the ACh has stimulated the muscle cell; thus, it is important in turning off muscle contraction (see Insight 10.2).

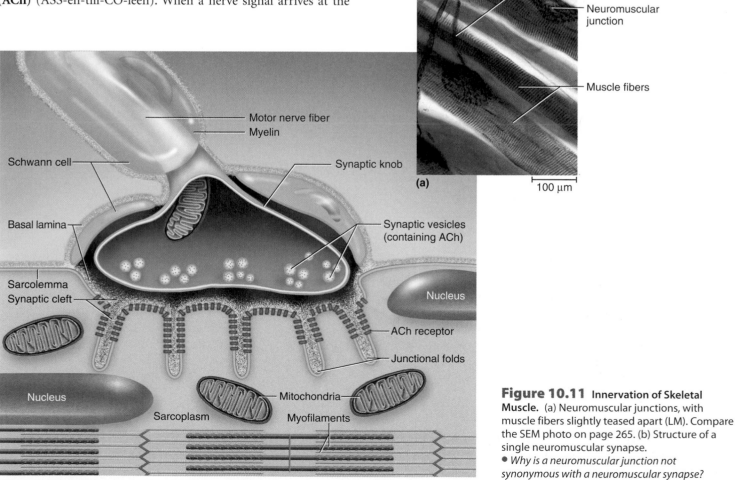

(a)

100 μm

(b)

**Figure 10.11** **Innervation of Skeletal Muscle.** (a) Neuromuscular junctions, with muscle fibers slightly teased apart (LM). Compare the SEM photo on page 265. (b) Structure of a single neuromuscular synapse.
● *Why is a neuromuscular junction not synonymous with a neuromuscular synapse?*

INSIGHT 10.2
## Clinical Application

### Neuromuscular Toxins and Paralysis

Toxins that interfere with synaptic function can paralyze the muscles. Some pesticides, for example, contain *cholinesterase inhibitors* that bind to AChE and prevent it from degrading ACh. This causes *spastic paralysis,* a state of continual contraction of the muscle, which poses the danger of suffocation if it affects the laryngeal and respiratory muscles. *Tetanus* (lockjaw) is a form of spastic paralysis caused by the toxin of a soil bacterium, *Clostridium tetani.* In the spinal cord, a chemical called glycine normally stops motor neurons from producing unwanted muscle contractions. The tetanus toxin blocks glycine release and thus causes overstimulation and spastic paralysis of the muscles.

*Flaccid paralysis* is a state in which the muscles are limp and cannot contract. This too can cause respiratory arrest if it affects the thoracic muscles. Flaccid paralysis can be caused by poisons such as curare (cue-RAH-ree) that compete with ACh for receptor sites but do not stimulate the muscle. Curare is extracted from certain plants and used by some South American natives to poison blowgun darts. It has been used to treat muscle spasms in some neurological disorders and to relax abdominal muscles for surgery, but other muscle relaxants have now replaced curare for most purposes.

*Botulism* is a type of food poisoning caused by a neuromuscular toxin secreted by the bacterium *Clostridium botulinum.* Botulinum toxin blocks the release of ACh and causes flaccid muscle paralysis. Purified botulinum toxin was approved by the U.S. Food and Drug Administration (FDA) in 2002 for cosmetically treating "frown lines" caused by muscle tautness between the eyebrows. Marketed as Botox Cosmetic (a prescription drug despite the name), it is injected in small doses into specific facial muscles. The wrinkles gradually disappear as muscle paralysis sets in over the next few hours. The effect lasts about 4 months until the muscles retighten and the wrinkles return. Botox treatment has become the fastest growing cosmetic medical procedure in the United States, with many people going for treatment every few months in their quest for a youthful appearance. It has begun to have some undesirable consequences, however, as it is sometimes administered by unqualified practitioners. Even some qualified physicians use it for treatments not yet approved by the FDA, and some host festive "Botox parties" for treatment of patients in assembly-line fashion.

### The Motor Unit

When a nerve signal approaches the end of an axon, it spreads out over all of its terminal branches and stimulates all the muscle fibers supplied by them. Thus, these muscle fibers contract in unison. Since they behave as a single functional unit, one nerve fiber and all the muscle fibers innervated by it are called a **motor unit.** The muscle fibers of a single motor unit are not all clustered together but are dispersed throughout a muscle (fig. 10.12). Thus, when they are stimulated, they cause a weak contraction over a wide area—not just a localized twitch in one small region.

Earlier it was stated that a motor nerve fiber supplies multiple muscle fibers. On average, there are about 200 muscle fibers per motor neuron. But where fine control is needed, we have *small motor units.* In the muscles of eye movement, for example, there are

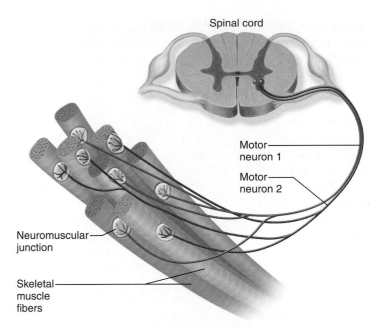

**Figure 10.12** **Motor Units.** A motor unit consists of one motor neuron and all skeletal muscle fibers that it innervates. Two motor units here are represented by the red and blue nerve and muscle fibers. Note that the muscle fibers of a motor unit are not clustered together, but distributed throughout the muscle and commingled with the fibers of other motor units.

about 3 to 6 muscle fibers per nerve fiber. Small motor units are not very strong, but they provide the fine degree of control needed for subtle movements. They also have small neurons that are easily stimulated. Where strength is more important than fine control, we have *large motor units.* The gastrocnemius muscle of the calf, for example, has about 1,000 muscle fibers per nerve fiber. Large motor units are much stronger, but have larger neurons that are harder to stimulate, and they do not produce such fine control.

One advantage of having multiple motor units in a muscle is that they are able to "work in shifts." Muscle fibers fatigue when subjected to continual stimulation. If all of the fibers in one of your postural muscles fatigued at once, for example, you might collapse. To prevent this, other motor units take over while the fatigued ones rest, and the muscle as a whole can sustain long-term contraction. Another advantage is that the strength of muscle contraction can be varied by activating more or fewer motor units.

## The Blood Supply

The muscular system as a whole receives about 1.25 L of blood per minute at rest—which is about one-quarter of the blood pumped by the heart. During heavy exercise, total cardiac output rises, and the muscular system's share of it is more than three-quarters, or 11.6 L/min. Working muscle has a great demand for glucose and oxygen. Blood capillaries ramify through the endomysium to reach every muscle fiber, sometimes so intimately associated with the muscle fibers that the fibers have surface indentations to accommodate them. The capillaries of skeletal muscle undulate or coil when the muscle is contracted (fig. 10.13), allowing them enough slack to stretch out straight, without breaking, when the muscle lengthens.

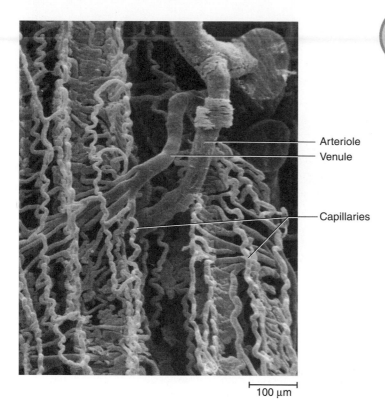

Arteriole
Venule

Capillaries

100 μm

**Figure 10.13** A Vascular Cast of the Blood Vessels in a Contracted Skeletal Muscle. This cast was prepared by injecting the blood vessels with a polymer, digesting away the tissue to leave a replica of the vessels, and photographing the cast through the SEM. (From R. G. Kessell and R. H. Kardon, *Tissues and Organs: A Text-Atlas of Scanning Electron Microscopy*, W. H. Freeman & Co., 1979)

## Before You Go On

*Answer the following questions to test your understanding of the preceding section:*

12. What special terms are given to the plasma membrane, cytoplasm, and smooth ER of a muscle cell?

13. Name the proteins that compose the thick and thin filaments of a muscle fiber and describe their structural arrangement.

14. Define *sarcomere*. Describe the striations of a sarcomere and sketch the arrangement of thick and thin filaments that accounts for the striations.

15. Describe the role of a synaptic knob, synaptic vesicles, synaptic cleft, and acetylcholine in neuromuscular function.

16. What is a motor unit? How do large and small motor units differ functionally?

17. Why is it important that the blood capillaries of a contracted muscle have an undulating or coiled arrangement?

# Functional Perspectives

### *Objectives*
When you have completed this section, you should be able to

- explain how a muscle fiber contracts and relaxes, and relate this to its ultrastructure;
- describe how muscle grows and shrinks with use and disuse; and
- discuss two physiological categories of muscle fibers and their respective advantages.

## Contraction and Relaxation

We noted earlier that a muscle fiber epitomizes the essential unity of form and function. Having examined the structure of a muscle fiber down to its molecular details, our task would be incomplete if we didn't ask ourselves what all of this is for. *Why* are all the molecules and organelles of the muscle fiber so closely packed and in such a precisely organized way? To answer that, we'll look briefly at the essential aspects of muscle contraction and relaxation. These form a cycle of events with four main phases:

1. **Excitation,** in which a nerve fiber releases ACh, ACh excites the muscle fiber, and a wave of electrical excitation spreads into the sarcoplasm by way of the T tubules.

2. **Excitation–contraction coupling,** consisting of events that link this electrical stimulus to the onset of muscle tension. Excitation of the T tubules induces the sarcoplasmic reticulum (SR) to release calcium ions, and calcium clears the way for the myosin of the thick filaments to bind to the actin of the thin filaments.

3. **Contraction,** in which the myosin heads repeatedly attach to the thin filaments and pull on them, causing the thin filaments to slide across the thick filaments and shorten the cell.

4. **Relaxation,** in which nerve signaling ceases, myosin is once again blocked from binding to actin, and muscle tension subsides.

Figure 10.14 shows a few of the finer steps of this process, numbered to correspond to the following description.

### Excitation

1. A nerve signal arrives at the synaptic knob.

2. The synaptic vesicles release ACh, which diffuses across the synaptic cleft and binds to receptors on the sarcolemma of the muscle fiber. This opens ion gates in the sarcolemma, resulting in sodium and potassium movements through the membrane that electrically excite the muscle fiber.

3. A self-propagating wave of excitation spreads down the length of the fiber and into the T tubules.

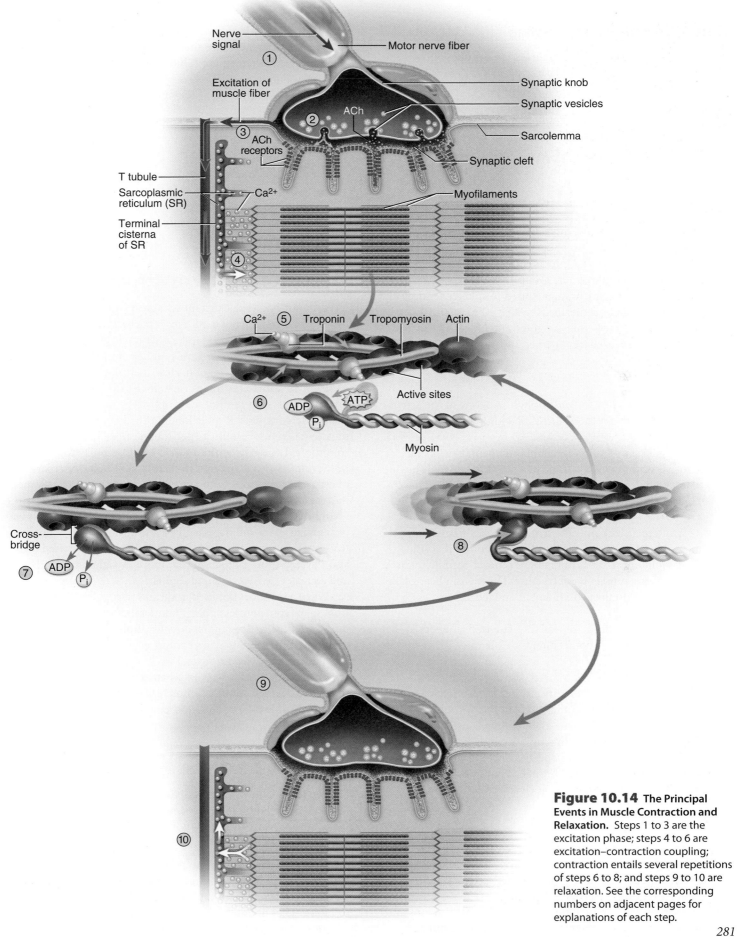

**Figure 10.14 The Principal Events in Muscle Contraction and Relaxation.** Steps 1 to 3 are the excitation phase; steps 4 to 6 are excitation–contraction coupling; contraction entails several repetitions of steps 6 to 8; and steps 9 to 10 are relaxation. See the corresponding numbers on adjacent pages for explanations of each step.

## Excitation–Contraction Coupling

(4) Electrical events in the T tubule lead to the opening of calcium gates in the sarcoplasmic reticulum. The SR releases a flood of calcium ions into the cytosol.

(5) Calcium ions bind to troponin molecules in the thin myofilaments. Troponin induces the long tropomyosin molecule to shift position, sinking into the groove between the two F actin filaments and exposing the active sites on the G actin.

(6) Meanwhile, myosin has been "waiting" in a flexed position, like a bent elbow, with a molecule of ATP bound to its head. The head contains an enzyme called *myosin ATPase,* which breaks down ATP into adenosine diphosphate (ADP) and an inorganic phosphate group ($P_i$). This is a *hydrolysis* reaction—one in which water is used to split a chemical bond in an organic molecule (the ATP). The energy liberated by this reaction straightens the myosin head into an extended, high-energy "cocked" position.

## Contraction

(7) Myosin forms a link, or *cross-bridge,* with one of the active sites of actin, and releases the ADP and $P_i$ .

(8) Myosin flexes and tugs on the thin filament, like flexing your elbow to pull in the rope of a boat anchor, and the thin filament slides a short distance along the thick filament. This movement is called the *power stroke.* Myosin binds a new ATP, lets go of the thin filament, breaks down the ATP, and recocks; this is the *recovery stroke.* Whenever one myosin head lets go of the thin filament, other myosin heads hold on, so the thin filament is never entirely released as long as the muscle is contracting. The myosin heads take turns pulling on the actin filament and letting go.

Steps 6 through 8 occur repeatedly. The overall effect is that the thin filament slides smoothly alongside the thick filament; this model of muscle contraction is therefore called the *sliding filament theory.* No myofilaments get shorter during contraction—they merely slide across each other. Since the thin filaments are connected through dystrophin to the sarcolemma and ultimately to the extracellular connective tissue, their sliding shortens the entire cell and its endomysium. If all the myosin heads in a muscle fiber executed a single cycle of power and recovery strokes, the muscle fiber would shorten about 1%. Through repetition of the process, however, a fiber can shorten by as much as 40%.

## Relaxation

(9) The first step needed to make a muscle fiber relax is to stop stimulating it. The motor neuron stops firing and releasing ACh, so the muscle fiber is no longer electrically excited.

(10) The sarcoplasmic reticulum reabsorbs the calcium ions and stores them until the next time the muscle is stimulated.

Without calcium, troponin moves back into the position that blocks the active sites and prevents myosin–actin cross-bridges from forming. Thus, the muscle can no longer maintain tension. It relaxes, and the action of gravity or an antagonistic muscle at the same joint stretches it back to its resting length.

### THINK ABOUT IT

*During muscle contraction, which band(s) of the muscle striations would you expect to become narrower or disappear? Which would remain the same width as in relaxed muscle? Explain.*

## Muscle Growth and Atrophy

It is common knowledge that muscles grow larger when exercised and shrink when they are not used. This is the basis for *resistance exercises* such as weight lifting. And yet, skeletal muscle fibers are incapable of mitosis. We have about the same number of muscle fibers in adulthood as we do in late childhood. How, then, does a muscle grow?

Exercise stimulates the muscle fiber to produce more protein myofilaments. As a result, the myofibrils grow thicker. At a certain point, a large myofibril splits longitudinally, so a well-conditioned muscle has more myofibrils per muscle fiber than does a weakly conditioned one. The entire muscle grows in bulk (thickness), not by the mitosis of existing cells (hyperplasia), but by the enlargement of cells that have existed since childhood (hypertrophy). Some authorities, however, think that entire muscle fibers (not just their myofibrils) may split longitudinally when they reach a certain size, thus giving rise to an increase in the number of fibers—not by mitosis but by a process more akin to tearing. Well-exercised muscles also develop more mitochondria, more myoglobin and glycogen, and a greater density of blood capillaries.

When a muscle is not used, it shrinks (atrophies). This can result from spinal cord injuries or other injuries that sever the nerve connections to a muscle *(denervation atrophy),* from lack of exercise *(disuse atrophy),* or from aging *(senescence atrophy).* The shrinkage of a limb that has been in a cast for several weeks is a good example of disuse atrophy. Muscle quickly regrows when exercise resumes, but if the atrophy becomes too advanced, muscle fibers die and are not replaced. Physical therapy is therefore important for maintaining muscle mass in people who are unable to use the muscles voluntarily.

## Physiological Classes of Muscle Fibers

Not all muscle fibers are metabolically alike or adapted to perform the same task. Some respond slowly but are relatively resistant to fatigue, while others respond more quickly but also fatigue quickly. Each primary type of fiber goes by several names:

- **Slow oxidative (SO), slow-twitch, red,** or **type I fibers.** These fibers have relatively abundant mitochondria, myoglobin, and blood capillaries, and therefore a relatively deep red color. They are well adapted to aerobic respiration, a means for making ATP that requires oxygen but does not generate lactic acid, a major contributor to muscle fatigue. Thus, these fibers do not fatigue easily. However, in response to a single stimulus, they exhibit a relatively long *twitch,* or contraction, lasting about 100 milliseconds (msec). The soleus muscle of the calf and the postural muscles of the back are composed mainly of these slow-twitch, fatigue-resistant fibers.

- **Fast glycolytic (FG), fast-twitch, white,** or **type II fibers.** These fibers are rich in enzymes for anaerobic fermentation, a process that is independent of oxygen but produces lactic acid. They respond quickly, with twitches as short as 7.5 msec, but because of the lactic acid, they fatigue more easily than SO fibers. They are poorer in mitochondria, myoglobin, and blood capillaries than SO fibers, so they are relatively pale (hence the expression *white* fibers). They are well adapted for quick responses but not for endurance. Thus, they are especially important in sports such as basketball that require stop-and-go activity and frequent changes of pace. The gastrocnemius muscle of the calf, biceps brachii of the arm, and the muscles of eye movement consist mainly of FG fibers.

Some authorities recognize two subtypes of FG fibers called types IIA and IIB. Type IIB is the common type just described, whereas IIA, or **intermediate fibers,** combine fast-twitch responses with aerobic fatigue-resistant metabolism. Type IIA fibers, however, are relatively rare except in some endurance-trained athletes. The fiber types can be differentiated histologically by using stains for certain mitochondrial enzymes and other cellular components (fig. 10.15). Table 10.2 summarizes the difference between SO and FG fibers.

All muscles are composed of both SO and FG fibers, but the proportions of these fiber types differ from one muscle to another. Muscles composed mainly of SO fibers are called *red muscles* and those composed mainly of FG fibers are called *white muscles.* People with different types and levels of physical activity differ in the proportion of one fiber type to another even in the same muscle, such as the *quadriceps femoris* of the anterior thigh (table 10.3). It is thought that people are born with a genetic predisposition for a certain ratio of fiber types. Those who go into competitive sports

| TABLE 10.2 | Classification of Skeletal Muscle Fibers | |
|---|---|---|
| **Properties** | **Slow Oxidative Fibers** | **Fast Glycolytic Fibers** |
| Relative diameter | Smaller | Larger |
| ATP synthesis | Aerobic | Anaerobic |
| Fatigue resistance | Good | Poor |
| ATP hydrolysis | Slow | Fast |
| Glycolysis | Moderate | Fast |
| Myoglobin content | Abundant | Low |
| Glycogen content | Low | Abundant |
| Mitochondria | Abundant and large | Fewer and smaller |
| Capillaries | Abundant | Fewer |
| Color | Red | White, pale |
| **Representative Muscles in Which Fiber Type Is Predominant** | | |
| | Soleus | Gastrocnemius |
| | Erector spinae | Biceps brachii |
| | Quadratus lumborum | Muscles of eye movement |

| TABLE 10.3 | Proportion of Slow- and Fast-Twitch Fibers in the Quadriceps Femoris of Male Athletes | |
|---|---|---|
| **Sample Population** | **Slow-Oxidative (SO)** | **Fast-Glycolytic (FG)** |
| Marathon runners | 82% | 18% |
| Swimmers | 74 | 26 |
| Average males | 45 | 55 |
| Sprinters and jumpers | 37 | 63 |

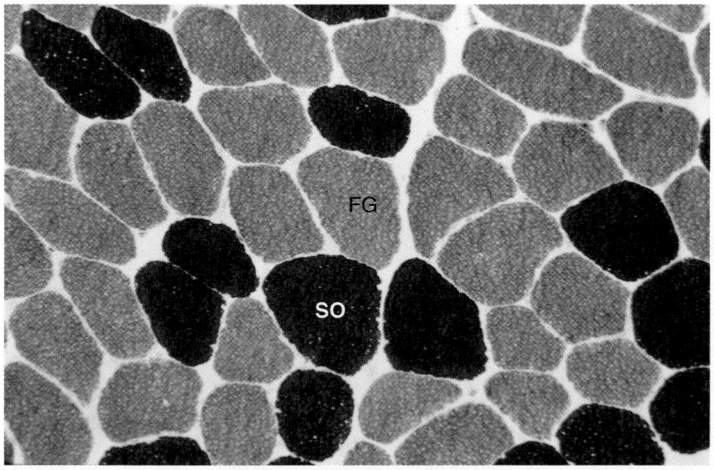

**Figure 10.15** **Muscle Stained to Distinguish Fast Glycolytic (FG) from Slow Oxidative (SO) Fibers.** Cross section.

discover the sports at which they can excel and gravitate toward those for which heredity has best equipped them. One person might be a "born sprinter" and another a "born marathoner."

We noted earlier that sometimes two or more muscles act across the same joint and superficially seem to have the same function. We have already seen why such muscles are not as redundant as they seem, such as differences in mechanical advantage. Another reason is that they may differ in the proportion of SO to FG fibers. For example, the gastrocnemius and soleus muscles of the calf both insert on the calcaneus through the calcaneal tendon, so they exert the same pull on the heel. The gastrocnemius, however, is a predominantly fast glycolytic muscle adapted for quick, powerful movements such as jumping, whereas the soleus is a predominantly slow oxidative muscle that does most of the work in endurance exercises such as jogging and skiing.

## Before You Go On

*Answer the following questions to test your understanding of the preceding section:*

18. What role does the sarcoplasmic reticulum play in muscle contraction? What role does it play in muscle relaxation?

19. Why does tropomyosin have to move before a muscle fiber can contract? What makes it move?

20. What role does ATP play in muscle contraction?

21. What is the mechanism of muscle growth? Describe the growth process in muscle and distinguish it from hyperplasia.

22. What are the basic functional differences between slow oxidative and fast glycolytic muscle fibers?

# Cardiac and Smooth Muscle

### Objectives

When you have completed this section, you should be able to

- describe cardiac muscle tissue and compare its structure and physiology to the other types; and

- describe smooth muscle tissue and compare its structure and physiology to the other types.

In this section, we will compare cardiac muscle and smooth muscle to skeletal muscle. Cardiac and smooth muscle have special structural and physiological properties related to their distinctive functions.

## Cardiac Muscle

Cardiac muscle constitutes most of the heart. Its form and function are discussed extensively in chapter 20 so that you will be able to relate these to the actions of the heart. Here, we only briefly compare it to skeletal and smooth muscle (table 10.4).

Cardiac muscle is striated like skeletal muscle, but otherwise exhibits several differences. Its *cardiocytes (myocytes)* are not long multinucleate fibers but short, stumpy, slightly branched cells. Microscopically, cardiac muscle exhibits characteristic dark lines called **intercalated** (in-TUR-kuh-LAY-ted) **discs** where the cells meet. These are steplike regions containing electrical gap junctions that allow the cells to communicate with each other, and various mechanical junctions that prevent the cells from pulling apart when they contract (see details in chapter 20). Each myocyte can join several others at its intercalated discs.

Cardiocytes usually have only one, centrally placed nucleus (occasionally two) (fig. 10.16a), often surrounded by glycogen. Cardiac muscle is very rich in glycogen and myoglobin, and it has especially large mitochondria that fill about 25% of the cell, compared to smaller mitochondria occupying about 2% of a skeletal muscle fiber. Cardiac muscle is therefore very well adapted to aerobic respiration and very resistant to fatigue, although it is highly vulnerable to interruptions in its oxygen supply. The sarcoplasmic reticulum is less developed than in skeletal muscle, but the T tubules are larger and admit supplemental calcium from the extracellular fluid. Cardiac myocytes have little capacity for mitosis. Furthermore, cardiac muscle has no satellite cells, so the repair of damaged cardiac muscle is primarily by fibrosis.

Cardiac muscle is innervated by the *autonomic nervous system (ANS)* rather than by somatic motor neurons. The ANS is a division of the nervous system that usually operates without one's

| TABLE 10.4 | Comparison of Skeletal, Cardiac, and Smooth Muscle | | |
|---|---|---|---|
| **Feature** | **Skeletal Muscle** | **Cardiac Muscle** | **Smooth Muscle** |
| Location | Associated with skeletal system | Heart | Walls of viscera and blood vessels, iris of eye, piloerectors of hair follicles |
| Cell shape | Long cylindrical fibers | Short branched cells | Fusiform cells |
| Cell length | 100 μm–30 cm | 50–100 μm | 50–200 μm |
| Cell width | 10–100 μm | 10–20 μm | 2–10 μm |
| Striations | Present | Present | Absent |
| Nuclei | Multiple nuclei, adjacent to sarcolemma | Usually one nucleus, near middle of cell | One nucleus, near middle of cell |
| Connective tissues | Endomysium, perimysium, epimysium | Endomysium only | Endomysium only |
| Sarcoplasmic reticulum | Abundant | Present | Scanty |
| T tubules | Present, narrow | Present, wide | Absent |
| Gap junctions | Absent | Present in intercalated discs | Present in single-unit smooth muscle |
| Ca²⁺ source | Sarcoplasmic reticulum | Sarcoplasmic reticulum and extracellular fluid | Mainly extracellular fluid |
| Innervation and control | Somatic motor fibers (voluntary) | Autonomic fibers (involuntary) | Autonomic fibers (involuntary) |
| Nervous stimulation required? | Yes | No | No |
| Mode of tissue repair | Limited regeneration, mostly fibrosis | Limited regeneration, mostly fibrosis | Relatively good capacity for regeneration |

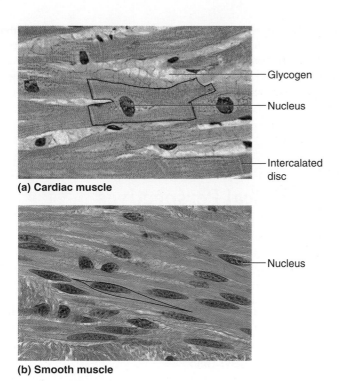

**Figure 10.16** Cardiac and Smooth Muscle.

- Glycogen
- Nucleus
- Intercalated disc

**(a) Cardiac muscle**

- Nucleus

**(b) Smooth muscle**

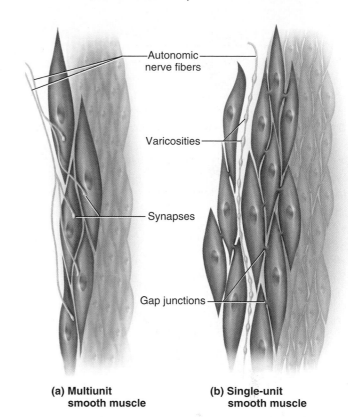

- Autonomic nerve fibers
- Varicosities
- Synapses
- Gap junctions

**(a) Multiunit smooth muscle**

**(b) Single-unit smooth muscle**

**Figure 10.17** Multiunit and Single-Unit Smooth Muscle. (a) Multiunit smooth muscle, in which each muscle cell receives its own nerve supply and contracts independently. (b) Single-unit smooth muscle, in which a nerve fiber passes through the tissue without synapsing with any specific muscle cell, and muscle cells are coupled by electrical gap junctions.

conscious awareness or control. It does not generate the heartbeat, but it modulates the heart rate and contraction strength. Cardiocytes pulsate rhythmically even without nervous stimulation; this property is called *autorhythmicity*. In an intact heart, their beating is triggered by a pacemaker, discussed in chapter 20.

## Smooth Muscle

Smooth muscle is composed of fusiform myocytes (fig. 10.16b). There is only one nucleus, located near the middle of the cell. Thick and thin filaments are both present, but they are not aligned with each other and produce no visible striations or sarcomeres; this is the reason for the name *smooth* muscle. Z discs are absent; instead, the thin filaments are attached by way of the cytoskeleton to **dense bodies,** little masses of protein scattered throughout the sarcoplasm and on the inner face of the sarcolemma.

The sarcoplasmic reticulum is scanty, and there are no T tubules. The calcium needed to activate smooth muscle contraction comes mainly from the extracellular fluid by way of calcium channels in the sarcolemma. During relaxation, calcium is pumped back out of the cell. Some smooth muscle has no nerve supply, but when nerve fibers are present, they come from the autonomic nervous system, like those of the heart.

Unlike skeletal and cardiac muscle, smooth muscle is capable of mitosis and hyperplasia. Thus, an organ such as the pregnant uterus can grow by adding more myocytes, and injured smooth muscle regenerates well.

There are two functional categories of smooth muscle called *multiunit* and *single-unit* types (fig. 10.17). **Multiunit smooth muscle** occurs in some of the largest arteries and pulmonary air

passages, in the piloerector muscles of the hair follicles, and in the iris of the eye. Its innervation, although autonomic, is otherwise similar to that of skeletal muscle—the terminal branches of a nerve fiber synapse with individual myocytes and form a motor unit. Each motor unit contracts independently of the others, hence the name of this muscle type.

**Single-unit smooth muscle** is more widespread. It occurs in most blood vessels and in the digestive, respiratory, urinary, and reproductive tracts—thus it is also called **visceral muscle.** The nerve fibers in this type of muscle do not synapse with individual muscle cells, but pass through the tissue and exhibit swellings called **varicosities** at which they release neurotransmitters. Neurotransmitters nonselectively stimulate multiple muscle cells in the vicinity of a varicosity. The muscle cells themselves are electrically coupled to each other by gap junctions. Thus, they directly stimulate each other and a large number of cells contract as a unit, almost as if they were a single cell. This is the reason that this muscle type is called *single-unit* smooth muscle.

In many of the hollow internal organs, visceral muscle forms two or more layers—typically an inner *circular layer,* in which the fibers encircle the organ, and an outer *longitudinal layer,* in which the fibers run lengthwise along the organ (fig. 10.18). When the circular layer of muscle contracts, it narrows the organ and may make it longer (like a roll of dough squeezed in your hands); when the longitudinal muscle contracts, it makes the organ shorter and thicker.

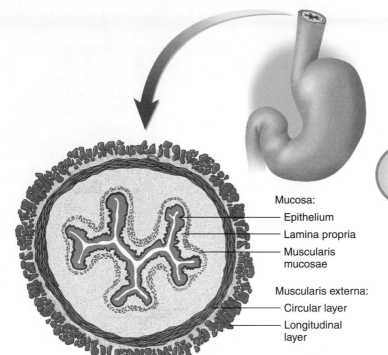

Mucosa:
— Epithelium
— Lamina propria
— Muscularis mucosae

Muscularis externa:
— Circular layer
— Longitudinal layer

**Figure 10.18** **Layers of Visceral Muscle in a Cross Section of the Esophagus.** Many hollow organs have alternating circular and longitudinal layers of smooth muscle.

Smooth muscle contracts and relaxes slowly, responding not only to nervous stimulation but also to chemicals and stretch. Its metabolism is mostly aerobic, but it has a very low energy requirement compared to skeletal and cardiac muscle, so it is highly fatigue-resistant. This enables smooth muscle to maintain a state of continual, partial contraction called **smooth muscle tone.** Smooth muscle tone maintains blood pressure by keeping the blood vessels partially constricted, and it prevents such organs as the stomach, intestines, urinary bladder, and uterus from becoming flaccid when empty. In the digestive tract and some other locations, smooth muscle is responsible for waves of contraction called **peristalsis** that propel the contents through an organ (food in the esophagus and urine in the ureters, for example).

Table 10.4 compares some properties of skeletal, cardiac, and smooth muscle.

## *Before You Go On*

*Answer the following questions to test your understanding of the preceding section:*

23. What organelles are more abundant and larger in cardiac muscle than in skeletal muscle? What is the functional significance of this?

24. What organelle is less developed in cardiac muscle than in skeletal muscle? How does this affect the activation of muscle contraction in the heart?

25. What factors make cardiac muscle more resistant to fatigue than skeletal muscle? What accounts for the relative fatigue resistance of smooth muscle?

26. How are single-unit and multiunit smooth muscle different? Which type is more abundant?

# Developmental and Clinical Perspectives

### *Objectives*
When you have completed this section, you should be able to

- describe how the three types of muscle develop in the embryo;
- describe the changes that occur in the muscular system in old age;
- discuss two muscle diseases, muscular dystrophy and myasthenia gravis; and
- briefly define and discuss several other disorders of the muscular system.

## Embryonic Development of Muscle

Muscular tissue arises from embryonic mesoderm, with the exception of the piloerector muscles of the skin and the muscles within the eye. As described in chapter 4, the mesoderm of the trunk forms segmentally arranged blocks of tissue called somites, which then divide into regions called the dermatomes, sclerotomes, and myotomes. Beginning in week 4, some mesodermal cells migrate to the center of a somite and form the myotome, which will give rise to major axial muscles such as the *erector spinae* of the back. Others migrate away from the somite to the limb buds and body wall, where they will give rise to limb, abdominal, thoracic, and other muscles.

In all of these locations, the mesodermal cells elongate into spindle-shaped **myoblasts**[16] and rapidly multiply (fig. 10.19). Myoblasts fuse into long multinucleate masses called the **primary myotubes,** with the nuclei in a chain down the core. These myotubes, the future muscle fibers, attach at each end to the developing tendons and skeleton. Internally, they begin assembling muscle proteins into sarcomeres, starting at the periphery of the myotube and progressing inward. Nuclei migrate to the periphery as the center becomes filled with myofibrils. Additional waves of myoblasts aggregate along the primary myotubes and form smaller *secondary* and *tertiary myotubes* (sometimes more in larger muscles) that fuse with the primary myotube to thicken the fiber.

By 9 weeks, most muscle groups are present, and nerve fibers have synapsed with the muscle fibers. The muscle fibers begin

[16]*myo* = muscle + *blast* = precursor

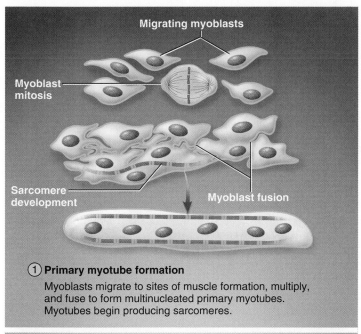

**1 Primary myotube formation**

Myoblasts migrate to sites of muscle formation, multiply, and fuse to form multinucleated primary myotubes. Myotubes begin producing sarcomeres.

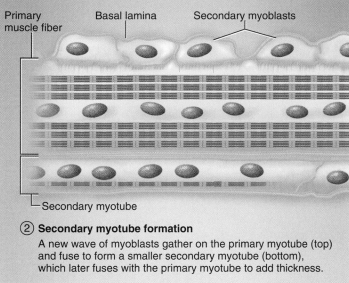

**2 Secondary myotube formation**

A new wave of myoblasts gather on the primary myotube (top) and fuse to form a smaller secondary myotube (bottom), which later fuses with the primary myotube to add thickness.

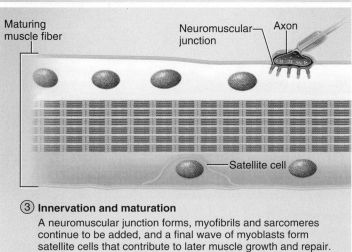

**3 Innervation and maturation**

A neuromuscular junction forms, myofibrils and sarcomeres continue to be added, and a final wave of myoblasts form satellite cells that contribute to later muscle growth and repair.

**Figure 10.19** Embryonic Development of Skeletal Muscle Fibers.

contracting in response to nervous stimulation by week 10. By week 17, the contractions are strong enough to be felt by the mother. It was once thought that the fetus first comes alive at this time, so this stage of development is called *quickening*.[17]

Late in fetal development, a final wave of myoblasts associate with the muscle fiber and become **satellite cells.** These are stem cells that persist throughout life. Some of them fuse with growing muscle fibers and contribute nuclei to it through childhood, and satellite cells may regenerate a limited amount of damaged skeletal muscle even in adults. The development of new muscle fibers by mitosis ends, according to various estimates, from week 24 of gestation to 1 year after birth. After that, all muscle growth is by hypertrophy (enlargement of existing fibers) or longitudinal, nonmitotic splitting of large fibers. After age 25, the number of fibers in each muscle begins to decline.

Cardiac muscle develops in association with an embryonic *heart tube* described in chapter 20. Mesenchymal cells near the heart tube differentiate into myoblasts, and these proliferate mitotically as they do in the development of skeletal muscle. But in contrast to skeletal muscle development, the myoblasts do not fuse. They remain joined to each other and develop intercalated discs at their points of adhesion. The heart begins beating in week 3. Mitosis in cardiac myocytes continues after birth and is active until about age 9, although there is now evidence of limited mitotic capability even in adults. There is understandable interest in being able to stimulate this process in hopes of promoting regeneration of cardiac muscle damaged by heart attacks.

Smooth muscle develops similarly from myoblasts associated with the embryonic gut, blood vessels, and other organs. As in cardiac muscle, these myoblasts never fuse with each other, but in single-unit smooth muscle, they do become interconnected through gap junctions.

## The Aging Muscular System

One of the most noticeable changes we experience with age is the loss of lean body mass (muscle) and accumulation of fat. The change is dramatically exemplified by CT scans of the thigh. In a young well-conditioned male, muscle accounts for 90% of the cross-sectional area of the midthigh, whereas in a frail 90-year-old woman, it is only 30%. Muscular strength and mass peak in the 20s; by the age of 80, most people have only half as much strength and endurance. A large percentage of people over age 75 cannot lift a 4.5 kg (10 lb) weight with their arms; such simple tasks as carrying a sack of groceries into the house may become impossible. The loss of strength is a major contributor to falls, fractures, and dependence on others for the routine activities of daily living. Fast glycolytic (fast-twitch) fibers exhibit the earliest and most severe atrophy, thus increasing reaction time and reducing coordination.

There are multiple reasons for the loss of strength. Aged muscle fibers have fewer myofibrils, so they are smaller and weaker. The sarcomeres are increasingly disorganized, and muscle mitochondria

[17]*quick* = alive

are smaller and have reduced quantities of oxidative enzymes. Aged muscle has less ATP, glycogen, and myoglobin; consequently, it fatigues quickly. Muscles also exhibit more fat and fibrous tissue with age, which limits their movement and blood circulation. With reduced circulation, muscle injuries heal more slowly and with more scar tissue.

But the weakness and easy fatigue of aged muscle also stems from the aging of other organ systems. There are fewer motor neurons in the spinal cord, and some muscle shrinkage may represent denervation atrophy. The remaining neurons produce less acetylcholine and show less efficient synaptic transmission, which makes the muscles slower to respond to stimulation. As muscle atrophies, motor units have fewer muscle fibers per motor neuron, and more motor units must be recruited to perform a given task. Tasks that used to be easy, such as buttoning the clothes or eating a meal, take more time and effort. The sympathetic nervous system is also less efficient in old age, and less effective in increasing the blood flow to the muscles during exercise. This contributes to reduced endurance.

The muscles can be significantly reconditioned, however, even by exercise begun late in life. A person in his or her 90s can increase muscle strength two- or threefold in 6 months with as little as 40 minutes of exercise per week.

## Diseases of the Muscular System

Diseases of muscular tissue are called **myopathies.** The muscular system suffers fewer diseases than any other organ system, but two of particular importance are muscular dystrophy and myasthenia gravis.

**Muscular dystrophy**[18] is a collective term for several hereditary diseases in which the skeletal muscles degenerate, lose strength, and are gradually replaced by fat and scar tissue. This new connective tissue impedes blood circulation, which in turn accelerates muscle degeneration, creating a fatal spiral of positive feedback. The most common form of the disease is *Duchenne*[19] *muscular dystrophy (DMD),* a sex-linked disease that occurs especially in males (about 1 in 3,500 male live births). It results from a defective gene for dystrophin. In the absence of dystrophin, the sarcolemma tears and the muscle fiber dies. DMD is not evident at birth, but difficulties appear as a child begins to walk. The child falls frequently and has difficulty standing up again. The disease affects the hips first, then the lower limbs, and progresses to the abdominal and spinal muscles. The muscles shorten as they atrophy, causing postural abnormalities such as scoliosis. DMD is incurable, but is treated with exercise to slow the atrophy and with braces to reinforce the weakened hips and correct the posture. Patients are usually confined to a wheelchair by early adolescence and rarely live beyond the age of 20.

**Myasthenia gravis**[20] **(MG)** (MY-ass-THEE-nee-uh GRAV-iss) is most prevalent in women from 20 to 40 years old. It is an autoimmune disease in which antibodies attack the neuromuscular junctions and trigger the destruction of ACh receptors. As a result, the muscle fibers become less and less sensitive to ACh. The effects often appear first in the facial muscles and include drooping eyelids (fig. 10.20) and double vision (due to weakness of the eye muscles). These signs are often followed by difficulty swallowing, weakness of the limbs, and poor physical endurance. Some people with MG die quickly as a result of respiratory failure, while others have normal life spans. The symptoms can be controlled with cholinesterase inhibitors, which retard the breakdown of ACh and prolong its action on the muscles, and with drugs that suppress the immune system and thus slow the attack on ACh receptors.

Some other disorders of the muscular system in general are briefly described in table 10.5, whereas disorders more specific to the axial or appendicular musculature are described in chapters 11 and 12.

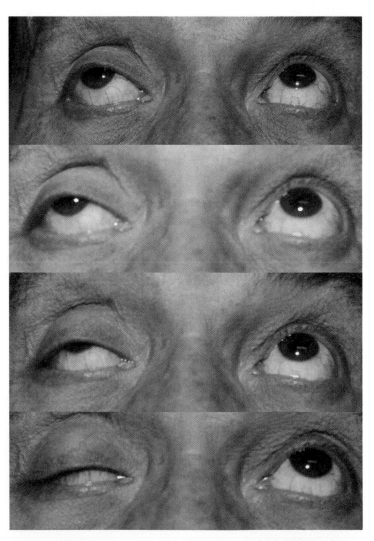

**Figure 10.20 Myasthenia Gravis (MG).** These photographs were taken when the patient was first told to gaze upward (top photo) and then at 30, 60, and 90 seconds. Note the inability to keep the right eyelid open. This drooping, or *ptosis,* is diagnostic of MG.

---

[18]*dys* = bad, abnormal + *trophy* = growth
[19]Guillaume B. A. Duchenne (1806–75), French physician
[20]*my* = muscle + *asthen* = weakness + *grav* = severe

| TABLE 10.5 | Disorders of the Muscular System |
|---|---|
| Charley horse | Slang for any painful tear, stiffness, and blood clotting in a muscle caused by contusion (a blow to the muscle causing hemorrhaging). |
| Contracture | Abnormal muscle shortening not caused by nervous stimulation. Can result from a persistence of calcium in the sarcoplasm after stimulation or from contraction of scar tissue. |
| Crush syndrome | A shocklike state following the massive crushing of muscles, associated with a high and potentially fatal fever, cardiac irregularities caused by $K^+$ released from the injured muscles, and kidney failure caused by blockage of the renal tubules with myoglobin released by the traumatized muscle. Myoglobin in the urine *(myoglobinuria)* is a common sign. |
| Delayed onset muscle soreness | Pain and stiffness felt from several hours to a day after strenuous exercise. Associated with microtrauma to the muscles, with disrupted Z discs, myofibrils, and plasma membranes, and with elevated blood levels of myoglobin and enzymes released by damaged muscle fibers. |
| Rhabdomyoma | A rare, benign muscle tumor, usually occurring in the tongue, neck, larynx, nasal cavity, throat, heart, or vulva. Treated by surgical removal. |
| Rhabdomyosarcoma | A malignant muscle tumor; the most common form of pediatric soft-tissue sarcoma, although accounting for <3% of childhood cancers and rarely seen in adults. Results from abnormal proliferation of myoblasts. Begins as a painless mass in a muscle but metastasizes rapidly. Diagnosed by biopsy and treated with surgery, chemotherapy, or radiation therapy. |

### Disorders Described Elsewhere

## *Before You Go On*

*Answer the following questions to test your understanding of the preceding section:*

27. What cells come between mesodermal cells and the muscle fiber in the stages of skeletal muscle development? Describe how several uninucleated cells transform into a multinucleated muscle fiber.

28. What is the principal difference between the way cardiac and smooth muscle form and the way skeletal muscle forms?

29. Describe the major changes seen in the muscular system in old age.

30. What is the root cause of Duchenne muscular dystrophy? What is the normal function of dystrophin?

31. How is synaptic function altered in myasthenia gravis? How does this synaptic dysfunction affect a person with MG?

32. In a game of baseball, the pitcher hits a man in the thigh with the ball. Which of the following conditions would this most likely cause: atrophy, a charley horse, contracture, crush syndrome, or a rhabdomyoma. Explain why the accident causes the condition you select.

# CHAPTER REVIEW

## REVIEW OF KEY CONCEPTS

### Muscle Types and Functions (p. 266)

1. The term *muscular system* refers only to skeletal muscles. The study of the muscular system is *myology*.

2. Skeletal muscle is voluntary striated muscle that is usually attached to bones. Its long slender cells are called *muscle fibers*. Cardiac muscle is involuntary striated muscle. Its cells are shaped like short logs with notched ends, and are called *myocytes* or *cardiocytes*. Smooth muscle is involuntary nonstriated muscle. Its cells, also called myocytes, are fusiform in shape.

3. Muscular tissue serves for movement, stability of the body, control of body passages and openings, and heat production.

4. Muscle cells have five properties that enable them to carry out their functions: excitability, conductivity, contractility, extensibility, and elasticity.

### General Anatomy of Muscles (p. 267)

1. A skeletal muscle is composed of muscular tissue, connective tissue, nervous tissue, and blood vessels.

2. The connective tissues of a muscle include a thin *endomysium* around each muscle fiber, a thicker *perimysium* that binds fibers into bundles called *fascicles,* and an *epimysium* that surrounds the entire muscle. Connective tissue sheets called *fasciae* separate neighboring muscles from each other and separate muscles into functional groups or *compartments*.

3. The strength of a muscle and direction of its pull are determined partly by the orientation of its fascicles. Muscles are classified into categories according to fascicle orientation: *fusiform, parallel, triangular, pennate,* and *circular*.

4. Some muscles have an *indirect attachment* to bone in which a fibrous *tendon* spans the distance between the muscular tissue and bone. Some tendons are flat sheets called *aponeuroses*. Other muscles have a *direct attachment* in which the muscle fibers extend nearly to the bone surface and the connective tissues of the muscle are continuous with the periosteum.

5. Most skeletal muscles attach to a different bone at each end, span at least one joint, and move one bone relative to another. The muscle attachment at the stationary end is called its *origin,* the attachment at the moving end is called the *insertion,* and the thicker midregion of the muscle is its *belly.*

The moving and stationary ends, however, may be reversed in different actions of the same muscle.

6. Some muscle insertions are on the fascia or tendon of another muscle or on collagen fibers of the dermis rather than on bones.

7. The effect produced by a muscle is called its *action.* Muscles work in functional groups that act on a single joint with different effects. In a given joint movement, a *prime mover* is the muscle that produces most of the force; a *synergist* is a muscle that aids the prime mover by adding power, stabilizing a joint, or modifying the direction of joint movement; an *antagonist* is a muscle that opposes the prime mover (such as an extensor that opposes a flexor); and a *fixator* is a muscle that holds a bone still.

8. *Intrinsic muscles* have both their origin and insertion within a specified region such as the head or hand; *extrinsic muscles* have their origin outside of a specified region, and they or their tendons extend into that region, such as muscles of the forearm whose tendons extend into the hand.

9. Many bones, especially long bones, act as levers when moved by the muscles. An *effort* is applied at one point on a lever to overcome a *load (resistance)* located at some other point; the lever rotates around a fixed *fulcrum.* The part of the lever from the fulcrum to the point of effort is the *effort arm,* and the part from the fulcrum to the load or point of resistance is the *resistance arm.*

10. Levers produce a gain in the speed, distance, or force of a movement. The ratio of the length of the effort arm to the length of the resistance arm is called the *mechanical advantage (MA)* of a lever. If MA > 1, a lever produces more force, but less speed or distance, than the force applied to it. If MA < 1, it produces a gain in speed or distance but exerts less force than the effort applied to it. When two or more muscles span and move the same joint, they may differ in MA and therefore in the qualities of the movement they produce.

11. A *first-class lever* has the effort at one end, resistance at the other end, and the fulcrum between the effort and resistance, as in a crowbar or the atlanto–occipital joint of the neck. A *second-class lever* has the fulcrum at one end, effort applied at the other end, and the load or resistance between the fulcrum and effort, as in a wheelbarrow

or in the way the mandible behaves as the mouth is opened. A *third-class lever* is one with the fulcrum at one end, the resistance at the other end, and the effort applied between the fulcrum and resistance, as in a canoe paddle or the action of the biceps brachii muscle on the forearm.

### Microscopic Anatomy of Skeletal Muscle (p. 274)

1. The key to understanding muscle contraction lies in the microscopic structure of individual skeletal muscle cells (muscle fibers).

2. A muscle fiber is a long, slender cell with multiple nuclei just inside the plasma membrane *(sarcolemma)*. The sarcolemma extends inward as tunnel-like *transverse (T) tubules* that cross the cell and open to the surface on both sides. The cytoplasm *(sarcoplasm)* is occupied mainly by *myofibrils,* which are threadlike bundles of protein filaments. Between the myofibrils, the muscle fiber has an abundance of mitochondria and smooth endoplasmic reticulum (ER). The cytoplasm also contains an abundance of *glycogen* (an energy-storage carbohydrate) and *myoglobin* (an oxygen-binding protein).

3. The smooth ER, or *sarcoplasmic reticulum,* forms an extensive branching network amid the myofibrils and has dilated *terminal cisternae* flanking each T tubule. It is a reservoir of calcium ions and has gated channels that can release a flood of calcium into the cytosol.

4. Each myofibril is a bundle of protein *myofilaments.* There are three kinds of myofilaments: *thick filaments* composed of a motor protein called *myosin; thin filaments* composed mainly of *actin,* but also containing the regulatory proteins *tropomyosin* and *troponin;* and *elastic filaments* composed of the protein *titin.*

5. Elastic filaments keep the thick and thin filaments aligned with each other, resist overstretching of a muscle, and aid in recoil of a muscle to its resting length. The work of contraction is carried out by the thick and thin filaments.

6. Several accessory proteins play various roles in sarcomere organization and function. *Dystrophin* is particularly important in linking the thin filaments to the sarcolemma and, indirectly, to extracellular proteins, thus transferring the force of sarcomere shortening to a shortening of the

entire cell and to a pull on the extracellular connective tissues.

7. In striated (skeletal and cardiac) muscle, myosin and actin are organized in such a way that they overlap and produce alternating dark *A bands* and light *I bands* that repeat at regular intervals along the length of the cell. These bands are called *striations.* The dark A bands consist of a midregion called the *H band* where only thick filaments occur, flanked by even darker regions where the thick and thin filaments overlap. The light A bands are bisected by a thin, dark line called a *Z disc.* The thin filaments and elastic filaments are anchored to the Z discs.

8. The region from one Z disc to the next is called a *sarcomere.* This is the functional unit of muscle contraction. When a muscle fiber contracts, the sarcomeres become shorter and the Z discs are pulled closer together.

9. Skeletal muscle contracts only when stimulated by a *somatic motor neuron.* The axon *(somatic motor fiber)* of one neuron branches at its tip and leads to typically a few hundred muscle fibers, but each muscle fiber receives only one nerve fiber.

10. The nerve and muscle fiber meet at a complex of synapses called a *neuromuscular junction.* Each tip of the nerve fiber ends in a dilated bulb, the *synaptic knob,* nestled in a depression of the muscle fiber sarcolemma. A narrow gap, the *synaptic cleft,* separates the synaptic bulb from the sarcolemma.

11. The synaptic knob contains *synaptic vesicles* filled with the chemical *acetylcholine (ACh).* The sarcolemma across from the knob has proteins that act as ACh receptors. An enzyme called *acetylcholinesterase (AChE),* found in the synaptic cleft and as part of the sarcolemma, breaks down ACh to terminate stimulation of the muscle fiber.

12. One nerve fiber and all the muscle fibers innervated by it are called a *motor unit,* because stimulation by that nerve fiber causes all these muscle fibers to contract in unison. Small motor units have as few as 3 to 6 muscle fibers per nerve fiber and produce precise, finely controlled movements, as in the muscles of eye movement. Large motor units may have up to 1,000 muscle fibers per nerve fiber and produce strong but not finely controlled movements, as in the muscles of the thigh and leg. Motor units can "work in shifts" so that fresh units take over the contraction of a muscle when other units fatigue. Activation of a greater number of motor units produces a stronger muscle contraction.

13. The muscular system receives from one-quarter of the blood pumped by the heart at rest, to three-quarters of it during ex-

ercise. Blood capillaries penetrate into the endomysium to reach every muscle fiber.

**Functional Perspectives (p. 280)**

1. Muscle contraction and relaxation occur in four steps: excitation, excitation–contraction coupling, contraction, and relaxation.

2. In *excitation,* a signal in the motor nerve fiber triggers the release of acetylcholine (ACh) from the synaptic vesicles. ACh crosses the synaptic cleft and binds with receptors on the muscle fiber. These receptors are gated $Na^+–K^+$ channels that open to allow flow of these ions through the sarcolemma, producing a voltage change. This sets off a chain reaction of electrical excitation that spreads along the fiber and down the T tubules to the interior of the muscle fiber.

3. In *excitation–contraction coupling,* electrical signals in the T tubules indirectly open the $Ca^{2+}$ channels of the sarcoplasmic reticulum, releasing $Ca^{2+}$ into the cytosol. $Ca^{2+}$ binds to the troponin molecules of the thin filaments. This induces tropomyosin to move away from the active sites on the actin, so these sites are exposed to the action of myosin.

4. In *contraction,* the heads of the myosin molecules are activated by ATP, swing forward into an extended or "cocked" position, bind to the active sites of actin, then flex and pull the actin filament a short distance. Each myosin head then binds and hydrolyzes a new ATP, detaches from actin, recocks, and repeats the process. By repetition of this process, the thin filament slides across the thick filament, pulling the Z discs closer together. The thin filaments are linked to the sarcolemma, so their movement shortens the cell as a whole.

5. In *relaxation,* the nerve signal stops, ACh is no longer released, and the existing ACh in the synaptic cleft is degraded by AChE. Stimulation of the muscle fiber therefore ceases. The sarcoplasmic reticulum pumps $Ca^{2+}$ back into its cisternae. As the $Ca^{2+}$ level in the cytosol falls, tropomyosin moves back into its resting position, blocking the active sites of actin. Myosin can no longer bind actin, and the muscle relaxes.

6. Muscles grow in response to *resistance exercise,* not by the mitotic production of more muscle fibers but by the production of more myofilaments and thickening of the fibers that already exist. Well-exercised muscles also develop more mitochondria, myoglobin, glycogen, and blood capillaries.

7. Muscle shrinkage, or *atrophy,* occurs when the nerve connection to a muscle is severed *(denervation atrophy),* a muscle is not exercised *(disuse atrophy),* or simply as a result of aging *(senescence atrophy).*

8. *Slow oxidative (SO) muscle fibers* employ aerobic respiration and are relatively fatigue-resistant, but have relatively long, slow twitches (contractions). Postural muscles of the back and the soleus muscle of the calf are composed predominantly of SO fibers.

9. *Fast glycolytic (FG) muscle fibers* employ anaerobic fermentation and fatigue relatively quickly, but produce quick twitches. The gastrocnemius muscle of the calf and the muscles of eye movement are composed predominantly of FG fibers.

10. *Intermediate fibers* are a type of FG fibers that combine fast twitches with aerobic fatigue-resistant metabolism. These are relatively rare except in some endurance-trained athletes.

**Cardiac and Smooth Muscle (p. 284)**

1. Cardiac muscle consists of short, thick *cardiocytes* connected to each other through electrical and mechanical junctions at their *intercalated discs.*

2. Cardiac muscle contracts spontaneously without need of nervous stimulation, although the nervous system does modify the heart rate and contraction strength.

3. Cardiac muscle has an abundance of myoglobin and glycogen and has numerous large mitochondria; thus, it is highly resistant to fatigue.

4. Smooth muscle cells contain myosin and actin like skeletal and cardiac muscle, but the myofilaments are not regularly aligned with each other, so there are no striations. Smooth muscle has no T tubules and has very little sarcoplasmic reticulum; the calcium needed to activate its contraction comes mainly from the extracellular fluid. Unlike skeletal and cardiac muscle, smooth muscle cells are capable of mitosis.

5. *Multiunit smooth muscle* is found in some blood vessels and pulmonary air passages, the iris, and piloerector muscles of the skin. In this type of muscle, each cell is innervated by a nerve fiber and contracts independently of other muscle cells.

6. Most smooth muscle is *single-unit smooth muscle (visceral muscle),* found in most blood vessels and in the digestive, respiratory, urinary, and reproductive tracts.

7. In single-unit smooth muscle, nerve fibers do not synapse with individual muscle cells. *Varicosities* of the nerve fiber release neurotransmitters, which diffuse to nearby muscle cells and may stimulate them to contract. The muscle cells are connected through electrical gap junctions and contract in unison.

8. Smooth muscle contracts and relaxes slowly and is very fatigue-resistant. It maintains muscle tone in organs such as the uterus,

bladder, and blood vessels, and produces waves of contraction called *peristalsis* in the digestive tract and other tubular organs.

## Developmental and Clinical Perspectives (p. 286)

1. Most skeletal muscle develops from embryonic mesoderm. Mesenchymal cells differentiate into *myoblasts,* which fuse to form multinucleated *myotubes.* Myofilaments and striations appear in the myotubes as they mature into functional muscle fibers. New muscle fibers are added until perhaps as late as 1 year of age; after that, the growth of muscles is primarily by cellular enlargement (hypertrophy) rather than an increase in cell number.

2. Cardiac and smooth muscle also develop from myoblasts, but the myoblasts do not fuse as they do in skeletal muscle. In cardiac muscle, myoblasts remain attached to each other and develop intercalated discs at their points of adhesion. In single-unit smooth muscle, they form gap junctions.

3. In old age, the skeletal muscles exhibit substantial atrophy and replacement of muscular tissue with fat and fibrous tissue. Aged muscle fibers exhibit fewer myofibrils and mitochondria, less glycogen and myoglobin, and more disorganized sarcomeres. Fewer motor neurons innervate the muscles, and those that do are less efficient at stimulating them. Reduced blood circulation to aged muscles also contributes to reduced endurance. Even in old age, however, moderate exercise can significantly enhance muscle performance.

4. *Muscular dystrophy* is a family of hereditary *myopathies* (muscle diseases) in which the skeletal muscles degenerate and are replaced by fat and scar tissue. *Duchenne muscular dystrophy,* the most common form, is a sex-linked trait affecting mostly boys. It results from the lack of a protein, *dystrophin,* that links actin to the sarcolemma. It is a crippling and incurable disease that usually claims the victim's life by the age of 20.

5. *Myasthenia gravis* is an autoimmune disease most commonly affecting young women. It is caused by autoantibodies that destroy ACh receptors and render muscle unresponsive to ACh. The result is muscular weakness, often first seen in facial muscles. Some victims die of respiratory failure, whereas some people live a normal life span with the aid of cholinesterase inhibitors and drugs to suppress the immune response.

6. Several other muscular system disorders are described in table 10.5.

## TESTING YOUR RECALL

1. A fascicle is bounded and defined by
   a. the endomysium.
   b. the fascia.
   c. the myofilaments.
   d. the epimysium.
   e. the perimysium.

2. Muscle cells must have all of the following properties *except* _____ to carry out their function.
   a. extensibility
   b. elasticity
   c. autorhythmicity
   d. contractility
   e. conductivity

3. If a tendon runs longitudinally throughout a muscle and fascicles insert obliquely on it along both sides, the muscle is classified as
   a. parallel.
   b. oblique.
   c. bipennate.
   d. convergent.
   e. multipennate.

4. A muscle that holds a bone still during a particular action is called
   a. a fixator.
   b. an antagonist.
   c. an agonist.
   d. a synergist.
   e. an intrinsic muscle.

5. Skeletal muscle fibers have _____, whereas smooth muscle cells do not.
   a. T tubules
   b. ACh receptors
   c. thick myofilaments
   d. thin myofilaments
   e. dense bodies

6. Smooth muscle cells have _____, whereas skeletal muscle fibers do not.
   a. T tubules
   b. ACh receptors
   c. thick myofilaments
   d. thin myofilaments
   e. dense bodies

7. ACh receptors are found in
   a. synaptic vesicles.
   b. terminal cisternae.
   c. thick filaments.
   d. thin filaments.
   e. junctional folds.

8. Single-unit smooth muscle cells can stimulate each other because they have
   a. a pacemaker.
   b. diffuse junctions.
   c. gap junctions.
   d. tight junctions.
   e. calcium pumps.

9. A second-class lever always has
   a. the fulcrum in the middle.
   b. the effort applied between the fulcrum and resistance.
   c. a mechanical advantage less than 1.
   d. a mechanical advantage greater than 1.
   e. the resistance at one end.

10. Slow oxidative muscle fibers have all of the following *except*
    a. an abundance of myoglobin.
    b. an abundance of glycogen.
    c. high fatigue resistance.
    d. a red color.
    e. a high capacity to synthesize ATP aerobically.

11. Acetylcholine is released from organelles called _____.

12. The region where a motor nerve fiber meets a skeletal muscle fiber is called a/an _____.

13. Parts of the sarcoplasmic reticulum called _____ lie on each side of a T tubule.

14. Thick myofilaments consist mainly of the protein _____.

15. Sheets of fibrous connective tissue called _____ separate a muscle or muscle group from neighboring muscles.

16. Muscle contains an oxygen-storage pigment called _____.

17. The _____ of skeletal muscle play the same role as dense bodies in smooth muscle.

18. A circular muscle that controls a body opening or passage is called a/an _____.

19. Skeletal muscle fibers develop by the fusion of embryonic cells called _____.

20. A wave of contraction passing along the esophagus or small intestine is called _____.

*Answers in the Appendix*

## TRUE OR FALSE

*Determine which five of the following statements are false, and briefly explain why.*

1. Pennate muscles are stronger than parallel muscles of comparable size.

2. A given muscle may be an agonist in one joint movement and an antagonist in a different movement of that joint.

3. Extrinsic muscles are not located entirely within the body region that they control.

4. Cardiac myocytes are of the fatigue-resistant, slow oxidative type.

5. One motor neuron can supply only one muscle fiber.

6. To initiate muscle contraction, calcium ions must bind to the myosin heads.

7. A first-class lever can have a mechanical advantage either greater than or less than 1.

8. Slow oxidative fibers are more fatigue-resistant than fast glycolytic fibers.

9. The blood vessels of a skeletal muscle are more wavy or coiled when a muscle is relaxed than when it contracts.

10. Well-exercised muscles generally gain in thickness by the addition of new muscle fibers.

***Answers in the Appendix***

## TESTING YOUR COMPREHENSION

1. Give two distinctly different reasons why two muscles that act across the same side of the same joint are not necessarily redundant in function.

2. What would be the consequences for muscular system function if muscle fibers were not elastic? What if they were not extensible?

3. For each of the following muscle pairs, state which muscle you think would have the higher percentage of fast glycolytic fibers: *(a)* Muscles that move the eyes or muscles of the upper throat that initiate swallowing? *(b)* The abdominal muscles employed in doing sit-ups or the muscles employed in handwriting? *(c)* Muscles of the tongue or the skeletal muscle sphincter of the anus? Explain each answer.

4. The forearm contains five flexor muscles that flex the wrist and fingers. Explain why it is better for them to have an indirect attachment rather than a direct attachment to the bones on which they act.

5. The brachialis muscle is the most powerful flexor of the elbow. Examine its bone attachments in figure 12.3 and table 12.3 (pp. 329 and 332). From a functional standpoint, identify what bone attachment would be its origin and what would be its insertion in a person lifting barbells. Then identify which would be the origin and insertion in a person climbing the face of a cliff. In light of your conclusions, concisely explain the imperfection in such conventional interpretations as presented by that table.

***Answers at aris.mhhe.com***

## ONLINE RESOURCES

Visit aprevealed.com to explore melt-away cadaver dissections, watch animations that clarify difficult concepts, review histological and radiological images, or take a quiz to assess your understanding of the material.

The Saladin *Human Anatomy*, 2e website at aris.mhhe.com features chapter-specific quizzes, labeling exercises, and other interactive tools to complement your study of human anatomy. If your instructor has provided an ARIS course code, you can also access assignments and information specific to your course.

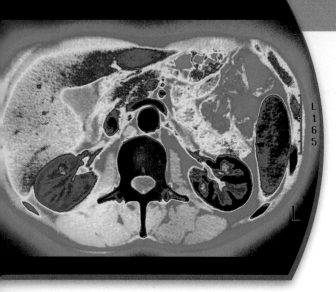

# The Axial Musculature

CT scan showing muscles of the body wall at the level of vertebra L1 (cross section)

## CHAPTER OUTLINE

## INSIGHTS

## BRUSHING UP

To understand this chapter, you may find it helpful to review the following concepts:
- Anatomy of the axial skeleton (chapter 7)
- Terminology of joint actions (pp. 243–249)
- Shapes of muscles (fusiform, pennate, circular, etc.) (p. 269)
- The meaning of muscle origin, insertion, and action (p. 270)
- Indirect versus direct muscle attachments (p. 269)
- Prime movers, synergists, antagonists, and fixators (p. 270)
- Intrinsic and extrinsic muscles (p. 271)

Anatomy & Physiology REVEALED®
aprevealed.com

**Muscular System**

There are about 600 skeletal muscles in the human body. Chapters 11 and 12 describe fewer than one-third of these. This chapter deals with the muscles that act on the axial division of the body—that is, on the head and trunk. Muscles that act on the limbs and limb girdles (the appendicular division) are described in chapter 12. This chapter opens with some tips to help you study the muscles more insightfully.

# Learning Approaches

## Objectives

When you have completed this section, you should be able to

- translate several Latin words commonly used in the naming of muscles;
- define the *origin, insertion, action,* and *innervation* of a muscle;
- describe the sources of the nerves to the head–neck and trunk muscles and explain the numbering system for the cranial and spinal nerves; and
- describe and practice some methods that will help in the learning of the skeletal muscles.

## How Muscles Are Named

Figure 11.1 shows an overview of the major superficial muscles. Learning the names of these and other muscles may seem a forbidding task at first, especially when some of them have such long Latin names as *depressor labii inferioris* and *flexor digiti minimi brevis.* Such names, however, typically describe some distinctive aspects of the structure, location, or action of a muscle, and become very helpful once we grow familiar with a few common Latin words. For example, the depressor labii inferioris is a muscle that lowers (depresses) the bottom (inferior) lip (labium), and the flexor digiti minimi brevis is a short (brevis) muscle that flexes the smallest (minimi) finger (digit). Several of the most common words in muscle names are interpreted in table 11.1, and others are explained in footnotes throughout the chapter. Familiarity with these terms and attention to the footnotes will help you translate muscle names and remember the location, appearance, and action of the muscles. You can listen to pronunciations of these muscle names on the CD-ROM or online versions of *Anatomy & Physiology | Revealed.*

## Muscle Innervation

The **innervation** of a muscle refers to the identity of the nerve that stimulates it. Knowing the innervation to each muscle enables clinicians to diagnose nerve, spinal cord, and brainstem injuries from their effects on muscle function, and to set realistic goals for rehabilitation. The innervations described in this chapter will be more

meaningful after you have studied the peripheral nervous system (chapters 14 and 15), but a brief orientation will be helpful here. The muscles are innervated by two groups of nerves:

- **Spinal nerves** arise from the spinal cord, emerge through the intervertebral foramina, and innervate muscles below the neck. Spinal nerves are identified by letters and numbers that refer to the adjacent vertebrae—for example, T6 for the sixth thoracic nerve and S2 for the second sacral nerve. Immediately after emerging from an intervertebral foramen, each spinal nerve branches into a *dorsal* and *ventral ramus.*[1] You will note references to nerve numbers and rami in many of the muscle tables. The term *plexus* in some of the tables refers to weblike networks of spinal nerves adjacent to the vertebral column. All of the spinal nerves named here are illustrated, and most are also discussed, in chapter 14.
- **Cranial nerves** arise from the base of the brain, emerge through the skull foramina, and innervate muscles of the head and neck. Cranial nerves are identified by roman numerals (CN I to CN XII) and by names given in chapter 15, although not all 12 of them innervate skeletal muscles.

## A Learning Strategy

The following suggestions can help you develop a rational strategy for learning the skeletal muscles as you first encounter them in the textbook and laboratory:

- Examine models, cadavers, dissected animals, or an anatomical atlas as you read about the muscles. Visual images are often easier to remember than words, and direct observation of a muscle may stick in your memory better than descriptive text or two-dimensional drawings.
- When studying a particular muscle, palpate it on yourself if possible. Contract the muscle to feel it bulge and sense its action. Doing so will make muscle locations and actions less abstract. Atlas B following chapter 12 shows where you can see and palpate several muscles on the living body.
- Locate the origins and insertions of muscles on an articulated skeleton. Some study skeletons are painted and labeled to show these. This will help you visualize the locations of muscles and understand how they produce particular joint actions.
- Study the derivations of the muscle names; look for descriptive meaning in their names.
- Say the names *aloud* to yourself or a study partner. It is harder to remember and spell terms you cannot pronounce, and silent pronunciation is not nearly as effective as speaking and hearing the names. Pronunciation guides are provided in the muscle tables for all but the most obvious cases.

[1] *ramus* = branch

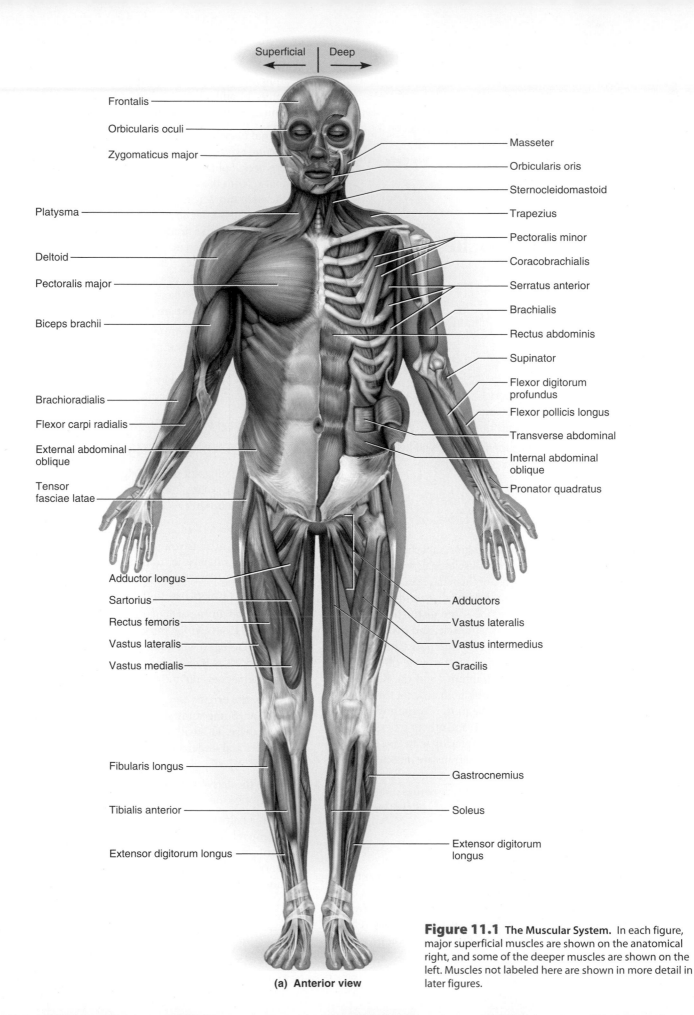

Superficial | Deep

Frontalis

Orbicularis oculi

Zygomaticus major

Masseter

Orbicularis oris

Sternocleidomastoid

Platysma

Trapezius

Pectoralis minor

Deltoid

Coracobrachialis

Pectoralis major

Serratus anterior

Biceps brachii

Brachialis

Rectus abdominis

Supinator

Brachioradialis

Flexor digitorum profundus

Flexor carpi radialis

Flexor pollicis longus

External abdominal oblique

Transverse abdominal

Internal abdominal oblique

Tensor fasciae latae

Pronator quadratus

Adductor longus

Sartorius

Adductors

Rectus femoris

Vastus lateralis

Vastus lateralis

Vastus intermedius

Vastus medialis

Gracilis

Fibularis longus

Gastrocnemius

Tibialis anterior

Soleus

Extensor digitorum longus

Extensor digitorum longus

**Figure 11.1** **The Muscular System.** In each figure, major superficial muscles are shown on the anatomical right, and some of the deeper muscles are shown on the left. Muscles not labeled here are shown in more detail in later figures.

(a) **Anterior view**

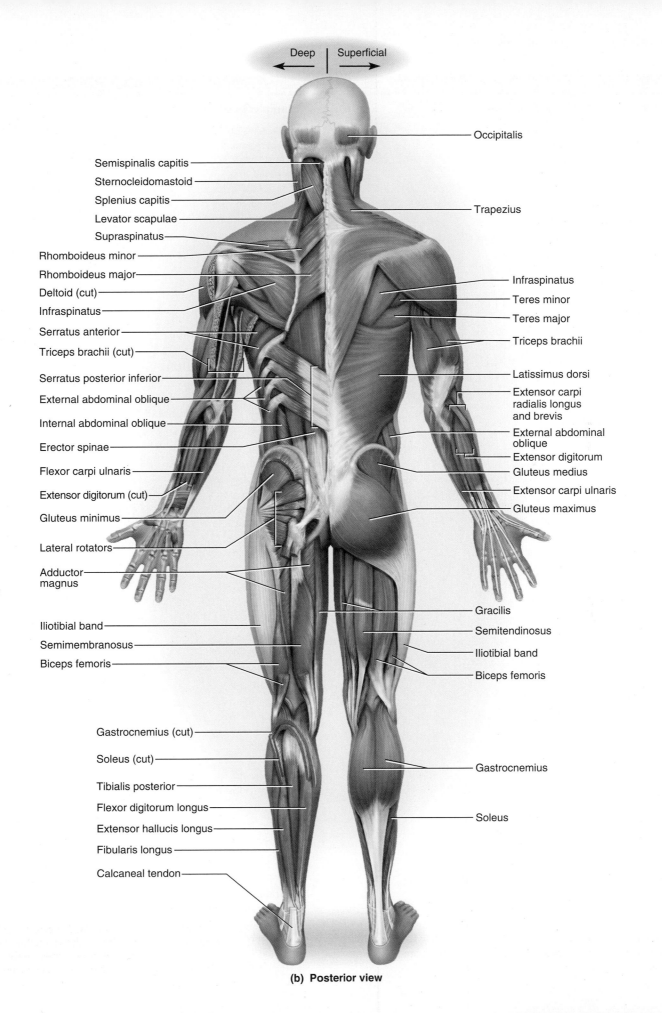

Deep | Superficial

Occipitalis

Semispinalis capitis

Sternocleidomastoid

Splenius capitis

Levator scapulae

Supraspinatus

Rhomboideus minor

Rhomboideus major

Deltoid (cut)

Infraspinatus

Serratus anterior

Triceps brachii (cut)

Serratus posterior inferior

External abdominal oblique

Internal abdominal oblique

Erector spinae

Flexor carpi ulnaris

Extensor digitorum (cut)

Gluteus minimus

Lateral rotators

Adductor magnus

Iliotibial band

Semimembranosus

Biceps femoris

Trapezius

Infraspinatus

Teres minor

Teres major

Triceps brachii

Latissimus dorsi

Extensor carpi radialis longus and brevis

External abdominal oblique

Extensor digitorum

Gluteus medius

Extensor carpi ulnaris

Gluteus maximus

Gracilis

Semitendinosus

Iliotibial band

Biceps femoris

Gastrocnemius (cut)

Soleus (cut)

Tibialis posterior

Flexor digitorum longus

Extensor hallucis longus

Fibularis longus

Calcaneal tendon

Gastrocnemius

Soleus

**(b) Posterior view**

| TABLE 11.1 | Words Commonly Used to Name Muscles | |
|---|---|---|
| **Criterion** | **Term and Meaning** | **Examples of Usage** |
| Size | Major (large) | Pectoralis major |
| | Maximus (largest) | Gluteus maximus |
| | Minor (small) | Pectoralis minor |
| | Minimus (smallest) | Gluteus minimus |
| | Longus (long) | Abductor pollicis longus |
| | Longissimus (longest) | Longissimus thoracis |
| | Brevis (short) | Extensor pollicis brevis |
| Shape | Rhomboideus (rhomboidal) | Rhomboideus major |
| | Trapezius (trapezoidal) | Trapezius |
| | Teres (round, cylindrical) | Pronator teres |
| | Deltoid (triangular) | Deltoid |
| | Quadratus (four-sided) | Pronator quadratus |
| Location | Capitis (of the head) | Splenius capitis |
| | Cervicis (of the neck) | Semispinalis cervicis |
| | Pectoralis (of the chest) | Pectoralis major |
| | Thoracis (of the thorax) | Spinalis thoracis |
| | Intercostal (between the ribs) | External intercostals |
| | Abdominis (of the abdomen) | Rectus abdominis |
| | Lumborum (of the lower back) | Quadratus lumborum |
| | Femoris (of the femur, or thigh) | Quadriceps femoris |
| | Fibularis (of the fibula) | Fibularis longus |
| | Brachii (of the arm) | Biceps brachii |
| | Carpi (of the wrist) | Flexor carpi ulnaris |
| | Digiti (of a finger or toe, singular) | Extensor digiti minimi |
| | Digitorum (of the fingers or toes, plural) | Flexor digitorum profundus |
| | Pollicis (of the thumb) | Opponens pollicis |
| | Indicis (of the index finger) | Extensor indicis |
| | Hallucis (of the great toe) | Abductor hallucis |
| | Superficialis (superficial) | Flexor digitorum superficialis |
| | Profundus (deep) | Flexor digitorum profundus |
| Number of heads | Biceps (two heads) | Biceps femoris |
| | Triceps (three heads) | Triceps brachii |
| | Quadriceps (four heads) | Quadriceps femoris |
| Orientation | Rectus (straight) | Rectus abdominis |
| | Transversus (transverse) | Transversus abdominis |
| | Oblique (slanted) | External abdominal oblique |
| Action | Adductor | Adductor pollicis |
| | Abductor | Abductor digiti minimi |
| | Flexor | Flexor carpi radialis |
| | Extensor | Extensor carpi radialis |
| | Pronator | Pronator teres |
| | Supinator | Supinator |
| | Levator | Levator scapulae |
| | Depressor | Depressor anguli oris |

## Before You Go On

*Answer the following questions to test your understanding of the preceding section:*

1. What is meant by the innervation of a muscle? Why is it important to know this? What two major groups of nerves innervate the skeletal muscles?

2. In table 11.1, pick a muscle name from the right column that you think meets each of the following descriptions: (*a*) lies beside the radius and straightens the wrist; (*b*) pulls down the corners of your mouth when you frown; (*c*) raises your shoulder blades; (*d*) moves your little finger laterally, away from the fourth digit; (*e*) is the largest muscle deep to the breast.

# Muscles of the Head and Neck

## Objectives

When you have completed this section, you should be able to

- name and locate the muscles that produce facial expressions;
- name and locate the muscles used for chewing and swallowing;
- name and locate the neck muscles that move the head; and
- identify the origin, insertion, action, and innervation of any of these muscles.

Muscles of the head and neck will be treated here from a regional and functional perspective, thus placing them in the following groups: muscles of facial expression, muscles of chewing and swallowing, and muscles that move the head as a whole (tables 11.2–11.4). In these tables and throughout the rest of the chapter, each muscle entry provides the following information:

- the name of the muscle;
- the pronunciation of the name, unless it is self-evident or uses words whose pronunciations have been provided in a recent entry;
- the actions of the muscle;
- the muscle's origin, indicated by the letter *O;*
- the muscle's insertion, indicated by the letter *I;* and
- the muscle's innervation, indicated by the letter *N.*

| **TABLE 11.2** | **Muscles of Facial Expression** |
| --- | --- |

Humans have much more expressive faces than other mammals because of a complex array of muscles that insert in the dermis and subcutaneous tissues (figs. 11.2 and 11.3). These muscles tense the skin and produce such expressions as a pleasant smile, a threatening scowl, a puzzled frown, or a flirtatious wink (fig. 11.4). They add subtle shades of meaning to our spoken words. Facial muscles also contribute directly to speech, chewing, and other oral functions. All but one of these muscles are innervated by the facial nerve (CN VII). This nerve is especially vulnerable to injury from lacerations and skull fractures, which can paralyze the muscles and cause parts of the face to sag. The only muscle in this table not innervated by the facial nerve is the levator palpebrae superioris, innervated by the oculomotor nerve (CN III).

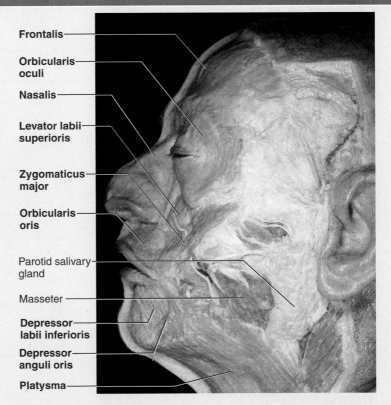

**Figure 11.2** **Some Facial Muscles of the Cadaver.** Boldface labels indicate muscles employed in facial expression.

**TABLE 11.2** Muscles of Facial Expression (continued)

**Figure 11.3** Muscles of Facial Expression. Boldface labels indicate muscles employed in facial expression.

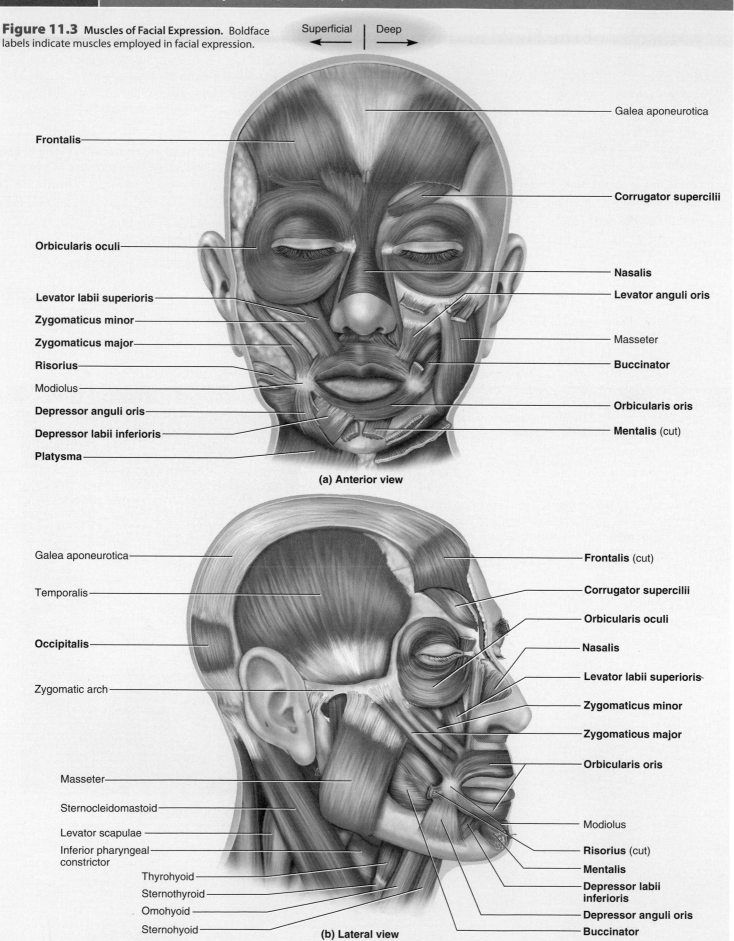

Superficial ← | → Deep

**(a) Anterior view**

- Frontalis
- Orbicularis oculi
- Levator labii superioris
- Zygomaticus minor
- Zygomaticus major
- Risorius
- Modiolus
- Depressor anguli oris
- Depressor labii inferioris
- Platysma
- Galea aponeurotica
- Corrugator supercilii
- Nasalis
- Levator anguli oris
- Masseter
- Buccinator
- Orbicularis oris
- Mentalis (cut)

**(b) Lateral view**

- Galea aponeurotica
- Temporalis
- Occipitalis
- Zygomatic arch
- Masseter
- Sternocleidomastoid
- Levator scapulae
- Inferior pharyngeal constrictor
- Thyrohyoid
- Sternothyroid
- Omohyoid
- Sternohyoid
- Frontalis (cut)
- Corrugator supercilii
- Orbicularis oculi
- Nasalis
- Levator labii superioris
- Zygomaticus minor
- Zygomaticus major
- Orbicularis oris
- Modiolus
- Risorius (cut)
- Mentalis
- Depressor labii inferioris
- Depressor anguli oris
- Buccinator

| **TABLE 11.2** | **Muscles of Facial Expression (continued)** |
|---|---|

**The Scalp.**   The *occipitofrontalis* overlies the dome of the cranium. It is divided into the *frontalis* of the forehead and *occipitalis* at the rear of the head, named for the frontal and occipital bones underlying them. They are connected to each other by a broad aponeurosis, the **galea aponeurotica**[2] (GAY-lee-uh AP-oh-new-ROT-ih-cuh).

**Frontalis (frun-TAY-lis)**   Elevates eyebrows in glancing upward and expressions of surprise or fright; draws scalp forward and wrinkles skin of forehead

**O:** Galea aponeurotica          **I:** Subcutaneous tissue of eyebrows          **N:** Facial n.

**Occipitalis (oc-SIP-ih-TAY-lis)**   Retracts scalp; fixes galea aponeurotica so frontalis can act on eyebrows

**O:** Superior nuchal line and temporal bone          **I:** Galea aponeurotica          **N:** Facial n.

**The Orbital and Nasal Regions.**   The *orbicularis oculi* is a sphincter of the eyelid that encircles and closes the eye. The *levator palpebrae superioris* lies deep to the orbicularis oculi, in the eyelid and orbital cavity (see fig. 17.20, p. 507), and opens the eye. Other muscles in this group move the eyelids and skin of the forehead and dilate the nostrils. Muscles within the orbit that move the eyeball itself are discussed in chapter 17.

**Orbicularis Oculi[3] (or-BIC-you-LERR-is OC-you-lye)**   Sphincter of the eyelids; closes eye in blinking, squinting, and sleep; aids in flow of tears across eye

**O:** Lacrimal bone, adjacent regions of frontal bone and maxilla, medial angle of eyelids          **I:** Upper and lower eyelids, skin around margin of orbit          **N:** Facial n.

**Levator Palpebrae Superioris[4] (leh-VAY-tur pal-PEE-bree soo-PEER-ee-OR-is)**   Elevates upper eyelid, opens eye

**O:** Lesser wing of sphenoid in posterior wall of orbit          **I:** Upper eyelid          **N:** Oculomotor n.

**Corrugator Supercilii[5] (COR-oo-GAY-tur SOO-per-SIL-ee-eye)**   Draws eyebrows medially and downward in frowning and concentration; reduces glare of bright sunlight

**O:** Medial end of supraorbital margin          **I:** Skin of eyebrow          **N:** Facial n.

**Nasalis[6] (nay-ZAIL-is)**   Widens nostrils; narrows internal air passage between vestibule and nasal cavity

**O:** Maxilla just lateral to nose          **I:** Bridge and alar cartilages of nose          **N:** Facial n.

**The Oral Region.**   The mouth is the most expressive part of the face, and lip movements are necessary for intelligible speech; thus, it is not surprising that the muscles here are especially diverse. The *orbicularis oris* is a complex of muscles in the lips that encircle the mouth; until recently it was misinterpreted as a sphincter or circular muscle, but it is actually composed of four independent quadrants that interlace and give only an appearance of circularity. Other muscles in this region approach the lips from all directions and thus draw the lips or angles (corners) of the mouth upward, laterally, and downward. Some of these have origins or insertions in a complex cord called the **modiolus**[7] just lateral to each angle of the lips (see fig. 11.3). Named for the hub of a cartwheel, the modiolus is a point of convergence of several muscles of the lower face. You can palpate it by inserting one finger just inside the corner of your lips and pinching the corner between the finger and thumb, feeling for a thick knot of tissue.

**Orbicularis Oris[8] (or-BIC-you-LERR-is OR-is)**   Encircles mouth, closes lips, protrudes lips as in kissing; uniquely developed in humans for speech

**O:** Modiolus of mouth          **I:** Submucosa and dermis of lips          **N:** Facial n.

**Levator Labii Superioris[9] (leh-VAY-tur LAY-bee-eye soo-PEER-ee-OR-is)**   Elevates and everts upper lip in sad, sneering, or serious expressions

**O:** Zygomatic bone and maxilla near inferior margin of orbit          **I:** Muscles of upper lip          **N:** Facial n.

**Levator Anguli Oris[10] (leh-VAY-tur ANG-you-lye OR-is)**   Elevates angle of mouth as in smiling

**O:** Maxilla just below infraorbital foramen          **I:** Muscles at angle of mouth          **N:** Facial n.

**Zygomaticus[11] Major (ZY-go-MAT-ih-cus)**   Draws angle of mouth upward and laterally as in laughing

**O:** Zygomatic bone          **I:** Superolateral angle of mouth          **N:** Facial n.

**Zygomaticus Minor**   Elevates upper lip, exposes upper teeth in smiling or sneering

**O:** Zygomatic bone          **I:** Muscles of upper lip          **N:** Facial n.

**Risorius[12] (rih-SOR-ee-us)**   Draws angle of mouth laterally in expressions of laughing, horror, or disdain

**O:** Zygomatic arch, fascia near ear          **I:** Modiolus of mouth          **N:** Facial n.

---

[2]*galea* = helmet + *apo* = above + *neuro* = nerves, brain
[3]*orb* = circle + *ocul* = eye
[4]*levat* = to raise + *palpebr* = eyelid + *superior* = upper
[5]*corrug* = wrinkle + *supercil* = eyebrow
[6]*nas* = nose
[7]*modiolus* = hub

[8]*orb* = circle + *or* = mouth
[9]*levat* = to raise + *labi* = lip + *superior* = upper
[10]*angul* = angle, corner + *or* = mouth
[11]*zygo* = join, unite (refers to zygomatic bone)
[12]*risor* = laughter

**TABLE 11.2** **Muscles of Facial Expression (continued)**

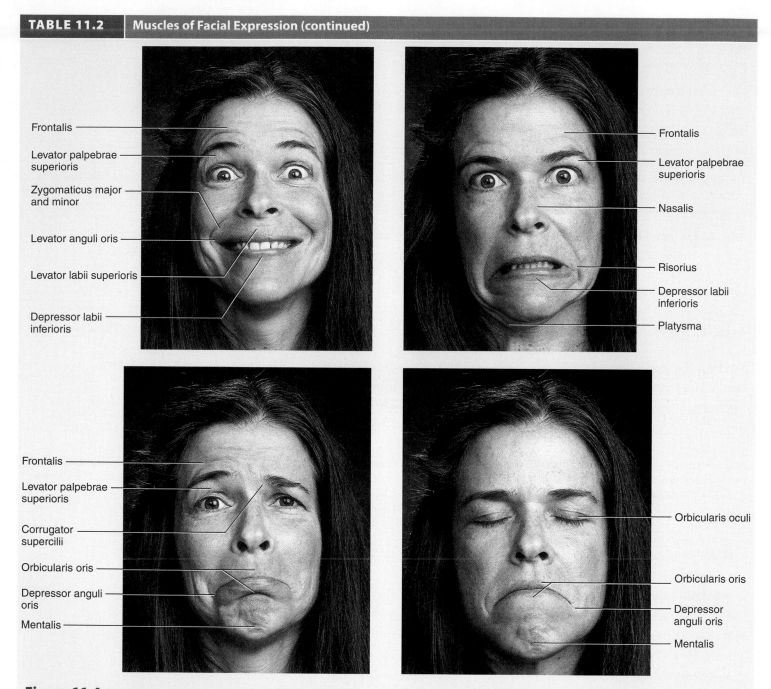

Frontalis

Levator palpebrae superioris

Zygomaticus major and minor

Levator anguli oris

Levator labii superioris

Depressor labii inferioris

Frontalis

Levator palpebrae superioris

Nasalis

Risorius

Depressor labii inferioris

Platysma

Frontalis

Levator palpebrae superioris

Corrugator supercilii

Orbicularis oris

Depressor anguli oris

Mentalis

Orbicularis oculi

Orbicularis oris

Depressor anguli oris

Mentalis

**Figure 11.4** **Expressions Produced by Several of the Facial Muscles.** The ordinary actions of these muscles are usually more subtle than these demonstrations.

● *Name an antagonist of each of these muscles: the depressor anguli oris, orbicularis oculi, and levator labii superioris.*

| TABLE 11.2 | Muscles of Facial Expression (continued) |
|---|---|

**Depressor Anguli Oris**[13]   Draws angle of mouth laterally and downward in opening mouth or sad expressions

   **O:** Inferior margin of mandibular body          **I:** Modiolus of mouth          **N:** Facial n.

**Depressor Labii Inferioris**[14]   Draws lower lip downward and laterally in chewing and expressions of melancholy or doubt

   **O:** Near mental protuberance          **I:** Skin and mucosa of lower lip          **N:** Facial n.

**The Mental and Buccal Regions.**   Adjacent to the oral orifice are the mental region (chin) and buccal region (cheeks). In addition to muscles already discussed that act directly on the lower lip, the mental region has a pair of small *mentalis muscles* extending from the upper margin of the mandible to the skin of the chin. In some people, these muscles are especially thick and have a visible dimple between them called the *mental cleft*. The *buccinator* is the muscle in the cheek. It has multiple functions in chewing, sucking, and blowing. If the cheek is inflated with air, compression of the buccinator blows it out. Sucking is achieved by contracting the buccinators to draw the cheeks inward, and then relaxing them. This action is especially important to nursing infants. To feel this action, hold your fingertips lightly on your cheeks as you make a kissing noise. You will notice the relaxation of the buccinators at the moment air is sharply drawn in through the pursed lips.

**Mentalis (men-TAY-lis)**   Elevates and protrudes lower lip in drinking, pouting, and expressions of doubt or disdain; elevates and wrinkles skin of chin

   **O:** Mandible near inferior incisors          **I:** Skin of chin at mental protuberance          **N:** Facial n.

**Buccinator**[15] **(BUC-sin-AY-tur)**   Compresses cheek against teeth and gums; directs food between molars; retracts cheek from teeth when mouth is closing to prevent biting cheek; expels air and liquid

   **O:** Alveolar processes on lateral surfaces of maxilla and mandible          **I:** Orbicularis oris; submucosa of cheek and lips          **N:** Facial n.

**The Cervical and Mental Region.**   The *platysma* is a thin superficial muscle of the upper chest and lower face. It is relatively unimportant, but when men shave, they tend to tense the platysma to make the concavity between the jaw and neck shallower and the skin tauter.

**Platysma**[16] **(plah-TIZ-muh)**   Draws lower lip and angle of mouth downward in expressions of horror or surprise; may aid in opening mouth widely

   **O:** Fascia of deltoid and pectoralis major          **I:** Mandible; skin and subcutaneous tissue of lower face          **N:** Facial n.

---

[13]*depress* = to lower + *angul* = angle, corner + *or* = mouth
[14]*labi* = lip + *inferior* = lower

[15]*buccinator* = trumpeter
[16]*platy* = flat

## TABLE 11.3    Muscles of Chewing and Swallowing

The following muscles contribute to facial expression and speech, but are primarily concerned with food manipulation.

**Extrinsic Muscles of the Tongue.**    The tongue is a very agile organ. It pushes food between the molars for chewing *(mastication)* and later forces the food into the pharynx for swallowing *(deglutition)*; it is also, of course, of crucial importance to speech. Both intrinsic and extrinsic muscles are responsible for its complex movements. The intrinsic muscles consist of a variable number of vertical fascicles that extend from the superior to the inferior sides of the tongue, transverse fascicles that extend from right to left, and longitudinal fascicles that extend from root to tip (see figs. 10.2c and 24.5b). The extrinsic muscles listed here connect the tongue to other structures in the head (fig. 11.5). Three of these are innervated by the hypoglossal nerve (CN XII), whereas the fourth is innervated by both the vagus (CN X) and accessory (CN XI) nerves.

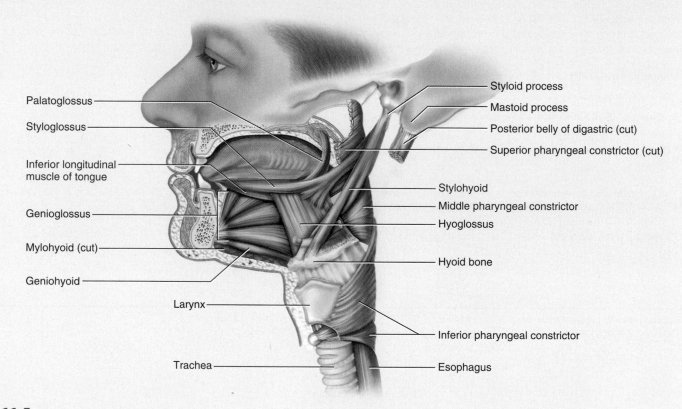

**Figure 11.5**  Muscles of the Tongue and Pharynx.

**Genioglossus**[17] **(JEE-nee-oh-GLOSS-us)**    Unilateral action draws tongue to one side; bilateral action depresses midline of tongue or protrudes tongue

  **O:** Superior mental spine on posterior surface of mental protuberance      **I:** Ventral surface of tongue from root to apex      **N:** Hypoglossal n.

**Hyoglossus**[18] **(HI-oh-GLOSS-us)**    Depresses tongue

  **O:** Body and greater horn of hyoid      **I:** Lateral and ventral surfaces of tongue      **N:** Hypoglossal n.

**Styloglossus**[19] **(STY-lo-GLOSS-us)**    Draws tongue upward and posteriorly

  **O:** Styloid process of temporal bone and ligament from styloid process to mandible      **I:** Dorsolateral surface of tongue      **N:** Hypoglossal n.

**Palatoglossus**[20] **(PAL-a-toe-GLOSS-us)**    Elevates root of tongue and closes oral cavity off from pharynx; forms palatoglossal arch at rear of oral cavity

  **O:** Soft palate      **I:** Lateral surface of tongue      **N:** Vagus and accessory nn.

---

[17]*genio* = chin + *gloss* = tongue
[18]*hyo* = hyoid bone + *gloss* = tongue

[19]*stylo* = styloid process + *gloss* = tongue
[20]*palato* = palate + *gloss* = tongue

| **TABLE 11.3** | **Muscles of Chewing and Swallowing (continued)** |
| --- | --- |

**Muscles of Chewing.**    Four pairs of muscles produce the biting and chewing movements of the mandible: the *temporalis, masseter,* and two pairs of *pterygoid muscles* (fig. 11.6). Their actions include *depression* to open the mouth for receiving food; *elevation* for biting off a piece of food or crushing it between the teeth; *protraction* so that the incisors meet in cutting off a piece of food, and *retraction* to draw the lower incisors behind the upper incisors and make the rear teeth meet; and *lateral* and *medial excursion,* the side-to-side movements that grind food between the rear teeth. The last four of these movements are shown in figure 9.15 (p. 247). All of these muscles are innervated by the mandibular nerve, which is a branch of the trigeminal (CN V).

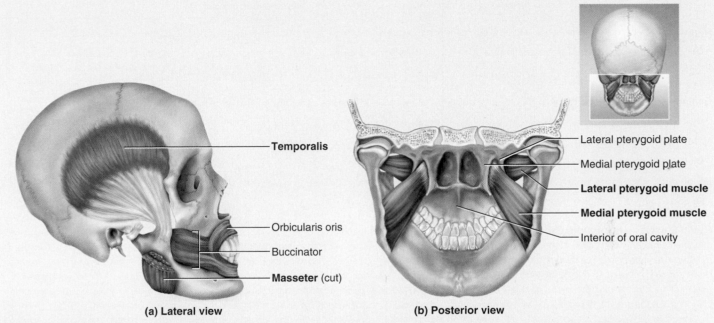

(a) Lateral view

Temporalis

Orbicularis oris

Buccinator

**Masseter** (cut)

(b) Posterior view

Lateral pterygoid plate

Medial pterygoid plate

**Lateral pterygoid muscle**

**Medial pterygoid muscle**

Interior of oral cavity

**Figure 11.6** **Muscles of Chewing.**  Boldface labels indicate muscles that act on the mandible in its chewing movements. (a) Right lateral view. In order to expose the insertion of the temporalis muscle on the mandible, part of the zygomatic arch and masseter muscle are removed. (b) View of the pterygoid muscles looking into the oral cavity from behind the skull.
● *Explain how the medial pterygoid muscles can produce both lateral and medial excursion of the mandible.*

**Temporalis**[21] **(TEM-po-RAY-liss)**    Elevation, retraction, and lateral and medial excursion of the mandible

**O:** Temporal lines and temporal fossa of cranium

**I:** Coronoid process and anterior border of mandibular ramus

**N:** Mandibular n.

**Masseter**[22] **(ma-SEE-tur)**    Elevation of the mandible, with smaller roles in protraction, retraction, and lateral and medial excursion

**O:** Zygomatic arch

**I:** Lateral surface of mandibular ramus and angle

**N:** Mandibular n.

**Medial Pterygoid**[23] **(TERR-ih-goyd)**    Elevation, protraction, and lateral and medial excursion of the mandible

**O:** Medial surface of lateral pterygoid plate, palatine bone, lateral surface of maxilla near molar teeth

**I:** Medial surface of mandibular ramus and angle

**N:** Mandibular n.

**Lateral Pterygoid**    Depression (in wide opening of the mouth), protraction, and lateral and medial excursion of the mandible

**O:** Lateral surfaces of lateral pterygoid plate and greater wing of sphenoid

**I:** Neck of mandible (just below condyle); articular disc and capsule of temporomandibular joint

**N:** Mandibular n.

---

[21]*temporalis* = of the temporal region of the head
[22]*masset* = chew

[23]*pteryg* = wing + *oid* = resembling (refers to pterygoid plate of sphenoid bone)

## TABLE 11.3 | Muscles of Chewing and Swallowing (continued)

**Hyoid Muscles—Suprahyoid Group.**　Several aspects of chewing, swallowing, and vocalizing are aided by eight pairs of *hyoid muscles* associated with the hyoid bone (fig. 11.7). The *suprahyoid group* is composed of the four pairs superior to the hyoid—the *digastric, geniohyoid, mylohyoid,* and *stylohyoid*. The digastric is an unusual muscle, named for its two bellies. Its *posterior belly* arises from the mastoid notch of the cranium and slopes downward and forward. The *anterior belly* arises from a trench called the *digastric fossa* on the inner surface of the mandibular body. It slopes downward and backward. The two bellies meet at a constriction, the *intermediate tendon*. This tendon passes through a connective tissue loop, the *fascial sling,* attached to the hyoid bone. Thus, when the two bellies of the digastric contract, they pull upward on the hyoid; but if the hyoid is fixed from below, the digastric aids in wide opening of the mouth. The lateral pterygoids are more important in wide mouth opening, with the digastrics coming into play only in extreme opening, as in yawning or taking a large bite of an apple. Cranial nerves V (trigeminal), VII (facial), and XII (hypoglossal) innervate these muscles; the trigeminal nerve gives rise to the mylohyoid nerve of the digastric and mylohyoid muscles.

**Digastric**[24]　Depresses mandible when hyoid is fixed; opens mouth widely, as when ingesting food or yawning; elevates hyoid when mandible is fixed

**O:** Mastoid notch of temporal bone, digastric fossa of mandible

**I:** Hyoid bone, via fascial sling

**N:** Posterior belly: facial n.
Anterior belly: mylohyoid n.
(a branch of the trigeminal n.)

**Geniohyoid**[25] **(JEE-nee-oh-HY-oyd)**　Depresses mandible when hyoid is fixed; elevates and protracts hyoid when mandible is fixed

**O:** Inferior mental spine of mandible

**I:** Hyoid bone

**N:** Spinal nerve C1 via hypoglossal n.

**Mylohyoid**[26]　Spans mandible from side to side and forms floor of mouth; elevates floor of mouth in initial stage of swallowing

**O:** Mylohyoid line near inferior margin of mandible

**I:** Hyoid bone

**N:** Mylohyoid n.

**Stylohyoid**　Elevates and retracts hyoid, elongating floor of mouth; roles in speech, chewing, and swallowing are not yet clearly understood

**O:** Styloid process of temporal bone

**I:** Hyoid bone

**N:** Facial n.

**Hyoid Muscles—Infrahyoid Group.**　The infrahyoid muscles are inferior to the hyoid bone. By fixing the hyoid from below, they enable the suprahyoid muscles to open the mouth. The *omohyoid* is unusual in that it arises from the shoulder, passes under the sternocleidomastoid, and then ascends to the hyoid bone. Like the digastric, it has two bellies. The *thyrohyoid,* named for the hyoid bone and the large shield-shaped *thyroid cartilage* of the larynx, helps prevent choking. It elevates the larynx during swallowing so that its superior opening is sealed by a flap of tissue, the *epiglottis*. You can feel this effect by placing your finger on the "Adam's apple" (the anterior prominence of the thyroid cartilage) and feeling it bob up as you swallow. The *sternothyroid* muscle then pulls the larynx down again so you can resume breathing; it is the only infrahyoid muscle with no connection to the hyoid bone. The *sternohyoid* lowers the hyoid bone after it has been elevated.

The infrahyoid muscles that act on the larynx are regarded as the *extrinsic muscles* of the larynx. The *intrinsic muscles,* considered in chapter 23, are concerned with control of the vocal cords and laryngeal opening. The *ansa cervicalis,*[27] which innervates three of these muscles, is a loop of nerve on the side of the neck formed by certain fibers from cervical nerves 1 to 3 (see fig. 14.13, p. 410). Cranial nerves IX (glossopharyngeal), X (vagus), and XII (hypoglossal) also innervate these muscles.

**Omohyoid**[28]　Depresses hyoid after it has been elevated

**O:** Superior border of scapula

**I:** Hyoid bone

**N:** Ansa cervicalis

**Sternohyoid**[29]　Depresses hyoid after it has been elevated

**O:** Manubrium of sternum, medial end of clavicle

**I:** Hyoid bone

**N:** Ansa cervicalis

**Thyrohyoid**[30]　Depresses hyoid; with hyoid fixed, elevates larynx as in singing high notes

**O:** Thyroid cartilage of larynx

**I:** Hyoid bone

**N:** Spinal nerve C1 via hypoglossal n.

**Sternothyroid**　Depresses larynx after it has been elevated in swallowing and vocalization; aids in singing low notes

**O:** Manubrium of sternum, costal cartilage 1

**I:** Thyroid cartilage of larynx

**N:** Ansa cervicalis

**Muscles of the Pharynx.**　The three pairs of *pharyngeal constrictors* encircle the pharynx on its posterior and lateral sides, forming a muscular funnel that aids in swallowing (see fig. 11.5).

**Pharyngeal Constrictors (three muscles)**　During swallowing, contract in order from *superior* to *middle* to *inferior constrictor* to drive food into esophagus

**O:** Medial pterygoid plate, mandible, hyoid, stylohyoid ligament, cricoid and thyroid cartilages of larynx

**I:** Median pharyngeal raphe (seam on posterior side of pharynx); basilar part of occipital bone

**N:** Glossopharyngeal and vagus nn.

---

[24]*di* = two + *gastr* = bellies
[25]*genio* = chin
[26]*mylo* = mill, molar tooth
[27]*ansa* = handle + *cervic* = neck + *alis* = of, belonging to

[28]*omo* = shoulder
[29]*sterno* = chest, sternum
[30]*thyro* = shield (refers to thyroid cartilage)

**TABLE 11.3**    **Muscles of Chewing and Swallowing (continued)**

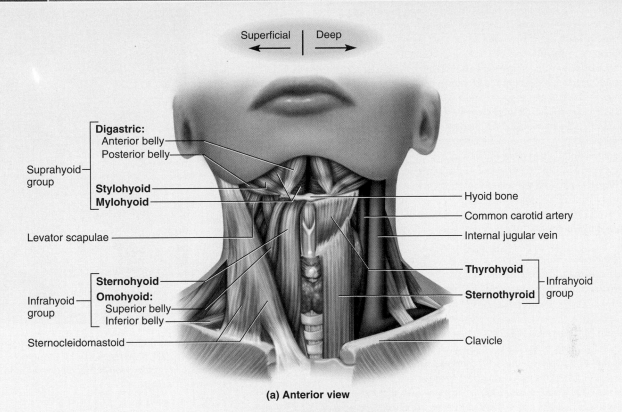

**(a) Anterior view**

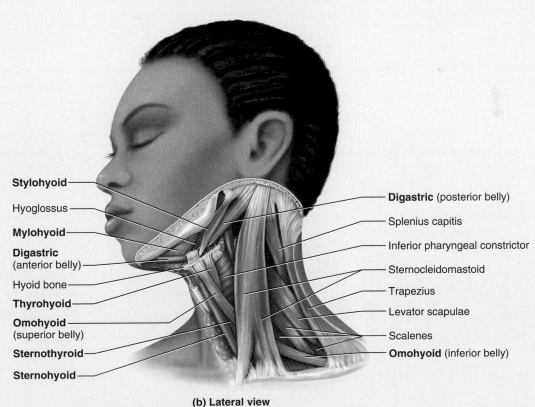

**(b) Lateral view**

**Figure 11.7** **Muscles of the Neck.** Boldface labels indicate muscles of the suprahyoid and infrahyoid groups. Another muscle of the suprahyoid group, the geniohyoid, lies deep to the mylohyoid and can be seen in figure 11.5.

| TABLE 11.4 | Muscles Acting on the Head |
|---|---|

Muscles that move the head originate on the vertebral column, thoracic cage, and pectoral girdle and insert on the cranial bones. Their actions include flexion (tipping the head forward), lateral flexion (tilting the head to one side), extension (holding the head erect), hyperextension (as in looking upward), and rotation (turning the head to look left or right). Flexion, extension, and hyperextension involve simultaneous action of the right and left muscles of a pair; the other actions require the muscle on one side to contract more strongly than its mate. Many head actions result from a combination of these movements—for example, looking up over the shoulder involves a combination of rotation and hyperextension.

Depending on the relations of the muscle origins and insertions, a muscle may cause a **contralateral**[31] movement of the head (toward the opposite side, as when contraction of a muscle on the left turns the face toward the right) or an **ipsilateral**[32] movement (toward the same side as the muscle, as when contraction of a muscle on the left tilts the head to the left).

The muscles of head movement are innervated mainly by cervical spinal nerves, with some contribution from CN XI (the accessory nerve) and thoracic nerves.

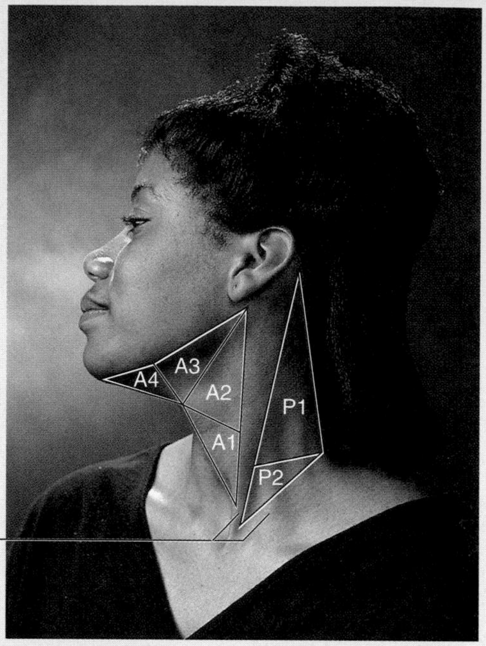

**Flexors of the Neck.** The prime mover of neck flexion is the *sternocleidomastoid*, a thick muscular cord that extends from the upper chest (sternum and clavicle) to the mastoid process behind the ear (fig. 11.7). This is most easily seen when the head is rotated to one side and slightly extended. To visualize the action of a single sternocleidomastoid, place the index finger of your left hand on your left mastoid process and the index finger of your right hand on your suprasternal notch. Now contract your left sternocleidomastoid to bring your two fingertips as close together as possible. You will see that this tilts your head so that your left ear approaches the shoulder and you look toward the right and slightly upward.

As the sternocleidomastoid passes obliquely across the neck, it divides it into *anterior* and *posterior triangles* (fig. 11.8). Other muscles and landmarks subdivide each of these into smaller triangles of surgical importance.

The three *scalenes*[33] (anterior, middle, and posterior), located on the side of the neck, are named for being arranged somewhat like a staircase. Their actions are similar so they are considered collectively.

**Anterior triangles**
A1. Muscular
A2. Carotid
A3. Submandibular
A4. Suprahyoid

**Posterior triangles**
P1. Occipital
P2. Omoclavicular

Sternocleidomastoid

**Figure 11.8** Triangles of the Neck. The sternocleidomastoid muscle separates the anterior triangles from the posterior triangles.
● *Name some of the major muscles found in triangles A1, A4, and P1.*

**Sternocleidomastoid**[34] **(STIR-no-CLY-do-MAST-oyd)** Unilateral action tilts head slightly upward and toward the opposite side, as in looking over one's contralateral shoulder. The most common action is probably rotating the head to the left and right. Bilateral action draws the head straight forward and down, as when eating or reading. Aids in deep breathing when head is fixed.

| | | |
|---|---|---|
| **O:** Manubrium of sternum, medial one-third of clavicle | **I:** Mastoid process and lateral half of superior nuchal line | **N:** Accessory n., spinal nerves C2–C3 |

**Scalenes (SCAY-leens) (anterior, middle, and posterior)** Unilateral contraction causes ipsilateral flexion or contralateral rotation (tilts head toward same shoulder, or rotates face away), depending on action of other muscles. Bilateral contraction flexes neck. If spine is fixed, scalenes elevate ribs 1–2 and aid in breathing.

| | | |
|---|---|---|
| **O:** Transverse processes of all cervical vertebrae (C1–C7) | **I:** Ribs 1–2 | **N:** Ventral rami of C3–C8 |

**Extensors of the Neck.** The extensors are located mainly in the nuchal region (back of the neck; fig. 11.9) and therefore tend to hold the head erect or draw it back. The *trapezius* is the most superficial of these. It extends from the nuchal region over the shoulders and halfway down the back (see fig. 11.14). It is named for the fact that the right and left trapezii together form a trapezoidal (diamond) shape. The *splenius* is a deeper, elongated muscle with *splenius capitis* and *splenius cervicis* regions in the head and neck, respectively. It is nicknamed the "bandage muscle" because of the way it wraps around still deeper neck muscles. One of those deeper muscles is the *semispinalis*, another elongated muscle with head, neck, and thoracic regions. Only the *semispinalis capitis* and *cervicis* are tabulated here; the semispinalis thoracis does not act on the neck, but is included in table 11.7.

**Trapezius**[35] **(tra-PEE-zee-us)** Extends and laterally flexes head. See also roles in scapular movement in table 12.1 (p. 327).

| | | |
|---|---|---|
| **O:** External occipital protuberance, medial one-third of superior nuchal line, nuchal ligament, spinous processes of vertebrae C7–T3 or T4 | **I:** Acromion and spine of scapula, lateral one-third of clavicle | **N:** Accessory n., ventral rami of C3–C4 |

---

[31]*contra* = other, opposite + *later* = side
[32]*ipsi* = same + *later* = side
[33]*scal* = staircase

[34]*sterno* = chest, sternum + *cleido* = hammer, clavicle + *masto* = breastlike, mastoid process
[35]*trapez* = table, trapezoid

| TABLE 11.4 | Muscles Acting on the Head (continued) |
|---|---|

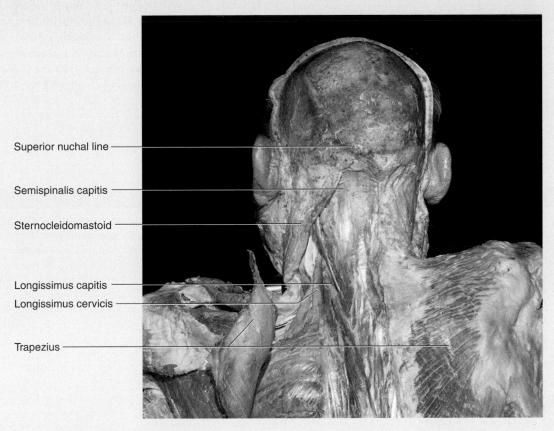

**Figure 11.9**  Muscles of the Shoulder and Nuchal Regions.

Labels:
- Superior nuchal line
- Semispinalis capitis
- Sternocleidomastoid
- Longissimus capitis
- Longissimus cervicis
- Trapezius

**Splenius Capitis[36] (SPLEE-nee-us CAP-ih-tiss) and Splenius Cervicis[37] (SIR-vih-sis)**  Acting unilaterally, produce ipsilateral flexion and slight rotation of head; extend head when acting bilaterally

**O:** Inferior half of nuchal ligament, spinous processes of vertebrae C7–T6

**I:** Mastoid process and occipital bone just inferior to superior nuchal line; cervical vertebrae C1–C2 or C3

**N:** Dorsal rami of middle cervical nn.

**Semispinalis Capitis (SEM-ee-spy-NAY-lis) and Semispinalis Cervicis**  Extend and contralaterally rotate head

**O:** Articular processes of vertebrae C4–C7, transverse processes of T1–T6

**I:** Occipital bone between nuchal lines, spinous processes of vertebrae C2–C5

**N:** Dorsal rami of cervical and thoracic nn.

### Think About It

*Of the muscles you have studied so far, name three that you would consider intrinsic muscles of the head and three that you would classify as extrinsic. Explain your reason for each.*

## Before You Go On

*Answer the following questions to test your understanding of the preceding section:*

3. Name two muscles that elevate the upper lip and two that depress the lower lip.

4. Name the four paired muscles of mastication and state where they insert on the mandible.

5. Distinguish between the functions of the suprahyoid and infrahyoid muscles.

6. List the prime movers of neck extension and flexion.

[36]*splenius* = bandage + *capitis* = of the head
[37]*cervicis* = of the neck

# Muscles of the Trunk

## Objectives

When you have completed this section, you should be able to

- name and locate the muscles of respiration and explain how they affect abdominal pressure;
- name and locate the muscles of the abdominal wall, back, and pelvic floor; and
- identify the origin, insertion, action, and innervation of any of these muscles.

In this section, we will examine muscles of the trunk of the body in three functional groups concerned with respiration, support of the abdominal wall and pelvic floor, and movement of the vertebral column (tables 11.5–11.8). In the illustrations, you will note some major muscles that are not discussed in the associated tables—for example, the pectoralis major and serratus anterior. Although they are *located in* the trunk, they *act upon* the limbs and limb girdles and are therefore discussed in chapter 12.

| **TABLE 11.5** | **Muscles of Respiration** |
| --- | --- |

We breathe primarily by means of muscles that enclose the thoracic cavity—the diaphragm, external intercostal muscles, and internal intercostal muscles (fig. 11.10).

The *diaphragm* is a muscular dome between the thoracic and abdominal cavities, bulging upward against the base of the lungs. It has openings for passage of the esophagus, major blood and lymphatic vessels, and nerves between the two cavities. Its fibers converge from the margins toward a fibrous **central tendon.** When the diaphragm contracts, it flattens slightly and enlarges the thoracic cavity, causing air intake *(inspiration);* when it relaxes, it rises and shrinks the thoracic cavity, expelling air *(expiration).*

Three layers of muscle lie between the ribs: the external, internal, and innermost intercostal muscles. The 11 pairs of *external intercostal muscles* constitute the most superficial layer. They extend from the rib tubercle posteriorly almost to the beginning of the costal cartilage anteriorly. Each one slopes downward and anteriorly from one rib to the next inferior one. The 11 pairs of *internal intercostal muscles* lie deep to the external intercostals and extend from the margin of the sternum to the angles of the ribs. They are thickest in the region between the costal cartilages and grow thinner in the region where they overlap the external intercostals. Their fibers slope downward and posteriorly from each rib to the one below, at nearly right angles to the external intercostals. The *innermost intercostal muscles* vary in number, as they are sometimes absent from the upper thoracic cage. Their fibers run in the same direction as the internal intercostals, and they are presumed to serve the same function. Intercostal nerves and blood vessels travel through the fascia between the inner and innermost intercostals (see fig. 14.12, p. 109).

The primary function of the intercostal muscles is to stiffen the thoracic cage during respiration so that it does not cave inward when the diaphragm descends. However, they also contribute to enlargement and contraction of the thoracic cage and thus add to the air volume that ventilates the lungs.

**Figure 11.10** Muscles of Respiration.

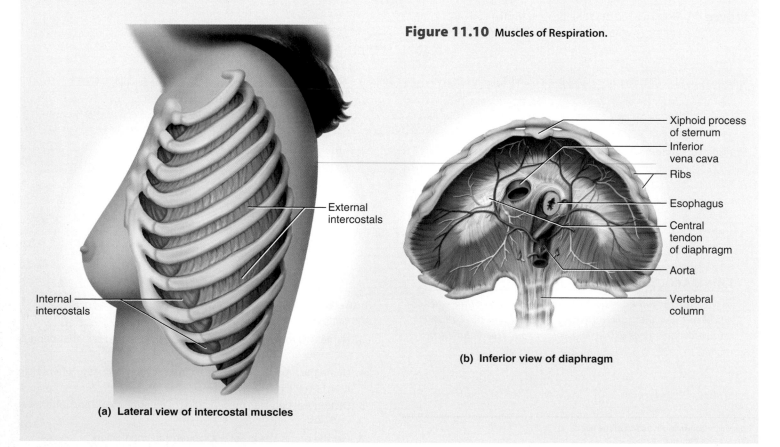

(a) **Lateral view of intercostal muscles**

(b) **Inferior view of diaphragm**

External intercostals

Internal intercostals

Xiphoid process of sternum

Inferior vena cava

Ribs

Esophagus

Central tendon of diaphragm

Aorta

Vertebral column

| TABLE 11.5 | Muscles of Respiration (continued) |
|---|---|

**Diaphragm**[38] **(DY-ah-fram)**   Prime mover of inspiration (responsible for about two-thirds of air intake); contracts in preparation for sneezing, coughing, crying, laughing, and weight lifting; contraction compresses abdominal viscera and aids in childbirth and expulsion of urine and feces

| **O:** Xiphoid process of sternum; ribs and costal cartilages 7–12; lumbar vertebrae | **I:** Central tendon of diaphragm | **N:** Phrenic nn. |
|---|---|---|

**External Intercostals**[39] **(IN-tur-COSS-tul)**   When scalenes fix rib 1, external intercostals elevate and protract ribs 2–12; this expands the thoracic cavity and creates a partial vacuum, causing inflow of air. Exercise a braking action during expiration so that expiration is not overly abrupt.

| **O:** Inferior margins of ribs 1–11 | **I:** Superior margin of next lower rib | **N:** Intercostal nn. |
|---|---|---|

**Internal Intercostals**   When quadratus lumborum and other muscles fix rib 12, internal intercostals depress and retract ribs; this compresses the thoracic cavity and expels air. Used only in forceful expiration, not in relaxed breathing.

| **O:** Superior margins and costal cartilages of ribs 2–12; margin of sternum | **I:** Inferior margin of next higher rib | **N:** Intercostal nn. |
|---|---|---|

**Innermost Intercostals**   Presumed to have the same action as the internal intercostals

| **O:** Superomedial surface of ribs 2–12; may be absent from upper ribs | **I:** Medial edge of costal groove of next higher rib | **N:** Intercostal nn. |
|---|---|---|

Many other muscles of the chest and abdomen contribute significantly to breathing (see Insight 11.1): the sternocleidomastoid and scalenes of the neck; pectoralis major and serratus anterior of the chest; latissimus dorsi of the lower back; internal and external abdominal obliques and transverse abdominal muscle; and even some of the anal muscles. The respiratory actions of all these muscles are described in chapter 23.

# INSIGHT 11.1

## Clinical Application

### Difficulty Breathing

Asthma, emphysema, heart failure, and other conditions can cause *dyspnea,* difficulty catching one's breath. People with dyspnea make increased use of accessory muscles to aid the diaphragm and intercostals in breathing, and often lean on a table or chair back to breathe more deeply. This action fixes the clavicles and scapulae so that the accessory muscles—such as the *pectoralis major* and *serratus anterior* (see chapter 12)—move the ribs instead of the bones of the pectoral girdle.

**THINK ABOUT IT**

*What muscles are eaten as "spare ribs"? What is the tough fibrous membrane between the meat and the bone?*

---

[38]*dia* = across + *phragm* = partition
[39]*inter* = between + *costa* = rib

## TABLE 11.6    Muscles of the Anterior Abdominal Wall

Unlike the thoracic cavity, the abdominal cavity has little skeletal support. It is enclosed, however, in layers of broad flat muscles whose fibers run in different directions, strengthening the abdominal wall on the same principle as the alternating layers of plywood. Three layers of muscle enclose the lateral abdominal region and extend about halfway across the anterior abdomen (fig. 11.11). The most superficial layer is the *external abdominal oblique.* Its fibers pass downward and anteriorly. The next deeper layer is the *internal abdominal oblique,* whose fibers pass upward and anteriorly, roughly perpendicular to those of the external oblique. The deepest layer is the *transverse abdominal (transversus abdominis),* with horizontal fibers. Anteriorly, a pair of vertical *rectus abdominis* muscles extend from sternum to pubis. These are divided into segments by three transverse **tendinous intersections,** giving them an appearance that bodybuilders nickname the "six pack."

The tendons of the oblique and transverse muscles are *aponeuroses*—broad fibrous sheets that continue medially and inferiorly (figs. 11.12 and 11.13). At the rectus abdominis, they diverge and pass around its anterior and posterior sides, enclosing the muscle in a vertical sleeve called the **rectus sheath.** They meet again at a median line called the **linea alba** between the rectus muscles. Another line, the **linea semilunaris,** marks the lateral boundary where the rectus sheath meets the aponeurosis. The aponeurosis of the external oblique also forms a cordlike **inguinal ligament** at its inferior margin. This extends obliquely from the anterior superior spine of the ilium to the pubis. The linea alba, linea semilunaris, and inguinal ligament are externally visible on a person with good muscle definition (see fig. B.2, p. 363).

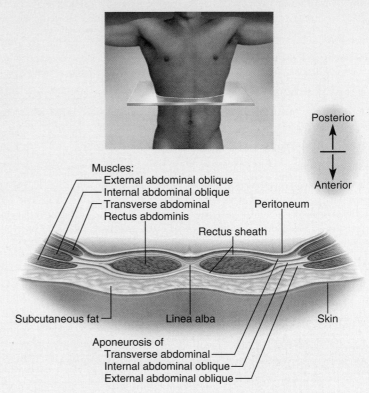

**Figure 11.11**  Cross Section of the Anterior Abdominal Wall.

**External Abdominal Oblique**    Supports abdominal viscera against pull of gravity; stabilizes vertebral column during heavy lifting; maintains posture; compresses abdominal organs, thus aiding in forceful expiration; aids in childbirth, urination, defecation, and vomiting. Unilateral contraction causes contralateral rotation of waist.

| | | |
|---|---|---|
| **O:** Ribs 5–12 | **I:** Anterior half of iliac crest, pubic symphysis, and superior margin of pubis | **N:** Ventral rami of spinal nerves T7–T12 |

**Internal Abdominal Oblique**    Same as external oblique except that unilateral contraction causes ipsilateral rotation of waist

| | | |
|---|---|---|
| **O:** Inguinal ligament, iliac crest, and thoracolumbar fascia | **I:** Ribs 10–12, costal cartilages 7–10, pubis | **N:** Ventral rami of spinal nerves T7–L1 |

**Transverse Abdominal**    Compresses abdominal contents, with same effects as external oblique, but does not contribute to movements of vertebral column

| | | |
|---|---|---|
| **O:** Inguinal ligament, iliac crest, thoracolumbar fascia, costal cartilages 7–12 | **I:** Linea alba, pubis, aponeurosis of internal oblique | **N:** Ventral rami of spinal nerves T7–L1 |

**Rectus[40] Abdominis (REC-tus ab-DOM-ih-nis)**    Flexes lumbar region of vertebral column, producing forward bending at the waist

| | | |
|---|---|---|
| **O:** Pubic symphysis and superior margin of pubis | **I:** Xiphoid process, costal cartilages 5–7 | **N:** Ventral rami of spinal nerves T6–T12 |

[40]*rectus* = straight

| TABLE 11.6 | Muscles of the Anterior Abdominal Wall (continued) |
|---|---|

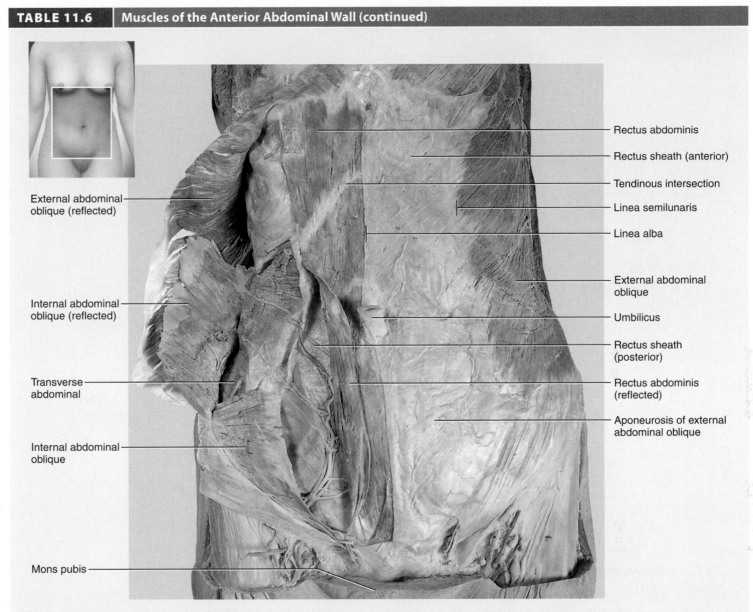

External abdominal oblique (reflected)

Internal abdominal oblique (reflected)

Transverse abdominal

Internal abdominal oblique

Mons pubis

Rectus abdominis

Rectus sheath (anterior)

Tendinous intersection

Linea semilunaris

Linea alba

External abdominal oblique

Umbilicus

Rectus sheath (posterior)

Rectus abdominis (reflected)

Aponeurosis of external abdominal oblique

**Figure 11.12** **Thoracic and Abdominal Muscles of the Cadaver.** The rectus sheath is removed on the anatomical right to expose the right rectus abdominis muscle. Inset shows area of dissection.

**TABLE 11.6** | **Muscles of the Anterior Abdominal Wall (continued)**

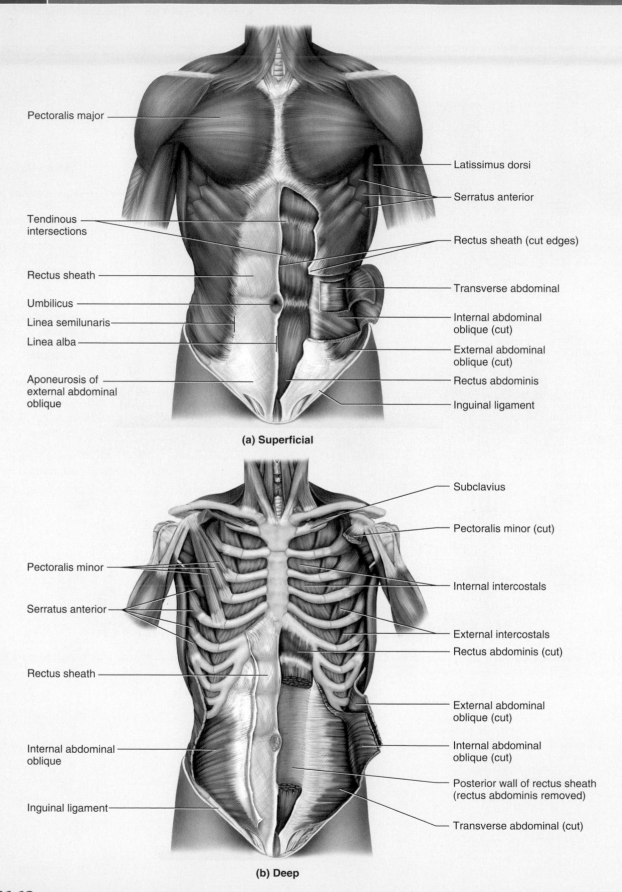

Pectoralis major

Latissimus dorsi

Serratus anterior

Tendinous intersections

Rectus sheath (cut edges)

Rectus sheath

Transverse abdominal

Umbilicus

Internal abdominal oblique (cut)

Linea semilunaris

Linea alba

External abdominal oblique (cut)

Aponeurosis of external abdominal oblique

Rectus abdominis

Inguinal ligament

**(a) Superficial**

Subclavius

Pectoralis minor (cut)

Pectoralis minor

Internal intercostals

Serratus anterior

External intercostals

Rectus abdominis (cut)

Rectus sheath

External abdominal oblique (cut)

Internal abdominal oblique

Internal abdominal oblique (cut)

Posterior wall of rectus sheath (rectus abdominis removed)

Inguinal ligament

Transverse abdominal (cut)

**(b) Deep**

**Figure 11.13 Thoracic and Abdominal Muscles.** (a) Superficial muscles. The left rectus sheath is cut away to expose the rectus abdominis muscle. (b) Deep muscles. On the anatomical right, the external abdominal oblique has been removed to expose the internal abdominal oblique, and the pectoralis major has been removed to expose the pectoralis minor. On the anatomical left, the internal abdominal oblique has been cut to expose the transverse abdominal, and the middle of the rectus abdominis has been cut out to expose the posterior rectus sheath.

● *Name at least three muscles that lie deep to the pectoralis major.*

| **TABLE 11.7** | **Muscles of the Back** |
|---|---|

Muscles of the back primarily extend, rotate, and laterally flex the vertebral column. The most prominent superficial back muscles are the latissimus dorsi and trapezius (fig. 11.14), but they are concerned with upper limb movements and covered in chapter 12. Deep to these are the *serratus posterior superior* and *inferior* (fig. 11.15). They extend from the vertebrae to the ribs. Their function and significance remain uncertain, so we will not consider them further.

Deep to these is a prominent muscle, the **erector spinae,** which runs vertically for the entire length of the back from the cranium to the sacrum. It is a thick muscle, easily palpated on each side of the vertebral column in the lumbar region. (Pork chops and T-bone steaks are erector spinae muscles.) As it ascends, it divides in the upper lumbar region into three parallel columns (figs. 11.15 and 11.16). The most lateral of these is the **iliocostalis,**[41] which is divided from inferior to superior into the *iliocostalis lumborum, iliocostalis thoracis,* and *iliocostalis cervicis* (lumbar, thoracic, and cervical regions). The next medial column is the **longissimus,**[42] divided from inferior to superior into the *longissimus thoracis, longissimus cervicis,* and *longissimus capitis* (thoracic, cervical, and cephalic regions). The most medial column is the **spinalis,** divided into *spinalis thoracis, spinalis cervicis,* and *spinalis capitis.* The functions of all three columns are sufficiently similar that we will treat them collectively as the erector spinae.

The major deep muscles are the *semispinalis thoracis* in the thoracic region and *quadratus lumborum* in the lumbar region. The erector spinae and quadratus lumborum are enclosed in a fibrous sheath called the **thoracolumbar fascia,** which is the origin of some of the abdominal and lumbar muscles. The *multifidus* is a collective name for a series of tiny muscles that connect adjacent vertebrae to each other from the cervical to lumbar region.

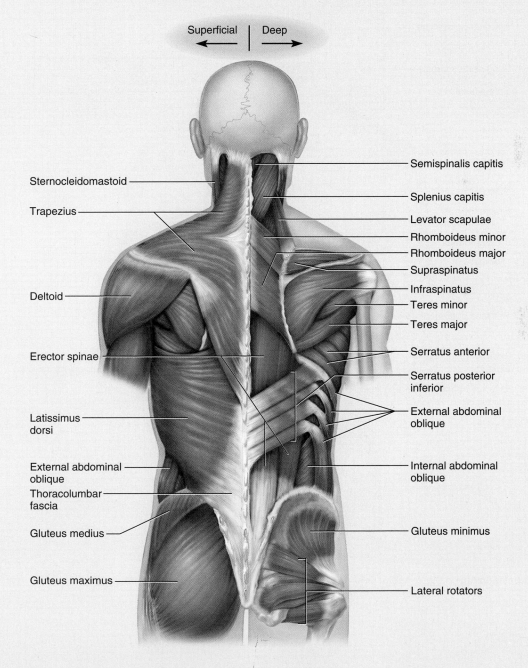

**Figure 11.14** **Neck, Back, and Gluteal Muscles.** The most superficial muscles are shown on the left and the next deeper layer on the right.

[41]*ilio* = ilium of the hip bone + *costalis* = pertaining to the ribs          [42]*longissimus* = longest

## TABLE 11.7   Muscles of the Back (continued)

**Erector Spinae[43] (eh-REC-tur SPY-nee)**   Extension and lateral flexion of vertebral column; the longissimus capitis also produces ipsilateral rotation of the head

**O:** Nuchal ligament, ribs 3–12, thoracic and lumbar vertebrae, median and lateral sacral crests, thoracolumbar fascia

**I:** Mastoid process, cervical and thoracic vertebrae, and all ribs

**N:** Dorsal rami of cervical to lumbar spinal nerves

**Semispinalis Thoracis (SEM-ee-spy-NAY-liss tho-RA-sis)**   Extension and contralateral rotation of vertebral column

**O:** Vertebrae T6–T10

**I:** Vertebrae C6–T4

**N:** Dorsal rami of cervical and thoracic spinal nerves

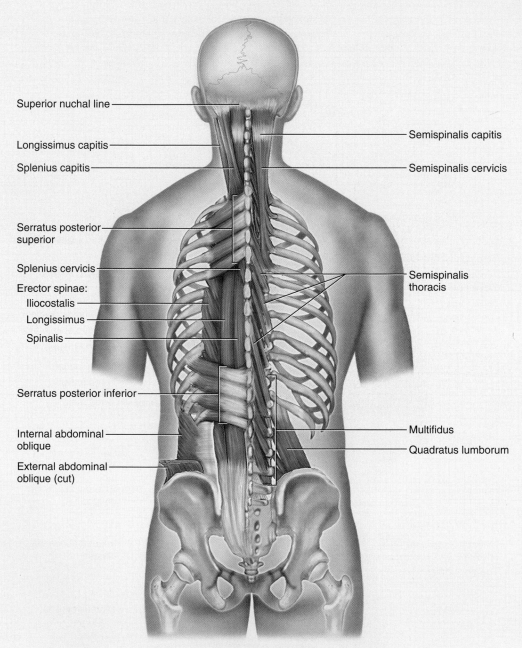

Superior nuchal line

Longissimus capitis

Splenius capitis

Serratus posterior superior

Splenius cervicis

Erector spinae:
  Iliocostalis
  Longissimus
  Spinalis

Serratus posterior inferior

Internal abdominal oblique

External abdominal oblique (cut)

Semispinalis capitis

Semispinalis cervicis

Semispinalis thoracis

Multifidus

Quadratus lumborum

**Figure 11.15   Muscles Acting on the Vertebral Column.**   Those on the right are deeper than those on the left.

[43]*erector* = that which straightens + *spinae* = of the spine

**TABLE 11.7** | **Muscles of the Back (continued)**

**Quadratus Lumborum**[44] **(quad-RAY-tus lum-BORE-um)** Aids respiration by fixing rib 12 and stabilizing inferior attachments of diaphragm. Unilateral contraction causes ipsilateral flexion of lumbar vertebral column; bilateral contraction extends lumbar vertebral column.

| | | |
|---|---|---|
| **O:** Iliac crest, iliolumbar ligament | **I:** Rib 12 and vertebrae L1–L4 | **N:** Ventral rami of spinal nerves T12–L4 |

**Multifidus**[45] **(mul-TIFF-ih-dus)** Stabilization of adjacent vertebrae, maintenance of posture, control of vertebral movement when erector spinae acts on vertebral column

| | | |
|---|---|---|
| **O:** Vertebrae C4–L5, posterior superior iliac spine, sacrum, aponeurosis of erector spinae | **I:** Laminae and spinous processes of vertebrae superior to origins | **N:** Dorsal rami of cervical to lumbar spinal nerves |

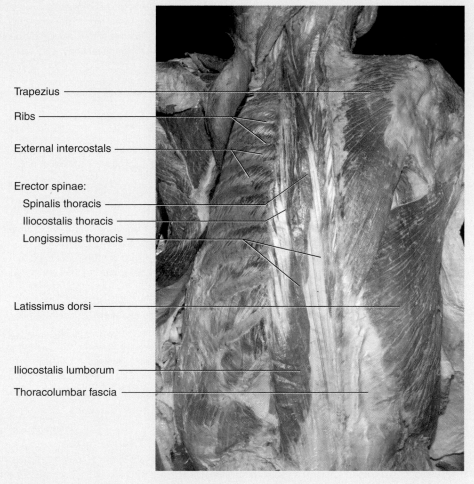

Trapezius
Ribs
External intercostals
Erector spinae:
Spinalis thoracis
Iliocostalis thoracis
Longissimus thoracis
Latissimus dorsi
Iliocostalis lumborum
Thoracolumbar fascia

**Figure 11.16** Deep Back Muscles of the Cadaver.

INSIGHT 11.2

## Clinical Application

### Heavy Lifting and Back Injuries

When a skeletal muscle is excessively stretched, its sarcomeres are so stretched that its thick and thin myofilaments have little or no overlap. When such a muscle is stimulated to contract, few of the myosin heads are able to attach to the actin filaments (see chapter 10), the contraction is very weak, and the muscle and connective tissues are subject to injury.

When you are fully bent over forward, as in touching your toes, the erector spinae is extremely stretched. Standing up from such a position is therefore initiated by the hamstring muscles on the back of the thigh and the gluteus maximus of the buttocks. The erector spinae joins in the action when it is partially contracted. Standing too suddenly or improperly lifting a heavy weight, however, can strain the erector spinae, cause painful muscle spasms, tear tendons and ligaments of the lower back, and rupture intervertebral discs. The lumbar muscles are adapted for maintaining posture, not for lifting. This is why it is important, in heavy lifting, to kneel and use the powerful extensor muscles of the thighs and buttocks to lift the load.

[44]*quadrat* = four-sided + *lumborum* = of the lumbar region

[45]*multi* = many + *fid* = branched, sectioned

| **TABLE 11.8** | **Muscles of the Pelvic Floor** |
|---|---|

The floor of the pelvic cavity is formed by three layers of muscles and fasciae that span the pelvic outlet and support the viscera (fig. 11.17). It is penetrated by the anal canal, urethra, and vagina, which open into a diamond-shaped region between the thighs called the **perineum** (PERR-ih-NEE-um). The perineum is bordered by four bony landmarks: the pubic symphysis anteriorly, the coccyx posteriorly, and the ischial tuberosities laterally. The anterior half of the perineum is the **urogenital triangle,** and the posterior half is the **anal triangle** (fig. 11.17a). These are especially important landmarks in obstetrics.

**Superficial Perineal Space.**    The pelvic floor is divided into three layers or *compartments*. The one just deep to the skin, called the **superficial perineal space** (fig. 11.17a), contains three muscles: the ischiocavernosus, bulbospongiosus, and superficial transverse perineal. The *ischiocavernosus muscles* converge like a V from the ischial tuberosities toward the penis or clitoris. In males, the *bulbospongiosus (bulbocavernosus) muscle* forms a sheath around the base (bulb) of the penis, and in females, it encloses the vagina like a pair of parentheses. *Cavernosus* in these names refers to the spongy, cavernous structure of the tissues in the penis and clitoris. The *superficial transverse perineal muscle* extends from the ischial tuberosities to a strong median fibromuscular anchorage, the **perineal body.** It is a weakly developed muscle and not always present, so it is not tabulated. The other two muscles of this layer primarily serve sexual functions.

**Ischiocavernosus[46] (ISS-kee-oh-CAV-er-NO-sus)**    Maintains erection of the penis or clitoris by compressing deep structures of the organ and forcing blood forward into its body

| | | |
|---|---|---|
| **O:** Ramus and tuberosity of ischium | **I:** Ensheaths deep structures of penis or clitoris | **N:** Pudendal n. |

**Bulbospongiosus[47] (BUL-bo-SPUN-jee-OH-sus)**    Expels remaining urine from urethra after bladder has emptied. Aids in erection of penis or clitoris. In males, spasmodic contractions expel semen during ejaculation. In females, contractions constrict vaginal orifice and expel secretions of greater vestibular glands (see fig. 26.21, p. 757).

| | | |
|---|---|---|
| **O:** Perineal body and median raphe | **I:** Male: Ensheaths root of penis<br>Female: Pubic symphysis | **N:** Pudendal n. |

**The Middle Compartment.**    In the middle compartment, the urogenital triangle is spanned by a thin triangular sheet called the **urogenital diaphragm.** This is composed of a fibrous membrane and two or three muscles: the *deep transverse perineal muscle* and the *external urethral sphincter* (fig. 11.17b), and in females only, a *compressor urethrae muscle*. The deep transverse perineal muscle, like its superficial counterpart mentioned earlier, is weakly developed and not tabulated; the two of them serve to anchor the perineal body on the median plane, and the perineal body, in turn, anchors other pelvic muscles. The anal triangle has one muscle at this level, the *external anal sphincter*.

**External Urethral Sphincter**    Retains urine in bladder until voluntarily voided; contractions help to expel final drops of urine or semen

| | | |
|---|---|---|
| **O:** Right and left ischiopubic rami | **I:** Encircles urethral orifice | **N:** Pudendal n., S2–S4, pelvic splanchnic n. |

**Compressor Urethrae**    Aids in urine retention; found in female only

| | | |
|---|---|---|
| **O:** Ischiopubic rami | **I:** Right and left compressor urethrae meet as muscular sheet inferior to external urethral sphincter | **N:** Pudendal n., S2–S4, pelvic splanchnic n. |

**External Anal Sphincter**    Retains feces in rectum until voluntarily voided

| | | |
|---|---|---|
| **O:** Coccyx, perineal body | **I:** Encircles anal canal and orifice | **N:** Pudendal n., S2–S4, pelvic splanchnic n. |

**The Pelvic Diaphragm.**    The deepest compartment, the **pelvic diaphragm,** consists of two muscle pairs shown in figure 11.17c: the *levator ani* and *coccygeus*. The levator ani forms most of the pelvic floor. It is a composite of three muscles. The greatest part of it is a broad, triangular *iliococcygeus*. It arises from a *tendinous arch* that forms the medial margin of a fascia over the obturator internus muscle. Medial and anterior to this are a pair of narrow muscles, the *pubococcygeus* and *puborectalis*, which arise from the pubis and flank the urethra, rectum, and (in females) vagina. The left and right levator ani muscles converge on the fibrous *anococcygeal body*, which, in turn, inserts on the coccyx. Posterior to the levator ani is the coccygeus muscle, extending from the ischial spine to the coccyx and forming about one-quarter of the pelvic diaphragm.

**Levator Ani[48] (leh-VAY-tur AY-nye)**    Compresses anal canal and reinforces external anal and urethral sphincters; supports uterus and other pelvic viscera; aids in the falling away of the feces; vertical movements affect pressure differences between abdominal and thoracic cavities and thus aid in breathing

| | | |
|---|---|---|
| **O:** Inner surface of lesser pelvis from pubis through tendinous arch of obturator internus to spine of ischium | **I:** Coccyx via anococcygeal body; walls of urethra, vagina, and anal canal | **N:** Pudendal n., S2–S3 |

**Coccygeus (coc-SIDJ-ee-us)**    Aids levator ani

| | | |
|---|---|---|
| **O:** Spine of ischium | **I:** Coccyx and adjacent border of sacrum | **N:** S3–S4 |

---

[46]*ischio* = ischium of the hip bone + *cavernosus* = corpus cavernosum of the penis or clitoris
[47]*bulbo* = bulb of the penis + *spongiosus* = corpus spongiosum of the penis
[48]*levat* = to elevate + *ani* = of the anus

**TABLE 11.8** Muscles of the Pelvic Floor

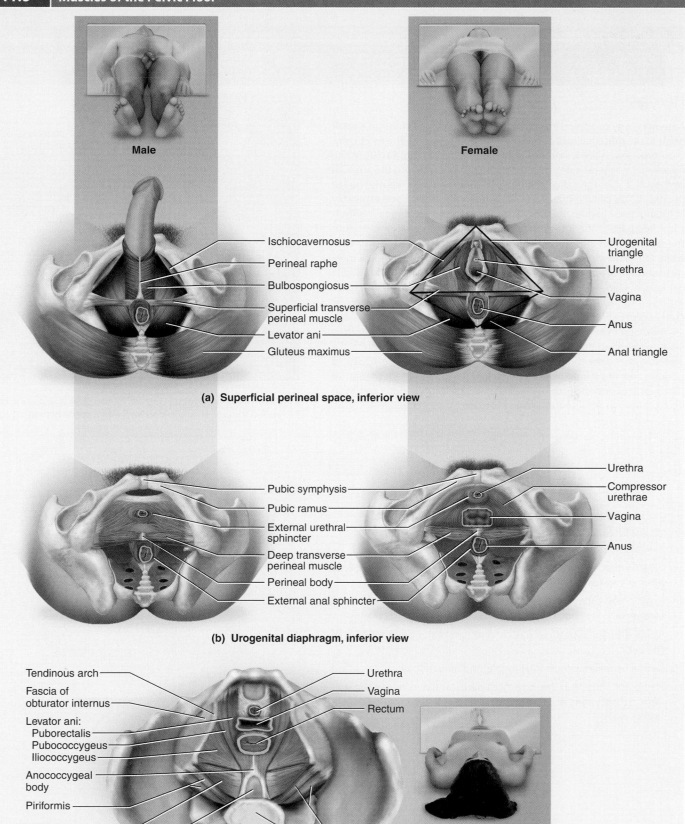

**Male**

**Female**

Ischiocavernosus

Perineal raphe

Bulbospongiosus

Superficial transverse perineal muscle

Levator ani

Gluteus maximus

Urogenital triangle

Urethra

Vagina

Anus

Anal triangle

**(a) Superficial perineal space, inferior view**

Pubic symphysis

Pubic ramus

External urethral sphincter

Deep transverse perineal muscle

Perineal body

External anal sphincter

Urethra

Compressor urethrae

Vagina

Anus

**(b) Urogenital diaphragm, inferior view**

Tendinous arch

Fascia of obturator internus

Levator ani:
Puborectalis
Pubococcygeus
Iliococcygeus

Anococcygeal body

Piriformis

Coccygeus

Coccyx

Urethra

Vagina

Rectum

Piriformis

Vertebra S1

**Female**

**(c) Pelvic diaphragm, superior view**

**Figure 11.17 Muscles of the Pelvic Floor.** (a) The superficial perineal space, with triangles of the perineum marked on the right. (b) The urogenital diaphragm; this is the next deeper layer after the muscles in part (a). (c) Superior view of the female pelvic diaphragm, the deepest layer, seen from within the pelvic cavity.

# INSIGHT 11.3

## Clinical Application

### Hernias

A hernia is any condition in which the viscera protrude through a weak point in the muscular wall of the abdominopelvic cavity. The most common type to require treatment is an *inguinal hernia* (fig. 11.18). In the male fetus, each testis descends from the pelvic cavity into the scrotum by way of a passage called the *inguinal canal* through the muscles of the groin. This canal remains a weak point in the pelvic floor, especially in infants and children. When pressure rises in the abdominal cavity, it can force part of the intestine or bladder into this canal or even into the scrotum. This also sometimes occurs in men who hold their breath while lifting heavy weights. When the diaphragm and abdominal muscles contract, pressure in the abdominal cavity can soar to 1,500 pounds per square inch—more than 100 times the normal pressure and quite sufficient to produce an inguinal hernia, or "rupture." Inguinal hernias rarely occur in women.

Two other sites of hernia are the diaphragm and navel. A *hiatal hernia* is a condition in which part of the stomach protrudes through the diaphragm into the thoracic cavity. This is most common in overweight people over 40. It may cause heartburn due to the regurgitation of stomach acid into the esophagus, but most cases go undetected. In an *umbilical hernia,* abdominal viscera protrude through the navel.

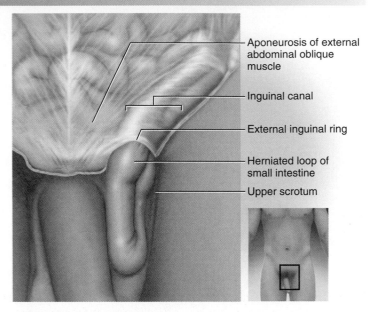

Aponeurosis of external abdominal oblique muscle

Inguinal canal

External inguinal ring

Herniated loop of small intestine

Upper scrotum

**Figure 11.18** **Inguinal Hernia.** A loop of small intestine has protruded through the inguinal canal into a space beneath the skin.

## Before You Go On

*Answer the following questions to test your understanding of the preceding section:*

7. Which muscles are used more often, the external intercostals or internal intercostals? Explain.

8. Explain how pulmonary ventilation affects abdominal pressure, and vice versa.

9. Name a major superficial muscle and two major deep muscles of the back.

10. Define *perineum, urogenital triangle,* and *anal triangle.*

11. Name one muscle in the superficial perineal space, one in the urogenital diaphragm, and one in the pelvic diaphragm. State the function of each.

# CHAPTER REVIEW

## REVIEW OF KEY CONCEPTS

### Learning Approaches (p. 295)

1. Learning muscle anatomy requires that one become familiar with a few Latin words that are used in naming muscles. These words describe such characteristics as the size, shape, location, number of heads, orientation, and action of a muscle (table 11.1).

2. Muscles below the neck are innervated by *spinal nerves,* which arise from the spinal cord and emerge through the intervertebral foramina. Spinal nerves are identified by a letter and number that refers to the vertebrae, such as spinal nerve T6 for the sixth thoracic nerve.

3. Muscles of the head and neck are innervated by *cranial nerves,* which arise from the brainstem and emerge through the skull foramina. Cranial nerves are identified by names (see chapter 15) and by roman numerals I through XII.

### Muscles of the Head and Neck (p. 299)

1. Humans and other primates have much more expressive faces than other animals, and they have correspondingly complex facial muscles.

2. The *occipitofrontalis* moves the scalp, eyebrows, and forehead (table 11.2).

3. The eyelid and other tissues around the eye are moved by the *orbicularis oculi, levator palpebrae superioris,* and *corrugator supercilii* (table 11.2).

4. The *nasalis* muscle flares the nostrils and compresses the air passages to the nasal cavity (table 11.2).

5. The lips are acted on by the *orbicularis oris, levator labii superioris, levator anguli oris, zygomaticus major* and *minor, risorius, depressor anguli oris, depressor labii inferioris,* and *mentalis* (table 11.2).

6. The cheeks are acted on by the *buccinator* muscles (table 11.2).

7. The *platysma* acts on the mandible and the skin of the neck (table 11.2).

8. The tongue is controlled by a set of unnamed *intrinsic muscles* and several *extrinsic muscles:* the *genioglossus, hyoglossus, styloglossus,* and *palatoglossus* (table 11.3).

9. Biting and chewing are achieved by the actions of the *temporalis, masseter, medial pterygoid,* and *lateral pterygoid* muscles on the mandible (table 11.3).

10. Four muscles are associated with the hyoid bone and located superior to it, and are thus called the *suprahyoid group:* the *digastric, geniohyoid, mylohyoid,* and *stylohyoid* (table 11.3). These muscles act on the mandible and hyoid bone to forcibly open the mouth and to aid in swallowing.

11. Another four muscles associated with the hyoid bone are inferior to it and therefore called the *infrahyoid group:* the *omohyoid, sternohyoid, thyrohyoid,* and *sternothyroid* (table 11.3). These muscles depress or fix the hyoid and elevate or depress the larynx, especially in association with swallowing.

12. The *superior, middle,* and *inferior pharyngeal constrictors* contract in sequence to force food down and into the esophagus (table 11.3).

13. The *sternocleidomastoid* and three *scalene* muscles flex the neck. The *trapezius, splenius capitis, splenius cervicis* and *semispinalis capitis* are the major extensors of the neck. Some of these are also employed in rotation of the head (table 11.4).

### Muscles of the Trunk (p. 310)

1. Breathing is achieved by the muscles of respiration, especially the *diaphragm, external intercostals,* and *internal intercostals* (table 11.5).

2. The abdominal wall is supported by the sheetlike *external abdominal oblique, internal abdominal oblique, transverse abdominal,* and *rectus abdominis* muscles, which support the abdominal viscera, stabilize the vertebral column during lifting, and aid in respiration, urination, defecation, vomiting, and childbirth (table 11.6).

3. The back has numerous complex muscles that extend, rotate, and laterally flex the vertebral column and aid in breathing. Some major back muscles include the *erector spinae* (which is subdivided into the *iliocostalis, longissimus,* and *spinalis* muscle columns); the *semispinalis thoracis;* the *quadratus lumborum;* and the *multifidus* (table 11.7).

4. The pelvic floor is spanned by three layers of muscles and fasciae (table 11.8). The anal canal, urethra, and vagina penetrate the pelvic floor muscles and open into the *perineum,* a diamond-shaped space between the thighs bordered by the pubic symphysis, coccyx, and ischial tuberosities. The anterior half of the perineum is the *urogenital triangle,* and the posterior half is the *anal triangle.*

5. The most superficial compartment of the pelvic floor is the *superficial perineal space.* Its two major muscles are the *ischiocavernosus* and *bulbospongiosus.*

6. The middle compartment of the pelvic floor, in the urogenital triangle, consists of the *urogenital diaphragm,* which is composed of a fibrous membrane and two muscles: the minor *deep transverse perineal muscle* and the *external urethral sphincter.* In the anal triangle, the middle compartment has one muscle, the *external anal sphincter.*

7. The deepest compartment of the pelvic floor is the *pelvic diaphragm.* It consists of two muscles, the *levator ani* and *coccygeus.*

## TESTING YOUR RECALL

1. Which of the following muscles is the prime mover in spitting out a mouthful of liquid?
   a. platysma
   b. buccinator
   c. risorius
   d. masseter
   e. palatoglossus

2. The word _____ in a muscle name indicates a function related to the head.
   a. cervicis
   b. carpi
   c. capitis
   d. hallucis
   e. teres

3. Which of these is *not* a suprahyoid muscle?
   a. genioglossus
   b. geniohyoid
   c. stylohyoid
   d. mylohyoid
   e. digastric

4. Which of these muscles is an extensor of the neck?
   a. external oblique
   b. sternocleidomastoid
   c. splenius capitis
   d. iliocostalis
   e. latissimus dorsi

5. Which of these muscles of the pelvic floor is the deepest?
   a. superficial transverse perineal
   b. bulbospongiosus
   c. ischiocavernosus
   d. deep transverse perineal
   e. levator ani

6. The facial nerve supplies all of the following muscles *except*
   a. the frontalis.
   b. the orbicularis oculi.
   c. the orbicularis oris.
   d. the depressor labii inferioris.
   e. the mylohyoid.

7. The _____ produce(s) lateral grinding movements of the jaw.
   a. pterygoids
   b. temporalis
   c. hyoglossus
   d. zygomaticus major and minor
   e. risorius

8. All of the following muscles act on the vertebral column *except*
   a. the serratus posterior superior.
   b. the iliocostalis thoracis.
   c. the longissimus thoracis.
   d. the spinalis thoracis.
   e. the multifidus.

9. A muscle that aids in chewing without moving the mandible is
   a. the temporalis.
   b. the mentalis.
   c. the buccinator.
   d. the levator anguli oris.
   e. the splenius cervicis.

10. Which of the following muscles raises the upper lip?
    a. levator palpebrae superioris
    b. orbicularis oris
    c. masseter
    d. zygomaticus minor
    e. mentalis

11. The prime mover of spinal extension is the _____.

12. Ejaculation results from contraction of the _____ muscle.

13. The muscle that opens your eyes is the _____.

14. As its name implies, the _____ nerve controls several muscles of the tongue.

15. The _____ muscle, named for its two bellies, opens the mouth.

16. The anterior half of the perineum is a region called the _____.

17. The abdominal aponeuroses converge on a median fibrous band on the abdomen called the _____.

18. The thyrohyoid muscle inserts on the thyroid cartilage of the _____.

19. The _____ muscles diverge like a V from the middle of the upper thorax to insertions behind the ears.

20. The largest muscle of the upper back is the _____.

*Answers in the Appendix*

## TRUE OR FALSE

*Determine which five of the following statements are false, and briefly explain why.*

1. The origin of the sternocleidomastoid is the mastoid process.

2. The largest deep muscle of the lower back is the quadratus lumborum.

3. The muscle used to stick out your tongue is the genioglossus.

4. The abdominal oblique muscles rotate the vertebral column.

5. Exhaling requires contraction of the internal intercostal muscles.

6. The digastric muscles form the floor of the mouth.

7. The scalenes are superficial to the trapezius.

8. Cutting the phrenic nerves would paralyze the prime mover of respiration.

9. The orbicularis oculi and orbicularis oris are sphincters.

10. All of the cranial nerves innervate muscles of the head and neck.

*Answers in the Appendix*

## TESTING YOUR COMPREHENSION

1. Name one antagonist of each of the following muscles: (*a*) orbicularis oculi, (*b*) genioglossus, (*c*) masseter, (*d*) sternocleidomastoid, (*e*) rectus abdominis.

2. Name one synergist of each of the following muscles: (*a*) temporalis, (*b*) diaphragm, (*c*) platysma, (*d*) semispinalis capitis, (*e*) bulbospongiosus.

3. Dental procedures, vaccination, HIV infection, and some other infections occasionally injure branches of the facial nerve and weaken or paralyze the affected muscles. Predict the problems that a person would have if the orbicularis oris and buccinator muscles were paralyzed by such a nerve lesion.

4. Removal of cancerous lymph nodes from the neck sometimes requires removal of the sternocleidomastoid on that side. How would this affect a patient's range of head movement?

5. Insight 10.2 (p. 279) remarked that the Food and Drug Administration approved Botox Cosmetic only for the treatment of frown lines between the eyebrows. From the knowledge you have gained in this chapter, name the muscles into which a physician following those guidelines would inject Botox.

*Answers at aris.mhhe.com*

# ONLINE RESOURCES

Visit aprevealed.com to explore melt-away cadaver dissections, watch animations that clarify difficult concepts, review histological and radiological images, or take a quiz to assess your understanding of the material.

The Saladin *Human Anatomy,* 2e website at aris.mhhe.com features chapter-specific quizzes, labeling exercises, and other interactive tools to complement your study of human anatomy. If your instructor has provided an ARIS course code, you can also access assignments and information specific to your course.

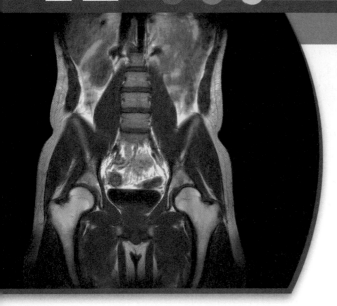

# The Appendicular Musculature

MRI scan showing muscles of the lumbar, pelvic, and upper femoral regions (frontal section)

## BRUSHING UP

To understand this chapter, you may find it helpful to review the following concepts:
- Terminology of the limb regions (p. 25)
- Anatomy of the appendicular skeleton (chapter 8)
- Terminology of joint actions (pp. 243–249)
- Shapes of muscles (fusiform, pennate, circular, etc.) (p. 269)
- The meaning of muscle origin, insertion, and action (p. 270)
- Prime movers, synergists, antagonists, and fixators (p. 270)
- Intrinsic and extrinsic muscles (p. 271)
- Muscle innervation (p. 295)
- Greek and Latin words commonly used to name muscles (p. 298, table 11.1)

Anatomy & Physiology REVEALED®
aprevealed.com

**Muscular System**

The appendicular musculature includes not only the muscles of the upper and lower limbs (appendages), but also several prominent muscles of the trunk that act on the limbs. In most vertebrate animals, these muscles serve for little more than locomotion, with such exceptions as digging (moles) and limited manipulation of objects (squirrels, raccoons). The upright locomotion of humans, however, has been associated with a number of evolutionary changes—large, heavily muscled lower limbs for standing, walking, and running, and upper limbs that have less muscular bulk but more mobile joints and an array of smaller muscles adapted for climbing and, more importantly, precise manipulation of objects. In this chapter, we examine the four major groups of appendicular muscles—those of the pectoral girdle, upper limb, pelvic girdle, and lower limb. We also consider several muscle injuries, which are more common in the appendicular region than in the axial region.

## Muscles Acting on the Shoulder and Upper Limb

### Objectives

When you have completed this section, you should be able to

- explain what muscle compartments are and describe how they are separated from each other;
- name and locate the muscles that act on the shoulder, arm, forearm, wrist, and hand;
- relate the actions of these muscles to the joint movements described in chapter 9; and
- describe the origin, insertion, and innervation of each muscle.

## Muscle Groups and Compartments

The upper and lower limbs have numerous muscles that serve primarily for movement of the body and manipulation of objects. Although their number presents a learning challenge, they are arranged in logical groups that make their functional relationships easier to understand. Their names alone are often helpful indications of their functions and locations. For example, *flexor carpi ulnaris* translates "flexor of the wrist (associated with) the ulna." As a flexor, it is found on the anterior side of the forearm so it can bend the wrist anteriorly, and the name further tells us that it is on the ulnar (medial) side of the forearm. You may find it helpful to review table 11.1 (p. 298) on the naming of muscles and to pay attention to the footnotes in this chapter until such terms as *flexor* and *ulnaris* become intuitively easy to remember.

## INSIGHT 12.1

### Clinical Application

#### Compartment Syndrome

The fasciae of the upper and lower limb enclose the muscle compartments very snugly. If a blood vessel in a compartment is damaged by overuse or contusion (a bruising injury), blood and tissue fluid accumulate in the compartment. The fasciae prevent the compartment from expanding to relieve the pressure. Mounting pressure on the muscles, nerves, and blood vessels triggers a sequence of degenerative events called *compartment syndrome.* Blood flow to the compartment is obstructed by pressure on its arteries. If *ischemia* (poor blood flow) persists for more than 2 to 4 hours, nerves begin to die, and after 6 hours, so does muscle tissue. Nerves can regenerate after the pressure is relieved, but muscle necrosis is irreversible. The breakdown of muscle releases myoglobin into the blood. *Myoglobinuria,* the presence of myoglobin in the urine, gives the urine a dark color and is one of the key signs of compartment syndrome and some other degenerative muscle disorders. Compartment syndrome is treated by immobilizing and resting the limb and, if necessary, making an incision *(fasciotomy)* to relieve the compartment pressure.

In the limbs, fibrous sheets of connective tissue, the *fasciae,* enclose spaces called **compartments.** Each compartment contains one or more functionally related muscles along with their nerve and blood supplies (fig. 12.1). In the ensuing tables, you will find muscles of the upper limb divided into anterior and posterior compartments, and those of the lower limb divided into anterior, posterior, medial, and lateral compartments. These major compartments are separated from each other by especially thick fasciae called **intermuscular septa,** and by the interosseous membranes of the forearm and leg (see chapter 8). In most limb regions, the muscle groups are further subdivided by thinner fasciae into superficial and deep layers. A serious problem called *compartment syndrome,* occurring when one of the muscles or blood vessels in a compartment is injured, is due partly to the fact that the muscles are so tightly bound by their fasciae (see Insight 12.1).

The upper limb is used for a broad range of both powerful and subtle actions, ranging from climbing, grasping, and throwing to writing, playing musical instruments, and manipulating small objects. Tables 12.1 through 12.5 group these into muscles that act on the scapula, those that act on the humerus and shoulder joint, those that act on the forearm and elbow joint, extrinsic (forearm) muscles that act on the wrist and hand, and intrinsic (hand) muscles that act on the fingers.

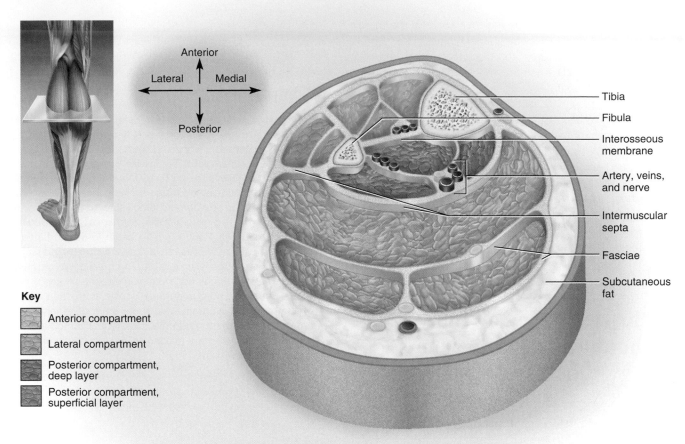

**Key**

- Anterior compartment
- Lateral compartment
- Posterior compartment, deep layer
- Posterior compartment, superficial layer

Anterior

Lateral ←→ Medial

Posterior

Tibia
Fibula
Interosseous membrane
Artery, veins, and nerve
Intermuscular septa
Fasciae
Subcutaneous fat

**Figure 12.1  Muscular Compartments.**  A cross section of the left leg slightly above midcalf, oriented the same way as the reader's.

---

| **TABLE 12.1** | **Muscles Acting on the Shoulder** |
|---|---|

Muscles that act on the pectoral girdle originate on the axial skeleton and insert on the clavicle and scapula. The scapula is only loosely attached to the thoracic cage and is capable of considerable movement (fig. 12.2)—rotation (as in raising and lowering the apex of the shoulder), elevation and depression (as in shrugging and lowering the shoulders), and protraction and retraction (pulling the shoulders forward and back). The clavicle braces the shoulder and moderates these movements.

**Anterior Group.**   Muscles of the pectoral girdle fall into anterior and posterior groups (fig. 12.3 in table 12.2). The major muscles of the anterior group are the *pectoralis minor* and *serratus anterior* (see fig. 11.13b, p. 314). The pectoralis minor arises by three heads from ribs 3 to 5 and converges on the coracoid process of the scapula. The serratus anterior arises from separate heads on all or nearly all of the ribs, wraps laterally around the chest and passes across the back between the rib cage and scapula, and inserts on the medial (vertebral) border of the scapula. Thus, when it contracts, the scapula glides laterally and slightly forward around the ribs.

**Pectoralis Minor (PECK-toe-RAY-liss)**   With serratus anterior, draws scapula laterally and forward around chest wall; with other muscles, rotates scapula and depresses apex of shoulder, as in reaching down to pick up a suitcase

|  **O:** Ribs 3–5 and overlying fascia | **I:** Coracoid process | **N:** Medial and lateral pectoral nn. |
|---|---|---|

**Serratus[1] Anterior (serr-AY-tus)**   With pectoralis minor, draws scapula laterally and forward around chest wall; protracts scapula, and is the prime mover in all forward-reaching and pushing actions; aids in rotating scapula to elevate apex of shoulder; fixes scapula during abduction of arm

|  **O:** All or nearly all ribs | **I:** Medial border of scapula | **N:** Long thoracic n. |
|---|---|---|

---

[1]*serrat* = scalloped, zigzag

**TABLE 12.1** | **Muscles Acting on the Shoulder (continued)**

**Lateral rotation**
Trapezius (superior part)
Serratus anterior

**Elevation**
Levator scapulae
Trapezius (superior part)
Rhomboideus major
Rhomboideus minor

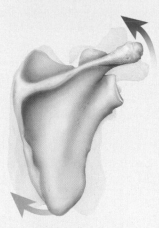
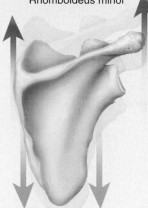

**Medial rotation**
Levator scapulae
Rhomboideus major
Rhomboideus minor

**Depression**
Trapezius (inferior part)
Serratus anterior

**Retraction**
Rhomboideus major
Rhomboideus minor
Trapezius

**Protraction**
Pectoralis minor
Serratus anterior

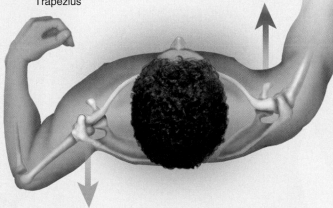

**Figure 12.2** Actions of Some Thoracic Muscles on the Scapula. Note that an individual muscle can contribute to multiple actions, depending on which fibers contract and what synergists act with it.

**Posterior Group.** The posterior muscles that act on the scapula include the large, superficial trapezius, already discussed (table 11.4), and three deep muscles: the *levator scapulae, rhomboideus minor,* and *rhomboideus major* (see fig. 11.14, p. 315). The action of the trapezius depends on whether its superior, middle, or inferior fibers contract and whether it acts alone or with other muscles. The levator scapulae and superior fibers of the trapezius rotate the scapula in opposite directions if either of them acts alone. If both act together, their opposite rotational effects balance each other and they elevate the scapula and shoulder, as when you lift a suitcase from the floor. Depression of the scapula occurs mainly by gravitational pull, but the trapezius and serratus anterior can depress it more rapidly and forcefully, as in swimming, hammering, and rowing.

**Trapezius (tra-PEE-zee-us)** Stabilizes scapula and shoulder during arm movements; elevates apex of shoulder; acts with other muscles to rotate and retract scapula. See also roles in head and neck movements in table 11.4.

**O:** External occipital protuberance, medial one-third of superior nuchal line, nuchal ligament, spinous processes of vertebrae C7–T3 or T4

**I:** Acromion and spine of scapula, lateral one-third of clavicle

**N:** Accessory n., ventral rami of C3–C4

**Levator Scapulae (leh-VAY-tur SCAP-you-lee)** Elevates scapula if cervical vertebrae are fixed; flexes neck laterally if scapula is fixed; retracts scapula and braces shoulder; rotates scapula and depresses apex of shoulder

**O:** Transverse processes of vertebrae C1–C4

**I:** Superior angle to medial border of scapula

**N:** C3–C4, and C5 via dorsal scapular n.

**Rhomboideus Minor (rom-BOY-dee-us)** Retracts scapula and braces shoulder; fixes scapula during arm movements

**O:** Spinous processes of vertebrae C7–T1, nuchal ligament

**I:** Medial border of scapula

**N:** Dorsal scapular n.

**Rhomboideus Major** Same as rhomboideus minor

**O:** Spinous processes of vertebrae T2–T5

**I:** Medial border of scapula

**N:** Dorsal scapular n.

327

## TABLE 12.2    Muscles Acting on the Arm

**Axial Muscles.**    Nine muscles cross the shoulder joint and insert on the humerus. Two are considered **axial muscles** because they originate primarily on the axial skeleton—the *pectoralis major* and *latissimus dorsi* (figs. 12.3 and 12.4). The pectoralis major is the thick, fleshy muscle of the mammary region, and the latissimus dorsi is a broad muscle of the back that extends from the waist to the axilla. These muscles bear the primary responsibility for attaching the arm to the trunk and are the prime movers of the shoulder joint.

**Pectoralis Major (PECK-toe-RAY-liss)**    Flexes, adducts, and medially rotates humerus, as in climbing or hugging. Aids in deep inspiration.

**O:** Medial half of clavicle, costal cartilages 1–7, aponeurosis of external oblique         **I:** Lateral lip of intertubercular sulcus of humerus         **N:** Medial and lateral pectoral nn.

**Latissimus Dorsi[2] (la-TISS-ih-mus DOR-sye)**    Adducts and medially rotates humerus; extends the shoulder joint as in pulling on the oars of a rowboat; produces backward swing of arm in such actions as walking and bowling. With hands grasping overhead objects, pulls body forward and upward, as in climbing. Aids in deep inspiration, sudden expiration such as sneezing and coughing, and prolonged forceful expiration as in singing or blowing a sustained note on a wind instrument.

**O:** Vertebrae T7–L5, lower three or four ribs, iliac crest, thoracolumbar fascia         **I:** Floor of intertubercular sulcus of humerus         **N:** Thoracodorsal n.

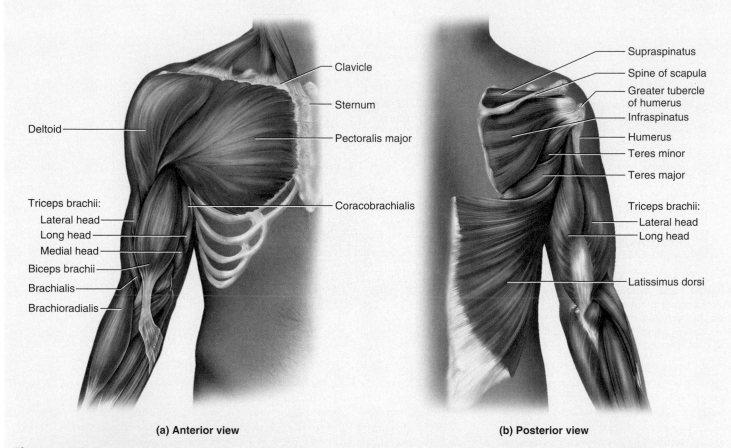

**(a) Anterior view**                    **(b) Posterior view**

**Figure 12.3** Pectoral and Brachial Muscles.  (a) Superficial muscles, anterior view. (b) Superficial muscles, posterior view (trapezius removed). (c) The biceps brachii, the superficial flexor of the elbow. (d) The brachialis, the deep flexor of the elbow, and the coracobrachialis and subscapularis, which act on the humerus.
• *What muscle serves as an antagonist of the pectoralis major?*

---

[2]*latissimus* = broadest + *dorsi* = of the back

| **TABLE 12.2** | **Muscles Acting on the Arm (continued)** |
|---|---|

**Scapular Muscles.**    The other seven muscles of the shoulder are considered **scapular muscles** because they originate on the scapula. Four of them form the rotator cuff and are treated in the next section. The most conspicuous scapular muscle is the *deltoid,* the thick, triangular muscle that caps the shoulder. This is a commonly used site for drug injections. Its anterior, lateral, and posterior fibers act like three different muscles.

**Deltoid**    Anterior fibers flex and medially rotate arm; lateral fibers abduct arm; posterior fibers extend and laterally rotate arm. Involved in arm swinging during such actions as walking or bowling and in adjustment of hand height for various manual tasks.

**O:** Acromion and spine of scapula; clavicle        **I:** Deltoid tuberosity of humerus        **N:** Axillary n.

**Teres Major (TERR-eez)**    Extends and medially rotates humerus; contributes to arm swinging

**O:** Inferior angle of scapula        **I:** Medial lip of intertubercular sulcus of humerus        **N:** Lower subscapular n.

**Coracobrachialis (COR-uh-co-BRAY-kee-AL-iss)**    Flexes and medially rotates arm; resists deviation of arm from frontal plane during abduction

**O:** Coracoid process        **I:** Medial aspect of humeral shaft        **N:** Musculocutaneous n.

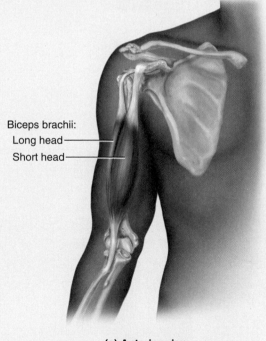

Biceps brachii:
Long head
Short head

**(c) Anterior view**

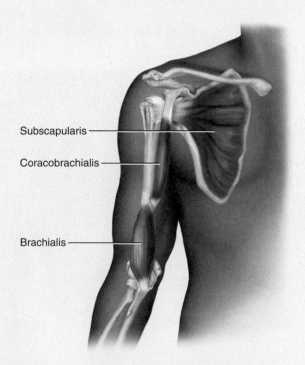

Subscapularis

Coracobrachialis

Brachialis

**(d) Anterior view**

### THINK ABOUT IT

*Since a muscle can only pull on a bone, and not push, antagonistic muscles are needed to produce opposite actions at a joint. Reconcile this fact with the observation that the deltoid muscle both flexes and extends the shoulder.*

**TABLE 12.2**    **Muscles Acting on the Arm (continued)**

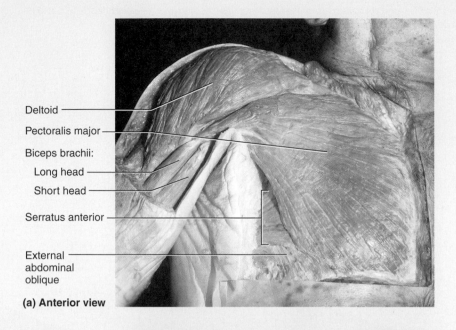

Deltoid

Pectoralis major

Biceps brachii:

Long head

Short head

Serratus anterior

External abdominal oblique

**(a) Anterior view**

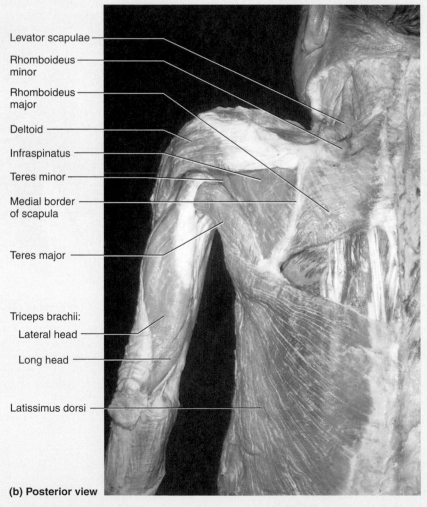

Levator scapulae

Rhomboideus minor

Rhomboideus major

Deltoid

Infraspinatus

Teres minor

Medial border of scapula

Teres major

Triceps brachii:

Lateral head

Long head

Latissimus dorsi

**(b) Posterior view**

**Figure 12.4** Pectoral and Brachial Muscles of the Cadaver.

| **TABLE 12.2** | **Muscles Acting on the Arm (continued)** |
| --- | --- |

**The Rotator Cuff.** Tendons of the remaining four scapular muscles form the **rotator cuff** (fig. 12.5). These muscles are nicknamed the "SITS muscles" for the first letters of their names—*supraspinatus, infraspinatus, teres minor,* and *subscapularis.* The first three muscles lie on the posterior side of the scapula (see fig. 12.3b). The supraspinatus and infraspinatus occupy the supraspinous and infraspinous fossae, above and below the scapular spine. The teres minor lies inferior to the infraspinatus. The subscapularis occupies the subscapular fossa on the anterior surface of the scapula, between the scapula and ribs (see fig. 12.3d). The tendons of these muscles merge with the joint capsule of the shoulder as they cross it en route to the humerus. They insert on the proximal end of the humerus, forming a partial sleeve around it. The rotator cuff reinforces the joint capsule and holds the head of the humerus in the glenoid cavity.

Rotator cuff injuries are common in sports and recreation. The tendon of the supraspinatus, especially, is easily damaged by strenuous circumduction (as in baseball pitching and bowling), falls (as in skiing), and hard blows from the side (as when a hockey player is slammed against the boards).

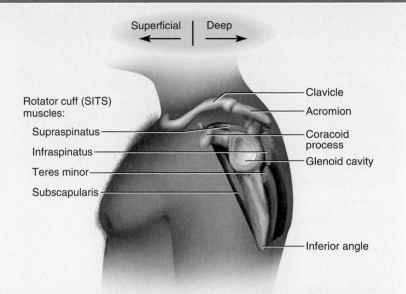

**Figure 12.5** **Rotator Cuff Muscles in Relation to the Scapula.** Lateral view. For posterior and anterior views of these muscles, see figure 12.3b, d.

**Supraspinatus[3] (SOO-pra-spy-NAY-tus)**   Aids deltoid in abduction of arm; resists downward slippage of humeral head when arm is relaxed or when carrying weight

| **O:** Supraspinous fossa of scapula | **I:** Greater tubercle of humerus | **N:** Suprascapular n. |
| --- | --- | --- |

**Infraspinatus[4] (IN-fra-spy-NAY-tus)**   Modulates action of deltoid, preventing humeral head from sliding upward; rotates humerus laterally

| **O:** Infraspinous fossa of scapula | **I:** Greater tubercle of humerus | **N:** Suprascapular n. |
| --- | --- | --- |

**Teres Minor (TERR-eez)**   Modulates action of deltoid, preventing humeral head from sliding upward as arm is abducted; rotates humerus laterally

| **O:** Lateral border and adjacent posterior surface of scapula | **I:** Greater tubercle of humerus; posterior surface of joint capsule | **N:** Axillary n. |
| --- | --- | --- |

**Subscapularis[5] (SUB-SCAP-you-LERR-iss)**   Modulates action of deltoid, preventing humeral head from sliding upward as arm is abducted; rotates humerus medially

| **O:** Subscapular fossa of scapula | **I:** Lesser tubercle of humerus, anterior surface of joint capsule | **N:** Upper and lower subscapular nn. |
| --- | --- | --- |

## INSIGHT 12.2

### Evolutionary Medicine

## Evolution of Limb Muscles

We can get deeper insights into human muscle functions by comparing our own muscles with those of other animals. The deltoid is a strong and prominent muscle in all hominoids (apes and humans). In its role as an abductor, it raises the arm above the shoulder—an action that a four-legged animal (quadruped) such as a horse or dog cannot perform. We take advantage of this whenever we reach for something on a high shelf or reach up for a handhold while climbing a ladder or rock wall. It is vitally important to monkeys and apes for climbing trees and swinging from overhead limbs.

The latissimus dorsi is another important muscle in climbing. We use this to pull the body up, as in rock climbing or performing pull-ups, and we condition it with "lat pulldown" exercises in fitness centers. In quadrupedal mammals, the latissimus dorsi binds the humerus to the trunk and produces a powerful backward thrust of the forelimb during walking and running.

---

[3]*supra* = above + *spin* = spine of scapula
[4]*infra* = below, under + *spin* = spine of scapula
[5]*sub* = below, under

| TABLE 12.3 | Muscles Acting on the Forearm |
|---|---|

The elbow and forearm are capable of four motions—flexion, extension, pronation, and supination—carried out by muscles in both the brachium and antebrachium (arm and forearm).

**Muscles with Bellies in the Arm (Brachium).** The principal elbow flexors are in the anterior compartment of the arm—the biceps brachii and brachialis (see fig. 12.3c, d). The *biceps brachii* appears as a large anterior bulge and commands considerable interest among bodybuilders, but the *brachialis* underlying it generates about 50% more power and is thus the prime mover of elbow flexion. The biceps is not only a flexor but also a powerful forearm supinator. It is named for its two heads: a *short head* whose tendon arises from the coracoid process of the scapula, and a *long head* whose tendon originates on the superior margin of the glenoid cavity, loops over the shoulder, and braces the humerus against the glenoid cavity (see p. 251). The two heads converge close to the elbow on a single distal tendon that inserts on the radius and on the fascia of the medial side of the upper forearm. Note that *biceps* is the singular term; there is no such word as *bicep*. To refer to the biceps muscles of both arms, the plural is *bicipites* (by-SIP-ih-teez).

The *triceps brachii* is a three-headed muscle in the posterior compartment and is the prime mover of elbow extension (see fig. 12.3b).

**Brachialis (BRAY-kee-AL-iss)** Prime mover of elbow flexion

| | | |
|---|---|---|
| **O:** Anterior surface of distal half of humerus | **I:** Coronoid process and tuberosity of ulna | **N:** Musculocutaneous n., radial n. |

**Biceps Brachii (BY-seps BRAY-kee-eye)** Rapid or forceful supination of forearm; synergist in elbow flexion; slight shoulder flexion; tendon of long head stabilizes shoulder by holding humeral head against glenoid cavity

| | | |
|---|---|---|
| **O:** Long head: superior margin of glenoid cavity<br>Short head: coracoid process | **I:** Tuberosity of radius, fascia of forearm | **N:** Musculocutaneous n. |

**Triceps Brachii (TRI-seps BRAY-kee-eye)** Extends elbow; long head extends and adducts humerus

| | | |
|---|---|---|
| **O:** Long head: inferior margin of glenoid cavity and joint capsule<br>Lateral head: posterior surface of proximal end of humerus<br>Medial head: posterior surface of entire humeral shaft | **I:** Olecranon, fascia of forearm | **N:** Radial n. |

**Muscles with Bellies in the Forearm (Antebrachium).** Most forearm muscles act on the wrist and hand, but two of them are synergists in elbow flexion and extension, and three of them function in pronation and supination. The *brachioradialis* is the large fleshy mass of the lateral (radial) side of the forearm just distal to the elbow (see figs. 12.3a and 12.7a). Its origin is on the distal end of the humerus and its insertion on the distal end of the radius. With the insertion so far from the fulcrum of the elbow, it does not generate as much force as the brachialis and biceps; it is effective mainly when those muscles have already partially flexed the elbow. The *anconeus* is a weak synergist of elbow extension on the posterior side of the elbow (see fig. 12.7e). Pronation is achieved by the *pronator quadratus* (the prime mover) near the wrist and the *pronator teres* near the elbow. Supination is usually achieved by the *supinator* of the upper forearm, with the biceps brachii aiding when additional speed or power is required (fig. 12.6).

**Brachioradialis (BRAY-kee-oh-RAY-dee-AL-iss)** Flexes elbow

| | | |
|---|---|---|
| **O:** Lateral supracondylar ridge of humerus | **I:** Lateral surface of radius near styloid process | **N:** Radial n. |

**Anconeus[6] (an-CO-nee-us)** Extends elbow; may help to control ulnar movement during pronation

| | | |
|---|---|---|
| **O:** Lateral epicondyle of humerus | **I:** Olecranon and posterior surface of ulna | **N:** Radial n. |

**Pronator Quadratus (PRO-nay-tur quad-RAY-tus)** Prime mover of forearm pronation; also resists separation of radius and ulna when force is applied to forearm through wrist, as in doing push-ups

| | | |
|---|---|---|
| **O:** Anterior surface of distal ulna | **I:** Anterior surface of distal radius | **N:** Median n. |

**Pronator Teres (PRO-nay-tur TERR-eez)** Assists pronator quadratus in pronation, but only in rapid or forceful action; weakly flexes elbow

| | | |
|---|---|---|
| **O:** Humeral shaft near medial epicondyle; coronoid process of ulna | **I:** Lateral surface of radial shaft | **N:** Median n. |

**Supinator (SOO-pih-NAY-tur)** Supinates forearm

| | | |
|---|---|---|
| **O:** Lateral epicondyle of humerus; supinator crest and fossa of ulna just distal to radial notch; anular and radial collateral ligaments of elbow | **I:** Proximal one-third of radius | **N:** Posterior interosseous n. |

---

[6]*anconeus* = elbow

| TABLE 12.3 | Muscles Acting on the Forearm (continued) |
|---|---|

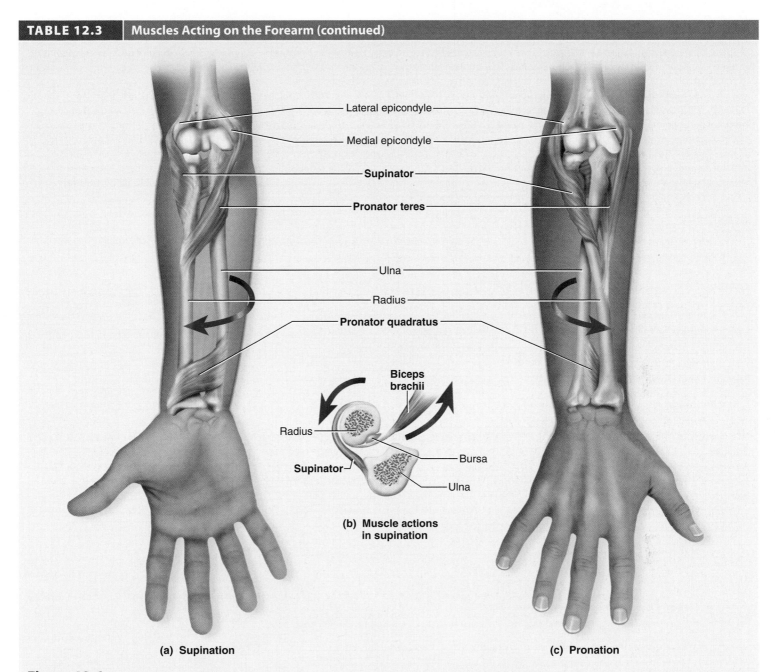

**Figure 12.6** **Actions of the Rotator Muscles on the Forearm.** (a) Supination. (b) Cross section just distal to the elbow, showing the synergistic action of the biceps brachii and supinator. (c) Pronation.

● *What do the names of the pronator teres and pronator quadratus indicate about their shapes?*

## TABLE 12.4 | Muscles Acting on the Wrist and Hand

The hand is acted upon by extrinsic muscles in the forearm and intrinsic muscles in the hand itself. The bellies of the extrinsic muscles form the fleshy roundness of the upper forearm (along with the brachioradialis, table 12.3), with their tendons extending into the wrist and hand. Their actions are mainly flexion and extension of the wrist and digits, but also include radial and ulnar flexion, finger abduction and adduction, and thumb opposition. These muscles are numerous and complex, but their names often describe their location, appearance, and function.

Many of them act on the **metacarpophalangeal joints,** between the metacarpal bones of the hand and the proximal phalanges of the fingers, and the **interphalangeal joints,** between the proximal and middle or the middle and distal phalanges (or proximal–distal in the thumb, which has no middle phalanx). The metacarpophalangeal joints form the knuckles at the bases of the fingers, and the interphalangeal joints form the second and third knuckles. Some tendons cross multiple joints before inserting on a middle or distal phalanx, and can flex or extend all the joints they cross.

Most tendons of the extrinsic muscles pass under a fibrous, braceletlike sheet called the **flexor retinaculum** on the anterior side of the wrist or the **extensor retinaculum** on the posterior side. These ligaments prevent the tendons from standing up like taut bowstrings when the muscles contract. The **carpal tunnel** is a tight space between the flexor retinaculum and carpal bones. The flexor tendons passing through the tunnel are enclosed in tendon sheaths that enable them to slide back and forth quite easily, although this region is very subject to painful inflammation—*carpal tunnel syndrome*—resulting from repetitive motion (see Insight 12.3 and fig. 12.9).

Fasciae divide the forearm muscles into anterior and posterior compartments and each compartment into superficial and deep layers (fig. 12.7). The muscles will be described in these four groups.

**Anterior (Flexor) Compartment, Superficial Layer.**   Most muscles of the anterior compartment are wrist and finger flexors that arise from a common tendon on the humerus (fig. 12.8a, b). At the distal end, the tendon of the *palmaris longus* passes over the flexor retinaculum, whereas the other tendons pass beneath it, through the carpal tunnel. The two prominent tendons you can palpate at the wrist belong to the palmaris longus on the medial side and the *flexor carpi radialis* on the lateral side (see fig. B.8a, p. 367). The latter is an important landmark for finding the radial artery, where the pulse is usually taken. The palmaris longus is absent on one or both sides (most commonly the left) in about 14% of people. To see if you have one, flex your wrist and touch the tips of your thumb and little finger together. If present, the palmaris longus tendon will stand up prominently on the wrist.

**Palmaris Longus (pal-MERR-iss)**   Anchors skin and fascia of palmar region; resists shearing forces when stress is applied to skin by such actions as climbing and tool use. Weakly developed and sometimes absent.

| | | |
|---|---|---|
| **O:** Medial epicondyle of humerus | **I:** Flexor retinaculum, palmar aponeurosis | **N:** Median n. |

**Flexor Carpi Radialis[7] (FLEX-ur CAR-pye RAY-dee-AL-iss)**   Flexes wrist; aids in radial flexion of wrist

| | | |
|---|---|---|
| **O:** Medial epicondyle of humerus | **I:** Base of metacarpals II–III | **N:** Median n. |

**Flexor Carpi Ulnaris[8] (ul-NAY-ris)**   Flexes wrist; aids in ulnar flexion of wrist

| | | |
|---|---|---|
| **O:** Medial epicondyle of humerus; medial margin of olecranon; posterior surface of ulna | **I:** Pisiform, hamate, metacarpal V | **N:** Ulnar n. |

**Flexor Digitorum Superficialis[9] (DIDJ-ih-TOE-rum SOO-per-FISH-ee-AY-lis)**   Flexes wrist, metacarpophalangeal, and interphalangeal joints depending on action of other muscles

| | | |
|---|---|---|
| **O:** Medial epicondyle of humerus; ulnar collateral ligament; coronoid process; superior half of radius | **I:** Middle phalanges II–V | **N:** Median n. |

**Anterior (Flexor) Compartment, Deep Layer.**   The following two flexors constitute the deep layer (fig. 12.8c). The *flexor digitorum profundus* flexes fingers II–V, but the thumb (pollex) has a flexor of its own—one of several muscles serving exclusively for thumb movements.

**Flexor Digitorum Profundus[10]**   Flexes wrist and metacarpophalangeal and interphalangeal joints of digits II–V; sole flexor of the distal interphalangeal joints

| | | |
|---|---|---|
| **O:** Proximal three-quarters of ulna; coronoid process; interosseous membrane | **I:** Distal phalanges II–V | **N:** Median n., ulnar n. |

**Flexor Pollicis[11] Longus (PAHL-ih-sis)**   Flexes phalanges of thumb

| | | |
|---|---|---|
| **O:** Radius, interosseous membrane | **I:** Distal phalanx I | **N:** Median n. |

---

[7]*carpi* = of the wrist + *radialis* = of the radius
[8]*carpi* = of the wrist + *ulnaris* = of the ulna
[9]*digitorum* = of the digits + *superficialis* = shallow, near the surface
[10]*digitorum* = of the digits + *profundus* = deep
[11]*pollicis* = of the thumb (pollex)

**TABLE 12.4** Muscles Acting on the Wrist and Hand (continued)

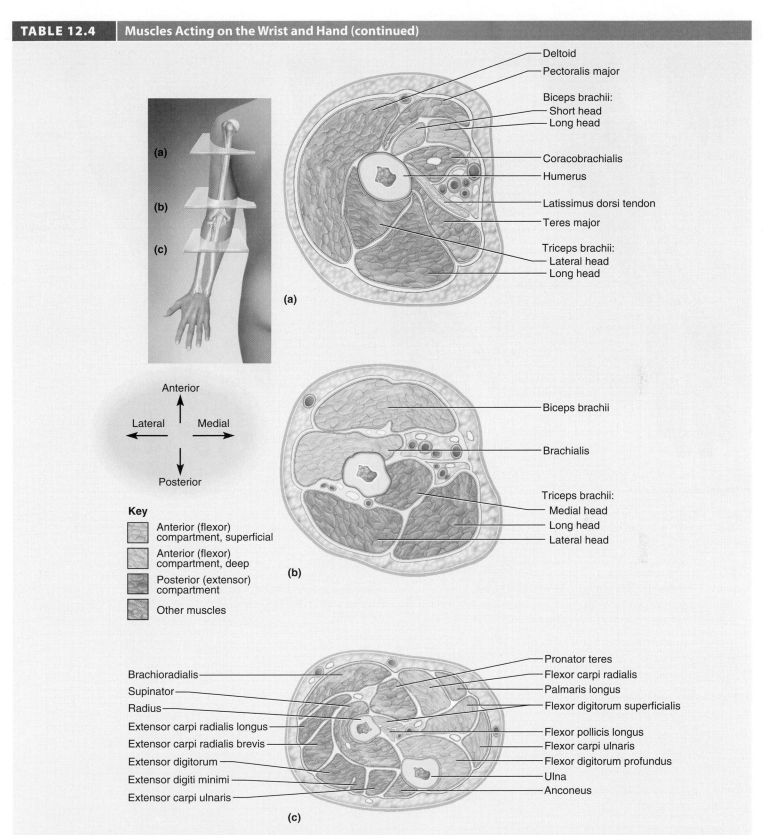

Key

- Anterior (flexor) compartment, superficial
- Anterior (flexor) compartment, deep
- Posterior (extensor) compartment
- Other muscles

**Figure 12.7** **Serial Cross Sections Through the Upper Limb.** Each section is taken at the correspondingly lettered level in the figure at the left and is pictured with the posterior muscle compartment facing the bottom of the page.

● *Why are the extensor pollicis longus and extensor indicis not seen in part (c)?*

**TABLE 12.4** Muscles Acting on the Wrist and Hand (continued)

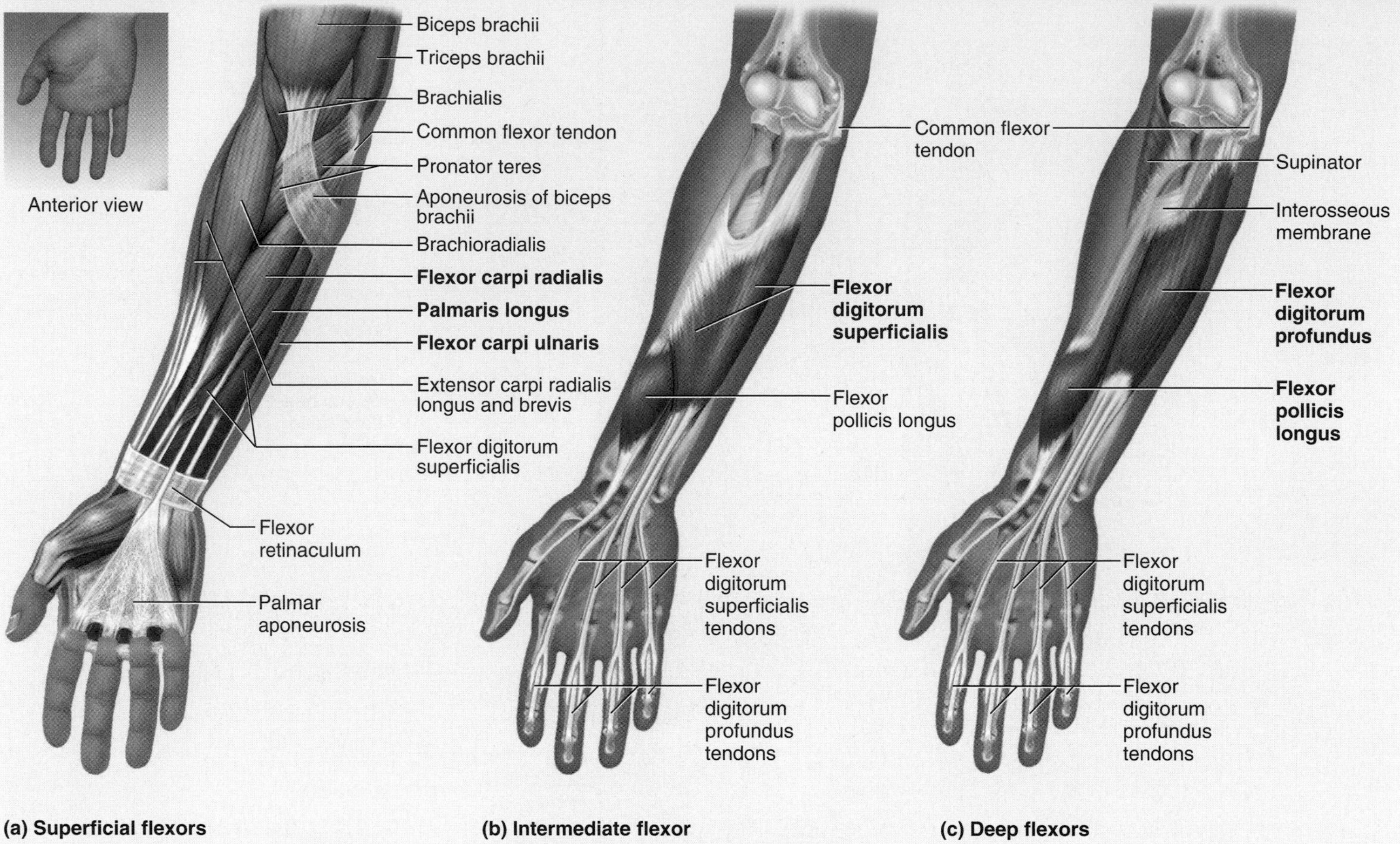

Anterior view

- Biceps brachii
- Triceps brachii
- Brachialis
- Common flexor tendon
- Pronator teres
- Aponeurosis of biceps brachii
- Brachioradialis
- **Flexor carpi radialis**
- **Palmaris longus**
- **Flexor carpi ulnaris**
- Extensor carpi radialis longus and brevis
- Flexor digitorum superficialis
- Flexor retinaculum
- Palmar aponeurosis

**(a) Superficial flexors**

- Common flexor tendon
- **Flexor digitorum superficialis**
- Flexor pollicis longus
- Flexor digitorum superficialis tendons
- Flexor digitorum profundus tendons

**(b) Intermediate flexor**

- Supinator
- Interosseous membrane
- **Flexor digitorum profundus**
- **Flexor pollicis longus**
- Flexor digitorum superficialis tendons
- Flexor digitorum profundus tendons

**(c) Deep flexors**

**Figure 12.8 Muscles of the Forearm.** Parts (a) to (c) are anterior views of the flexor muscles, and parts (d) and (e) are posterior views of the extensor muscles. Muscles labeled in boldface are (a) superficial flexors; (b) the flexor digitorum superficialis, deep to the muscles in (a) but also classified as a superficial flexor; (c) deep flexors; (d) superficial extensors; and (e) deep extensors.

**Posterior (Extensor) Compartment, Superficial Layer.** Muscles of the posterior compartment are mostly wrist and finger extensors and share a single tendon arising from the humerus (fig. 12.8d). The first of these, the *extensor digitorum,* has four distal tendons that can easily be seen and palpated on the back of the hand when the fingers are strongly extended (see fig. B.8b, p. 367). It serves digits II through V, and the other muscles in this group each serve a single digit. From lateral to medial, these extensors are as follows.

**Extensor Carpi Radialis Longus** Extends wrist; aids in radial flexion of wrist

**O:** Lateral supracondylar ridge of humerus     **I:** Base of metacarpal II     **N:** Radial n.

**Extensor Carpi Radialis Brevis (BREV-iss)** Extends wrist; aids in radial flexion of wrist

**O:** Lateral epicondyle of humerus     **I:** Base of metacarpal III     **N:** Posterior interosseous n.

**Extensor Digitorum** Extends wrist and metacarpophalangeal and interphalangeal joints of digits II–V; tends to spread digits apart when extending metacarpophalangeal joints

**O:** Lateral epicondyle of humerus     **I:** Dorsal surfaces of phalanges II–V     **N:** Posterior interosseous n.

**Extensor Digiti Minimi[12] (DIDJ-ih-ty MIN-ih-my)** Extends wrist and all joints of little finger

**O:** Lateral epicondyle of humerus     **I:** Proximal phalanx V     **N:** Posterior interosseous n.

**Extensor Carpi Ulnaris** Extends and fixes wrist when fist is clenched or hand grips an object; aids in ulnar flexion of wrist

**O:** Lateral epicondyle of humerus; posterior surface of ulnar shaft     **I:** Base of metacarpal V     **N:** Posterior interosseous n.

[12]*digiti* = of the finger + *minim* = smallest

| TABLE 12.4 | Muscles Acting on the Wrist and Hand (continued) |
|---|---|

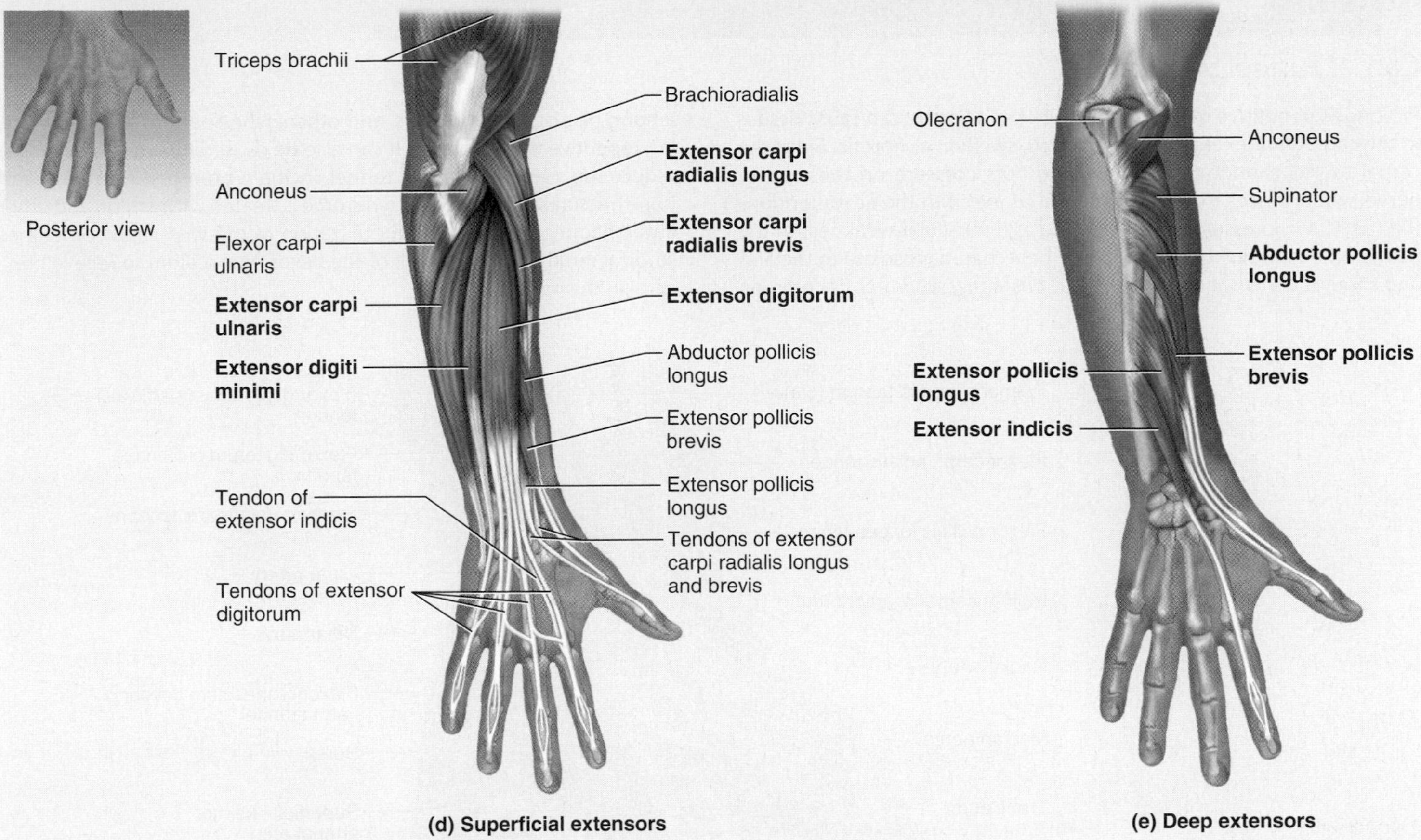

Posterior view

Triceps brachii
Anconeus
Flexor carpi ulnaris
**Extensor carpi ulnaris**
**Extensor digiti minimi**
Tendon of extensor indicis
Tendons of extensor digitorum

Brachioradialis
**Extensor carpi radialis longus**
**Extensor carpi radialis brevis**
**Extensor digitorum**
Abductor pollicis longus
Extensor pollicis brevis
Extensor pollicis longus
Tendons of extensor carpi radialis longus and brevis

**(d) Superficial extensors**

Olecranon
**Extensor pollicis longus**
**Extensor indicis**

Anconeus
Supinator
**Abductor pollicis longus**
**Extensor pollicis brevis**

**(e) Deep extensors**

**Posterior (Extensor) Compartment, Deep Layer.**   The deep muscles that follow serve only the thumb and index finger (fig. 12.8e). By strongly abducting and extending the thumb into a hitchhiker's position, you may see a deep dorsolateral pit at the base of the thumb, with a taut tendon on each side of it (see fig. B.8b, p. 367). This depression is called the *anatomical snuffbox* because it was once fashionable to place a pinch of snuff here and inhale it. It is bordered laterally by the tendons of the *abductor pollicis longus* and *extensor pollicis brevis,* and medially by the tendon of the *extensor pollicis longus.* These muscles from lateral to medial are as follows.

**Abductor Pollicis Longus**   Abducts thumb in frontal (palmar) plane (radial abduction); extends thumb at carpometacarpal joint

  **O:** Posterior surfaces of radius and ulna; interosseous membrane       **I:** Trapezium, base of metacarpal I       **N:** Posterior interosseous n.

**Extensor Pollicis Brevis**   Extends metacarpal I and proximal phalanx of thumb

  **O:** Shaft of radius,  interosseous membrane       **I:** Proximal phalanx I       **N:** Posterior interosseous n.

**Extensor Pollicis Longus**   Extends distal phalanx I; aids in extending proximal phalanx I and metacarpal I; adducts and laterally rotates thumb

  **O:** Posterior surface of ulna, interosseous membrane       **I:** Distal phalanx I       **N:** Posterior interosseous n.

**Extensor Indicis[13] (IN-dih-sis)**   Extends wrist and index finger

  **O:** Posterior surface of ulna, interosseous membrane       **I:** Middle and distal phalanges of index finger       **N:** Posterior interosseous n.

**THINK ABOUT IT**

*Why are the prime movers of finger extension and flexion located in the forearm rather than in the hand, closer to the fingers?*

[13]*indicis* = of the index finger

# INSIGHT 12.3

## Clinical Application

### Carpal Tunnel Syndrome

Prolonged, repetitive motions of the wrist and fingers can cause tissues in the carpal tunnel to become inflamed, swollen, or fibrotic. Since the carpal tunnel cannot expand, swelling puts pressure on the median nerve, which passes through the carpal tunnel with the flexor tendons (fig. 12.9). This pressure causes tingling and muscular weakness in the palm and lateral side of the hand and pain that may radiate to the arm and shoulder. This condition, called *carpal tunnel syndrome*, is common among pianists, meat cutters, and others who spend long hours making repetitive wrist motions. It can also be caused by other factors that reduce the size of the carpal tunnel, including tumors, infections, and bone fractures. Carpal tunnel syndrome is treated with aspirin and other anti-inflammatory drugs, immobilization of the wrist, and sometimes surgical removal of part or all of the flexor retinaculum to relieve pressure on the nerve.

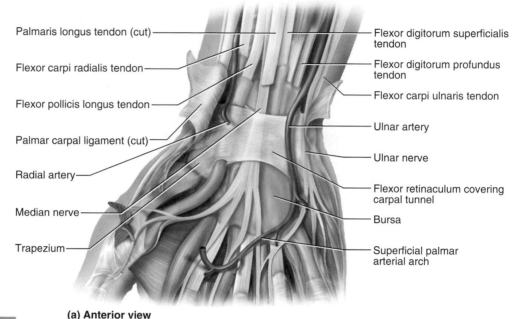

**(a) Anterior view**

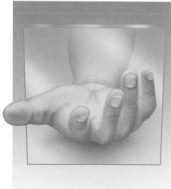

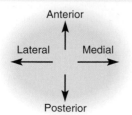

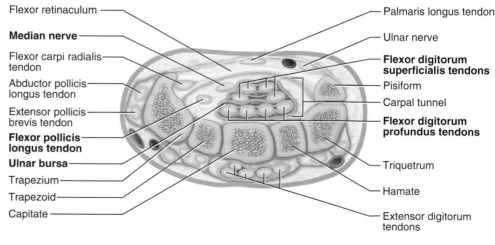

**(b) Cross section**

**Figure 12.9  The Carpal Tunnel.** (a) Dissection of the wrist (anterior aspect) showing the tendons, nerve, and bursae that pass under the flexor retinaculum. (b) Cross section of the wrist, viewed as if from the distal end of a person's right arm extended toward you with the palm up. Note how the flexor tendons and median nerve are confined in the tight space between the carpal bones and flexor retinaculum. That tight packing and repetitive sliding movements of the flexor tendons through the tunnel contribute to carpal tunnel syndrome.

**TABLE 12.5**   **Intrinsic Muscles of the Hand**

The intrinsic muscles of the hand assist the flexors and extensors in the forearm and make finger movements more precise. They are divided into three groups: the *thenar group* at the base of the thumb, the *hypothenar group* at the base of the little finger, and the *midpalmar group* between these (fig. 12.10).

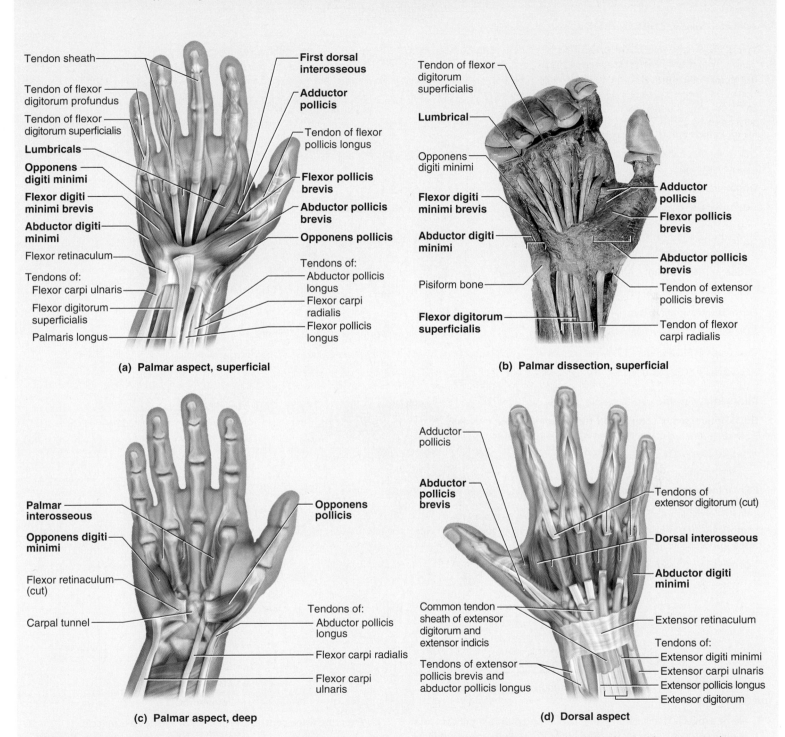

(a) **Palmar aspect, superficial**

(b) **Palmar dissection, superficial**

(c) **Palmar aspect, deep**

(d) **Dorsal aspect**

**Figure 12.10  Intrinsic Muscles of the Hand.** The boldfaced labels in parts (a), (c), and (d) indicate the muscles that belong to the respective layers.

| TABLE 12.5 | Intrinsic Muscles of the Hand (continued) |
| --- | --- |

**Thenar[14] Group.**   The thenar group of muscles form the thick, fleshy mass *(thenar eminence)* at the base of the thumb, and the *adductor pollicis* forms the web between the thumb and palm. All are concerned with thumb movements. The adductor pollicis has an *oblique head* that extends from the capitate bone of the wrist to the ulnar side of the base of the thumb, and a *transverse head* that extends from metacarpal III to the same insertion as the oblique head.

**Adductor Pollicis**   Draws thumb toward palm as in gripping a tool

  **O:** Capitate; bases of metacarpals III; anterior ligaments of wrist; tendon sheath of flexor carpi radialis　　　**I:** Medial surface of base of proximal phalanx I　　　**N:** Ulnar n.

**Abductor Pollicis Brevis**   Abducts thumb in sagittal plane

  **O:** Mainly flexor retinaculum; also scaphoid, trapezium, and abductor pollicis longus tendon　　　**I:** Lateral surface of proximal phalanx I　　　**N:** Median n.

**Flexor Pollicis Brevis**   Flexes metacarpophalangeal joint of thumb

  **O:** Trapezium, trapezoid, capitate, anterior ligaments of wrist, flexor retinaculum　　　**I:** Proximal phalanx I　　　**N:** Median n., ulnar n.

**Opponens Pollicis (op-PO-nenz)**   Flexes metacarpal I to oppose thumb to fingertips

  **O:** Trapezium, flexor retinaculum　　　**I:** Metacarpal I　　　**N:** Median n.

**Hypothenar Group.**   The hypothenar group forms the fleshy mass *(hypothenar eminence)* at the base of the little finger. All of these muscles are concerned with movement of that digit.

**Abductor Digiti Minimi**   Abducts little finger, as in spreading fingers apart

  **O:** Pisiform, tendon of flexor carpi ulnaris　　　**I:** Medial surface of proximal phalanx V　　　**N:** Ulnar n.

**Flexor Digiti Minimi Brevis**   Flexes little finger at metacarpophalangeal joint

  **O:** Hamulus of hamate bone, flexor retinaculum　　　**I:** Medial surface of proximal phalanx V　　　**N:** Ulnar n.

**Opponens Digiti Minimi**   Flexes metacarpal V at carpometacarpal joint when little finger is moved into opposition with tip of thumb; deepens palm of hand

  **O:** Hamulus of hamate bone, flexor retinaculum　　　**I:** Medial surface of metacarpal V　　　**N:** Ulnar n.

**Midpalmar Group.**   The midpalmar group occupies the hollow of the palm. It has 11 small muscles divided into three groups.

**Dorsal Interosseous[15] Muscles (IN-tur-OSS-ee-us) (four muscles)**   Abduct fingers; strongly flex metacarpophalangeal joints but extend interphalangeal joints, depending on action of other muscles; important for grip strength

  **O:** Each with two heads arising from facing surfaces of adjacent metacarpals　　　**I:** Proximal phalanges II–IV　　　**N:** Ulnar n.

**Palmar Interosseous Muscles (three muscles)**   Adduct fingers; other actions same as for dorsal interosseous muscles

  **O:** Metacarpals I, II, IV, V　　　**I:** Proximal phalanges II, IV, V　　　**N:** Ulnar n.

**Lumbricals[16] (LUM-brick-ulz) (four muscles)**   Extend interphalangeal joints; contribute to ability to pinch objects between fleshy pulp of thumb and finger, instead of these digits meeting by the edges of their nails

  **O:** Tendons of flexor digitorum profundus　　　**I:** Proximal phalanges II–V　　　**N:** Median n., ulnar n.

## Before You Go On

*Answer the following questions to test your understanding of the preceding section:*

1. Name a muscle that inserts on the scapula and plays a significant role in each of the following actions: (*a*) pushing a stalled car, (*b*) paddling a canoe, (*c*) squaring the shoulders in military attention, (*d*) lifting the shoulder to carry a heavy box on it, and (*e*) lowering the shoulder to grasp a suitcase handle.

2. Describe three contrasting actions of the deltoid muscle.

3. Name the four rotator cuff muscles and describe the scapular surfaces against which they lie.

4. Name the prime movers of elbow flexion and extension.

5. Identify three functions of the biceps brachii.

6. Name three extrinsic muscles and two intrinsic muscles that flex the phalanges.

---

[14]*thenar* = of the palm
[15]*inter* = between + *osse* = bones
[16]*lumbrical* = resembling an earthworm

# Muscles Acting on the Hip and Lower Limb

### Objectives

When you have completed this section, you should be able to

- name and locate the muscles that act on the hip, knee, ankle, and toe joints;
- relate the actions of these muscles to the joint movements described in chapter 9; and
- describe the origin, insertion, and innervation of each muscle.

The largest muscles are found in the lower limb. Unlike those of the upper limb, they are adapted less for precision than for the strength needed to stand, maintain balance, walk, and run. Several of them cross and act on two or more joints, such as the hip and knee. To avoid confusion in this discussion, remember that in the anatomical sense the word *leg* refers only to that part of the limb between the knee and ankle. The term *foot* includes the tarsal region (ankle), metatarsal region, and toes. Tables 12.6 through 12.9 group the muscles of the lower limb into those that act on the femur and hip joint, those that act on the leg and knee joint, extrinsic (leg) muscles that act on the foot and ankle joint, and intrinsic (foot) muscles that act on the arches and toes.

| TABLE 12.6 | Muscles Acting on the Hip and Thigh |
| --- | --- |

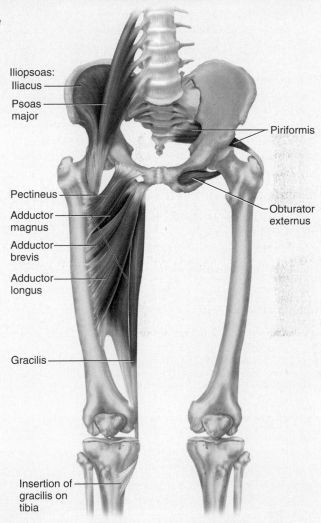

**Figure 12.11** Muscles That Act on the Hip and Femur. Anterior view.

**Anterior Muscles of the Hip.** Most muscles that act on the femur originate on the hip bone. The two principal anterior muscles are the *iliacus,* which fills most of the broad iliac fossa of the pelvis, and the *psoas major,* a thick rounded muscle that arises mainly from the lumbar vertebrae (fig. 12.11). Collectively, they are called the **iliopsoas** and share a common tendon to the femur.

**Iliacus[17] (ih-LY-uh-cus)** Flexes thigh at hip when trunk is fixed; flexes trunk at hip when thigh is fixed, as in bending forward in a chair or sitting up in bed; balances trunk during sitting

> **O:** Iliac crest and fossa, superolateral region of sacrum, anterior sacroiliac and iliolumbar ligaments  **I:** Lesser trochanter and nearby shaft of femur  **N:** Femoral n.

**Psoas[18] Major (SO-ass)** Same as iliacus

> **O:** Bodies and intervertebral discs of vertebrae T12–L5, transverse processes of lumbar vertebrae  **I:** Lesser trochanter and nearby shaft of femur  **N:** Ventral rami of lumbar spinal nn.

---

[17]*ili* = loin, flank
[18]*psoa* = loin

| **TABLE 12.6** | **Muscles Acting on the Hip and Thigh (continued)** |
|---|---|

**Lateral and Posterior Muscles of the Hip.**   On the lateral and posterior sides of the hip are the *tensor fasciae latae* and three gluteal muscles. The **fascia lata** is a fibrous sheath that encircles the thigh like a subcutaneous stocking and tightly binds its muscles. On the lateral surface, it combines with the tendons of the gluteus maximus and tensor fasciae latae to form the **iliotibial band,** which extends from the iliac crest to the lateral condyle of the tibia (see figs. 12.13 and 12.14). The tensor fasciae latae tautens the iliotibial band and braces the knee, especially when the opposite foot is lifted.

The gluteal muscles are the *gluteus maximus, gluteus medius,* and *gluteus minimus* (fig. 12.12). The gluteus maximus is the largest of these and forms most of the lean mass of the buttock. It is an extensor of the hip joint that produces the backswing of the leg in walking and provides most of the lift when you climb stairs. It generates its maximum force when the thigh is flexed at a 45° angle to the trunk. This is the advantage in starting a foot race from a crouched position. The gluteus medius is deep and lateral to the gluteus maximus. Its name refers to its size, not its position. The gluteus minimus is the smallest and deepest of the three.

**Tensor Fasciae Latae[19] (TEN-sur FASH-ee-ee LAY-tee)**   Extends knee, laterally rotates tibia, aids in abduction and medial rotation of femur; during standing, steadies pelvis on femoral head and steadies femoral condyles on tibia

|  |  |  |
|---|---|---|
| **O:** Iliac crest, anterior superior spine, deep surface of fascia lata | **I:** Lateral condyle of tibia via iliotibial band | **N:** Superior gluteal n. |

**Gluteus Maximus[20]**   Extends thigh at hip as in stair climbing (rising to next step) or running and walking (backswing of limb); abducts thigh; elevates trunk after stooping; prevents trunk from pitching forward during walking and running; helps stabilize femur on tibia

|  |  |  |
|---|---|---|
| **O:** Posterior gluteal line of ilium, on posterolateral surface from iliac crest to posterior superior spine; coccyx; dorsal surface of lower sacrum; aponeurosis of erector spinae | **I:** Gluteal tuberosity of femur; lateral condyle of tibia via iliotibial band | **N:** Inferior gluteal n. |

**Gluteus Medius and Gluteus Minimus**   Abduct and medially rotate thigh; during walking, shift weight of trunk toward limb with foot on the ground as other foot is lifted

|  |  |  |
|---|---|---|
| **O:** Most of lateral surface of ilium between crest and acetabulum | **I:** Greater trochanter of femur | **N:** Superior gluteal n. |

**Lateral Rotators.**   Inferior to the gluteus minimus and deep to the other two gluteal muscles are six muscles called the **lateral rotators,** named for their action on the femur (fig. 12.12). Their action is most clearly visualized when you cross your legs to rest an ankle on your knee, causing your femur to rotate and the knee to point laterally. Thus, they oppose medial rotation by the gluteus medius and minimus. Most of them also abduct or adduct the femur. The abductors are important in walking because when we lift one foot from the ground, they shift the body weight to other leg and prevent us from falling.

**Gemellus[21] Superior (jeh-MEL-us)**   Laterally rotates extended thigh; abducts flexed thigh. Sometimes absent.

|  |  |  |
|---|---|---|
| **O:** Ischial spine | **I:** Greater trochanter of femur | **N:** Nerve to obturator internus |

**Gemellus Inferior**   Same actions as gemellus superior

|  |  |  |
|---|---|---|
| **O:** Ischial tuberosity | **I:** Greater trochanter of femur | **N:** Nerve to quadratus femoris |

**Obturator[22] Externus (OB-too-RAY-tur)**   Not well understood; thought to laterally rotate thigh in climbing

|  |  |  |
|---|---|---|
| **O:** External surface of obturator membrane; pubic and ischial rami | **I:** Femur between head and greater trochanter | **N:** Obturator n. |

**Obturator Internus**   Not well understood; thought to laterally rotate extended thigh and abduct flexed thigh

|  |  |  |
|---|---|---|
| **O:** Ramus of ischium; inferior ramus of pubis; anteromedial surface of lesser pelvis | **I:** Greater trochanter of femur | **N:** Nerve to obturator internus |

**Piriformis[23] (PIR-ih-FOR-mis)**   Laterally rotates extended thigh; abducts flexed thigh

|  |  |  |
|---|---|---|
| **O:** Anterior surface of sacrum; gluteal surface of ilium; capsule of sacroiliac joint | **I:** Greater trochanter of femur | **N:** Spinal nn. L5–S2 |

**Quadratus Femoris[24] (quad-RAY-tus FEM-oh-ris)**   Laterally rotates thigh

|  |  |  |
|---|---|---|
| **O:** Ischial tuberosity | **I:** Intertrochanteric crest of femur | **N:** Nerve to quadratus femoris |

**Medial (Adductor) Compartment of the Thigh.**   Fasciae divide the thigh into three compartments: the *anterior (extensor) compartment, posterior (flexor) compartment,* and *medial (adductor) compartment.* Muscles of the anterior and posterior compartments function mainly as extensors and flexors of the knee, respectively, and are treated in table 12.7. The five muscles of the medial compartment act primarily as adductors of the thigh (see fig. 12.11), but some of them cross both the hip and knee joints and have additional actions as follows.

**Adductor Brevis**   Adducts thigh

|  |  |  |
|---|---|---|
| **O:** Body and inferior ramus of pubis | **I:** Linea aspera and spiral line of femur | **N:** Obturator n. |

**Adductor Longus**   Adducts and medially rotates thigh; flexes thigh at hip

|  |  |  |
|---|---|---|
| **O:** Body and inferior ramus of pubis | **I:** Linea aspera of femur | **N:** Obturator n. |

---

[19]*fasc* = band + *lat* = broad
[20]*glut* = buttock + *maxim* = largest
[21]*gemellus* = twin

[22]*obtur* = to close, stop up
[23]*piri* = pear + *form* = shaped
[24]*quadrat* = four-sided + *femoris* = of the thigh or femur

**TABLE 12.6** | **Muscles Acting on the Hip and Thigh (continued)**

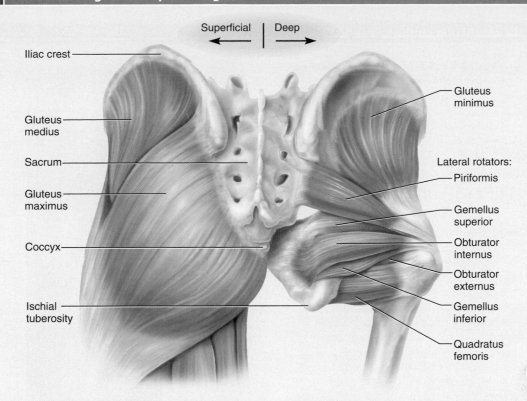

Superficial | Deep

Iliac crest

Gluteus medius

Sacrum

Gluteus maximus

Coccyx

Ischial tuberosity

Gluteus minimus

Lateral rotators:
Piriformis

Gemellus superior

Obturator internus

Obturator externus

Gemellus inferior

Quadratus femoris

**Figure 12.12 Gluteal Muscles.** Posterior view. Superficial muscles are shown on the left and deep muscles on the right.
• *Describe two everyday movements of the body that employ the power of the gluteus maximus.*

**Adductor Magnus**    Adducts and medially rotates thigh; extends thigh at hip

  **O:** Inferior ramus of pubis; ramus and tuberosity of ischium     **I:** Linea aspera, gluteal tuberosity, and medial supracondylar line of femur     **N:** Obturator n., tibial n.

**Gracilis[25] (GRASS-ih-lis)**    Flexes and medially rotates tibia at knee

  **O:** Body and inferior ramus of pubis; ramus of ischium     **I:** Medial surface of tibia just below condyle     **N:** Obturator n.

**Pectineus[26] (pec-TIN-ee-us)**    Flexes and adducts thigh

  **O:** Superior ramus of pubis     **I:** Spiral line of femur     **N:** Femoral n.

---

## INSIGHT 12.4

### Clinical Application

### Intramuscular Injections

Muscles with thick bellies are commonly used for intramuscular (I.M.) drug injections. Since drugs injected into these muscles are absorbed into the bloodstream gradually, it is safe to administer relatively large doses (up to 5 mL) that could be dangerous or even fatal if injected directly into the bloodstream. I.M. injections also cause less tissue irritation than subcutaneous injections.

Knowledge of subsurface anatomy is necessary to avoid damaging nerves or accidentally injecting a drug into a blood vessel. Anatomical knowledge also enables a clinician to position a patient so that the muscle is relaxed, making the injection less painful.

Amounts up to 2 mL are commonly injected into the deltoid muscle about two finger widths below the acromion. A misplaced injection into the deltoid can injure the axillary nerve and cause atrophy of the muscle. Drug doses over 2 mL are commonly injected into the gluteus medius, in the superolateral quadrant of the gluteal area, at a safe distance from the sciatic nerve and major gluteal blood vessels. Injections are often given to infants and young children in the vastus lateralis of the thigh, because their deltoid and gluteal muscles are not well developed.

---

[25]*gracil* = slender
[26]*pectin* = comb

**TABLE 12.7** | **Muscles Acting on the Knee and Leg**

**Figure 12.13** Anterior Superficial Thigh Muscles of the Cadaver. Left limb.

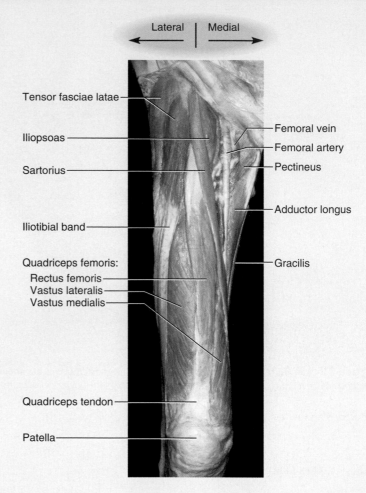

Lateral | Medial

Tensor fasciae latae

Iliopsoas

Sartorius

Iliotibial band

Quadriceps femoris:
Rectus femoris
Vastus lateralis
Vastus medialis

Quadriceps tendon

Patella

Femoral vein
Femoral artery
Pectineus

Adductor longus

Gracilis

The following muscles form most of the mass of the thigh and produce their most obvious actions on the knee joint. Some of them, however, cross both the hip and knee joints and produce actions at both, moving the femur, tibia, and fibula.

**Anterior (Extensor) Compartment of the Thigh.** The anterior compartment of the thigh contains the large *quadriceps femoris* muscle, the prime mover of knee extension and the most powerful muscle of the body (figs. 12.13 and 12.14; see also fig. 12.20). As the name implies, it has four heads: the *rectus femoris, vastus lateralis, vastus medialis,* and *vastus intermedius*. All four converge on a single **quadriceps (patellar) tendon,** which extends to the patella, then continues as the **patellar ligament** and inserts on the tibial tuberosity. (Remember that a tendon usually extends from muscle to bone, and a ligament from bone to bone.) The patellar ligament is struck with a rubber reflex hammer to test the knee-jerk reflex. The quadriceps extends the knee when you stand up, take a step, or kick a ball. One of its heads, the rectus femoris, contributes to running by acting with the ilopsoas to flex the hip in each airborne phase of the leg's cycle of motion. It also flexes the hip in such actions as high kicks, stair climbing, or simply in drawing the leg forward during a stride.

Crossing the quadriceps from the lateral side of the hip to the medial side of the knee is the narrow, straplike *sartorius,* the longest muscle of the body. It flexes the hip and knee joints and laterally rotates the thigh, as in crossing the legs. It is colloquially called the "tailor's muscle," after the cross-legged stance of a tailor supporting his work on the raised knee.

**Quadriceps Femoris (QUAD-rih-seps FEM-oh-ris)**   All heads insert on tibia through a common tendon and extend the knee, in addition to the actions of individual heads below.

**Rectus femoris**   Extends knee; flexes thigh at hip; flexes trunk on hip if thigh is fixed

| **O:** Ilium at anterior inferior spine and superior margin of acetabulum; capsule of hip joint | **I:** Patella, tibial tuberosity, lateral and medial condyles of tibia | **N:** Femoral n. |

**Vastus[27] lateralis**   Extends knee; retains patella in groove on femur during knee movements

| **O:** Femur at greater trochanter and intertrochanteric line, gluteal tuberosity, and linea aspera | **I:** Same as rectus femoris | **N:** Same as rectus femoris |

**Vastus medialis**   Same as vastus lateralis

| **O:** Femur at intertrochanteric line, spiral line, linea aspera, and medial supracondylar line | **I:** Same as rectus femoris | **N:** Same as rectus femoris |

**Vastus intermedius**   Extends knee

| **O:** Anterior and lateral surfaces of femoral shaft | **I:** Same as rectus femoris | **N:** Same as rectus femoris |

**Sartorius[28]**   Aids in knee and hip flexion, as in sitting or climbing; abducts and laterally rotates thigh

| **O:** On and near anterior superior spine of ilium | **I:** Medial surface of proximal end of tibia | **N:** Femoral n. |

[27]*vastus* = large, extensive
[28]*sartor* = tailor

**TABLE 12.7** | **Muscles Acting on the Knee and Leg (continued)**

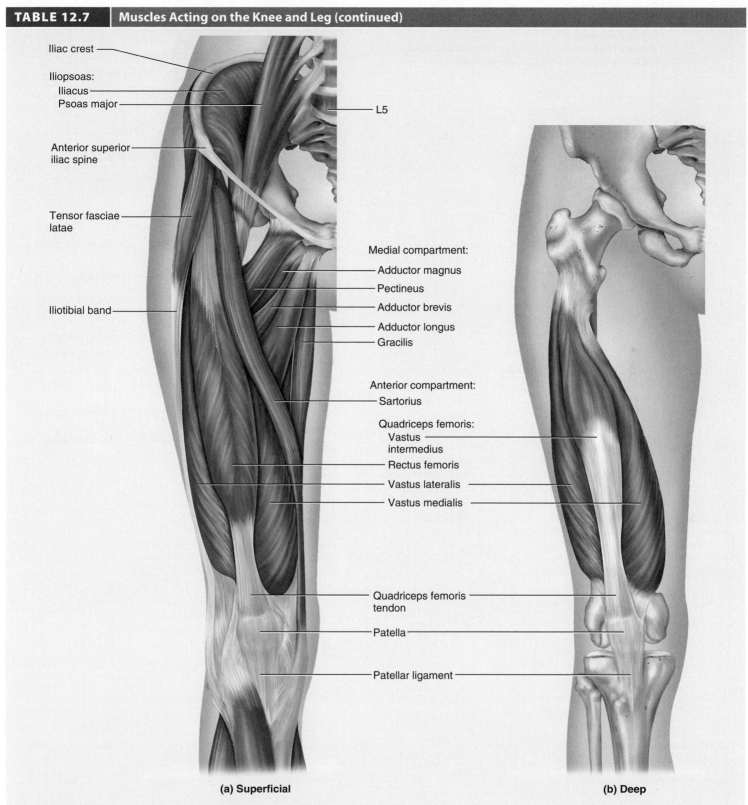

Iliac crest

Iliopsoas:
  Iliacus
  Psoas major

L5

Anterior superior
iliac spine

Tensor fasciae
latae

Iliotibial band

Medial compartment:
  Adductor magnus
  Pectineus
  Adductor brevis
  Adductor longus
  Gracilis

Anterior compartment:
  Sartorius

Quadriceps femoris:
  Vastus
  intermedius
  Rectus femoris
  Vastus lateralis
  Vastus medialis

Quadriceps femoris
tendon

Patella

Patellar ligament

**(a) Superficial**

**(b) Deep**

**Figure 12.14  Anterior Muscles of the Thigh.**  (a) Superficial muscles. (b) Rectus femoris and other muscles removed to expose the other three heads of the quadriceps femoris.

**TABLE 12.7** | **Muscles Acting on the Knee and Leg (continued)**

**Figure 12.15 Gluteal and Thigh Muscles.** Posterior view. The gluteus maximus is cut to expose the origins of the hamstring muscles.

● *Note the tendinous band that crosses the semitendinous muscle. Name another muscle that is subdivided by one or more transverse tendinous bands.*

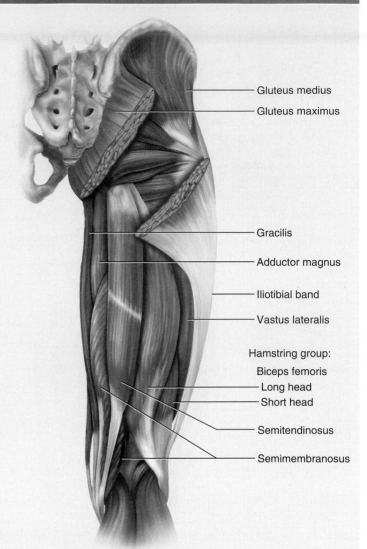

- Gluteus medius
- Gluteus maximus
- Gracilis
- Adductor magnus
- Iliotibial band
- Vastus lateralis
- Hamstring group:
- Biceps femoris
- Long head
- Short head
- Semitendinosus
- Semimembranosus

**Posterior (Flexor) Compartment of the Thigh.** The posterior compartment contains three muscles colloquially known as the **hamstring muscles;** from lateral to medial, they are the *biceps femoris, semitendinosus,* and *semimembranosus* (fig. 12.15). The pit at the back of the knee, known anatomically as the popliteal fossa, is colloquially called the *ham.* The tendons of these muscles can be felt as prominent cords on both sides of the pit—the biceps tendon on the lateral side and the semimembranosus and semitendinosus tendons on the medial side. When wolves attack large prey, they often attempt to sever the hamstring tendons, because this renders the prey helpless. The hamstrings flex the knee, and aided by the gluteus maximus, they extend the hip during walking and running. The semitendinosus is named for its unusually long tendon. This muscle also is usually bisected by a transverse or oblique tendinous band. The semimembranosus is named for the flat shape of its superior attachment.

**Biceps Femoris** Flexes knee; extends hip; elevates trunk from stooping posture; laterally rotates tibia on femur when knee is flexed; laterally rotates femur when hip is extended; counteracts forward bending at hips

| **O:** Long head: ischial tuberosity | **I:** Head of fibula | **N:** Tibial n., common |
| Short head: linea aspera and lateral supracondylar line of femur | | fibular n. |

**Semitendinosus[29] (SEM-ee-TEN-din-OH-sus)** Same as semimembranosus

| **O:** Ischial tuberosity | **I:** Medial surface of upper tibia | **N:** Tibial n. |

**Semimembranosus[30] (SEM-ee-MEM-bran-OH-sus)** Flexes knee; medially rotates tibia on femur when knee is flexed; medially rotates femur when hip is extended; counteracts forward bending at hips

| **O:** Ischial tuberosity | **I:** Medial condyle and nearby margin of tibia; intercondylar line and lateral condyle of femur; ligament of popliteal region | **N:** Tibial n. |

**Posterior Compartment of the Leg.** Most muscles in the posterior compartment of the leg act on the ankle and foot and are reviewed in table 12.8, but the popliteus acts on the knee (see fig. 12.18b).

**Popliteus[31] (pop-LIT-ee-us)** Rotates tibia medially on femur if femur is fixed (as in sitting), or rotates femur laterally on tibia if tibia is fixed (as in standing); unlocks knee to allow flexion; may prevent forward dislocation of femur during crouching

| **O:** Lateral condyle of femur; lateral meniscus and joint capsule | **I:** Posterior surface of upper tibia | **N:** Tibial n. |

---

[29]*semi* = half + *tendinosus* = tendinous
[30]*semi* = half + *membranosus* = membranous
[31]*poplit* = ham (pit) of the knee

# INSIGHT 12.5

## Clinical Application

### Hamstring Injuries

Hamstring injuries are common among sprinters, soccer players, and other athletes who depend on quick extension of the knee to kick or jump forcefully. Rapid knee extension stretches the hamstrings and often tears the proximal tendons where they originate on the ischial tuberosity. These muscle strains are excruciatingly painful. Hamstring injuries often result from failure to warm up adequately before competition or practice.

---

| TABLE 12.8 | Muscles Acting on the Foot |
|---|---|

The fleshy mass of the leg is formed by a group of **crural muscles,** which act on the foot (fig. 12.16). These muscles are tightly bound by fasciae which compress them and aid in the return of blood from the legs. The fasciae separate the crural muscles into anterior, lateral, and posterior compartments (see fig. 12.20b).

**Anterior (Extensor) Compartment of the Leg.**  Muscles of the anterior compartment dorsiflex the ankle and prevent the toes from scuffing the ground during walking. From lateral to medial, these muscles are the *fibularis tertius, extensor digitorum longus* (extensor of toes II–V), *extensor hallucis longus* (extensor of the great toe), and *tibialis anterior.* Their tendons are held tightly against the ankle and kept from bowing by two **extensor retinacula** similar to the one at the wrist (fig. 12.17).

**Fibularis (Peroneus[32]) Tertius[33] (FIB-you-LERR-iss TUR-she-us)**  Dorsiflexes and everts foot during walking, helps toes clear the ground during forward swing

| **O:** Medial surface of lower one-third of fibula, interosseous membrane | **I:** Metatarsal V | **N:** Deep fibular (peroneal) n. |
|---|---|---|

**Extensor Digitorum Longus (DIDJ-ih-TOE-rum)**  Extends toes II–V, dorsiflexes foot, tautens plantar aponeurosis

| **O:** Lateral condyle of tibia, shaft of fibula, interosseous membrane | **I:** Middle and distal phalanges II–V | **N:** Deep fibular (peroneal) n. |
|---|---|---|

**Extensor Hallucis Longus (ha-LOO-sis)**  Extends great toe, dorsiflexes foot

| **O:** Anterior surface of middle of fibula, interosseous membrane | **I:** Distal phalanx I | **N:** Deep fibular (peroneal) n. |
|---|---|---|

**Tibialis[34] Anterior (TIB-ee-AY-lis)**  Dorsiflexes and inverts foot; resists backward tipping of body (as when standing on a moving boat deck); helps support medial longitudinal arch of foot

| **O:** Lateral condyle and lateral margin of proximal half of tibia; interosseous membrane | **I:** Medial cuneiform, metatarsal I | **N:** Deep fibular (peroneal) n. |
|---|---|---|

**Posterior (Flexor) Compartment of the Leg, Superficial Group.**  The posterior compartment has superficial and deep muscle groups. The three muscles of the superficial group are plantar flexors: the *gastrocnemius, soleus,* and *plantaris* (fig. 12.18). The first two of these, collectively known as the *triceps surae,*[35] insert on the calcaneus by way of the **calcaneal (Achilles) tendon.** This is the strongest tendon of the body but is nevertheless a common site of sports injuries resulting from sudden stress. The plantaris, a weak synergist of the triceps surae, is a relatively unimportant muscle and is absent from many people; it is not tabulated here. Surgeons often use the plantaris tendon for tendon grafts needed in other parts of the body.

**Gastrocnemius[36] (GAS-trock-NEE-me-us)**  Plantar flexes foot, flexes knee; active in walking, running, and jumping

| **O:** Condyles and popliteal surface of femur, lateral supracondylar line, capsule of knee joint | **I:** Calcaneus | **N:** Tibial n. |
|---|---|---|

**Soleus[37] (SO-lee-us)**  Plantar flexes foot; steadies leg on ankle during standing

| **O:** Posterior surface of head and proximal one-fourth of fibula; middle one-third of tibia; interosseous membrane | **I:** Calcaneus | **N:** Tibial n. |
|---|---|---|

---

[32]*perone* = pinlike (fibula)
[33]*fibularis* = of the fibula + *tert* = third
[34]*tibialis* = of the tibia
[35]*sura* = calf of leg
[36]*gastro* = belly + *cnem* = leg
[37]Named for its resemblance to a flatfish (sole)

**TABLE 12.8**   **Muscles Acting on the Foot (continued)**

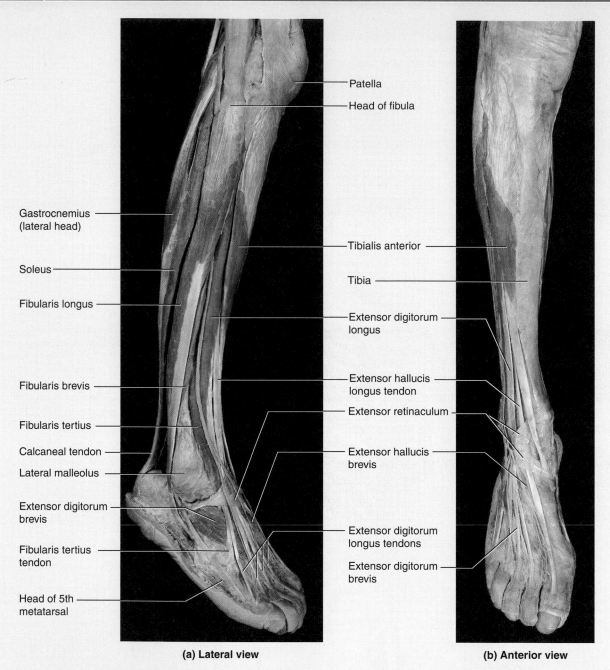

Patella
Head of fibula

Gastrocnemius (lateral head)

Soleus

Fibularis longus

Tibialis anterior

Tibia

Extensor digitorum longus

Fibularis brevis

Extensor hallucis longus tendon

Fibularis tertius

Extensor retinaculum

Calcaneal tendon

Lateral malleolus

Extensor hallucis brevis

Extensor digitorum brevis

Fibularis tertius tendon

Extensor digitorum longus tendons

Extensor digitorum brevis

Head of 5th metatarsal

(a) Lateral view

(b) Anterior view

**Figure 12.16** Superficial Crural Muscles. Right leg of the cadaver.

**THINK ABOUT IT**

*Not everyone has the same muscles. From the information provided in this chapter, identify two muscles that are lacking in some people.*

| TABLE 12.8 | Muscles Acting on the Foot (continued) |
|---|---|

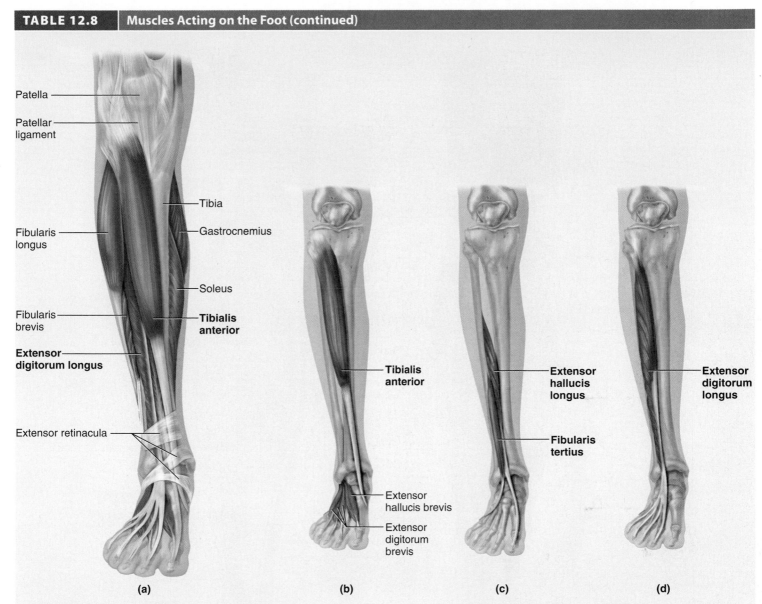

(a)     (b)     (c)     (d)

**Figure 12.17** **Muscles of the Leg, Anterior Compartment.** Boldface labels identify muscles belonging to the anterior compartment. (a) Superficial anterior view of the leg. Some muscles of the posterior and lateral compartments are also partially visible. (b–d) Individual muscles of the anterior compartment of the leg and dorsal aspect of the foot.

● *Palpate the hard anterior surface of your own tibia at midshaft, then continue medially until you feel muscle. What muscle is that?*

| TABLE 12.8 | Muscles Acting on the Foot (continued) |
|---|---|

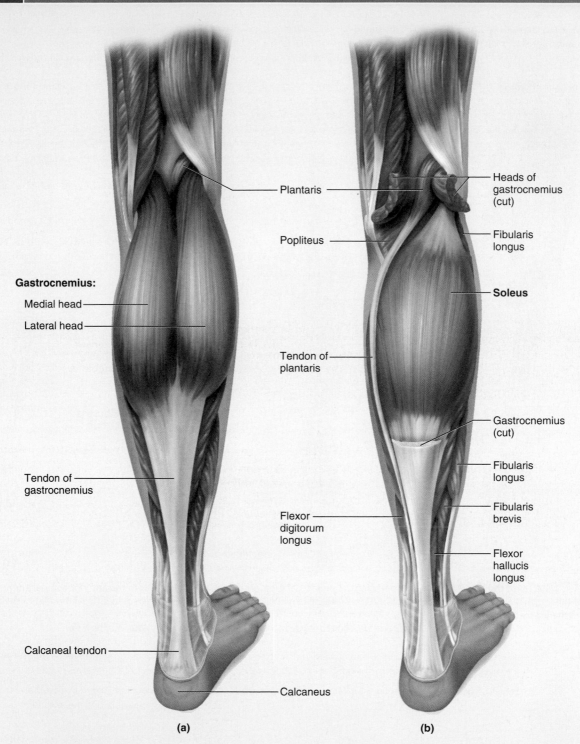

Plantaris

Popliteus

Gastrocnemius:

Medial head

Lateral head

Tendon of plantaris

Tendon of gastrocnemius

Calcaneal tendon

Calcaneus

Heads of gastrocnemius (cut)

Fibularis longus

Soleus

Gastrocnemius (cut)

Fibularis longus

Fibularis brevis

Flexor digitorum longus

Flexor hallucis longus

(a)    (b)

**Figure 12.18** **Superficial Muscles of the Leg, Posterior Compartment.** (a) The gastrocnemius. (b) The soleus, deep to the gastrocnemius and sharing the calcaneal tendon with it.

| TABLE 12.8 | Muscles Acting on the Foot (continued) |
|---|---|

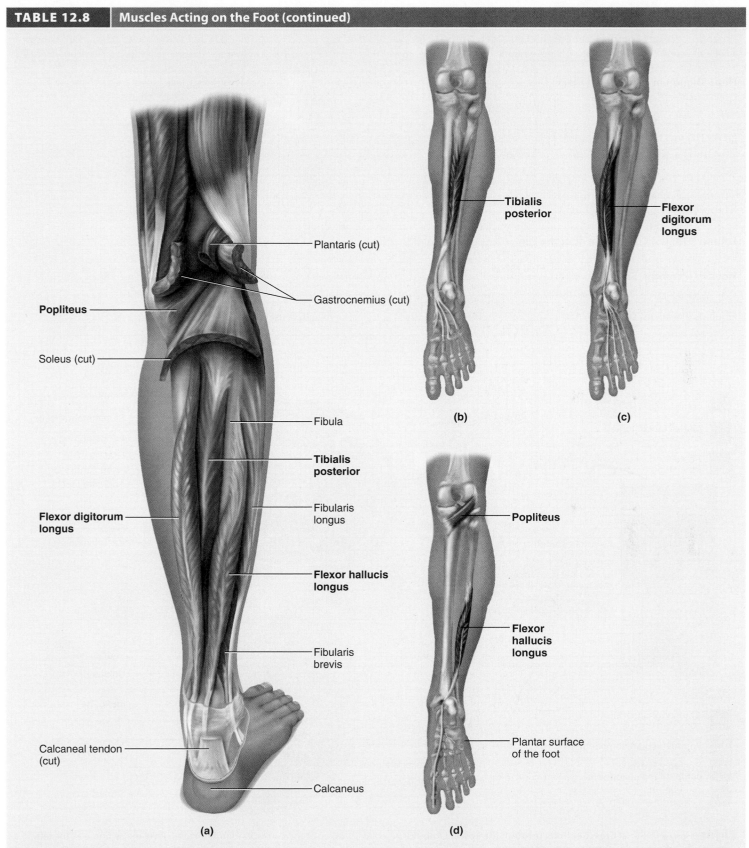

Plantaris (cut)

Gastrocnemius (cut)

**Popliteus**

Soleus (cut)

Fibula

**Tibialis posterior**

Fibularis longus

**Flexor digitorum longus**

**Flexor hallucis longus**

Fibularis brevis

Calcaneal tendon (cut)

Calcaneus

**(a)**

**Tibialis posterior**

**(b)**

**Flexor digitorum longus**

**(c)**

**Popliteus**

**Flexor hallucis longus**

Plantar surface of the foot

**(d)**

**Figure 12.19 Deep Muscles of the Leg, Posterior and Lateral Compartments.** (a) Muscles deep to the soleus. (b–d) Exposure of some individual deep muscles with the foot plantar flexed (sole facing viewer).

| **TABLE 12.8** | **Muscles Acting on the Foot (continued)** |
|---|---|

**Posterior (Flexor) Compartment of the Leg, Deep Group.**   There are four muscles in the deep group (fig. 12.19). The *flexor digitorum longus, flexor hallucis longus,* and *tibialis posterior* are plantar flexors. The fourth muscle, the *popliteus,* was described in table 12.7 because it acts on the knee rather than on the foot.

**Flexor Digitorum Longus**   Flexes phalanges of digits II–V as foot is raised from ground; stabilizes metatarsal heads and keeps distal pads of toes in contact with ground in toe-off and tiptoe movements

**O:** Posterior surface of tibial shaft     **I:** Distal phalanges II–V     **N:** Tibial n.

**Flexor Hallucis Longus**   Same actions as flexor digitorum longus, but for great toe (digit I)

**O:** Inferior two-thirds of fibula and interosseous membrane     **I:** Distal phalanx I     **N:** Tibial n.

**Tibialis Posterior**   Inverts foot; may assist in strong plantar flexion or control pronation of foot during walking

**O:** Posterior surface of proximal half of tibia, fibula, and interosseous membrane     **I:** Navicular, medial cuneiform, metatarsals II–IV     **N:** Tibial n.

**Lateral (Fibular) Compartment of the Leg.**   The lateral compartment includes the *fibularis brevis* and *fibularis longus* (figs. 12.16a, 12.17a, 12.20b). They plantar flex and evert the foot. Plantar flexion is important not only in standing on tiptoes but in providing lift and forward thrust each time you take a step.

**Fibularis (Peroneus) Brevis**   Maintains concavity of sole during toe-off and tiptoeing; may evert foot and limit inversion and help steady leg on foot

**O:** Lateral surface of distal two-thirds of fibula     **I:** Base of metatarsal V     **N:** Superficial fibular (peroneal) n.

**Fibularis (Peroneus) Longus**   Maintains concavity of sole during toe-off and tiptoeing; everts and plantar flexes foot

**O:** Head and lateral surface of proximal two-thirds of fibula     **I:** Medial cuneiform, metatarsal I     **N:** Superficial fibular (peroneal) n.

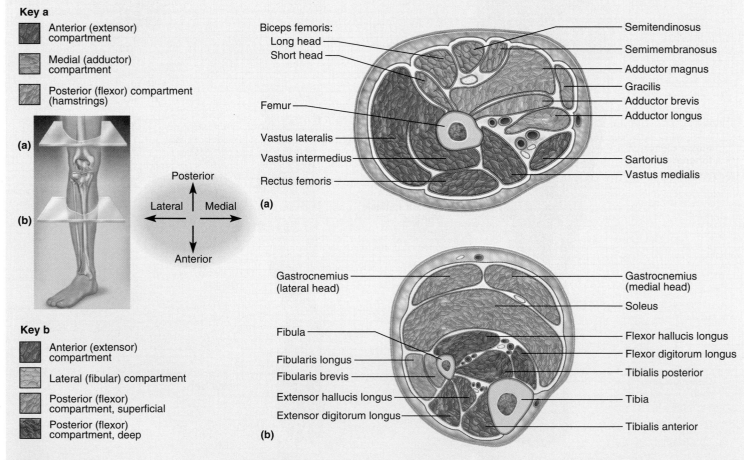

**Figure 12.20** Serial Cross Sections Through the Lower Limb.   Each section is taken at the correspondingly lettered level in the figure at the left.

| **TABLE 12.9** | **Intrinsic Muscles of the Foot** |
| --- | --- |

The intrinsic muscles of the foot help to support the arches and act on the toes in ways that aid locomotion. Several of them are similar in name and location to the intrinsic muscles of the hand.

**Dorsal Aspect of Foot.**   Only one of the intrinsic muscles, the *extensor digitorum brevis,* is on the dorsal side of the foot (see fig. 12.17b). The medial slip of this muscle, serving the great toe, is sometimes called the *extensor hallucis brevis.*

**Extensor Digitorum Brevis**   Extends proximal phalanx I and all phalanges of digits II–IV

| | | |
| --- | --- | --- |
| **O:** Calcaneus, inferior extensor retinaculum of ankle | **I:** Proximal phalanx I, tendons of extensor digitorum longus to digits II–IV | **N:** Deep fibular (peroneal) n. |

**Ventral Layer 1 (most superficial).**   All remaining intrinsic muscles are on the ventral aspect of the foot or between the metatarsal bones. They are grouped in four layers (fig. 12.21). Dissecting into the foot from the plantar surface, one first encounters a tough fibrous sheet, the **plantar aponeurosis,** between the skin and muscles. It diverges like a fan from the calcaneus to the bases of all the toes and serves as an origin for several ventral muscles. The ventral muscles include the stout *flexor digitorum brevis* on the midline of the foot, with four tendons that supply all digits except the hallux. It is flanked by the *abductor digiti minimi* laterally and the *abductor hallucis* medially.

**Flexor Digitorum Brevis**   Flexes digits II–IV; supports arches of foot

| | | |
| --- | --- | --- |
| **O:** Calcaneus, plantar aponeurosis | **I:** Middle phalanges II–V | **N:** Medial plantar n. |

**Abductor Digiti Minimi**[38]   Abducts and flexes little toe; supports arches of foot

| | | |
| --- | --- | --- |
| **O:** Calcaneus, plantar aponeurosis | **I:** Proximal phalanx V | **N:** Lateral plantar n. |

**Abductor Hallucis**   Abducts great toe; supports arches of foot

| | | |
| --- | --- | --- |
| **O:** Calcaneus, plantar aponeurosis, flexor retinaculum | **I:** Proximal phalanx I | **N:** Medial plantar n. |

**Ventral Layer 2.**   The next deeper layer consists of the thick *quadratus plantae* in the middle of the foot and the four *lumbrical muscles* located between the metatarsals (fig. 12.21b).

**Quadratus Plantae**[39] **(quad-RAY-tus PLAN-tee)**   Same as flexor digitorum longus (table 12.8); flexion of digits II–V and associated locomotor functions

| | | |
| --- | --- | --- |
| **O:** Two heads on the medial and lateral sides of calcaneus | **I:** Distal phalanges II–V via flexor digitorum longus tendons | **N:** Lateral plantar n. |

**Lumbricals (LUM-brick-ulz)**   Flex toes II–V

| | | |
| --- | --- | --- |
| **O:** Tendon of flexor digitorum longus | **I:** Proximal phalanges II–V | **N:** Lateral and medial plantar nn. |

**Ventral Layer 3.**   The muscles of this layer serve only the great and little toes (fig. 12.21c). They are the *flexor digiti minimi brevis, flexor hallucis brevis,* and *adductor hallucis.* The adductor hallucis has an *oblique head* that extends diagonally from the midplantar region to the base of the great toe, and a *transverse head* that passes across the bases of digits II–IV and meets the long head at the base of the great toe.

**Flexor Digiti Minimi Brevis**   Flexes little toe

| | | |
| --- | --- | --- |
| **O:** Metatarsal V, sheath of fibularis longus | **I:** Proximal phalanx V | **N:** Lateral plantar n. |

**Flexor Hallucis Brevis**   Flexes great toe

| | | |
| --- | --- | --- |
| **O:** Cuboid, lateral cuneiform, tibialis posterior tendon | **I:** Proximal phalanx I | **N:** Medial plantar n. |

**Adductor Hallucis**   Adducts great toe

| | | |
| --- | --- | --- |
| **O:** Metatarsals II–IV, fibularis longus tendon, ligaments at bases of digits III–V | **I:** Proximal phalanx I | **N:** Lateral plantar n. |

**Ventral Layer 4 (deepest).**   This layer consists only of the small interosseous muscles located between the metatarsal bones—four dorsal and three plantar (fig. 12.21d, e). Each dorsal interosseous muscle is bipennate and originates on two adjacent metatarsals. The plantar interosseous muscles are unipennate and originate on only one metatarsal each.

**Dorsal Interosseous Muscles (four muscles)**   Abduct toes II–IV

| | | |
| --- | --- | --- |
| **O:** Each with two heads arising from facing surfaces of two adjacent metatarsals | **I:** Proximal phalanges II–IV | **N:** Lateral plantar n. |

**Plantar Interosseous Muscles (three muscles)**   Adduct toes III–V

| | | |
| --- | --- | --- |
| **O:** Medial aspect of metatarsals III–V | **I:** Proximal phalanges III–V | **N:** Lateral plantar n. |

[38]*digiti* = of the toe + *minim* = smallest
[39]*quadrat* = four-sided + *plantae* = of the plantar region

**TABLE 12.9** Intrinsic Muscles of the Foot (continued)

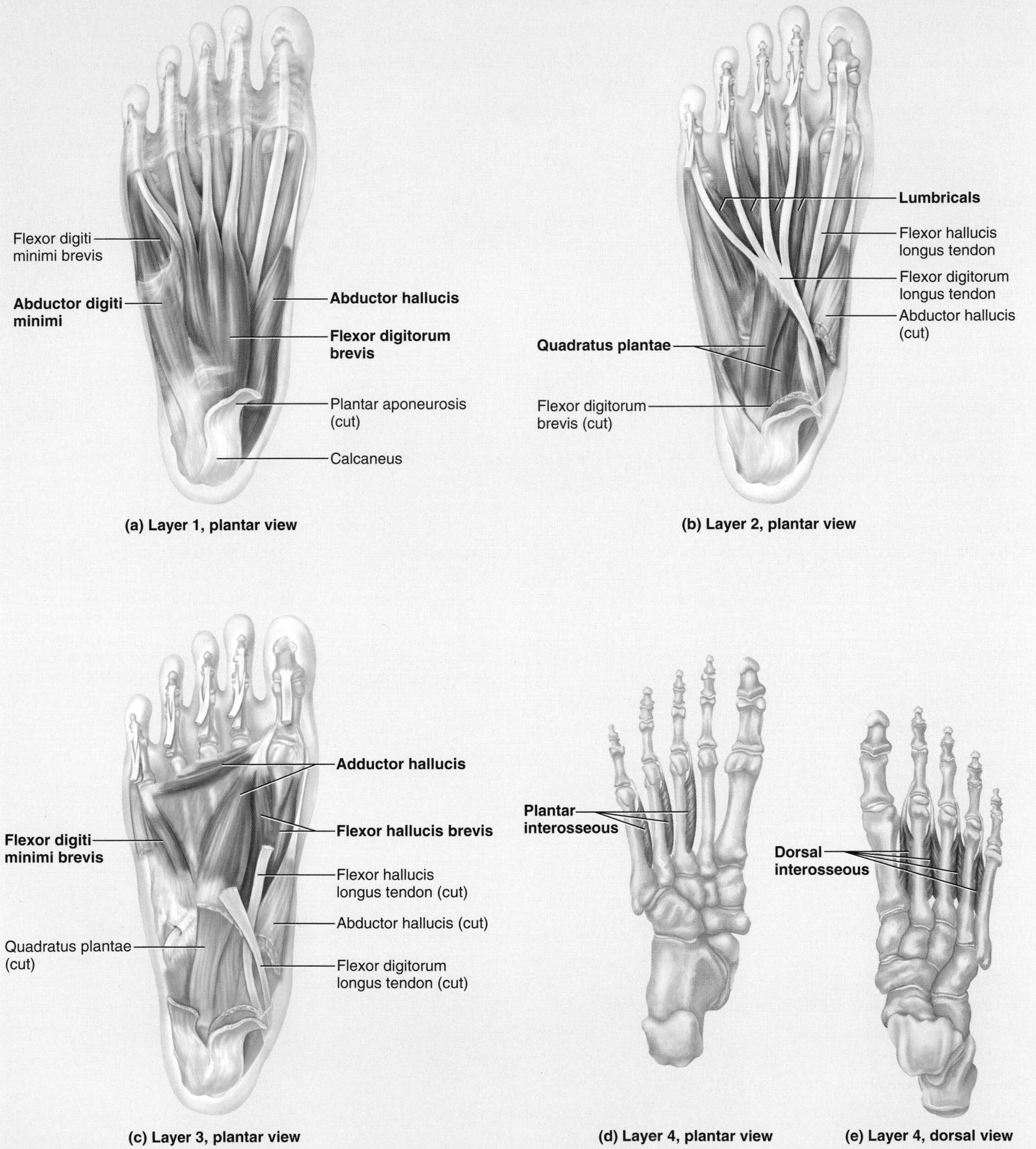

Flexor digiti minimi brevis

**Abductor digiti minimi**

**Abductor hallucis**

**Flexor digitorum brevis**

Plantar aponeurosis (cut)

Calcaneus

**(a) Layer 1, plantar view**

**Lumbricals**

Flexor hallucis longus tendon

Flexor digitorum longus tendon

Abductor hallucis (cut)

**Quadratus plantae**

Flexor digitorum brevis (cut)

**(b) Layer 2, plantar view**

**Adductor hallucis**

**Flexor hallucis brevis**

**Flexor digiti minimi brevis**

Flexor hallucis longus tendon (cut)

Abductor hallucis (cut)

Quadratus plantae (cut)

Flexor digitorum longus tendon (cut)

**(c) Layer 3, plantar view**

**Plantar interosseous**

**Dorsal interosseous**

**(d) Layer 4, plantar view**

**(e) Layer 4, dorsal view**

**Figure 12.21** **Intrinsic Muscles of the Foot.** (a–d) First through fourth layers, respectively, in ventral (plantar) views. (e) Fourth layer, dorsal view. The muscles belonging to each layer are shown in color and with boldface labels.

## *Before You Go On*

*Answer the following questions to test your understanding of the preceding section:*

7. In the middle of a stride, you have one foot on the ground and you are about to swing the other leg forward. What muscles produce the movements of that leg?

8. Name the muscles that cross both the hip and knee joints and produce actions at both.

9. List the major actions of the muscles of the anterior, medial, and posterior compartments of the thigh.

10. Describe the role of plantar flexion and dorsiflexion in walking. What muscles produce these actions?

# Muscle Injuries

### *Objectives*

When you have completed this section, you should be able to

- explain how to reduce the risk of muscle injuries; and

- define several types of muscle injuries often incurred in sports and recreation.

Although the muscular system suffers fewer diseases than most organ systems, it is particularly vulnerable to injuries resulting from sudden and intense stress placed on muscles and tendons. Each year, thousands of athletes from high school to professional level sustain some type of muscle injury, as do increasing numbers of people who have taken up running and other forms of physical conditioning. Overzealous exertion without proper preparation and warm-up is frequently the cause. Some of the most common athletic injuries are briefly described in table 12.10. (See table 10.5, p. 289, for more general disorders of the muscular system).

Most athletic injuries can be prevented by proper conditioning. A person who suddenly takes up vigorous exercise may not have sufficient muscle and bone mass to withstand the stresses such exercise entails. These must be developed gradually. Stretching exercises keep ligaments and joint capsules supple and therefore reduce injuries. Warm-up exercises promote more efficient and less injurious musculoskeletal function in several ways. Most of all, moderation is important, as most injuries simply result from overuse of the muscles. "No pain, no gain" is a dangerous misconception.

Muscular injuries can be treated initially with "RICE": **R**est to prevent further injury and allow repair to occur; **I**ce to reduce swelling; **C**ompression with an elastic bandage to prevent fluid accumulation and swelling; and **E**levation of an injured limb to promote drainage of blood from the affected area and limit further swelling. If these measures are not enough, anti-inflammatory drugs such as hydrocortisone and aspirin may be employed.

## *Before You Go On*

*Answer the following questions to test your understanding of the preceding section:*

11. Explain why stretching exercises may reduce the incidence of muscle injuries.

12. Explain the reason for each of the four treatments in the RICE approach to muscle injuries.

| TABLE 12.10 | Muscle Injuries |
|---|---|
| **Baseball finger** | Tears in the extensor tendons of the fingers resulting from the impact of a baseball with the extended fingertip |
| **Blocker's arm** | Abnormal calcification in the lateral margin of the forearm as a result of repeated impact such as occurs in football |
| **Pitcher's arm** | Inflammation at the origin of the wrist flexors resulting from hard wrist flexion in releasing a baseball |
| **Pulled groin** | Strain in the adductor muscles of the thigh; common in gymnasts and dancers who perform splits and high kicks |
| **Pulled hamstrings** | Strained hamstring muscles or a partial tear in the tendinous origin, often with a hematoma (blood clot) in the fascia lata; frequently caused by repetitive kicking (as in football and soccer) or long, hard running |
| **Rider's bones** | Calcification in the tendons of the thigh adductors; results from prolonged abduction of the thighs when riding horses |
| **Shinsplints** | General term for several kinds of injury with pain in the crural region—tendinitis of the tibialis posterior, inflammation of the tibial periosteum, and anterior compartment syndrome. May result from unaccustomed jogging, walk-a-thons, walking on snowshoes, or any vigorous activity of the legs after a period of inactivity |
| **Tennis elbow** | Inflammation at the origin of the extensor carpi muscles on the lateral epicondyle of the humerus occurs when these muscles are repeatedly tensed during backhand strokes and then strained by sudden impact with the tennis ball. Any activity that requires rotary movements of the forearm and a firm grip of the hand (for example, using a screwdriver) can cause the symptoms of tennis elbow. |
| **Tennis leg** | Partial tear in the lateral origin of the gastrocnemius; results from repeated strains put on the muscle while supporting the body weight on the toes |

### Disorders Described Elsewhere

# CHAPTER REVIEW

## REVIEW OF KEY CONCEPTS

### Muscles Acting on the Shoulder and Upper Limb (p. 325)

1. Muscles of the limbs are organized in functional groups contained in *compartments* set apart by interosseous membranes, intermuscular septa, and thinner fasciae. Within a compartment, muscle groups may also be separated by fasciae into superficial, deep, and sometimes more layers.

2. Muscles that act on the pectoral girdle originate on the axial skeleton and insert on the clavicle and scapula. They fall into an anterior group that includes the *pectoralis minor* and *serratus anterior,* and a posterior group that includes the superficial *trapezius* and three deeper muscles: the *levator scapulae, rhomboideus minor,* and *rhomboideus major* (table 12.1).

3. Muscles that act on the arm (humerus) originate mainly on the pectoral girdle and axial skeleton and cross the shoulder joint. These include the *pectoralis major, latissimus dorsi, deltoid, teres major, coracobrachialis,* and four *rotator cuff (SITS)* muscles: the *supraspinatus, infraspinatus, teres minor,* and *subscapularis* (table 12.2).

4. Muscles that act on the forearm and elbow are located in both the arm (the *biceps brachii, brachialis,* and *triceps brachii*) and the forearm (the *brachioradialis, anconeus, pronator quadratus, pronator teres,* and *supinator*) (table 12.3).

5. Most muscles whose origins and bellies are in the forearm have insertions in, and act on, the wrist and hand (table 12.4). Several of them, however, have origins on the humerus and also cross the elbow joint. Therefore, they also contribute slightly to actions of the elbow.

6. Anterior compartment muscles are mainly flexors of the wrist and hand. Most of their tendons pass under a *flexor retinaculum* on the anterior side of the wrist. The space between the flexor retinaculum and carpal bones is called the *carpal tunnel.*

7. Superficial muscles of the anterior compartment include the *palmaris longus* and *flexor carpi radialis,* which form the two most prominent tendons of the anterior wrist, and the *flexor carpi ulnaris* and *flexor digitorum superficialis.* The deep muscles of the anterior compartment include the *flexor digitorum profundus* and *flexor pollicis longus.*

8. Posterior compartment muscles are mainly extensors of the wrist and hand. Their tendons pass under an *extensor retinaculum* on the posterior side of the wrist. Superficial muscles of the posterior compartment include the *extensor carpi radialis longus, extensor carpi radialis brevis, extensor digitorum, extensor digiti minimi,* and *extensor carpi ulnaris.* Deep muscles of the posterior compartment include the *abductor pollicis longus, extensor pollicis brevis, extensor pollicis longus,* and *extensor indicis.*

9. Intrinsic muscles of the hand assist the forearm muscles and make movements of the digits more precise. They are divided into a thenar, hypothenar, and midpalmar group (table 12.5).

10. The *thenar group* muscles form the thick fleshy mass at the base of the thumb and the web between the thumb and palm. They move the thumb. They include the *adductor pollicis, abductor pollicis brevis, flexor pollicis brevis,* and *opponens pollicis.*

11. The *hypothenar group* muscles form the fleshy *hypothenar eminence* at the base of the little finger, and are concerned with movements of that digit. They include the *abductor digiti minimi, flexor digiti minimi brevis,* and *opponens digiti minimi.*

12. The *midpalmar group* of muscles span the palm and include four *dorsal interosseous muscles,* three *palmar interosseous muscles,* and four *lumbrical muscles,* located between the metacarpal bones. They act on digits II through V.

### Muscles Acting on the Hip and Lower Limb (p. 341)

1. Most muscles that act on the femur originate on the hip bone (table 12.6). The two major anterior muscles of this group are the *iliacus* and the *psoas major,* collectively called the *iliopsoas.*

2. Superficial muscles on the lateral and posterior sides of the hip include the *tensor fasciae latae, gluteus maximus, gluteus medius,* and *gluteus minimus.* The tendons of the first two of these muscles join the *fascia lata* to form the fibrous *iliotibial band* on the lateral aspect of the thigh.

3. Deep muscles on the lateral aspect of the hip, known as the *lateral rotators,* include the *gemellus superior, gemellus inferior, obturator externus, obturator internus, piriformis,* and *quadratus femoris.* The principal actions of these muscles are abduction and lateral rotation of the femur.

4. Fasciae divide the other thigh muscles into a *medial (adductor) compartment,* anterior *(extensor) compartment,* and *posterior (flexor) compartment.*

5. Muscles of the medial compartment act as adductors of the femur. These include the *adductor brevis, adductor longus, adductor magnus, gracilis,* and *pectineus* (table 12.6).

6. Muscles of the anterior compartment act mainly as extensors of the knee. They include the *sartorius* and the four heads of the *quadriceps femoris: rectus femoris, vastus lateralis, vastus medialis,* and *vastus intermedius.*

7. Muscles of the posterior compartment act as extensors of the hip and flexors of the knee. These are the *biceps femoris, semitendinosus,* and *semimembranosus,* known colloquially as the *hamstring muscles.*

8. Muscles of the leg are divided into anterior, posterior, and lateral compartments (table 12.8). Most of them act on the foot.

9. Anterior compartment muscles of the leg include the *fibularis tertius, extensor digitorum longus, extensor hallucis longus,* and *tibialis anterior.*

10. Superficial posterior compartment muscles include the *popliteus,* which acts on the knee, and two muscles, the *gastrocnemius* and *soleus,* collectively also known as the *triceps surae* (these two share the calcaneal tendon to the heel).

11. Deep posterior compartment muscles include the *flexor digitorum longus, flexor hallucis longus,* and *tibialis posterior.*

12. Lateral compartment muscles include the *fibularis brevis* and *fibularis longus.*

13. Intrinsic muscles of the foot support the arches and act on the toes, and resemble intrinsic muscles of the hand. The *extensor digitorum brevis* is located dorsally. The others are ventral and are arranged in layers (table 12.9).

14. The layer 1 (most superficial) intrinsic muscles of the foot are the *flexor digitorum brevis, abductor digiti minimi,* and *abductor hallucis;* layer 2 comprises the *quadratus plantae* and four *lumbrical muscles;* layer 3 includes the *adductor hallucis, flexor digiti minimi brevis,* and *flexor hallucis brevis;* and layer 4 (deepest) includes four *dorsal interosseous muscles* and three *plantar interosseous muscles.*

### Muscle Injuries (p. 355)

1. Athletic and recreational injuries to the appendicular muscles are especially common, and often result from overly zealous or vigorous exercise without proper conditioning or warm-up. Table 12.10 defines many well-known injuries of the appendicular muscles.

# TESTING YOUR RECALL

1. Which of the following muscles could you most easily do without?
   a. flexor digitorum profundus
   b. trapezius
   c. palmaris longus
   d. triceps brachii
   e. tibialis anterior

2. Which of the following has the least in common with the other four?
   a. vastus intermedius
   b. vastus lateralis
   c. vastus medialis
   d. rectus femoris
   e. biceps femoris

3. The triceps surae is a muscle group composed of
   a. the flexor hallucis longus and brevis.
   b. the gastrocnemius and soleus.
   c. lateral, medial, and long heads.
   d. the biceps brachii and triceps brachii.
   e. the vastus lateralis, medialis, and intermedius.

4. The interosseous muscles lie between
   a. the ribs.
   b. the tibia and fibula.
   c. the radius and ulna.
   d. the metacarpal bones.
   e. the phalanges.

5. Which of these muscles does *not* contribute to the rotator cuff?
   a. the supraspinatus
   b. the infraspinatus
   c. the subscapularis
   d. the teres major
   e. the teres minor

6. Which of these actions is *not* performed by the trapezius?
   a. extension of the neck
   b. depression of the scapula
   c. elevation of the scapula
   d. rotation of the scapula
   e. adduction of the humerus

7. Both the hands and feet are acted upon by a muscle or muscles called
   a. the extensor digitorum.
   b. the abductor digiti minimi.
   c. the flexor digitorum profundus.
   d. the abductor hallucis.
   e. the flexor digitorum longus.

8. Which of the following muscles does *not* extend the hip joint?
   a. rectus femoris
   b. gluteus maximus
   c. biceps femoris
   d. semitendinosus
   e. semimembranosus

9. Both the gastrocnemius and _____ muscles insert on the heel by way of the calcaneal tendon.
   a. semimembranosus
   b. tibialis posterior
   c. tibialis anterior
   d. soleus
   e. plantaris

10. Which of these is *not* in the anterior compartment of the thigh?
    a. semimembranosus
    b. rectus femoris
    c. vastus intermedius
    d. vastus lateralis
    e. sartorius

11. The major superficial muscle of the shoulder, where injections are often given, is the _____.

12. If a muscle has the word *hallucis* in its name, it must cause movement of the _____.

13. Pronation of the forearm is achieved by two muscles, the pronator _____ just distal to the elbow and the pronator _____ near the wrist.

14. The three large muscles on the posterior side of the thigh are collectively known by the colloquial name of _____ muscles.

15. Connective tissue bands called _____ prevent flexor tendons from rising like bowstrings.

16. The web between your thumb and palm consists mainly of the _____ muscle.

17. The patella is embedded in the tendon of the _____ muscle.

18. The _____ muscle, named for its origin and insertion, originates on the coracoid process of the scapula, inserts on the humerus, and adducts the arm.

19. The most medial adductor muscle of the thigh is the long, slender _____.

20. The _____ and _____ are hip flexors that originate on the pelvis and lumbar vertebrae and converge on a shared tendon that inserts on the lesser trochanter of the femur.

***Answers in the Appendix***

# TRUE OR FALSE

*Determine which five of the following statements are false, and briefly explain why.*

1. All plantar flexors in the posterior compartment of the calf insert on the heel by way of the calcaneal tendon.

2. The trapezius can act as both a synergist and antagonist of the levator scapulae.

3. To push someone away from you, you would use the serratus anterior muscle more than the trapezius.

4. Both the extensor digitorum and extensor digiti minimi extend the little finger.

5. The interosseous muscles are fusiform.

6. The actions of the palmaris longus and plantaris muscles are weak and relatively dispensable.

7. The psoas major is an antagonist of the rectus femoris.

8. Rapid flexion of the knee often causes hamstring injuries.

9. Curling your toes employs the quadratus plantae muscle.

10. The tibialis posterior and tibialis anterior are synergists.

***Answers in the Appendix***

## TESTING YOUR COMPREHENSION

1. Radical mastectomy, once a common treatment for breast cancer, involved removal of the pectoralis major along with the breast. What functional impairments would result from this? What synergists could a physical therapist train a patient to use to recover some lost function?

2. Table 12.6 describes a simple test for determining whether you have a palmaris longus muscle. Why do you think the other major tendon of the anterior wrist, the flexor carpi radialis tendon, does not stand out conspicuously in such a test?

3. Poorly conditioned, middle-aged people may suffer a rupture of the calcaneal tendon when the foot is suddenly dorsiflexed. Explain each of the following signs of a ruptured calcaneal tendon: (*a*) a prominent lump typically appears in the calf; (*b*) the foot can be dorsiflexed farther than usual; and (*c*) the patient cannot plantar flex the foot very effectively.

4. Women who habitually wear high heels may suffer painful "high heel syndrome" when they go barefoot or wear flat shoes. What muscle(s) and tendon(s) are involved? Explain.

5. A student moving out of a dormitory kneels down, in correct fashion, to lift a heavy box of books. What prime movers are involved as he straightens his legs to lift the box?

*Answers at aris.mhhe.com*

## ONLINE RESOURCES

Visit aprevealed.com to explore melt-away cadaver dissections, watch animations that clarify difficult concepts, review histological and radiological images, or take a quiz to assess your understanding of the material.

The Saladin *Human Anatomy,* 2e website at aris.mhhe.com features chapter-specific quizzes, labeling exercises, and other interactive tools to complement your study of human anatomy. If your instructor has provided an ARIS course code, you can also access assignments and information specific to your course.

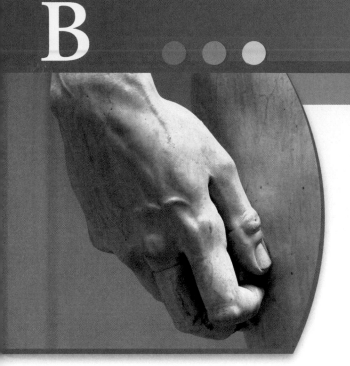

Michelangelo's *David* (detail)

# Surface Anatomy

Anatomy &
Physiology | **REVEALED**®
aprevealed.com

**Muscular System**

# The Importance of External Anatomy

In the study of human anatomy, it is easy to become so preoccupied with internal structure that we forget the importance of what we can see and feel externally. Yet external anatomy and appearance are major concerns in giving a physical examination and in many aspects of patient care. A knowledge of the body's surface landmarks is essential to one's competence in physical therapy, cardiopulmonary resuscitation, surgery, making X-rays and electrocardiograms, giving injections, drawing blood, listening to heart and respiratory sounds, measuring the pulse and blood pressure, and finding pressure points to stop arterial bleeding, among other procedures. A misguided attempt to perform some of these procedures while disregarding or misunderstanding external anatomy can be very harmful and even fatal to a patient.

Having just studied skeletal and muscular anatomy in the preceding chapters, this is an opportune time for you to study the body surface. Much of what we see there reflects the underlying structure of the superficial bones and muscles. A broad photographic overview of surface anatomy is given in atlas A (p. 26). In the following pages, we examine the body literally from head (fig. B.1) to toe (fig. B.14), studying its regions in more detail. To make the most profitable use of this atlas, refer back to the skeletal and muscular anatomy in chapters 7 to 12. Relate drawings of the clavicles in chapter 8 to the photograph in figure B.1, for example. Study the shape of the scapula in chapter 8 and see how much of it you can trace on the photographs in figure B.3. See if you can relate the tendons visible on the hand (fig. B.8) to the muscles of the forearm illustrated in chapter 12.

For learning surface anatomy, there is a resource available to you that is far more valuable than any laboratory model or textbook illustration—your own body. For the best understanding of human structure, compare the art and photographs in this book with your body or with structures visible on a study partner. In addition to bones and muscles, you can palpate a number of superficial arteries, veins, tendons, ligaments, and cartilages, among other structures. By palpating regions such as the shoulder, elbow, or ankle, you can develop a mental image of the subsurface structures better than you can obtain by looking at two-dimensional textbook images. And the more you can study with other people, the more you will appreciate the variations in human structure and be able to apply your knowledge to your future patients or clients, who will not look quite like any textbook diagram or photograph you have ever seen. Through comparisons of art, photography, and the living body, you will get a much deeper understanding of the body than if you were to study this atlas in isolation from the earlier chapters.

At the end of this atlas, you can test your knowledge of externally visible muscle anatomy. The two photographs in figure B.15 have 30 numbered muscles and a list of 26 names, some of which are shown more than once in the photographs and some of which are not shown at all. Identify the muscles to your best ability without looking back at the previous illustrations, and then check your answers in the appendix at the back of the book.

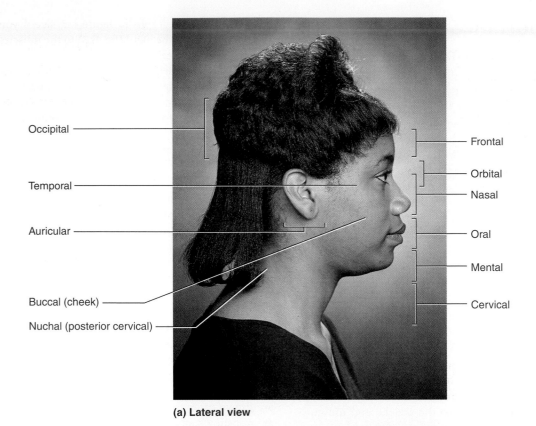

Occipital

Temporal

Auricular

Buccal (cheek)

Nuchal (posterior cervical)

Frontal

Orbital

Nasal

Oral

Mental

Cervical

**(a) Lateral view**

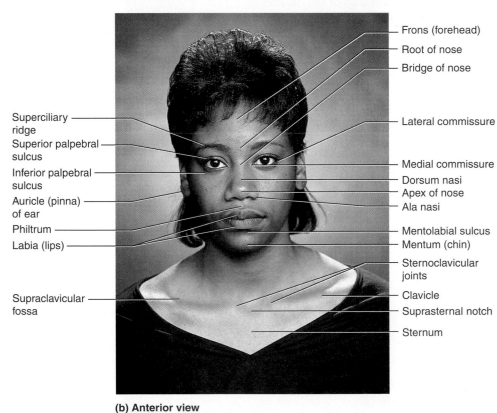

Superciliary
ridge

Superior palpebral
sulcus

Inferior palpebral
sulcus

Auricle (pinna)
of ear

Philtrum

Labia (lips)

Supraclavicular
fossa

Frons (forehead)

Root of nose

Bridge of nose

Lateral commissure

Medial commissure

Dorsum nasi

Apex of nose

Ala nasi

Mentolabial sulcus

Mentum (chin)

Sternoclavicular
joints

Clavicle

Suprasternal notch

Sternum

**(b) Anterior view**

**Figure B.1** **The Head and Neck.** (a) Anatomical regions of the head. (b) Features of the facial region and upper thorax.
• *What muscle underlies the region of the philtrum? What muscle forms the slope of the shoulder?*

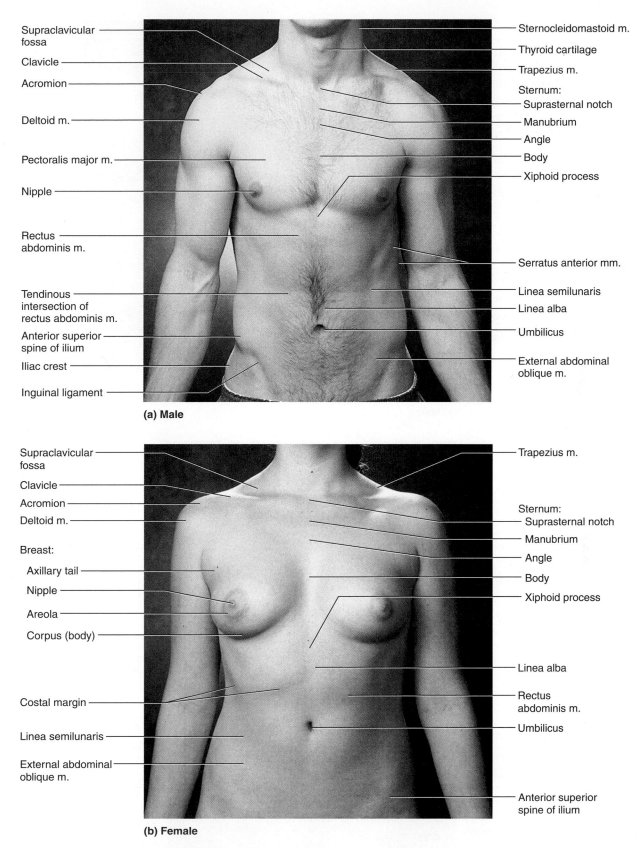

Supraclavicular fossa
Clavicle
Acromion
Deltoid m.
Pectoralis major m.
Nipple
Rectus abdominis m.
Tendinous intersection of rectus abdominis m.
Anterior superior spine of ilium
Iliac crest
Inguinal ligament

Sternocleidomastoid m.
Thyroid cartilage
Trapezius m.
Sternum:
Suprasternal notch
Manubrium
Angle
Body
Xiphoid process
Serratus anterior mm.
Linea semilunaris
Linea alba
Umbilicus
External abdominal oblique m.

**(a) Male**

Supraclavicular fossa
Clavicle
Acromion
Deltoid m.
Breast:
Axillary tail
Nipple
Areola
Corpus (body)
Costal margin
Linea semilunaris
External abdominal oblique m.

Trapezius m.
Sternum:
Suprasternal notch
Manubrium
Angle
Body
Xiphoid process
Linea alba
Rectus abdominis m.
Umbilicus
Anterior superior spine of ilium

**(b) Female**

**Figure B.2** **The Thorax and Abdomen, Anterior View.** All of the features labeled are common to both sexes, though some are labeled only on the photograph that shows them best.

● *The V-shaped tendons on each side of the suprasternal notch in part (a) belong to what muscles?*

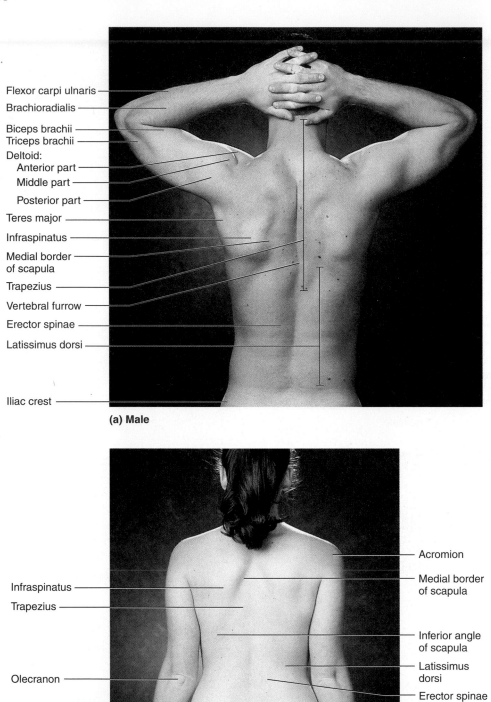

Flexor carpi ulnaris
Brachioradialis
Biceps brachii
Triceps brachii
Deltoid:
   Anterior part
   Middle part
   Posterior part
Teres major
Infraspinatus
Medial border
of scapula
Trapezius
Vertebral furrow
Erector spinae
Latissimus dorsi

Iliac crest

**(a) Male**

Acromion
Medial border
of scapula

Inferior angle
of scapula
Latissimus
dorsi
Erector spinae

Sacrum

Coccyx
Natal cleft

Greater
trochanter
of femur
Gluteal fold

Infraspinatus
Trapezius

Olecranon

Iliac crest

Gluteus medius
Gluteus maximus

Hamstring muscles

**(b) Female**

**Figure B.3** **The Back and Gluteal Region.** All of the features labeled are common to both sexes, though some are labeled only on the photograph that shows them best.

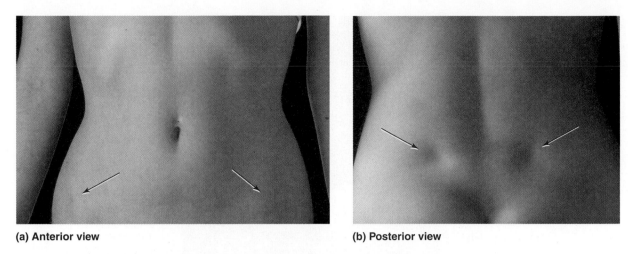

**(a) Anterior view**                    **(b) Posterior view**

**Figure B.4**  **The Pelvic Region.**  (a) The anterior superior spines of the ilium are marked by anterolateral protuberances (arrows). (b) The posterior superior spines are marked in some people by dimples in the sacral region (arrows).

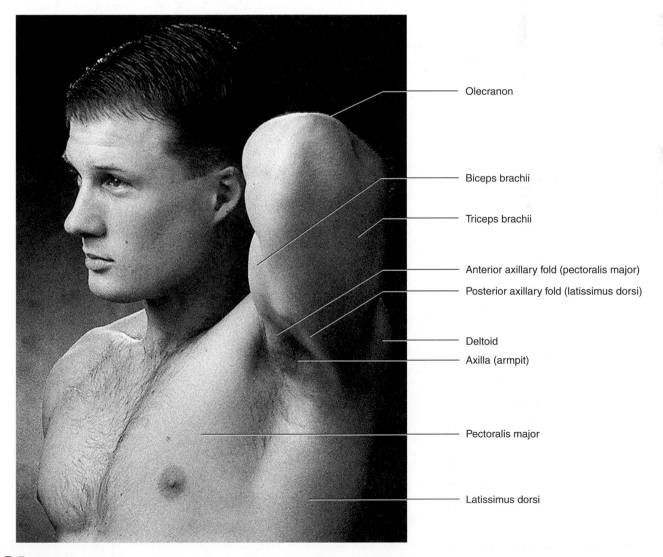

Olecranon

Biceps brachii

Triceps brachii

Anterior axillary fold (pectoralis major)
Posterior axillary fold (latissimus dorsi)

Deltoid

Axilla (armpit)

Pectoralis major

Latissimus dorsi

**Figure B.5**  The Axillary Region.

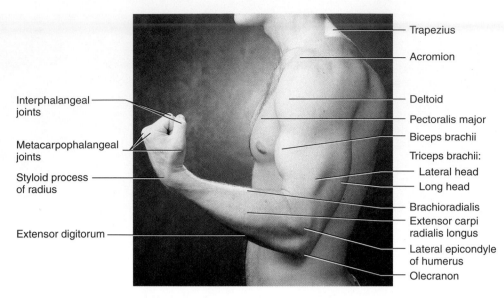

Trapezius

Acromion

Interphalangeal joints

Deltoid

Pectoralis major

Metacarpophalangeal joints

Biceps brachii

Triceps brachii:

Lateral head

Long head

Styloid process of radius

Brachioradialis

Extensor carpi radialis longus

Extensor digitorum

Lateral epicondyle of humerus

Olecranon

**Figure B.6** The Upper Limb, Lateral View.

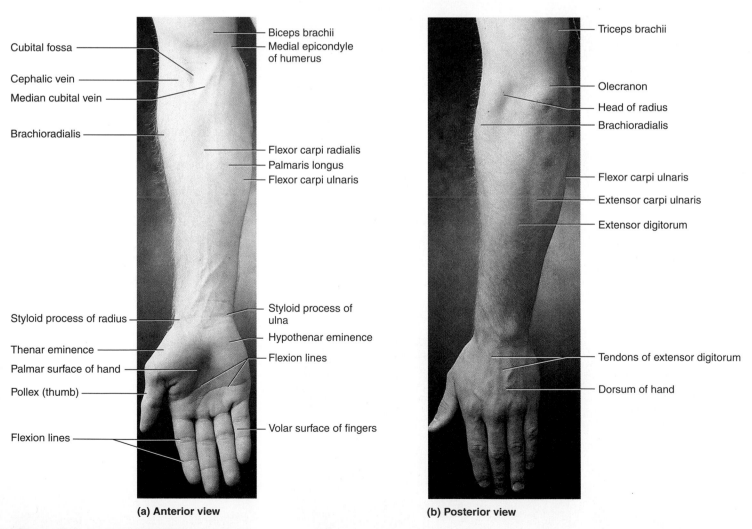

Cubital fossa

Biceps brachii

Medial epicondyle of humerus

Cephalic vein

Median cubital vein

Brachioradialis

Flexor carpi radialis

Palmaris longus

Flexor carpi ulnaris

Styloid process of radius

Styloid process of ulna

Thenar eminence

Hypothenar eminence

Palmar surface of hand

Flexion lines

Pollex (thumb)

Flexion lines

Volar surface of fingers

**(a) Anterior view**

Triceps brachii

Olecranon

Head of radius

Brachioradialis

Flexor carpi ulnaris

Extensor carpi ulnaris

Extensor digitorum

Tendons of extensor digitorum

Dorsum of hand

**(b) Posterior view**

**Figure B.7** The Right Antebrachium (Forearm).
● *Only two tendons of the extensor digitorum are labeled, but how many tendons does this muscle have in all?*

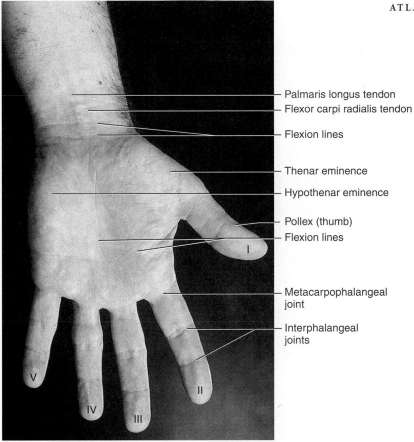

Palmaris longus tendon
Flexor carpi radialis tendon
Flexion lines
Thenar eminence
Hypothenar eminence
Pollex (thumb)
Flexion lines
Metacarpophalangeal joint
Interphalangeal joints

**(a) Anterior (palmar) view**

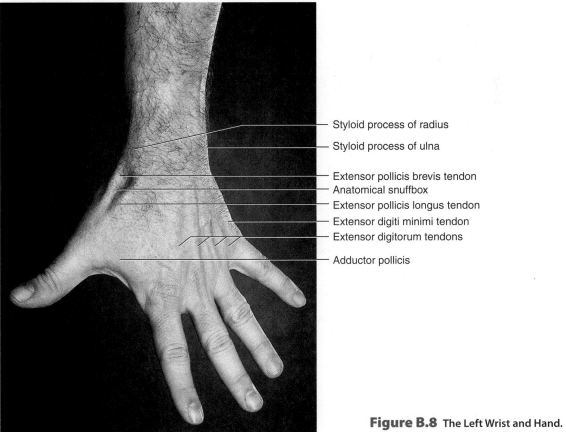

Styloid process of radius
Styloid process of ulna
Extensor pollicis brevis tendon
Anatomical snuffbox
Extensor pollicis longus tendon
Extensor digiti minimi tendon
Extensor digitorum tendons
Adductor pollicis

**(b) Posterior (dorsal) view**

**Figure B.8** **The Left Wrist and Hand.**
● *Mark the spot on one or both photographs where a saddle joint could be found.*

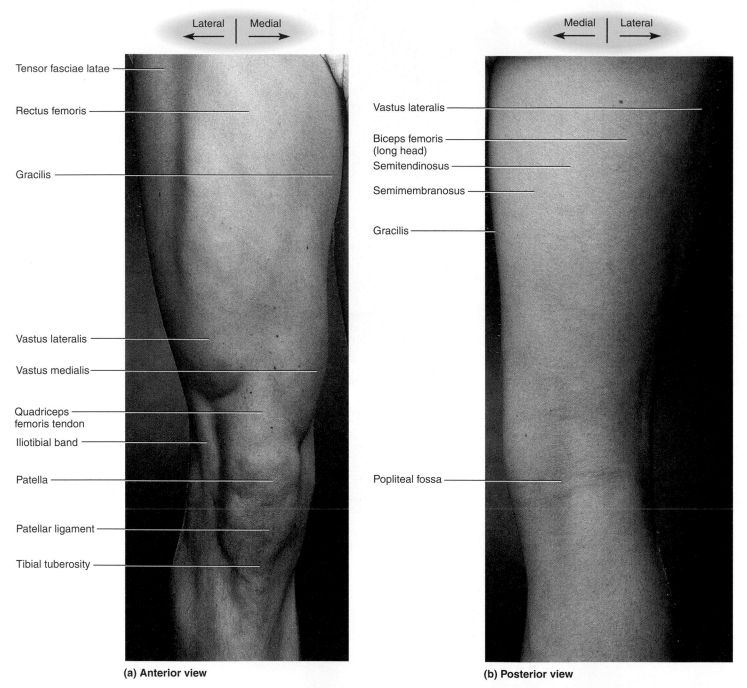

Lateral ← | → Medial

Tensor fasciae latae

Rectus femoris

Gracilis

Vastus lateralis

Vastus medialis

Quadriceps femoris tendon

Iliotibial band

Patella

Patellar ligament

Tibial tuberosity

**(a) Anterior view**

Medial ← | → Lateral

Vastus lateralis

Biceps femoris (long head)

Semitendinosus

Semimembranosus

Gracilis

Popliteal fossa

**(b) Posterior view**

**Figure B.9**  **The Right Thigh and Knee.**  Locations of posterior thigh muscles are indicated, but the boundaries of the individual muscles are rarely visible on a living person.

● *Mark the spot on (a) where the vastus intermedius would be found.*

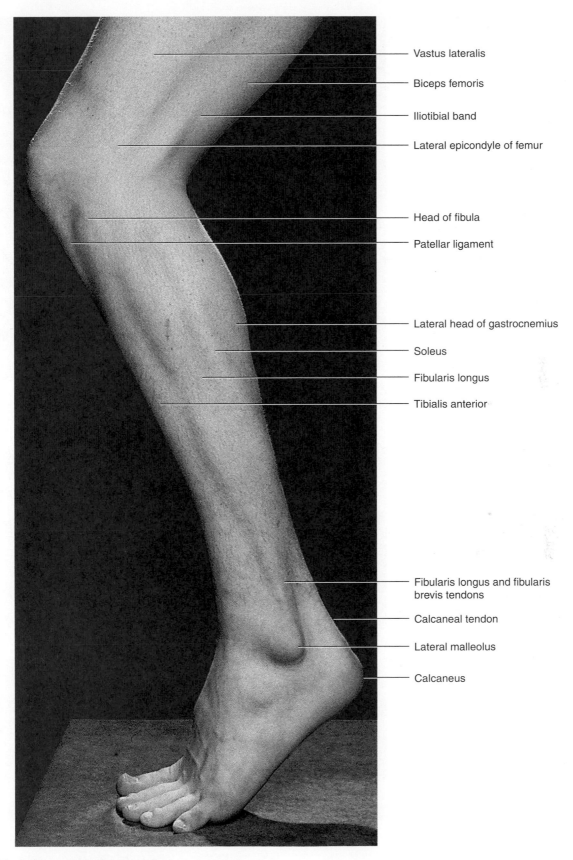

Vastus lateralis

Biceps femoris

Iliotibial band

Lateral epicondyle of femur

Head of fibula

Patellar ligament

Lateral head of gastrocnemius

Soleus

Fibularis longus

Tibialis anterior

Fibularis longus and fibularis brevis tendons

Calcaneal tendon

Lateral malleolus

Calcaneus

**Figure B.10** **The Left Leg and Foot, Lateral View.**
• *The lateral malleolus is part of what bone?*

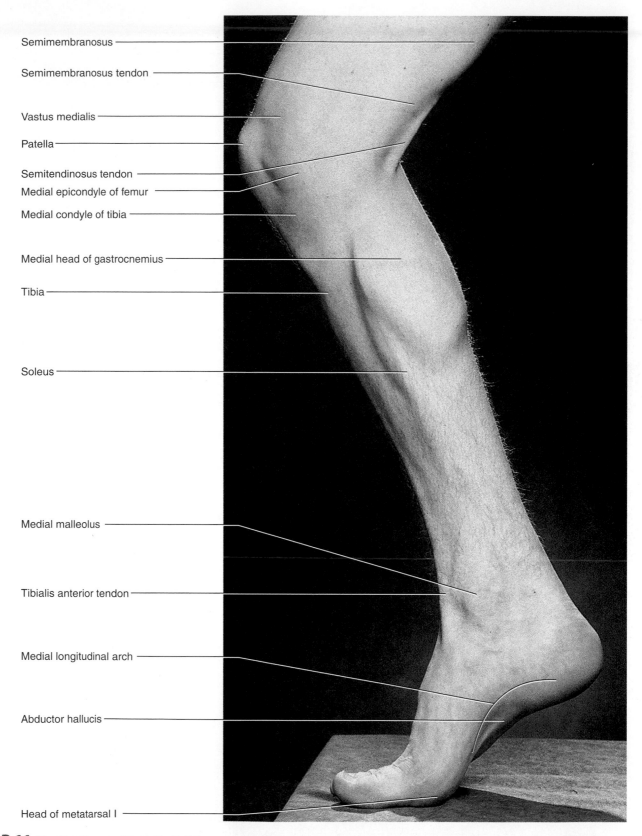

Semimembranosus

Semimembranosus tendon

Vastus medialis

Patella

Semitendinosus tendon
Medial epicondyle of femur

Medial condyle of tibia

Medial head of gastrocnemius

Tibia

Soleus

Medial malleolus

Tibialis anterior tendon

Medial longitudinal arch

Abductor hallucis

Head of metatarsal I

**Figure B.11** The Right Leg and Foot, Medial View.

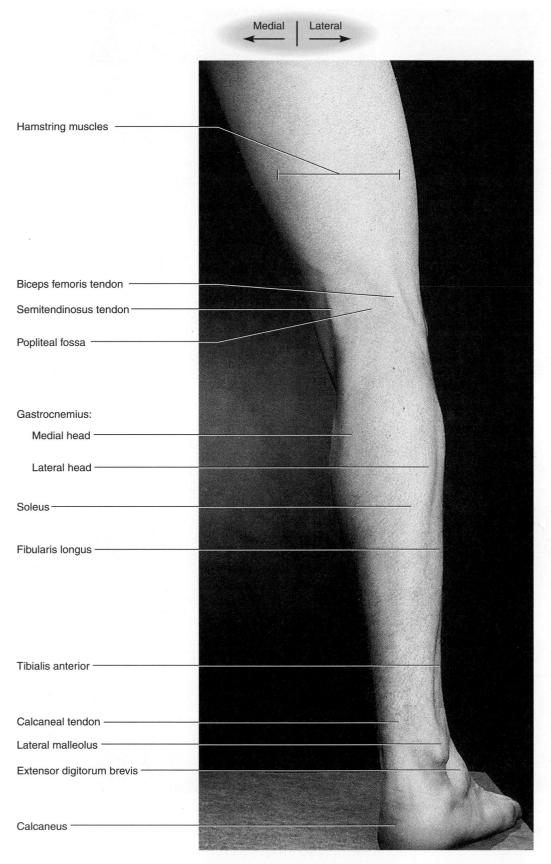

Medial | Lateral

Hamstring muscles

Biceps femoris tendon

Semitendinosus tendon

Popliteal fossa

Gastrocnemius:

Medial head

Lateral head

Soleus

Fibularis longus

Tibialis anterior

Calcaneal tendon

Lateral malleolus

Extensor digitorum brevis

Calcaneus

**Figure B.12** The Right Leg and Foot, Posterior View.

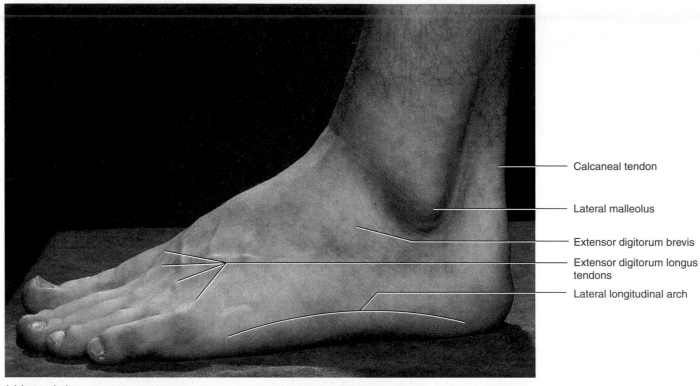

Calcaneal tendon

Lateral malleolus

Extensor digitorum brevis

Extensor digitorum longus tendons

Lateral longitudinal arch

**(a) Lateral view**

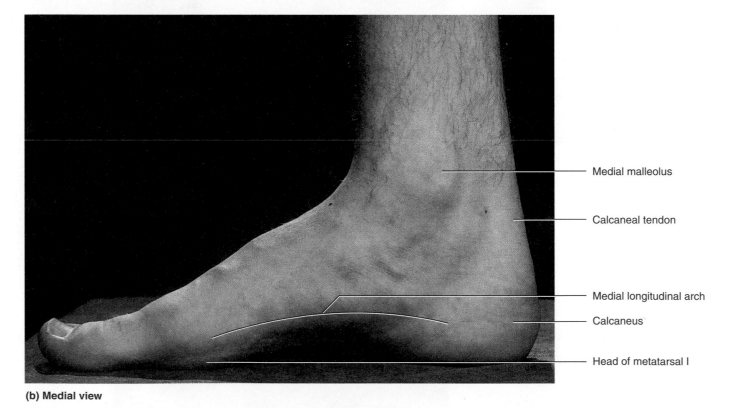

Medial malleolus

Calcaneal tendon

Medial longitudinal arch

Calcaneus

Head of metatarsal I

**(b) Medial view**

**Figure B.13** The Foot.

• *Indicate the location of middle phalanx I on each photograph.*

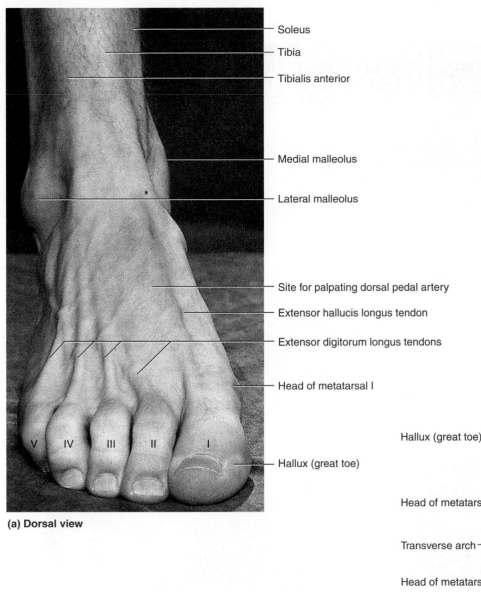

- Soleus
- Tibia
- Tibialis anterior
- Medial malleolus
- Lateral malleolus
- Site for palpating dorsal pedal artery
- Extensor hallucis longus tendon
- Extensor digitorum longus tendons
- Head of metatarsal I
- Hallux (great toe)

V  IV  III  II  I

**(a) Dorsal view**

- Hallux (great toe)
- Head of metatarsal I
- Transverse arch
- Head of metatarsal V
- Abductor digiti minimi
- Abductor hallucis
- Medial longitudinal arch
- Lateral longitudinal arch
- Lateral malleolus
- Calcaneus

II
III
IV
V
I

**Figure B.14** **The Foot.** Compare the arches in part (b) to the skeletal anatomy in figure 8.14 (p. 224).

**(b) Plantar view**

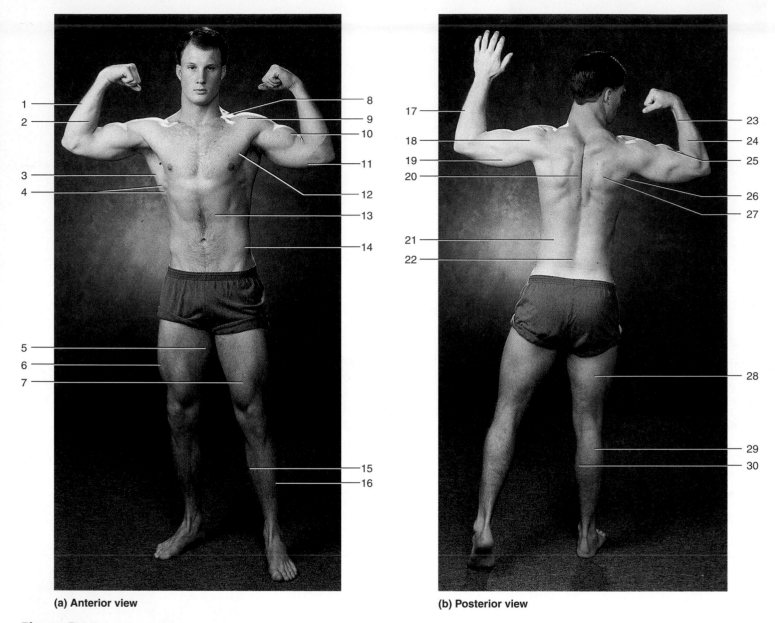

**(a) Anterior view**

**(b) Posterior view**

**Figure B.15 Muscle Test.** To test your knowledge of muscle anatomy, match the 30 labeled muscles on these photographs to the alphabetical list of muscles that follows. Answer as many as possible without referring back to the previous illustrations. Some of these names will be used more than once, since the same muscle may be shown from different perspectives, and some of these names will not be used at all. The answers are in the appendix.

| | | | | | |
|---|---|---|---|---|---|
| a. | biceps brachii | j. | infraspinatus | s. | sternocleidomastoid |
| b. | brachioradialis | k. | latissimus dorsi | t. | subscapularis |
| c. | deltoid | l. | pectineus | u. | teres major |
| d. | erector spinae | m. | pectoralis major | v. | tibialis anterior |
| e. | external oblique | n. | rectus abdominis | w. | trapezius |
| f. | flexor carpi ulnaris | o. | rectus femoris | x. | triceps brachii |
| g. | gastrocnemius | p. | serratus anterior | y. | vastus lateralis |
| h. | gracilis | q. | soleus | z. | vastus medialis |
| i. | hamstrings | r. | splenius capitis | | |

# Nervous Tissue

A Purkinje cell, a neuron from the cerebellum of the brain

## INSIGHTS

## BRUSHING UP

To understand this chapter, you may find it helpful to review the following concepts:
- General structure of nerve cells, especially the soma, dendrites, and axon (p. 92)
- Early embryonic development (pp. 110–112)
- Introduction to synapses and neurotransmitters (p. 277)

Anatomy & Physiology REVEALED®
aprevealed.com

**Nervous System**

The next five chapters are concerned with the nervous system. This is a system of great complexity and mystery. It is the foundation of all our conscious experiences, personality, and behavior. It profoundly intrigues biologists, physicians, psychologists, and even philosophers. Understanding this fascinating system is regarded by many as the ultimate challenge facing the behavioral and life sciences.

We begin our study at the simplest organizational level—the nerve cells (neurons) and cells called neuroglia that support their function in various ways. We then progress to the organ level to examine the spinal cord (chapter 14), brain (chapter 15), autonomic nervous system (chapter 16), and sense organs (chapter 17).

# Overview of the Nervous System

### Objectives
When you have completed this section, you should be able to
- describe the function of the nervous system;
- describe the major anatomical subdivisions of the nervous system;
- explain the functional differences between these anatomical subdivisions; and
- define nerve, ganglion, receptor, and effector.

If the body is to maintain homeostasis and function effectively, its trillions of cells must work together in a coordinated fashion. If each cell behaved without regard to what others are doing, the result would be physiological chaos and death. We have two organ systems dedicated to maintaining internal coordination—the **endocrine system,** which communicates by means of chemical messengers (hormones) secreted into the blood, and the **nervous system** (fig.13.1), which employs electrical and chemical means to send messages very quickly from cell to cell. The study of the nervous system is called **neurobiology.** Its primary subdisciplines are **neuroanatomy** and **neurophysiology.**

The nervous system carries out its coordinating task in three basic steps: (1) Through sense organs and simple sensory nerve endings, it receives information about changes in the body and external environment and it transmits coded messages to the spinal cord and brain. (2) The spinal cord and brain process this information, relate it to past experience, and determine what response, if any, is appropriate to the circumstances. (3) The spinal cord and brain issue commands primarily to muscle and gland cells to carry out such responses.

The nervous system has two major anatomical subdivisions (fig. 13.2):

- The **central nervous system (CNS)** consists of the brain and spinal cord, which are enclosed and protected by the cranium and vertebral column.

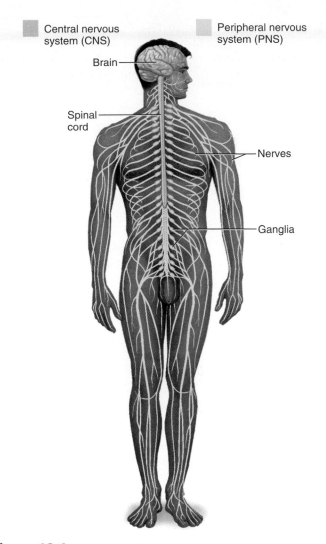

**Figure 13.1** The Nervous System.
● Which division, the CNS or PNS, is likely to suffer the most frequent injuries? Why?

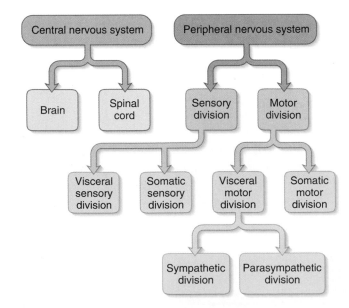

**Figure 13.2** Subdivisions of the Nervous System.

The **peripheral nervous system (PNS)** consists of all the nervous system except the brain and spinal cord. It is composed of nerves and ganglia. A **nerve** is a bundle of nerve fibers (axons) wrapped in fibrous connective tissue. Nerves emerge from the CNS through foramina of the skull and vertebral column and carry signals to and from other organs of the body. A **ganglion**[1] (plural, *ganglia*) is a knotlike swelling in a nerve where the cell bodies of neurons are concentrated.

The peripheral nervous system is functionally divided into *sensory* and *motor* divisions, and each of these is further divided into *somatic* and *visceral* divisions.

- The **sensory (afferent**[2]**) division** carries sensory signals from various **receptors** (sense organs and simple sensory nerve endings) to the CNS. This is the pathway that informs the CNS of stimuli within and around the body.
  - The **somatic**[3] **sensory division** carries signals from receptors in the skin, muscles, bones, and joints.
  - The **visceral sensory division** carries signals mainly from the viscera of the thoracic and abdominal cavities, such as the heart, lungs, stomach, and urinary bladder.
- The **motor (efferent**[4]**) division** carries signals from the CNS to gland and muscle cells that carry out the body's responses. Cells and organs that respond to commands from the nervous system are called **effectors.**
  - The **somatic motor division** carries signals to the skeletal muscles. This output produces muscular contractions that are under voluntary control, as well as involuntary muscle contractions called *somatic reflexes.*
  - The **visceral motor division (autonomic**[5] **nervous system)** carries signals to glands, cardiac muscle, and smooth muscle. We usually have no voluntary control over these effectors, and this system operates at an unconscious level. The responses of this system and its effectors are *visceral reflexes.* The autonomic nervous system has two further divisions:
    - The **sympathetic division** tends to arouse the body for action—for example, by accelerating the heartbeat and increasing respiratory airflow—but it inhibits digestion.
    - The **parasympathetic division** adapts the body for energy intake and conservation. It stimulates digestion but slows down the heartbeat and reduces respiratory airflow, for example.

The foregoing terminology may give the impression that the body has several nervous systems—central, peripheral, sensory, motor, somatic, and visceral. These are just terms of convenience, however. There is only one nervous system, and these subsystems are interconnected parts of the whole.

---

[1]*gangli* = knot
[2]*af* = *ad* = toward + *fer* = to carry
[3]*somat* = body + *ic* = pertaining to
[4]*ef* = *ex* = out, away + *fer* = to carry
[5]*auto* = self + *nom* = law, governance

## Before You Go On

*Answer the following questions to test your understanding of the preceding section:*

1. Define *receptor* and *effector*. Give two examples of each.
2. Distinguish between the central and peripheral nervous systems, and between the visceral and somatic divisions of the sensory and motor systems.
3. What is another name for the visceral motor nervous system? What are the two subdivisions of this system? How do they differ in their effects on the body?

# Nerve Cells (Neurons)

## Objectives
When you have completed this section, you should be able to
- describe the properties that neurons must have to carry out their function;
- identify and define three functional classes into which all neurons fall;
- describe the structure of a representative neuron; and
- describe some variations in neuron structure.

## Universal Properties of Neurons

The functional unit of the nervous system is the **nerve cell,** or **neuron;** neurons carry out the system's communicative role. These cells have three fundamental physiological properties that are necessary to this function:

1. **Excitability (irritability).** All cells possess excitability, the ability to respond to environmental changes called **stimuli.** Neurons have developed this property to the highest degree.
2. **Conductivity.** Neurons respond to stimuli by producing traveling electrical signals that quickly reach other cells at distant locations.
3. **Secretion.** When the electrical signal reaches the end of a nerve fiber, the neuron usually secretes a chemical called a *neurotransmitter* that crosses a small gap between cells and stimulates the next cell.

## Functional Classes of Neurons

There are three general classes of neurons (fig. 13.3) corresponding to the three major aspects of nervous system function listed earlier:

1. **Sensory (afferent) neurons** are specialized to detect stimuli such as light, heat, pressure, and chemicals and to transmit information about them to the CNS. These neurons can begin

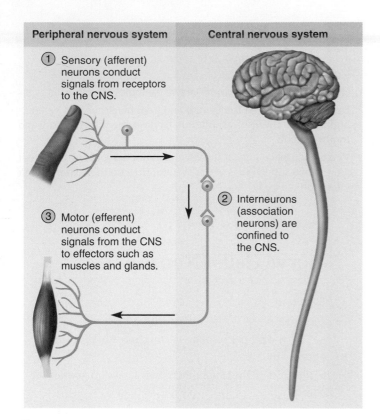

**Peripheral nervous system**

① Sensory (afferent) neurons conduct signals from receptors to the CNS.

③ Motor (efferent) neurons conduct signals from the CNS to effectors such as muscles and glands.

**Central nervous system**

② Interneurons (association neurons) are confined to the CNS.

**Figure 13.3** **Functional Classes of Neurons.** Sensory (afferent) neurons carry signals to the central nervous system (CNS); interneurons are contained entirely within the CNS and carry signals from one neuron to another; and motor (efferent) neurons carry signals from the CNS to muscles and glands.

●*How do the origins of the words* afferent *and* efferent *relate to the functions of the respective neurons?*

in almost any organ of the body but always end in the brain or spinal cord; the word *afferent* refers to signal conduction *toward* the CNS. Some sensory receptors, such as pain and smell receptors, are themselves neurons. In other cases, such as taste and hearing, the receptor is a separate cell that communicates directly with a sensory neuron.

2. **Interneurons**[6] (**association neurons**) lie entirely within the CNS. They receive signals from many other neurons and carry out the *integrative* function of the nervous system—that is, they process, store, and retrieve information and "make decisions" about how the body responds to stimuli. About 90% of human neurons are interneurons. The word *interneuron* refers to the fact that they lie *between*, and interconnect, the incoming sensory pathways and the outgoing motor pathways of the CNS.

3. **Motor (efferent) neurons** send signals predominantly to muscle and gland cells, the effectors that carry out the body's responses to stimuli. They are called *motor* neurons because most of them lead to muscle cells, and *efferent* neurons to signify that they conduct signals *away from* the CNS.

[6]*inter* = between

## Structure of a Neuron

There are several varieties of neurons, as we shall see, but a good starting point for discussing neuron stucture is a motor neuron of the spinal cord (fig. 13.4). The control center of the neuron is its **soma,**[7] or **cell body.** It has a single, centrally located nucleus with a large nucleolus. The cytoplasm contains mitochondria, lysosomes, a Golgi complex, numerous inclusions, and an extensive rough endoplasmic reticulum and cytoskeleton. The cytoskeleton consists of a dense mesh of microtubules and **neurofibrils** (bundles of actin filaments) that compartmentalize the rough ER into dark-staining regions called *Nissl*[8] *bodies,* unique to neurons (fig. 13.4c, d). Nissl bodies are a helpful clue to identifying neurons in tissue sections with mixed cell types. Mature neurons lack centrioles and apparently undergo no further mitosis after adolescence, but they are unusually long-lived cells, capable of functioning for over a hundred years. Even in old age, however, there are unspecialized stem cells in the CNS that divide and develop into new neurons.

The major cytoplasmic inclusions in a neuron are glycogen granules, lipid droplets, melanin, and a golden brown pigment called *lipofuscin*[9] (LIP-oh-FEW-sin)—produced when lysosomes digest worn-out organelles and other products. Lipofuscin collects with age and pushes the nucleus to one side of the cell. Lipofuscin granules are also called "wear-and-tear granules" because they are most abundant in old neurons.

The soma of a neuron usually gives rise to a few thick processes that branch into a vast number of **dendrites**[10]—named for their striking resemblance to the bare branches of a tree in winter. The dendrites are the primary site for receiving signals from other neurons. Some neurons have only one dendrite and some have thousands. The more dendrites a neuron has, the more information it can receive from other cells and incorporate into its decision making. As tangled as the dendrites may seem, they provide exquisitely precise pathways for the reception and processing of neural information.

On one side of the soma is a mound called the **axon hillock,** from which the **axon (nerve fiber)** originates. The axon hillock and nearby portion of the axon *(initial segment)* are collectively called the **trigger zone,** because this is where the neuron first generates **action potentials**—electrical changes that constitute the nerve signal. An axon is specialized for rapid conduction of nerve signals to points remote from the soma. It is cylindrical and relatively unbranched for most of its length; however, it may give rise to a few branches called *axon collaterals* along the way, and most axons branch extensively at their distal end. Its cytoplasm is called the **axoplasm** and its membrane the **axolemma.**[11] A neuron never has more than one axon, and some neurons in the retina and brain have none.

Somas range from 5 to 135 μm in diameter, while axons range from 1 to 20 μm in diameter and from a few millimeters to more than a meter long. Such dimensions are more impressive when we scale them up to the size of familiar objects. If the soma of a spinal

[7]*soma* = body
[8]Franz Nissl (1860–1919), German neuropathologist
[9]*lipo* = fat, lipid + *fusc* = dusky, brown
[10]*dendr* = tree, branch + *ite* = little
[11]*axo* = axis, axon + *lemma* = husk, peel, sheath

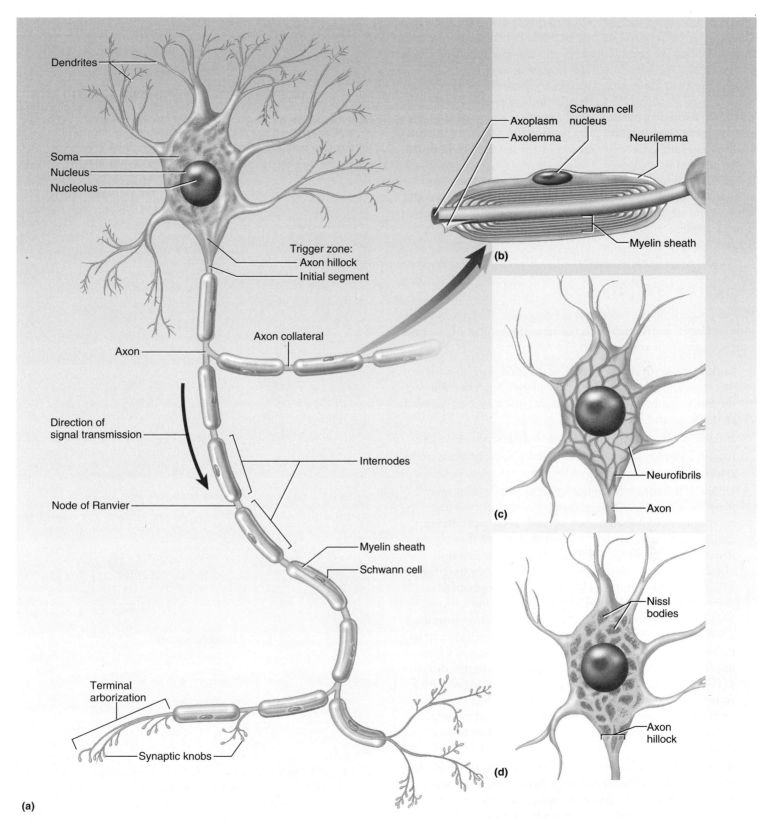

**Figure 13.4** **A Representative Neuron.** The Schwann cells and myelin sheath are explained later in this chapter. (a) A multipolar neuron such as a spinal motor neuron. (b) Detail of myelin sheath. (c) Neurofibrils of the soma. (d) Nissl bodies, stained masses of rough ER separated by the bundles of neurofibrils shown in part (c).

● *What feature of this neuron is the basis for classifying it as multipolar? (Relate this figure to the discussion of fig. 13.5.)*

motor neuron were the size of a tennis ball, its dendrites would form a huge bushy mass that could fill a 30-seat classroom from floor to ceiling. Its axon would be up to a mile long but a little narrower than a garden hose. This is quite a point to ponder. The neuron must assemble molecules and organelles in its "tennis ball" soma and deliver them through its "mile-long garden hose" to the end of the axon. In a process called *axonal transport,* neurons employ *motor proteins* that can carry organelles and macromolecules as they crawl along the cytoskeleton of the nerve fiber to distant destinations in the cell.

At the distal end, an axon usually has a **terminal arborization**[12]— an extensive complex of fine branches. Each branch ends in a **synaptic knob (terminal button).** The synaptic knob is a little swelling that forms a junction *(synapse*[13]*)* with a muscle cell, gland cell, or another neuron. Synapses are described in detail later in this chapter.

## Neuronal Variety

Not all neurons fit every detail of the preceding description. Neurons are classified structurally according to the number of processes extending from the soma (fig. 13.5):

- **Multipolar neurons** are those, like the preceding, that have one axon and two or more (usually many) dendrites. This is the most common type of neuron and includes most neurons of the brain and spinal cord.

- **Bipolar neurons** have one axon and one dendrite. Examples include olfactory cells of the nasal cavity, some neurons of the retina, and sensory neurons of the inner ear.

- **Unipolar neurons** have only a single process leading away from the soma. They are represented by the neurons that carry sensory signals to the spinal cord. These neurons are also called *pseudounipolar*[14] because they start out as bipolar neurons in the embryo, but their two processes fuse into one as the neuron matures. A short distance away from the soma, the process branches like a T, with a *peripheral fiber* carrying signals from the source of sensation and a *central fiber* continuing into the spinal cord. In most other neurons, a dendrite carries signals toward the soma, and an axon carries them away. In unipolar neurons, however, there is one long fiber that bypasses the soma and carries nerve signals directly to the spinal cord. The dendrites are the branching receptive endings in the skin or other place of origin, while the rest of the fiber is considered to be the axon (defined in these neurons by the presence of myelin and the ability to generate action potentials).

- **Anaxonic neurons** have multiple dendrites but no axon. They communicate over short distances through their dendrites and do not produce action potentials. Anaxonic neurons are found in the brain, retina, and adrenal medulla. In the retina, they help in visual processes such as the perception of contrast.

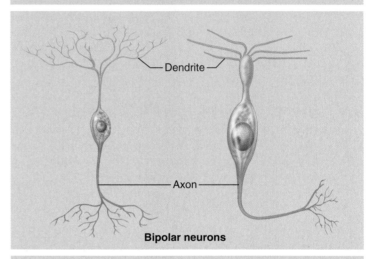

**Multipolar neurons**

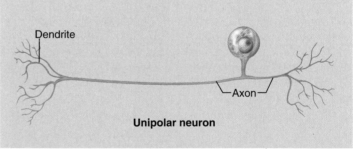

**Bipolar neurons**

**Unipolar neuron**

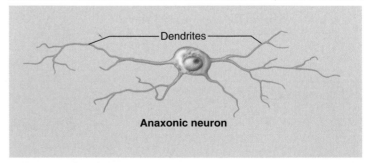

**Anaxonic neuron**

**Figure 13.5** **Variation in Neuron Structure.** *Top row, left to right:* Two multipolar neurons of the brain: a pyramidal cell and Purkinje cell. *Second row, left to right:* Two bipolar neurons: a bipolar cell of the retina and an olfactory neuron. *Third row:* A unipolar neuron of the type involved in the senses of touch and pain. *Bottom row:* An anaxonic neuron (amacrine cell) of the retina.

---

[12]*arbor* = treelike
[13]*syn* = together + *aps* = to touch, join
[14]*pseudo* = false

## Before You Go On

*Answer the following questions to test your understanding of the preceding section:*

4. Explain why neurons could not function without the properties of excitability, conductivity, and secretion.

5. Distinguish between sensory neurons, interneurons, and motor neurons.

6. Define each of the following and explain its importance to neuronal function: dendrites, soma, axon, and synaptic knob.

7. Sketch a multipolar, bipolar, unipolar, and anaxonic neuron and next to each sketch, state one place where such a neuron could be found.

# Supportive Cells (Neuroglia)

### Objectives

When you have completed this section, you should be able to

- name the cells that aid neuron function and state their locations and functions;

- describe the myelin sheath that is formed around certain nerve fibers;

- describe how the speed of nerve signal conduction varies with nerve fiber diameter and the presence or absence of myelin; and

- explain the relevance of neuroglia to the regeneration of damaged nerve fibers.

There are about a trillion ($10^{12}$) neurons in the nervous system—10 times as many neurons in one person as there are stars in our galaxy! Yet the neurons are outnumbered as much as 50 to 1 by supportive cells called **neuroglia** (noo-ROG-lee-uh), or **glial (GLEE-ul) cells.** Glial cells protect the neurons and aid their function. The word *glia,* which means "glue," implies one of their roles—they bind neurons together. In the fetus, glial cells form a scaffold that guides young migrating neurons to their destinations. Wherever a mature neuron is not in synaptic contact with another cell, it is covered with glial cells. This prevents neurons from contacting each other except at points specialized for signal transmission, and thus gives precision to their conduction pathways.

## Types of Neuroglia

There are six major categories of neuroglia, each with a unique function (table 13.1). Four types occur in the central nervous system (fig. 13.6):

1. **Oligodendrocytes**[15] (OL-ih-go-DEN-dro-sites) somewhat resemble an octopus; they have a bulbous body with as many as 15 armlike processes. Each process reaches out to a nerve fiber and spirals around it like electrical tape wrapped repeatedly around a wire. This spiral wrapping, called the *myelin sheath,* insulates the nerve fiber from the extracellular fluid and speeds up signal conduction in the nerve fiber.

2. **Ependymal**[16] (ep-EN-dih-mul) **cells** resemble a cuboidal epithelium lining the internal cavities of the brain and spinal cord. Unlike epithelial cells, however, they have no basement membrane and they exhibit rootlike processes that penetrate into the underlying nervous tissue. Ependymal cells produce a significant fraction of the *cerebrospinal fluid (CSF),* a clear liquid that bathes the CNS and fills its internal cavities. Some of them have patches of cilia on their apical surfaces that help to circulate the CSF. Ependymal cells and CSF are considered in more detail in chapter 15, (p. 428).

3. **Microglia** are small macrophages that develop from stem cells related to the white blood cells called monocytes. They wander through the CNS and phagocytize dead nervous tissue, microorganisms, and other foreign matter. They become concentrated in areas damaged by infection, trauma, or stroke. Pathologists look for clusters of microglia in histological sections of the brain as a clue to sites of injury.

| TABLE 13.1 | Types of Glial Cells | |
|---|---|---|
| **Type** | **Location** | **Functions** |
| Oligodendrocytes | CNS | Form myelin in brain and spinal cord |
| Ependymal cells | CNS | Line cavities of brain and spinal cord; secrete and circulate cerebrospinal fluid |
| Microglia | CNS | Phagocytize and destroy microorganisms, foreign matter, and dead nervous tissue |
| Astrocytes | CNS | Cover brain surface and nonsynaptic regions of neurons; form supportive framework for the CNS; stimulate formation of blood–brain barrier; nourish neurons and secrete growth stimulants; influence synaptic signaling between neurons; help to regulate composition of the extracellular fluid in the CNS; form scar tissue to replace damaged nervous tissue |
| Schwann cells | PNS | Form neurilemma around all PNS nerve fibers and myelin around most of them; aid in regeneration of damaged nerve fibers |
| Satellite cells | PNS | Surround somas of neurons in the ganglia; function uncertain |

[15]*oligo* = few + *dendro* = branches + *cyte* = cell

[16]*ependyma* = upper garment

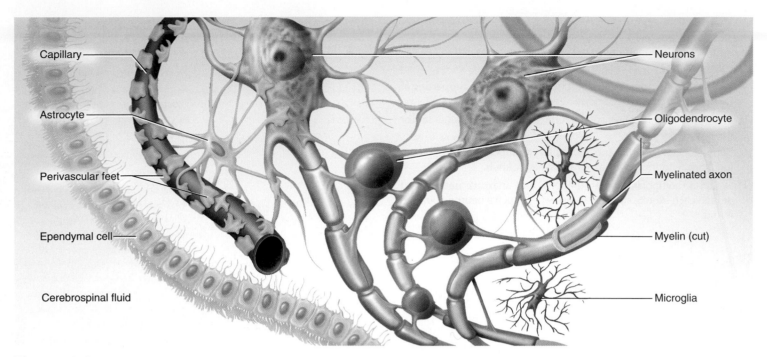

Capillary

Astrocyte

Perivascular feet

Ependymal cell

Cerebrospinal fluid

Neurons

Oligodendrocyte

Myelinated axon

Myelin (cut)

Microglia

**Figure 13.6** Neuroglia of the Central Nervous System.

4. **Astrocytes**[17] are the most abundant glial cells in the CNS and constitute over 90% of the tissue in some areas of the brain. They cover the entire brain surface and most nonsynaptic regions of the neurons in the gray matter of the CNS. They are named for their many-branched, somewhat starlike shape. They have the most diverse functions of any glia:

- They form a supportive framework for the nervous tissue.

- They have extensions called *perivascular feet,* which contact the blood capillaries and stimulate them to form a tight seal called the *blood–brain barrier.* This barrier isolates the blood from the brain tissue and limits what substances are able to get to the brain cells, thus protecting the neurons (see chapter 15, p. 428).

- They convert blood glucose to lactate and supply this to the neurons for nourishment.

- They secrete proteins called *nerve growth factors* that promote neuron growth and synapse formation.

- They communicate electrically with neurons and may influence future synaptic signaling between neurons.

- They regulate the chemical composition of the tissue fluid. When neurons transmit signals, they release neurotransmitters and potassium ions. Astrocytes absorb these substances and prevent them from reaching excessive levels in the tissue fluid.

- When neurons are damaged, astrocytes form hardened scar tissue and fill space formerly occupied by the neurons. This process is called *astrocytosis* or *sclerosis.*

The other two types of glial cells occur in the peripheral nervous system:

5. **Schwann**[18] (shwon) **cells** (**neurilemmocytes**) envelop nerve fibers of the PNS, forming a sleeve around them called the *neurilemma* (fig. 13.4). In most cases, a Schwann cell winds repeatedly around a nerve fiber and produces a myelin sheath between the neurilemma and nerve fiber. This is similar to the myelin sheath produced by oligodendrocytes in the CNS, but there are differences in the way myelin is produced, as described later. In addition to myelinating peripheral nerve fibers, Schwann cells assist in the regeneration of damaged fibers.

6. **Satellite cells** surround the neuron cell bodies in ganglia of the PNS. Little is known of their function.

# INSIGHT 13.1

## Clinical Application

### Glial Cells and Brain Tumors

A tumor consists of a mass of rapidly dividing cells. Mature neurons, however, have little capacity for mitosis and seldom form tumors. Some brain tumors arise from the meninges (protective membranes of the CNS) or arise by metastasis from tumors elsewhere, such as malignant melanoma and colon cancer. Most adult brain tumors, however, are composed of glial cells, which are mitotically active throughout life. Such tumors, called *gliomas,*[19] grow rapidly and are highly malignant. Because of the blood–brain barrier, brain tumors usually do not yield to chemotherapy and must be treated with radiation or surgery.

---

[17]*astro* = star + *cyte* = cell

[18]Theodore Schwann (1810–82), German histologist
[19]*glia* = glial cells + *oma* = tumor

# Myelin

The **myelin** (MY-eh-lin) **sheath** is an insulating layer around a nerve fiber, somewhat like the rubber insulation on a wire. It is formed by oligodendrocytes in the central nervous system and Schwann cells in the peripheral nervous system. Since it consists of the plasma membranes of these glial cells, its composition is like that of plasma membranes in general. It is about 20% protein and 80% lipid, the latter including phospholipids, glycolipids, and cholesterol. Myelin imparts a glistening white color to certain regions of nervous tissue, such as the *white matter* of the brain and spinal cord.

Production of the myelin sheath is called **myelination.** In the PNS, a Schwann cell spirals repeatedly around a single nerve fiber, laying down as many as a hundred compact layers of its own membrane with almost no cytoplasm between the membranes (fig. 13.7a). These layers constitute the myelin sheath. The Schwann cell spirals

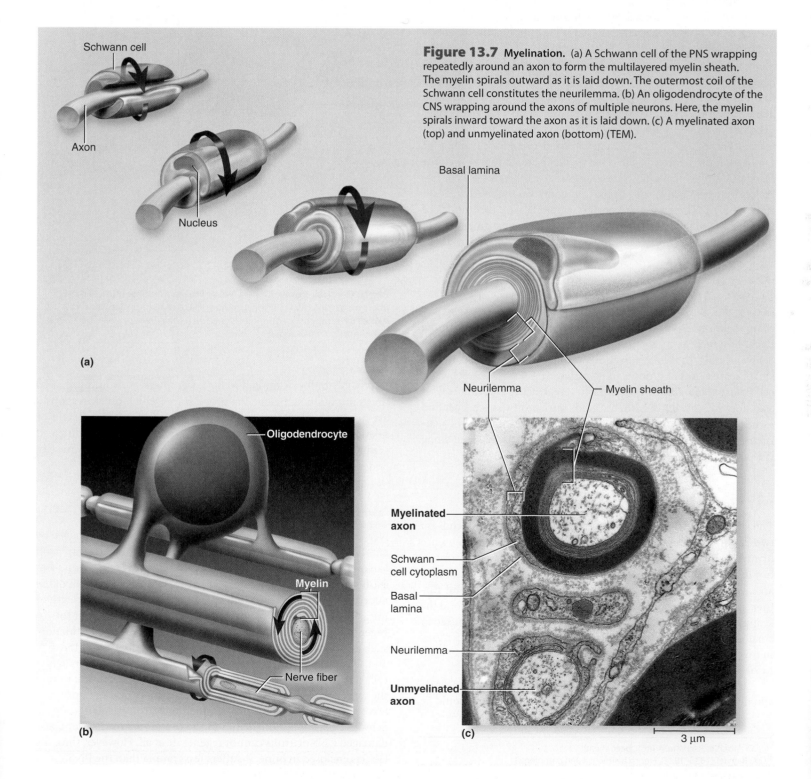

**Figure 13.7** **Myelination.** (a) A Schwann cell of the PNS wrapping repeatedly around an axon to form the multilayered myelin sheath. The myelin spirals outward as it is laid down. The outermost coil of the Schwann cell constitutes the neurilemma. (b) An oligodendrocyte of the CNS wrapping around the axons of multiple neurons. Here, the myelin spirals inward toward the axon as it is laid down. (c) A myelinated axon (top) and unmyelinated axon (bottom) (TEM).

**(a)**

Schwann cell

Axon

Nucleus

Basal lamina

Neurilemma

Myelin sheath

**(b)**

Oligodendrocyte

Myelin

Nerve fiber

**(c)**

Myelinated axon

Schwann cell cytoplasm

Basal lamina

Neurilemma

Unmyelinated axon

3 μm

outward as it wraps the nerve fiber, finally ending with a thick outermost coil called the **neurilemma**[20] (noor-ih-LEM-ah). Here, the bulging body of the Schwann cell contains its nucleus and most of its cytoplasm. External to the neurilemma is a basal lamina and then a thin sleeve of fibrous connective tissue called the *endoneurium*.

To visualize this myelination process, imagine that you wrap an almost-empty tube of toothpaste tightly around a pencil. The pencil represents the axon, and the spiral layers of toothpaste tube (with the toothpaste squeezed out) represent the myelin. The toothpaste would be forced to one end of the tube, which would form a bulge on the external surface of the wrapping, like the body of the Schwann cell.

In the CNS, each oligodendrocyte reaches out to myelinate several nerve fibers in its immediate vicinity (fig. 13.7b). Since it is anchored to multiple nerve fibers, it cannot migrate around any one of them like a Schwann cell does. It must push newer layers of myelin under the older ones, so myelination spirals inward toward the nerve fiber. Nerve fibers of the CNS have no neurilemma or endoneurium.

In both the PNS and CNS, a nerve fiber is much longer than the reach of a single glial cell, so it requires many Schwann cells or oligodendrocytes to cover one fiber. Consequently, the myelin sheath is segmented. The gaps between the segments are called **nodes of Ranvier**[21] (RON-vee-AY), and the myelin-covered segments from one gap to the next are called **internodes**. The internodes are about 0.2 to 1.0 mm long.

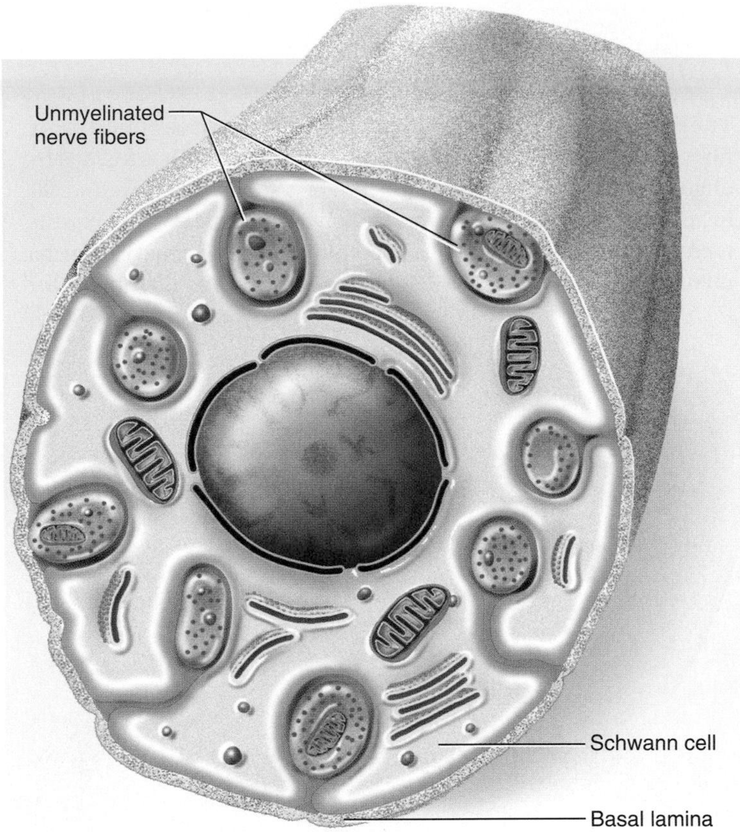

## Unmyelinated Nerve Fibers

Many nerve fibers in the CNS and PNS are unmyelinated. In the PNS, however, even the unmyelinated fibers are enveloped in Schwann cells. In this case, one Schwann cell harbors from 1 to 12 small nerve fibers in grooves in its surface (fig. 13.8). The Schwann cell's plasma membrane does not spiral repeatedly around the fiber as it does in a myelin sheath, but folds once around each fiber and somewhat overlaps itself along the edges. This wrapping is the neurilemma. A basal lamina surrounds the entire Schwann cell along with its nerve fibers.

## Myelin and Signal Conduction

The speed at which a signal travels along a nerve fiber depends on two factors: the diameter of the fiber and the presence or absence of myelin. Signal conduction occurs along the surface of a fiber, not deep within its axoplasm. Large fibers have more surface area and conduct signals more rapidly than small fibers. Myelin further speeds signal conduction for physiological reasons beyond the scope of this book. Nerve signals travel about 0.5 to 2.0 m/sec in small unmyelinated fibers (2–4 μm in diameter) and 3 to 15 m/sec in myelinated fibers of the same size. In large myelinated fibers (up to 20 μm in diameter), they travel as fast as 120 m/sec.

One might wonder why all of our nerve fibers are not large, myelinated, and fast, but if this were so, our nervous system would be

Unmyelinated nerve fibers

Schwann cell

Basal lamina

**Figure 13.8** **Unmyelinated Nerve Fibers.** Multiple unmyelinated fibers are enclosed in channels in the surface of a single Schwann cell.
● *What is the functional disadvantage of an unmyelinated nerve fiber? What is its anatomical advantage?*

impossibly bulky or limited to far fewer fibers. Slow unmyelinated fibers are quite sufficient for processes in which quick responses are not particularly important, such as secreting stomach acid or dilating the pupil. Fast myelinated fibers are employed where speed is more important, as in motor commands to the skeletal muscles and sensory signals for vision and balance.

## Schwann Cells and Nerve Regeneration

Nerve fibers in the peripheral nervous system are often damaged by cuts and other injuries, but if the cell body remains intact, an axon can often regenerate. Two things are required for regeneration of an axon: a neurilemma and an endoneurium. The Schwann cells of the neurilemma secrete *nerve growth factors* that stimulate regrowth of the axon, and the Schwann cells and endoneurium together form a **regeneration tube** that guides the growing axon to its destination, such as a muscle fiber. The axon grows down the middle of the tube and, if successful, it reestablishes synaptic contact with its target cell. The process is not perfect—some injured neurons fail to find the target cell, and some simply die. Nerve injuries therefore may leave a person with some loss of fine motor control. There are no Schwann cells or endoneurium in the central nervous system, and damaged CNS neurons cannot regenerate at all. However, since the CNS is enclosed in bone, it suffers less trauma than the PNS.

---

[20]*neuri* = nerve + *lemma* = husk, peel, sheath
[21]L. A. Ranvier (1835–1922), French histologist and pathologist

# INSIGHT 13.2

## Clinical Application

### Diseases of the Myelin Sheath

Multiple sclerosis and Tay–Sachs disease are degenerative disorders of the myelin sheath. In *multiple sclerosis*[22] *(MS),* the oligodendrocytes and myelin sheaths of the CNS deteriorate and are replaced by hardened scar tissue, especially between the ages of 20 and 40. Nerve conduction is disrupted with effects that depend on what part of the CNS is involved—numbness, double vision, blindness, speech defects, neurosis, or tremors. Patients experience variable cycles of milder and worse symptoms until they eventually become bedridden. The cause of MS remains uncertain; most hypotheses suggest that it is an *autoimmune disease*—a disorder in which one's immune system turns against one's own tissues—perhaps triggered by a virus in genetically susceptible individuals. There is no cure. There is conflicting evidence as to how much it shortens a patient's life expectancy, if at all. A few die within a year of diagnosis, but many people live with MS for 25 or 30 years.

*Tay–Sachs*[23] *disease* is a hereditary disorder seen mainly in infants of Eastern European Jewish ancestry. It results from the abnormal accumulation of a glycolipid called $GM_2$ (ganglioside) in the myelin sheath. $GM_2$ is normally decomposed by a lysosomal enzyme, but this enzyme is lacking from those who inherit the recessive Tay–Sachs gene from both parents. As $GM_2$ accumulates, it disrupts the conduction of nerve signals, and the victim typically suffers blindness, loss of coordination, and dementia. Signs begin to appear before the child is a year old and most victims die by the age of 3 or 4. Asymptomatic adult carriers can be identified by a blood test and advised by genetic counselors on the risk of their children having the disease.

## *Before You Go On*

Answer the following questions to test your understanding of the preceding section:

8. From memory, make your own table of the six kinds of glial cells and the functions of each. Which type has the most varied functions?

9. Summarize the major ways in which oligodendrocytes and Schwann cells differ in the way they produce a myelin sheath, and state where the glial cell body of each type is located relative to the myelin and nerve fiber.

10. Compare the signal conduction speed in myelinated fibers versus unmyelinated ones. Why aren't *all* nerve fibers in the body myelinated?

11. Explain why damaged nerve fibers in the PNS can regenerate but damaged fibers in the CNS cannot.

---

[22]*scler* = hard, tough + *osis* = condition
[23]Warren Tay (1843–1927), English physician; Bernard Sachs (1858–1944), American neurologist

# Synapses and Neural Circuits

### Objectives

When you have completed this section, you should be able to

- describe the synaptic junctions between one neuron and another;
- describe the variety of interconnections that exist between two neurons; and
- describe four basic variations in the circuitry or "wiring patterns" of the nervous system.

No neuron functions in isolation from others; neurons work in groups of cells that are connected in patterns similar to the electrical circuits of radios and other electronic devices. In this section, we examine the connections between neurons and the functional circuits of neuron groups.

## Synapses

The meeting point between a neuron and any other cell is called a **synapse.** The other cell may be an epithelial, muscular, glandular, or other cell type, but in most cases it is another neuron. Synapses make *neural integration* (information processing) possible; each is a "decision-making" device that determines whether a second cell will respond to signals from the first. Without synapses, signals would simply be transmitted automatically from receptors to effectors, effectors would respond to every stimulus, and the nervous system would be incapable of any decision making. But in reality, one neuron can have an enormous number of synapses and thus a great deal of information-processing capability (fig. 13.9). For example, a spinal motor neuron receives about 8,000 synaptic contacts from other neurons on its dendrites and another 2,000 on its soma. In part of the brain called the cerebellum, one neuron can have as many as 100,000 synapses. The cerebral cortex (the main information-processing tissue of the brain) is estimated to have 100

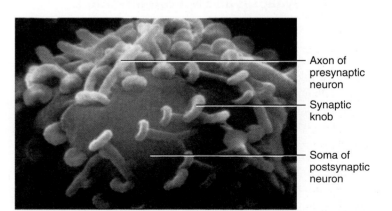

**Figure 13.9** Synaptic Knobs on the Soma of a Neuron in a Marine Slug, *Aplysia* (SEM).
● *To which of the three classes of synapses (compare fig. 13.10) would these belong?*

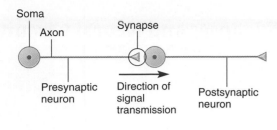

**Figure 13.10** Synaptic Relationships Between Neurons. (a) Pre- and postsynaptic neurons. (b) Types of synapses defined by the site of contact on the postsynaptic neuron.

trillion ($10^{14}$) synapses. To get some impression of this number, imagine trying to count them. Even if you could count two synapses per second, night and day without a coffee break, and you were immortal, it would take you 1.6 million years.

A nerve signal arrives at a synapse by way of the **presynaptic neuron,** then continues on its way via the **postsynaptic neuron** (fig. 13.10a). When a presynaptic axon ends at the dendrite of a postsynaptic neuron, the two cells are said to form an **axodendritic synapse.** When the presynaptic axon terminates on the soma of the next cell, they form an **axosomatic synapse.** When it terminates on the axon of the next cell, they form an **axoaxonic synapse** (fig. 13.10b).

## Chemical Synapses and Neurotransmitters

A **chemical synapse** is a junction at which the presynaptic neuron releases a neurotransmitter to stimulate the postsynaptic cell. The neuromuscular junction (NMJ) described in chapter 10, (p. 278) is an example of this. The NMJ and many other synapses employ *acetylcholine* as a neurotransmitter. Postsynaptic neurons of the sympathetic nervous system use *norepinephrine.*

Some neurotransmitters are *excitatory* and tend to cause the postsynaptic cell to generate a nerve signal. Some widely used excitatory neurotransmitters in the central nervous system (CNS) are *glutamate* in the brain and *aspartate* in the spinal cord. Other neurotransmitters are *inhibitory* and suppress responses in the postsynaptic cell. The most widely used inhibitory neurotransmitters in the CNS are *gamma-aminobutyric acid (GABA)* in the brain and *glycine* in the spinal cord. Some other well-known neurotransmitters are *dopamine, serotonin, histamine,* and *beta-endorphin.* There are over 100 known neurotransmitters.

At a chemical synapse, a terminal branch of the presynaptic nerve fiber ends in a swelling, the **synaptic knob.** The knob is separated from the next cell by a 20- to 40-nm gap called the **synaptic cleft** (fig. 13.11). The knob contains membrane-bounded secretory vesicles called **synaptic vesicles,** which contain the neurotransmitter. Many of these vesicles are "docked" at release sites on the inside of the plasma membrane, ready to release their neurotransmitter on demand. Neurotransmitter release is achieved by exocytosis (see p. 56). A reserve pool of synaptic vesicles is located a little farther away from the membrane, clustered near the release sites and tethered to the cytoskeleton by protein microfilaments. These vesicles stand by and "step forward" to dock on the membrane and release their neurotransmitter after the previously docked vesicles have expended their contents. Synaptic vesicles are found in a few cells other than neurons, such as the sensory cells of taste, hearing, and equilibrium. They release neurotransmitter to stimulate a nearby nerve cell.

A postsynaptic neuron does not show such conspicuous specializations. At this end, a neuron has no synaptic vesicles and cannot release neurotransmitters. Its membrane does, however, contain proteins that function as neurotransmitter receptors, and it may be folded to increase its receptor-laden surface area and, therefore, its sensitivity to the neurotransmitter. A signal always travels in only one direction across a chemical synapse, from the presynaptic cell with synaptic vesicles to the postsynaptic cell with neurotransmitter receptors. This one-way transmission ensures the precise routing of nerve signals in the body.

Synaptic transmission begins when a nerve signal arrives at the end of the presynaptic neuron and triggers the exocytosis of synaptic vesicles. Neurotransmitter is released into the synaptic cleft, diffuses across to the postsynaptic cell, and binds to receptors on that cell's membrane. Depending on the neurotransmitter and the type of receptor, this may either stimulate or inhibit the postsynaptic cell. The postsynaptic cell "decides" whether or not to initiate a new nerve signal based on the composite effects of excitatory and inhibitory input through the many synapses on its dendrites and soma.

## Electrical Synapses

Another type of synapse, called an **electrical synapse,** connects some neurons, neuroglia, and cardiac and single-unit smooth muscle cells. Here, adjacent cells are joined by gap junctions that allow ions to diffuse directly from one cell into the next. These junctions have the advantage of quick transmission because there is no delay for the release and binding of neurotransmitter. Their disadvantage, however, is that they cannot integrate information and make decisions.

## Neural Pools and Circuits

Neurons function in ensembles called **neural pools.** One neural pool may consist of thousands to millions of interneurons concerned with a particular body function—one to control the rhythm of your breathing, one to move your limbs rhythmically as you walk, one to regulate your sense of hunger, and another to interpret smells, for example. The functioning of a neural pool hinges on the anatomical organization of its neurons, much like the functioning of a radio depends on the particular way its transistors, diodes,

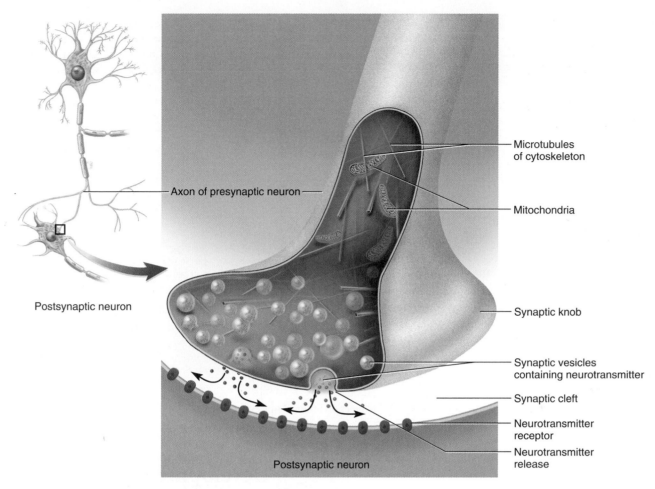

**Figure 13.11**  Structure of a Chemical Synapse.

and capacitors are laid out. The interconnections between neurons are called **neural circuits.** A wide variety of neural functions result from the operation of four principal kinds of circuits (fig. 13.12):

1. In a **diverging circuit,** one nerve fiber branches and synapses with several postsynaptic cells. Each of those may synapse with several more, so input from just one neuron may produce output through dozens more. Such a circuit allows one motor neuron of the brain, for example, to ultimately cause thousands of muscle fibers to contract.

2. A **converging circuit** is the opposite of a diverging circuit—input from many different sources is funneled to one neuron or neural pool. Through neural convergence, a respiratory center in the brainstem receives input from other parts of the brain, from receptors for blood chemistry in the arteries, and from stretch receptors in the lungs. The respiratory center can then produce an output that takes all of these factors into account and sets an appropriate pattern of breathing.

3. In a **reverberating circuit,** neurons stimulate each other in a linear sequence such as A → B → C → D, but neuron C sends an axon collateral back to A. As a result, every time C fires, it not only stimulates output neuron D, but also restimulates A and starts the process over. Such a circuit produces a repetitive

output that lasts until one or more neurons in the circuit fail to fire or until an inhibitory signal from another source stops one of them from firing. A reverberating circuit sends repetitious signals to the diaphragm and intercostal muscles, for example, to make you inhale. When the circuit stops firing, you exhale; the next time it fires, you inhale again. Reverberating circuits may also be involved in short-term memory (for example, in the way a telephone number "echoes" in your memory from the time you look it up in the phone book until the time you dial it), and they may play a role in the uncontrolled "storms" of neural activity that occur in epilepsy.

4. In a **parallel after-discharge circuit,** an input neuron diverges to stimulate several chains of neurons. Each chain has a different number of synapses, but eventually they all reconverge on the same output neuron. Each synapse delays a nerve signal by about 0.5 millisecond, so the more synapses there are in a pathway, the longer it takes a nerve signal to get through that pathway to the output neuron. The output neuron, receiving signals from multiple pathways, may go on firing for some time after the input has ceased. Unlike a reverberating circuit, this type has no feedback loop. Once all the neurons in the circuit have fired, the output ceases. Continued firing after the stimulus stops is called *after-discharge.* It explains why you can

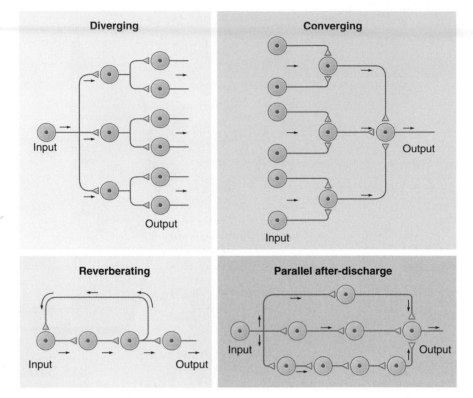

**Figure 13.12** **Four Types of Neural Circuits.** Arrows indicate the direction of signal transmission.

stare at a lamp, then close your eyes or turn the lamp off and continue to see an image of it for a while. Such a circuit is also important to certain reflexes—for example, when a brief pain produces a longer-lasting output to the limb muscles and causes you to draw back your hand or foot from danger. (See the discussion of *reflex arcs* in chapter 14, p. 416.)

## Before You Go On

*Answer the following questions to test your understanding of the preceding section:*

12. At a given synapse, what features are present on the presynaptic neuron that are absent from the postsynaptic neuron?

13. In synaptic transmission, where does a neurotransmitter come from? How does it affect the postsynaptic neuron?

14. Name any four neurotransmitters and state some functional differences between them.

15. What is an electrical synapse? Where can electrical synapses be found? Identify an advantage and a disadvantage of an electrical synapse compared to a chemical synapse.

16. What is the difference between a neural pool and a neural circuit?

17. Name the four types of neural circuits and briefly describe the functional differences between them, or an advantage of each type for certain purposes.

## Developmental and Clinical Perspectives

### Objectives
When you have completed this section, you should be able to

- describe how the nervous system develops in an embryo; and

- describe a few birth defects that result from abnormalities of this developmental process.

## Development of the Nervous System

Some aspects of nervous system development, or **neurulation,** were briefly discussed in chapter 4 (p. 112). Further understanding of this process will form a basis for understanding the brain and spinal cord anatomy presented in chapters 14 and 15.

The first embryonic trace of the central nervous system appears early in the third week of development. A dorsal streak called the *neuroectoderm* appears along the length of the embryo and thickens to form a **neural plate** (fig. 13.13). This is destined to give rise to most neurons and to all glial cells except microglia, which come from mesoderm. As development progresses, the neural plate sinks and the edges of it thicken, thus forming a **neural groove** with a raised **neural fold** along each side. The neural folds then fuse along the midline, somewhat like a closing zipper, beginning in the cervical

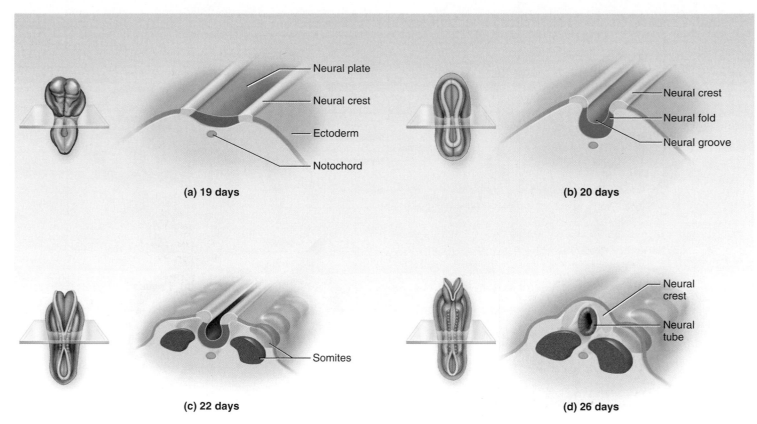

**Figure 13.13** **Formation of the Neural Tube.** The left-hand figure in each case is a dorsal view of the embryo, and the right-hand figure is a three-dimensional representation of the tissues at the indicated level of the respective embryo.

(neck) region of the neural groove and progressing rostrally (toward the head) and caudally (toward the tail). By 4 weeks, this process creates a hollow channel called the **neural tube.** For a time, the neural tube is open to the amniotic fluid at the rostral and caudal ends. These openings close at 25 and 27 days, respectively. The lumen of the neural tube becomes a fluid-filled space that later constitutes the *central canal* of the spinal cord and *ventricles* of the brain.

Following closure, the neural tube separates from the overlying ectoderm, sinks a little deeper, and grows lateral processes that later give rise to motor nerve fibers. Some ectodermal cells that originally lay along the margin of the neural groove separate from the rest and form a longitudinal column on each side called the **neural crest.** Neural crest cells give rise to most of the peripheral nervous system, including the sensory and autonomic nerves and ganglia, Schwann cells, the adrenal medulla (a gland described on p. 537), the two inner membranes *(meninges)* around the brain and spinal cord, melanocytes of the skin, and the dermis and some of the bones of the head and neck, as well as a few other structures.

By the fourth week, the neural tube exhibits three anterior dilations, or *primary vesicles,* called the **forebrain** *(prosencephalon[24])* (PROSS-en-SEF-uh-lon), **midbrain** *(mesencephalon[25])* (MEZ-en-SEF-uh-lon), and **hindbrain** *(rhombencephalon[26])* (ROM-ben-SEF-uh-lon) (fig. 13.14). While these vesicles develop, the neural tube bends at the junction of the hindbrain and spinal cord to form the **cervical flexure,** and in the midbrain region to form the **cephalic flexure.**

By the fifth week, the neural tube undergoes further flexion and subdivides into five *secondary vesicles.* The forebrain divides into two of them, the **telencephalon**[27] (TEL-en-SEFF-uh-lon) and **diencephalon**[28] (DY-en-SEF-uh-lon); the midbrain remains undivided and retains the name **mesencephalon;** and the hindbrain divides into two vesicles, the **metencephalon**[29] (MET-en-SEF-uh-lon) and **myelencephalon**[30] (MY-el-en-SEF-uh-lon). The telencephalon has a pair of lateral outgrowths that later become the *cerebral hemispheres,* and the diencephalon exhibits a pair of small cuplike *optic vesicles* that become the retinas of the eyes. Figure 13.14c shows structures of the fully developed brain that arise from each of the secondary vesicles.

In week 14, Schwann cells and oligodendrocytes begin spiraling around the nerve fibers, laying down layers of myelin and giving the fibers a white appearance. Yet very little myelin is present in the brain even at birth, and there is little visible distinction between the *gray matter* and *white matter* of the newborn brain. Myelination

---

[24]*pros* = before, in front + *encephal* = brain
[25]*mes* = middle
[26]*rhomb* = rhombus

[27]*tele* = end, remote
[28]*di* = through, between
[29]*met* = behind, beyond, distal to
[30]*myel* = spinal cord

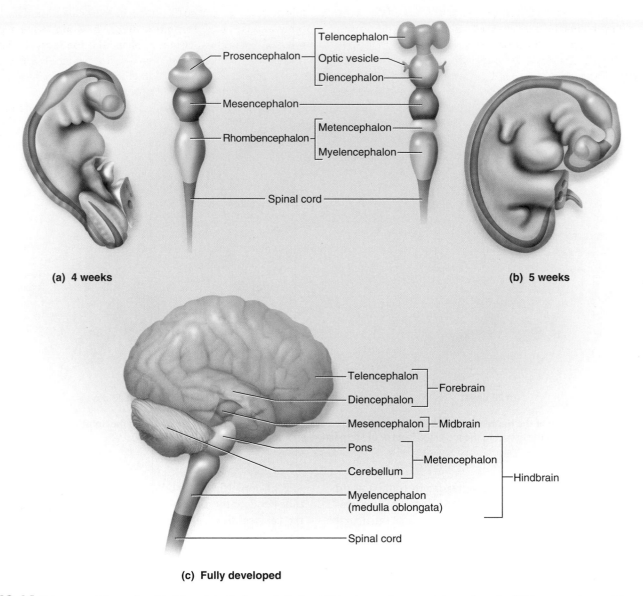

(a) 4 weeks

(b) 5 weeks

Telencephalon
Optic vesicle
Diencephalon

Prosencephalon

Mesencephalon

Rhombencephalon

Metencephalon

Myelencephalon

Spinal cord

Telencephalon ┐
                │ Forebrain
Diencephalon ┘

Mesencephalon ├ Midbrain

Pons ┐
     │ Metencephalon ┐
Cerebellum ┘          │
                      │ Hindbrain
Myelencephalon        │
(medulla oblongata) ┘

Spinal cord

(c) Fully developed

**Figure 13.14** **Primary and Secondary Vesicles of the Embryonic Brain.** (a) The three primary vesicles at 4 weeks. (b) The secondary vesicles at 5 weeks. (c) The fully developed brain, color-coded to relate its structures to the secondary embryonic vesicles.

proceeds rapidly in infancy, and it is this, far more than the multiplication or enlargement of neurons, that accounts for most postnatal brain growth. Myelination is not completed until late adolescence. Since myelin has such a high lipid content, dietary fat is important to early nervous system development. Well-meaning parents can do their children significant harm by giving them the sort of low-fat diets (skimmed milk, etc.) that may be beneficial to an adult.

In the third month of development, the spinal cord extends for the full length of the embryo. As the vertebrae develop (see p. 204), *spinal nerves* arise from the cord and pass straight laterally to emerge between the vertebrae, through the intervertebral foramina. Subsequently, however, the vertebral column grows faster than the spinal cord. By birth, the cord ends in the vertebral canal of the third lumbar vertebra (L3), and by adulthood, it ends at the level of L1 to L2. As the vertebral column elongates, the spinal nerve roots elongate,

so they still emerge between the same vertebrae, but the lower vertebral canal is occupied by a bundle of nerve roots instead of spinal cord. The resulting adult anatomy is described in chapter 14.

## Developmental Disorders of the Nervous System

The central nervous system is subject to multiple aberrations in embryonic development. Approximately 1 out of 100 live-born infants exhibit major defects in brain development. Common among these are **neural tube defects (NTDs)** such as **spina bifida** (SPY-nuh BIF-ih-duh). Spina bifida occurs when one or more vertebrae fail to form a complete neural arch for enclosure of the spinal cord. It is especially common in the lumbosacral region. The mildest form, *spina bifida occulta,*[31] involves only one to a few vertebrae and causes no functional problems. Its only external sign is a dimple or patch of hairy pigmented skin on the lower back. *Spina bifida cystica*[32] is more serious (fig. 13.15). A sac protrudes from the spine and may contain parts of the spinal cord and nerve roots, meninges, and cerebrospinal fluid. In extreme cases, inferior spinal cord function is absent, causing paralysis of the lower limbs and urinary bladder and lack of bowel control. Bladder paralysis can lead to chronic urinary infections and renal failure. Women can significantly reduce the risk of bearing a child with spina bifida by taking supplemental folic acid (a B vitamin). However, this works only if taken habitually before the egg is fertilized; folic acid supplements are ineffective if begun after a woman already knows she is pregnant.

Other severe neural tube defects include microcephaly and anencephaly. In **microcephaly,**[33] the face is of normal size but the brain and calvaria are abnormally small. Microcephaly is accompanied by profound mental retardation. **Anencephaly**[34] results from failure of the rostral end of the neural tube to close. This leaves the brain exposed to the amniotic fluid. The brain tissue degenerates, most of the brain is absent at birth, and the head is relatively flat or truncated above the eyes. Such infants generally die within a few hours. Neural tube defects sometimes run in families but can also be caused by teratogens and nutritional deficiencies.

Other disorders of the nervous system are described in chapters 14 through 17.

---

[31]*bifid* = divided, forked + *occult* = hidden
[32]*cyst* = sac, bladder
[33]*micro* = small + *cephal* = head
[34]*an* = without + *encephal* = brain

## *Before You Go On*

*Answer the following questions to test your understanding of the preceding section:*

18. How does the neural crest originate? What cells or tissues arise from it?

19. Where does closure of the neural tube begin? What are the last regions to close?

20. What single adult structure arises from all five of the secondary vesicles of the neural tube?

21. When does myelination begin? When does it end?

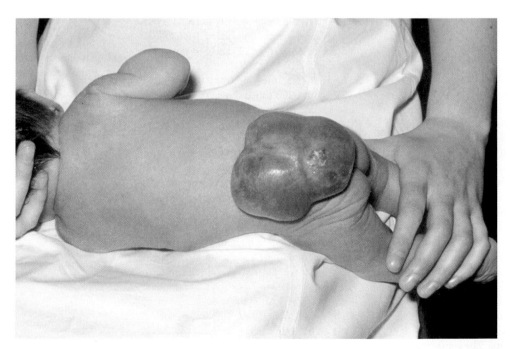

**Figure 13.15** Spina Bifida Cystica. The sac in the lumbar region is called a myelomeningocele.

# CHAPTER REVIEW

## REVIEW OF KEY CONCEPTS

### Overview of the Nervous System (p. 376)

1. The nervous and endocrine systems are the body's two principal mechanisms of internal communication and coordination. The nervous system is specialized for the rapid transmission of signals from cell to cell.
2. The two major divisions of the nervous system are the *central nervous system (CNS)* (brain and spinal cord) and the *peripheral nervous system (PNS)* (nerves and ganglia).
3. The PNS has *sensory (afferent)* and *motor (efferent)* divisions. Each of these, in turn, has subdivisions called the visceral and somatic divisions. The *visceral division* innervates organs of the body cavities such as the heart and stomach, and the *somatic division* innervates the skin, muscles, bones, and joints.
4. The visceral motor division is also called the *autonomic nervous system*. It innervates glands, cardiac muscle, and smooth muscle, and controls unconscious, involuntary visceral reflexes. It consists of *sympathetic* and *parasympathetic* divisions, which often have contrasting effects on the same target organs.

### Nerve Cells (Neurons) (p. 377)

1. The functional unit of the nervous system is the *neuron*. Neurons are able to communicate only because they possess the properties of excitability, conductivity, and secretion.
2. There are three functional classes of neurons: *sensory (afferent) neurons,* which convey signals to the CNS; *interneurons,* contained entirely within the CNS; and *motor (efferent) neurons,* which convey signals away from the CNS to effectors such as muscle and gland cells.
3. A neuron consists of a *soma* (cell body); usually multiple *dendrites,* which receive signals and convey them to the soma; and a single *axon* (nerve fiber), which carries nerve signals away from the soma. The soma contains the nucleus and protein-synthesizing organelles of the cell. The axon arises from an *axon hillock.* This and the first segment of the axon are the *trigger zone,* where action potentials are generated. The axon branches into a *terminal arborization* at its distal end, and each branch ends in a dilated *synaptic knob.*
4. Neurons are described as *multipolar* (with an axon and two or more dendrites), *bipolar* (with an axon and one dendrite), *unipolar* (with only a single process arising from the soma), or *anaxonic* (with dendrites but no axon).

### Supportive Cells (Neuroglia) (p. 381)

1. Most cells of the nervous system are not neurons but *neuroglia (glial cells).*
2. Four kinds of neuroglia occur in the CNS: *oligodendrocytes* (which produce myelin); *ependymal cells* (which line the internal cavities of the CNS and produce cerebrospinal fluid); *microglia* (macrophages of the CNS); and *astrocytes* (with numerous roles in the supportive framework of the CNS, the blood–brain barrier, nourishment of neurons, homeostatic maintenance of the extracellular fluid, and repair of damaged CNS tissue).
3. Two kinds of glial cells occur in the PNS: *Schwann cells* (which produce a neurilemma and myelin) and *satellite cells* (of little-known function).
4. *Myelin* is an insulating sheath around certain nerve fibers. It consists of spiral layers of plasma membrane arising from oligodendrocytes in the CNS and Schwann cells in the PNS.
5. In the PNS, the outermost coil of the Schwann cell is called the *neurilemma.* It is covered with a basal lamina and then a thin connective tissue sheath, the *endoneurium.*
6. One glial cell myelinates only a short segment of a nerve fiber. Therefore the myelin sheath around a nerve fiber is segmented, with long *internodes* separated by interruptions of the myelin sheath called *nodes of Ranvier.*
7. Schwann cells also envelop *unmyelinated neurons,* but enfold them in only one coil of plasma membrane and do not form myelin around them. Each Schwann cell can have several surface grooves, each accommodating an unmyelinated nerve fiber.
8. The velocity of a nerve signal depends on the diameter of a nerve fiber and whether it is covered with myelin, which speeds up the signal. Thus, nerve signals travel relatively slowly (up to 2 m/sec) in unmyelinated fibers; faster in myelinated fibers of the same diameter; and fastest (up to 120 m/sec) in large myelinated fibers.
9. A neurilemma and endoneurium are required for the regeneration of damaged nerve fibers; they form a *regeneration tube* that guides a regrowing nerve fiber to its target cell. They are absent from the CNS, and damaged fibers there cannot regenerate.

### Synapses and Neural Circuits (p. 385)

1. The point where a nerve fiber ends at a target cell (such as another neuron or a muscle or gland cell) is called a *synapse.* Synapses are the decision-making, information-processing points in the nervous system; the more synapses a neuron or neural circuit has, the more data the neuron or circuit can process.
2. With respect to the direction of signal transmission, the neuron before the synapse is called the *presynaptic neuron,* and the one after the synapse is the *postsynaptic neuron.*
3. A presynaptic neuron can terminate on the dendrites, soma, or axon of a postsynaptic neuron; such junctions are respectively called *axodendritic, axosomatic,* and *axoaxonic synapses.*
4. A *chemical synapse* is one at which the presynaptic neuron releases a chemical *neurotransmitter,* which diffuses across the *synaptic cleft* and binds to receptors on the postsynaptic cell.
5. Some familiar neurotransmitters are acetylcholine, norepinephrine, glutamate, aspartate, GABA, glycine, dopamine, serotonin, histamine, and beta-endorphin. There are many others.
6. Neurotransmitters are stored in *synaptic vesicles* of the presynaptic neuron. The arrival of a nerve signal stimulates the release of neurotransmitter by vesicle exocytosis.
7. Some cells are linked by *electrical synapses* (gap junctions)—cardiac and single-unit smooth muscle, and some neurons and neuroglia. Electrical synapses allow for very rapid signal transmission but no decision making.
8. Neurons function in groups called *neural pools,* aggregations of neurons collectively dedicated to a certain purpose such as breathing or sensory perception. Within a pool, the neurons are connected along pathways called *neural circuits.*
9. There are four principal types of neural circuits: *diverging, converging, reverberating,* and *parallel after-discharge circuits.*

### Developmental and Clinical Perspectives (p. 388)

1. The early stages of central nervous system development are a middorsal thickening of ectoderm called the *neural plate,* developing into a *neural groove* flanked by raised *neural folds,* and then developing into an enclosed *neural tube.*

2. A longitudinal column of ectodermal tissue separates from the neural groove on each side to become the *neural crest;* this gives rise to sensory and sympathetic neurons, neuroglia, and other cell types.

3. The neural tube develops anterior dilations that form three *primary vesicles (forebrain, midbrain,* and *hindbrain),* then undergoes flexion and subdivision of the forebrain and hindbrain, producing five *secondary vesicles.*

4. Myelination begins in the fourth month, but most brain myelination occurs after birth.

5. The spinal cord initially occupies the entire vertebral canal, but the vertebral column grows faster than the spinal cord, and by adulthood, the spinal cord ends at the level of vertebrae L1 to L2.

6. *Neural tube defects (NTDs)* are deformities of the brain or spinal cord that result from failure of the neural tube to close or otherwise to develop normally. NTDs range from the relatively mild *spina bifida occulta* to the more serious *spina bifida cystica, microcephaly,* and *anencephaly.* NTDs can be genetic or caused by teratogens and nutritional deficiencies.

## TESTING YOUR RECALL

1. The integrative functions of the nervous system are performed mainly by
   a. afferent neurons.
   b. efferent neurons.
   c. neuroglia.
   d. sensory neurons.
   e. interneurons.

2. Neurons arise from embryonic
   a. endoderm.
   b. epidermis.
   c. mesoderm.
   d. mesenchyme.
   e. ectoderm.

3. The soma of a mature neuron lacks
   a. a nucleus.
   b. endoplasmic reticulum.
   c. lipofuscin.
   d. centrioles.
   e. ribosomes.

4. The glial cells that destroy microorganisms in the CNS are
   a. microglia.
   b. satellite cells.
   c. ependymal cells.
   d. oligodendrocytes.
   e. astrocytes.

5. A friend takes a flash photograph of you, and you continue to see an image of the flash unit for several seconds afterward. This phenomenon is the result of a ____ circuit.
   a. diverging
   b. converging
   c. presynaptic
   d. reverberating
   e. parallel after-discharge

6. Neurotransmitters are found in
   a. the cell bodies of neurons.
   b. the dendrites.
   c. the axon hillock.
   d. the synaptic knob.
   e. the postsynaptic plasma membrane.

7. Another name for the axon of a neuron is
   a. nerve fiber.
   b. neurofibril.
   c. neurilemma.
   d. axoplasm.
   e. endoneurium.

8. Nerves that directly control the motility of the stomach or rate of the heartbeat would belong to
   a. the central nervous system.
   b. the somatic sensory division.
   c. the somatic motor division.
   d. the visceral motor division.
   e. the visceral sensory division.

9. The glial cells that guide migrating neurons in the developing fetal brain are
   a. astrocytes.
   b. oligodendrocytes.
   c. satellite cells.
   d. ependymal cells.
   e. microglia.

10. Which of the following appears earlier than all the rest in prenatal development of the nervous system?
    a. the neural groove
    b. the primary vesicles
    c. the neural plate
    d. the neural crest
    e. the neural tube

11. Neurons that convey information to the CNS are called sensory, or _____, neurons.

12. Motor effects that depend on repetitive output from a neural pool are most likely to use the _____ type of neural circuit.

13. Prenatal degeneration of the forebrain results in a birth defect called _____.

14. Neurons receive incoming signals by way of specialized processes called _____.

15. In the central nervous system, cells called _____ perform one of the same functions that Schwann cells do in the peripheral nervous system.

16. A/an _____ synapse is formed when a presynaptic neuron synapses with the cell body of a postsynaptic neuron.

17. All of the nervous system except the brain and spinal cord is called the _____.

18. The _____ and _____ are necessary for regeneration of damaged nerve fibers in the peripheral nervous system.

19. In the peripheral nervous system, the somas of the neurons are concentrated in enlarged, knotlike structures called _____ connected to the nerves.

20. At a given synapse, the _____ neuron has neurotransmitter receptors.

***Answers in the Appendix***

## TRUE OR FALSE

*Determine which five of the following statements are false, and briefly explain why.*

1. Adult neurons are incapable of mitosis.

2. Most neurons have more dendrites than axons.

3. Dendrites never contain synaptic vesicles.

4. Interneurons connect sense organs to the CNS.

5. Nerve signals travel faster in myelinated nerve fibers than in unmyelinated ones.

6. The myelin sheath covers the neurilemma of a nerve fiber.

7. Nodes of Ranvier are present only in myelinated fibers of the PNS.

8. Interneurons occur in the brain, spinal cord, and ganglia of the PNS.

9. Unipolar neurons cannot produce action potentials because they have no axon.

10. There are more glial cells than neurons in the nervous system.

*Answers in the Appendix*

## TESTING YOUR COMPREHENSION

1. Suppose some hypothetical disease prevented the formation of astrocytes in the fetal brain. How would you expect this to affect brain development?

2. How would nervous system function be affected if both the presynaptic and postsynaptic neurons at every synapse had both synaptic vesicles and neurotransmitter receptors?

3. What unusual characteristic of neurons can be attributed to their lack of centrioles?

4. Of the three properties of neurons described on page 377, which ones are also characteristic of skeletal muscle fibers (see chapter 10)? Explain why these properties are needed by both types of cells. Which one is absent from skeletal muscle? Explain why neurons require this property but skeletal muscle does not.

5. What division or subdivision of the peripheral nervous system would control each of the following: constriction of the pupils in bright light; the movements of your hand as you write; the sensation of a stomachache; blinking as a particle of dust is blown toward your eye; your awareness of the position of your hand as you touch your nose with your eyes closed? Briefly explain each answer.

*Answers at aris.mhhe.com*

## ONLINE RESOURCES

Visit aprevealed.com to explore melt-away cadaver dissections, watch animations that clarify difficult concepts, review histological and radiological images, or take a quiz to assess your understanding of the material.

The Saladin *Human Anatomy,* 2e website at aris.mhhe.com features chapter-specific quizzes, labeling exercises, and other interactive tools to complement your study of human anatomy. If your instructor has provided an ARIS course code, you can also access assignments and information specific to your course.

# 14

# The Spinal Cord and Spinal Nerves

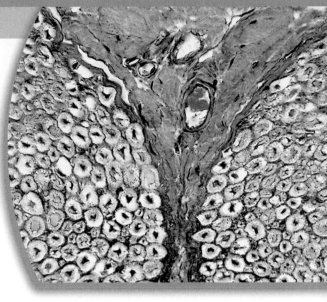

Cross section of a nerve showing parts of two fascicles (bundles) of nerve fibers (maroon)

## CHAPTER OUTLINE

## INSIGHTS

## BRUSHING UP

To understand this chapter, you may find it helpful to review the following concepts:
- Embryonic folding and organogenesis (p. 111)
- Divisions of the nervous system (p. 376)
- Functional classes of neurons (p. 377)
- Embryonic development of the spinal cord (p. 388)

Anatomy & Physiology | REVEALED®
aprevealed.com

**Nervous System**

Every year in the United States, thousands of people become paralyzed by spinal cord injuries that result from automobile and motorcycle accidents, contact sports, and falls. Although the spinal cord is protected by the vertebral column, damage may occur as a result of vertebral fractures or viral infections. Because the spinal cord serves as a pathway for messages between the brain and the rest of the body, spinal cord injuries often have a devastating effect on one's quality of life. Their treatment is one of the most lively areas of medical research today.

As physical therapists are well aware, the consequences of spinal cord injury can vary greatly, but include paralysis of the lower limbs (*paraplegia*) or all four limbs (*quadriplegia*), respiratory paralysis, loss of sensation or motor control in more limited regions of the body, and disorders of bladder and bowel control and sexual function. Therapists who treat spinal patients must know spinal cord anatomy and function to understand their patients' functional deficits and prospects for improvement and to plan an appropriate regimen of treatment. Such anatomical knowledge is necessary, as well, for understanding *hemiplegia*—paralysis of one or both limbs on either the left or right side of the body—even though this usually results from strokes or other brain injuries rather than spinal cord injuries. The spinal cord is the "information highway" that connects the brain with the lower body; it contains the neural routes that explain why a lesion to a specific part of the brain results in a functional loss in a specific locality in the lower body.

In this chapter, we will study not only the spinal cord but also the spinal nerves that arise from it with ladderlike regularity at intervals along its length. Thus, we will examine components of both the central and peripheral nervous systems, but these components are so closely related, structurally and functionally, that it is appropriate to consider them together. Similarly, the brain and cranial nerves will be considered together in the following chapter. These two chapters therefore elevate our study of the nervous system from the cellular level (chapter 13) to the organ and system levels.

## The Spinal Cord

### *Objectives*
When you have completed this section, you should be able to

- name the two types of tissue in the central nervous system and state their locations;
- describe the gross and microscopic anatomy of the spinal cord; and
- name the major conduction pathways of the spinal cord and state their functions.

## Functions

The spinal cord serves three principal functions:

1. **Conduction.** The spinal cord contains bundles of nerve fibers that conduct information up and down the body, connecting different levels of the trunk with each other and with the brain. It enables sensory information to reach the brain, motor commands to reach the effectors, and input received at one level of the cord to affect output from another level.

2. **Locomotion.** Walking involves repetitive, coordinated contractions of several muscle groups in the limbs. Motor neurons in the brain initiate walking and determine its speed, distance, and direction, but the simple repetitive muscle contractions that put one foot in front of another, over and over, are coordinated by groups of neurons called **central pattern generators** in the cord. These neural circuits produce the sequence of outputs to the extensor and flexor muscles that cause alternating movements of the lower limbs.

3. **Reflexes.** Reflexes are involuntary stereotyped responses to stimuli. They involve the brain, spinal cord, and peripheral nerves.

## Surface Anatomy

The **spinal cord** (fig. 14.1) is a cylinder of nervous tissue that arises from the brainstem at the foramen magnum of the skull. It passes down the vertebral canal as far as the inferior margin of the first lumbar vertebra (L1) or slightly beyond. In adults, it averages about 1.8 cm thick and 45 cm long. Thus, it occupies only the upper two-thirds of the vertebral canal; the lower one-third is described shortly. The cord gives rise to 31 pairs of spinal nerves. The first pair pass between the skull and vertebra C1, and the rest pass through the intervertebral foramina. Although the spinal cord is not visibly segmented, the part supplied by each pair of spinal nerves is called a *segment.* The cord exhibits longitudinal grooves on its ventral and dorsal sides—the *ventral median fissure* and *dorsal median sulcus,* respectively.

The spinal cord is divided into **cervical, thoracic, lumbar,** and **sacral regions.** It may seem odd that it has a sacral region when the cord itself ends well above the sacrum. These regions, however, are named for the level of the vertebral column from which the spinal nerves emerge, not for the vertebrae that contain the cord itself.

The cord widens at two points along its course: a **cervical enlargement** in the inferior cervical region, where it gives rise to nerves of the upper limbs; and a similar **lumbar enlargement** in the lumbosacral region, where it gives rise to nerves of the pelvic region and lower limbs. Inferior to the lumbar enlargement, the cord tapers to a point called the **medullary cone (conus medullaris).** The lumbar enlargement and medullary cone give off a bundle of nerve roots that occupy the vertebral canal from L2 to S5. This bundle, named the **cauda equina**[1] (CAW-duh ee-KWY-nah) for its resemblance to a horse's tail, innervates the pelvic organs and lower limbs.

### THINK ABOUT IT
*Spinal cord injuries commonly result from fractures of vertebrae C5 to C6, but never from fractures of L3 to L5. Explain both observations.*

---

[1]*cauda* = tail + *equin* = horse

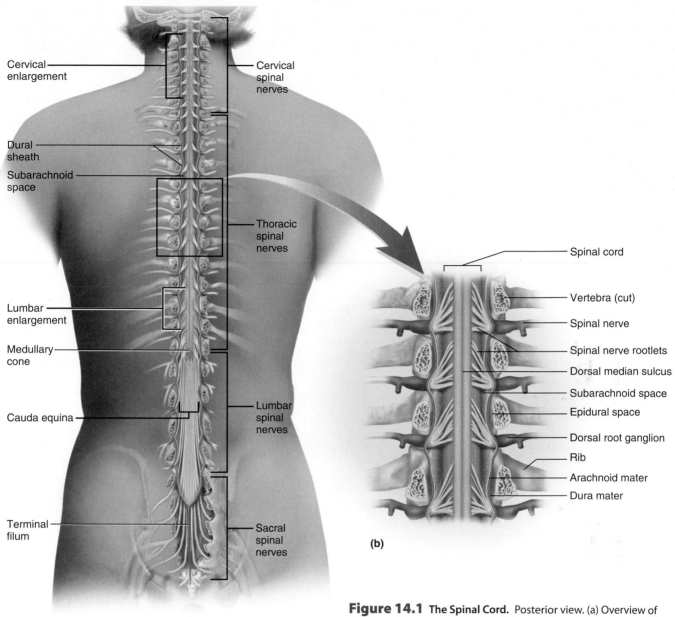

**(a)**

**Figure 14.1  The Spinal Cord.**  Posterior view. (a) Overview of spinal cord structure. (b) Detail of the spinal cord and associated nerves, meninges, and vertebrae.

## Meninges of the Spinal Cord

The spinal cord and brain are enclosed in three connective tissue membranes called **meninges** (meh-NIN-jeez)—singular, *meninx*[2] (MEN-inks). These membranes separate the soft tissue of the central nervous system from the bones of the vertebrae and skull. From superficial to deep, they are the dura mater, arachnoid mater, and pia mater (fig. 14.2).

The **dura mater**[3] (DOO-ruh MAH-tur) forms a loose-fitting sleeve called the **dural sheath** around the spinal cord. It is a tough collagenous membrane about as thick as a rubber kitchen glove.

The space between the sheath and vertebral bone, called the **epidural space,** is occupied by blood vessels, adipose tissue, and loose connective tissue (fig. 14.2a). Anesthetics are sometimes introduced to this space to block pain signals during childbirth or surgery; this procedure is called *epidural anesthesia.*

The **arachnoid**[4] (ah-RACK-noyd) **mater** consists of a simple squamous epithelium, the *arachnoid membrane,* adhering to the inside of the dura, and a loose mesh of collagenous and elastic fiber spanning the gap between the arachnoid membrane and the p mater. This gap, called the **subarachnoid space,** is filled with ce brospinal fluid (CSF), a clear liquid discussed on p. 428. Inferio

---

[2]*menin* = membrane
[3]*dura* = tough + *mater* = mother, womb

[4]*arachn* = spider, spider web + *oid* = resembling

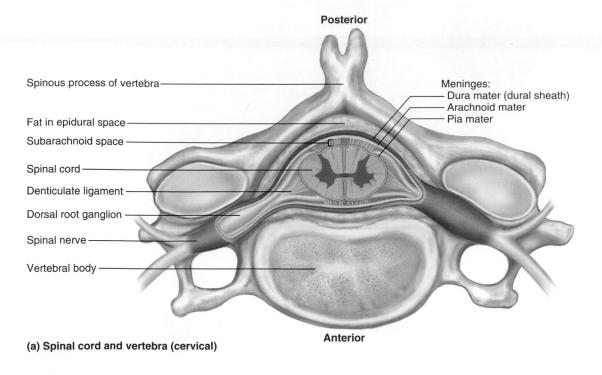

Posterior

Spinous process of vertebra

Fat in epidural space

Subarachnoid space

Spinal cord

Denticulate ligament

Dorsal root ganglion

Spinal nerve

Vertebral body

Meninges:
Dura mater (dural sheath)
Arachnoid mater
Pia mater

Anterior

**(a) Spinal cord and vertebra (cervical)**

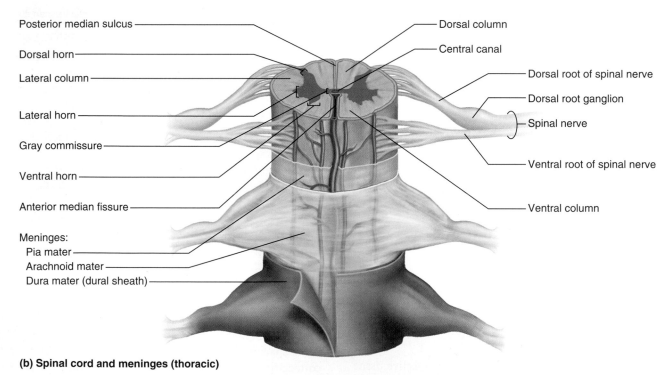

Posterior median sulcus

Dorsal horn

Lateral column

Lateral horn

Gray commissure

Ventral horn

Anterior median fissure

Meninges:
Pia mater
Arachnoid mater
Dura mater (dural sheath)

Dorsal column

Central canal

Dorsal root of spinal nerve

Dorsal root ganglion

Spinal nerve

Ventral root of spinal nerve

Ventral column

**(b) Spinal cord and meninges (thoracic)**

**Figure 14.2** **Cross Section of the Spinal Cord.** (a) Relationship to the vertebra, meninges, and spinal nerve. (b) Detail of the spinal cord, meninges, and spinal nerves.

the medullary cone, the subarachnoid space is called the **lumbar cistern,** a space occupied by the cauda equina and CSF.

The **pia**[5] (PEE-uh) **mater** is a delicate, translucent membrane that closely follows the contours of the spinal cord. It continues

beyond the medullary cone as a fibrous strand, the *terminal filum,* forming part of the **coccygeal ligament** that anchors the cord to vertebra L2 (see fig. 14.1a). At regular intervals along the cord, extensions of the pia called **denticulate ligaments** extend through the arachnoid to the dura, anchoring the cord and preventing side-to-side movements.

---

[5]*pia* = tender, soft

# Cross-Sectional Anatomy

Figure 14.2a shows the relationship of the spinal cord to a vertebra and spinal nerve, and figure 14.2b shows the cord itself in more detail. The spinal cord, like the brain, consists of two kinds of nervous tissue called gray and white matter. **Gray matter** has a relatively dull color because it contains little myelin. It contains the somas, dendrites, and proximal parts of the axons of neurons. It is the site of synaptic contact between neurons and therefore the site of all synaptic integration (information processing) in the central nervous system. **White matter** contains an abundance of myelinated axons, which give it a bright, pearly white appearance. It is composed of bundles of axons, called **tracts,** that carry signals from one part of the CNS to another. In silver-stained nervous tissue sections, gray matter tends to have a brown or golden color and white matter a lighter tan to yellow color.

## Gray Matter

The spinal cord has a central core of gray matter that looks somewhat butterfly- or H-shaped in cross sections. The core consists mainly of two **dorsal (posterior) horns,** which extend toward the dorsolateral surfaces of the cord, and two thicker **ventral (anterior) horns,** which extend toward the ventrolateral surfaces. The right and left sides are connected by a **gray commissure.** In the middle of the commissure is the **central canal,** which is collapsed in most areas of the adult spinal cord, but in some places (and in young children) remains open, lined with ependymal cells, and filled with CSF. The canal is a remnant of the lumen of the embryonic neural tube (see p. 389).

Near its attachment to the spinal cord, a spinal nerve branches into a *dorsal root* and *ventral root.* The dorsal root carries sensory nerve fibers, which enter the dorsal horn of the cord and sometimes synapse with an interneuron there. Such interneurons are especially numerous in the cervical and lumbar enlargements and are quite

## INSIGHT 14.1
### Clinical Application

#### Spinal Taps

Several neurological diseases are diagnosed in part by examining cerebrospinal fluid for bacteria, blood, white blood cells, or abnormalities of chemical composition. CSF is obtained by a procedure called a *spinal tap,* or *lumbar puncture.* The patient leans forward or lies on one side with the spine flexed, thus spreading the vertebral laminae and spinous processes apart. The skin over the lumbar vertebrae is anesthetized, and a needle is inserted between the spinous processes of L3 and L4 (sometimes L4 and L5). This is the safest place to obtain CSF because the spinal cord does not extend this far and is not exposed to injury by the needle. At a depth of 4 to 6 cm, the needle punctures the dura mater and enters the lumbar cistern. CSF normally drips out at a rate of about 1 drop per second. A lumbar puncture is not performed if a patient has signs of high intracranial pressure, because the sudden release of pressure (causing CSF to jet from the puncture) can cause fatal herniation of the brainstem and cerebellum into the vertebral canal.

evident in histological sections at these levels. The ventral horns contain the large somas of the somatic motor neurons. Axons from these neurons exit by way of the ventral root of the spinal nerve and lead to the skeletal muscles. The spinal nerve roots are described more fully later in this chapter.

In the thoracic and lumbar regions, an additional **lateral horn** is visible on each side of the gray matter. It contains neurons of the sympathetic nervous system, which send their axons out of the cord by way of the ventral root along with the somatic efferent fibers.

## White Matter

The white matter of the spinal cord surrounds the gray matter. It consists of bundles of axons that course up and down the cord and provides avenues of communication between different levels of the CNS. These bundles are arranged in three pairs called **columns,** or **funiculi**[6] (few-NIC-you-lie)—a **dorsal (posterior), lateral,** and **ventral (anterior) column** on each side. Each column consists of subdivisions called **tracts,** or **fasciculi**[7] (fah-SIC-you-lye).

# Spinal Tracts

Knowledge of the locations and functions of the spinal tracts is essential in diagnosing and managing spinal cord injuries. **Ascending tracts** carry sensory information up the cord and **descending tracts** conduct motor impulses down. All nerve fibers in a given tract have a similar origin, destination, and function. Many of these fibers, as you will see, have their origin or destination in a region called the *brainstem.* Described more fully in chapter 15 (see fig. 15.7, p. 432), this is a vertical stalk that supports the large *cerebellum* at the rear of the head and, even larger, two globes called the *cerebral hemispheres* that dominate the brain. In the following discussion, you will find references to brainstem and other regions where the spinal cord tracts begin and end. Spinal cord anatomy will grow in meaning as you study the brain.

Several of these tracts undergo **decussation**[8] (DEE-cuh-SAY-shun) as they pass up or down the brainstem and spinal cord—meaning that they cross over from the left side of the body to the right, or vice versa. As a result, the left side of the brain receives sensory information from the right side of the body and sends its motor commands to that side, while the right side of the brain senses and controls the left side of the body. A stroke that damages motor centers of the right side of the brain can thus cause paralysis of the left limbs, and vice versa. When the origin and destination of a tract are on opposite sides of the body, we say they are **contralateral**[9] to each other. When a tract does not decussate, so the origin and destination of its fibers are on the same side of the body, we say they are **ipsilateral.**[10]

The major spinal cord tracts are summarized in table 14.1 and figure 14.3. Bear in mind that each tract is repeated on the right and left sides of the spinal cord.

[6]*funicul* = little rope, cord
[7]*fascicul* = little bundle
[8]*decuss* = to cross, form an X
[9]*contra* = opposite + *later* = side
[10]*ipsi* = the same + *later* = side

| TABLE 14.1 | Major Spinal Tracts | | |
|---|---|---|---|
| **Tract** | **Column** | **Decussation** | **Functions** |
| **Ascending (Sensory) Tracts** | | | |
| Cuneate fasciculus | Dorsal | In medulla | Sensations of limb and trunk position and movement, deep touch, viscera pain, and vibration, from level T6 up |
| Gracile fasciculus | Dorsal | In medulla | Same as cuneate fasciculus, below level T6 |
| Spinothalamic | Lateral and ventral | In spinal cord | Sensations of light touch, tickle, itch, temperature, pain, and pressure |
| Spinoreticular | Lateral and ventral | In spinal cord (some fibers) | Sensation of pain from tissue injury |
| Dorsal spinocerebellar | Lateral | None | Feedback from muscles (proprioception) |
| Ventral spinocerebellar | Lateral | In spinal cord | Same as dorsal spinocerebellar |
| **Descending (Motor) Tracts** | | | |
| Lateral corticospinal | Lateral | In medulla | Fine control of limbs |
| Ventral corticospinal | Ventral | None | Fine control of limbs |
| Tectospinal | Ventral | In midbrain | Reflexive head-turning in response to visual and auditory stimuli |
| Lateral reticulospinal | Lateral | None | Balance and posture; regulation of awareness of pain |
| Medial reticulospinal | Ventral | None | Same as lateral reticulospinal |
| Lateral vestibulospinal | Ventral | None | Balance and posture |
| Medial vestibulospinal | Ventral | In medulla (some fibers) | Control of head position |

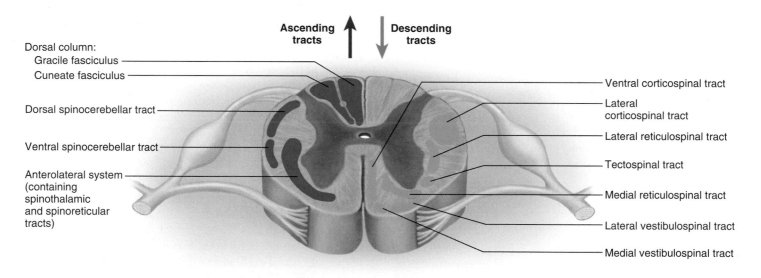

**Figure 14.3** **Tracts of the Spinal Cord.** All of the illustrated tracts occur on both sides of the cord, but only the ascending sensory tracts are shown on the left (red), and only the descending motor tracts on the right (green).
● *If you were told that this is a cross section either at level T4 or T10, how could you determine which is correct?*

## Ascending Tracts

Ascending tracts carry sensory signals up the spinal cord. Sensory signals typically travel across three neurons from their origin in the receptors to their destination in the sensory areas of the brain: a **first-order neuron** that detects a stimulus and conducts a signal to the spinal cord or brainstem; a **second-order neuron** that contin-

ues as far as a "gateway" called the *thalamus* at the upper end of the brainstem; and a **third-order neuron** that carries the signal the rest of the way to the sensory region of the cerebral cortex. The axons of these neurons are called the *first-* through *third-order nerve fibers.* Deviations from the pathway described here will be noted for some of the sensory systems to follow.

The major ascending tracts are as follows. The names of most ascending tracts consist of the prefix *spino-* followed by a root denoting the destination of its fibers in the brain.

- The **gracile**[11] **fasciculus** (GRAS-el fah-SIC-you-lus) (fig. 14.4a) carries signals from the midthoracic and lower parts of the body. Below vertebra T6, it composes the entire dorsal column. At T6, it is joined by the cuneate fasciculus, discussed next. The gracile fasciculus consists of first-order nerve fibers that travel up the ipsilateral side of the spinal cord and terminate at the *gracile nucleus* in the medulla oblongata of the brainstem. These fibers carry signals for vibration, visceral pain, deep and discriminative touch (touch whose location one can precisely identify), and especially *proprioception*[12] from the lower limbs and lower trunk. (Proprioception is the nonvisual sense of the position and movements of the body.)

- The **cuneate**[13] (CUE-nee-ate) **fasciculus** (fig. 14.4a) joins the gracile fasciculus at the T6 level. It occupies the lateral portion of the dorsal column and forces the gracile fasciculus medially. It carries the same type of sensory signals, originating from level T6 and up (from the upper limb and chest). Its fibers end in the *cuneate nucleus* on the ipsilateral side of the medulla oblongata. In the medulla, second-order fibers of the gracile and cuneate systems decussate and form the **medial lemniscus**[14] (lem-NIS-cus), a tract of nerve fibers that leads the rest of the way up the brainstem to the thalamus. Third-order fibers go from the thalamus to the cerebral cortex. Because of decussation, the signals carried by the gracile and cuneate fasciculi ultimately go to the contralateral cerebral hemisphere.

- The **spinothalamic** (SPY-no-tha-LAM-ic) **tract** (fig. 14.4b) and some smaller tracts form the *anterolateral system,* which passes up the anterior and lateral columns of the spinal cord. The spinothalamic tract carries signals for pain, temperature, pressure, tickle, itch, and light or crude touch. Light touch is the sensation produced by stroking hairless skin with a feather or cotton wisp, without indenting the skin; crude touch is touch whose location one can only vaguely identify. In this pathway, first-order neurons end in the dorsal horn of the spinal cord near the point of entry. Here they synapse with second-order neurons, which decussate to the opposite side of the spinal cord and form the ascending spinothalamic tract. These fibers lead all the way to the thalamus. Third-order neurons continue from there to the cerebral cortex. Because of its decussation, the spinothalamic tract ultimately sends its signals to the contralateral cerebral hemisphere.

- The **spinoreticular tract** also travels up the anterolateral system. It carries pain signals resulting from tissue injury. The first-order sensory neurons enter the dorsal horn and immediately synapse with second-order neurons. These decussate to the opposite anterolateral system, ascend the cord, and end in a loosely organized core of gray matter called the *reticular formation* in the medulla and pons. Third-order neurons continue from the pons to the thalamus, and fourth-order neurons complete the path from there to the cerebral cortex. The reticular formation is further described in chapter 15, and the role of the spinoreticular tract in pain sensation is further discussed in chapter 17.

- The **dorsal** and **ventral spinocerebellar** (SPY-no-SERR-eh-BEL-ur) **tracts** travel through the lateral column and carry proprioceptive signals from the limbs and trunk to the cerebellum, a large motor control area at the rear of the brain. The first-order neurons of this system originate in the muscles and tendons and end in the dorsal horn of the spinal cord. Second-order neurons send their fibers up the spinocerebellar tracts and end in the cerebellum. Fibers of the dorsal tract travel up the ipsilateral side of the spinal cord. Those of the ventral tract cross over and travel up the contralateral side but then cross back in the brainstem to enter the ipsilateral side of the cerebellum. Both tracts provide the cerebellum with feedback needed to coordinate muscle action, as discussed in chapter 15.

## Descending Tracts

Descending tracts carry motor signals down the brainstem and spinal cord. A descending motor pathway typically involves two neurons called the upper and lower motor neurons. The **upper motor neuron** begins with a soma in the cerebral cortex or brainstem and has an axon that terminates on a **lower motor neuron** in the brainstem or spinal cord. The axon of the lower motor neuron then leads the rest of the way to the muscle or other target organ. The names of most descending tracts consist of a word root denoting the point of origin in the brain, followed by the suffix *-spinal.* The major descending tracts are described here.

- The **corticospinal** (COR-tih-co-SPY-nul) **tracts** carry motor signals from the cerebral cortex for precise, finely coordinated limb movements. The fibers of this system form ridges called *pyramids* on the ventral surface of the medulla oblongata, so these tracts were once called *pyramidal tracts.* Most corticospinal fibers decussate in the lower medulla and form the **lateral corticospinal tract** on the contralateral side of the spinal cord. A few fibers remain uncrossed and form the **ventral corticospinal tract** on the ipsilateral side (fig. 14.5). Fibers of the ventral tract decussate lower in the spinal cord, however, so even they control contralateral muscles.

- The **tectospinal** (TEC-toe-SPY-nul) **tract** begins in a midbrain region called the *tectum* ("roof") and crosses to the contralateral side of the midbrain. It descends through the brainstem to the upper spinal cord on that side, going only as far as the neck. It is involved in reflex turning of the head, especially in response to sights and sounds.

- The **lateral** and **medial reticulospinal** (reh-TIC-you-lo-SPY-nul) **tracts** originate in the *reticular formation* of the brainstem. They control muscles of the upper and lower limbs, especially to maintain posture and balance. They also contain *descending analgesic pathways* that reduce the transmission of pain signals to the brain (see p. 492).

---

[11]*gracil* = thin, slender
[12]*proprio* = one's own + *cept* = receive, sense
[13]*cune* = wedge
[14]*lemniscus* = ribbon

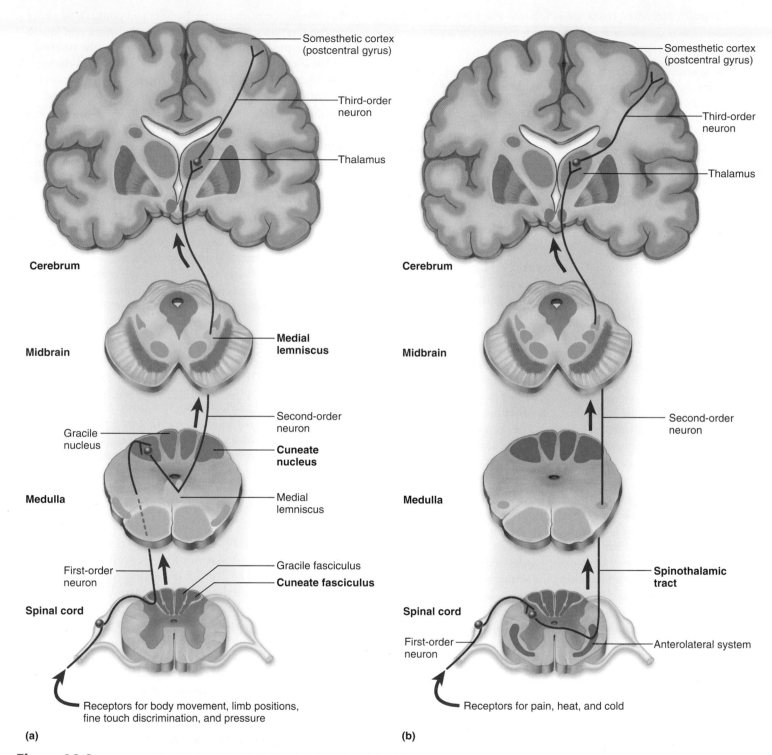

**Figure 14.4 Some Ascending Tracts of the CNS.** The spinal cord, medulla oblongata, and midbrain are shown in cross section and the cerebrum and thalamus (top) in frontal section. Nerve signals enter the spinal cord at the bottom of the figure and carry somatosensory information to the cerebral cortex at the top. (a) The cuneate fasciculus and medial lemniscus. (b) The spinothalamic tract.
● *On the basis of this figure, explain why the* right *cerebral hemisphere perceives heat and cold on the* left *side of the body. What is the name of the phenomenon that accounts for this transmission of sensory information from one side of the body to the opposite side of the brain?*

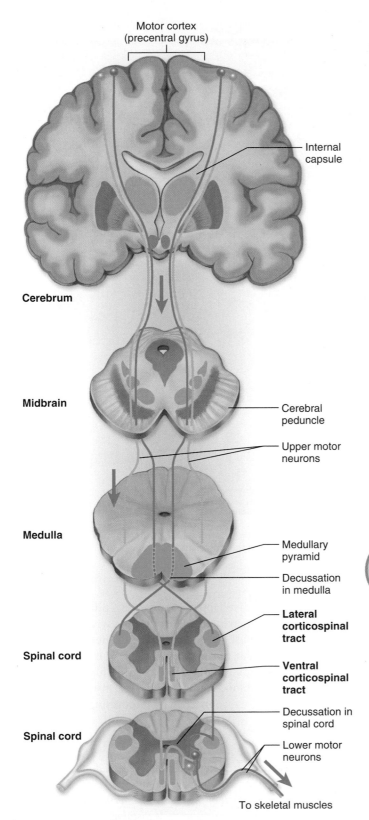

**Figure 14.5 Two Descending Tracts of the CNS.** The lateral and ventral corticospinal tracts, which carry signals for voluntary muscle contraction. Nerve signals originate in the cerebral cortex at the top of the figure and carry motor commands down the spinal cord. Pathways shown at the bottom right are duplicated on the left.

- The **lateral** and **medial vestibulospinal** (vess-TIB-you-lo-SPY-nul) **tracts** begin in the brainstem *vestibular nuclei,* which receive impulses for balance from the inner ear. The lateral vestibulospinal tract passes down the ventral column of the spinal cord and facilitates neurons that control the extensor muscles of the limbs, thus inducing the limbs to stiffen and straighten. This is an important reflex in responding to body tilt and keeping one's balance. The medial vestibulospinal tract splits into ipsilateral and contralateral fibers that descend through the ventral column on both sides of the spinal cord and terminate in the neck. It plays a role in the control of head position.

*Rubrospinal tracts* are prominent in other mammals, where they aid in muscle coordination. Although often pictured in illustrations of human anatomy, they are almost nonexistent in humans and have little functional importance.

## Before You Go On

*Answer the following questions to test your understanding of the preceding section:*

1. Name the four major regions and two enlargements of the spinal cord.

2. Describe the distal (inferior) end of the spinal cord and the contents of the vertebral canal from level L2 to S5.

3. Sketch a cross section of the spinal cord showing the dorsal and ventral horns. Where are the gray and white matter? Where are the columns and tracts?

4. Give an anatomical explanation as to why a stroke in the right cerebral hemisphere can paralyze the limbs on the left side of the body.

# The Spinal Nerves

### Objectives
When you have completed this section, you should be able to

- describe the attachment of a spinal nerve to the spinal cord;

- trace the branches of a spinal nerve distal to its attachment;

- name the five plexuses of spinal nerves and describe their general anatomy;

- name some major nerves that arise from each plexus; and

- explain the relationship of dermatomes to the spinal nerves.

## General Anatomy of Nerves and Ganglia

The spinal cord communicates with the rest of the body by way of the spinal nerves. Before we discuss those specific nerves, however, it is necessary to be familiar with the structure of nerves and ganglia in general.

# INSIGHT 14.2

## Clinical Application

### Poliomyelitis and Amyotrophic Lateral Sclerosis

*Poliomyelitis*[15] and *amyotrophic lateral sclerosis*[16] (ALS) are two diseases that result from the destruction of motor neurons. In both diseases, the skeletal muscles atrophy from lack of innervation.

Poliomyelitis is caused by the poliovirus, which destroys motor neurons in the brainstem and ventral horn of the spinal cord. Signs of polio include muscle pain, weakness, and loss of some reflexes, followed by paralysis, muscular atrophy, and sometimes respiratory arrest. The virus spreads through water contaminated by feces. Historically, polio afflicted many children who contracted the virus from contaminated swimming pools. For a time, the polio vaccine nearly eliminated new cases, but the disease has lately begun to reemerge among children in some parts of the world.

ALS is also known as Lou Gehrig[17] disease after the baseball player who had to retire from the sport because of it. It is marked not only by the degeneration of motor neurons and atrophy of the muscles, but also sclerosis (scarring) of the lateral regions of the spinal cord—hence its name. Most cases occur when astrocytes fail to reabsorb the neurotransmitter glutamate from the tissue fluid, allowing it to accumulate to a neurotoxic level. The early signs of ALS include muscular weakness and difficulty in speaking, swallowing, and using the hands. Sensory and intellectual functions remain unaffected, as evidenced by the accomplishments of astrophysicist and best-selling author Stephen Hawking (fig. 14.6), who was stricken with ALS while he was in college. Despite near-total paralysis, he remains highly productive and communicates with the aid of a speech synthesizer and computer. Tragically, many people are quick to assume that those who have lost most of their ability to communicate their ideas and feelings have no ideas and feelings to communicate. To a victim, this may be more unbearable than the loss of motor function itself.

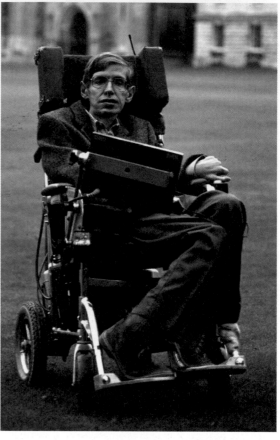

**Figure 14.6**  Stephen Hawking (1942–  ), Lucasian Professor of Mathematics at Cambridge University.

---

A **nerve** is a cordlike organ composed of numerous nerve fibers (axons) bound together by connective tissue (fig. 14.7). If we compare a nerve fiber to a wire carrying an electrical current in one direction, a nerve would be comparable to an electrical cable composed of thousands of wires carrying currents in opposite directions. A nerve contains anywhere from a few nerve fibers to more than a million. Nerves usually have a pearly white color and resemble frayed string as they divide into smaller and smaller branches.

Nerve fibers of the peripheral nervous system are ensheathed in Schwann cells, which form a neurilemma and often a myelin sheath around the axon (see p. 383). External to the neurilemma, each fiber is surrounded by a basal lamina and then a thin sleeve of loose connective tissue called the **endoneurium.** In most nerves, the nerve fibers are gathered in bundles called **fascicles,** each wrapped in a sheath called the **perineurium.** The perineurium is composed of up to 20 layers of overlapping, squamous, epithelium-like cells. Several fascicles are then bundled together and wrapped in an outer **epineurium** to compose the nerve as a whole. The epineurium consists of dense irregular fibrous connective tissue and protects the nerve from stretching and injury. Nerves have a high metabolic rate and need a plentiful blood supply, which is furnished by blood vessels that penetrate these connective tissue coverings.

### THINK ABOUT IT

*How does the structure of a nerve compare to that of a skeletal muscle? Which of the descriptive terms for nerves have similar counterparts in muscle histology?*

Peripheral nerve fibers are of two kinds: *sensory (afferent) fibers* carry signals from sensory receptors to the CNS, and *motor (efferent) fibers* carry signals from the CNS to muscles and glands. Both sensory and motor fibers can also be described as *somatic* or *visceral* and as *general* or *special* depending on the organs they innervate (table 14.2).

---

[15]*polio* = gray matter + *myel* = spinal cord + *itis* = inflammation
[16]*a* = without + *myo* = muscle + *troph* = nourishment
[17]Lou Gehrig (1903–41), American baseball player

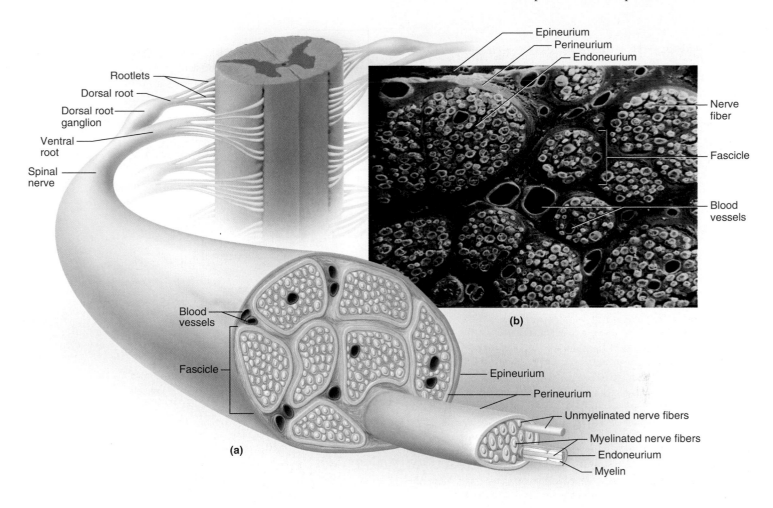

**Figure 14.7** **Anatomy of a Nerve.** (a) A spinal nerve and its association with the spinal cord. (b) Cross section of a nerve (SEM). Myelinated nerve fibers appear in the photograph as white rings and unmyelinated fibers as solid gray. [(b) From Richard E. Kessel and Randy H. Kardon, *Tissues and Organs: A Text-Atlas of Scanning Electron Microscopy,* 1979, W. H. Freeman and Company.]

| TABLE 14.2 | The Classification of Nerve Fibers |
|---|---|
| **Class** | **Description** |
| Afferent fibers | Carry sensory signals from receptors to the CNS |
| Efferent fibers | Carry motor signals from the CNS to effectors |
| Somatic fibers | Innervate skin, skeletal muscles, bones, and joints |
| Visceral fibers | Innervate blood vessels, glands, and viscera |
| General fibers | Innervate widespread organs such as muscles, skin, glands, viscera, and blood vessels |
| Special fibers | Innervate more localized organs in the head, including the eyes, ears, olfactory and taste receptors, and muscles of chewing, swallowing, and facial expression |

A **mixed nerve** consists of both sensory and motor fibers and thus conducts signals in two directions, although any one fiber within the nerve conducts signals one way only. Most nerves are mixed. **Sensory nerves,** composed entirely of sensory axons, are less common; they include the olfactory and optic nerves discussed in chapter 15 (p. 452). Nerves that carry only motor fibers are called **motor nerves.** Many nerves often described as motor are actually mixed because they carry sensory signals of proprioception from the muscle back to the CNS.

If a nerve resembles a thread, a **ganglion**[18] resembles a knot in the thread. A ganglion is a cluster of cell bodies (somas) outside the CNS. It is enveloped in an epineurium continuous with that of the nerve. Among the somas are bundles of nerve fibers leading into and out of the ganglion. Figure 14.8 shows a type of ganglion associated with the spinal nerves.

---

[18]*gangli* = knot

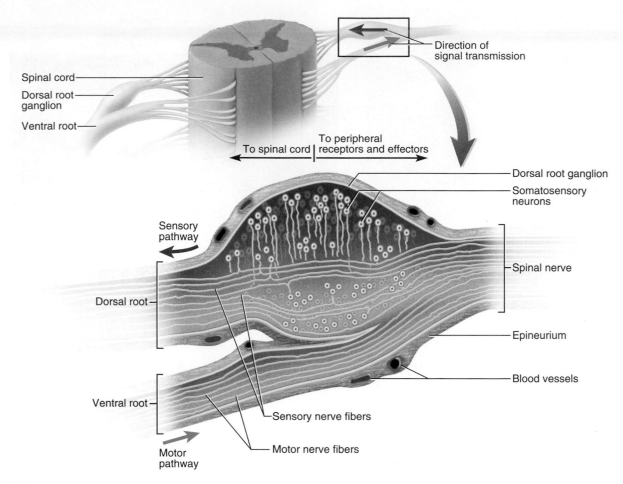

**Figure 14.8** **Anatomy of a Ganglion.** Longitudinal section. The dorsal root ganglion contains the somas of sensory neurons conducting signals from peripheral sense organs to the spinal cord. Below this is the ventral root of the spinal nerve, which conducts motor signals away from the spinal cord, toward muscles and other peripheral effectors. (The ventral root is not part of the ganglion.)
● *To which morphological category of neurons (see p. 380) do the somatosensory neurons in this figure belong?*

## Spinal Nerves

There are 31 pairs of **spinal nerves:** 8 cervical (C1–C8), 12 thoracic (T1–T12), 5 lumbar (L1–L5), 5 sacral (S1–S5), and 1 coccygeal (Co) (fig. 14.9). The first cervical nerve emerges between the skull and atlas, and the others emerge through intervertebral foramina, including the anterior and posterior foramina of the sacrum and the sacral hiatus.

### Proximal Branches

Each spinal nerve has two points of attachment to the spinal cord. As a spinal nerve passes through the intervertebral foramen, it divides into a branch called the **dorsal root,** which passes dorsally (posteriorly) toward the back of the spinal cord, and a branch called the **ventral root,** which passes ventrally (anteriorly) toward the front of the spinal cord (fig. 14.10).

Shortly after the branch point, the dorsal root expands into a **dorsal root ganglion,** which contains the somas of the sensory neurons carrying signals to the spinal cord (see fig. 14.8). The dorsal root then divides into six to eight **rootlets** that enter the dorsal horn of

the cord (figs. 14.1b and 14.11). Ventrally, another six to eight rootlets leave the spinal cord and converge to form the ventral root.

The dorsal and ventral roots merge, penetrate the dural sac, enter the intervertebral foramen, and there form the spinal nerve proper. Thus, the spinal nerve is a mixed nerve, carrying sensory information to the spinal cord by way of the dorsal root and motor commands away from the cord by way of the ventral root. The dorsal and ventral roots are shortest in the cervical region and become longer inferiorly. The roots that arise from segments L2 to Co of the cord form the cauda equina. Some viruses invade the central nervous system by way of these roots (see Insight 14.3).

### Distal Branches

Distal to the vertebrae, the branches of a spinal nerve are more complex (fig. 14.12). Immediately after emerging from the intervertebral foramen, the nerve divides into a **dorsal ramus,**[19] a

---

[19]*ramus* = branch

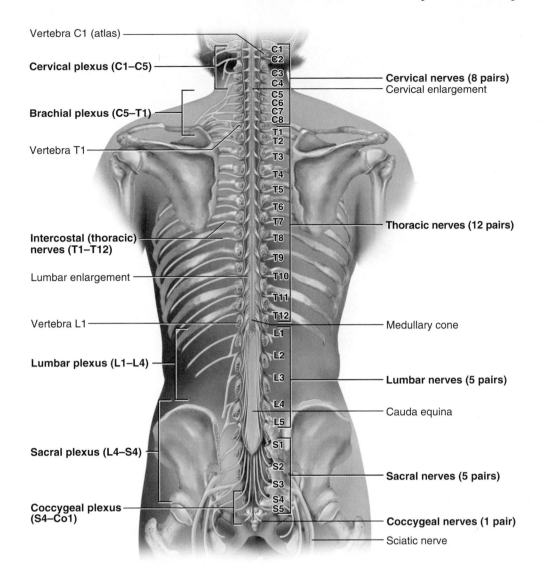

Vertebra C1 (atlas)
Cervical plexus (C1–C5)
Brachial plexus (C5–T1)
Vertebra T1
Intercostal (thoracic) nerves (T1–T12)
Lumbar enlargement
Vertebra L1
Lumbar plexus (L1–L4)
Sacral plexus (L4–S4)
Coccygeal plexus (S4–Co1)

Cervical nerves (8 pairs)
Cervical enlargement
Thoracic nerves (12 pairs)
Medullary cone
Lumbar nerves (5 pairs)
Cauda equina
Sacral nerves (5 pairs)
Coccygeal nerves (1 pair)
Sciatic nerve

C1 C2 C3 C4 C5 C6 C7 C8 T1 T2 T3 T4 T5 T6 T7 T8 T9 T10 T11 T12 L1 L2 L3 L4 L5 S1 S2 S3 S4 S5

**Figure 14.9** **The Spinal Nerve Roots and Plexuses.** Posterior view.

**ventral ramus,** and a small **meningeal branch.** Thus, each spinal nerve branches on both ends—into dorsal and ventral *roots* approaching the spinal cord, and dorsal and ventral *rami* leading away from the vertebral column.

The meningeal branch (see fig. 14.10) reenters the vertebral canal and innervates the meninges, vertebrae, and spinal ligaments. The dorsal ramus innervates the muscles and joints in that region of the spine and the skin of the back. The larger ventral ramus innervates the ventral and lateral skin and muscles of the trunk and gives rise to nerves of the limbs.

### THINK ABOUT IT

*Do you think the meningeal branch is sensory, motor, or mixed? Explain your reasoning.*

The ventral ramus differs from one region of the trunk to another. In the thoracic region, it forms an **intercostal nerve** that travels along the inferior margin of a rib and innervates the skin and intercostal muscles (thus contributing to breathing), as well as the internal oblique, external oblique, and transversus abdominis muscles. All other ventral rami form the *nerve plexuses* described next.

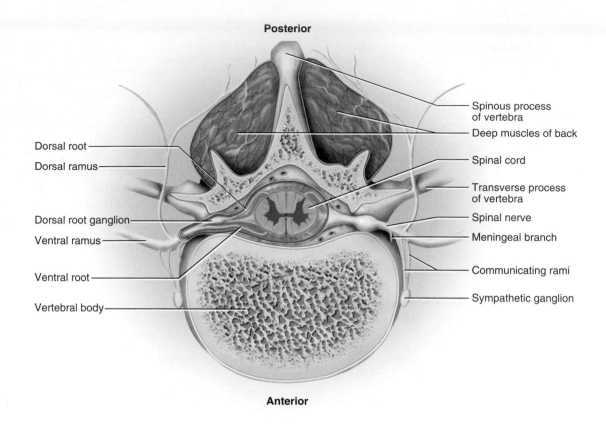

**Figure 14.10** **Branches of a Spinal Nerve in Relation to the Spinal Cord and Vertebra.** Cross section.

**Figure 14.11** **The Point of Entry of Two Spinal Nerves into the Spinal Cord.** Posterior (dorsal) view with vertebrae cut away. Note that each dorsal root divides into several rootlets that enter the spinal cord. A segment of the spinal cord is the portion receiving all the rootlets of one spinal nerve.
● *What would be the consequences of surgically cutting the spinal nerve rootlets shown in this photograph?*

INSIGHT 14.3 ●●●
## Clinical Application

## Shingles

Chickenpox *(varicella),* a common disease of early childhood, is caused by the *varicella-zoster* virus. It produces an itchy rash that usually clears up without complications. The virus, however, remains for life in the dorsal root ganglia, kept in check by the immune system. If the immune system is compromised, however, the virus can travel down the sensory nerves by axonal transport and cause *shingles (herpes zoster).* This is particularly common after the age of 50. Shingles is characterized by a painful trail of skin discoloration and fluid-filled vesicles along the path of the nerve. These signs usually appear in the chest and waist, often on just one side of the body. There is no cure, and the vesicles generally heal spontaneously within 1 to 3 weeks. In the meantime, aspirin and steroidal ointments can help to relieve the pain and inflammation of the lesions. Antiviral drugs such as acyclovir can shorten the course of an episode of shingles, but only if taken within the first 2 to 3 days of outbreak. Even after the lesions disappear, however, some people suffer intense pain along the course of the nerve *(postherpetic neuralgia, PHN),* lasting for months or even years. PHN has proven very difficult to treat, but pain relievers and antidepressants are of some help. Childhood vaccination against varicella reduces the risk of shingles later in life.

## Nerve Plexuses

Except in the thoracic region, the ventral rami branch and anastomose (merge) repeatedly to form five weblike nerve plexuses: the small **cervical plexus** in the neck, the **brachial plexus** near the shoulder, the **lumbar plexus** of the lower back, the **sacral plexus** immediately inferior to this, and finally, the tiny **coccygeal plexus** adjacent to the lower sacrum and coccyx. A general view of these plexuses is shown in figure 14.9; they are illustrated and described in tables 14.3 through 14.6. The spinal nerve roots that give rise to each plexus are indicated in violet in each table. Some of these roots give rise to smaller branches called *trunks, anterior divisions, posterior divisions,* and *cords,* which are color-coded and explained in the individual tables.

The nerves tabulated here have somatosensory and motor functions. *Somatosensory* means that they carry sensory signals from bones, joints, muscles, and the skin, in contrast to sensory input from the viscera or from special sense organs such as the eyes and ears. (See chapter 17, p. 487 for explanation of the different modes of sensory function.) These somatosensory signals are for touch, heat, cold, stretch, pressure, pain, and other sensations. One of the most important sensory roles of these nerves is *proprioception,* in which the brain receives information about body position and movements from nerve endings in the muscles, tendons, and joints. The brain uses this information to adjust muscle actions and thereby maintain equilibrium (balance) and coordination.

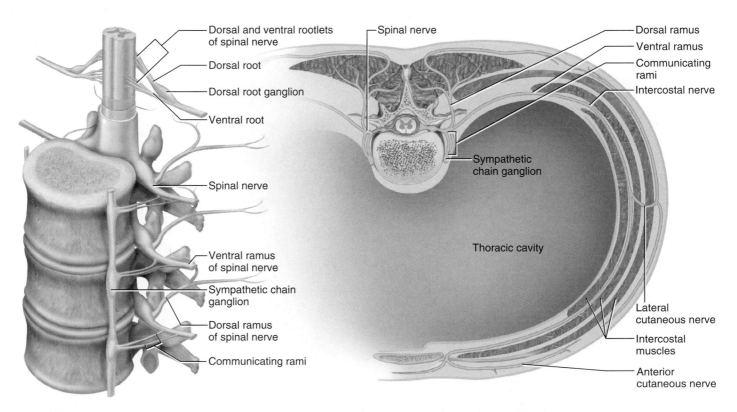

**(a) Anterolateral view**                    **(b) Cross section**

**Figure 14.12 Rami of the Spinal Nerves.** (a) Anterolateral view of the spinal nerves and their subdivisions in relation to the spinal cord and vertebrae. (b) Cross section of the thorax showing innervation of muscles and skin of the chest and back. This section is cut through the intercostal muscles between two ribs.

The motor function of these nerves is primarily to stimulate the contraction of skeletal muscles. These nerves also carry autonomic fibers to the blood vessels of the skin, muscles, and other organs, thus adjusting blood flow to changing local needs.

The following tables identify the areas of skin innervated by the sensory fibers and the muscle groups innervated by the motor fibers of the individual nerves. The muscle tables in chapters 11 and 12 provide a more detailed breakdown of the muscles supplied by each nerve and the actions they perform. You may assume that for each muscle, these nerves also carry autonomic fibers to its blood vessels and sensory fibers from its proprioceptors.

| TABLE 14.3 | The Cervical Plexus |
|---|---|

The cervical plexus (fig. 14.13) receives fibers from the ventral rami of nerves C1 to C5 and gives rise to the nerves listed below, in order from superior to inferior. The most important of these are the *phrenic*[20] *nerves*, which travel down each side of the mediastinum, innervate the diaphragm, and play an essential role in breathing (see fig. 16.3, p. 471). In addition to the major nerves listed here, there are several motor branches that innervate the geniohyoid, thyrohyoid, scalene, levator scapulae, trapezius, and sternocleidomastoid muscles.

| Nerve | Composition | Cutaneous and Other Sensory Innervation | Muscular Innervation (Motor and Proprioceptive) |
|---|---|---|---|
| Lesser occipital n. | Somatosensory | Upper third of medial surface of external ear, skin posterior to ear, posterolateral neck | (None) |
| Great auricular n. | Somatosensory | Most of the external ear, mastoid region, region from parotid salivary gland (see fig. 11.2) to slightly inferior to angle of mandible | (None) |
| Transverse cervical n. | Somatosensory | Anterior and lateral neck, underside of chin | (None) |
| Ansa cervicalis | Mixed | (None) | Omohyoid, sternohyoid, and sternothyroid muscles |
| Supraclavicular nn. | Somatosensory | Lower anterior and lateral neck, shoulder, anterior chest | (None) |
| Phrenic n. | Mixed | Diaphragm, pleura, and pericardium | Diaphragm |

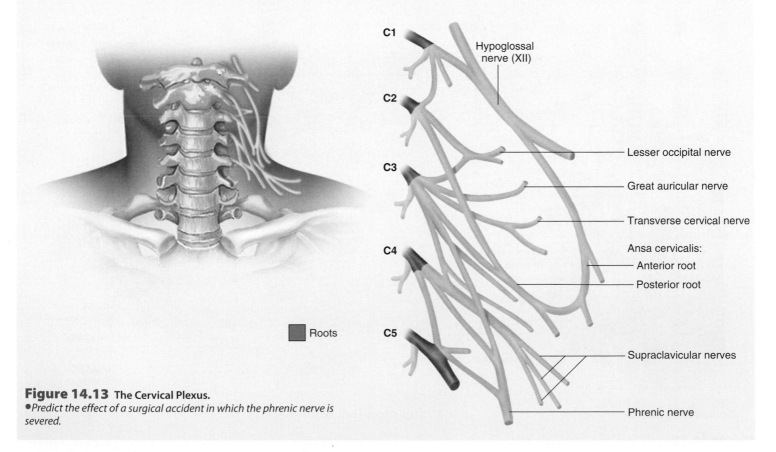

**Figure 14.13** The Cervical Plexus.
● *Predict the effect of a surgical accident in which the phrenic nerve is severed.*

---

[20]*phren* = diaphragm

## TABLE 14.4 | The Brachial Plexus

The brachial plexus (figs. 14.14 and 14.15) is formed predominantly by the ventral rami of nerves C5 to T1 (C4 and T2 make smaller contributions). It passes over the first rib into the axilla and innervates the upper limb and some muscles of the neck and shoulder. The subdivisions of this plexus are called *roots, trunks, divisions,* and *cords* (color-coded in fig. 14.14). The five **roots** are the ventral rami of C5 through T1. Roots C5 and C6 converge to form the **upper trunk;** C7 continues as the **middle trunk;** and C8 and T1 converge to form the **lower trunk.** Each trunk divides into an **anterior** and **posterior division;** as the body is dissected from the anterior surface of the shoulder inward, the posterior divisions are found behind the anterior ones. Finally, the six divisions merge to form three large fiber bundles—the **lateral, posterior,** and **medial cords.** From these cords arise the following major nerves, listed in order of the illustration from superior to inferior.

| Nerve | Composition | Cord of Origin | Cutaneous and Joint Innervation (Sensory) | Muscular Innervation (Motor and Proprioceptive) |
|---|---|---|---|---|
| Musculocutaneous n. | Mixed | Lateral | Skin of anterolateral forearm; elbow joint | Brachialis, biceps brachii, and coracobrachialis muscles |
| Axillary n. | Mixed | Posterior | Skin of lateral shoulder and arm; shoulder joint | Deltoid and teres minor muscles |
| Radial n. | Mixed | Posterior | Skin of posterior arm; posterior and lateral forearm and wrist; joints of elbow, wrist, and hand | Mainly extensor muscles of posterior arm and forearm (see tables 12.3 and 12.4) |
| Median n. | Mixed | Lateral and medial | Skin of lateral two-thirds of hand; tips of digits I–IV; joints of hand | Mainly forearm flexors; thenar group and lumbricals I–II of hand (see tables 12.3 to 12.5) |
| Ulnar n. | Mixed | Medial | Skin of palmar and medial hand and digits III–V; joints of elbow and hand | Some forearm flexors; adductor pollicis; hypothenar group; interosseous muscles; lumbricals III–IV (see tables 12.4 and 12.5) |

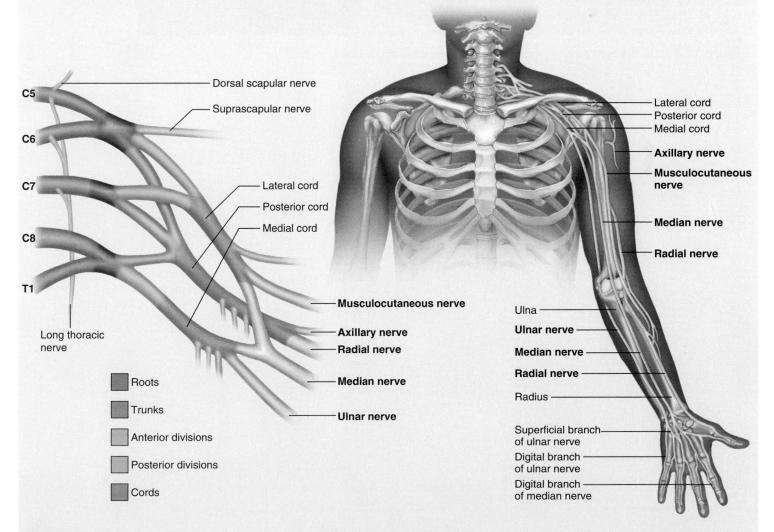

**Figure 14.14 The Brachial Plexus.** The labeled nerves innervate muscles tabulated in chapter 12, and those in boldface are further detailed in this table.

**TABLE 14.4** | **The Brachial Plexus (continued)**

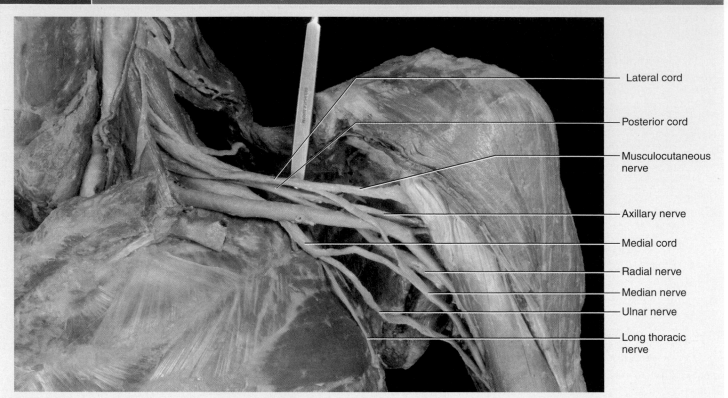

Lateral cord

Posterior cord

Musculocutaneous nerve

Axillary nerve

Medial cord

Radial nerve

Median nerve

Ulnar nerve

Long thoracic nerve

**Figure 14.15** **The Brachial Plexus of a Cadaver.** Anterior view of the left shoulder.

| TABLE 14.5 | The Lumbar Plexus |
|---|---|

The lumbar plexus (fig. 14.16) is formed from the ventral rami of nerves L1 to L4 and some fibers from T12. With only five roots and two divisions, it is less complex than the brachial plexus. It gives rise to the following nerves.

| Nerve | Composition | Cutaneous and Joint Innervation (Sensory) | Muscular Innervation (Motor and Proprioceptive) |
|---|---|---|---|
| Iliohypogastric n. | Mixed | Skin of lower anterior abdominal and posterolateral gluteal regions | Internal and external abdominal oblique and transverse abdominal muscles |
| Ilioinguinal n. | Mixed | Skin of upper medial thigh; male scrotum and root of penis; female labia majora | Internal abdominal oblique |
| Genitofemoral n. | Mixed | Skin of middle anterior thigh; male scrotum; female labia majora | Male cremaster muscle (see p. 738) |
| Lateral femoral cutaneous n. | Somatosensory | Skin of anterior and upper lateral thigh | (None) |
| Femoral n. | Mixed | Skin of anterior, medial, and lateral thigh and knee; skin of medial leg and foot; hip and knee joints | Iliacus, pectineus, quadriceps femoris, and sartorius muscles |
| Obturator n. | Mixed | Skin of medial thigh; hip and knee joints | Obturator externus; medial (adductor) thigh muscles (see table 12.6) |

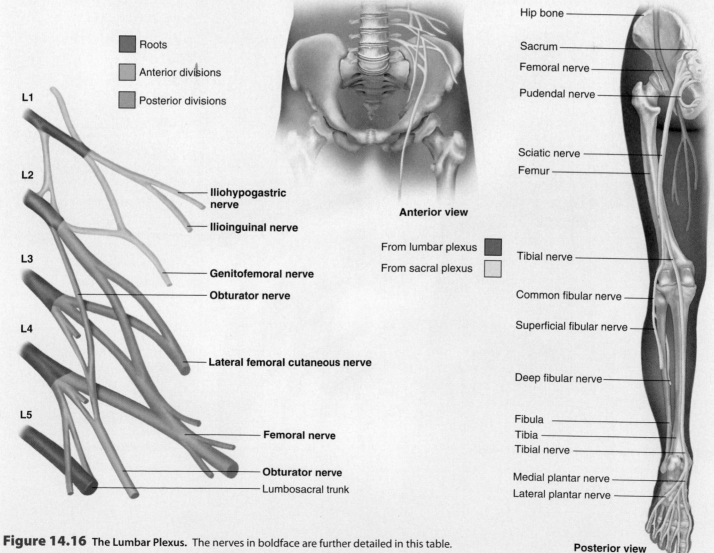

Roots

Anterior divisions

Posterior divisions

L1

L2

L3

L4

L5

**Iliohypogastric nerve**

**Ilioinguinal nerve**

**Genitofemoral nerve**

**Obturator nerve**

**Lateral femoral cutaneous nerve**

**Femoral nerve**

**Obturator nerve**

Lumbosacral trunk

**Anterior view**

From lumbar plexus

From sacral plexus

Hip bone

Sacrum

Femoral nerve

Pudendal nerve

Sciatic nerve

Femur

Tibial nerve

Common fibular nerve

Superficial fibular nerve

Deep fibular nerve

Fibula

Tibia

Tibial nerve

Medial plantar nerve

Lateral plantar nerve

**Posterior view**

**Figure 14.16 The Lumbar Plexus.** The nerves in boldface are further detailed in this table.

## TABLE 14.6 | The Sacral and Coccygeal Plexuses

The sacral plexus is formed from the ventral rami of nerves L4, L5, and S1 through S4. It has six roots and anterior and posterior divisions. Since it is connected to the lumbar plexus by fibers that run through the *lumbosacral trunk*, the two plexuses are sometimes referred to collectively as the *lumbosacral plexus*. The coccygeal plexus is a tiny plexus formed from the ventral rami of S4, S5, and Co (fig. 14.17).

The *tibial* and *common fibular nerves* travel together through a connective tissue sheath; they are referred to collectively as the **sciatic** (sy-AT-ic) **nerve.** The sciatic nerve passes through the greater sciatic notch of the pelvis, extends for the length of the thigh, and ends at the popliteal fossa. Here, the tibial and common fibular nerves diverge and follow their separate paths into the leg. The tibial nerve descends through the leg and then gives rise to the medial and plantar nerves in the foot. The common fibular nerve divides into deep and superficial fibular nerves. The sciatic nerve is a common focus of injury and pain (see Insight 14.4).

| Nerve | Composition | Cutaneous and Joint Innervation (Sensory) | Muscular Innervation (Motor and Proprioceptive) |
|---|---|---|---|
| Superior gluteal n. | Mixed | (None) | Gluteus minimus, gluteus medius, and tensor fasciae latae muscles |
| Inferior gluteal n. | Mixed | (None) | Gluteus maximus muscle |
| Posterior cutaneous n. | Somatosensory | Skin of gluteal region, perineum, posterior and medial thigh, popliteal fossa, and upper posterior leg | (None) |
| Tibial n. | Mixed | Skin of posterior leg; plantar skin; knee and foot joints | Hamstring muscles; posterior muscles of leg (see tables 12.6 and 12.7); most intrinsic foot muscles (via plantar nerves) (see table 12.8) |
| Fibular (peroneal) n. (common, deep, and superficial) | Mixed | Skin of anterior distal third of leg, dorsum of foot, and toes I–II; knee joint | Biceps femoris muscle; anterior and lateral muscles of leg; extensor digitorum brevis muscle of foot (see tables 12.7 to 12.9) |
| Pudendal n. | Mixed | Skin of penis and scrotum of male; clitoris, labia majora and minora, and lower vagina of female | Muscles of perineum (see table 11.8) |

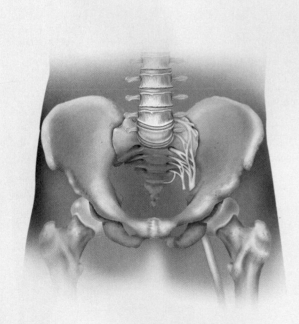
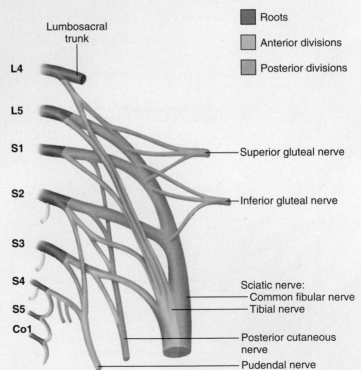

**Figure 14.17** The Sacral and Coccygeal Plexuses.

## Cutaneous Innervation and Dermatomes

Each spinal nerve except C1 receives sensory input from a specific area of skin called a **dermatome**,[21] derived from the embryonic dermatomes described in chapter 4. A *dermatome map* (fig. 14.18) is a diagram of the cutaneous regions innervated by each spinal nerve. Such a map is oversimplified, however, because the dermatomes overlap at their edges by as much as 50%. Therefore, severance of one sensory nerve root does not entirely deaden sensation from a dermatome. It is necessary to sever or anesthetize three successive spinal nerves to produce a total loss of sensation from one dermatome. Spinal nerve damage is assessed by testing the dermatomes with pinpricks and noting areas in which the patient has no sensation.

---

[21]*derma* = skin + *tome* = segment, part

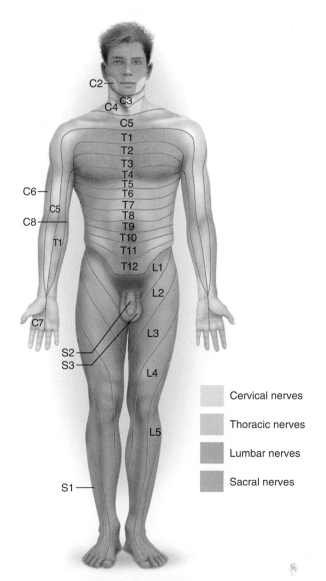

Cervical nerves

Thoracic nerves

Lumbar nerves

Sacral nerves

**Figure 14.18** **A Dermatome Map of the Anterior Aspect of the Body.** Each zone of the skin is innervated by sensory branches of the spinal nerves indicated by the labels. Nerve C1 does not innervate the skin.

INSIGHT 14.4 ●●●●

### Clinical Application

### Spinal Nerve Injuries

The radial and sciatic nerves are especially vulnerable to injury. The radial nerve, which passes through the axilla, may be compressed against the humerus by improperly adjusted crutches, causing *crutch paralysis.* A similar injury often resulted from the discredited practice of trying to correct a dislocated shoulder by putting a foot in a person's armpit and pulling on the arm. One consequence of radial nerve injury is *wrist drop*—the fingers, hand, and wrist are chronically flexed because the extensor muscles supplied by the radial nerve are paralyzed.

Because of its position and length, the sciatic nerve of the hip and thigh is the most vulnerable nerve in the body. Trauma to this nerve produces *sciatica,* a sharp pain that travels from the gluteal region along the posterior side of the thigh and leg as far as the ankle. Ninety percent of cases result from a herniated intervertebral disc or osteoarthritis of the lower spine, but sciatica can also be caused by pressure from a pregnant uterus, dislocation of the hip, injections in the wrong area of the buttock, or sitting for a long time on the edge of a hard chair. Men sometimes suffer sciatica because of the habit of sitting on a wallet carried in the hip pocket.

### *Before You Go On*

*Answer the following questions to test your understanding of the preceding section:*

5. What is meant by the dorsal and ventral roots of a spinal nerve? Which of these is sensory, and which is motor?

6. Where are the somas of the dorsal root located? Where are the somas of the ventral root?

7. List the five plexuses of spinal nerves and state where each one is located.

8. State which plexus gives rise to each of the following nerves: axillary, ilioinguinal, obturator, phrenic, pudendal, radial, and sciatic.

## Somatic Reflexes

### *Objectives*

When you have completed this section, you should be able to

- define *reflex* and explain how reflexes differ from other motor actions;

- describe the general components of a typical reflex arc; and

- describe some common variations in reflex arcs.

**Reflexes** are quick, involuntary, stereotyped reactions of glands or muscles to stimulation. This definition sums up four important properties of a reflex:

1. Reflexes *require stimulation*—they are not spontaneous actions but responses to sensory input.

2. Reflexes are *quick*—they generally involve few if any interneurons and minimal synaptic delay.

3. Reflexes are *involuntary*—they occur without intent, often without our awareness, and they are difficult to suppress. Given an adequate stimulus, the response is essentially automatic. You may become conscious of the stimulus that evoked a reflex, and this awareness may enable you to correct or avoid a potentially dangerous situation, but awareness is not a part of the reflex itself. It may come after the reflex action has been completed, and some reflexes occur even if the spinal cord has been severed so that no stimuli reach the brain.

4. Reflexes are *stereotyped*—they occur in essentially the same way every time; the response is very predictable.

**Visceral reflexes** are responses of glands, cardiac muscle, and smooth muscle. They are controlled by the autonomic nervous system and discussed in chapter 16 (p. 468). **Somatic reflexes** are responses of skeletal muscles, such as the quick withdrawal of your hand from a hot stove or the lifting of your foot when you step on something sharp. They are controlled by the somatic nervous system. Somatic reflexes will be briefly discussed here from the anatomical standpoint. They have traditionally been called *spinal reflexes*, although this is a misleading expression for two reasons: (1)

Spinal reflexes are not exclusively somatic; the autonomic (visceral) reflexes also involve the spinal cord. (2) Some somatic reflexes are mediated more by the brain than by the spinal cord.

A somatic reflex employs a rather simple neural pathway called a **reflex arc,** from a sensory nerve ending to the spinal cord or brainstem and back to a skeletal muscle. The components of a reflex arc are as follows:

1. *Somatic receptors* in the skin, a muscle, or a tendon. These include simple nerve endings for heat and pain in the skin, specialized stretch receptors called *muscle spindles* embedded in the skeletal muscles, and other types (see chapter 17, p. 488).

2. *Afferent nerve fibers,* which carry information from these receptors into the dorsal horn of the spinal cord.

3. An *integrating center,* a point of synaptic contact between neurons in the gray matter of the spinal cord or brainstem. In most reflex arcs, there are one or more interneurons in the integrating center. Synaptic events in the integrating center determine whether the efferent (output) neuron issues a signal to the muscle.

4. *Efferent nerve fibers,* which originate in the ventral horn of the spinal cord and carry motor impulses to the skeletal muscles.

5. *Skeletal muscles,* the somatic effectors that carry out the response.

In the simplest type of reflex arc, there is no interneuron. The afferent neuron synapses directly with an efferent neuron, so this kind of pathway is called a **monosynaptic reflex arc** (fig. 14.19). Synaptic delay is minimal, and the response is especially quick.

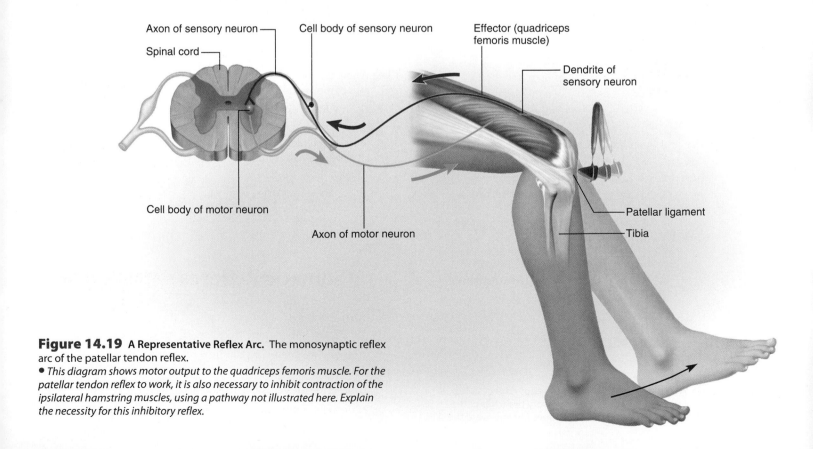

**Figure 14.19 A Representative Reflex Arc.** The monosynaptic reflex arc of the patellar tendon reflex.
● *This diagram shows motor output to the quadriceps femoris muscle. For the patellar tendon reflex to work, it is also necessary to inhibit contraction of the ipsilateral hamstring muscles, using a pathway not illustrated here. Explain the necessity for this inhibitory reflex.*

Most reflex arcs, however, have one or more interneurons, and indeed often involve multineuron circuits with many synapses. Such reflex arcs produce more prolonged muscular responses and, by way of diverging circuits, may stimulate multiple muscles at once.

## THINK ABOUT IT

*There is actually a second synapse in a "monosynaptic" reflex arc. Identify its location.*

A reflex like the one diagrammed in figure 14.19 is described as an **ipsilateral reflex** because the CNS input and output are on the same side of the body. Others such as the crossed extension reflex (table 14.7) are called **contralateral reflexes** because the sensory input enters the spinal cord on one side of the body and the motor output leaves on the opposite side. In an **intersegmental reflex,** the sensory signal enters the spinal cord at one level (segment), and the motor output leaves the cord from a higher or lower level. For example, if you step on something sharp and lift your foot from the ground, some motor output leaves the spinal cord higher up and goes to trunk muscles that flex your waist. This shifts your center of gravity over the leg still on the ground, preventing you from falling over.

Table 14.7 describes several types of somatic reflexes. These reflexes are controlled primarily by the cerebrum and cerebellum of the brain, but a weak response is mediated through the spinal cord and persists even if the spinal cord is severed from the brain. The spinal component can be more pronounced if the stimulus is sudden or intense, as in the clinical testing of the knee-jerk (patellar) reflex and other stretch reflexes.

## Before You Go On

*Answer the following questions to test your understanding of the preceding section:*

9. Define *reflex*. Distinguish between somatic and visceral reflexes.

10. List and define the five components of a typical somatic reflex arc.

11. Describe a situation in which each of the following would be functionally relevant: an ipsilateral, a contralateral, and an intersegmental reflex arc.

# Clinical Perspectives

### Objectives
When you have completed this section, you should be able to

- describe some effects of spinal cord injuries; and
- define the types of paralysis and explain the basis for their differences.

Some developmental abnormalities of the spinal cord are described in chapter 13. In children and adults, the most significant disorder of the spinal cord is trauma. Each year in the United States, 10,000 to 12,000 people become paralyzed by spinal cord trauma, usually as a result of vertebral fractures. The group at greatest risk is males from 16 to 30 years old, because of their high-risk behaviors. Fifty-five percent of their injuries are from automobile and motorcycle accidents, 18% from sports, and 15% from gunshot and stab wounds. Elderly people are also at above-average risk because of falls, and in times of war, battlefield injuries account for many cases.

Complete *transection* (severance) of the spinal cord causes immediate loss of motor control at and below the level of the injury. Victims also lose all sensation from the level of injury and below, although some patients temporarily feel burning pain within one or two dermatomes of the level of the lesion.

## THINK ABOUT IT

*Respiratory paralysis typically results from spinal cord transection above level C4, but not from injuries below that level. Explain.*

In the early stage, victims exhibit a syndrome (a suite of signs and symptoms) called **spinal shock.** The muscles below the level of injury exhibit flaccid paralysis (inability to contract) and an absence of reflexes because of the lack of stimulation from higher levels of the CNS. For 8 days to 8 weeks after the accident, the patient typically lacks bladder and bowel reflexes and thus retains urine and feces. Lacking sympathetic stimulation to the blood vessels, a patient may exhibit *neurogenic shock* in which the vessels dilate and blood pressure drops dangerously low. Spinal shock can last from a few days to 3 months, but typically lasts 7 to 20 days.

| TABLE 14.7 | Types of Somatic Reflexes |
|---|---|
| Stretch reflex | Increased muscle tension in response to stretch. Serves to maintain equilibrium and posture, stabilize joints, and make joint actions smoother and better coordinated. The knee-jerk reflex (patellar reflex, fig. 14.19) is a familiar monosynaptic spinal reflex. |
| Flexor reflex | Contraction of flexor muscles resulting in withdrawal of a limb from an injurious stimulus, as in withdrawal from a burn or pinprick. |
| Crossed extension reflex | Contraction of extensor muscles in one limb when the flexor muscles of the opposite limb contract. Stiffens one leg, for example, when the opposite leg is lifted from the ground, so that one does not fall over. |
| Golgi tendon reflex | Inhibition of muscle contraction when a tendon is excessively stretched, thus preventing tendon injuries. |

As spinal shock subsides, somatic reflexes begin to reappear, at first in the toes and progressing to the feet and legs. Autonomic reflexes also reappear. Contrary to the earlier urinary and fecal retention, a patient now has the opposite problem, incontinence, as the rectum and bladder empty reflexively in response to stretch. Both the somatic and autonomic nervous systems typically exhibit exaggerated reflexes, a state called *hyperreflexia* or the *mass reflex reaction*. Stimuli such as a full bladder or cutaneous touch can trigger an extreme cardiovascular reaction. The systolic blood pressure, normally about 120 mmHg, jumps to as high as 300 mmHg, sometimes causing a stroke. Pressure receptors in the major arteries sense this rise in blood pressure and activate a reflex that slows the heart, sometimes to a rate as low as 30 or 40 beats/minute *(bradycardia)*. Men at first lose the capacity for erection and ejaculation. They may recover these functions later and become capable of climaxing and fathering children, but still lack sexual sensation.

The most serious permanent effect of spinal cord trauma is paralysis. The flaccid paralysis of spinal shock later changes to spastic paralysis as reflexes are regained, but lack inhibitory control from the brain. Spastic paralysis typically starts with chronic flexion of the hips and knees *(flexor spasms)* and progresses to a state in which the limbs become straight and rigid *(extensor spasms)*. Three forms of muscle paralysis are **paraplegia,** a paralysis of both lower limbs resulting from spinal cord lesions at levels T1 to L1; **quadriplegia,** the paralysis of all four limbs resulting from lesions above level C5; and **hemiplegia,** paralysis of one side of the body, usually resulting not from spinal cord injuries but from a stroke or other brain lesion. Spinal cord lesions from C5 to C7 can produce a state of partial quadriplegia—total paralysis of the lower limbs and partial paralysis *(paresis,* or weakness) of the upper limbs.

Treatment of spinal cord injuries is an area of intense medical research today, with hopes for recovery of spinal functions stimulated by new insights into the physiological mechanisms of spinal cord tissue death and the potential for embryonic stem cells to regenerate damaged cord tissue.

Table 14.8 describes some injuries and other disorders of the spinal cord and spinal nerves.

## *Before You Go On*

*Answer the following questions to test your understanding of the preceding section:*

12. Describe the signs of spinal shock.

13. Describe the difference between flaccid paralysis and spastic paralysis.

14. Distinguish between the causes of paraplegia, quadriplegia, and hemiplegia.

| TABLE 14.8 | Some Disorders of the Spinal Cord and Spinal Nerves |
|---|---|
| **Guillain-Barré syndrome** | An acute demyelinating nerve disorder often triggered by viral infection, resulting in muscle weakness, elevated heart rate, unstable blood pressure, shortness of breath, and sometimes death from respiratory paralysis |
| **Neuralgia** | General term for nerve pain, often caused by pressure on spinal nerves from herniated intervertebral discs or other causes |
| **Paresthesia** | Abnormal sensations of prickling, burning, numbness, or tingling; a symptom of nerve trauma or other peripheral nerve disorders |
| **Peripheral neuropathy** | Any loss of sensory or motor function due to nerve injury; also called *nerve palsy* |
| **Rabies (hydrophobia)** | A disease usually contracted from animal bites, involving viral infection that spreads via somatic motor nerve fibers to the CNS and then out of the CNS via autonomic nerve fibers, leading to seizures, coma, and death; invariably fatal if not treated before CNS symptoms appear |
| **Spinal meningitis** | Inflammation of the spinal meninges due to viral, bacterial, or other infection |

### Disorders Described Elsewhere

# CHAPTER REVIEW

## REVIEW OF KEY CONCEPTS

### The Spinal Cord (p. 396)

1. The spinal cord conducts signals up and down the body, contains *central pattern generators* that control locomotion, and mediates many reflexes.

2. The spinal cord occupies the vertebral canal from vertebrae C1 to L1. A bundle of nerve roots called the *cauda equina* occupies the canal from C2 to S5.

3. The cord is divided into *cervical, thoracic, lumbar,* and *sacral regions,* named for the levels of the vertebral column through which the spinal nerves emerge. The portion served by each spinal nerve is called a *segment* of the cord.

4. *Cervical* and *lumbar enlargements* are wide points in the cord marking the emergence of nerves that control the limbs.

5. The spinal cord is enclosed in three fibrous *meninges.* From superficial to deep, these are the *dura mater, arachnoid mater,* and *pia mater.* An *epidural space* exists between the dura mater and vertebral bone, and a *subarachnoid space* between the arachnoid and pia mater.

6. The pia mater issues periodic *denticulate ligaments* that anchor it to the dura, and continues inferiorly as a *coccygeal ligament* that anchors the cord to vertebra L2.

7. In cross section, the spinal cord exhibits a central H-shaped core of *gray matter* surrounded by white matter. The gray matter contains the somas, dendrites, and synapses, whereas the white matter consists of nerve fibers (axons).

8. The *dorsal horn* of the gray matter receives afferent (sensory) nerve fibers from the dorsal root of the spinal nerve. The *ventral horn* contains the somas that give rise to the efferent (motor) nerve fibers of the ventral root. A *lateral horn* in the thoracic and lumbar regions contains somas of the sympathetic neurons.

9. The white matter is divided into *dorsal, lateral,* and *ventral columns* on each side of the cord. Each column consists of one or more *tracts,* or bundles of nerve fibers. The nerve fibers in a given tract are similar in origin, destination, and function.

10. *Ascending tracts* carry sensory information up the cord to the brain. Their names and functions are listed in table 14.1.

11. From receptor to cerebral cortex, sensory signals typically travel through three neurons (first- through third-order) and cross over *(decussate)* from one side of the body to the other in the spinal cord or brainstem. Thus, the right cerebral cortex receives sensory input from the left side of the body (from the neck down), and vice versa.

12. *Descending tracts* carry motor commands from the brain downward. Their names and functions are also listed in table 14.1.

13. Motor signals typically begin in an *upper motor neuron* in the cerebral cortex and travel to a *lower motor neuron* in the brainstem or spinal cord. The latter neuron's axon leaves the CNS in a cranial or spinal nerve leading to a muscle.

### The Spinal Nerves (p. 403)

1. A nerve is a cordlike organ composed of nerve fibers (axons) and connective tissue.

2. Each nerve fiber is enclosed in its own fibrous sleeve called an *endoneurium.* Nerve fibers are bundled in groups called *fascicles* separated from each other by a *perineurium.* A fibrous *epineurium* covers the entire nerve.

3. Nerve fibers are classified as *afferent* or *efferent* depending on the direction of signal conduction, *somatic* or *visceral* depending on the types of organs they innervate, and *special* or *general* depending on the locations of the organs they innervate (table 14.2).

4. A *sensory nerve* is composed of afferent fibers only, a *motor nerve* of efferent fibers only, and a *mixed nerve* is composed of both. Most nerves are mixed.

5. A *ganglion* is a swelling along the course of a nerve containing the cell bodies of the peripheral neurons.

6. There are 31 pairs of *spinal nerves,* which enter and leave the spinal cord and emerge mainly through the intervertebral foramina. Within the vertebral canal, each branches into a *dorsal root,* which carries sensory signals to the dorsal horn of the spinal cord, and a *ventral root,* which receives motor signals from the ventral horn. The dorsal root has a swelling, the *dorsal root ganglion,* containing the somas of somatic sensory neurons.

7. Distal to the intervertebral foramen, each spinal nerve branches into a *dorsal ramus, ventral ramus,* and *meningeal branch.*

8. The ventral ramus gives rise to *intercostal nerves* in the thoracic region and *nerve plexuses* in all other regions. The nerve plexuses are weblike networks adjacent to the verte-

bral column: the *cervical, brachial, lumbar, sacral,* and *coccygeal plexus.* The nerves arising from each plexus are described in tables 14.3 through 14.6.

### Somatic Reflexes (p. 415)

1. A reflex is a quick, involuntary, stereotyped reaction of a gland or muscle to a stimulus.

2. *Visceral reflexes* are reactions of glands, cardiac muscle, and smooth muscle, controlled by the autonomic nervous system. *Somatic (spinal) reflexes* are responses of skeletal muscles, controlled by the somatic nervous system.

3. A somatic reflex employs a simple neural pathway called a *reflex arc,* in which signals travel from a somatic receptor through an afferent nerve fiber to the spinal cord or brainstem, an integrating center in the CNS, an efferent nerve fiber leaving the CNS, and finally to a skeletal muscle.

4. A *monosynaptic reflex arc* has no interneuron between the afferent and efferent neurons; thus, it has minimal synaptic delay and especially quick responses. Most reflex arcs, however, are polysynaptic, involving one or more interneurons.

5. *Ipsilateral reflex arcs* have the sensory input and motor output on the same side of the CNS; *contralateral reflex arcs* have their output on the side opposite from the input; and *intersegmental reflex arcs* have their output at a different vertical level of the spinal cord than their input. Four specific classes of somatic reflexes are described in table 14.7.

### Clinical Perspectives (p. 417)

1. Trauma is the most common disorder of the spinal cord, usually resulting from accidents.

2. Complete transection of the spinal cord immediately abolishes sensation and motor control in areas below the injury. *Spinal shock* typically lasts up to 20 days from the injury. Somatic and autonomic reflexes then begin to reappear and may be exaggerated *(hyperreflexia).* Flaccid paralysis is typically replaced by spastic paralysis as reflex functions return. *Paraplegia* and *quadriplegia* are common consequences of spinal cord injury, while *hemiplegia* usually results from a brain lesion.

3. Other disorders of the spinal cord and spinal nerves are described in table 14.8.

## TESTING YOUR RECALL

1. Below L2, the vertebral canal is occupied by a bundle of spinal nerve roots called
   a. the terminal filum.
   b. the descending tracts.
   c. the gracile fasciculus.
   d. the medullary cone.
   e. the cauda equina.

2. The brachial plexus gives rise to all of the following nerves *except*
   a. the axillary nerve.
   b. the radial nerve.
   c. the obturator nerve.
   d. the median nerve.
   e. the ulnar nerve.

3. Between the dura mater and vertebral bone, one is most likely to find
   a. arachnoid mater.
   b. denticulate ligaments.
   c. cartilage.
   d. adipose tissue.
   e. spongy bone.

4. Which of these tracts carry motor signals destined for the postural muscles?
   a. the gracile fasciculus
   b. the cuneate fasciculus
   c. spinothalamic tract
   d. vestibulospinal tracts
   e. tectospinal tract

5. A patient has a gunshot wound that caused a bone fragment to nick the spinal cord. The patient now feels no pain or temperature sensations from that level of the body down. Most likely, the _____ was damaged.
   a. gracile fasciculus
   b. medial lemniscus
   c. tectospinal tract
   d. lateral corticospinal tract
   e. spinothalamic tract

6. Which of these is *not* a region of the spinal cord?
   a. cervical
   b. thoracic
   c. pelvic
   d. lumbar
   e. sacral

7. In the spinal cord, the somas of the lower motor neurons are found in
   a. the cauda equina.
   b. the dorsal horns.
   c. the ventral horns.
   d. the dorsal root ganglia.
   e. the fasciculi.

8. The outermost connective tissue wrapping of a nerve is called the
   a. epineurium.
   b. perineurium.
   c. endoneurium.
   d. arachnoid mater.
   e. dura mater.

9. The intercostal nerves between the ribs arise from which spinal nerve plexus?
   a. cervical
   b. brachial
   c. lumbar
   d. sacral
   e. none of them

10. All somatic reflexes share all of the following properties *except*
    a. they are quick.
    b. they are monosynaptic.

c. they require stimulation.
d. they are involuntary.
e. they are stereotyped.

11. Outside the CNS, the somas of neurons are clustered in swellings called _____.

12. Distal to the intervertebral foramen, a spinal nerve branches into a dorsal and ventral _____.

14. The cerebellum receives feedback from the muscles and joints by way of the _____ tracts of the spinal cord.

14. Motor innervation of the leg proper comes predominantly from the _____ plexus.

15. Neural circuits called _____ in the spinal cord produce the rhythmic muscular contractions of walking.

16. The _____ nerves arise from the cervical plexus and innervate the diaphragm.

17. The crossing of a nerve fiber or tract from the right side of the CNS to the left, or vice versa, is called _____.

18. The nonvisual awareness of the body's position and movements is called _____.

19. The _____ ganglion contains the somas of neurons that carry sensory signals to the spinal cord.

20. The sciatic nerve is a composite of two nerves, the _____ and _____.

*Answers in the Appendix*

## TRUE OR FALSE

*Determine which five of the following statements are false, and briefly explain why.*

1. The gracile fasciculus is a descending spinal tract.

2. At the inferior end, the adult spinal cord ends before the vertebral column does.

3. Each spinal cord segment has only one pair of spinal nerves.

4. Some spinal nerves are sensory and others are motor.

5. The dura mater adheres tightly to the bone of the vertebral canal.

6. The dorsal and ventral horns of the spinal cord are composed of gray matter.

7. The corticospinal tracts carry motor signals down the spinal cord.

8. The dermatomes are nonoverlapping regions of skin innervated by different spinal nerves.

9. Somatic reflexes are those that do not involve the brain.

10. The Golgi tendon reflex acts to inhibit muscle contraction.

*Answers in the Appendix*

## TESTING YOUR COMPREHENSION

1. Jillian is thrown from a horse. She strikes the ground with her chin, causing severe hyperextension of the neck. Emergency medical technicians properly immobilize her neck and transport her to a hospital, but she dies 5 minutes after arrival. An autopsy shows multiple fractures of vertebrae C1, C6, and C7 and extensive damage to the spinal cord. Explain why she died rather than being left quadriplegic.

2. Wallace is the victim of a hunting accident. A bullet grazed his vertebral column, and bone fragments severed the left half of his spinal cord at segments T8 through T10. Since the accident, Wallace has had a condition called *dissociated sensory loss,* in which he feels no sensations of deep touch or limb position on the *left* side of his body below the injury and no sensations of pain or heat on the *right* side. Explain what spinal tract(s) the injury has affected and why these sensory losses are on opposite sides of the body.

3. Anthony gets into a fight between rival gangs. As an attacker comes at him with a knife, he turns to flee, but stumbles. The attacker stabs him on the medial side of the right gluteal fold, and Anthony collapses. He loses all use of his right limb, being unable to extend his hip, flex his knee, or move his foot. He never fully recovers these lost functions. Explain what nerve injury Anthony has most likely suffered.

4. Stand with your right shoulder, hip, and foot firmly against a wall. Raise your left foot from the floor without losing contact with the wall at any point. What happens? Why? What principle of this chapter does this demonstrate?

5. When a patient needs a tendon graft, surgeons sometimes use the tendon of the palmaris longus, a relatively dispensable muscle of the forearm. The median nerve lies nearby and looks very similar to this tendon. There have been cases where a surgeon mistakenly removed a section of this nerve instead of the tendon. What effects do you think such a mistake would have on the patient?

*Answers at aris.mhhe.com*

## ONLINE RESOURCES

 Visit aprevealed.com to explore melt-away cadaver dissections, watch animations that clarify difficult concepts, review histological and radiological images, or take a quiz to assess your understanding of the material.

 The Saladin *Human Anatomy,* 2e website at aris.mhhe.com features chapter-specific quizzes, labeling exercises, and other interactive tools to complement your study of human anatomy. If your instructor has provided an ARIS course code, you can also access assignments and information specific to your course.

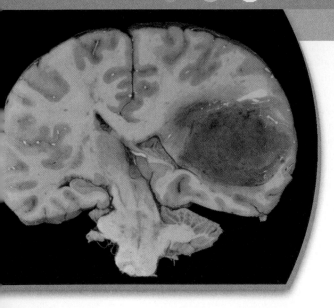

# The Brain and Cranial Nerves

Frontal section of a brain with a large tumor (glioblastoma) in the left cerebral hemisphere

## BRUSHING UP

To understand this chapter, you may find it helpful to review the following concepts:
- Anatomy of the cranium (pp. 179–188)
- Glial cells and their functions (p. 381)
- Embryonic development of the central nervous system (pp. 388–390)
- Meninges (pp. 397–398)
- Gray and white matter (p. 399)
- Tracts of the spinal cord (pp. 399–403)
- Structure of nerves and ganglia (pp. 403–405)

Anatomy & Physiology REVEALED®
aprevealed.com

**Nervous System**

The mystique of the brain continues to intrigue modern biologists and psychologists even as it did the philosophers of antiquity. Aristotle thought that the brain was a radiator for cooling the blood, but generations earlier, Hippocrates had expressed a more accurate view. "Men ought to know," he said, "that from the brain, and from the brain only, arise our pleasures, joy, laughter and jests, as well as our sorrows, pains, griefs and tears. Through it, in particular, we think, see, hear, and distinguish the ugly from the beautiful, the bad from the good, the pleasant from the unpleasant."

Brain function is so strongly associated with what it means to be alive and human that the cessation of brain activity is taken as a clinical criterion of death even when other organs of the body are still functioning. With its hundreds of neural pools and trillions of synapses, the brain performs sophisticated tasks beyond our present understanding. Still, all of our mental functions, no matter how complex, are ultimately based on the cellular activities described in chapter 13. The relationship of the mind or personality to the cellular function of the brain is a question that will provide fertile ground for scientific study and philosophical debate long into the future.

This chapter is a study of the brain and the cranial nerves directly connected to it. Here we will plumb some of the mysteries of motor control, sensation, emotion, thought, language, personality, memory, dreams, and plans. Your study of this chapter is one brain's attempt to understand itself.

# Overview of the Brain

## Objectives
When you have completed this section, you should be able to

- describe the major subdivisions and anatomical landmarks of the brain;
- state the locations of the gray and white matter of the brain;
- describe the meninges of the brain;
- describe a system of fluid-filled chambers within the brain;
- discuss the production, flow, and function of the cerebrospinal fluid in these chambers; and
- explain the significance of the brain barrier system.

In the evolution of the central nervous system from the simplest vertebrate animals to humans, the spinal cord has changed very little while the brain has changed a great deal. In fishes and amphibians, the brain weighs about the same as the spinal cord, but in humans, it weighs 55 times as much. It averages about 1,600 g (3.5 lb) in men and 1,450 g in women. The difference in weight is proportional to body size, not intelligence. The Neanderthal people had larger brains than modern humans do.

The human brain has a high opinion of itself: Ours is the most sophisticated brain when compared to others in terms of awareness of the environment, adaptability to environmental variation and change,

quick execution of complex decisions, fine motor control and mobility of the body, and behavioral complexity. Over the course of human evolution, the brain has shown its greatest growth in areas concerned with vision, memory, and motor control of the prehensile hand.

## Major Landmarks

Before we consider the form and function of specific regions of the brain, it will help to get a general overview of its major landmarks (figs. 15.1 and 15.2). These will provide important points of reference as we progress through a more detailed study.

Two directional terms often used to describe brain anatomy are *rostral* and *caudal*. **Rostral**[1] means "toward the nose" and **caudal**[2] means "toward the tail." These are apt descriptions for an animal such as a laboratory rat, on which so much neuroscience research has been done. The terms are retained for human neuroanatomy as well, but in references to the human brain, *rostral* means toward the forehead and *caudal* means toward the spinal cord. In the spinal cord and brainstem, which are vertically oriented, *rostral* means higher and *caudal* means lower.

The brain is divided into three major portions—the *cerebrum, cerebellum,* and *brainstem.* The **cerebrum** (seh-REE-brum or SER-eh-brum) constitutes about 83% of its volume and consists of a pair of half-globes called the **cerebral hemispheres.** Each hemisphere is marked by thick folds called **gyri**[3] (JY-rye; singular, *gyrus*) separated by shallow grooves called **sulci**[4] (SUL-sye; singular, *sulcus*). A very deep groove, the **longitudinal fissure,** separates the right and left hemispheres from each other. At the bottom of this fissure, the hemispheres are connected by a thick bundle of nerve fibers called the **corpus callosum**[5]—a prominent landmark for anatomical description (fig. 15.2).

The **cerebellum**[6] (SER-eh-BEL-um) lies inferior to the cerebrum and occupies the posterior cranial fossa. It is also marked by gyri, sulci, and fissures. The cerebellum is the second-largest region of the brain; it constitutes about 10% of its volume but contains over 50% of its neurons.

Authorities differ on how they define the **brainstem.** This book treats it as that which remains of the brain if the cerebrum and cerebellum are removed. Its major components, from rostral to caudal, are the *diencephalon, midbrain, pons,* and *medulla oblongata.* The most common alternative definition includes only the last three of these.

In a living person, the brainstem is oriented like a vertical stalk with the cerebrum perched on top of it like a mushroom cap. Postmortem changes give it a more oblique angle in the cadaver and consequently in many medical illustrations. Caudally, the brainstem ends at the foramen magnum of the skull, and the central nervous system (CNS) continues below this as the spinal cord.

---

[1]*rostr* = nose
[2]*caud* = tail
[3]*gyr* = turn, twist
[4]*sulc* = furrow, groove
[5]*corpus* = body + *call* = thick
[6]*cereb* = brain + *ellum* = little

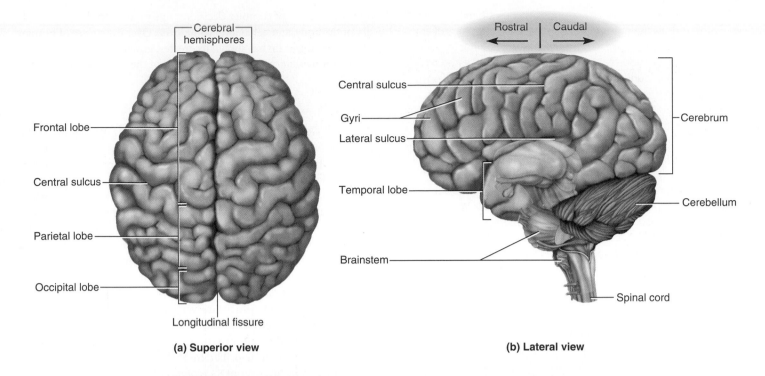

**(a) Superior view**

**(b) Lateral view**

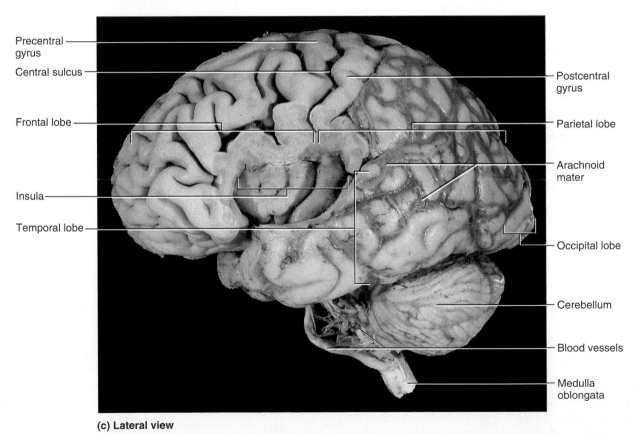

**(c) Lateral view**

**Figure 15.1  Surface Anatomy of the Brain.**  (a) Superior view of the cerebral hemispheres. (b) Left lateral view, with the brainstem in orange. The portion of the brainstem above the cerebellum is represented as showing through the cerebrum to convey its location. (c) The partially dissected brain of a cadaver. Part of the left hemisphere is cut away to expose the insula. The arachnoid mater is removed from the anterior (rostral) half of the brain to expose the gyri and sulci; the arachnoid mater with its blood vessels is seen on the posterior (caudal) half. Blood vessels of the brainstem are left in place.
● *After studying the meninges, determine which of the three had to be removed to expose* any *of the anatomy visible in part (c).*

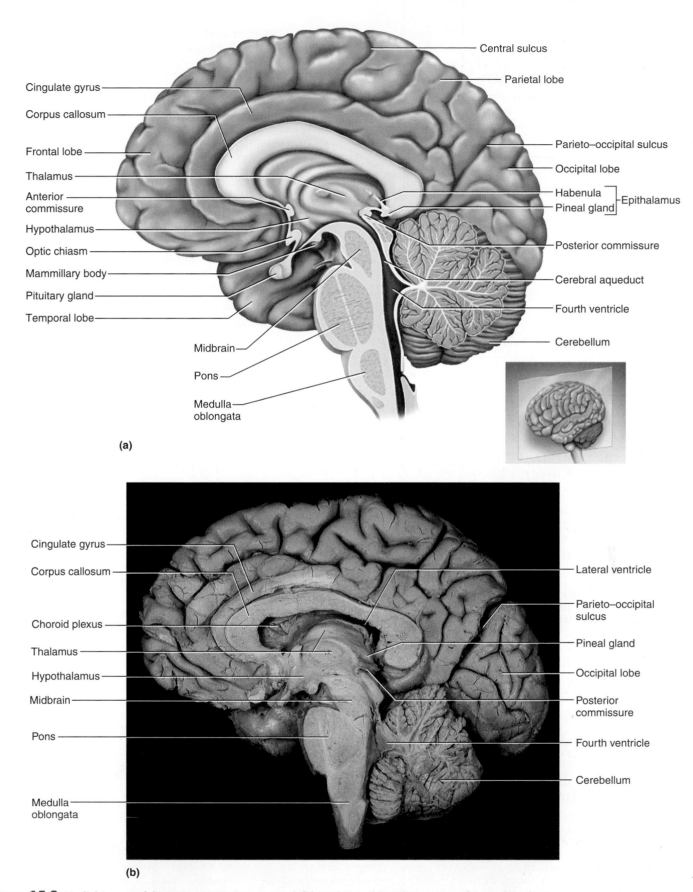

**Figure 15.2** **Medial Aspect of the Brain.** (a) Median section, left lateral view. (b) Median section of the cadaver brain.

## Gray and White Matter

The brain, like the spinal cord, is composed of gray and white matter. Gray matter—the site of the neuron cell bodies, dendrites, and synapses—forms a surface layer called the **cortex** over the cerebrum and cerebellum, and deeper masses called **nuclei** surrounded by white matter (see fig. 15.4c). The white matter thus lies deep to the cortical gray matter in most of the brain, opposite from the relationship of gray and white matter in the spinal cord. As in the spinal cord, the white matter is composed of **tracts,** or bundles of axons, which here connect one part of the brain to another and to the spinal cord. It gets its bright white color from myelin. The tracts are described later in more detail.

## Meninges

The brain is enveloped in three connective tissue membranes, the meninges, which lie between the nervous tissue and bone. As in the spinal cord, these are the dura mater, arachnoid mater, and pia mater (fig. 15.3). They protect the brain and provide a structural framework for arteries, veins, and *dural sinuses.* In the cranial cavity, the dura mater consists of two layers—an outer *periosteal layer,* equivalent to the periosteum of the cranial bones, and an inner *meningeal layer.* Only the meningeal layer continues into the vertebral canal, where it forms the dural sac around the spinal cord. The cranial dura mater lies closely against the cranial bone, with no intervening epidural space like the one in the vertebral canal. It is attached to the cranial bone in limited places—around the foramen magnum, the sella turcica, the crista galli, and the sutures of the skull.

In some places, the two layers of dura are separated by **dural sinuses,** spaces that collect blood that has circulated through the brain. Two major dural sinuses are the **superior sagittal sinus,** found just under the cranium along the midsagittal line, and the **transverse sinus,** which runs horizontally from the rear of the head toward each ear. These sinuses meet like an inverted T at the back of the brain and ultimately empty into the internal jugular veins of the neck. The anatomy of the dural sinuses is detailed in chapter 21.

In certain places, the meningeal layer of the dura mater folds inward to separate major parts of the brain from each other: the *falx*[7] *cerebri* (falks SER-eh-bry) extends into the longitudinal fissure as a vertical wall between the right and left cerebral hemispheres, and is shaped like the curved blade of a sickle; the *tentorium*[8] (ten-TOE-ree-um) *cerebelli* stretches horizontally like a roof over the posterior cranial fossa and separates the cerebellum from the overlying cerebrum; and the vertical *falx cerebelli* partially separates the right and left halves of the cerebellum on the inferior side.

The arachnoid mater and pia mater are similar to those of the spinal cord. The arachnoid mater is a transparent membrane over the brain surface, visible in the caudal half of the cerebrum in figure 15.1c.

---

[7]*falx* = sickle
[8]*tentorium* = tent

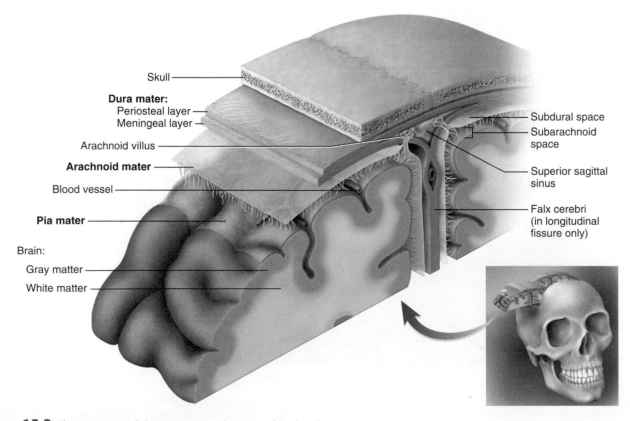

**Figure 15.3** The Meninges of the Brain. Frontal section of the head.

A *subarachnoid space* separates the arachnoid from the pia, and in some places, a *subdural space* separates the dura from the arachnoid. The pia mater is a very thin, delicate membrane that closely follows all the contours of the brain surface, even dipping into the sulci. It is not usually visible without a microscope.

# Ventricles and Cerebrospinal Fluid

The brain has four internal chambers called **ventricles.** The largest are the two **lateral ventricles,** which form an arc in each cerebral hemisphere (fig. 15.4). Through a pore called the **interventricular foramen,** each lateral ventricle is connected to the **third ventricle,** a narrow median space inferior to the corpus callosum. From

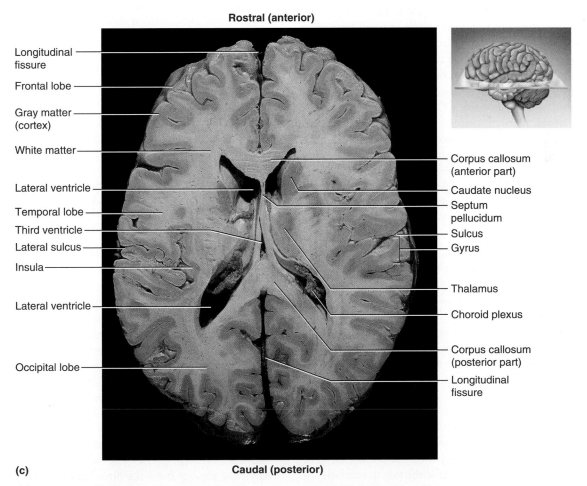

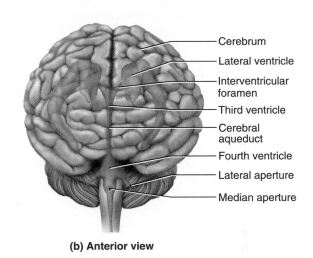

**Figure 15.4  Ventricles of the Brain.** (a) Right lateral view. (b) Anterior view. (c) Superior view of a horizontal section of the cadaver brain, showing the lateral ventricles and some other features of the cerebrum.

# INSIGHT 15.1   ●●●

## Clinical Application

## Meningitis

*Meningitis*—inflammation of the meninges—is one of the most serious diseases of infancy and childhood. It occurs especially between 3 months and 2 years of age. Meningitis is caused by a variety of bacteria and viruses that invade the CNS by way of the nose and throat, often following respiratory, throat, or ear infections. The pia mater and arachnoid are most often affected, and from here the infection can spread to the adjacent nervous tissue. In bacterial meningitis, the brain swells, the ventricles enlarge, and the brainstem may exhibit hemorrhages. Signs include a high fever, stiff neck, drowsiness, and intense headache and may progress to vomiting, loss of sensory and motor functions, and coma. Death can occur within hours of the onset. Infants and toddlers with a high fever should therefore receive immediate medical attention.

Meningitis is diagnosed partly by examining the cerebrospinal fluid (CSF) for bacteria and white blood cells. The CSF is obtained by making a *lumbar puncture (spinal tap)* between two lumbar vertebrae and drawing fluid from the subarachnoid space (see Insight 14.1).

here, a canal called the **cerebral aqueduct** passes down the core of the midbrain and leads to the **fourth ventricle,** a small triangular chamber between the pons and cerebellum (see fig. 15.2). Caudally, this space narrows and forms a **central canal** that extends through the medulla oblongata into the spinal cord.

On the floor or wall of each ventricle, there is a spongy mass of blood capillaries called a **choroid** (CO-royd) **plexus** (fig. 15.4c), named for its histological resemblance to the chorion of a fetus. Ependymal cells, a type of neuroglia, cover each choroid plexus, the entire interior surface of the ventricles, and the canals of the brain and spinal cord. The choroid plexuses produce cerebrospinal fluid.

**Cerebrospinal fluid (CSF)** is a clear, colorless liquid that fills the ventricles and canals of the CNS and bathes its external surface. The brain produces about 500 mL of CSF per day, but the fluid is constantly reabsorbed at the same rate and only 100 to 160 mL are present at one time. About 40% of it is formed in the subarachnoid space external to the brain, 30% by the general ependymal lining of the brain ventricles, and 30% by the choroid plexuses. CSF formation begins with the filtration of plasma through the blood capillaries of the brain. The ependymal cells chemically modify the filtrate as it passes through them into the ventricles and subarachnoid space.

The CSF is not a stationary fluid but continually flows through and around the CNS, driven partly by its own pressure and partly by rhythmic pulsations of the brain produced by each heartbeat. The CSF secreted in the lateral ventricles flows through the interventricular foramina into the third ventricle (fig. 15.5), then down the cerebral aqueduct to the fourth ventricle. The third and fourth ventricles and their choroid plexuses add more CSF along the way. A small amount of CSF fills the central canal of the spinal cord, but ultimately, all of it escapes through three pores in the walls of the fourth ventricle—a *median aperture* and two *lateral apertures.* These lead into the subarachnoid space on the surface of the brain and spinal cord. CSF is

absorbed from this space by **arachnoid villi,** cauliflower-like extensions of the arachnoid meninx that protrude through the dura mater into the superior sagittal sinus of the brain. CSF penetrates the walls of the arachnoid villi and mixes with the blood in the sinus.

Cerebrospinal fluid serves three purposes:

1. **Buoyancy.** Because the brain and CSF are very similar in density, the brain neither sinks nor floats in the CSF. It hangs from delicate specialized fibroblasts of the arachnoid meninx. A human brain removed from the body weighs about 1,500 g, but when suspended in CSF, its effective weight is only about 50 g. By analogy, consider how much easier it is to lift another person when you are standing in a lake than it is on land. This buoyancy effect allows the brain to attain considerable size without being impaired by its own weight. If the brain rested heavily on the floor of the cranium, the pressure would kill the nervous tissue.

2. **Protection.** CSF also protects the brain from striking the cranium when the head is jolted. If the jolt is severe, however, the brain still may strike the inside of the cranium or suffer shearing injury from contact with the angular surfaces of the cranial floor. This is one of the common findings in child abuse (shaken child syndrome) and in head injuries (concussions) from auto accidents, boxing, and the like.

3. **Chemical stability.** The flow of CSF rinses metabolic wastes from the nervous tissue and homeostatically regulates its chemical environment. Slight changes in CSF composition can cause malfunctions of the nervous system. For example, a high glycine concentration disrupts the control of temperature and blood pressure, and a high pH causes dizziness and fainting.

### THINK ABOUT IT

*What effect would you expect from a small brain tumor that blocked the left interventricular foramen?*

# Blood Supply and the Brain Barrier System

Although the brain constitutes only 2% of the adult body weight, it receives 15% of the blood (about 750 mL/min) and consumes 20% of the oxygen and glucose. But despite its critical importance to the brain, blood is also a source of agents such as bacterial toxins that can harm the brain tissue. Consequently, there is a brain barrier system that strictly regulates what substances get from the bloodstream into the tissue fluid of the brain.

One component of this system is the **blood–brain barrier (BBB),** which seals nearly all of the blood capillaries throughout the brain tissue. In the developing brain, astrocytes reach out and contact the capillaries with their perivascular feet. They do not fully surround the capillary, but stimulate the formation of tight junctions between the *endothelial cells* that line it. These junctions and the basement membrane around them constitute the BBB. Anything passing from the blood into the tissue fluid has to pass through the endothelial cells themselves, which are more selective than gaps between the cells can be.

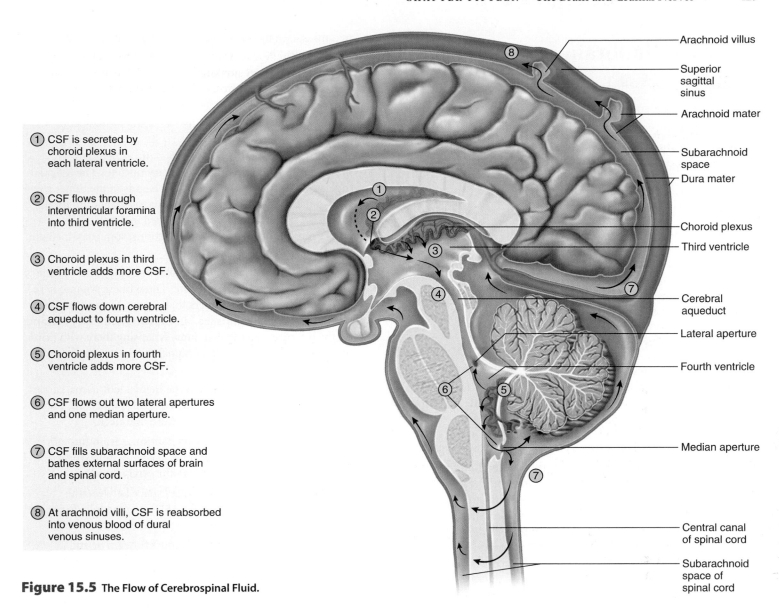

① CSF is secreted by choroid plexus in each lateral ventricle.

② CSF flows through interventricular foramina into third ventricle.

③ Choroid plexus in third ventricle adds more CSF.

④ CSF flows down cerebral aqueduct to fourth ventricle.

⑤ Choroid plexus in fourth ventricle adds more CSF.

⑥ CSF flows out two lateral apertures and one median aperture.

⑦ CSF fills subarachnoid space and bathes external surfaces of brain and spinal cord.

⑧ At arachnoid villi, CSF is reabsorbed into venous blood of dural venous sinuses.

Arachnoid villus
Superior sagittal sinus
Arachnoid mater
Subarachnoid space
Dura mater
Choroid plexus
Third ventricle
Cerebral aqueduct
Lateral aperture
Fourth ventricle
Median aperture
Central canal of spinal cord
Subarachnoid space of spinal cord

**Figure 15.5** The Flow of Cerebrospinal Fluid.

At the choroid plexuses, there is a similar **blood–CSF barrier,** composed of ependymal cells joined by tight junctions. Tight junctions are absent from ependymal cells elsewhere, because it is important to allow exchanges between the brain tissue and CSF. That is, there is no brain–CSF barrier.

The brain barrier system (BBS) is highly permeable to water, glucose, lipid-soluble substances such as oxygen and carbon dioxide, and drugs such as alcohol, caffeine, nicotine, and anesthetics. While the BBS is an important protective device, it is an obstacle to the delivery of drugs such as antibiotics and cancer drugs, and thus complicates the treatment of brain diseases.

The BBB is absent from patches called **circumventricular organs (CVOs)** on the walls of the third and fourth ventricles. Here, the blood has direct access to the brain tissue, enabling the brain to monitor and respond to fluctuations in blood chemistry. Unfortunately, the CVOs also afford a route for the human immunodeficiency virus (HIV) to invade the brain.

## Before You Go On

*Answer the following questions to test your understanding of the preceding section:*

1. List the three major parts of the brain and describe their locations.

2. Define *gyrus* and *sulcus*.

3. Name the parts of the brainstem from caudal to rostral.

4. Name the three meninges from superficial to deep.

5. Describe three functions of the cerebrospinal fluid.

6. Where does the CSF originate, and what route does it take through and around the CNS?

7. Name the two components of the brain barrier system and explain the importance of this system.

# The Hindbrain and Midbrain

## Objectives
When you have completed this section, you should be able to
- list the components of the hindbrain and midbrain;
- describe the major features of their anatomy; and
- explain the functions of each hindbrain and midbrain region.

We will survey the functional anatomy of the brain in a caudal to rostral direction, beginning with the hindbrain and its relatively simple functions, and progressing to the forebrain, the seat of such complex functions as thought, memory, and emotion. This survey will be organized around the five secondary vesicles of the embryonic brain and their mature derivatives, as described in chapter 13.

## The Medulla Oblongata

The embryonic hindbrain differentiates into two subdivisions, the myelencephalon and metencephalon (see fig. 13.14). The myelencephalon gives rise to just one structure, the **medulla oblongata** (meh-DULL-uh OB-long-GAH-ta).

The medulla begins at the foramen magnum of the skull and extends for 3 cm rostrally, ending at a groove marking the boundary between medulla and pons. The medulla contains all nerve fibers that travel between the brain and spinal cord. The last four (most caudal) pairs of cranial nerves begin or end at nuclei in the medulla. The medulla also contains several nuclei concerned with basic physiological functions: a **cardiac center,** which regulates the rate and force of the heartbeat; a **vasomotor center,** which regulates blood pressure and flow by dilating and constricting blood vessels; two **respiratory centers,** which regulate the rate and depth of breathing; and others involved in speech, coughing, sneezing, salivation, swallowing, gagging, vomiting, and sweating.

The external anatomy of the medulla oblongata is shown in figure 15.6. The anterior surface bears a pair of clublike ridges, the **pyramids.** Resembling side-by-side baseball bats, the pyramids are wider at the rostral end, taper caudally, and are separated by a longitudinal groove, the *anterior median fissure,* continuous with that of the spinal cord (fig. 15.6a). Lateral to each pyramid is a prominent bulge called the **olive.** The dorsal surface of the medulla exhibits two pairs of ridges, the gracile and cuneate fasciculi, a continuation of the ones in the spinal cord (p. 401).

Figure 15.7c shows some of the internal structure of the medulla oblongata. Cross sections at other levels would reveal different structures, but in this representative section, we see the following:

- The **corticospinal tracts,** seen anteriorly (at the bottom of the figure). These tracts occupy the pyramids and consist of nerve fibers that descend from the cerebral cortex carrying motor signals to the spinal cord. About 90% of these fibers cross over (decussate) to the opposite side of the brainstem at a point called the *pyramidal decussation,* near the caudal end of the

pyramids, (see fig. 15.6a). As a result, muscles below the neck are controlled by the contralateral side of the brain.

- The **inferior olivary nucleus,** a wavy layer of gray matter immediately posterior to each corticospinal tract, occupying the olive. This nucleus receives signals from many levels of the brain and spinal cord and relays them mainly to the cerebellum.

- The **reticular formation,** a vaguely defined region of gray matter posterior to the inferior olivary nucleus. The reticular formation is an elongated body that begins in the upper spinal cord and ascends through the medulla, pons, and midbrain. It consists of numerous nuclei involved in many of the body's most basic physiological functions, some of which are discussed later in this chapter.

- The **gracile** and **cuneate nuclei,** where sensory fibers of the corresponding fasciculi terminate. These fibers synapse here with second-order nerve fibers that decussate and form the ribbonlike **medial lemniscus.**[9] In the lemniscus, they continue up the brainstem to the thalamus, synapsing there with third-order neurons that convey the signals to the cerebrum and one's conscious awareness.

- The **tectospinal tract,** dorsal to the medial lemniscus, carries motor signals on their way to the cervical spinal cord. This tract mediates movements of the head and neck.

- The **dorsal spinocerebellar tract** continues from the spinal cord into the dorsolateral margins of the medulla. It carries sensory information destined for the cerebellum.

- The **fourth ventricle** is a CSF-filled space between the medulla and cerebellum (see fig. 15.2); the medulla forms its anterior boundary but does not completely contain it.

- Cranial nerves IX, X, part of XI, and XII begin or end in the medulla oblongata. Their Latin names and individual functions are provided in table 15.3, starting on page 453. At the level of the tissue section in figure 15.7c, we see the nuclei of two of these, the vagus (X) and hypoglossal (XII) nerves. The trigeminal nerve (V) emerges from the pons, but its nucleus extends into the medulla and is also visible in this figure. Collectively, the sensory functions of cranial nerves IX to XII include touch, pressure, temperature, taste, and pain. Their motor functions include chewing, swallowing, speech, respiration, cardiovascular control, gastrointestinal motility and secretion, and head, neck, and shoulder movements.

## The Pons

The metencephalon develops into two structures, the pons and cerebellum. The **pons**[10] measures about 2.5 cm long. Most of it forms a broad anterior bulge in the brainstem just rostral to the medulla (fig. 15.6a). Posteriorly, the pons consists mainly of two

---

[9]*lemn = ribbon + iscus = little*
[10]*pons = bridge*

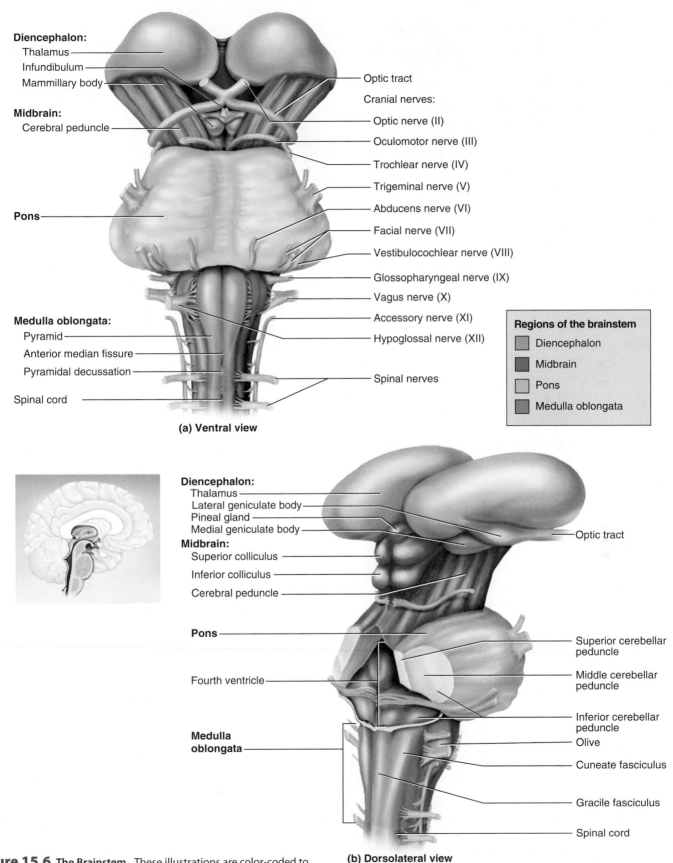

**Diencephalon:**
Thalamus
Infundibulum
Mammillary body

**Midbrain:**
Cerebral peduncle

**Pons**

**Medulla oblongata:**
Pyramid
Anterior median fissure
Pyramidal decussation

Spinal cord

Optic tract

Cranial nerves:

Optic nerve (II)
Oculomotor nerve (III)
Trochlear nerve (IV)
Trigeminal nerve (V)
Abducens nerve (VI)
Facial nerve (VII)
Vestibulocochlear nerve (VIII)
Glossopharyngeal nerve (IX)
Vagus nerve (X)
Accessory nerve (XI)
Hypoglossal nerve (XII)

Spinal nerves

**Regions of the brainstem**
Diencephalon
Midbrain
Pons
Medulla oblongata

**(a) Ventral view**

**Diencephalon:**
Thalamus
Lateral geniculate body
Pineal gland
Medial geniculate body

**Midbrain:**
Superior colliculus
Inferior colliculus
Cerebral peduncle

**Pons**

Fourth ventricle

**Medulla oblongata**

Optic tract

Superior cerebellar peduncle

Middle cerebellar peduncle

Inferior cerebellar peduncle

Olive

Cuneate fasciculus

Gracile fasciculus

Spinal cord

**(b) Dorsolateral view**

**Figure 15.6** **The Brainstem.** These illustrations are color-coded to match the embryonic origins in figure 13.14. The boundary between the middle and inferior cerebellar peduncles is indistinct. Authorities vary on whether to include the diencephalon in the brainstem.

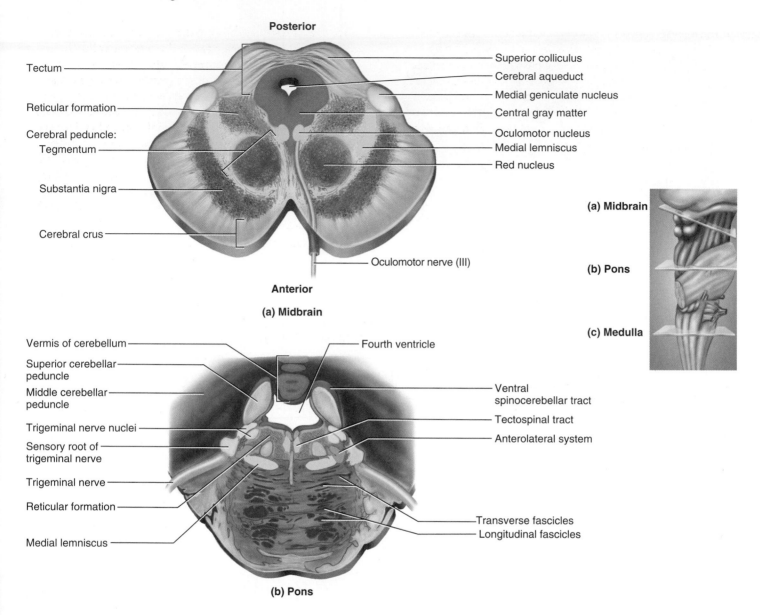

**Posterior**

Tectum

Reticular formation

Cerebral peduncle:
Tegmentum

Substantia nigra

Cerebral crus

Superior colliculus

Cerebral aqueduct

Medial geniculate nucleus

Central gray matter

Oculomotor nucleus

Medial lemniscus

Red nucleus

Oculomotor nerve (III)

**Anterior**

**(a) Midbrain**

Vermis of cerebellum

Superior cerebellar peduncle

Middle cerebellar peduncle

Trigeminal nerve nuclei

Sensory root of trigeminal nerve

Trigeminal nerve

Reticular formation

Medial lemniscus

Fourth ventricle

Ventral spinocerebellar tract

Tectospinal tract

Anterolateral system

Transverse fascicles

Longitudinal fascicles

**(b) Pons**

**(a) Midbrain**

**(b) Pons**

**(c) Medulla**

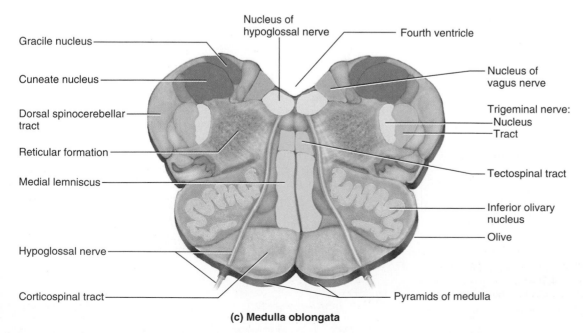

Gracile nucleus

Cuneate nucleus

Dorsal spinocerebellar tract

Reticular formation

Medial lemniscus

Hypoglossal nerve

Corticospinal tract

Nucleus of hypoglossal nerve

Fourth ventricle

Nucleus of vagus nerve

Trigeminal nerve:
Nucleus
Tract

Tectospinal tract

Inferior olivary nucleus

Olive

Pyramids of medulla

**(c) Medulla oblongata**

**Figure 15.7** **Cross Sections of the Brainstem.** The level of each section is shown in the figure on the right, and all sections are shown with the posterior surface uppermost. (a) The midbrain, cut obliquely to pass through the superior colliculi. (b) The pons. The straight edges indicate cut edges of the peduncles where the cerebellum was removed. (c) The medulla oblongata.

• *Trace the route taken through all three of these sections by fibers from the gracile and cuneate fasciculi described in chapter 14.*

pairs of thick stalks called *peduncles* that attach it to the cerebellum (fig. 15.6b); these are the cut edges of the upper half of figure 15.7b. The peduncles are further described with the cerebellum. The pons contains several nuclei involved in basic physiological functions including sleep, respiration, and bladder control.

In cross section, the pons exhibits continuations of the reticular formation, medial lemniscus, and tectospinal tract, all mentioned previously, as well as the following:

- Continuations of two spinal cord sensory tracts described in chapter 14—the **anterolateral system,** which contains the *spinothalamic tract* en route to the thalamus, and the **ventral spinocerebellar tract,** carrying signals en route to the cerebellum.

- Cranial nerves V through VIII begin or end in the pons, although we see only V (the trigeminal nerve) at the level of the cross section in figure 15.7b. The other three nerves emerge from the groove between the pons and medulla (see fig. 15.24). Their individual names and functions are provided in table 15.3. Collectively, the sensory functions of these four nerves include hearing, equilibrium, taste, and facial sensations such as touch and pain. Their motor functions include eye movements, facial expressions, chewing, swallowing, and the secretion of saliva and tears.

- Tracts of white matter in the anterior half of the pons (lower half of the figure), including transverse fascicles that cross from left to right and connect the two hemispheres of the cerebellum, and longitudinal fascicles that course up and down the pons carrying signals ascending to the thalamus and signals descending from the cerebrum to the cerebellum and medulla.

- Part of the fourth ventricle is seen bordered by the pons, the tail-like *vermis* of the cerebellum, and the superior cerebellar peduncles.

Even though the cerebellum is part of the metencephalon, it is not part of the brainstem. It will be clearer to continue this brainstem discussion with the midbrain and then return to the cerebellum.

## The Midbrain

The embryonic mesencephalon produces just one mature brain structure, the **midbrain**—a short segment of the brainstem that connects the hindbrain and forebrain (see figs. 15.2 and 15.8). The midbrain, too, contains continuations of the reticular formation and medial lemniscus. The cerebral aqueduct—the channel connecting the third ventricle to the fourth—passes through the midbrain and furnishes a useful landmark in figure 15.7a. Relative to the aqueduct, the cross section of the pons exhibits the following structures:

- The **central (periaqueductal) gray matter,** a region of gray matter surrounding the aqueduct. This functions with the reticular formation in controlling our awareness of pain (see chapter 16).

- The **tectum,**[11] a rooflike region dorsal to the aqueduct. The tectum exhibits four bulges collectively called the

*corpora quadrigemina*[12]—a rostral pair called the superior colliculi and a caudal pair called the inferior colliculi (see fig. 15.6b). The **superior colliculi**[13] (col-LIC-you-lye) function in visual attention, such as visually tracking moving objects and reflexively turning the eyes and head in response to a visual stimulus—for example, to look at something you catch sight of in your peripheral vision. The **inferior colliculi** receive and process auditory input from lower levels of the brainstem and relay it to other parts of the brain, especially the thalamus. They are sensitive to time delays between sounds heard by the two ears and thus aid in locating the source of a sound in space, and they function in auditory reflexes such as turning the head toward a sound or the startle response to a loud noise.

- The **tegmentum,**[14] the main mass of the midbrain, located ventral to the aqueduct. The tegmentum contains the **red nucleus,** named for the pink color it gets from a high density of blood vessels. Fibers from the red nucleus form the *rubrospinal tract* in most mammals, but in humans its connections go mainly to and from the cerebellum, with which it collaborates in fine motor control.

- The **substantia nigra**[15] (sub-STAN-she-uh NY-gruh), a dark gray to black nucleus pigmented with melanin, located between the tegmentum and cerebral crura (discussed next). This is a motor center that relays inhibitory signals to the thalamus and basal nuclei (both discussed later). It improves motor performance by suppressing unwanted muscle contractions. Degeneration of the substantia nigra leads to the uncontrollable muscle tremors of Parkinson disease (see p. 461).

- The **cerebral crura** (CROO-ra; singular, *crus*[16]), which anchor the cerebrum to the brainstem. The crura, tegmentum, and substantia nigra collectively form the *cerebral peduncle.* Corticospinal and other tracts from the cerebrum descend through the crura on their way to lower levels of the brainstem and spinal cord.

- Cranial nerves III and IV, both concerned with eye movements, originate in the midbrain; only III (the oculomotor nerve) is visible at the level of the section in figure 15.7a.

This figure also shows the *medial geniculate nucleus,* but this is part of the thalamus, not the midbrain. It just happens to lie in the plane of this section. The *superior cerebellar peduncles* connect to the midbrain, but are not seen at this level.

## The Reticular Formation

The **reticular**[17] **formation** is a loosely organized web of gray matter that runs vertically through all levels of the brainstem and has connections with many areas of the cerebrum (fig. 15.8). It occupies much of the space between the white fiber tracts and the more

---

[11]*tectum* = roof, cover

[12]*corpora* = bodies + *quadrigemina* = quadruplets
[13]*colli* = hill + *cul* = little
[14]*tegmen* = cover
[15]*substantia* = substance + *nigra* = black
[16]*crus* = leg
[17]*ret* = network + *icul* = little

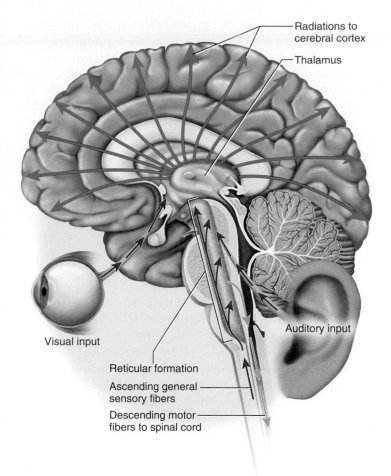

Radiations to
cerebral cortex

Thalamus

Visual input

Reticular formation

Ascending general
sensory fibers

Descending motor
fibers to spinal cord

Auditory input

**Figure 15.8 The Reticular Formation.** The formation consists of over 100 nuclei scattered through the brainstem. Red arrows indicate routes of input to the reticular formation; blue arrows indicate the radiating relay of signals from the thalamus to the cerebral cortex; and green arrows indicate output from the reticular formation to the spinal cord.

● *Locate components of the reticular formation in all three parts of figure 15.7.*

anatomically distinct brainstem nuclei. It consists of more than 100 small neural networks without well-defined boundaries. The functions of these networks include the following:

- **Somatic motor control.** Some motor neurons of the cerebral cortex and cerebellum send their axons to reticular formation nuclei, which then give rise to the *reticulospinal tracts* of the spinal cord. These tracts adjust muscle tension to maintain tone, balance, and posture, especially during body movements. The reticular formation also relays signals from the eyes and ears to the cerebellum so the cerebellum can integrate visual, auditory, and vestibular (balance and motion) stimuli into its role in motor coordination. Other reticular formation motor nuclei include *gaze centers,* which enable the eyes to track and fixate on objects, and *central pattern generators*—neural pools that produce rhythmic signals to the muscles of breathing and swallowing.

- **Cardiovascular control.** The reticular formation includes the previously mentioned cardiac and vasomotor centers of the medulla oblongata.

- **Pain modulation.** The reticular formation is one route by which pain signals from the lower body reach the cerebral cortex. It is also the origin of the *descending analgesic fibers* discussed in chapter 17 (p. 492). The nerve fibers in these pathways act in the spinal cord to block the transmission of pain signals to the brain.

- **Sleep and consciousness.** The reticular formation has projections to the cerebral cortex and thalamus that allow it some control over what sensory signals reach the cerebrum and come to our conscious attention. It plays a central role in states of consciousness such as alertness and sleep. Injury to the reticular formation can result in irreversible coma.

- **Habituation.** This is the process in which the brain learns to ignore repetitive, inconsequential stimuli while remaining sensitive to others. In a noisy city, for example, a person can sleep through traffic sounds but wake promptly to the sound of an alarm clock or a crying baby. The reticular formation screens out insignificant stimuli, preventing them from arousing cerebral centers of consciousness while it permits important sensory signals to pass. Reticular formation nuclei that modulate activity of the cerebral cortex are called the *reticular activating system* or *extrathalamic cortical modulatory system.*

## The Cerebellum

The **cerebellum** is the largest part of the hindbrain and second-largest part of the brain as a whole. It consists of right and left **cerebellar hemispheres** connected by a narrow wormlike bridge, the **vermis**[18] (fig. 15.9). Each hemisphere exhibits slender, parallel folds called **folia**[19] separated by shallow sulci. The cerebellum has a surface cortex of gray matter and a deeper layer of white matter. In a sagittal section, the white matter shows a branching fernlike pattern called the **arbor vitae.**[20] Each hemisphere also has four masses of gray matter called **deep nuclei** embedded in the white matter. All cerebellar input goes to the cortex and all output comes from the deep nuclei.

The cerebellum is connected to the brainstem by three pairs of stalks called **cerebellar peduncles**[21] (peh-DUN-culs): two *inferior peduncles* connecting it to the medulla oblongata, two *middle peduncles* to the pons, and two *superior peduncles* to the midbrain (see fig. 15.6b). These consist of thick bundles of nerve fibers that carry signals into and out of the cerebellum. Connections between the cerebellum and brainstem are complex, but overlooking some exceptions, we can draw a few generalizations. Most spinal input to the cerebellum comes from the spinocerebellar tracts and travels through the inferior peduncles; input from the rest of the brain enters by way of the middle peduncles; and the superior peduncles carry most cerebellar output.

The cerebellum monitors body movements by means of information coming from the muscles and joints via the spinocerebellar

[18]*verm* = worm
[19]*foli* = leaf
[20]*arbor* = tree + *vitae* = of life
[21]*ped* = foot + *uncle* = little

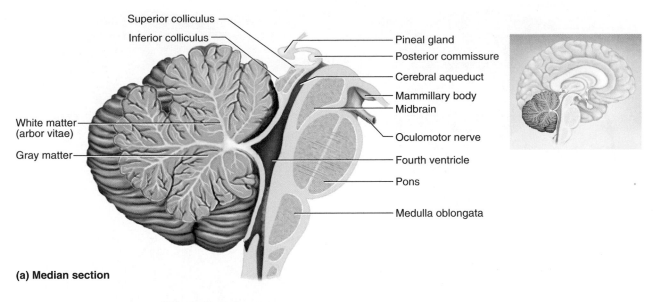

**(a) Median section**

Superior colliculus
Inferior colliculus
White matter (arbor vitae)
Gray matter
Pineal gland
Posterior commissure
Cerebral aqueduct
Mammillary body
Midbrain
Oculomotor nerve
Fourth ventricle
Pons
Medulla oblongata

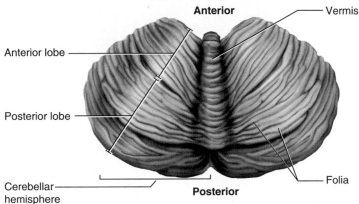

**Anterior**
Vermis
Anterior lobe
Posterior lobe
Cerebellar hemisphere
Folia
**Posterior**

**(b) Superior view**

**Figure 15.9** The Cerebellum.
(a) Median section, showing relationship to the brainstem. (b) Superior view.

tracts (fig. 15.10a). The middle peduncles carry signals from the cerebrum about what the muscles were commanded to do, enabling the cerebellum to compare the command with the performance. These peduncles also carry information from the eyes and ears for hearing and the perception of body position and movement. Output through the superior peduncles leads to various points in the midbrain and thalamus. The thalamus relays cerebellar signals to the cerebral cortex so that the cerebrum can make fine adjustments in muscle performance (fig. 15.10b).

Although it is only 10% of the mass of the brain, the cerebellum has about 60% as much surface area as the cerebral cortex and contains more than half of all brain neurons—about 100 billion of them. Its tiny, densely spaced **granule cells** are the most abundant neurons in the entire brain. Its most distinctive neurons, however, are the large globose **Purkinje**[22] (pur-KIN-jee) **cells.** These have a tremendous profusion of dendrites compressed into a single plane

like a flat tree (see fig. 13.5a, p. 380, and the photograph on p. 375). Purkinje cells are arranged in single file, with these thick dendritic planes parallel to each other like books on a shelf. Their axons travel to the deep nuclei, where they synapse on output neurons that issue fibers to the brainstem.

The function of the cerebellum was unknown in the 1950s. By the 1970s, it had come to be regarded as a control center of motor coordination. Now, however, positron emission tomography (PET), functional magnetic resonance imaging (fMRI), and behavioral studies of people with cerebellar lesions have created a much more expansive view of cerebellar function. It appears that the main role of the cerebellum is the evaluation of certain kinds of sensory input; monitoring the movements of muscles is only a part of that general role. People with cerebellar lesions exhibit serious deficits in locomotor ability, but also in several sensory, linguistic, emotional, and other nonmotor functions. More will be said of these later in the chapter.

Table 15.1 summarizes the hindbrain and midbrain functions discussed in the last several pages.

[22]Johannes E. von Purkinje (1787–1869), Bohemian anatomist

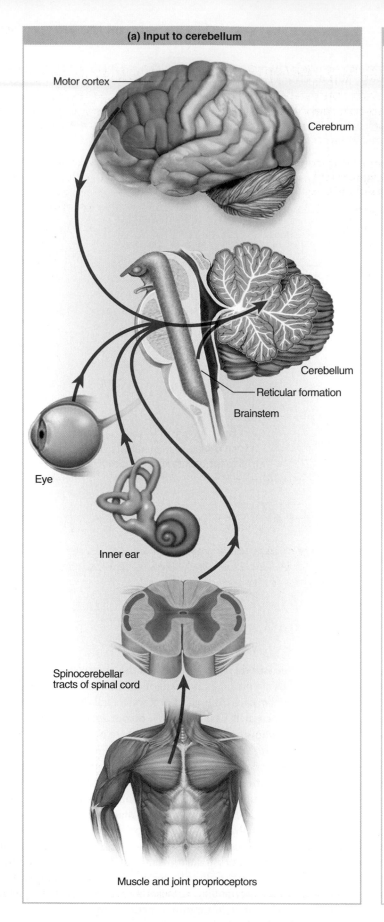

Motor cortex

Cerebrum

Cerebellum

Reticular formation

Brainstem

Eye

Inner ear

Spinocerebellar
tracts of spinal cord

Muscle and joint proprioceptors

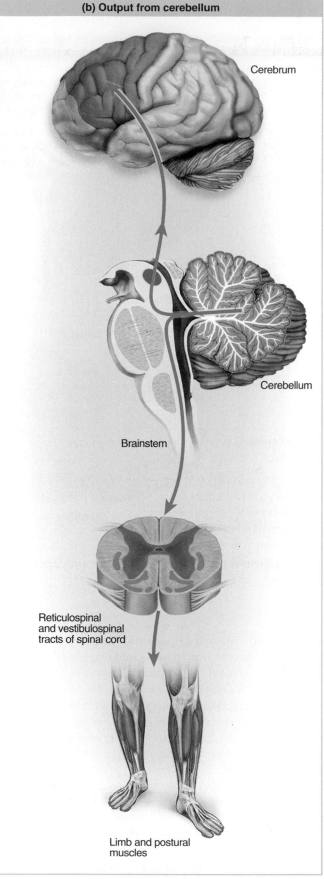

Cerebrum

Cerebellum

Brainstem

Reticulospinal
and vestibulospinal
tracts of spinal cord

Limb and postural
muscles

**Figure 15.10** **Principal Pathways of Cerebellar Input and Output.** (a) Afferent pathways sending input to the cerebellum. (b) Efferent pathways sending output from the cerebellum to the cerebrum and muscles.

| TABLE 15.1 | Hindbrain and Midbrain Functions |
|---|---|
| Medulla oblongata | Origin or termination of cranial nerves IX–XII. Sensory nuclei receive input from the taste buds, pharynx, and thoracic and abdominal viscera. Motor nuclei include the cardiac center (adjusts the rate and force of the heartbeat), vasomotor center (controls blood vessel diameter and blood pressure), two respiratory centers (control the rate and depth of breathing), and centers involved in speech, coughing, sneezing, salivation, swallowing, gagging, vomiting, sweating, gastrointestinal secretion, and movements of the tongue and head. |
| Pons | Sensory terminations and motor origins of cranial nerves V–VIII. Sensory nuclei receive input from the face, eye, oral and nasal cavities, sinuses, and meninges, concerned with pain, touch, temperature, taste, hearing, and equilibrium. Cranial nerve motor nuclei control chewing, swallowing, eye movements, middle- and inner-ear reflexes, facial expression, and secretion of tears and saliva. Other nuclei of pons relay signals from cerebrum to cerebellum (provide most of the input to the cerebellum) or function in sleep, respiration, bladder control, and posture. |
| Midbrain | Origin of cranial nerves III–IV (concerned with eye movements). Red nucleus is concerned with fine motor control. Substantia nigra relays inhibitory signals to thalamus and basal nuclei of forebrain. Central gray matter modulates awareness of pain. Superior colliculi concerned with visual attention and tracking movements of eyes, and visual reflexes such as shifting gaze to objects seen moving in peripheral vision. Inferior colliculi relay auditory signals to thalamus and mediate auditory reflexes such as the startle response to a loud noise. |
| Reticular formation | A network of over 100 nuclei extending throughout brainstem, including some nuclei described earlier in this table. Involved in somatic motor control, equilibrium, visual attention, breathing, swallowing, cardiovascular control, pain modulation, sleep, and consciousness. |
| Cerebellum | Muscular coordination, fine motor control, muscle tone, posture, equilibrium, judging passage of time; some involvement in emotion, processing tactile input, spatial perception, and language. |

## *Before You Go On*

Answer the following questions to test your understanding of the preceding section:

8. Name several functions controlled by nuclei of the medulla.
9. Describe the anatomical and functional relationship of the pons to the cerebellum.
10. What are the functions of the corpora quadrigemina, substantia nigra, and central gray matter?
11. Describe the reticular formation and list several of its functions.
12. Describe the general functions of the cerebellum.

# The Forebrain

### *Objectives*
When you have completed this section, you should be able to

- name the three major components of the diencephalon and describe their locations and functions;
- identify the five lobes of the cerebrum and discuss their functions;
- describe the three types of tracts in the cerebral white matter;
- describe the distinctive cell types and histological arrangement of the cerebral cortex; and
- discuss the locations and functions of the basal nuclei and limbic system.

The forebrain consists of the diencephalon and cerebrum. As noted earlier, some authorities treat the diencephalon as the most rostral part of the brainstem, while others exclude it from the brainstem.

## The Diencephalon

The embryonic diencephalon has three major derivatives: the *thalamus*, *hypothalamus*, and *epithalamus*. These structures surround the third ventricle of the brain.

### The Thalamus

Each side of the brain has a **thalamus**,[23] an ovoid mass perched at the superior end of the brainstem beneath the cerebral hemisphere (see figs. 15.4c, 15.6, and 15.15). The thalami constitute about four-fifths of the diencephalon. Each one protrudes medially into the third ventricle and laterally into the lateral ventricle. In about 70% of people, the two thalami are joined medially by a narrow *intermediate mass.*

The thalamus is composed of at least 23 nuclei, but we will consider only five major functional groups into which most of these are classified: the anterior, posterior, medial, lateral, and ventral groups. These regions and their functions are shown in figure 15.11a.

Generally speaking, the thalamus is the "gateway to the cerebral cortex." Nearly all sensory input and other information going to the cerebrum passes by way of synapses in the thalamic nuclei, including signals for taste, smell, hearing, equilibrium, vision, and such somesthetic senses as touch, pain, pressure, heat,

---

[23]*thalamus* = chamber, inner room

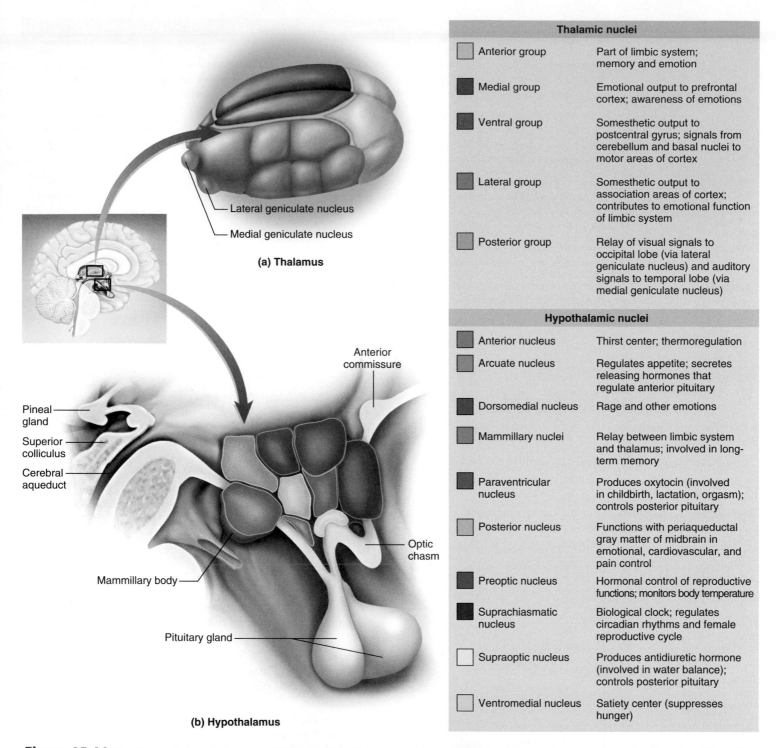

| Thalamic nuclei | |
|---|---|
| Anterior group | Part of limbic system; memory and emotion |
| Medial group | Emotional output to prefrontal cortex; awareness of emotions |
| Ventral group | Somesthetic output to postcentral gyrus; signals from cerebellum and basal nuclei to motor areas of cortex |
| Lateral group | Somesthetic output to association areas of cortex; contributes to emotional function of limbic system |
| Posterior group | Relay of visual signals to occipital lobe (via lateral geniculate nucleus) and auditory signals to temporal lobe (via medial geniculate nucleus) |

| Hypothalamic nuclei | |
|---|---|
| Anterior nucleus | Thirst center; thermoregulation |
| Arcuate nucleus | Regulates appetite; secretes releasing hormones that regulate anterior pituitary |
| Dorsomedial nucleus | Rage and other emotions |
| Mammillary nuclei | Relay between limbic system and thalamus; involved in long-term memory |
| Paraventricular nucleus | Produces oxytocin (involved in childbirth, lactation, orgasm); controls posterior pituitary |
| Posterior nucleus | Functions with periaqueductal gray matter of midbrain in emotional, cardiovascular, and pain control |
| Preoptic nucleus | Hormonal control of reproductive functions; monitors body temperature |
| Suprachiasmatic nucleus | Biological clock; regulates circadian rhythms and female reproductive cycle |
| Supraoptic nucleus | Produces antidiuretic hormone (involved in water balance); controls posterior pituitary |
| Ventromedial nucleus | Satiety center (suppresses hunger) |

(a) Thalamus

Lateral geniculate nucleus
Medial geniculate nucleus

Anterior commissure
Pineal gland
Superior colliculus
Cerebral aqueduct
Optic chasm
Mammillary body
Pituitary gland

(b) Hypothalamus

**Figure 15.11** **The Diencephalon.** Only some of the nuclei of the thalamus and hypothalamus are shown, and some of their functions listed. These lists are by no means complete. The third component of the diencephalon, the epithalamus, is not shown here; see figure 15.2a.

and cold. The thalamic nuclei filter this information and relay only a small portion of it to the cerebral cortex.

The thalamus also plays a key role in motor control; it relays signals from the cerebellum to the cerebrum and provides feedback loops between the cerebral cortex and *basal nuclei* (deep cerebral motor centers described later). Finally, the thalamus is involved in the memory and emotional functions of the *limbic system,* a complex of structures (also described later) that includes the cerebral cortex of the temporal and frontal lobes and some of the anterior thalamic nuclei. The role of the thalamus in motor and sensory circuits is further discussed later in this chapter and in chapter 17.

## The Hypothalamus

The **hypothalamus** forms part of the walls and floor of the third ventricle. It extends anteriorly to the *optic chiasm* (ky-AZ-um), where the optic nerves meet, and posteriorly to and including a pair of humps called the *mammillary*[24] *bodies* (see fig. 15.2a). The mammillary bodies each contain three to four *mammillary nuclei*. Their primary function is to relay signals from the limbic system to the thalamus. The pituitary gland is attached to the hypothalamus by a stalk *(infundibulum)* between the optic chiasm and mammillary bodies.

The hypothalamus is the major control center of the autonomic nervous system and endocrine system and plays an essential role in the homeostatic regulation of nearly all organs of the body. Its nuclei include centers concerned with a wide variety of visceral functions (fig. 15.11b):

- **Hormone secretion.** The hypothalamus secretes hormones that control the anterior pituitary gland. Acting through the pituitary, it regulates growth, metabolism, reproduction, and stress responses. It also produces two hormones that are stored in the posterior pituitary gland—*oxytocin* concerned with labor contractions, lactation, and emotional bonding, and *antidiuretic hormone* concerned with water conservation. It sends nerve signals to the posterior pituitary to stimulate release of these hormones at appropriate times.

- **Autonomic effects.** The hypothalamus is a major integrating center for the autonomic nervous system. It sends descending fibers to nuclei lower in the brainstem that influence heart rate, blood pressure, pupillary diameter, and gastrointestinal secretion and motility, among other functions.

- **Thermoregulation.** The *hypothalamic thermostat* consists of a collection of neurons, concentrated especially in the preoptic nucleus, that monitor body temperature. When the body temperature rises above normal, heat-sensitive neurons in this center send signals to a heat-loss center in the anterior hypothalamus. The heat-loss center activates mechanisms for lowering the body temperature: widening the blood vessels of the skin (cutaneous vasodilation) so more heat is lost from the body surface, and sweating so heat is carried away by evaporating water. If the body temperature falls below normal, cold-sensitive neurons in the thermostat send signals to a heat-promoting center located near the mammillary bodies in the posterior hypothalamus. The heat-promoting center activates mechanisms for conserving heat and raising the body temperature: narrowing blood vessels of the skin (cutaneous vasoconstriction) to retain the warm blood deeper in the body, and shivering (muscle tremors that release heat by breaking down ATP).

- **Food and water intake.** Neurons of the *hunger* and *satiety centers* monitor blood glucose and amino acid levels and produce sensations of hunger and satisfaction of the appetite. Hypothalamic neurons called *osmoreceptors* monitor the osmolarity of the blood and stimulate the hypothalamic *thirst center* when the body is dehydrated. Thus, our drives to eat and drink are under hypothalamic control.

- **Sleep and circadian rhythms.** The caudal part of the hypothalamus is part of the reticular formation. In this region are nuclei that regulate falling asleep and waking. Superior to the optic chiasm, the hypothalamus contains a *suprachiasmatic nucleus* that controls our *circadian rhythm* (24-hour cycle of activity).

- **Emotional responses.** The hypothalamus contains nuclei for a variety of emotional responses including anger, aggression, fear, pleasure, and contentment; and for sexual drive, copulation, and orgasm. The mammillary bodies provide a pathway by which emotional states can affect visceral function—for example, when anxiety accelerates the heart or upsets the stomach.

- **Memory.** In addition to their role in emotional circuits, the mammillary bodies lie in the pathway from the hippocampus to the thalamus. The hippocampus is a center for the creation of new memories—the cerebrum's "teacher"—so as intermediaries between the hippocampus and cerebral cortex, the mammillary bodies are essential for the acquisition of new memories.

## The Epithalamus

The **epithalamus** consists mainly of the **pineal gland** (an endocrine gland discussed in chapter 18), the **habenula** (a relay from the limbic system to the midbrain), and a thin roof over the third ventricle (see fig. 15.2a).

# The Cerebrum

The embryonic telencephalon becomes the cerebrum, the largest and most conspicuous part of the human brain. Your cerebrum enables you to turn these pages, read and comprehend the words, remember ideas, talk about them with your peers, and take an examination. It is the seat of sensory perception, voluntary motor actions, memory, and mental processes such as thought, judgment, and imagination, which most distinguish humans from other animals. It is the most complex and challenging frontier of neurobiology.

## Gross Anatomy

The cerebrum so dwarfs and conceals the other structures that people often think of "cerebrum" and "brain" as synonymous. Its major anatomical landmarks were described on page 423 and should be reviewed if necessary (see figs. 15.1 and 15.2)—especially the two *cerebral hemispheres*, separated by the *longitudinal fissure* but connected by a prominent fiber tract, the *corpus callosum;* and the conspicuous wrinkles, or *gyri*, of each hemisphere, separated by grooves called *sulci*. The folding of the cerebral surface into gyri allows a greater amount of cortex to fit in the cranial cavity. The gyri give the cerebrum a surface area of about 2,500 cm$^2$, comparable

---

[24]*mammill* = nipple, little breast

to 4.5 pages of this book. If the cerebrum were smooth-surfaced, it would have only one-third as much area and proportionately less information-processing capability. This extensive folding is one of the greatest differences between the human brain and the relatively smooth-surfaced brains of most other mammals.

Some gyri have consistent and predictable anatomy; others vary from brain to brain and from the right hemisphere to the left. Certain unusually prominent sulci divide each hemisphere into five anatomically and functionally distinct lobes, listed next. The first four of these are visible superficially and are named for the cranial bones overlying them (fig. 15.12); the fifth lobe is not visible from the surface.

1. The **frontal lobe** lies immediately behind the frontal bone, superior to the orbits. From the forehead, it extends caudally to a wavy vertical groove, the **central sulcus.** It is concerned with cognition (thought) and other "higher" mental processes, speech, and motor control.

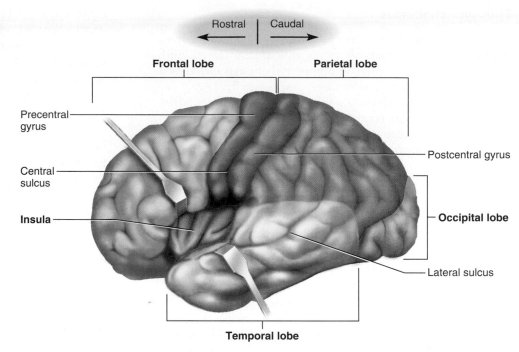

**Figure 15.12**  **Lobes of the Cerebrum.**  The frontal and temporal lobes are retracted slightly to reveal the insula.

2. The **parietal lobe** forms the uppermost part of the brain and underlies the parietal bone. Starting at the central sulcus, it extends caudally to the **parieto–occipital sulcus,** visible on the medial surface of each hemisphere (see fig. 15.2). It is the primary site for receiving and interpreting signals of the *general senses* described later in this chapter, as well as signals for taste, one of the *special senses.*

3. The **occipital lobe** is at the rear of the head, caudal to the parieto–occipital sulcus and underlying the occipital bone. It is the principal visual center of the brain.

4. The **temporal lobe** is a lateral, horizontal lobe deep to the temporal bone, separated from the parietal lobe above it by a deep **lateral sulcus.** Among its functions are hearing, smell, learning, memory, and some aspects of vision and emotion.

5. The **insula**[25] is a small mass of cortex deep to the lateral sulcus, made visible only by retracting or cutting away some of the overlying cerebrum (see figs. 15.1c, 15.4c, and 15.15). It is less understood than the other lobes because it is less accessible to testing in living subjects, but it apparently plays roles in taste, hearing, and visceral sensation.

## The Cerebral White Matter

Most of the volume of the cerebrum is white matter. This is composed of glia and myelinated nerve fibers that conduct signals from one region of the cerebrum to another and between the cerebrum

and lower brain centers. These fibers travel in bundles called tracts. There are three types of cerebral tracts (fig. 15.13):

1. **Projection tracts** extend vertically between higher and lower brain or spinal cord centers and carry information between the cerebrum and the rest of the body. The corticospinal tracts, for example, carry motor signals from the cerebrum to the brainstem and spinal cord. Other projection tracts carry signals upward to the cerebral cortex. Superior to the brainstem, such tracts form a dense band called the *internal capsule* between the thalamus and basal nuclei (described shortly), then radiate in a diverging, fanlike array (the *corona radiata*[26]) to specific areas of the cortex.

2. **Commissural tracts** cross from one cerebral hemisphere to the other through bridges called **commissures** (COM-ih-shurs). The great majority of commissural fibers pass through the corpus callosum. A few pass through the much smaller **anterior** and **posterior commissures** (fig. 15.2a). Commissural tracts enable the two cerebral hemispheres to communicate with each other.

3. **Association tracts** connect different regions of the same hemisphere. *Long association fibers* connect different lobes to each other, whereas *short association fibers* connect different gyri within a single lobe. Among their roles, association tracts link perceptual and memory centers of the brain; for example, they enable you to smell a rose, name it, and picture what it looks like.

---

[25]*insula* = island

[26]*corona* = crown + *radiata* = radiating

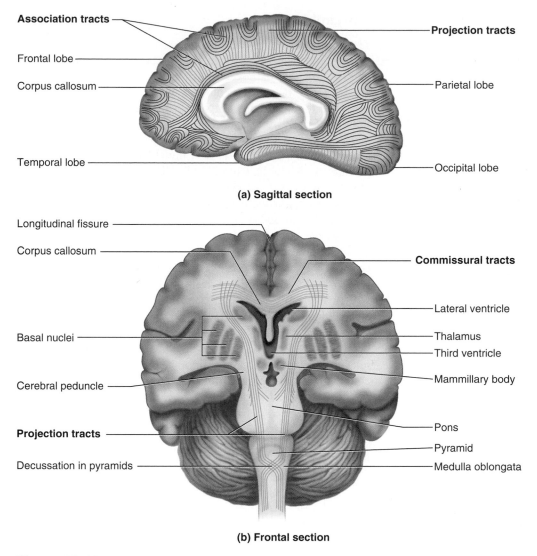

**Figure 15.13** Tracts of Cerebral White Matter.   (a) Sagittal section, showing association (red) and projection (green) tracts. (b) Frontal section, showing commissural (yellow) and projection tracts.

that synapse with other neurons in the cortex or in deeper regions of the brain. Pyramidal cells are the output neurons of the cerebrum—they are the only cerebral neurons whose fibers leave the cortex and connect with other parts of the CNS.

About 90% of the human cerebral cortex is a six-layered tissue called **neo-cortex**[28] because of its relatively recent evolutionary origin. Although vertebrates have existed for about 600 million years, the neocortex did not develop significantly until about 60 million years ago, when there was a sharp increase in the diversity of mammals. It attained its highest development by far in the primates. The six layers of neocortex, numbered in figure 15.14, vary from one part of the cerebrum to another in relative thickness, cellular composition, synaptic connections, size of the neurons, and destination of their axons. Layer IV is thickest in sensory regions and layer V in motor regions, for example. All axons that leave the cortex and enter the white matter arise from layers III, V, and VI.

Some regions of cerebral cortex have fewer than six layers. The earliest type of cerebral cortex to appear in vertebrate evolution was a one- to five-layered tissue called *paleocortex* (PALE-ee-oh-cor-tex), limited in humans to part of the insula and certain areas of the temporal lobe concerned with smell. The next to evolve was a three-layered *archicortex* (AR-kee-cor-tex), found in the human hippocampus. The neocortex was the last to evolve.

## The Cerebral Cortex

Neural integration is carried out in the gray matter of the cerebrum, which is found in three places—the cerebral cortex, basal nuclei, and limbic system. The **cerebral cortex**[27] is a layer about 2 to 3 mm thick covering the surface of the hemispheres. It constitutes about 40% of the mass of the brain and contains 14 to 16 billion neurons. It possesses two principal types of neurons called stellate and pyramidal cells (fig. 15.14). **Stellate cells** have spheroidal somas with dendrites projecting for short distances in all directions. They are concerned largely with receiving sensory input and processing information on a local level. **Pyramidal cells** are tall and conical (triangular in tissue sections). Their apex points toward the brain surface and has a thick dendrite with many branches and small, knobby *dendritic spines*. The base gives rise to horizontally oriented dendrites and an axon that passes into the white matter. The axon also has collaterals

## The Basal Nuclei

The **basal nuclei** are masses of cerebral gray matter buried deep in the white matter, lateral to the thalamus (fig. 15.15). They are often called *basal ganglia*, but the word *ganglion* is best restricted to clusters of neurons outside the CNS. Neuroanatomists disagree on how many brain centers to classify as basal nuclei, but agree on at least three: the **caudate**[29] **nucleus, putamen,**[30] and **globus pallidus.**[31] The putamen and globus pallidus are also collectively called the *lentiform*[32] *nucleus,* named for its lenslike shape. The putamen and caudate nucleus are collectively called the *corpus striatum* because of their striped appearance. The basal nuclei are involved in motor control, as discussed later.

---

[27]*cortex* = bark, rind

[28]*neo* = new
[29]*caudate* = tailed, tail-like
[30]*putam* = pod, husk
[31]*glob* = globe, ball + *pall* = pale
[32]*lenti* = lens + *form* = shape

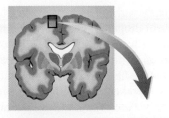

**Figure 15.14** Histology of the Neocortex. Neurons are arranged in six layers.
● Are the long processes leading upward from each pyramidal cell dendrites or axons?

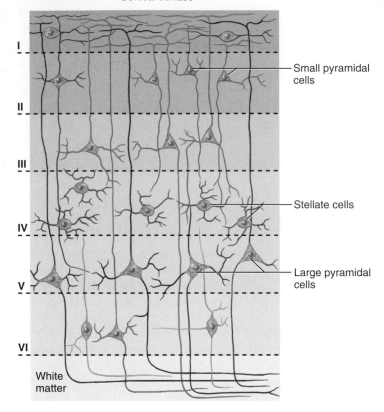

Cortical surface

I

II

III

IV

V

VI

White matter

Small pyramidal cells

Stellate cells

Large pyramidal cells

## The Limbic System

The **limbic**[33] system is an important center of emotion and learning. It was originally described in the 1850s as a ring of structures on the medial side of the cerebral hemisphere, encircling the corpus callosum and thalamus. Its most anatomically prominent components are the **cingulate**[34] (SING-you-let) **gyrus** that arches over the top of the corpus callosum in the frontal and parietal lobes, the **hippocampus**[35] in the medial temporal lobe (fig. 15.16), and the **amygdala**[36] (ah-MIG-da-luh) immediately rostral to the hippocampus, also in the temporal lobe. There are still differences of opinion on what structures to consider as parts of the limbic system, but those three are agreed upon. Other components include the mammillary bodies and other hypothalamic nuclei, some thalamic nuclei, parts of the basal nuclei, and parts of the frontal lobe cortex. Limbic system components are interconnected through a complex loop of fiber tracts allowing for somewhat circular patterns of feedback among its nuclei and cortical neurons. All of these structures are bilaterally paired; there is a limbic system in each cerebral hemisphere.

The limbic system was long thought to be associated with smell because of its close association with olfactory pathways, but beginning in the early 1900s and continuing even now, experiments have abundantly demonstrated more significant roles in emotion and memory. Most limbic system structures have centers for both gratification and aversion. Stimulation of a gratification center produces a sense of pleasure or reward; stimulation of an aversion center

---

[33]*limbus* = border
[34]*cingul* = girdle
[35]*hippocampus* = sea horse, named for its shape
[36]*amygdala* = almond

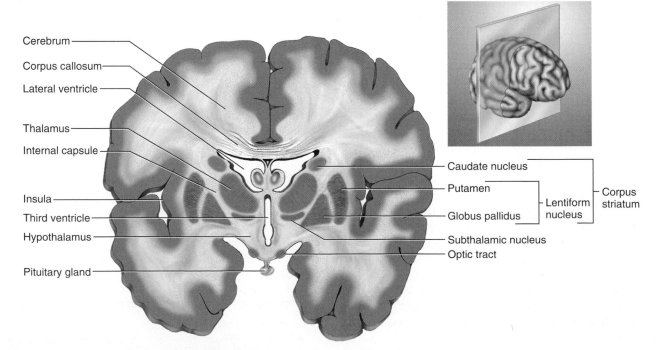

Cerebrum

Corpus callosum

Lateral ventricle

Thalamus

Internal capsule

Insula

Third ventricle

Hypothalamus

Pituitary gland

Caudate nucleus

Putamen

Globus pallidus

Subthalamic nucleus

Optic tract

Lentiform nucleus

Corpus striatum

**Figure 15.15** The Basal Nuclei. Frontal section of the brain.

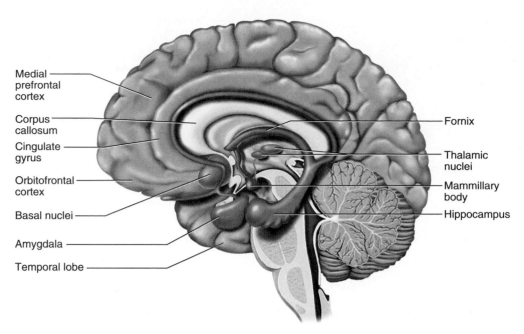

Medial prefrontal cortex

Corpus callosum

Cingulate gyrus

Orbitofrontal cortex

Basal nuclei

Amygdala

Temporal lobe

Fornix

Thalamic nuclei

Mammillary body

Hippocampus

**Figure 15.16 The Limbic System.** This ring of structures includes important centers of learning and emotion. In the frontal lobe, there is no sharp rostral boundary to limbic system components.

produces unpleasant sensations such as fear or sorrow. Gratification centers dominate some limbic structures, such as the *nucleus accumbens* (not illustrated), while aversion centers dominate others such as the amygdala. The roles of the amygdala in emotion and the hippocampus in memory are described in the next section, on higher forebrain functions.

## Higher Forebrain Functions

We will here examine a number of "higher" functions of the forebrain—sensory awareness, motor control, language, emotion, thought, and memory. These processes call attention especially to the cerebral cortex, but are not limited to the cerebrum; they involve also the diencephalon and cerebellum. It is impossible in many cases to assign a specific function to a specific brain region. Functions of the brain do not have such easily defined boundaries as its anatomy. Some functions overlap anatomically, some cross anatomical boundaries from one region to another, and some functions such as consciousness and memory are widely distributed through the cerebrum.

As a general principle for the functional discussion of the cerebrum, we distinguish between primary cortex and association cortex. **Primary cortex** consists of those regions that receive input directly from the sense organs or brainstem, or issue motor nerve fibers directly to the brainstem for distribution of the motor commands to cranial and spinal nerves. **Association cortex** consists of all regions other than the primary cortex, involved in integrative functions such as interpretation of sensory input, planning of motor output, cognitive (thought) processes, and the storage and retrieval of memories. About 75% of the mass of the cerebral cortex is association cortex. Typically an area of primary cortex has an as-

sociation area immediately adjacent to it, concerned with the same general function. For example, the primary visual cortex, which receives input from the eyes, is bordered by visual association cortex, which interprets and makes cognitive sense of the visual stimuli. Some areas of association cortex are *multimodal*—instead of processing information from a single sensory source, they receive input from multiple senses and integrate this into our overall perception of our surroundings. The association cortex of the frontal lobe is a very important center of cognitive and emotional function, the **prefrontal cortex.**

### Special Senses

The *special senses* are taste, smell, hearing, equilibrium, and vision, mediated by relatively complex sense organs in the head. Signals from these organs are routed to widely separated areas of primary sensory cortex in the cerebrum. From an area of primary sensory cortex, signals are relayed to a nearby association area, where the present sensory experience is integrated with memory and made identifiable and intelligible. Here we will only briefly identify the regions of cerebral cortex concerned with each of the special senses (fig. 15.17). Chapter 17 details the pathways taken from the sense organs to these areas of the cerebrum.

- **Vision.** Visual signals are received by the **primary visual cortex** in the far posterior region of the occipital lobe. This is bordered anteriorly by the **visual association area,** which includes all the remainder of the occipital lobe and much of the inferior temporal lobe. The association area integrates information so we can identify what we see.

- **Hearing.** Auditory signals are received by the **primary auditory cortex** in the superior region of the temporal lobe and in the nearby insula. The **auditory association area** occupies areas of temporal lobe inferior to the primary auditory cortex and deep within the lateral sulcus. This is where we become capable of recognizing spoken words, a familiar piece of music, or a voice on the telephone.

- **Equilibrium.** Signals from the inner ear for equilibrium (balance and the sense of motion) project mainly to the cerebellum and several brainstem nuclei concerned with head and eye movements and visceral functions. Some fibers of this system, however, are routed through the thalamus to areas of association cortex in the roof of the lateral sulcus and near the lower end of the central sulcus. This is the seat of consciousness of our body movements and orientation in space.

- **Taste.** Gustatory signals are received by the **primary gustatory cortex** in the inferior end of the postcentral gyrus of the

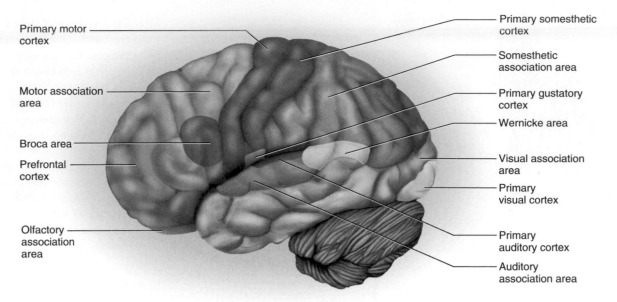

**Figure 15.17** **Some Functional Regions of the Cerebral Cortex.** The Broca and Wernicke areas for language abilities are found in only one hemisphere, usually the left. The other regions shown here are mirrored in both hemispheres.

parietal lobe (discussed shortly) and an anterior region of the insula. The gustatory association cortex is integrated with the association area for smell.

- **Smell.** The primary olfactory cortex lies in the medial surface of the temporal lobe and inferior surface of the frontal lobe. The **orbitofrontal cortex** (see fig. 15.16) contains an association area that integrates gustatory, olfactory, and visual information to create a sense of the overall flavor and desirability (or rejection) of food.

## General Senses

The *general (somesthetic* or *somatosensory) senses* are widely distributed over the body and have relatively simple receptors (see chapter 17). They include such senses as touch, pressure, stretch, temperature, and pain. Somesthetic signals arising from the neck down travel up the spinal cord in the gracile and cuneate fasciculi and spinothalamic tracts. Somesthetic nerve fibers decussate in the spinal cord or medulla before reaching the thalamus (see table 14.1 and fig. 14.4). Consequently, these signals ultimately arrive in the contralateral cerebral cortex—stimuli on the right side of the body are perceived in the left cerebral hemisphere, and vice versa. The thalamus routes all somesthetic signals to one specific fold of the cerebrum, the **postcentral gyrus.** This gyrus lies immediately caudal to the central sulcus and forms the anterior border of the parietal lobe (fig. 15.1c). It rises from the lateral sulcus up to the crown of the head and then descends into the longitudinal fissure. The cortex of this gyrus is called the **primary somesthetic**[37] **cortex** (fig. 15.18).

This gyrus is like an upside-down sensory map of the contralateral side of the body, traditionally diagrammed as a *sensory ho-*

*munculus*[38] (fig. 15.18b). As the diagram shows, receptors in the lower limb project to superior and medial parts of the gyrus, and receptors in the face project to the inferior and lateral parts. There is a point-for-point correspondence, or **somatotopy,**[39] between an area of the body and an area of the postcentral gyrus. The reason for the bizarre, distorted appearace of the homunculus is that the amount of cerebral tissue devoted to a given body region is proportional to how richly innervated and sensitive that region is, not to its size. Thus, the hands and face are represented by a much larger region of somesthetic cortex than the trunk is.

The **somesthetic association area** is found in the parietal lobe posterior to the postcentral gyrus and in the roof of the lateral sulcus (see fig. 15.17).

## Motor Control

The intention to contract a skeletal muscle begins in the **motor association (premotor) area** of the frontal lobes (fig. 15.17). This is where we plan our behavior—where neurons compile a program for the degree and sequence of muscle contractions required for an action such as dancing, typing, or speaking. The program is then transmitted to neurons of the **precentral gyrus** (primary motor area), which is the most posterior gyrus of the frontal lobe, immediately anterior to the central sulcus (fig. 15.1c). Neurons here send signals to the brainstem and spinal cord that ultimately result in muscle contractions.

The precentral gyrus, like the postcentral one, exhibits somatotopy. The neurons for toe movements, for example, are deep in the longitudinal fissure on the medial side of the gyrus. The summit of the gyrus controls the trunk, shoulder, and arm, and the inferolateral region controls the facial muscles. This map is diagrammed as a *motor homunculus* (fig. 15.19b). Like the sensory homunculus,

---

[37]*som* = body + *esthet* = sensation

[38]*hom* = man + *unculus* = little
[39]*somato* = body + *top* = place

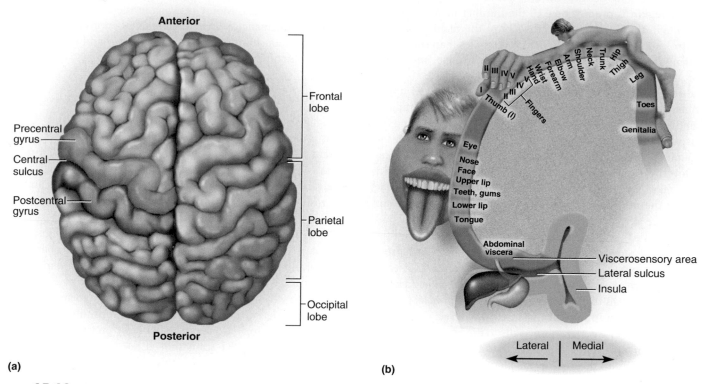

**Figure 15.18** **The Primary Somesthetic Area (Postcentral Gyrus).** (a) Superior view of the brain showing the location of the postcentral gyrus (violet). (b) Sensory homunculus, drawn so that body parts are in proportion to the amount of cortex dedicated to their sensation.

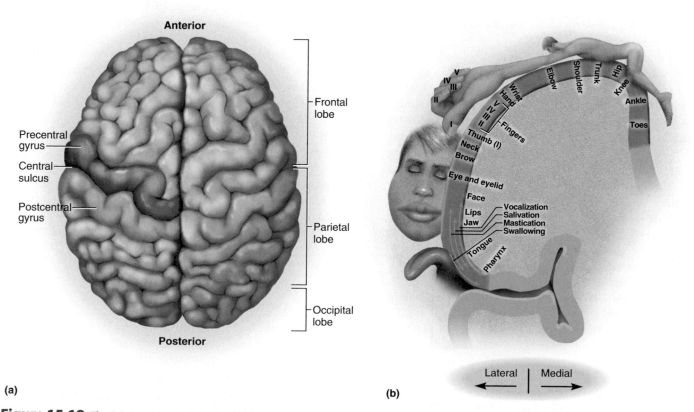

**Figure 15.19** **The Primary Motor Area (Precentral Gyrus).** (a) Superior view of the brain showing the location of the precentral gyrus (blue). (b) Motor homunculus, drawn so that body parts are in proportion to the amount of primary motor cortex dedicated to their control.
• *Which body regions are controlled by the largest area of motor cortex—regions with a few large muscles or regions with many small muscles?*

it has a distorted look because the amount of cortex devoted to a given body region is proportional to the number of muscles and motor units in that region, not to the size of the region. Areas of fine control, such as the hands, have more muscles than such areas as the trunk and thigh, more motor units per muscle, and larger areas of motor cortex to control them.

The pyramidal cells of the precentral gyrus are called **upper motor neurons.** Their fibers project caudally, with about 19 million fibers ending in nuclei of the brainstem and 1 million forming the corticospinal tracts. These tracts decussate in the pyramids of the medulla oblongata and then continue into the spinal cord. Therefore, below the neck, each precentral gyrus controls muscles on the contralateral side of the body. In the brainstem or spinal cord, the fibers from the upper motor neurons synapse with **lower motor neurons** whose axons innervate the skeletal muscles.

Other areas of the brain important in muscle control are the basal nuclei and cerebellum. The basal nuclei receive signals from the cerebral cortex and direct their output back to the cortex. Nearly all areas of cerebral cortex, except for the primary visual and auditory areas, send signals to the basal nuclei. The basal nuclei process these and issue their output to the thalamus, which relays these signals back to the cerebral cortex—especially to the prefrontal cortex, motor association area, and precentral gyrus. The basal nuclei thus lie in a feedback circuit involved in the planning and execution of movement.

Among other functions, the basal nuclei assume control of highly practiced behaviors that one carries out with little thought—writing, typing, driving a car, using scissors, or tying one's shoes, for example. They also control the onset and cessation of planned movements and the repetitive movements at the shoulder and hip that occur during walking.

Lesions of the basal nuclei cause movement disorders called **dyskinesias.**[40] Some dyskinesias are characterized by abnormally inhibited movements—for example, difficulty rising from a chair or beginning to walk and a slow shuffling walk, as seen in Parkinson disease (see p. 461). Smooth, easy movements require the excitation of agonistic muscles and inhibition of their antagonists. In Parkinson disease, the antagonists are not inhibited. Therefore, opposing muscles at a joint fight each other, making it a struggle to move as one wishes. Other dyskinesias are characterized by exaggerated or unwanted movements, such as flailing of the limbs (*ballismus*) in Huntington disease.

The cerebellum is highly important in motor coordination. It aids in learning motor skills, maintains muscle tone and posture, smooths muscle contractions, coordinates eye and body movements, and coordinates the motions of different joints with each other (such as the shoulder and elbow in pitching a baseball). The cerebellum acts as a comparator in motor control. It receives information from the upper motor neurons of the cerebrum about what movements are intended, and information from proprioceptors in the muscles and joints about the actual performance of the movement (see fig. 15.10). The Purkinje cells of the cerebellum compare the two. If there is a discrepancy between the intent and the performance, they signal the deep cerebellar nuclei, which, in turn, relay signals to the thalamus and cerebral cortex. Motor neurons in the cortex then correct the muscle performance to match the intent. Lesions of the cerebellum can result in a clumsy, awkward gait (*ataxia*) and make some tasks such as climbing stairs virtually impossible.

## Language

Language includes several abilities—reading, writing, speaking, and understanding spoken and printed words—assigned to different regions of cerebral cortex. The **Wernicke**[41] (WUR-nih-kee) **area** is responsible for the recognition of spoken and written language. It lies just posterior to the lateral sulcus, usually in the left hemisphere, at the "crossroads" between visual, auditory, and somesthetic areas of the cortex (see fig. 15.17). It is a sensory association area that receives input from all these neighboring regions of primary sensory cortex. The *angular gyrus,* part of the parietal lobe caudal and superior to the Wernicke area, is important in the ability to read and write.

When we intend to speak, the Wernicke area formulates phrases according to learned rules of grammar and transmits a plan of speech to the **Broca**[42] **area,** located in the inferior prefrontal cortex of the same hemisphere. PET scans show a rise in the metabolic activity of the Broca area as we prepare to speak. The Broca area generates a motor program for the muscles of the larynx, tongue, cheeks, and lips to produce speech. This program is then transmitted to the primary motor cortex, which executes it—that is, it issues commands to the lower motor neurons that supply the relevant muscles.

The emotional aspect of language is controlled by regions in the opposite hemisphere that mirror the Wernicke and Broca areas. Opposite the Broca area is the *affective language area.* Lesions to this area result in *aprosody*—flat, emotionless speech. The cortex opposite the Wernicke area is concerned with recognizing the emotional content of another person's speech. Lesions here can result in such problems as the inability to understand a joke. Lesions in the language areas of the brain tend to produce a variety of language deficits called **aphasias**[43] (ah-FAY-zee-uhs). They may include a complete inability to speak; slow speech with difficulty choosing words; invention of words that only approximate the correct ones; babbling, incomprehensible speech filled with invented words and illogical word order; inability to comprehend another person's written or spoken words; or inability to name objects that a person sees. Since cranial nerves VII and XII (the facial and hypoglossal nerves) control several of the muscles of speech, speech deficits can also result from lesions to these nerves or their brainstem nuclei.

### THINK ABOUT IT

*Mr. Thompson has had a stroke that destroyed his Wernicke area. Ms. Meyers has had a stroke that destroyed her Broca area. What differences in language deficits would you expect between these two patients?*

---

[40]*dys* = bad, abnormal, difficult + *kines* = movement

[41]Karl Wernicke (1848–1904), German neurologist
[42]Pierre Paul Broca (1824–80), French surgeon and anthropologist
[43]*a* = without + *phas* = speech

## Emotion

Emotional feelings and memories are not exclusively cerebral functions, but rather result from an interaction between areas of the prefrontal cortex and the diencephalon. The hypothalamus and amygdala play especially important roles in emotion. Experiments by Swiss physiologist Walter Hess, leading to a 1949 Nobel Prize, showed that stimulation of various nuclei of the hypothalamus in cats could induce rage, attack, and other emotional responses. Nuclei involved in the senses of reward and punishment have been identified in the hypothalamus of cats, rats, monkeys, and other animals.

The *amygdala,* one of the most important centers of human emotion, is a major component of the limbic system described earlier. It receives processed information from the senses of vision, hearing, taste, smell, and general somesthetic and visceral senses. Thus, it is able to mediate emotional responses to such stimuli as a disgusting odor, a foul taste, a beautiful image, pleasant music, or a stomachache. It is especially important in the sense of fear. Output from the amygdala goes in two directions of special interest: (1) Some output projects to the hypothalamus and lower brainstem and thus influences the somatic and visceral motor systems. An emotional response to a sight or sound may, through these connections, make one's heart race, make the hair stand on end (piloerection), or induce vomiting. (2) Other output projects to areas of the prefrontal cortex that mediate conscious control and expression of the emotions, such as our ability to express love or control anger.

Many important aspects of personality depend on an intact, functional amygdala and hypothalamus. When specific regions of the amygdala or hypothalamus are destroyed or artificially stimulated, humans and other animals exhibit blunted or exaggerated expressions of anger, fear, aggression, self-defense, pleasure, pain, love, sexuality, and parental affection, as well as abnormalities in learning, memory, and motivation.

## Cognition

Cognition[44] is the range of mental processes by which we acquire and use knowledge—sensory perception, thought, reasoning, judgment, memory, imagination, and intuition. Cognitive abilities of various kinds are widely distributed through the association areas of the cerebral cortex. This is the most difficult area of brain research and the most incompletely understood area of cerebral function. Much of what we know about cognitive functions of the brain has come from studies of patients with brain lesions—areas of tissue destruction resulting from cancer, stroke, and trauma. The many brain injuries incurred in World War I and II yielded a special abundance of insights into regional brain functions. More recently, imaging methods such as positron emission tomography (PET) and functional magnetic resonance imaging (fMRI), described on page 4, have yielded much more sophisticated insights into brain function. These methods allow a researcher to scan a person's brain while that person is performing various cognitive or motor tasks and to see which brain regions are most active in different mental and task states (fig. 15.20).

Attention to objects in the environment is based in the parietal lobe on the side opposite the Broca and Wernicke speech centers. Lesions here can produce *contralateral neglect syndrome,* in which a patient seems unaware of objects on one side of the body, ignores all words on the left side of a page of reading, or fails even to recognize, dress, and take care of the left side of his or her own body. Such patients are also unable to find their way around—say, to describe the route from home to work, or navigate within a familiar building.

The prefrontal cortex is concerned with many of our most distinctive abilities, such as abstract thought, foresight, judgment, responsibility, a sense of purpose, and a sense of socially appropriate behavior. Lesions here tend to render a person easily distracted

[44]*cognit* = to know, to learn

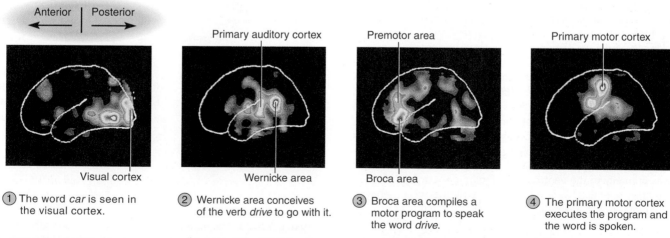

**Figure 15.20  PET Scans of the Brain During Performance of a Language Task.** These scans represent computer-averaged images of the brains of one or more subjects who were shown a word (car) in print and asked to speak a word (such as drive) related to it. The most active brain areas are shown in red and the least active in blue. Such studies have shown that the Broca and Wernicke areas are not involved in simply repeating a word, but are active when a person must evaluate a word and choose an appropriate response. PET scans also show that different neural pools take over a task as a person practices and becomes more proficient at it.

from a task, irresponsible, exceedingly stubborn, unable to anticipate future events, and incapable of any ambition or planning for the future (Insight 15.2).

The cerebellum also has lately shown a surprising amount of cognitive function. It exhibits increased PET activity in analyzing visual and tactile input, solving spatial puzzles, judging the passage of time, planning and scheduling activities, discriminating similar-sounding words, and performing other language tasks. For example, if a person is given a noun such as *apple* and asked to think of a related verb such as *eat*, the cerebellum is more active than when the person is asked simply to repeat *apple*. Touching sandpaper activates the cerebellum to some degree, but not as much as when one is asked to compare the texture of two different sandpapers. The cerebellum also helps in making short-term predictions about movement, such as where a baseball will be in a second or two so that one can catch it. People with cerebellar lesions have difficulty with emotional overreaction and impulse control. Many children with attention deficit–hyperactivity disorder (ADHD) have abnormally small cerebellums.

## Memory

Memory is one of the cognitive functions, but warrants special attention. There are two kinds of memory—**procedural memory,** the retention of motor skills such as how to tie one's shoes, play the violin, or type on a keyboard; and **declarative memory,** the retention of events and facts that one can put into words, such as names, dates, or facts inportant to an upcoming examination. At the cellular level, both forms of memory probably involve the same processes: the creation of new synaptic contacts and physiological changes that make synaptic transmission more efficient along certain pathways.

The limbic system has important roles in the establishment of memories. The amygdala creates emotional memories, such as the chilling fear of being stung when a wasp alights on the skin. The *hippocampus* (see fig. 15.16) is critical to the creation of long-term declarative memories. It does not store memories, but organizes sensory and cognitive experiences into a unified long-term memory. The hippocampus learns from sensory input while an experience

---

INSIGHT 15.2

### Medical History

## An Accidental Lobotomy

Accidental but nonfatal destruction of parts of the brain has afforded many clues to the function of various regions. One of the most famous incidents occurred in 1848 to Phineas Gage, a laborer on a railroad construction project in Vermont. Gage was packing blasting powder into a hole with a 3 1/2 ft tamping iron when the powder prematurely exploded. The tamping rod was blown out of the hole and passed through Gage's maxilla, orbit, and the frontal lobe of his brain before emerging from his skull near the hairline and landing 50 ft away (fig. 15.21). Gage went into convulsions, but later sat up and conversed with his crewmates as they drove him to a physician in an oxcart. On arrival, he stepped out on his own and told the physician, "Doctor, here is business enough for you." His doctor, John Harlow, reported that he could insert his index finger all the way into Gage's wound. Yet 2 months later, Gage was walking around town carrying on his normal business.

He was not, however, the Phineas Gage people had known. Before the accident, he had been a competent, responsible, financially prudent man, well liked by his associates. In an 1868 publication on the incident, Harlow said that following the accident, Gage was "fitful, irreverent, indulging at times in the grossest profanity." He became irresponsible, lost his job, worked for a while as a circus sideshow attraction, and died a vagrant 12 years later.

A 1994 computer analysis of Gage's skull indicated that the brain injury was primarily to the ventromedial region of both frontal lobes. In Gage's time, scientists were reluctant to attribute social behavior and moral judgment to any region of the brain. These functions were strongly tied to issues of religion and ethics and were considered inaccessible to scientific analysis. Based partly on Phineas Gage and other brain injury patients like him, neuroscientists today recognize that planning, moral judgment, and emotional control are among the functions of the prefrontal cortex.

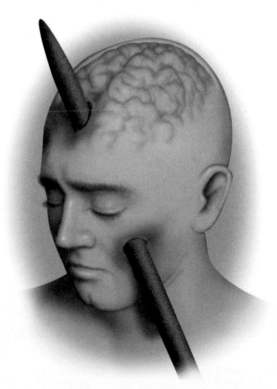

**Figure 15.21** Phineas Gage's 1848 Accident. Gage suffered frontal lobe damage when a tamping bar flew upward, entered his maxilla, passed through the orbit and between the two frontal lobes, and exited the top of his head near the hairline. The accident resulted in permanent personality changes that helped to define some functions of the frontal lobes.

is happening, but it has a short memory. Later, perhaps when one is sleeping, it plays this memory repeatedly to the cerebral cortex, which is a "slow learner" but forms longer-lasting memories. This process of "teaching the cerebral cortex" until a long-term memory is established is called **memory consolidation.** Lesions of the hippocampus do not abolish old memories, but abolish the ability to form new ones.

Long-term memories are stored in various areas of the cerebral cortex. The memory of language (vocabulary and grammatical rules) resides in the Wernicke area. Our memory of faces, voices, and familiar objects is stored in the superior temporal lobe. Memories of one's social role, appropriate behavior, goals, and plans are stored in the prefrontal cortex. Procedural memories are stored in the motor association area, basal nuclei, and cerebellum.

## Cerebral Lateralization

The two cerebral hemispheres look identical at a glance, but close examination reveals a number of differences. For example, in women the left temporal lobe is longer than the right. In left-handed people, the left frontal, parietal, and occipital lobes are usually wider than those on the right. The two hemispheres also differ in some of their functions (fig. 15.22). Neither hemisphere is "dominant," but each is specialized for certain tasks. This difference in function is called **cerebral lateralization.**

One hemisphere, usually the left, is called the *categorical hemisphere.* It is specialized for spoken and written language and for

the sequential and analytical reasoning employed in such fields as science and mathematics. This hemisphere seems to break information into fragments and analyze it in a linear way. The other hemisphere, usually the right, is called the *representational hemisphere.* It perceives information in a more integrated, holistic way. It is the seat of imagination and insight, musical and artistic skill, perception of patterns and spatial relationships, and comparison of sights, sounds, smells, and tastes.

Figure 15.23 shows some of the forebrain structures in a coronal tissue section and a corresponding MRI image of the cerebrum. Table 15.2 summarizes the forebrain functions described in the last several pages.

## *Before You Go On*

*Answer the following questions to test your understanding of the preceding section:*

13. What is the role of the thalamus in sensory function?

14. List at least six functions of the hypothalamus.

15. Name the five lobes of the cerebrum and describe their locations and boundaries.

16. Where are the basal nuclei located? What is their general function?

17. Where is the limbic system located? What component of it is involved in emotion? What component is involved in memory?

18. Describe the locations and functions of the somesthetic, visual, auditory, and frontal association areas.

19. Describe the somatotopy of the primary motor cortex and primary sensory cortex.

20. What are the roles of the Wernicke area, Broca area, and precentral gyrus in language?

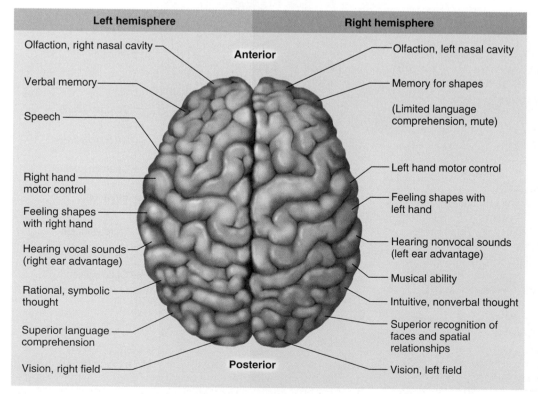

**Figure 15.22 Lateralization of Cerebral Functions.** The two cerebral hemispheres are not functionally identical.
• *If a person is described as "left-brained," does this mean he or she makes little use of the right hemisphere?*

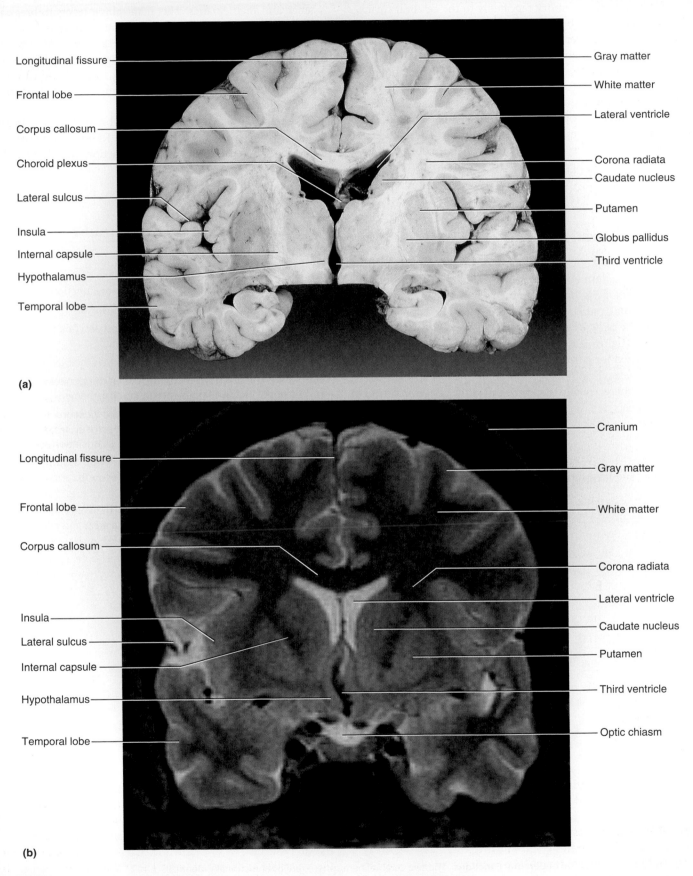

Longitudinal fissure

Frontal lobe

Corpus callosum

Choroid plexus

Lateral sulcus

Insula

Internal capsule

Hypothalamus

Temporal lobe

Gray matter

White matter

Lateral ventricle

Corona radiata

Caudate nucleus

Putamen

Globus pallidus

Third ventricle

**(a)**

Longitudinal fissure

Frontal lobe

Corpus callosum

Insula

Lateral sulcus

Internal capsule

Hypothalamus

Temporal lobe

Cranium

Gray matter

White matter

Corona radiata

Lateral ventricle

Caudate nucleus

Putamen

Third ventricle

Optic chiasm

**(b)**

**Figure 15.23 Coronal Sections of the Cerebrum.** (a) Tissue section. (b) A corresponding MRI image.

| TABLE 15.2 | Forebrain Functions |
|---|---|
| **Diencephalon** | |
| Thalamus | Sensory processing; relay of sensory and other signals to cerebrum; relay of cerebral output to other parts of brain |
| Hypothalamus | Hormone synthesis; control of pituitary secretion; autonomic responses affecting heart rate, blood pressure, pupillary diameter, digestive secretion and motility, and other visceral functions; thermoregulation; hunger and thirst; sleep and circadian rhythms; emotional responses; sexual function; memory |
| Epithalamus | Hormone secretion; relay of signals between midbrain and limbic system |
| **Cerebral lobes** | |
| Frontal lobe | Smell; motor aspects of speech; voluntary control of skeletal muscles; procedural memory; cognitive functions such as abstract thought, judgment, responsibility, foresight, ambition, planning, and ability to stay focused on a task |
| Parietal lobe | Somesthetic senses, taste, awareness of body movement and orientation, language recognition, nonmotor aspects of speech |
| Occipital lobe | Vision |
| Temporal lobe | Hearing, smell, interpreting visual information, learning, memory, emotion |
| Insula | Hearing, taste, visceral sensation |
| **Basal nuclei** | Motor control; procedural memory |
| **Limbic system** | Learning, emotion, gratification (pleasure) and aversion responses |

# The Cranial Nerves

## Objectives

When you have completed this section, you should be able to

- list the 12 cranial nerves by name and number;
- identify where each cranial nerve originates and terminates; and
- state the functions of each cranial nerve.

To be functional, the brain must communicate with the rest of the body. Most of its input and output travels by way of the spinal cord, but it also communicates by way of the **cranial nerves,** which arise primarily from the base of the brain, exit the cranium through its foramina, and lead to muscles and sense organs primarily in the head and neck. There are 12 pairs of cranial nerves, numbered I to XII starting with the most rostral (fig. 15.24). Each nerve also has a descriptive name such as *optic nerve* and *vagus nerve.* The cranial nerves are illustrated and described in table 15.3.

## Classification

Cranial nerves are traditionally classified as sensory (I, II, and VIII), motor (III, IV, VI, XI, and XII), or mixed (V, VII, IX, and X). In reality, only cranial nerves I and II (for smell and vision) are purely sensory, whereas all the rest contain both afferent and efferent fibers and are therefore mixed nerves. Those traditionally classified as motor not only stimulate muscle contractions but also contain afferent fibers of proprioception, which provide your brain with un-

conscious feedback for controlling muscle contraction and which make you consciously aware of such things as the position of your tongue and orientation of your head. Cranial nerve VIII, concerned with hearing and equilibrium, is traditionally classified as sensory, but it has motor fibers that return signals to the inner ear and "tune" it to sharpen our sense of hearing. The nerves traditionally classified as mixed have sensory functions quite unrelated to their motor functions—for example, the facial nerve (VII) has a sensory role in taste and a motor role in controlling facial expressions.

In order to teach the traditional classification (which is relevant for such purposes as board examinations and comparison to other books), yet remind you that all but two of these nerves are mixed, table 15.3 describes many of the nerves as *predominantly* sensory or motor.

## Nerve Pathways

The motor fibers of the cranial nerves begin in nuclei of the brainstem and lead to glands and muscles. The sensory fibers begin in receptors located mainly in the head and neck and lead mainly to the brainstem. Pathways for the special senses are described in chapter 17. Sensory fibers for proprioception begin in the muscles innervated by the motor fibers of the cranial nerves, but they often travel to the brain in a different nerve than the one that supplies the motor innervation.

Most cranial nerves carry fibers between the brainstem and ipsilateral receptors and effectors. Thus, a lesion to one side of the brainstem causes a sensory or motor deficit on the same side of the head. This contrasts with lesions to the motor and somesthetic cortex of the cerebrum, which, as we saw earlier, cause sensory and motor deficits on the contralateral side of the body. The exceptions are the optic nerve (cranial nerve I), where half the fibers decussate to the opposite side of

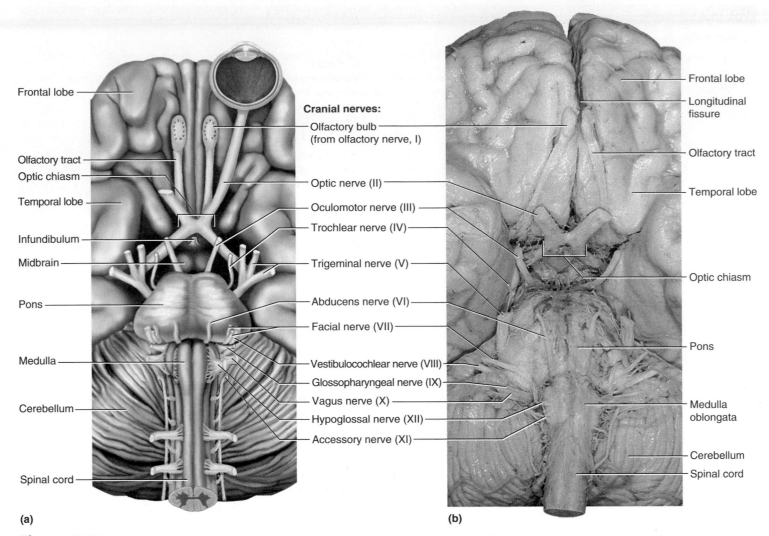

**Figure 15.24** **The Cranial Nerves.** (a) Base of the brain, showing the 12 pairs of cranial nerves. (b) Cranial nerves of the cadaver brain.

the brain (see chapter 17), and the trochlear nerve (cranial nerve IV), in which all efferent fibers go to a muscle of the contralateral eye.

## An Aid to Memory

Generations of biology and medical students have relied on mnemonic (memory-aiding) phrases and ditties, ranging from the sublimely silly to the unprintably ribald, to help them remember the cranial nerves and other anatomy. An old classic began, "On old Olympus' towering tops . . . ," with the first letter of each word matching the first letter of each cranial nerve (olfactory, optic, oculomotor, etc.). Some cranial nerves have changed names, however, since that passage was devised. One of the author's former students devised a better mnemonic that can remind you of the first two to four letters of most cranial nerves:

| | |
|---|---|
| **Ol**d | **ol**factory (I) |
| **Op**ie | **op**tic (II) |
| **oc**casionally | **oc**ulomotor (III) |
| **tr**ies | **tr**ochlear (IV) |
| **trig**onometry | **trig**eminal (V) |
| **a**nd | **a**bducens (VI) |
| **f**eels | **f**acial (VII) |
| **v**ery | **v**estibulocochlear (VIII) |
| **glo**omy, | **glo**ssopharyngeal (IX) |
| **va**gue, | **va**gus (X) |
| **a**nd | **a**ccessory (XI) |
| **hypo**active. | **hypo**glossal (XII) |

Another common mnemonic, but using only the first letter of each nerve's name, is "Oh, once one takes the anatomy final, very good vacation ahead." The first two letters of *ahead* represent nerves XI and XII.

| TABLE 15.3 | The Cranial Nerves |
|---|---|

Cranial nerves listed as mixed or sensory are agreed by all authorities to be either mixed or purely sensory. Those classified as predominantly motor or sensory have fibers of the other type as well. Motor nerves also contain proprioceptive sensory fibers, but these may come from different muscles than the ones innervated by the motor fibers.

**I. Olfactory Nerve.**    This is the nerve for the sense of smell. It consists of several separate fascicles that pass independently through the cribriform plate in the roof of the nasal cavity. It is not visible on brains removed from the skull because these fascicles are severed by removal of the brain.

| Composition | Function | Origin | Termination | Cranial Passage | Effect of Damage | Clinical Test |
|---|---|---|---|---|---|---|
| Sensory | Smell | Olfactory mucosa in nasal cavity | Olfactory bulbs | Cribriform foramina of ethmoid bone | Impaired sense of smell | Determine whether subject can smell (not necessarily identify) aromatic substances such as coffee, vanilla, clove oil, or soap |

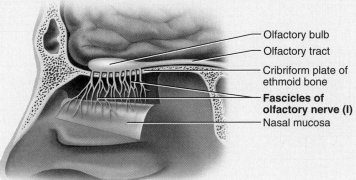

**Figure 15.25** The Olfactory Nerve (I).

**II. Optic Nerve.**    This is the nerve for vision.

| Composition | Function | Origin | Termination | Cranial Passage | Effect of Damage | Clinical Test |
|---|---|---|---|---|---|---|
| Sensory | Vision | Retina | Thalamus and midbrain | Optic foramen | Blindness in part or all of visual field | Inspect retina with ophthalmoscope; test peripheral vision and visual acuity |

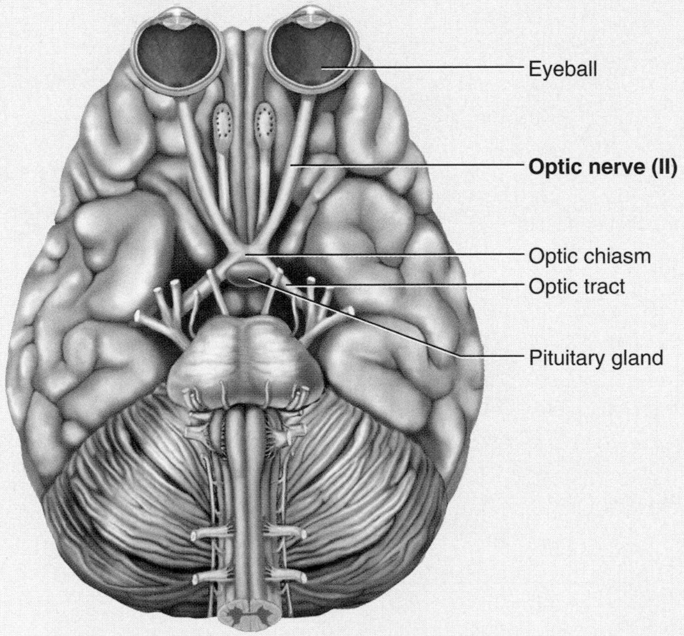

**Figure 15.26** The Optic Nerve (II).

| **TABLE 15.3** | **The Cranial Nerves (continued)** |
|---|---|

**III. Oculomotor[45] Nerve (OC-you-lo-MO-tur).**   This nerve controls muscles that turn the eyeball up, down, and medially, as well as controlling the iris, lens, and upper eyelid.

| Composition | Function | Origin | Termination | Cranial Passage | Effect of Damage | Clinical Test |
|---|---|---|---|---|---|---|
| Predominantly motor | Eye movements, opening of eyelid, pupillary constriction, focusing | Midbrain | Somatic fibers to levator palpebrae superioris; superior, medial, and inferior rectus muscles; and inferior oblique muscle of eye. Autonomic fibers enter eyeball and lead to constrictor of iris and ciliary muscle of lens. | Superior orbital fissure | Drooping eyelid; dilated pupil; inability to move eye in some directions; tendency of eye to rotate laterally at rest; double vision; difficulty focusing | Look for differences in size and shape of right and left pupils; test pupillary response to light; test ability to track moving objects |

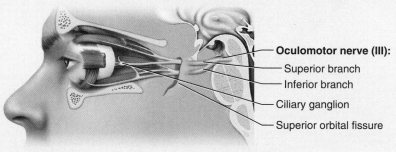

**Figure 15.27**  The Oculomotor Nerve (III).

**IV. Trochlear[46] Nerve (TROCK-lee-ur).**   This nerve controls a muscle that rotates the eyeball medially and slightly depresses the eyeball when the head turns.

| Composition | Function | Origin | Termination | Cranial Passage | Effect of Damage | Clinical Test |
|---|---|---|---|---|---|---|
| Predominantly motor | Eye movements | Midbrain | Superior oblique muscle of eye | Superior orbital fissure | Double vision and inability to rotate eye inferolaterally; eye points superolaterally and subject tends to tilt head toward affected side | Test ability of eye to rotate inferolaterally |

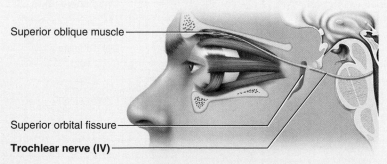

**Figure 15.28**  The Trochlear Nerve (IV).

---

[45]*oculo* = eye + *motor* = mover
[46]*trochlea* = pulley (for a loop through which the muscle's tendon passes)

| TABLE 15.3 | The Cranial Nerves (continued) |
|---|---|

**V. Trigeminal[47] Nerve (tri-JEM-ih-nul).**   This is the largest of the cranial nerves and the most important sensory nerve of the face. It forks into three divisions: *ophthalmic (V₁)*, *maxillary (V₂)*, and *mandibular (V₃)*.

| Composition | Function | Origin | Termination | Cranial Passage | Effect of Damage | Clinical Test |
|---|---|---|---|---|---|---|
| **Ophthalmic division (V₁)**<br><br>Sensory | Touch, temperature, and pain sensations from upper face | Superior region of face as illustrated; surface of eyeball; lacrimal (tear) gland; superior nasal mucosa; frontal and ethmoid sinuses | Pons | Superior orbital fissure | Loss of sensation from upper face | Test corneal reflex (blinking in response to light touch to eyeball) |
| **Maxillary division (V₂)**<br><br>Sensory | Same as V₁, lower on face | Middle region of face as illustrated; nasal mucosa; maxillary sinus; palate; upper teeth and gums | Pons | Foramen rotundum and infraorbital foramen | Loss of sensation from middle face | Test sense of touch, pain, and temperature with light touch, pinpricks, and hot and cold objects |
| **Mandibular division (V₃)**<br><br>Mixed | *Sensory:* Same as V₁ and V₂ lower on face<br><br>*Motor:* mastication | *Sensory:* Inferior region of face as illustrated; anterior two-thirds of tongue (but not taste buds); lower teeth and gums; floor of mouth; dura mater<br><br>*Motor:* Pons | *Sensory:* Pons<br><br>*Motor:* Anterior belly of digastric; masseter, temporalis, mylohyoid, and pterygoid muscles; tensor tympani muscle of middle ear | Foramen ovale | Loss of sensation; impaired chewing | Assess motor functions by palpating masseter and temporalis while subject clenches teeth; test ability to move mandible from side to side and to open mouth against resistance |

# INSIGHT 15.3

## Clinical Application

# Some Cranial Nerve Disorders

*Trigeminal neuralgia*[48] (*tic douloureux*[49]) is a syndrome characterized by recurring episodes of intense stabbing pain in the trigeminal nerve. The cause is unknown; there is no visible change in the nerve. It usually occurs after the age of 50 and mostly in women. The pain lasts only a few seconds to a minute or two, but it strikes at unpredictable intervals and sometimes up to a hundred times a day. The pain usually occurs in a specific zone of the face, such as around the mouth and nose. It may be triggered by touch, drinking, tooth brushing, or washing the face. Analgesics (pain relievers) give only limited relief. Severe cases are treated by cutting the nerve, but this also deadens most other sensation in that side of the face.

*Bell*[50] *palsy* is a degenerative disorder of the facial nerve, probably due to a virus. It is characterized by paralysis of the facial muscles on one side with resulting distortion of the facial features, such as sagging of the mouth or lower eyelid. The paralysis may interfere with speech, prevent closure of the eye, and sometimes inhibit tear secretion. There may also be a partial loss of the sense of taste. Bell palsy may appear abruptly, sometimes overnight, and often disappears spontaneously within 3 to 5 weeks.

[47]*tri* = three + *gem* = born (*trigem* = triplets)
[48]*neur* = nerve + *algia* = pain
[49]*tic* = twitch, spasm + *douloureux* = painful

[50]Sir Charles Bell (1774–1842), Scottish physician

**TABLE 15.3**   **The Cranial Nerves (continued)**

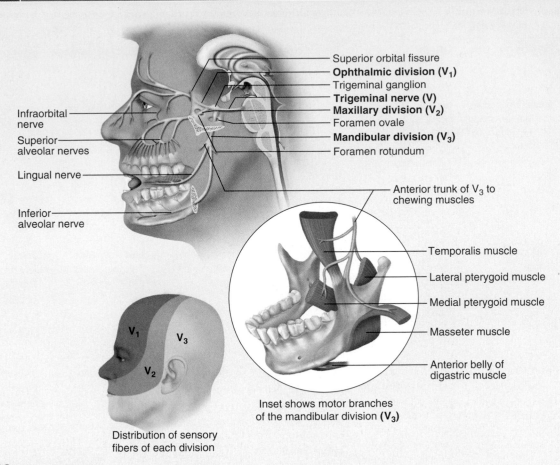

**Figure 15.29** The Trigeminal Nerve (V).

**VI. Abducens[51] Nerve (ab-DOO-senz).**   This nerve controls a muscle that turns the eyeball laterally.

| Composition | Function | Origin | Termination | Cranial Passage | Effect of Damage | Clinical Test |
|---|---|---|---|---|---|---|
| Predominantly motor | Lateral eye movement | Inferior pons | Lateral rectus muscle of eye | Superior orbital fissure | Inability to turn eye laterally; at rest, eye turns medially because of action of antagonistic muscles | Test lateral eye movement |

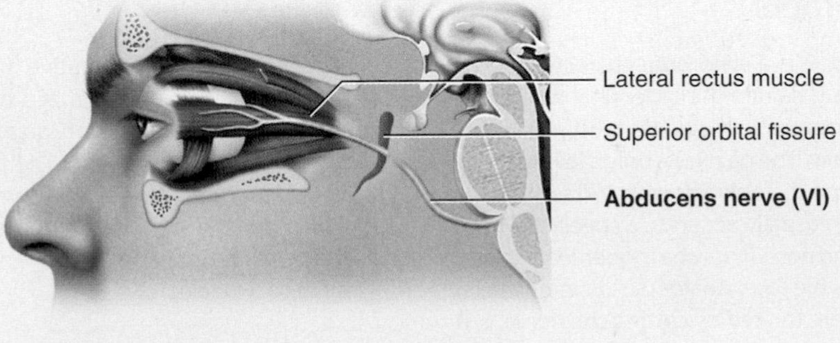

**Figure 15.30** The Abducens Nerve (VI).

---

[51]*ab* = away + *duc* = to lead or turn

| TABLE 15.3 | The Cranial Nerves (continued) |
|---|---|

**VII. Facial Nerve.** This is the major motor nerve of the facial muscles. It divides into five prominent branches: *temporal, zygomatic, buccal, mandibular,* and *cervical.*

| Composition | Function | Origin | Termination | Cranial Passage | Effect of Damage | Clinical Test |
|---|---|---|---|---|---|---|
| Mixed | *Sensory:* Taste *Motor:* Facial expression; secretion of tears, saliva, nasal and oral mucus | *Sensory:* Taste buds of anterior two-thirds of tongue *Motor:* Pons | *Sensory:* Thalamus *Motor:* Somatic fibers to digastric muscle, stapedius muscle of middle ear, stylohyoid muscle, muscles of facial expression. Autonomic fibers to submandibular and sublingual salivary glands, tear glands, nasal and palatine glands. | Internal acoustic meatus and stylomastoid foramen | Inability to control facial muscles; sagging due to loss of muscle tone; distorted sense of taste, especially for sweets | Test anterior two-thirds of tongue with substances such as sugar, salt, vinegar, and quinine; test response of tear glands to ammonia fumes; test subject's ability to smile, frown, whistle, raise eyebrows, close eyes, etc. |

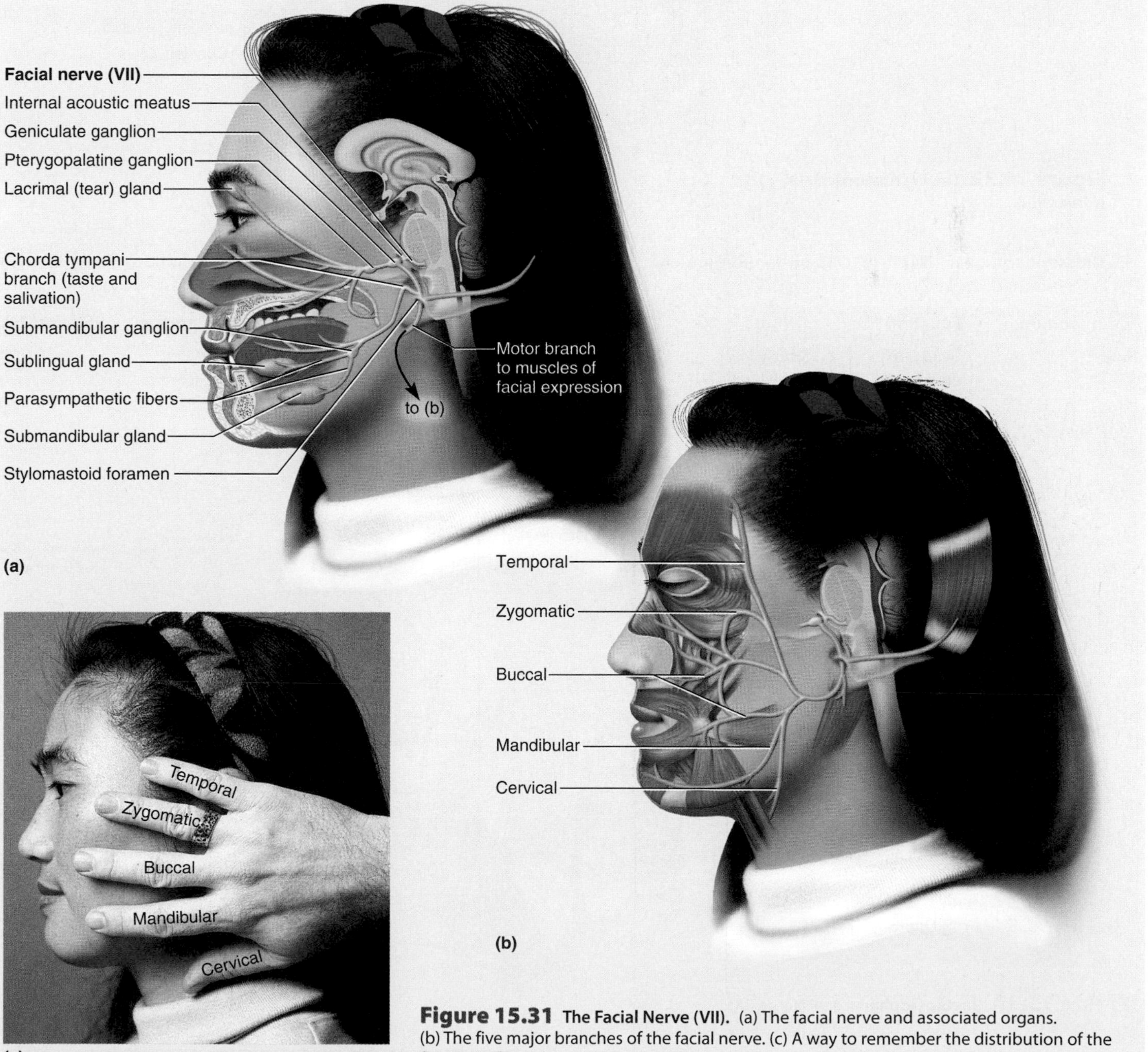

(a)

(b)

(c)

**Figure 15.31  The Facial Nerve (VII).**  (a) The facial nerve and associated organs. (b) The five major branches of the facial nerve. (c) A way to remember the distribution of the five major branches.

| TABLE 15.3 | The Cranial Nerves (continued) |

**VIII. Vestibulocochlear[52] Nerve (vess-TIB-you-lo-COC-lee-ur).** This is the nerve of hearing and equilibrium, but it also has motor fibers that lead to cells of the cochlea that tune the sense of hearing (see chapter 17).

| Composition | Function | Origin | Termination | Cranial Passage | Effect of Damage | Clinical Test |
|---|---|---|---|---|---|---|
| Predominantly sensory | Hearing and equilibrium | *Sensory:* Cochlea, vestibule, and semicircular ducts of inner ear<br><br>*Motor:* Pons | *Sensory:* Fibers for hearing end in medulla; fibers for equilibrium end at junction of medulla and pons<br><br>*Motor:* Outer hair cells of cochlea of inner ear | Internal acoustic meatus | Nerve deafness, dizziness, nausea, loss of balance, and nystagmus (involuntary rhythmic oscillation of eyes from side to side) | Look for nystagmus; test hearing, balance, and ability to walk a straight line |

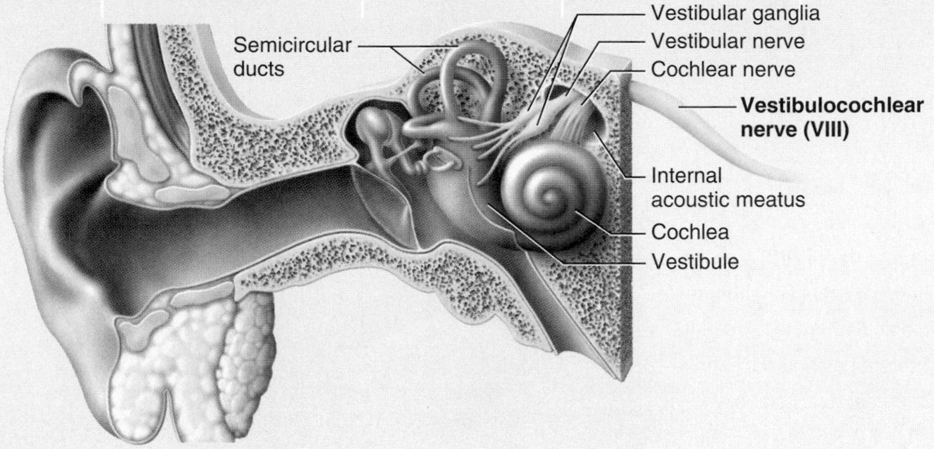

**Figure 15.32** The Vestibulocochlear Nerve (VIII).

**IX. Glossopharyngeal[53] Nerve (GLOSS-oh-fah-RIN-jee-ul).** This is a complex, mixed nerve with numerous sensory and motor functions in the head, neck, and thoracic regions, including sensation from the tongue, throat, and outer ear; control of food ingestion; and some aspects of cardiovascular and respiratory function.

| Composition | Function | Origin | Termination | Cranial Passage | Effect of Damage | Clinical Test |
|---|---|---|---|---|---|---|
| Mixed | *Sensory:* Taste; touch, pressure, pain and temperature sensations from tongue and outer ear; regulation of blood pressure and respiration<br><br>*Motor:* Salivation, swallowing, gagging | *Sensory:* Pharynx; middle and outer ear; posterior one-third of tongue (including taste buds); internal carotid artery<br><br>*Motor:* Medulla oblongata | *Sensory:* Medulla oblongata<br><br>*Motor:* Parotid salivary gland; glands of posterior tongue; stylopharyngeal muscle (which dilates pharynx during swallowing) | Jugular foramen | Loss of bitter and sour taste; impaired swallowing | Test gag reflex, swallowing, and coughing; note any speech impediments; test posterior one-third of tongue with bitter and sour substances |

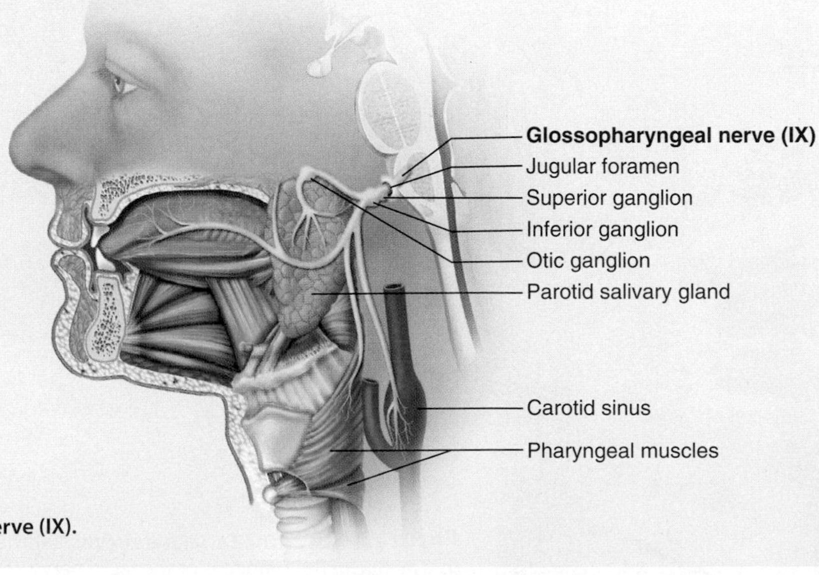

**Figure 15.33** The Glossopharyngeal Nerve (IX).

---

[52]*vestibul* = entryway (vestibule of the inner ear) + *cochlea* = conch, snail (cochlea of the inner ear)

[53]*glosso* = tongue + *pharyng* = throat + *eal* = pertaining to

| TABLE 15.3 | The Cranial Nerves (continued) |
| --- | --- |

**X. Vagus[54] Nerve (VAY-gus).**   The vagus has the most extensive distribution of any cranial nerve, supplying not only organs in the head and neck but also most viscera of the thoracic and abdominal body cavities. It plays major roles in the control of cardiac, pulmonary, digestive, and urinary functions.

| Composition | Function | Origin | Termination | Cranial Passage | Effect of Damage | Clinical Test |
| --- | --- | --- | --- | --- | --- | --- |
| Mixed | *Sensory:* Taste; sensations of hunger, fullness, and gastrointestinal discomfort<br><br>*Motor:* Swallowing, speech, deceleration of heart, broncho-constriction, gastro-intestinal secretion and motility | *Sensory:* Thoracic and abdominal viscera, root of tongue, pharynx, larynx, epiglottis, outer ear, dura mater<br><br>*Motor:* Medulla oblongata | *Sensory:* Medulla oblongata<br><br>*Motor:* Tongue, palate, pharynx, larynx, lungs, heart, liver, spleen, digestive tract, kidney, ureter | Jugular foramen | Hoarseness or loss of voice; impaired swallowing and gastrointestinal motility; fatal if both vagus nerves are damaged | Examine palatal movements during speech; check for abnormalities of swallowing, absence of gag reflex, weak hoarse voice, inability to cough forcefully |

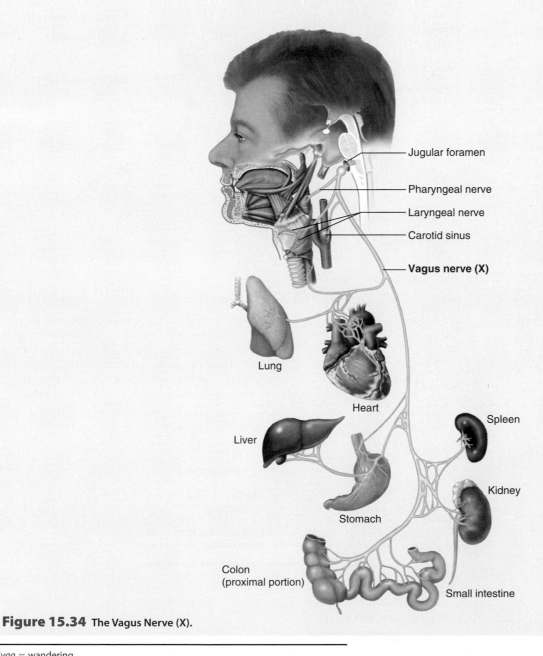

Jugular foramen

Pharyngeal nerve

Laryngeal nerve

Carotid sinus

**Vagus nerve (X)**

Lung

Heart

Liver

Spleen

Stomach

Kidney

Colon (proximal portion)

Small intestine

**Figure 15.34** The Vagus Nerve (X).

[54]*vag* = wandering

**TABLE 15.3** | **The Cranial Nerves (continued)**

**XI. Accessory Nerve.** This nerve takes an unusual path. Unlike any other spinal nerve, it does not arise entirely from the brain. A small root does arise from the medulla oblongata, but a larger root arises from the cervical spinal cord. The latter root ascends alongside the spinal cord and enters the cranial cavity through the foramen magnum. It then joins the smaller root for a short distance, and they exit the cranium together through the jugular foramen, bundled with the vagus and glossopharyngeal nerves. The accessory nerve controls mainly swallowing and neck and shoulder muscles.

| Composition | Function | Origin | Termination | Cranial Passage | Effect of Damage | Clinical Test |
|---|---|---|---|---|---|---|
| Predominantly motor | Swallowing; head, neck, and shoulder movements | Medulla oblongata and spinal cord segments C1 to C6 | Palate; pharynx; trapezius and sternocleidomastoid muscles | Jugular foramen | Impaired movement of head, neck, and shoulders; difficulty shrugging shoulder on damaged side; paralysis of sternocleidomastoid, causing head to turn toward injured side | Test ability to rotate head and shrug shoulders against resistance |

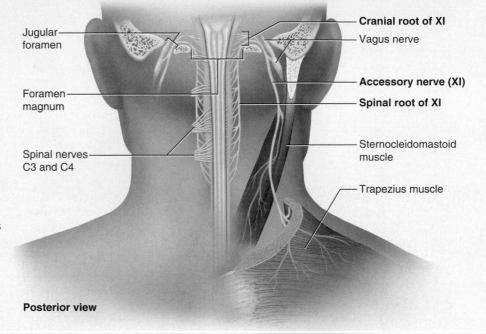

**Figure 15.35** **The Accessory Nerve (XI).** A posterior view showing the dual origin of the accessory nerve from the cervical spinal cord and medulla oblongata. The spinal root enters the cranial cavity through the foramen magnum, picks up the cranial root from the medulla, then exits the cranium through the jugular foramen and innervates neck and shoulder muscles.

Jugular foramen
Foramen magnum
Spinal nerves C3 and C4
Cranial root of XI
Vagus nerve
Accessory nerve (XI)
Spinal root of XI
Sternocleidomastoid muscle
Trapezius muscle

**Posterior view**

**XII. Hypoglossal[55] Nerve (HY-po-GLOSS-ul).** This nerve controls tongue movements.

| Composition | Function | Origin | Termination | Cranial Passage | Effect of Damage | Clinical Test |
|---|---|---|---|---|---|---|
| Predominantly motor | Tongue movements of speech, food manipulation, and swallowing | Medulla oblongata | Intrinsic and extrinsic muscles of tongue | Hypoglossal canal | Impaired speech and swallowing; inability to protrude tongue if both right and left nerves are damaged; deviation of tongue toward injured side, and atrophy on that side, if only one nerve is damaged | Note deviations of tongue as subject protrudes and retracts it; test ability to protrude tongue against resistance |

Hypoglossal canal
Intrinsic muscles of the tongue
Extrinsic muscles of the tongue
Hypoglossal nerve (XII)

**Figure 15.36** **The Hypoglossal Nerve (XII).**

---

[55]*hypo* = below + *gloss* = tongue + *al* = pertaining to

## *Before You Go On*

*Answer the following questions to test your understanding of the preceding section:*

21. List the purely sensory cranial nerves by name and number, and state the function of each.

22. What is the only cranial nerve to extend beyond the head–neck region? In general terms, where does it lead?

23. If the oculomotor, trochlear, or abducens nerve were damaged, the effect would be similar in all three cases. What would that effect be?

24. Which cranial nerve carries sensory signals from the largest area of the face?

25. Name two cranial nerves involved in the sense of taste and describe where their sensory fibers originate.

# Developmental and Clinical Perspectives

### *Objectives*

When you have completed this section, you should be able to

- describe some ways in which neural function and cerebral anatomy change in old age; and

- discuss Alzheimer and Parkinson diseases at the levels of neurotransmitter function and brain anatomy.

## The Aging Central Nervous System

In chapter 13, we examined development of the nervous system at the beginning of life. As so many of us are regretfully aware, the nervous system also exhibits some marked changes at the other end of the life span. The nervous system reaches its peak development and efficiency around age 30. By age 75, the average brain weighs slightly less than half what it did at age 30. The cerebral gyri are narrower, the sulci are wider, the cortex is thinner, and there is more space between the brain and meninges. The remaining neurons show signs that their metabolism is slowing down, such as less rough ER and Golgi complex. Old neurons accumulate lipofuscin pigment and begin to show *neurofibrillary tangles*—dense mats of cytoskeletal elements in their cytoplasm. In the extracellular material, *senile plaques* appear, especially in people with Down syndrome and Alzheimer disease. These are composed of cells and altered nerve fibers surrounding a core of *amyloid protein*.

Old neurons are also less efficient at signal conduction and transmission. The degeneration of myelin sheaths slows down conduction along the axon. The neurons have fewer synapses, and for multiple reasons, signals are not transmitted across the synapses as well as in the younger years: The neurons produce less neurotransmitter, they have fewer receptors, and the neuroglia around the synapses is more leaky and allows neurotransmitter to diffuse away. Target cells have fewer receptors for norepinephrine, and the sympathetic nervous system thus becomes less able to regulate such variables as body temperature and blood pressure.

Not all functions of the central nervous system are equally affected by aging. Language skills and long-term memory hold up better than motor coordination, intellectual function, and short-term memory. Elderly people are often better at remembering things in the distant past than remembering recent events.

## Two Neurodegenerative Diseases

Like a machine with a great number of moving parts, the nervous system is highly subject to malfunctions. Neurological disorders fill many volumes of medical textbooks and can hardly be touched upon here. We have considered meningitis, one peculiar case of the effects of cerebral trauma, and two cranial nerve disorders in Insights 15.1 through 15.3; several other neurological disorders are briefly described in table 15.4. We will close with a brief look at two of the most common brain dysfunctions, Alzheimer and Parkinson diseases. Both of these relate to neurotransmitter imbalances in the brain, and are considered to be *neurodegenerative diseases*. A basic understanding of these two diseases lends added clinical relevance to some areas of the brain studied in this chapter.

**Alzheimer[56] disease (AD)** affects about 11% of the U.S. population over the age of 65 and 47% by age 85. It accounts for nearly half of all nursing home admissions and is a leading cause of death among the elderly. AD may begin before the age of 50 with symptoms so slight and ambiguous that early diagnosis is difficult. One of its first symptoms is memory loss, especially for recent events. As the disease progresses, patients exhibit reduced attention span and may become disoriented and lost in previously familiar places. The AD patient may become moody, confused, paranoid, combative, or hallucinatory, and may eventually lose even the ability to read, write, talk, walk, and eat. Death ensues from pneumonia or other complications of confinement and immobility.

Diagnosis of AD is confirmed on autopsy. There is atrophy of some of the gyri of the cerebral cortex and hippocampus. Neurofibrillary tangles and senile plaques are abundant (fig. 15.37). Cholinergic neurons are in reduced supply, and the level of acetylcholine in affected areas of the brain is consequently low. Intense research efforts are currently geared toward identifying the cause of AD and developing treatment strategies. Researchers have identified three genes on chromosomes 1, 14, and 21 for various forms of early- and late-onset AD.

**Parkinson[57] disease (PD),** also called *paralysis agitans* or *parkinsonism,* is a progressive loss of motor function typically beginning in a person's 50s or 60s. It is due to degeneration of dopamine-releasing neurons in the substantia nigra of the midbrain. A gene has recently been identified for a hereditary form of PD, but most cases are nonhereditary and of little-known cause. Dopamine is an inhibitory neurotransmitter that normally prevents excessive activity in the basal nuclei. Degeneration of the dopamine-releasing neurons leads to hyperactivity of the basal nuclei and, therefore, involuntary muscle contractions. These

---

[56]Alois Alzheimer (1864–1915), German neurologist
[57]James Parkinson (1755–1824), British physician

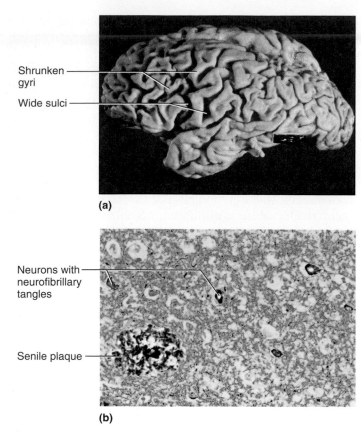

Shrunken gyri

Wide sulci

(a)

Neurons with neurofibrillary tangles

Senile plaque

(b)

**Figure 15.37 Alzheimer Disease.** (a) Brain of a person who died of AD. Note the shrunken gyri and wide sulci. (b) Cerebral tissue from a person with AD. Neurofibrillary tangles are present in the neurons, and a senile plaque is evident in the extracellular matrix.

take such forms as shaking of the hands (tremor) and compulsive "pill-rolling" motions of the thumb and fingers. In addition, the facial muscles may become rigid and produce a staring, expressionless face with a slightly open mouth. The patient's range of motion diminishes. He or she takes smaller steps and develops a slow, shuffling gait with a forward-bent posture and a tendency to fall forward. Speech becomes slurred and handwriting becomes cramped and eventually illegible. Tasks such as buttoning clothes and preparing food become increasingly laborious.

Patients cannot be expected to recover from PD, but drugs and physical therapy can lessen the severity of its effects. A surgical technique called *pallidotomy* has been used since the 1940s to alleviate severe tremors. It involves the destruction of a small portion of the globus pallidus, one of the basal nuclei. Pallidotomy fell out of favor in the late 1960s when the drug L-DOPA came into common use. By the early 1990s, however, the limitations of L-DOPA had become apparent, while MRI- and CT-guided methods had improved surgical precision and reduced the risks of pallidotomy. The procedure has thus made a comeback. Other surgical treatments for parkinsonism target certain nuclei in and near the thalamus, relieving symptoms by ablating (destroying) small areas of tissue or implanting stimulating electrodes.

## Before You Go On

*Answer the following questions to test your understanding of the preceding section:*

26. Describe two respects in which neurons function less efficiently in old age.

27. Describe some changes seen in the brain with aging.

28. Describe the neuroanatomical and behavioral changes seen in Alzheimer and Parkinson diseases.

| TABLE 15.4 | Some Disorders Associated with the Brain and Cranial Nerves |
|---|---|
| **Cerebral palsy** | Muscular incoordination resulting from damage to the motor areas of the brain during fetal development, birth, or infancy; causes include prenatal rubella infection, drugs, and radiation exposure; oxygen deficiency during birth; and hydrocephalus |
| **Concussion** | Damage to the brain typically resulting from a blow, often with loss of consciousness, disturbances of vision or equilibrium, and short-term amnesia |
| **Encephalitis** | Inflammation of the brain, accompanied by fever, usually caused by mosquito-borne viruses or herpes simplex virus; causes neural degeneration and necrosis; can lead to delirium, seizures, and death |
| **Epilepsy** | Disorder causing sudden, massive discharge of neurons (seizures) resulting in motor convulsions, sensory and psychic disturbances, and often impaired consciousness; may result from birth trauma, tumors, infections, drug or alcohol abuse, or congenital brain malformation |
| **Migraine headache** | Recurring headaches often accompanied by nausea, vomiting, dizziness, and aversion to light, often triggered by such factors as weather changes, stress, hunger, red wine, or noise; more common in women and sometimes hereditary |
| **Schizophrenia** | A thought disorder involving delusions, hallucinations, inappropriate emotional responses to situations, incoherent speech, and withdrawal from society, resulting from hereditary or developmental abnormalities in neural networks |

### Disorders Described Elsewhere

# CHAPTER REVIEW

## REVIEW OF KEY CONCEPTS

### Overview of the Brain (p. 423)

1. The adult brain weighs 1,450 to 1,600 g. It is divided into the *cerebrum, cerebellum,* and *brainstem.* The cerebrum and cerebellum are conspicuously marked by surface *gyri* (folds) and *sulci* (grooves).

2. The brain is composed of two kinds of nervous tissue: *gray matter* and *white matter.* Gray matter constitutes the surface *cortex* and deeper *nuclei* of the cerebrum and cerebellum, and nuclei of the brainstem. White matter lies deep to the cortex and consists of *tracts* of myelinated nerve fibers.

3. The brain is surrounded by dura mater, arachnoid mater, and pia mater. The dura mater is divided into two layers, *periosteal* and *meningeal,* which in some places are separated by a blood-filled *dural sinus.* In some places, the dura folds inward to separate major brain regions. A *subdural space* separates some areas of dura from the arachnoid, and a *subarachnoid space* separates arachnoid from pia.

4. The brain has four internal, interconnected chambers: two *lateral ventricles* in the cerebral hemispheres, a *third ventricle* between the hemispheres, and a *fourth ventricle* between the pons and cerebellum.

5. The ventricles and canals of the CNS are lined with ependymal cells, and each ventricle contains a *choroid plexus* of blood capillaries.

6. These spaces are filled with cerebrospinal fluid (CSF), which is produced by the ependyma and choroid plexuses and in the subarachnoid space around the brain. The CSF of the ventricles flows from the lateral to the third and then fourth ventricle, out through foramina in the fourth, into the subarachnoid space around the brain and spinal cord, and finally returns to the blood by way of arachnoid villi.

7. CSF provides buoyancy, physical protection, and chemical stability for the CNS.

8. The brain has a high demand for glucose and oxygen and thus receives a copious blood supply.

9. The *blood–brain barrier* and *blood–CSF barrier* tightly regulate what substances can escape the blood and reach the nervous tissue.

### The Hindbrain and Midbrain (p. 430)

1. The *medulla oblongata* is the most caudal part of the brain, just inside the foramen magnum. It conducts signals up and down the brainstem and between the brainstem and cerebellum, and contains nuclei involved in numerous visceral functions and some muscular control. Cranial nerves IX through XII arise from the medulla. Most descending motor fibers decussate in the medullary pyramids.

2. The *pons* is immediately rostral to the medulla. It conducts signals up and down the brainstem and between the brainstem and cerebellum. Cranial nerve V arises from the pons, and nerves VI through VIII arise between the pons and medulla.

3. The *midbrain* is rostral to the pons. It conducts signals up and down the brainstem and between the brainstem and cerebellum, and gives rise to cranial nerves III and IV. It includes important centers for vision, hearing, pain, and motor control.

4. The *reticular formation* is a loosely organized network of gray matter in the core of the brainstem, including over 100 small neural networks. Because of the number and variety of nuclei, it has wide-ranging functions in motor control, visceral function, pain modulation, sleep, and consciousness.

5. The *cerebellum* is the largest part of the hindbrain and receives most of its input by way of the pons. It has three pairs of *cerebellar peduncles* that attach it to the medulla, pons, and midbrain.

6. Histologically, the cerebellum exhibits a fernlike pattern of white matter called the *arbor vitae,* deep *nuclei* of gray matter embedded in the white matter, and unusually large neurons called *Purkinje cells.*

7. The cerebellum is concerned mainly with motor coordination, equilibrium, and memory of motor skills, but it also has emotional and cognitive functions.

### The Forebrain (p. 437)

1. The forebrain consists of the diencephalon and cerebrum.

2. The *diencephalon* is composed of the *thalamus, hypothalamus,* and *epithalamus.*

3. Almost all sensory signals pass through the *thalamus,* which processes them and relays coded signals to the appropriate regions of the cerebral cortex; it is the "gateway to the cerebral cortex." It also relays signals from the cerebral cortex to other regions of the brain. Figure 15.11 summarizes the functions of its major nuclei.

4. The *hypothalamus* is inferior to the thalamus and forms the walls and floor of the third ventricle. It is a major homeostatic control center and acts through the pituitary gland and autonomic nervous system to regulate many fundamental visceral functions. It is also involved in emotion and memory.

5. The *epithalamus* lies above the thalamus and includes the *pineal gland* (an endocrine gland) and *habenula* (a relay from limbic system to midbrain).

6. The cerebrum is the largest part of the brain. It is divided into two hemispheres separated by the longitudinal fissure. The hemispheres are prominently marked with gyri and sulci. The two hemispheres are connected chiefly through a large fiber tract, the *corpus callosum.*

7. Each hemisphere has five lobes: *frontal, parietal, occipital,* and *temporal lobes* and the *insula.*

8. Nerve fibers of the cerebral white matter are bundled in tracts of three kinds: *projection tracts* that extend between higher and lower brain centers, *commissural tracts* that cross between the right and left cerebral hemispheres through the corpus callosum and the *anterior* and *posterior commissures;* and *association tracts* that connect different lobes and gyri within a single hemisphere.

9. The cerebral cortex is gray matter with two types of neurons: *stellate cells* and *pyramidal cells.* All output from the cortex travels by way of axons of the pyramidal cells. Most of the cortex is *neocortex,* in which there are six layers of nervous tissue. Evolutionarily older parts of the cerebrum have one- to five-layered *paleocortex* and *archicortex.*

10. The *basal nuclei* are masses of cerebral gray matter lateral to the thalamus, concerned with motor control. They include the *caudate nucleus, putamen,* and *globus pallidus.*

11. The *limbic system* is a loop of specialized structures on the medial border of each cerebral hemisphere. Its major components include the *cingulate gyrus, hippocampus,* and *amygdala.* Parts of the hypothalamus, thalamus, basal nuclei, and prefrontal cortex are also often regarded as belonging to the limbic system. Major functions of the limbic system include memory and emotion.

12. The cerebral cortex includes areas of *primary cortex* that either directly receive sensory input or provide the cerebral output to the muscular system, and much more extensive *association areas* that integrate

sensory information, plan motor outputs, and are the seat of memory and other cognitive processes.

13. The *special senses* originate in relatively complex sense organs of the head and involve distinct regions of primary sensory cortex and association areas. Vision resides in the occipital lobe and inferior temporal lobe; hearing in the superior temporal lobe; equilibrium in the cerebellum and brainstem, but with centers of consciousness of body movements and position low in the parietal lobe; taste in the parietal lobe and insula; smell in the frontal and temporal lobes; and there is an association area in the frontal lobe for taste and smell combined.

14. The primary cortex for *somesthetic sensation* is in the postcentral gyrus of the parietal lobe, where there is a point-for-point correspondence *(somatotopy)* with specific regions on the contralateral side of the body. The somesthetic association area is a large region of parietal lobe caudal to this gyrus.

15. Motor control resides in the *motor association area* and *precentral gyrus* of the frontal lobe. The precentral gyrus shows a somatotopic correspondence with muscles on the contralateral side of the body. It contains the *upper motor neurons* whose axons project to *lower motor neurons* in the brainstem and spinal cord.

16. The basal nuclei and cerebellum play important roles in motor coordination and learned motor skills (procedural memory).

17. Language is coordinated largely by the Wernicke and Broca areas. Recognizing language and formulating what one will say or write occur in the Wernicke area; the Broca area compiles the motor program of speech; and commands to the muscles of speech originate in the precentral gyrus.

18. Emotional responses are controlled by the hypothalamus, amygdala, and prefrontal cortex.

19. Cognitive functions are widely distributed through the association cortex of all the cerebral lobes. The prefrontal cortex is the seat of many of our most distinctively human cognitive abilities such as social judgment and abstract thought.

20. The limbic system, especially the hippocampus, is an important site for the cre-
ation of new memories although not for memory storage; it essentially "teaches the cerebral cortex," which stores memories for the long term. The amygdala is important in creating emotional memories, such as associating fear with dangerous situations.

21. The brain exhibits *cerebral lateralization:* Some functions are coordinated mainly by the left hemisphere and others by the right. The *categorical hemisphere* (in most people, the left) is responsible for verbal and mathematical skills and logical, linear thinking. The *representational hemisphere* (usually the right) is a seat of imagination, insight, spatial perception, musical skill, and other "holistic" functions.

### The Cranial Nerves (p. 451)

1. Twelve pairs of *cranial nerves* arise from the floor of the brain, pass through foramina of the skull, and lead primarily to structures in the head and neck.

2. Cranial nerves I and II are purely sensory. All the rest are mixed, although the sensory components of some are only proprioceptive and aid in motor control, so they are often regarded as motor nerves (III, IV, VI, XI, and XII).

3. The olfactory nerve (I) carries the sensory signals for smell.

4. The optic nerve (II) carries the sensory signals for vision.

5. The oculomotor nerve (III) carries motor signals that control eye movements, opening of the eyelids, pupillary constriction, and focusing of the lens.

6. The trochlear nerve (IV) carries motor signals for eye movement.

7. The trigeminal nerve (V) is a large nerve with three branches (ophthalmic, maxillary, and mandibular). It is the main sensory nerve of the face, and it carries motor signals for mastication.

8. The abducens nerve (VI) carries motor signals for eye movement. Cranial nerves III, IV, and VI control different muscles of the eye.

9. The facial nerve (VII) carries sensory signals for taste and motor signals that control facial expression and the secretion of saliva, tears, and nasal and oral mucus.

10. The vestibulocochlear nerve (VIII) carries sensory signals of hearing and equilibrium
and carries motor signals to the inner ear for tuning the sense of hearing.

11. The glossopharyngeal nerve (IX) carries sensory signals for taste, touch, pressure, pain, and temperature sensations from the tongue; for touch, pain, and temperature sensations from the outer ear; and for regulation of blood pressure and respiration. It also carries motor signals for salivation, swallowing, and gagging.

12. The vagus nerve (X) has the most extensive distribution of all cranial nerves, with branches leading not only to organs in the head and neck, but also to most viscera of the thoracic and abdominal cavities. It carries sensory signals for taste, hunger, fullness, and gastrointestinal discomfort, and motor signals for swallowing, speech, and regulation of pulmonary, cardiovascular, and gastrointestinal functions.

13. The accessory nerve (XI) carries motor signals for swallowing and for head, neck, and shoulder movements.

14. The hypoglossal nerve (XII) carries motor signals for the tongue movements of speech, food manipulation, and swallowing.

### Developmental and Clinical Perspectives (p. 461)

1. The brain exhibits substantial atrophy in old age, and neurons exhibit less efficient signal conduction and synaptic transmission.

2. Alzheimer disease (AD) is the most common neurodegenerative disease of old age and a major cause of death in the elderly. It involves memory deficits, personality derangement, and a loss of motor and cognitive skills. At the structural level, AD shows neurofibrillary tangles and senile plaques in the cerebral tissue, a loss of cholinergic neurons, and a low level of acetylcholine in affected areas of the brain.

3. Parkinson disease (PD) results from degeneration of dopamine-releasing neurons of the midbrain substantia nigra and is characterized by involuntary muscle contractions and progressive difficulty in motor tasks such as walking and speech. It is incurable, but medical and surgical treatments can reduce its severity and progression.

## TESTING YOUR RECALL

1. Which of these is caudal to the hypothalamus?
   a. the thalamus
   b. the optic chiasm
   c. the cerebral aqueduct
   d. the pituitary gland
   e. the corpus callosum

2. Hearing is associated mainly with
   a. the limbic system.
   b. the prefrontal cortex.
   c. the occipital lobe.
   d. the temporal lobe.
   e. the parietal lobe.

3. The blood–CSF barrier is formed by
   a. blood capillaries.
   b. endothelial cells.
   c. protoplasmic astrocytes.
   d. oligodendrocytes.
   e. ependymal cells.

4. The pyramids of the medulla oblongata contain
   a. descending corticospinal fibers.
   b. commissural fibers.
   c. ascending spinocerebellar fibers.
   d. fibers going to and from the cerebellum.
   e. ascending spinothalamic fibers.

5. Which of the following is *not* involved in vision?
   a. the temporal lobe
   b. the occipital lobe
   c. the midbrain tectum
   d. the trochlear nerve
   e. the vagus nerve

6. While studying in a noisy cafeteria, you get sleepy and doze off for a few minutes. You awaken with a start and realize that all the cafeteria sounds have just "come back." While you were dozing, this auditory input was blocked from reaching your auditory cortex by
   a. the temporal lobe.
   b. the thalamus.
   c. the reticular activating system.
   d. the medulla oblongata.
   e. the vestibulocochlear nerve.

7. Because of a brain lesion, a certain patient never feels full, but eats so excessively that she now weighs nearly 600 pounds. The lesion is most likely in her
   a. hypothalamus.
   b. amygdala.
   c. hippocampus.
   d. basal nuclei.
   e. pons.

8. The _____ is most closely associated with the cerebellum in embryonic development and remains its primary source of input fibers throughout life.
   a. telencephalon
   b. thalamus
   c. midbrain
   d. pons
   e. medulla

9. Damage to the _____ nerve could result in defects of eye movement.
   a. optic
   b. vagus
   c. trigeminal
   d. facial
   e. abducens

10. All of the following *except* the _____ nerve begin or end in the orbit.
    a. optic
    b. oculomotor
    c. trochlear
    d. abducens
    e. accessory

11. The right and left cerebral hemispheres are connected to each other by a thick C-shaped bundle of fibers called the _____.

12. The brain has four chambers called _____ filled with _____ fluid.

13. In a medial section, the cerebellar white matter exhibits a branching pattern called the _____.

14. Part of the limbic system involved in forming new memories is the _____.

15. Cerebrospinal fluid is secreted partly by a mass of blood capillaries called the _____ in each ventricle.

16. The primary motor area of the cerebrum is the _____ gyrus of the frontal lobe.

17. Your personality is determined mainly by which lobe of the cerebrum?

18. Areas of cerebral cortex that identify or interpret sensory information are called _____.

19. Linear, analytical, and verbal thinking occurs in the _____ hemisphere of the cerebrum, which is on the left in most people.

20. The motor pattern for speech is generated in an area of cortex called the _____ and then transmitted to the primary motor cortex to be carried out.

***Answers in the Appendix***

## TRUE OR FALSE

*Determine which five of the following statements are false, and briefly explain why.*

1. The two hemispheres of the cerebellum are separated by the longitudinal fissure.

2. Degeneration of the substantia nigra causes Alzheimer disease.

3. The midbrain is caudal to the thalamus.

4. The Broca area is ipsilateral to the Wernicke area.

5. Most of the cerebrospinal fluid is produced by the choroid plexuses.

6. Hearing is a function of the occipital lobe.

7. Respiration is controlled by nuclei in both the pons and medulla oblongata.

8. The trigeminal nerve carries sensory signals from a larger area of the face than the facial nerve does.

9. Unlike other cranial nerves, the vagus nerve extends far beyond the head–neck region.

10. The optic nerve controls movements of the eye.

***Answers in the Appendix***

## TESTING YOUR COMPREHENSION

1. Which cranial nerve conveys pain signals to the brain in each of the following situations: (*a*) sand blows into your eye; (*b*) you bite the rear of your tongue; and (*c*) your stomach hurts from eating too much?

2. How would a lesion in the cerebellum and a lesion in the basal nuclei differ in their effects on skeletal muscle function?

3. Suppose that a neuroanatomist performed two experiments on an animal with the same basic spinal and brainstem structure as a human's: In experiment 1, he selectively transected (cut across) the pyramids on the ventral side of the medulla oblongata, and in experiment 2, he selectively transected the gracile and cuneate fasciculi on the dorsal side. How would the outcomes of the two experiments differ?

4. A person can survive destruction of an entire cerebral hemisphere but cannot survive destruction of the hypothalamus, which is a much smaller mass of brain tissue. Explain this difference and describe some ways that destruction of a cerebral hemisphere would affect one's quality of life.

5. What would be the most obvious effects of lesions that destroyed each of the following: (*a*) the hippocampus, (*b*) the amygdala, (*c*) the Broca area, (*d*) the occipital lobe, and (*e*) the hypoglossal nerve?

*Answers at aris.mhhe.com*

## ONLINE RESOURCES

Visit aprevealed.com to explore melt-away cadaver dissections, watch animations that clarify difficult concepts, review histological and radiological images, or take a quiz to assess your understanding of the material.

The Saladin *Human Anatomy,* 2e website at aris.mhhe.com features chapter-specific quizzes, labeling exercises, and other interactive tools to complement your study of human anatomy. If your instructor has provided an ARIS course code, you can also access assignments and information specific to your course.

# The Autonomic Nervous System and Visceral Reflexes

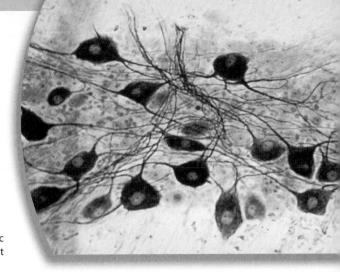

Autonomic neurons in the myenteric plexus of the digestive tract

## BRUSHING UP

To understand this chapter, you may find it helpful to review the following concepts:
- Innervation of smooth muscle (p. 285)
- Overview of the nervous system (pp. 376–377)
- Neurotransmitters and receptors (p. 386)
- General anatomy of nerves and ganglia (pp. 403–405)
- Branches of the spinal nerves (pp. 406–407)
- The hypothalamus (p. 439)
- The limbic system (p. 442)
- Cranial nerves, especially III, VII, IX, and X (pp. 453–460)

We are consciously aware of many of the activities of our nervous system discussed in the preceding chapters—the general and special senses, our cognitive processes and emotions, and our voluntary movements. But there is another branch of the nervous system that operates in comparative secrecy, usually without our willing it, thinking about it, or even being able to consciously modify or suppress it.

This secretive agent is called the *autonomic nervous system (ANS)*. Its name means "self-governed,"[1] as it is almost fully independent of our will. Its job is to regulate such fundamental states and life processes as heart rate, blood pressure, body temperature, respiratory airflow, pupillary diameter, digestion, energy metabolism, defecation, and urination. In short, the ANS quietly manages a multitude of unconscious processes responsible for the body's homeostasis.

Walter Cannon (1871–1945), the American physiologist who coined such expressions as *homeostasis* and the *fight or flight reaction*, dedicated his career to the study of the autonomic nervous system. He found that an animal can live without a functional sympathetic nervous system (one of the two divisions of the ANS), but it must be kept warm and free of stress. It cannot regulate its body temperature, tolerate any strenuous exertion, or even survive on its own. Indeed, the ANS is more necessary for survival than are many functions of the somatic nervous system; an absence of autonomic function is fatal because the body cannot maintain homeostasis without it. Thus, for an understanding of bodily function, the mode of action of many drugs, and other aspects of health care, we must be especially aware of how the ANS works.

# General Properties of the Autonomic Nervous System

## Objectives

When you have completed this section, you should be able to

- explain how the autonomic and somatic nervous systems differ in form and function;
- explain what a visceral reflex is and describe some examples; and
- explain how the two divisions of the autonomic nervous system differ in general function.

## General Actions

The **autonomic nervous system (ANS)** can be defined as a motor nervous system that controls glands, cardiac muscle, and smooth muscle. It is also called the **visceral motor system** to distinguish it from the somatic motor system, which controls the skeletal muscles

(see fig. 13.2, p. 376). The primary target organs of the ANS are the viscera of the thoracic and abdominal cavities and some structures of the body wall, including cutaneous blood vessels, sweat glands, and piloerector muscles.

The somatic and visceral motor systems are often described as voluntary and involuntary, respectively. The somatic motor system innervates voluntary (skeletal) muscle, which is usually under the control of one's will (volition). Cardiac and smooth muscle are involuntary muscles; like glands, they are not usually subject to voluntary control. This voluntary–involuntary distinction is not, however, as clear-cut as it once seemed. Some skeletal muscle responses are quite involuntary, such as the somatic reflexes, and some skeletal muscles are difficult or impossible to control, such as the middle-ear muscles. On the other hand, therapeutic uses of biofeedback (see Insight 16.1) show that some people can learn to voluntarily control such visceral functions as blood pressure.

Visceral effectors do not depend on the autonomic nervous system to function, but only to adjust (modulate) their activity to the body's changing needs. The heart, for example, goes on beating even if all autonomic nerves to it are severed, but the ANS modulates the heart rate in conditions of rest and exercise. If the somatic nerves to a skeletal muscle are severed, the muscle exhibits flaccid paralysis—it no longer contracts at all. But if the autonomic nerves to cardiac or smooth muscle are severed, the muscle often exhibits exaggerated responses (*denervation hypersensitivity*).

## Visceral Reflexes

The ANS is responsible for the body's **visceral reflexes**—unconscious, automatic, stereotyped responses to stimulation, much like the somatic reflexes discussed in chapter 14, but involving visceral receptors and effectors and somewhat slower responses. Some authorities regard the visceral afferent (sensory) pathways as part of the ANS, but most prefer to limit the term *ANS* to the efferent (motor) pathways. Regardless of this preference, however, autonomic activity involves a visceral reflex arc that includes receptors (nerve

## INSIGHT 16.1

### Clinical Application

## Biofeedback

*Biofeedback* is a technique in which an instrument produces auditory or visual signals in response to changes in a subject's blood pressure, heart rate, muscle tone, skin temperature, brain waves, or other physiological variables. It gives the subject awareness of changes that he or she would not ordinarily notice. Some people can be trained to control these variables in order to produce a certain tone or color of light from the apparatus. Eventually they can control them without the aid of the monitor. Biofeedback is not a quick, easy, infallible, or inexpensive cure for all ills, but it has been used successfully to treat hypertension, stress, and migraine headaches.

---

[1]*auto* = self + *nom* = rule

endings that detect stretch, tissue damage, blood chemicals, body temperature, and other internal stimuli), afferent neurons leading to the CNS, interneurons in the CNS, efferent neurons carrying motor signals away from the CNS, and finally effectors.

For example, high blood pressure activates a visceral *baroreflex*.[2] It stimulates stretch receptors called *baroreceptors* in the carotid arteries and aorta, and they transmit signals via the glossopharyngeal nerves to the medulla oblongata (fig. 16.1). The medulla integrates this input with other information and transmits efferent signals back to the heart by way of the vagus nerves. The vagus nerves slow down the heart and reduce blood pressure, thus completing a homeostatic negative feedback loop. A separate baroreflex arc accelerates the heart when blood pressure above the heart drops—for example, when we change from lying down to standing up and gravity draws blood away from the upper body.

---

[2]*baro* = pressure

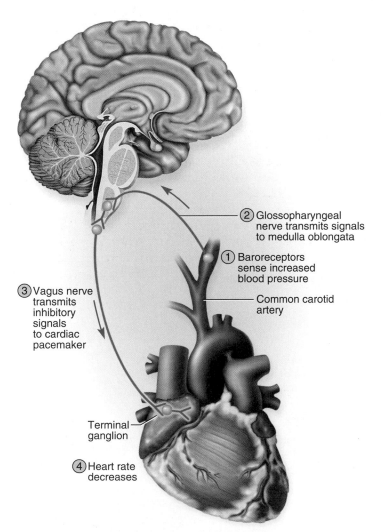

**Figure 16.1** **An Autonomic Reflex Arc.** A rise in blood pressure is detected by baroreceptors in the carotid artery. The glossopharyngeal nerve transmits signals to the medulla oblongata, resulting in parasympathetic output from the vagus nerve that reduces the heart rate and lowers blood pressure.

Labels within figure:
② Glossopharyngeal nerve transmits signals to medulla oblongata
① Baroreceptors sense increased blood pressure
Common carotid artery
③ Vagus nerve transmits inhibitory signals to cardiac pacemaker
Terminal ganglion
④ Heart rate decreases

Another example of a visceral reflex is the autonomic response to chilling of the body. Cooling of the skin stimulates nerve endings called *cold receptors.* Nerve signals travel through spinal nerve fibers to the spinal cord and then up the spinothalamic tracts to the brainstem. This input is directed to the hypothalamic thermostat, a neural pool in the preoptic nucleus of the anterior hypothalamus. Neurons here also respond directly to cooling of the blood that circulates through the hypothalamus. In response, they transmit signals to the heat-promoting center of the posterior hypothalamus. Output from the heat-promoting center travels by nerve fibers that descend through the brainstem to the spinal cord and exit the cord through sympathetic pathways described later in this chapter. Sympathetic nerve fibers ultimately reach the blood vessels of the skin, stimulating contraction of the smooth muscle of the vessel walls. The resulting vasoconstriction diverts blood away from the skin surface, thus helping to reduce heat loss. Hypothalamic output can also increase muscle tone and induce shivering to generate additional body heat, but since this involves the skeletal muscles, it is a somatic reflex rather than a visceral one. Both the visceral and somatic components of thermoregulation, however, admirably exemplify the negative feedback loops that maintain homeostasis: A deviation from the homeostatic set point is detected (chilling of the body); signals are sent to neural integrating centers (the preoptic nucleus and the heat-promoting center of the hypothalamus), and responses are activated (cutaneous vasoconstriction, increased muscle tone, shivering) that return body temperature to the set point.

## Divisions of the Autonomic Nervous System

The ANS has two subsystems, the *sympathetic* and *parasympathetic divisions.* These divisions differ in anatomy and function, but they often innervate the same target organs and may have cooperative or contrasting effects on them. The **sympathetic division** adapts the body in many ways for physical activity—it increases alertness, heart rate, blood pressure, pulmonary airflow, blood glucose concentration, and blood flow to cardiac and skeletal muscle, but at the same time, it reduces blood flow to the skin and digestive tract. Cannon referred to extreme sympathetic responses as the "fight or flight" reaction because they come into play when an animal must attack, defend itself, or flee from danger. In our own lives, this reaction occurs in many situations involving arousal, exercise, competition, stress, danger, trauma, anger, or fear. Ordinarily, however, the sympathetic division has more subtle effects that we notice barely, if at all. The **parasympathetic division,** by comparison, has a calming effect on many body functions. It is associated with reduced energy expenditure and normal bodily maintenance, including such functions as digestion and waste elimination. This can be thought of as the "resting and digesting" state.

This does not mean that the body alternates between states where one system or the other is active. Normally both systems are active simultaneously. They exhibit a background rate of activity called **autonomic tone,** and the balance between *sympathetic tone* and *parasympathetic tone* shifts in accordance with the body's changing needs. Parasympathetic tone, for example, maintains smooth muscle tone in the intestines and holds the resting heart rate down to about 70 to 80 beats/minute. If the parasympathetic vagus nerves to the heart are cut, the heart beats at its own intrinsic rate of about 100 beats/min. Sympathetic tone keeps most blood vessels partially constricted and thus maintains blood pressure. A loss of sympathetic tone can cause such a rapid drop in blood pressure that a person goes into shock.

Neither division has universally excitatory or calming effects. The sympathetic division, for example, excites the heart but inhibits digestive and urinary functions, while the parasympathetic division has the opposite effects.

## Neural Pathways

Although the ANS is often categorized as part of the peripheral nervous system (see fig. 13.2), it has components in both the central and peripheral nervous systems. It includes control nuclei in the hypothalamus and other regions of the brainstem, motor neurons in the spinal cord and peripheral ganglia, and nerve fibers that travel through the spinal and cranial nerves described in chapters 14 and 15.

The autonomic motor pathway to a target organ differs significantly from somatic motor pathways. In somatic pathways, a motor neuron in the brainstem or spinal cord issues a myelinated axon that reaches all the way to a skeletal muscle. In autonomic pathways, the signal must travel across two neurons to get to the target organ, and it must cross a synapse where these neurons meet in an autonomic ganglion (fig. 16.2). The first neuron, called the **preganglionic neuron,** has a soma in the brainstem or spinal cord. Its axon terminates in a ganglion, where it synapses with a **postganglionic neuron** whose axon extends the rest of the way to the target cells. (Some call this cell the *ganglionic neuron* since its soma is in the ganglion and only its axon is truly postganglionic.) The axons of these neurons are called the *pre-* and *postganglionic fibers.*

Differences between the somatic and autonomic nervous systems are summarized in table 16.1.

| TABLE 16.1 | Comparison of the Somatic and Autonomic Nervous Systems | |
|---|---|---|
| **Feature** | **Somatic** | **Autonomic** |
| Effectors | Skeletal muscle | Glands, smooth muscle, cardiac muscle |
| Control | Usually voluntary | Usually involuntary |
| Efferent pathways | One nerve fiber from CNS to effector; no ganglia | Two nerve fibers from CNS to effector; synapse at a ganglion |
| Neurotransmitters | Acetylcholine (ACh) | ACh and norepinephrine (NE) |
| Effect on target cells | Always excitatory | Excitatory or inhibitory |
| Effect of denervation | Flaccid paralysis | Denervation hypersensitivity |

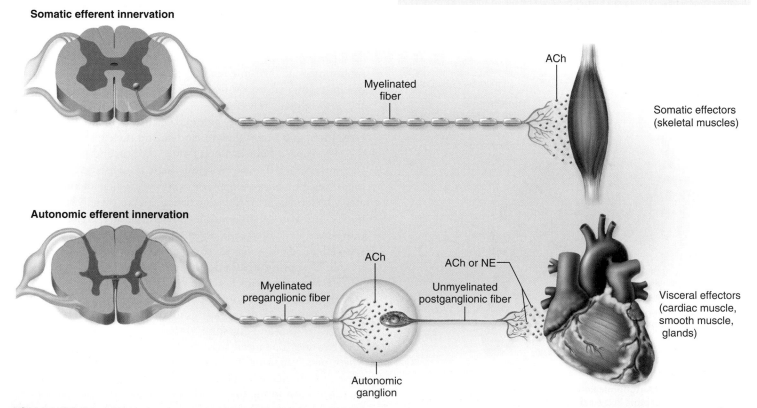

**Somatic efferent innervation**

Myelinated fiber

ACh

Somatic effectors (skeletal muscles)

**Autonomic efferent innervation**

Myelinated preganglionic fiber

ACh

ACh or NE

Unmyelinated postganglionic fiber

Autonomic ganglion

Visceral effectors (cardiac muscle, smooth muscle, glands)

**Figure 16.2** **Comparison of Somatic and Autonomic Efferent Pathways.** The entire distance from CNS to effector is spanned by one neuron in the somatic system and two neurons in the autonomic system. Only acetylcholine (ACh) is employed as a neurotransmitter by the somatic neuron and the autonomic preganglionic neuron, but autonomic postganglionic neurons can employ either ACh or norepinephrine (NE).

## Before You Go On

*Answer the following questions to test your understanding of the preceding section:*

1. How does the autonomic nervous system differ from the somatic motor system?

2. How does a visceral reflex resemble a somatic reflex? How does it differ?

3. What are the two divisions of the ANS? How do they functionally differ from each other?

4. Define *preganglionic* and *postganglionic neuron*. Why are these terms not used in describing the somatic motor system?

# Anatomy of the Autonomic Nervous System

### Objectives

When you have completed this section, you should be able to

- identify the anatomical components and nerve pathways of the sympathetic and parasympathetic divisions;

- discuss the relationship of the adrenal glands to the sympathetic nervous system; and

- describe the enteric nervous system of the digestive tract and explain its significance.

## The Sympathetic Division

The sympathetic division is also called the *thoracolumbar division* because it arises from the thoracic and lumbar regions of the spinal cord. It has relatively short preganglionic and long postganglionic fibers. The preganglionic somas are in the lateral horns and nearby regions of the gray matter of the spinal cord. Their fibers exit by way of spinal nerves T1 to L2 and lead to the nearby **sympathetic chain** of ganglia (**paravertebral[3] ganglia**). This is a longitudinal series of ganglia that lie adjacent to the vertebral column from the cervical to the coccygeal level. They are interconnected by longitudinal nerve cords (figs. 16.3 and 16.4). The number of ganglia varies from person to person, but usually there are 3 cervical *(superior, middle,* and *inferior),* 11 thoracic, 4 lumbar, 4 sacral, and 1 coccygeal ganglion in each chain.

It may seem odd that sympathetic ganglia exist in the cervical, sacral, and coccygeal regions considering that sympathetic fibers arise only from the thoracic and lumbar regions of the spinal cord (levels T1 to L2). But as shown in figure 16.4, nerve cords from the thoracic region ascend to the ganglia in the neck, and cords from the lumbar region descend to the sacral and coccygeal ganglia. Consequently, sympathetic nerve fibers are distributed to every level of the body. As a general rule, the head receives sympathetic output arising from spinal cord segment T1, the neck from T2, the thorax and upper limbs from T3 to T6, the abdomen from T7 to T11, and the lower limbs from T12 to L2. There is considerable overlap and individual variation in this pattern, however.

In the thoracolumbar region, each paravertebral ganglion is connected to a spinal nerve by two branches called *communicating rami* (fig. 16.5). The preganglionic fibers are small myelinated fibers that travel from the spinal nerve to the ganglion by way of

---

[3]*para* = next to + *vertebr* = vertebral column

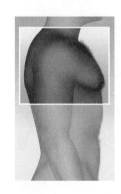

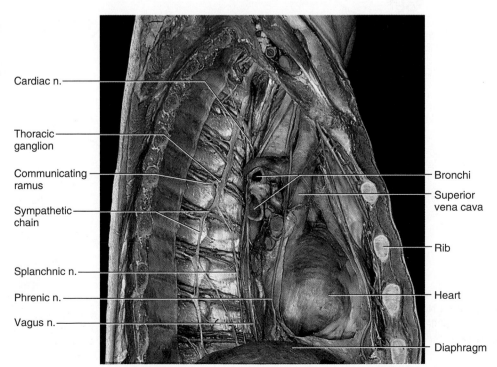

**Figure 16.3** **The Sympathetic Chain Ganglia.** Right lateral view of the thoracic cavity. (n. = nerve)

Cardiac n.

Thoracic ganglion

Communicating ramus

Sympathetic chain

Splanchnic n.

Phrenic n.

Vagus n.

Bronchi

Superior vena cava

Rib

Heart

Diaphragm

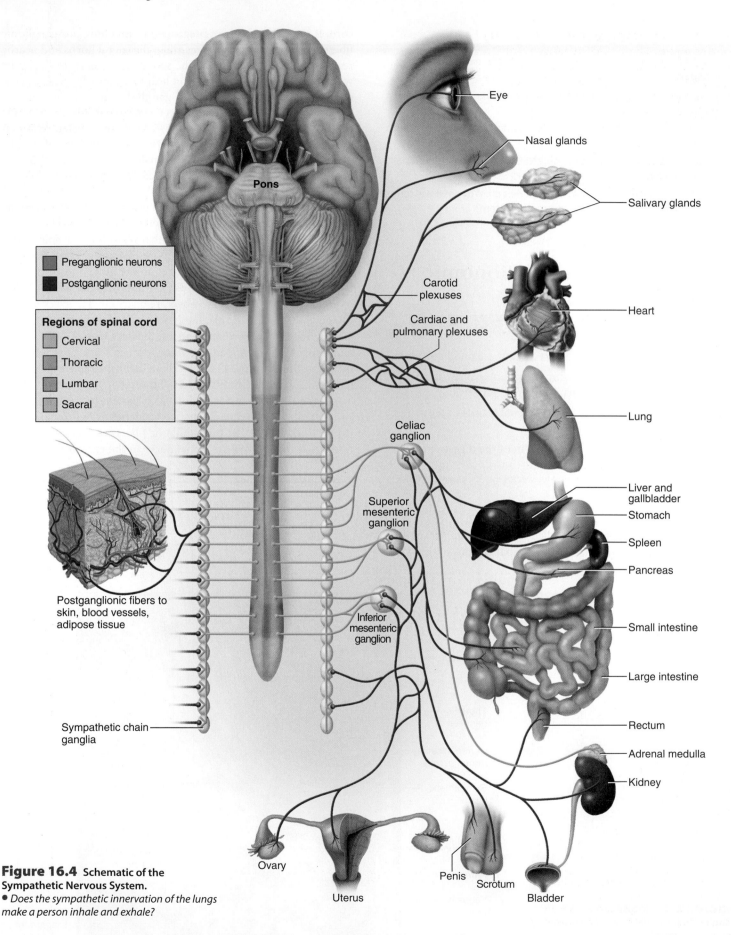

**Figure 16.4** Schematic of the Sympathetic Nervous System.
• *Does the sympathetic innervation of the lungs make a person inhale and exhale?*

Pons

Preganglionic neurons
Postganglionic neurons

**Regions of spinal cord**
Cervical
Thoracic
Lumbar
Sacral

Postganglionic fibers to skin, blood vessels, adipose tissue

Sympathetic chain ganglia

Eye

Nasal glands

Salivary glands

Carotid plexuses

Cardiac and pulmonary plexuses

Heart

Lung

Celiac ganglion

Superior mesenteric ganglion

Inferior mesenteric ganglion

Liver and gallbladder
Stomach
Spleen
Pancreas

Small intestine

Large intestine

Rectum

Adrenal medulla

Kidney

Ovary

Penis
Scrotum

Uterus

Bladder

the **white communicating ramus,**[4] which gets its color and name from the myelin. Unmyelinated postganglionic fibers leave the ganglion by various routes including a **gray communicating ramus,** named for its lack of myelin and duller color. This ramus forms a bridge back to the spinal nerve. Postganglionic fibers travel by way of the gray ramus and spinal nerve to the target organs.

### THINK ABOUT IT

*Would autonomic postganglionic fibers have faster or slower conduction speeds than somatic motor fibers? Why? (See hints in chapter 13.)*

After entering the sympathetic chain, preganglionic fibers may follow any of three courses:

- Some end in the ganglion that they enter and synapse immediately with a postganglionic neuron.
- Some travel up or down the chain and synapse in ganglia at other levels. It is these fibers that link the paravertebral ganglia

---

[4]*ramus* = branch

into a chain. They are the only route by which ganglia at the cervical, sacral, and coccygeal levels receive input.

- Some pass through the chain without synapsing and continue as *splanchnic* (SPLANK-nic) *nerves,* to be considered shortly.

Nerve fibers leave the paravertebral ganglia by three routes: spinal, sympathetic, and splanchnic nerves. These are numbered in figure 16.5 to correspond to the following descriptions:

( 1 )  **The spinal nerve route.** Some postganglionic fibers exit a ganglion by way of the gray ramus, return to the spinal nerve or its subdivisions, and travel the rest of the way to the target organ. This is the route to most sweat glands, piloerector muscles, and blood vessels of the skin and skeletal muscles.

( 2 )  **The sympathetic nerve route.** Other postganglionic fibers leave the chain by way of sympathetic nerves that extend to the heart, lungs, esophagus, and thoracic blood vessels. These nerves form a **carotid plexus** around each carotid artery and issue fibers from there to effectors in the head— including sweat, salivary, and nasal glands; piloerector

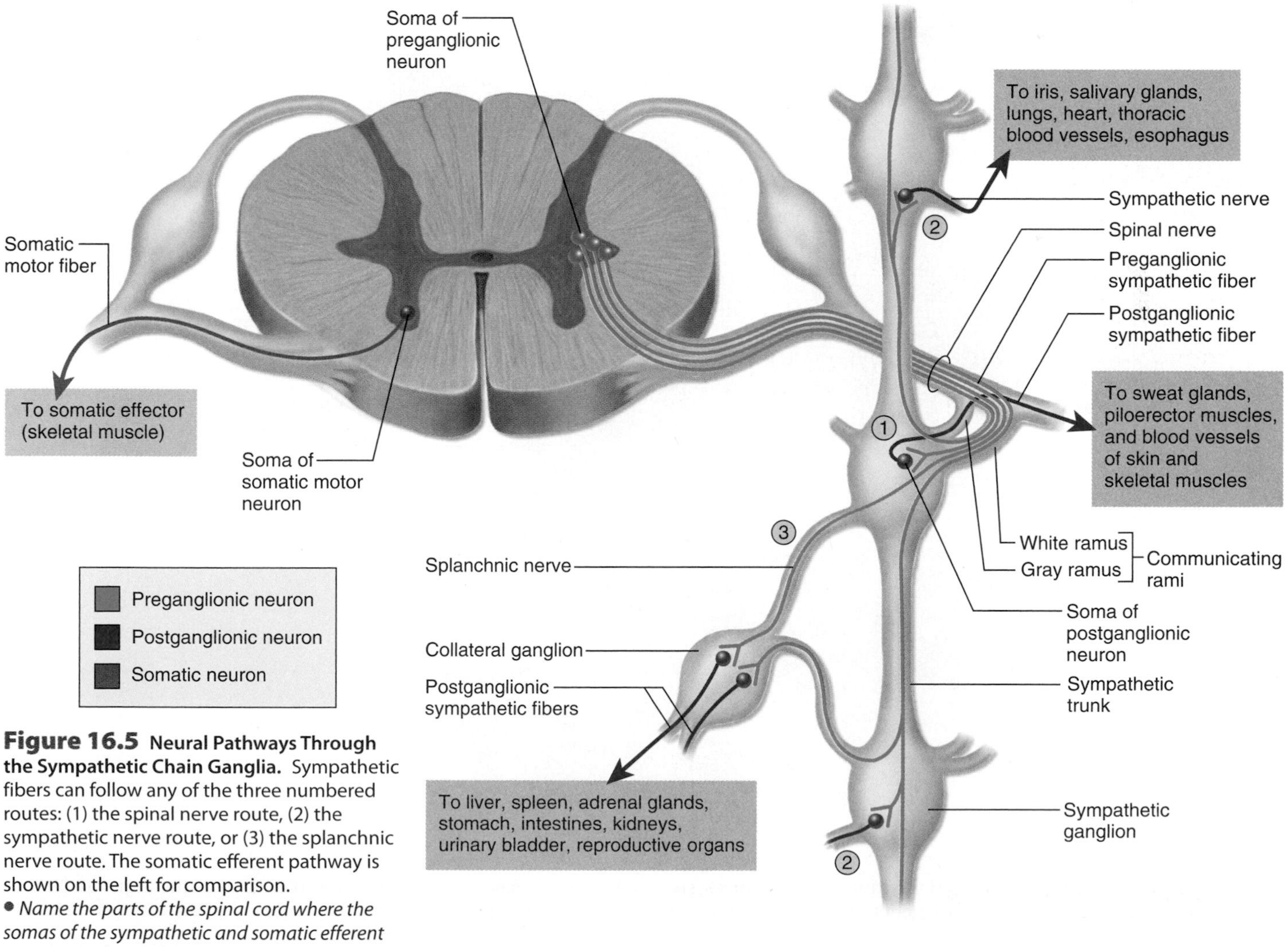

**Figure 16.5 Neural Pathways Through the Sympathetic Chain Ganglia.** Sympathetic fibers can follow any of the three numbered routes: (1) the spinal nerve route, (2) the sympathetic nerve route, or (3) the splanchnic nerve route. The somatic efferent pathway is shown on the left for comparison.
● *Name the parts of the spinal cord where the somas of the sympathetic and somatic efferent neurons are located.*

muscles; blood vessels; and dilators of the iris. Some fibers from the superior and middle cervical ganglia form *cardiac nerves* to the heart. (The cardiac nerves also contain parasympathetic fibers.)

**(3)** **The splanchnic[5] nerve route.** Some of the fibers that arise from spinal nerves T5 to T12 pass through the sympathetic ganglia without synapsing. Beyond the ganglia, they continue as **splanchnic nerves,** which lead to a second set of ganglia called **collateral (prevertebral) ganglia.** Here the preganglionic fibers synapse with the postganglionics.

The collateral ganglia contribute to a network called the **abdominal aortic plexus** wrapped around the aorta (fig. 16.6). There are three major collateral ganglia in this

[5]*splanchn* = viscera

plexus—the **celiac, superior mesenteric,** and **inferior mesenteric ganglion**—located at points where arteries of the same names branch off the aorta. The postganglionic fibers accompany these arteries and their branches to the target organs. Table 16.2 summarizes the innervation to and from the three major collateral ganglia.

The term *solar plexus* is used by some authorities as a collective name for the celiac and superior mesenteric ganglia, and by others as a synonym for the celiac ganglion only. The term comes from the nerves radiating from the ganglion like rays of the sun.

In summary, effectors in the muscles and body wall are innervated mainly by sympathetic fibers in the spinal nerves; effectors in the head and thoracic cavity by sympathetic nerves; and effectors in the abdominal cavity by splanchnic nerves.

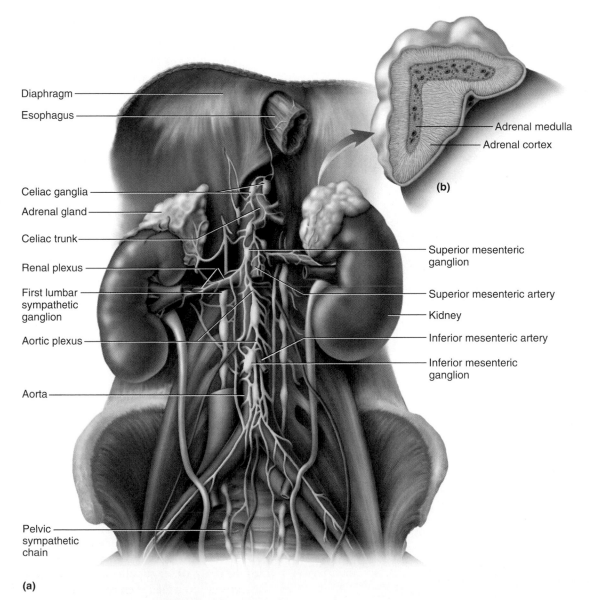

Diaphragm
Esophagus
Adrenal medulla
Adrenal cortex

**(b)**

Celiac ganglia
Adrenal gland
Celiac trunk
Renal plexus
First lumbar sympathetic ganglion
Aortic plexus
Aorta
Pelvic sympathetic chain

Superior mesenteric ganglion
Superior mesenteric artery
Kidney
Inferior mesenteric artery
Inferior mesenteric ganglion

**(a)**

**Figure 16.6** **Abdominal Components of the Sympathetic Nervous System.** (a) Collateral ganglia, abdominal aortic plexus, and adrenal glands. (b) The adrenal gland, frontal section. Only the adrenal medulla plays a role in the sympathetic nervous system; the adrenal cortex has unrelated roles described in chapter 18.

| TABLE 16.2 | Innervation To and From the Collateral Ganglia | | | | |
|---|---|---|---|---|---|
| **Sympathetic Ganglia** | $\longrightarrow$ | **Collateral Ganglion** | $\longrightarrow$ | **Postganglionic Target Organs** | |
| Thoracic ganglia 5 to 9 or 10 | $\longrightarrow$ | Celiac ganglion | $\longrightarrow$ | Stomach, spleen, liver, small intestine, and kidneys | |
| Thoracic ganglia 9 and 10 | $\longrightarrow$ | Celiac and superior mesenteric ganglia | $\longrightarrow$ | Small intestine and colon | |
| Lumbar ganglia | $\longrightarrow$ | Inferior mesenteric ganglion | $\longrightarrow$ | Rectum, urinary bladder, and reproductive organs | |

There is no simple one-to-one relationship between pregangli-onic and postganglionic neurons in the sympathetic division. For one thing, each postganglionic cell may receive synapses from multiple preganglionic cells, thus exhibiting the principle of *neural convergence* discussed in chapter 13. Furthermore, each preganglionic fiber branches and synapses with multiple postganglionic fibers, thus showing *neural divergence*. Most sympathetic preganglionic neurons synapse with 10 to 20 postganglionic neurons. This means that when one preganglionic neuron fires, it can excite multiple postganglionic fibers leading to different target organs. The sympathetic division thus tends to have relatively widespread effects—as suggested by the name *sympathetic*.[6]

## The Adrenal Glands

The paired **adrenal**[7] **(suprarenal) glands** rest like hats on the superior poles of the kidneys (fig. 16.6a). Each adrenal is actually two glands with different functions and embryonic origins. The outer rind, the **adrenal cortex,** secretes steroid hormones discussed in chapter 18. The inner core, the **adrenal medulla,** is essentially a sympathetic ganglion (fig. 16.6b). It consists of modified postganglionic neurons without dendrites or axons. Sympathetic preganglionic fibers penetrate through the cortex and terminate on these cells. The sympathetic nervous system and adrenal medulla are so closely related in development and function that they are referred to collectively as the *sympathoadrenal system.* When stimulated, the adrenal medulla secretes a mixture of hormones into the bloodstream—about 85% epinephrine (adrenaline), 15% norepinephrine (noradrenaline), and a trace of dopamine.

## The Parasympathetic Division

The parasympathetic division is also called the *craniosacral division* because it arises from the brain and sacral region of the spinal cord; its fibers travel in certain cranial and sacral nerves. Somas of the preganglionic neurons are located in the pons, medulla oblongata, and segments S2 to S4 of the spinal cord (fig. 16.7). They issue long preganglionic fibers that end in **terminal ganglia** in or near the target organ (see fig. 16.1). (If a terminal ganglion is embedded in the wall of a target organ, it is also called an *intramural*[8] *ganglion.*) Thus, the parasympathetic division has long preganglionic fibers, reaching almost all the way to the target cells, and short postganglionic fibers that cover the rest of the distance.

There is some neural divergence in the parasympathetic division, but much less than in the sympathetic. The parasympathetic division has a ratio of fewer than five postganglionic fibers to every preganglionic. Furthermore, the preganglionic fiber reaches the target organ before even this slight divergence occurs. The parasympathetic division is therefore more selective than the sympathetic in its stimulation of target organs.

Parasympathetic fibers leave the brainstem by way of the following four cranial nerves. The first three supply all parasympathetic innervation to the head, and the last one supplies viscera of the thoracic and abdominal cavities.

1. **Oculomotor nerve (III)** (see p. 454). The oculomotor nerve carries parasympathetic fibers that control the lens and pupil of the eye. The preganglionic fibers enter the orbit and terminate in the *ciliary ganglion.* Postganglionic fibers enter the eyeball and innervate the *ciliary muscle,* which thickens the lens, and the *pupillary constrictor,* which narrows the pupil.

2. **Facial nerve (VII)** (see p. 457). The facial nerve carries parasympathetic fibers that regulate the tear glands, salivary glands, and nasal glands. Soon after the facial nerve emerges from the pons, its parasympathetic fibers split away and form two smaller branches. The upper branch ends at the *pterygopalatine ganglion* near the junction of the maxilla and palatine bones. Postganglionic fibers then continue to the tear glands and glands of the nasal cavity, palate, and other areas of the oral cavity. The lower branch, called the *chorda tympani,* crosses the middle-ear cavity and ends at the *submandibular ganglion* near the angle of the mandible. Postganglionic fibers from here supply salivary glands in the floor of the mouth.

3. **Glossopharyngeal nerve (IX)** (see p. 458). The glossopharyngeal nerve carries parasympathetic fibers concerned with salivation. The preganglionic fibers leave this nerve soon after its origin and form the *tympanic nerve.* A continuation of this nerve crosses the middle-ear cavity and ends in the *otic*[9] *ganglion* near the foramen ovale. The postganglionic fibers then follow the trigeminal nerve to the *parotid salivary gland* just in front of the earlobe.

4. **Vagus nerve (X)** (see p. 459). The vagus nerve carries about 90% of all parasympathetic preganglionic fibers. It travels down the neck and forms three networks in the mediastinum—the **cardiac plexus** near the base (upper end) of the heart, which supplies fibers to the heart; the **pulmonary plexus** near the medial entrance (hilum) of each lung, whose

---

[6]*sym* = together + *path* = feeling
[7]*ad* = near + *ren* = kidney

[8]*intra* = within + *mur* = wall
[9]*ot* = ear + *ic* = pertaining to

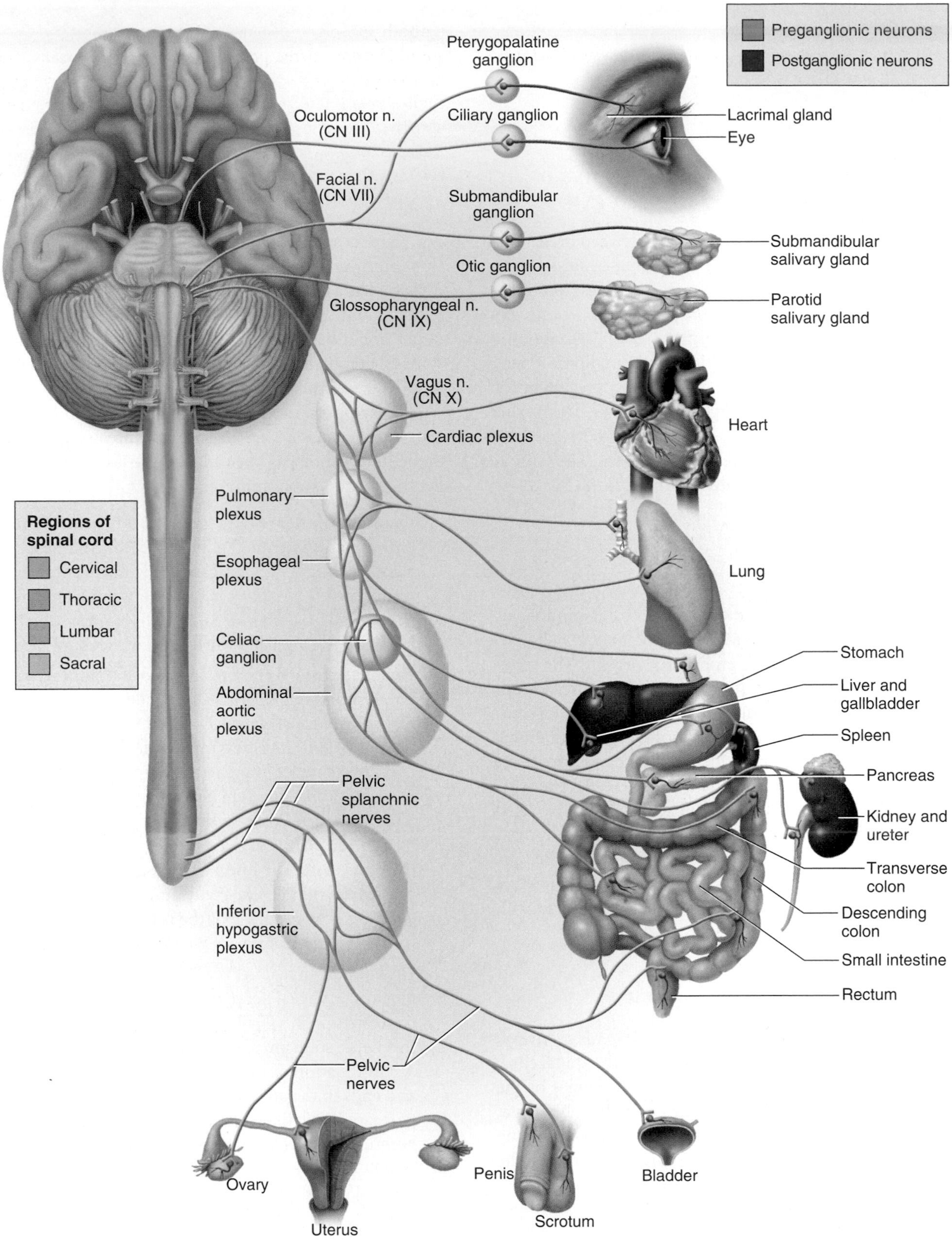

**Figure 16.7** Schematic of the Parasympathetic Nervous System.
● *Which nerve carries the most parasympathetic nerve fibers?*

fibers accompany the bronchi and blood vessels into the lungs; and the **esophageal plexus,** which enmeshes the distal half of the esophagus and whose fibers regulate swallowing.

At the lower end of the esophagus, the esophageal plexus gives off anterior and posterior **vagal trunks,** each of which contains fibers from both the right and left vagus nerves. These penetrate the diaphragm, enter the abdominal cavity, and contribute to the extensive *abdominal aortic plexus* mentioned earlier. As noted earlier, sympathetic fibers synapse here. The parasympathetic fibers, however, pass through the plexus without synapsing. They synapse farther along, in terminal ganglia in or near the liver, pancreas, stomach, small intestine, kidney, ureter, and proximal half of the colon.

The remaining parasympathetic fibers arise from levels S2 to S4 of the spinal cord. They travel a short distance in the ventral rami of the spinal nerves and then form **pelvic splanchnic nerves** that lead to the **inferior hypogastric plexus.** Some parasympathetic fibers synapse here, but most pass through this plexus and travel by way of pelvic nerves to the terminal ganglia in their target organs: the distal half of the large intestine, the rectum, urinary bladder, and reproductive organs. With few exceptions, the parasympathetic system does not innervate body wall structures (sweat glands, piloerector muscles, or cutaneous blood vessels).

The sympathetic and parasympathetic divisions of the ANS are compared in table 16.3.

### THINK ABOUT IT

*Would autonomic functions be affected if the ventral roots of the cervical spinal nerves were damaged? Why or why not?*

## The Enteric Nervous System

The digestive tract has a nervous system of its own called the **enteric[10] nervous system.** Unlike the ANS proper, it does not arise from the brainstem or spinal cord, but like the ANS, it innervates

---

[10]*enter* = intestines + *ic* = pertaining to

| TABLE 16.3 | Comparison of the Sympathetic and Parasympathetic Divisions | |
|---|---|---|
| **Feature** | **Sympathetic** | **Parasympathetic** |
| Origin in CNS | Thoracolumbar | Craniosacral |
| Location of ganglia | Paravertebral ganglia adjacent to spinal column and prevertebral ganglia anterior to it | Terminal ganglia near or within target organs |
| Fiber lengths | Short preganglionic Long postganglionic | Long preganglionic Short postganglionic |
| Neuronal divergence | Extensive | Minimal |
| Effects of system | Often widespread and general | More local and specific |

smooth muscle and glands. Thus, opinions differ on whether it should be considered part of the ANS. It consists of about 100 million neurons embedded in the wall of the digestive tract (see photograph on p. 467)—perhaps more neurons than there are in the spinal cord—and it has its own reflex arcs. The enteric nervous system regulates the motility of the esophagus, stomach, and intestines and the secretion of digestive enzymes and acid. To function normally, however, these digestive activities also require regulation by the sympathetic and parasympathetic systems. The enteric nervous system is discussed in more detail in chapter 24.

## Before You Go On

*Answer the following questions to test your understanding of the preceding section:*

5. Explain why the sympathetic division is also called the thoracolumbar division even though its paravertebral ganglia extend all the way from the cervical to the sacral region.

6. Describe or diagram the structural relationships among the following: preganglionic fiber, postganglionic fiber, ventral ramus, gray ramus, white ramus, and paravertebral ganglion.

## INSIGHT 16.2

### Clinical Application

### Megacolon

The importance of the enteric nervous system becomes vividly clear when it is absent. Such is the case in a hereditary defect called *Hirschsprung disease.*[11] During normal embryonic development, neural crest cells migrate to the large intestine and establish the enteric nervous system. In Hirschsprung disease, however, they fail to supply the distal parts of the large intestine, leaving the sigmoid colon and rectum (see fig. 24.16, p. 703) without enteric ganglia. In the absence of these ganglia, the sigmoidorectal region lacks motility, constricts permanently, and will not allow feces to pass. Feces accumulate and become impacted above the constriction, resulting in *megacolon*—a massive dilation of the bowel accompanied by abdominal distension and chronic constipation. The most life-threatening complications are colonic gangrene, perforation of the bowel, and bacterial infection of the peritoneum *(peritonitis).* The treatment of choice is surgical removal of the affected segment and attachment of the healthy colon directly to the anal canal.

Hirschsprung disease is usually evident even in the newborn, which fails to have its first bowel movement. It affects four times as many infant boys as girls, and although its incidence in the general population is about 1 in 5,000 live births, it occurs in about 1 out of 10 infants with Down syndrome.

Hirschsprung disease is not the only cause of megacolon. In Central and South America, biting insects called *kissing bugs* transmit parasites called *trypanosomes* to humans. These parasites, similar to the ones that cause African sleeping sickness, cause *Chagas*[12] disease. Among other effects, they destroy the autonomic ganglia of the enteric nervous system, leading to a massively enlarged and often gangrenous colon.

---

[11]Harald Hirschsprung (1830–1916), Danish physician
[12]Carlos Chagas (1879–1934), Brazilian physician

7. Explain in anatomical terms why the parasympathetic division affects target organs more selectively than the sympathetic division does.

8. Trace the pathway of a parasympathetic fiber of the vagus nerve from the medulla oblongata to the small intestine.

# Autonomic Effects

### Objectives

When you have completed this section, you should be able to

- name the neurotransmitters employed by the ANS and define terms for neurons and synapses with different neurotransmitter and receptor types;

- in terms of neurotransmitters and receptors, explain why the two divisions of the ANS can have contrasting effects on the same organs;

- explain how the two divisions of the ANS interact when they both innervate the same organ; and

- describe how the central nervous system regulates the ANS.

# Neurotransmitters and Receptors

As noted earlier, the two divisions of the ANS often have contrasting effects on an organ. For example, the sympathetic division accelerates the heart, and the parasympathetic division slows it down. But this does not mean the sympathetic division is stimulatory and the parasympathetic division inhibitory to every organ. Each division stimulates some organs and inhibits others. For example, the parasympathetic division stimulates the contraction of intestinal smooth muscle but inhibits cardiac muscle. The sympathetic division has the opposite effects on these two muscular tissues. Several other examples of such contrasting effects are given in table 16.4. Cases where one division has no effect are usually because it provides little or no innervation to that tissue or organ.

How can different autonomic neurons have such contrasting effects? There are two fundamental reasons: (1) sympathetic and parasympathetic neurons secrete different neurotransmitters, and (2) cells respond in different ways even to the same neurotransmitter depending on what type of receptors they have for it. The basic categories of autonomic neurotransmitters and receptors are as follows (fig. 16.8).

| TABLE 16.4 | Effects of the Sympathetic and Parasympathetic Nervous Systems | |
|---|---|---|
| **Target** | **Effect of Sympathetic Stimulation** | **Effect of Parasympathetic Stimulation** |
| Pupil of eye | Dilation | Constriction |
| Lens of eye | Relaxation for far vision | Contraction for near vision |
| Lacrimal (tear) glands | None | Secretion |
| Sweat glands | Secretion | Usually no effect but produces palmar sweating |
| Piloerector muscles | Hair erection | No effect |
| Heart rate | Increased | Decreased |
| Blood vessels of most viscera | Vasoconstriction | Usually no effect but dilates gastrointestinal blood vessels |
| Blood vessels of skeletal muscles | Vasodilation | No effect |
| Blood vessels of skin | Vasoconstriction | Usually no effect but dilates some facial blood vessels, causing blushing |
| Bronchioles | Bronchodilation | Bronchoconstriction |
| Kidneys | Reduced urine output | No effect |
| Muscle of bladder wall | No effect | Contraction, emptying bladder |
| Salivary glands | Thick mucous secretion | Thin serous secretion |
| Gastrointestinal motility | Decreased | Increased |
| Gastrointestinal secretion | Decreased | Increased |
| Liver | Glycogen breakdown | Glycogen synthesis |
| Pancreatic enzyme secretion | Decreased | Increased |
| Penis and clitoris | Loss of erection | Erection |
| Ejaculation (smooth muscle roles—sperm propulsion and glandular secretion) | Stimulation | No effect |

- **Acetylcholine (ACh).** This neurotransmitter is secreted by the preganglionic neurons in both divisions and the postganglionic neurons of the parasympathetic division. A few sympathetic postganglionics also secrete ACh—those that innervate sweat glands and some blood vessels. Any nerve fiber that secretes ACh is called a **cholinergic** (CO-li-NUR-jic) **fiber,** and any receptor that binds it is called a **cholinergic receptor** (table 16.5). There are two categories of cholinergic receptors:
  - **Muscarinic** (MUSS-cuh-RIN-ic) **receptors.** These are named for muscarine, a mushroom toxin used in their discovery. All cardiac muscle, smooth muscle, and gland cells that receive cholinergic innervation have muscarinic receptors. Because of different subclasses of muscarinic receptors, ACh excites some cells and inhibits others.
  - **Nicotinic** (NIC-oh-TIN-ic) **receptors.** These are named for another botanical toxin helpful to their discovery—nicotine. They occur at the synapses where autonomic preganglionic neurons stimulate the postganglionic cells; on cells of the adrenal medulla; and at the neuromuscular junctions of skeletal muscle fibers. ACh excites all cells with nicotinic receptors.
- **Norepinephrine (NE).** This neurotransmitter is secreted by nearly all sympathetic postganglionic neurons. Nerve fibers that secrete it are called **adrenergic fibers,** and the receptors for it are called **adrenergic receptors.** (NE is also called noradrenaline, the origin of the term *adrenergic.*) There are two principal categories of NE receptors:
  - **α-adrenergic receptors.** These usually have excitatory effects. For example, the binding of NE to the alpha receptors of uterine muscle promotes labor contractions.
  - **β-adrenergic receptors.** These are usually inhibitory. For example, the binding of NE to the beta receptors of uterine muscle relaxes it.

There are exceptions to both of these adrenergic effects because of physiologically different subclasses of both α- and β-adrenergic receptors, but we will not delve into such details.

## Dual Innervation

Most of the viscera receive nerve fibers from both the sympathetic and parasympathetic divisions and thus are said to have **dual innervation.** In such cases, the two divisions may have either *antagonistic* or *cooperative effects* on the same organ. Antagonistic effects oppose each other. Thus, the sympathetic division dilates the pupil, and the parasympathetic division constricts it (fig. 16.9), among other examples already discussed and contrasted in table 16.4. Cooperative effects occur when the two divisions act on different effector cells in an organ to produce a unified overall effect. For example, the parasympathetic division stimulates the secretion of salivary enzymes, and the sympathetic division stimulates the secretion of salivary mucus.

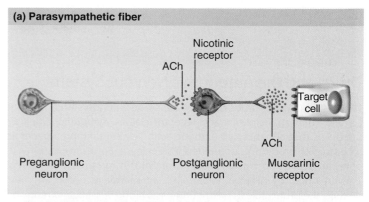

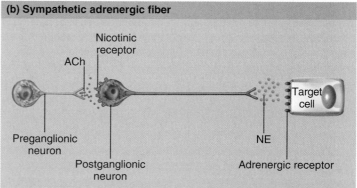

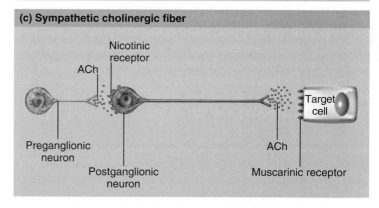

**Figure 16.8** **Neurotransmitters and Receptors of the Autonomic Nervous System.** (a) All parasympathetic fibers are cholinergic. (b) Most sympathetic postganglionic fibers are adrenergic; they secrete norepinephrine (NE), and the target cell bears adrenergic receptors. (c) A few sympathetic postganglionic fibers are cholinergic; they secrete acetylcholine (ACh), and the target cell has cholinergic receptors of the muscarinic class.

| TABLE 16.5 | Locations of Cholinergic and Adrenergic Fibers in the ANS | |
|---|---|---|
| **Division** | **Preganglionic Fibers** | **Postganglionic Fibers** |
| Sympathetic | Always cholinergic | Mostly adrenergic; a few cholinergic |
| Parasympathetic | Always cholinergic | Always cholinergic |

# INSIGHT 16.3 ●●●

## Clinical Application

### Drugs and the Autonomic Nervous System

The design of many drugs has been based on an understanding of autonomic neurotransmitters and receptor classes. *Sympathomimetics*[13] are drugs that enhance sympathetic action by stimulating adrenergic receptors or promoting norepinephrine release. For example, phenylephrine, found in such cold medicines as Chlor-Trimeton and Dimetapp, aids breathing by stimulating certain α-adrenergic receptors and thus dilating the bronchioles, constricting nasal blood vessels, and reducing swelling in the nasal mucosa. *Sympatholytics*[14] are drugs that suppress sympathetic action by inhibiting norepinephrine release or binding to adrenergic receptors without stimulating them. Propranolol, for example, is a *β-blocker* used to treat hypertension. It blocks the action of epinephrine and norepinephrine on β-adrenergic receptors of the heart and blood vessels.

*Parasympathomimetics* enhance parasympathetic effects. Pilocarpine, for example, relieves glaucoma (excessive pressure within the eye) by dilating a vessel that drains fluid from the eye. *Parasympatholytics* inhibit ACh release or block its receptors. Atropine, for example, blocks muscarinic receptors and is sometimes used to dilate the pupils for eye examinations and to dry the mucous membranes of the respiratory tract before inhalation anesthesia. It is an extract of the deadly nightshade plant, *Atropa belladonna*.[15] Women of the Middle Ages used nightshade to dilate their pupils, which was regarded as a beauty enhancement.

The branch of medicine that deals with the effects of drugs on the nervous system—especially drugs that mimic, enhance, or inhibit the action of neurotransmitters—is called *neuropharmacology*.

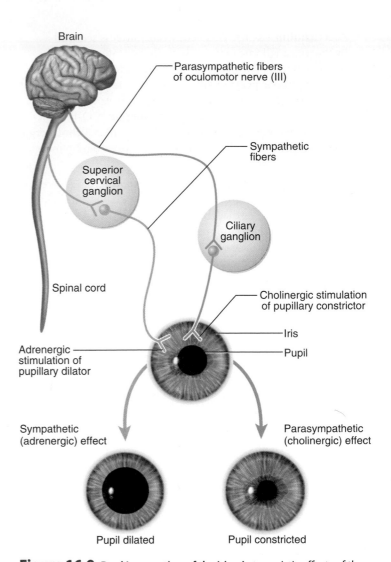

**Figure 16.9** **Dual Innervation of the Iris.** Antagonistic effects of the sympathetic (yellow) and parasympathetic (blue) divisions on the iris.
● *If a person is in a state of fear, would you expect the pupils to be dilated or constricted? Why?*

Dual innervation is not always necessary for the ANS to produce opposite effects on an organ. The adrenal medulla, piloerector muscles, sweat glands, and many blood vessels receive only sympathetic fibers. An example of control without dual innervation is the regulation of blood flow. The sympathetic fibers to a blood vessel have a baseline sympathetic tone that keeps the vessels in a state of partial constriction called *vasomotor tone* (fig. 16.10). An increase in sympathetic stimulation causes vasoconstriction by increasing smooth muscle contraction. A drop in sympathetic stimulation allows the smooth muscle to relax and the vessel to dilate.

## Central Control of Autonomic Function

In spite of its name, the ANS is not an independent nervous system. All of its output originates in the CNS, and it receives input from the cerebral cortex, hypothalamus, medulla oblongata, and somatic division of the PNS.

Effects of the cerebral cortex on autonomic function are evident when anger raises the blood pressure, fear makes the heart race, thoughts of good food make the stomach rumble, and sexual thoughts or images increase blood flow to the genitals. The limbic system (p. 442π) is involved in many emotional responses and has extensive connections with the hypothalamus, an important autonomic control center. Thus, the limbic system provides a pathway connecting sensory and mental experiences with the autonomic nervous system.

The hypothalamus contains many nuclei for primitive autonomic functions, including hunger, thirst, thermoregulation, and sexual response. Artificial stimulation of different regions of the hypothalamus can activate the arousal response typical of the sympathetic nervous system or have the calming effects typical of the parasympathetic. Output from the hypothalamus travels largely to nuclei in more caudal regions of the brainstem and from there to the cranial nerves and the sympathetic preganglionic neurons in the spinal cord.

---

[13]*mimet* = imitate, mimic
[14]*lyt* = break down, destroy
[15]*bella* = beautiful, fine + *donna* = woman

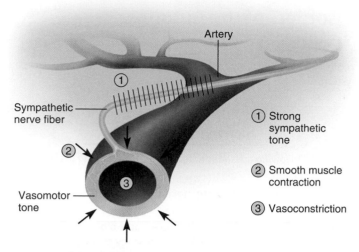

Artery

Sympathetic nerve fiber

① Strong sympathetic tone

② Smooth muscle contraction

③ Vasoconstriction

Vasomotor tone

**(a) Vasoconstriction**

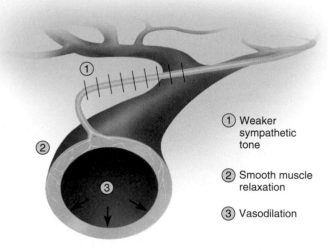

① Weaker sympathetic tone

② Smooth muscle relaxation

③ Vasodilation

**(b) Vasodilation**

**Figure 16.10** **Sympathetic and Vasomotor Tone.**
(a) Vasoconstriction in response to a high rate of sympathetic nerve firing. (b) Vasodilation in response to a low rate of sympathetic nerve firing. Smooth muscle relaxation allows blood pressure within the vessel to push the vessel wall outward. Black lines crossing each nerve fiber represent action potentials, with a high firing frequency in (a) and a lower frequency in (b).

The midbrain, pons, and medulla oblongata house the nuclei of cranial nerves that mediate several autonomic responses: the oculomotor nerve (pupillary constriction), facial nerve (lacrimal, nasal, palatine, and salivary gland secretion), glossopharyngeal nerve (salivation, blood pressure regulation), and vagus nerve (the chief parasympathetic supply to the thoracic and abdominal viscera).

The spinal cord also contains autonomic control nuclei. Such autonomic responses as the defecation and micturition (urination) reflexes are regulated here. Fortunately, the brain is able to inhibit these responses consciously, but when injuries sever the spinal cord from the brain, the autonomic spinal reflexes alone control the elimination of urine and feces.

## *Before You Go On*

*Answer the following questions to test your understanding of the preceding section:*

9. To what neurotransmitters do the terms *adrenergic* and *cholinergic* refer?

10. Why is a single autonomic neurotransmitter able to have opposite effects on different target cells?

11. What are the two ways in which the sympathetic and parasympathetic divisions can interact when they both innervate the same target organ? Give examples.

12. How can the sympathetic nervous system have contrasting effects in a target organ without dual innervation?

13. What system in the brain connects our conscious thoughts and feelings with the autonomic control centers of the hypothalamus?

14. List some autonomic responses that are controlled by nuclei in the hypothalamus.

15. What is the role of the midbrain, pons, and medulla in autonomic control?

16. Name some visceral reflexes controlled by the spinal cord.

# Developmental and Clinical Perspectives

### *Objectives*
When you have completed this section, you should be able to

- describe the embryonic origins of the autonomic neurons and ganglia;

- describe some consequences of aging of the autonomic nervous system; and

- describe a few disorders of autonomic function.

## Development and Aging of the Autonomic Nervous System

Preganglionic neurons of the autonomic nervous system develop from the *neural tube* described in chapter 13; their somas remain embedded in the brainstem and spinal cord for life. Autonomic ganglia and postganglionic neurons, however, develop from the *neural crest* adjacent to the neural tube. During the fifth week of embryonic development, some neural crest cells migrate and assume positions alongside the vertebral bodies to become the sympathetic chain ganglia; others assume positions alongside the aorta to form the abdominal aortic plexus; and others migrate to the heart, lungs, digestive tract, and other viscera to form the terminal ganglia of the parasympathetic division.

The adrenal medulla arises from cells that separate from a nearby sympathetic ganglion, and thus ultimately comes from neural crest (ectodermal) cells. During its development, the medulla is surrounded by cells of mesodermal origin that produce the outer layer of the adrenal gland, the adrenal cortex (which is not part of the autonomic nervous system).

The efficiency of the ANS declines in old age, like that of the rest of the nervous system (see chapter 15). Target organs of the ANS have fewer neurotransmitter receptors in old age and are thus less responsive to autonomic stimulation. As a result, elderly people may experience dry eyes and more eye infections; slower and less effective adaptation of the eye to changing light intensities, and poorer night vision; less efficient control of blood pressure; and reduced intestinal motility and increasing constipation. Because of reduced efficiency of the baroreflex described earlier in this chapter, some elderly people experience *orthostatic hypotension,* a drop in blood pressure when they stand up, sometimes causing dizziness, loss of balance, or fainting.

## Disorders of the Autonomic Nervous System

Table 16.6 describes some dysfunctions of the autonomic nervous system.

## *Before You Go On*

*Answer the following questions to test your understanding of the preceding section:*

17. How do the pre- and postganglionic neurons of the ANS differ in embryonic origin?

18. Briefly state how the intestines, eyes, and blood pressure are affected in old age by the declining efficiency of the autonomic nervous system.

| TABLE 16.6 | Some Disorders of the Autonomic Nervous System |
|---|---|
| Achalasia[16] of the cardia | A defect in autonomic innervation of the esophagus, resulting in impaired swallowing, accompanied by failure of the lower esophageal sphincter to relax and allow food to pass into the stomach. (The region of the stomach at its junction with the esophagus is called the *cardia.*) Results in enormous dilation of the esophagus and inability to keep food down. Most common in young adults; cause remains poorly understood. |
| Horner[17] syndrome | Chronic unilateral pupillary constriction, sagging of the eyelid, withdrawal of the eye into the orbit, flushing of the skin, and lack of facial perspiration. Results from lesions in the cervical ganglia, upper thoracic spinal cord, or brainstem that interrupt sympathetic innervation of the head. |
| Raynaud[18] disease | Intermittent attacks of paleness, cyanosis, and pain in the fingers and toes, caused when cold or emotional stress triggers excessive vasoconstriction in the digits; most common in young women. In extreme cases, causes gangrene and may require amputation. Sometimes treated by severing sympathetic nerves to the affected regions. |

### Disorders Described Elsewhere

---

[16]*a* = without + *chalas* = relaxation
[17]Johann F. Horner (1831–86), Swiss ophthalmologist
[18]Maurice Raynaud (1834–81), French physician

# CHAPTER REVIEW

## REVIEW OF KEY CONCEPTS

### General Properties of the Autonomic Nervous System (p. 468)

1. The autonomic nervous system (ANS) carries out many visceral reflexes that are crucial to homeostasis. It is a visceral motor system that acts on glands, cardiac muscle, and smooth muscle.

2. Functions of the ANS are largely, but not entirely, unconscious and involuntary.

3. Autonomic innervation is not necessary for smooth or cardiac muscle to contract, but the ANS does modulate their activity. It functions through *visceral reflex* arcs similar to those of the somatic reflexes except for the type of effector at the end of the arc.

4. The *sympathetic division* of the ANS prepares the body for physical activity and is especially active in stressful "fight or flight" situations.

5. The *parasympathetic division* has a calming effect on many body functions, but stimulates digestion; it is especially active in "resting and digesting" states.

6. Although the balance of activity may shift from one division to the other, both divisions are normally active simultaneously. Each maintains a background level of activity called *autonomic tone.*

7. The ANS is composed of nuclei in the brainstem, motor neurons in the spinal cord and ganglia, and nerve fibers in the cranial and spinal nerves.

8. Most autonomic efferent pathways, unlike somatic motor pathways, involve two neurons: a *preganglionic neuron* whose axon travels to a peripheral ganglion, and a *postganglionic neuron* whose axon leads the rest of the way to the target cells.

### Anatomy of the Autonomic Nervous System (p. 471)

1. Sympathetic (thoracolumbar) preganglionic neurons arise from thoracic and lumbar segments of the spinal cord. They travel through spinal nerves T1 through L2 to a *sympathetic chain* of ganglia adjacent to the vertebral column.

2. The sympathetic chain extends for the entire length of the vertebral column, from cervical to coccygeal, but it is directly attached to the spinal cord only at levels T1 through L2. Above and below that, nerve fibers that enter the chain ascend and descend to ganglia at higher and lower levels. The chain usually has 3 cervical, 11 thoracic, 4 lumbar, 4 sacral, and 1 coccygeal ganglion.

3. Most preganglionic fibers synapse with postganglionic neurons in one of the ganglia of this chain, sometimes at a higher or lower level than the ganglion at which they enter. Some fibers pass through the chain without synapsing.

4. Preganglionic sympathetic fibers travel from the spinal nerve to the sympathetic ganglion by way of a white communicating ramus.

5. Postganglionic fibers may leave the ganglion through a gray communicating ramus that returns to the spinal nerve, or through sympathetic nerves that lead to target organs of the head and thorax. Other sympathetic fibers pass through the ganglia without synapsing and travel by way of *splanchnic nerves* to synapses in the ganglia of the *abdominal aortic plexus.* The *celiac, superior mesenteric,* and *inferior mesenteric ganglia* of this plexus then give off postganglionic fibers to the abdominopelvic viscera.

6. Sympathetic pathways show substantial neural divergence, with most preganglionic neurons synapsing with 10 to 20 postganglionic neurons. Sympathetic stimulation therefore tends to have widespread effects on multiple target organs.

7. The *adrenal medulla* is a modified sympathetic ganglion composed of modified neurons. These cells secrete mainly epinephrine and norepinephrine into the blood when stimulated.

8. The parasympathetic division issues relatively long preganglionic fibers through cranial nerves III, VII, IX, and X, and spinal nerves S2 through S4, to their target organs.

9. Parasympathetic preganglionic fibers in cranial nerves III, VII, and IX terminate in the *ciliary ganglion* (III), *pterygopalatine* and *submandibular ganglia* (VII), and *otic ganglion* (IX) in the head; postganglionic fibers complete the route to such target organs as the eye, tear glands, salivary glands, and nasal glands.

10. The vagus nerve (X) carries about 90% of all parasympathetic preganglionic fibers, innervates viscera of the thoracic and abdominal cavities, and has the most extensive and complex pathway. It forms *cardiac, pulmonary,* and *esophageal plexuses* in the thoracic cavity, then penetrates the diaphragm as a pair of *vagal trunks* and contributes to the abdominal aortic plexus.

11. The parasympathetic fibers arising from the sacral spinal cord form *pelvic splanchnic nerves,* which lead to the *inferior hypogastric plexus.* From there, *pelvic nerves* lead to the viscera of the pelvic cavity.

12. Parasympathetic preganglionic fibers end in *terminal ganglia* in or near the target organ. Relatively short postganglionic fibers complete the route to specific target cells.

13. The wall of the digestive tract contains an *enteric nervous system,* sometimes considered part of the ANS because it innervates smooth muscle and glands of the tract.

### Autonomic Effects (p. 478)

1. The autonomic effects on a target cell depend on the neurotransmitter released and the type of receptors that the target cell has.

2. *Cholinergic* fibers secrete acetylcholine (ACh) and include all preganglionic fibers, all parasympathetic postganglionic fibers, and some sympathetic postganglionic fibers.

3. ACh binds to two classes of cholinergic receptors called *muscarinic* and *nicotinic* receptors. The binding of ACh to a muscarinic receptor has excitatory effects on some cells and inhibitory effects on others, owing to different subclasses of muscarinic receptors. Binding to a nicotinic receptor is always excitatory.

4. Most sympathetic postganglionic fibers are *adrenergic* and secrete norepinephrine (NE). NE binds to two major classes of receptors called alpha and beta receptors. Binding to an α-adrenergic receptor is usually excitatory, and binding to a β-adrenergic receptor is usually inhibitory, but there are exceptions to both owing to subclasses of each receptor type.

5. Many organs receive *dual innervation* by both sympathetic and parasympathetic fibers. In such cases, the two divisions may have either antagonistic or cooperative effects on the organ.

6. The sympathetic division can have contrasting effects on an organ even without dual innervation, by increasing or decreasing the firing rate of the sympathetic neuron.

7. All autonomic output originates in the CNS and is subject to control by multiple levels of the CNS.

8. The hypothalamus is an especially important center of autonomic control, but the cerebral cortex, midbrain, pons, and medulla oblongata are also involved in autonomic responses.

9. Some autonomic reflexes such as defecation, micturition, and sexual responses are regulated by nuclei in the spinal cord.

**Developmental and Clinical Perspectives (p. 481)**

1. Preganglionic neurons of the ANS develop from the neural tube. Postganglionic neurons, ganglia, and the adrenal medulla develop from the neural crest.

2. The ANS becomes less efficient with age, resulting in such conditions as dry eyes and eye infections; poorer adaptation to changing light intensities, and deficient night vision; and inefficient control of blood pressure, sometimes resulting in orthostatic hypotension; and reduced intestinal motility.

3. Dysfunctions of the ANS include achalasia of the cardia, Horner syndrome, and Raynaud syndrome (table 16.6), and Hirschsprung disease (see Insight 16.2).

# TESTING YOUR RECALL

1. The autonomic nervous system innervates all of these *except*
   a. cardiac muscle.
   b. skeletal muscle.
   c. smooth muscle.
   d. salivary glands.
   e. blood vessels.

2. Muscarinic receptors bind
   a. epinephrine.
   b. norepinephrine.
   c. acetylcholine.
   d. cholinesterase.
   e. neuropeptides.

3. All of the following cranial nerves except the _____ carry parasympathetic fibers.
   a. vagus
   b. facial
   c. oculomotor
   d. glossopharyngeal
   e. hypoglossal

4. Which of the following cranial nerves carries sympathetic fibers?
   a. oculomotor
   b. facial
   c. trigeminal
   d. vagus
   e. none of the cranial nerves

5. Which of these ganglia is *not* involved in the sympathetic division?
   a. intramural
   b. superior cervical
   c. paravertebral
   d. inferior mesenteric
   e. celiac

6. Epinephrine is secreted by
   a. sympathetic preganglionic fibers.
   b. sympathetic postganglionic fibers.
   c. parasympathetic preganglionic fibers.
   d. parasympathetic postganglionic fibers.
   e. the adrenal medulla.

7. The major autonomic control center within the CNS is
   a. the cerebral cortex.
   b. the limbic system.
   c. the midbrain.
   d. the hypothalamus.
   e. the sympathetic chain ganglia.

8. The gray communicating ramus contains
   a. visceral sensory fibers.
   b. parasympathetic motor fibers.
   c. sympathetic preganglionic fibers.
   d. sympathetic postganglionic fibers.
   e. somatic motor fibers.

9. The neural crest gives rise to all of the following *except*
   a. sympathetic chain ganglia.
   b. the celiac ganglion.
   c. parasympathetic preganglionic neurons.
   d. parasympathetic postganglionic neurons.
   e. the adrenal medulla.

10. Which of these does *not* result from sympathetic stimulation?
    a. dilation of the pupil
    b. acceleration of the heart
    c. digestive secretion
    d. bronchodilation
    e. piloerection

11. Nerve fibers that secrete norepinephrine are called _____ fibers.

12. _____ is a state in which a target organ receives both sympathetic and parasympathetic fibers.

13. _____ is a state of continual background activity of the sympathetic and parasympathetic divisions.

14. Most parasympathetic preganglionic fibers are found in the _____ nerve.

15. The digestive tract has a semi-independent nervous system called the _____ nervous system.

16. The embryonic tissue that gives rise to all autonomic ganglia and postganglionic neurons, but not to any preganglionic neurons, is the _____.

17. The adrenal medulla consists of modified postganglionic neurons of the _____ nervous system.

18. The sympathetic nervous system has short _____ and long _____ nerve fibers.

19. Orthostatic hypotension is the result of inefficiency of the _____ reflex.

20. Sympathetic stimulation of blood vessels maintains a state of partial vasoconstriction called _____.

*Answers in the Appendix*

## TRUE OR FALSE

*Determine which five of the following statements are false, and briefly explain why.*

1. The parasympathetic nervous system shuts down when the sympathetic nervous system is active, and vice versa.

2. Some blood vessels of the skin receive parasympathetic innervation.

3. Voluntary control of the ANS is not possible.

4. The sympathetic nervous system stimulates digestion.

5. Some sympathetic postganglionic fibers are cholinergic.

6. Urination and defecation cannot occur without signals from the brain to the bladder and rectum.

7. Some parasympathetic nerve fibers are adrenergic.

8. Parasympathetic effects are more localized and specific than sympathetic effects.

9. The parasympathetic division shows less neural divergence than the sympathetic division does.

10. The two divisions of the ANS have antagonistic effects on the iris.

***Answers in the Appendix***

## TESTING YOUR COMPREHENSION

1. You are dicing raw onions while preparing dinner, and the vapor makes your eyes water. Describe the afferent and efferent pathways involved in this response.

2. Suppose you are walking alone at night when you hear a dog growling close behind you. Describe the ways your sympathetic nervous system would prepare you to deal with this situation.

3. Suppose that the cardiac nerves were destroyed. How would this affect the heart and the body's ability to react to a stressful situation?

4. What would be the advantage to a wolf in having its sympathetic nervous system stimulate the piloerector muscles? What happens in a human when the sympathetic system stimulates these muscles?

5. Pediatric literature has reported cases of poisoning of children with Lomotil, an antidiarrheic medicine. Lomotil works by means of the morphinelike effects of its chief ingredient, diphenoxylate, but it also contains atropine. Considering the mode of action described for atropine in Insight 16.3, why might it contribute to the antidiarrheic effect of Lomotil? In atropine poisoning, would you expect the pupils to be dilated or constricted? The skin to be moist or dry? The heart rate to be elevated or depressed? The bladder to retain urine or void uncontrollably? Explain each answer.

***Answers at aris.mhhe.com***

## ONLINE RESOURCES

Visit aprevealed.com to explore melt-away cadaver dissections, watch animations that clarify difficult concepts, review histological and radiological images, or take a quiz to assess your understanding of the material.

The Saladin *Human Anatomy,* 2e website at aris.mhhe.com features chapter-specific quizzes, labeling exercises, and other interactive tools to complement your study of human anatomy. If your instructor has provided an ARIS course code, you can also access assignments and information specific to your course.

# The Circulatory System I—Blood

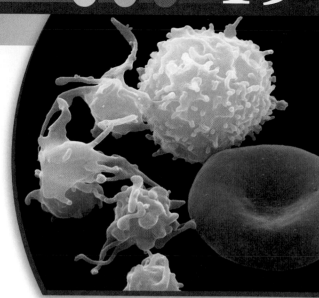

Blood cells and platelets (SEM)

## INSIGHTS

## BRUSHING UP

To understand this chapter, you may find it helpful to review the following concepts:
- Osmosis (p. 54)
- Blood as a connective tissue (p. 89)
- Red bone marrow (p. 160)
- Erythropoietin (p. 541)

Anatomy & Physiology REVEALED®
aprevealed.com

**Cardiovascular System**

**B**lood has always had a special mystique. From time immemorial, people have seen blood flow from the body and with it, the life of the individual. People thus presumed that blood carried a mysterious "vital force," and Roman gladiators drank it to fortify themselves for battle. Even today, we become especially alarmed when we find ourselves bleeding, and the emotional impact of blood is enough to make many people faint at the sight of it. From ancient Egypt to nineteenth-century America, physicians drained "bad blood" from their patients to treat everything from gout to headaches, from menstrual cramps to mental illness. It was long thought that hereditary traits were transmitted through the blood, and people still use such unfounded expressions as "I have one-quarter Cherokee blood."

Scarcely anything meaningful was known about blood until its cells were seen with the first microscopes. Even though blood is a uniquely accessible tissue, most of what we know about it dates only to the last 50 years. Recent developments in this field have empowered us to save and improve the lives of countless people who would otherwise suffer or die.

# Introduction

### *Objectives*
When you have completed this section, you should be able to
- describe the functions and major components of the circulatory system;
- describe the components and physical properties of blood; and
- describe the composition of blood plasma.

## Functions of the Circulatory System

The **circulatory system** consists of the heart, blood vessels, and blood. The term **cardiovascular system**[1] refers only to the heart and blood vessels, which are the subject of chapters 20 and 21. The study of blood, specifically, is called **hematology.**[2]

The fundamental purpose of the circulatory system is to transport substances from place to place in the blood. Blood is the liquid medium in which these materials travel, blood vessels ensure the proper routing of blood to its destinations, and the heart is the pump that keeps the blood flowing.

More specifically, the functions of the circulatory system are as follows:

### Transport
- The blood carries oxygen from the lungs to all of the body's tissues, while it picks up carbon dioxide from those tissues and carries it to the lungs to be removed from the body.

- It picks up nutrients from the digestive tract and delivers them to all of the body's tissues.
- It carries metabolic wastes to the kidneys for removal.
- It carries hormones from endocrine cells to their target cells.
- It transports a variety of stem cells from the bone marrow and other origins to the tissues where they lodge and mature.

### Protection
- The blood plays several roles in inflammation, a mechanism for limiting the spread of infection.
- White blood cells destroy microorganisms and cancer cells.
- Antibodies and other blood proteins neutralize toxins and help to destroy pathogens (disease agents).
- Platelets secrete factors that initiate blood clotting and other processes for minimizing blood loss.

### Regulation
- By absorbing or giving off fluid under different conditions, the blood capillaries help to stabilize fluid distribution in the body.
- By buffering acids and bases, blood proteins help to stabilize the pH of the extracellular fluids.
- Shifts in blood flow help to regulate body temperature by routing blood to the skin for heat loss or retaining blood deeper in the body for heat retention.

Considering the importance of efficiently transporting nutrients, wastes, hormones, and especially oxygen from place to place, it is easy to understand why an excessive loss of blood is quickly fatal, and why the circulatory system needs mechanisms for minimizing such losses.

## Components and General Properties of Blood

All of the foregoing functions depend, of course, on the characteristics of the blood. Adults generally have about 4 to 6 liters of blood. It is a liquid connective tissue composed, like other connective tissues, of cells and an extracellular matrix. The matrix is the blood **plasma,** a clear, light yellow fluid constituting a little over half of the blood volume. Suspended in the plasma are the **formed elements**—cells and cell fragments including the red blood cells, white blood cells, and platelets (fig. 19.1). The term *formed element* is used to denote that these are membrane-enclosed bodies with a definite structure visible with the microscope. Strictly speaking, they cannot all be called cells because the platelets, as explained later, are merely fragments of certain bone marrow cells. The formed elements are classified as follows:

Erythrocytes[3] (red blood cells, RBCs)

Platelets

---

[1]*cardio* = heart + *vas* = vessel
[2]*hem, hemato* = blood + *logy* = study of

[3]*erythro* = red + *cyte* = cell

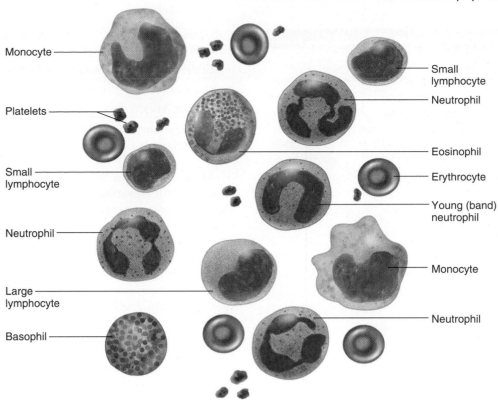

**Figure 19.1** **The Formed Elements of Blood.**
● *What do erythrocytes and platelets lack that the other formed elements have?*

Leukocytes[4] (white blood cells, WBCs)

    Granulocytes

        Neutrophils

        Eosinophils

        Basophils

    Agranulocytes

        Lymphocytes

        Monocytes

Thus, there are seven kinds of formed elements: the erythrocytes, platelets, and five kinds of leukocytes. The five leukocyte types are divided into two categories, the *granulocytes* and *agranulocytes*, on grounds explained later.

The ratio of formed elements to plasma can be seen by taking a sample of blood in a tube and spinning it for a few minutes in a centrifuge (fig. 19.2). Erythrocytes, the densest elements, settle to the bottom of the tube and typically constitute about 37% to 52% of the total volume of whole blood. Leukocytes and platelets settle into a narrow cream- or buff-colored layer called the *buffy coat* just above the erythrocytes; they total 1% or less of the blood volume. At the top of the tube is the plasma, usually constituting about 47% to 63% of the volume.

Some general properties of blood are listed in table 19.1. Some of the terms in that table are defined later in this chapter.

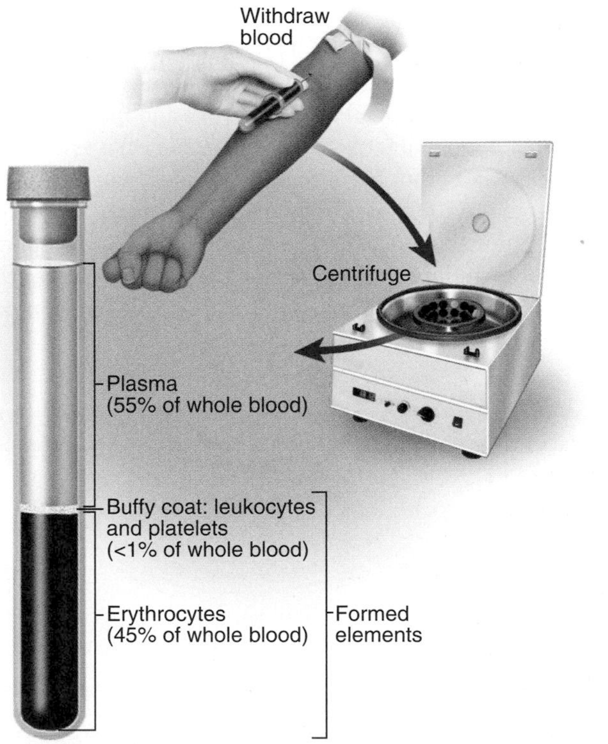

Withdraw
blood

Centrifuge

Plasma
(55% of whole blood)

Buffy coat: leukocytes
and platelets
(<1% of whole blood)

Erythrocytes
(45% of whole blood)

Formed
elements

**Figure 19.2** **Separating the Plasma and Formed Elements of Blood.** A small sample of blood is taken in a glass tube and spun in a centrifuge to separate the cells from the plasma. Erythrocytes are the densest components and settle to the bottom of the tube; platelets and WBCs are next; and plasma remains at the top of the tube. The percentage composed of erythrocytes is called the hematocrit.

[4]*leuko* = white + *cyte* = cell

| TABLE 19.1 | General Properties of Blood* |
|---|---|
| Mean fraction of body weight | 8% |
| Volume in adult body | Female: 4–5 L; male: 5–6 L |
| Volume/body weight | 80–85 mL/kg |
| Mean temperature | 38°C (100.4°F) |
| pH | 7.35–7.45 |
| Viscosity (relative to water) | Whole blood: 4.5–5.5; plasma: 2.0 |
| Osmolarity | 280–296 mOsm/L |
| Mean salinity (mainly NaCl) | 0.9% |
| Hematocrit (packed cell volume) | Female: 37%–48%<br>Male: 45%–52% |
| Hemoglobin | Female: 12–16 g/dL<br>Male: 13–18 g/dL |
| Mean RBC count | Female: 4.2–5.4 million/μL<br>Male: 4.6–6.2 million/μL |
| Platelet count | 130,000–360,000/μL |
| Total WBC count | 5,000–10,000/μL |

*Values vary slightly depending on the testing methods used.

## Blood Plasma

Even though blood plasma has no anatomy that we can study visually, we cannot ignore its importance as the matrix of this liquid connective tissue we call blood. Plasma is a complex mixture of water, proteins, nutrients, electrolytes, nitrogenous wastes, hormones, and gases (table 19.2). When the blood clots and the solids are removed, the remaining fluid is the blood **serum.** Serum is essentially identical to plasma except for the absence of the clotting protein fibrinogen.

Protein is the most abundant plasma solute by weight, totaling 6 to 9 grams per deciliter (g/dL). Plasma proteins play a variety of roles including clotting, defense, and transport of other solutes such as iron, copper, lipids, and hydrophobic hormones. There are

| TABLE 19.2 | Composition of Blood Plasma |
|---|---|
| Water | 92% by weight |
| Proteins | Albumins, globulins, fibrinogen, other clotting factors, enzymes, and others |
| Nutrients | Glucose, amino acids, lactic acid, lipids (cholesterol, fatty acids, lipoproteins, triglycerides, and phospholipids), iron, trace elements, and vitamins |
| Electrolytes | Salts of sodium, potassium, magnesium, calcium, chloride, bicarbonate, phosphate, and sulfate |
| Nitrogenous wastes | Urea, uric acid, creatinine, creatine, bilirubin, and ammonia |
| Hormones | All hormones are transported in the blood |
| Gases | Oxygen, carbon dioxide, and nitrogen |

three major categories of proteins: the albumins, globulins, and fibrinogen (table 19.3). Many other plasma proteins are indispensable to survival, but they account for less than 1% of the total.

### THINK ABOUT IT

*Based on your body weight, estimate the volume (in liters) and weight (in kilograms) of your own blood.*

**Albumin** is the smallest and most abundant plasma protein. It serves to transport various plasma solutes and buffer the pH of the blood. It also makes a major contribution to two physical properties of blood: its *viscosity* (thickness, or resistance to flow) and *osmolarity* (the concentration of particles that cannot pass through the walls of the blood vessels). Through its effects on these two variables, changes in albumin concentration can significantly affect blood volume, pressure, and flow. **Globulins** are divided into three subclasses; from smallest to largest in molecular weight, they are the alpha (α), beta (β), and gamma (γ) globulins. Globulins play various roles in solute transport, clotting, and immunity. **Fibrinogen** is a soluble precursor of *fibrin,* a sticky protein that forms the framework of a blood clot. Some of the other plasma proteins are enzymes involved in the clotting process.

The liver produces as much as 4 g of plasma protein per hour, contributing all of the major proteins except gamma globulins. The gamma globulins come from *plasma cells*—connective tissue cells that are descended from white blood cells called *B lymphocytes.*

| TABLE 19.3 | Major Proteins of the Blood Plasma |
|---|---|
| **Proteins** | **Functions** |
| **Albumin (60%)*** | Major contributor to blood viscosity and osmolarity; transports lipids, hormones, calcium, and other solutes; buffers blood pH |
| **Globulins (36%)*** | |
| Alpha (α) globulins | |
| Haptoglobulin | Transports hemoglobin released by dead erythrocytes |
| Ceruloplasmin | Transports copper |
| Prothrombin | Promotes blood clotting |
| Others | Transport lipids, fat-soluble vitamins, and hormones |
| Beta (β) globulins | |
| Transferrin | Transports iron |
| Complement proteins | Aid in destruction of toxins and microorganisms |
| Others | Transport lipids |
| Gamma (γ) globulins | Antibodies; combat pathogens |
| **Fibrinogen (4%)*** | Becomes fibrin, the major component of blood clots |

*Percentage of the total plasma protein by weight

*How could a disease such as liver cancer or hepatitis result in impaired blood clotting?*

## Before You Go On

*Answer the following questions to test your understanding of the preceding section:*

1. List some transport, protective, and regulatory functions of the blood.

2. What are the two principal components of the blood? Outline the classification of its formed elements.

3. List the three major classes of plasma proteins. Which one is missing from blood serum?

4. What are the functions of blood albumin?

# Erythrocytes

### Objectives

When you have completed this section, you should be able to

- describe the morphology and functions of erythrocytes (RBCs);

- explain some clinical measurements of RBC and hemoglobin quantities;

- describe the structure and function of hemoglobin;

- discuss the formation, life span, death, and disposal of RBCs; and

- explain the chemical and immunological basis and the clinical significance of blood types.

**Erythrocytes,** or **red blood cells (RBCs),** have two principal functions: (1) to pick up oxygen from the lungs and deliver it to tissues elsewhere, and (2) to pick up carbon dioxide from the tissues and unload it in the lungs. RBCs are the most abundant formed elements of the blood and therefore the most obvious things one sees upon its microscopic examination. They are also the most critical to survival; while a severe deficiency of leukocytes or platelets can be fatal within a few days, a severe deficiency of erythrocytes can be fatal within a few minutes. It is the lack of life-giving oxygen, carried by erythrocytes, that leads rapidly to death in cases of major trauma or hemorrhage.

## Form and Function

An erythrocyte is a discoid cell with a thick rim and a thin sunken center. It is about 7.5 μm in diameter and 2.0 μm thick at the rim (fig. 19.3). While most cells, including white blood cells, have an abundance of organelles, RBCs lose nearly all organelles during their development and are thus remarkably devoid of internal structure. When viewed with the transmission electron microscope, the interior of an RBC appears uniformly gray. Lacking mitochondria,

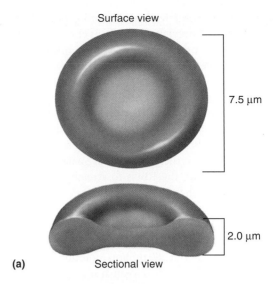

Surface view

7.5 μm

2.0 μm

**(a)**  Sectional view

**(b)**

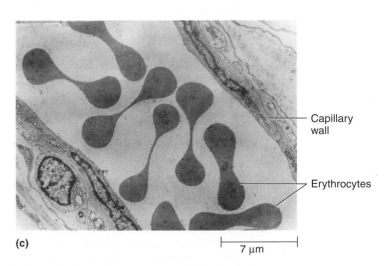

Capillary wall

Erythrocytes

**(c)**     7 μm

**Figure 19.3  The Structure of Erythrocytes.** (a) Dimensions and shape of an erythrocyte. (b) Erythrocytes on the tip of a hypodermic needle (SEM). (c) Erythrocytes in a blood capillary (TEM). Note the lack of internal structure in the cells.

● *Why do erythrocytes look caved in at the center?*

RBCs rely exclusively on anaerobic fermentation to produce ATP. The lack of aerobic respiration prevents them from consuming the oxygen they must transport to other tissues. Lacking a nucleus and DNA, RBCs also are incapable of protein synthesis and mitosis.

The plasma membrane of a mature RBC has glycoproteins and glycolipids on the outer surface that determine a person's blood type. On the inner surface of the membrane are two cytoskeletal proteins, *spectrin* and *actin,* which give it resilience and durability. This is especially important when RBCs pass through small blood capillaries and sinusoids. Many of these passages are narrower than the diameter of an RBC, forcing the RBCs to stretch, bend, and fold as they squeeze through. When they enter larger vessels, RBCs spring back to their discoid shape, like an air-filled inner tube.

With no space occupied by organelles, RBCs can carry more hemoglobin for a given cell volume. Their cytoplasm consists mainly of a 33% solution of hemoglobin (about 280 million molecules per cell). Hemoglobin is known especially for its oxygen-transport function, but it also aids in the transport of carbon dioxide and the buffering of blood pH. While the lack of a nucleus makes an RBC unable to divide or repair itself, it has an overriding advantage: the biconcave shape of the cell gives it a much greater ratio of surface area to volume, which enables $O_2$ and $CO_2$ to diffuse quickly to and from the hemoglobin.

## Quantity of Erythrocytes

The quantity of circulating erythrocytes is critically important to health, because it determines the amount of oxygen the blood can carry. Two of the most routine measurements in hematology are measures of RBC quantity: the **RBC count** and the **hematocrit,**[5] or **packed cell volume (PCV).** The RBC count is normally 4.6 to 6.2 million RBCs/$\mu$L in men and 4.2 to 5.4 million/$\mu$L in women. (A microliter, $\mu$L, is the same volume as a cubic millimeter, $mm^3$; RBC counts are also expressed as RBCs/$mm^3$.) The hematocrit is the percentage of blood volume composed of RBCs (see fig. 19.2). In men, it normally ranges between 45% and 52%; in women, between 37% and 48%.

## Hemoglobin

The red color of blood is due to its **hemoglobin (Hb),** an iron-containing gas-transport protein normally found only in the RBCs. Hemoglobin consists of four protein chains called **globins** (fig. 19.4a). In adult hemoglobin, two of these, the *alpha ($\alpha$) chains,* are 141 amino acids long, and the other two, the *beta ($\beta$) chains,* are 146 amino acids long. A nonprotein component called the **heme** group is bound to each protein chain (fig. 19.4b). At the center of each heme is a ferrous ion ($Fe^{2+}$), the binding site for oxygen. Having four heme groups, each hemoglobin molecule can transport up to 4 $O_2$. About 5% of the $CO_2$ in the bloodstream is also transported by hemoglobin, but this is bound to the globin component rather than to the heme, and a hemoglobin molecule can therefore transport both gases simultaneously. The **hemoglobin concentration** of whole blood is normally 13 to 18 g/dL in men and 12 to 16 g/dL in women.

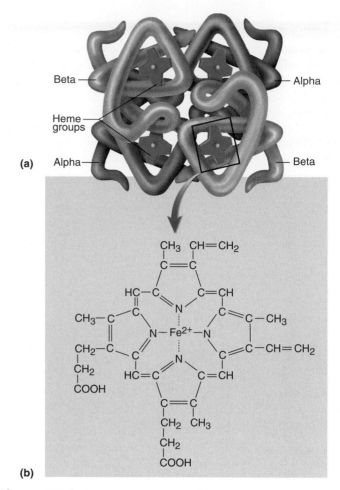

**(a)**

**(b)**

**Figure 19.4** **The Structure of Hemoglobin.** (a) The hemoglobin molecule consists of two alpha proteins and two beta proteins, with a nonprotein heme group bound to each. (b) Structure of the heme group.
● *Where does oxygen bind to this molecule?*

## The Erythrocyte Life Cycle

The production of red blood cells is called **erythropoiesis**[6] (eh-RITH-ro-poy-EE-sis). It is one aspect of the more general process called **hemopoiesis** (HE-mo-poy-EE-sis), the production of all formed elements of the blood. A knowledge of hemopoiesis provides a foundation for understanding leukemia, anemia, and other blood disorders. We will survey some general aspects of hemopoiesis before examining erythropoiesis specifically.

The tissues that produce blood cells are called **hemopoietic tissues.** The first hemopoietic tissues of the human embryo form in the *yolk sac,* a membrane associated with all vertebrate embryos (see fig. 4.5, p. 111). In most vertebrates (fish, amphibians, reptiles, and birds), this sac encloses the egg yolk, transfers its nutrients to the growing embryo, and produces the forerunners of the first blood cells. Even animals that don't lay eggs, however, have a yolk sac that retains its hemopoietic function. (It is also the source of cells that later produce eggs and sperm.) Cell clusters called *blood*

---

[5]*hemato* = blood + *crit* = to separate

[6]*erythro* = red + *poiesis* = formation of

islands form here by the third week of human development. They produce primitive *stem cells* that migrate into the embryo proper and colonize the bone marrow, liver, spleen, and thymus. Here, the stem cells multiply and give rise to blood cells throughout fetal development. The liver stops producing blood cells around the time of birth. The spleen stops producing RBCs soon after, but it continues to produce lymphocytes for life.

From infancy onward, the red bone marrow produces all seven kinds of formed elements, while lymphocytes are produced not only there but also in the lymphatic tissues and organs—especially the thymus, tonsils, lymph nodes, spleen, and patches of lymphatic tissue in the mucous membranes. Blood formation in the bone

marrow and lymphatic organs is called, respectively, **myeloid**[7] and **lymphoid hemopoiesis.**

All formed elements trace their origins to a common type of bone marrow stem cell, the **pluripotent stem cell (PPSC)** (formerly called a hemocytoblast[8]). PPSCs are so-named because they have the potential to develop into multiple mature cell types. They multiply at a relatively slow rate and thus maintain a small population in the bone marrow. Some of them go on to differentiate into a variety of more specialized cells called **colony-forming units (CFUs),** each type destined to produce one or another class of formed elements. Through a series of **precursor cells,** the CFUs divide and differentiate into mature formed elements.

Erythropoiesis itself begins when a PPSC becomes an *erythrocyte colony-forming unit (ECFU)* (fig. 19.5). The hormone *erythropoietin (EPO)* stimulates the ECFU to develop into a *proerythroblast,* followed by an *erythroblast.* Erythroblasts multiply and synthesize hemoglobin. When this task is completed, the nucleus shrivels and is discharged from the cell. The cell is now called a *reticulocyte,*[9] named for a temporary network composed of clusters of ribosomes *(polyribosomes).* Reticulocytes leave the bone marrow and enter the circulating blood. When the last of the polyribosomes disintegrate and disappear, the cell is a mature erythrocyte. Normally, about 0.5% to 1.5% of the circulating RBCs are reticulocytes, but this percentage rises when the body is making RBCs especially rapidly, as when compensating for blood loss.

The entire process of transformation from PPSC to mature RBC takes 3 to 5 days and involves four major developments—a reduction in cell size, an increase in cell number, the synthesis of hemoglobin, and the loss of the nucleus and other organelles. The process normally generates about 2.5 million RBCs per second, or 20 mL of packed RBCs per day.

The average RBC lives about 120 days after its release from the bone marrow. As it ages, its membrane proteins (especially spectrin) deteriorate, and the membrane grows increasingly fragile. Without a nucleus or ribosomes, an RBC cannot synthesize new spectrin. Eventually, it ruptures as it tries to flex its way through narrow capillaries and sinusoids. The spleen has been called an

---

## INSIGHT 19.1

### Evolutionary Medicine

## The Packaging of Hemoglobin

The gas-transport pigments of earthworms, snails, and many other animals are dissolved in the plasma rather than contained in blood cells. You might wonder why human hemoglobin must be contained in RBCs. The main reason is osmotic. The osmolarity of blood depends on the number of particles in solution. A "particle," for this purpose, can be a sodium ion, an albumin molecule, or a whole cell. If all the hemoglobin contained in the RBCs were free in the plasma, it would drastically increase blood osmolarity, since each RBC contains about 280 million molecules of hemoglobin. The circulatory system would osmotically absorb excess water and become enormously congested. Circulation would be severely impaired. The blood simply could not contain that much free hemoglobin and support life. On the other hand, if it contained a safe level of free hemoglobin, it could not transport enough oxygen to support the high metabolic demand of the human body. By having our hemoglobin packaged in RBCs, we are able to have much more of it and hence to have more efficient gas transport and more active metabolism.

Another reason for packaging the hemoglobin in RBCs is that some of the body's capillaries (*fenestrated capillaries* found in the kidneys and endocrine glands, for example) are permeable to proteins. Hemoglobin would leak out into the tissues if it were not contained in cells too big to pass through the capillary wall.

---

[7]*myel* = bone marrow
[8]*hemo* = blood + *cyto* = cell + *blast* = precursor
[9]*reticulo* = little network + *cyte* = cell

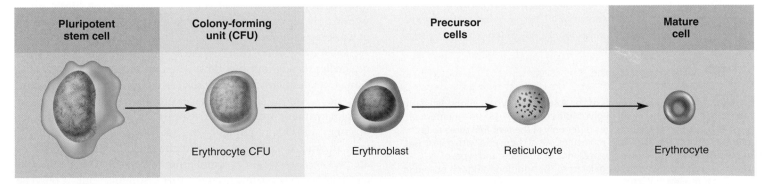

**Figure 19.5 Erythropoiesis.** Stages in the development of erythrocytes.

Pluripotent stem cell | Colony-forming unit (CFU) | Precursor cells | Mature cell

Erythrocyte CFU | Erythroblast | Reticulocyte | Erythrocyte

"erythrocyte graveyard" because RBCs have an especially difficult time passing through its small channels. Here the old cells become trapped, broken up, and destroyed.

The 120-day life span of an RBC is often described as relatively short, owing to the fact that it lacks protein synthesis organelles and cannot repair itself. However, this is actually a relatively long life compared to other formed elements. Most leukocytes (which have nuclei) live less than a week, and platelets live about 10 days. Only monocytes and lymphocytes outlive the RBCs.

## Blood Types

There are numerous genetically determined *blood groups* in the human population, each of which contains multiple **blood types.** The most familiar of these are the ABO group (with blood types A, B, AB, and O) and Rh group (with blood types Rh-positive and Rh-negative). These types differ with respect to the chemical composition of glycolipids on the RBC surface (fig. 19.6). These molecules act as *antigens,* substances capable of evoking an immune reaction. The blood plasma contains *antibodies* that react against incompatible antigens on foreign RBCs. The RBC antigens and plasma antibodies thus determine the compatibility of donor and recipient blood in transfusions. In the event of an incompatibility in Rh type between the mother and fetus, they can also cause a severe anemia in the newborn infant.

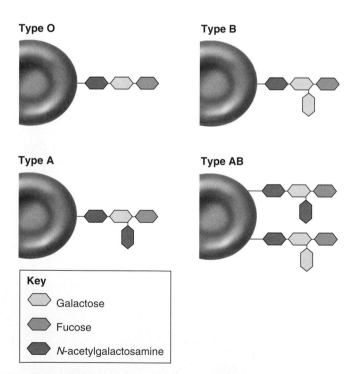

**Figure 19.6 Chemical Basis of the ABO Blood Types.** Blood types are determined by the chemistry of glycolipids of the RBC plasma membrane. Types A, B, AB, and O erythrocytes differ only in the terminal three to four carbohydrates of the glycolipid molecules. All of them end with galactose and fucose, but they differ in the presence or absence, and type, of additional sugar bonded to the galactose. The additional sugar is absent in type O; it is N-acetylgalactosamine in type A; it is another galactose in type B; and type AB cells have both the type A and B chains.

## Before You Go On

*Answer the following questions to test your understanding of the preceding section:*

5. What are the two main functions of RBCs?
6. Define *hematocrit* and *RBC count,* and state some normal clinical values for each.
7. Describe the structure of a hemoglobin molecule. Explain where $O_2$ and $CO_2$ are carried on a hemoglobin molecule.
8. Name the stages in the production of an RBC, and state the differences between them.
9. Explain what plasma and RBC components are responsible for blood types, and why blood types are clinically important.

# Leukocytes

### Objectives
When you have completed this section, you should be able to
- describe the appearance of the five kinds of leukocytes;
- explain the function of WBCs in general and the individual roles of each WBC type;
- describe the formation and life history of WBCs; and
- describe the production, death, and disposal of leukocytes.

## Form and Function

**Leukocytes,** or **white blood cells (WBCs),** are the least abundant formed elements, totaling only 5,000 to 10,000 WBCs/µL. Yet we cannot live long without them, because they afford protection against infectious microorganisms and other pathogens. WBCs are easily recognized in stained blood films because they have conspicuous nuclei that stain from light violet to dark purple with the most common blood stains. They are much more abundant in the body than their low number in blood films would suggest, because they spend only a few hours in the bloodstream, then migrate through the walls of the capillaries and venules and spend the rest of their lives in the connective tissues. It's as if the bloodstream were merely the subway that the WBCs take to work; in blood films, we see only the ones on their way to work, not the WBCs already at work in the tissues.

Leukocytes differ from erythrocytes in that they retain their organelles throughout life; thus, when viewed with the transmission electron microscope, they show a complex internal structure (fig. 19.7). Among these organelles are the usual instruments of protein synthesis—the nucleus, rough endoplasmic reticulum, ribosomes, and Golgi complex—for leukocytes must synthesize proteins in order to carry out their functions. Some of these proteins are packaged into lysosomes and other organelles, which appear as conspicuous cytoplasmic granules that distinguish one WBC type from another.

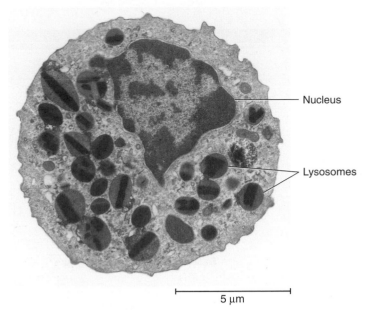

**Figure 19.7** **Structure of an Eosinophil.** In contrast to an RBC, the WBC cytoplasm is crowded with organelles, including a nucleus.

## Types of Leukocytes

As outlined at the beginning of this chapter, there are five kinds of leukocytes (table 19.4). They are distinguished from each other by their relative size and abundance, the size and shape of their nuclei, the presence or absence of certain cytoplasmic granules, the coarseness and staining properties of those granules, and most importantly by their functions. All WBCs have lysosomes called **nonspecific (azurophilic**[10]**) granules** in the cytoplasm, so-named because they absorb the blue or violet dyes of blood stains. Three of the five WBC types—neutrophils, eosinophils, and basophils—are called **granulocytes** because they also have various types of **specific granules** that stain conspicuously and distinguish each cell type from the others. These granules contain enzymes and other chemicals employed in defense against pathogens. The two remaining WBC types—monocytes and lymphocytes—are called **agranulocytes** because they lack specific granules. Nonspecific granules

[10]*azuro* = blue + *philic* = loving

| TABLE 19.4 | The White Blood Cells (Leukocytes) |
|---|---|

**Neutrophils**

| Percent of WBCs | 60%–70% |
|---|---|
| Mean count | 4,150 cells/µL |
| Diameter | 9–12 µm |

**Appearance***

Nucleus usually with 3–5 lobes in S- or C-shaped array
Fine reddish to violet granules in cytoplasm

**Differential Count**

Increases in bacterial infections

**Functions**

Phagocytosis of bacteria
Release of antimicrobial chemicals

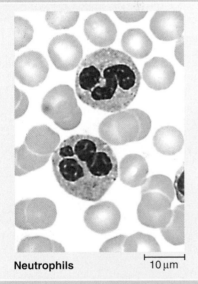

**Neutrophils**   10 µm

**Eosinophils**

| Percent of WBCs | 2%–4% |
|---|---|
| Mean count | 170 cells/µL |
| Diameter | 10–14 µm |

**Appearance***

Nucleus usually has two large lobes connected by thin strand
Large orange-pink granules in cytoplasm

**Differential Count**

Fluctuates greatly from day to night, seasonally, and with phase of menstrual cycle
Increases in parasitic infections, allergies, collagen diseases, and diseases of spleen and central nervous system

**Functions**

Phagocytosis of antigen–antibody complexes, allergens, and inflammatory chemicals
Release enzymes that weaken or destroy parasites such as worms

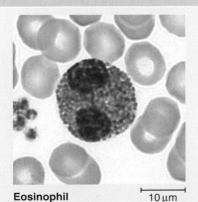

**Eosinophil**   10 µm

| TABLE 19.4 | The White Blood Cells (Leukocytes) (continued) |
|---|---|

## Basophils

| | |
|---|---|
| Percent of WBCs | <0.5%–1% |
| Mean count | 40 cells/µL |
| Diameter | 8–10 µm |

**Appearance***

Nucleus large and irregularly shaped, but typically obscured from view
Coarse, abundant, dark violet granules in cytoplasm

**Differential Count**

Relatively stable
Increases in chicken pox, sinusitis, diabetes mellitus, myxedema, and polycythemia

**Functions**

Secrete histamine (a vasodilator), which increases blood flow to a tissue
Secrete heparin (an anticoagulant), which promotes mobility of other WBCs by preventing clotting

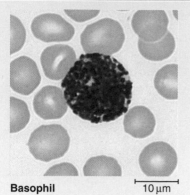

**Basophil**          10 µm

## Monocytes

| | |
|---|---|
| Percent of WBCs | 3%–8% |
| Mean count | 460 cells/µL |
| Diameter | 12–15 µm |

**Appearance***

Nucleus ovoid, kidney-shaped, or horseshoe-shaped
Abundant light violet cytoplasm with sparse, fine granules
Sometimes very large with stellate or polygonal shapes

**Differential Count**

Increases in viral infections and inflammation

**Functions**

Differentiate into macrophages (large phagocytic cells of the tissues)
Phagocytize pathogens, dead neutrophils, and debris of dead cells
"Present" antigens to activate other cells of immune system

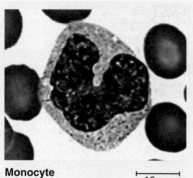

**Monocyte**          10 µm

## Lymphocytes

| | |
|---|---|
| Percent of WBCs | 25%–33% |
| Mean count | 2,200 cells/µL |
| Diameter | |
|    Small class | 5–8 µm |
|    Medium class | 10–12 µm |
|    Large class | 14–17 µm |

**Appearance***

Nucleus round, ovoid, or slightly dimpled on one side, of uniform dark violet color
In small lymphocytes, nucleus fills nearly all of the cell and leaves only a scanty rim of clear, light blue cytoplasm
In larger lymphocytes, cytoplasm is more abundant; large lymphocytes may be hard to differentiate from monocytes

**Differential Count**

Increases in diverse infections and immune responses

**Functions**

Several functional classes indistinguishable by light microscopy
Destroy cancer cells, cells infected with viruses, and foreign cells
"Present" antigens to activate other cells of immune system
Coordinate actions of other immune cells
Secrete antibodies
Serve in immune memory

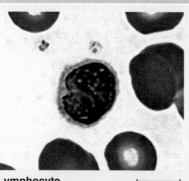

**Lymphocyte**          10 µm

*Appearance pertains to blood films dyed with Wright's stain.

are inconspicuous to the light microscope, and these cells therefore have relatively clear-looking cytoplasm.

## Granulocytes

- **Neutrophils** (NEW-tro-fills) are the most abundant WBCs—generally about 4,150 cells/μL and constituting 60% to 70% of the circulating leukocytes. The nucleus is clearly visible and, in a mature neutrophil, typically consists of three to five lobes connected by slender nuclear strands. These strands are sometimes so delicate that they are scarcely visible, and the neutrophil may seem as if it had multiple nuclei. Young neutrophils have an undivided nucleus often shaped like a band or a knife puncture; thus they are called *band cells* or *stab cells.* Neutrophils are also called *polymorphonuclear leukocytes (PMNs)* because of their varied nuclear shapes.

  The cytoplasm contains fine reddish to violet specific granules, which contain lysozyme and other antimicrobial agents. Neutrophils are named for the way these granules take up histological stains at pH 7—some stain with acidic dyes and others with basic dyes. The individual granules are very small, barely visible with the light microscope, but their combined staining gives the cytoplasm a pale lilac color.

  The neutrophil count rises—a condition called *neutrophilia*—in response to bacterial infections. The primary task of the neutrophils is to destroy bacteria, which they achieve in two ways. One is to phagocytize and digest them. The other is to release a potent mix of toxic chemicals, including hypochlorite (HClO) (the active agent in household bleach) and the superoxide anion ($O_2^-$), which reacts with hydrogen ions to produce hydrogen peroxide ($H_2O_2$). Just as bleach and hydrogen peroxide are often used around the home as disinfectants, they are deadly to bacteria in the tissues. These chemicals form a **killing zone** around the neutrophil, lethal to the invaders but also to the neutrophil itself. Neutrophils are thus the body's suicidal guardians against infection.

- **Eosinophils** (EE-oh-SIN-oh-fills) are harder to find in a blood film because they are only 2% to 4% of the WBC total, typically numbering about 170 cells/μL. The eosinophil count fluctuates greatly, however, from day to night, seasonally, and with the phase of the menstrual cycle. It rises *(eosinophilia)* in allergies, parasitic infections, collagen diseases, and diseases of the spleen and central nervous system. Although relatively scanty in the blood, eosinophils are abundant in the mucous membranes of the respiratory, digestive, and lower urinary tracts. The eosinophil nucleus usually has two large lobes connected by a thin strand, and the cytoplasm has an abundance of coarse rosy to orange-colored specific granules. Eosinophils secrete chemicals that weaken or destroy relatively large parasites such as hookworms and tapeworms, too big for any one WBC to phagocytize. Eosinophils also phagocytize and dispose of inflammatory chemicals, antigen–antibody complexes (masses of antigen molecules stuck together by antibodies), and allergens (foreign antigens that trigger allergies).

- **Basophils** (BASE-oh-fills) are the rarest of the WBCs and, indeed, of all formed elements. They number about 40 cells/μL and constitute from less than 0.5% to about 1% of the WBC count. They can be recognized mainly by an abundance of very coarse, dark violet specific granules. The nucleus is largely hidden from view by these granules, but is large, pale, and typically S- or U-shaped. Basophils secrete two chemicals that aid in the body's defense processes: (1) **histamine,** a vasodilator that widens the blood vessels, speeds the flow of blood to an injured tissue, and makes the blood vessels more permeable so that blood components such as neutrophils and clotting proteins can get into the connective tissues more quickly; and (2) **heparin,** an anticoagulant that inhibits blood clotting and thus promotes the mobility of other WBCs in the area. They also release chemical signals that attract eosinophils and neutrophils to a site of infection.

## Agranulocytes

- **Monocytes** (MON-oh-sites) are the largest WBCs, often two or three times the diameter of an RBC. They number about 460 cells/μL and about 3% to 8% of the WBC count. The nucleus is large and clearly visible, often a relatively light violet, and typically ovoid, kidney-shaped, or horseshoe-shaped. The cytoplasm is abundant and contains sparse, fine granules. In prepared blood films, monocytes often assume sharply angular to spiky shapes (see fig. 19.1). The monocyte count rises in inflammation and viral infections. Monocytes go to work only after leaving the bloodstream and transforming into large tissue cells called **macrophages**[11] (MAC-ro-fay-jez). Macrophages are highly phagocytic cells that consume up to 25% of their own volume per hour. They destroy dead or dying host and foreign cells, pathogenic chemicals and microorganisms, and other foreign matter. They also chop up or "process" foreign antigens and "display" fragments of them on the cell surface to alert the immune system to the presence of a pathogen. Thus, they and a few other cells are called *antigen-presenting cells (APCs).* There are several kinds of macrophages in the body descended from monocytes or from the same hemopoietic stem cells as monocytes. Macrophages of the loose connective tissues are generally called simply *macrophages* or sometimes *histiocytes.* Macrophages in some other localities have special names:

  - **dendritic cells** in the epidermis (see p. 131) and the mucous membranes of the mouth, esophagus, and vagina;

  - **microglia,** a type of neuroglia in the central nervous system (see p. 381);

  - **alveolar macrophages** in the pulmonary alveoli (see p. 673); and

  - **hepatic macrophages (Kupffer cells)** in the liver sinusoids (see p. 707).

---

[11]*macro* = big + *phage* = eater

- **Lymphocytes** (LIM-fo-sites) include the smallest WBCs; at 5 to 17 μm in diameter, they range from smaller than RBCs to two and a half times as large, but those in circulating blood are generally at the small end of the range. They are second to neutrophils in abundance and are thus quickly spotted when you examine a blood film. They number about 2,200 cells/μL and are 25% to 33% of the WBC count. The lymphocyte nucleus is round, ovoid, or slightly dimpled on one side. It usually stains dark violet and fills nearly the entire cell, especially in small lymphocytes. The cytoplasm, which stains a clear light blue color, thus forms a narrow and often barely detectable rim around the nucleus, although it is more abundant in the larger lymphocytes. Small lymphocytes are sometimes difficult to distinguish from basophils, but most basophils are conspicuously grainy whereas the lymphocyte nucleus is uniform or merely mottled. Basophils also lack the rim of clear cytoplasm seen in most lymphocytes. Large lymphocytes are sometimes difficult to distinguish from monocytes.

The lymphocyte count increases in diverse infections and immune responses. Some of them function in nonspecific defense of the body against viruses and cancer, but most of them are involved in specific *immunity,* a defense in which the body recognizes a certain antigen it has encountered before and mounts such a quick response that a person notices little or no illness. The various lymphocytes are not distinguishable by light microscopy, but differ in their functions. As you will see in chapter 22, there are three functional classes of lymphocytes—*NK (natural killer) cells, B cells,* and *T cells,* which attack different categories of pathogens.

## The Leukocyte Life Cycle

**Leukopoiesis** (LOO-co-poy-EE-sis), the production of white blood cells, begins with the same pluripotent stem cells (PPSCs) as erythropoiesis. Some PPSCs differentiate into the distinct types of colony-forming units, which then go on to produce the following cell lines (fig. 19.8):

1. *Myeloblasts,* which ultimately differentiate into the three types of granulocytes (neutrophils, eosinophils, and basophils).

2. *Monoblasts,* which look identical to myeloblasts but lead ultimately to monocytes.

3. *Lymphoblasts,* which give rise to three types of lymphocytes (B lymphocytes, T lymphocytes, and natural killer cells).

Granulocytes and monocytes stay in the red bone marrow until they are needed; the marrow contains 10 to 20 times as many of these cells as the circulating blood does. Lymphocytes, by contrast, begin developing in the bone marrow but then migrate elsewhere. **B lymphocytes (B cells)** mature in the bone marrow and some remain there, while others disperse and colonize the lymph nodes, spleen, tonsils, and mucous membranes. To remember their site of maturation, it may help to think "B for bone marrow," although these cells were actually named for an organ in chickens (the *bursa*

## INSIGHT 19.2

### Clinical Application

## The Complete Blood Count

One of the most common clinical procedures, in both routine physical examinations and the diagnosis of disease, is a *complete blood count (CBC).* The CBC yields a highly informative profile of data on multiple blood values: the number of RBCs, WBCs, and platelets per microliter of blood; the relative numbers (percentages) of each WBC type, called a *differential WBC count;* hematocrit; hemoglobin concentration; and various *RBC indices* such as RBC size *(mean corpuscular volume, MCV)* and hemoglobin concentration per RBC *(mean corpuscular hemoglobin, MCH).*

RBC and WBC counts used to require the microscopic examination of films of diluted blood on a calibrated slide, and a differential WBC count required examination of stained blood films. Today, most laboratories use *electronic cell counters.* These devices draw a blood sample through a very narrow tube with sensors that identify cell types and measure cell sizes and hemoglobin content. These counters give faster and more accurate results based on much larger numbers of cells than the old visual methods. However, cell counters still misidentify some cells, and a medical technologist must review the results for suspicious abnormalities and identify cells that the instrument cannot.

The wealth of information gained from a CBC is too vast to give more than a few examples here. Various forms of anemia are indicated by low RBC counts or abnormalities of RBC size, shape, and hemoglobin content. A platelet deficiency can indicate an adverse drug reaction. A high neutrophil count suggests bacterial infection, and a high eosinophil count suggests an allergy or parasitic infection. Elevated numbers of specific WBC types or WBC stem cells can indicate various forms of leukemia. If a CBC does not provide enough information or if it suggests other disorders, additional tests may be done, such as coagulation time and bone marrow biopsy.

---

*of Fabricius)* where they were discovered. **T lymphocytes (T cells)** begin development in the bone marrow but then migrate to the thymus (a gland in the mediastinum just above the heart) and mature there. In this case, the *T* really does stand for *thymus.* Mature T lymphocytes disperse from the thymus and colonize the same organs as B lymphocytes. **Natural killer (NK) cells** develop in the bone marrow like B cells.

Circulating WBCs do not stay in the blood for very long. Granulocytes circulate for 4 to 8 hours and then migrate into the tissues, where they live for another 4 or 5 days. Monocytes travel in the blood for 10 or 20 hours, then migrate into the tissues and transform into a variety of macrophages, which live as long as a few years. Lymphocytes, responsible for long-term immunity, have a life span ranging from weeks to decades.

When leukocytes die, they are generally phagocytized and digested by macrophages. Dead neutrophils, however, are responsible for the creamy color of pus, and are sometimes disposed of by the rupture of a blister onto the skin surface.

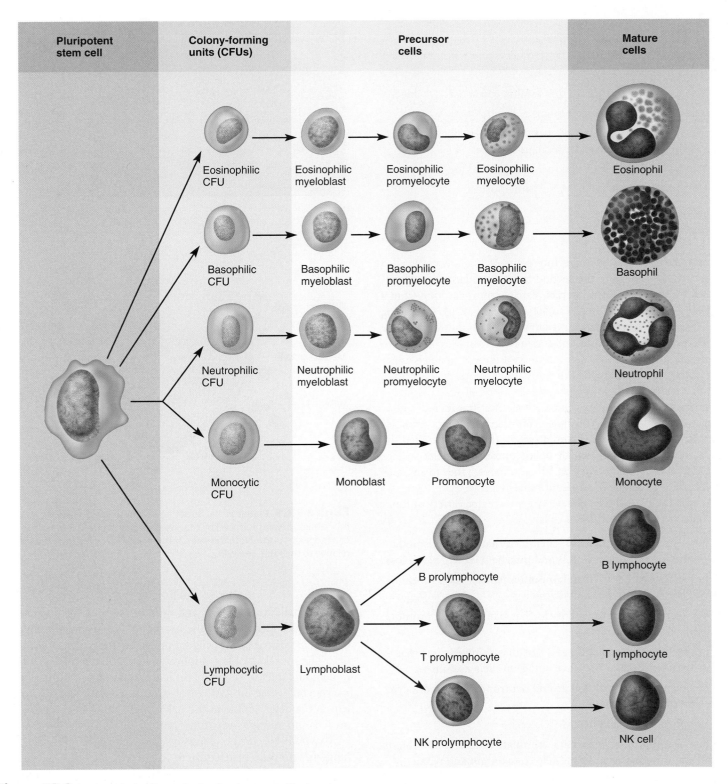

| Pluripotent stem cell | Colony-forming units (CFUs) | Precursor cells | | | Mature cells |
|---|---|---|---|---|---|
| | Eosinophilic CFU | Eosinophilic myeloblast | Eosinophilic promyelocyte | Eosinophilic myelocyte | Eosinophil |
| | Basophilic CFU | Basophilic myeloblast | Basophilic promyelocyte | Basophilic myelocyte | Basophil |
| | Neutrophilic CFU | Neutrophilic myeloblast | Neutrophilic promyelocyte | Neutrophilic myelocyte | Neutrophil |
| | Monocytic CFU | Monoblast | Promonocyte | | Monocyte |
| | Lymphocytic CFU | Lymphoblast | B prolymphocyte | | B lymphocyte |
| | | | T prolymphocyte | | T lymphocyte |
| | | | NK prolymphocyte | | NK cell |

**Figure 19.8 Leukopoiesis.** Stages in the development of leukocytes.

● *Explain the meaning and relevance of the combining form* myelo-, *seen in so many of these cell names.*

## Before You Go On

*Answer the following questions to test your understanding of the preceding section:*

10. What is the purpose of WBCs in general?

11. Name the five kinds of WBCs and state the specific functions of each.

12. Describe the key features that enable one to microscopically identify each WBC type.

13. What are macrophages? What class of WBCs do they arise from? Name some types of macrophages.

# Platelets

## Objectives

When you have completed this section, you should be able to

- describe the structure of blood platelets;
- explain the multiple roles played by platelets in hemostasis and blood vessel maintenance;
- describe platelet production and state their longevity; and
- describe the general processes of hemostasis.

## Form and Function

**Platelets** are not cells but small fragments of marrow cells called *megakaryocytes.* They are the second most abundant formed elements, after erythrocytes; a normal platelet count in blood from a fingerstick ranges from 130,000 to 400,000 platelets/µL (averaging about 250,000). The platelet count can vary greatly, however, under different physiological conditions and in blood samples taken from various places in the body. In spite of their numbers, platelets are so small (2 to 4 µm in diameter) that they contribute even less than the WBCs to the blood volume.

Platelets have a complex internal structure that includes lysosomes, mitochondria, microtubules and microfilaments, granules filled with platelet secretions, and a system of channels called the **open canalicular system,** which opens onto the platelet surface (fig. 19.9a). They have no nucleus. When activated, they form pseudopods and are capable of ameboid movement.

Despite their small size, platelets have a greater variety of functions than any of the true blood cells:

- They secrete *vasoconstrictors,* chemicals that cause spasmodic constriction of broken vessels and thus help reduce blood loss.
- They stick together to form temporary *platelet plugs* to seal small breaks in injured blood vessels.
- They secrete *procoagulants,* or clotting factors, which promote blood clotting.
- They initiate the formation of a clot-dissolving enzyme that dissolves blood clots that have outlasted their usefulness.
- They secrete chemicals that attract neutrophils and monocytes to sites of inflammation.
- They phagocytize and destroy bacteria.
- They secrete *growth factors* that stimulate mitosis in fibroblasts and smooth muscle and thus help to maintain and repair blood vessels.

## Platelet Production

The production of platelets is a division of hemopoiesis called **thrombopoiesis.** (Platelets are occasionally called *thrombocytes,*[12] but this term is now usually reserved for nucleated true cells in

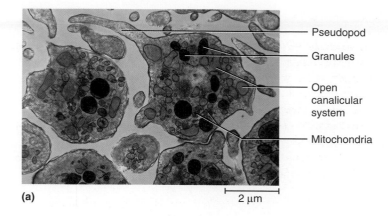

(a)

2 µm

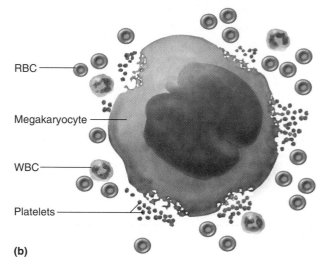

RBC

Megakaryocyte

WBC

Platelets

(b)

**Figure 19.9** Platelets. (a) Structure of blood platelets (TEM). (b) Platelets being produced by the shredding of the peripheral cytoplasm of a megakaryocyte. Note the sizes of the megakaryocyte and platelets relative to the RBCs and WBCs.

other animals such as birds and reptiles.) Some pluripotent stem cells produce receptors for the hormone *thrombopoietin,* thus becoming *megakaryoblasts,* cells committed to the platelet-producing line. The megakaryoblast duplicates its DNA repeatedly without undergoing nuclear or cytoplasmic division. The result is a **megakaryocyte**[13] (meg-ah-CAR-ee-oh-site), a gigantic cell up to 150 µm in diameter, visible to the naked eye, with a huge multilobed nucleus and multiple sets of chromosomes (fig. 19.9b). Most megakaryocytes live in the bone marrow, but some of them colonize the lungs and produce platelets there.

A megakaryocyte develops infoldings of the plasma membrane that divide its marginal cytoplasm into little compartments. The cytoplasm breaks up along these lines of weakness into tiny fragments that enter the bloodstream. Some of these fragments are already functional platelets, but others are larger particles that break up into platelets as they pass through the lungs. About 25% to 40% of the platelets are stored in the spleen and released as needed. The remainder circulate freely in the blood and live for about 10 days.

---

[12]*thrombo* = clotting + *cyte* = cell

[13]*mega* = giant + *karyo* = nucleus + *cyte* = cell

## Hemostasis

**Hemostasis**[14] is the cessation of bleeding. The details of hemostasis are beyond the scope of an anatomy textbook, but the basic roles of platelets in the process will be briefly surveyed here. Upon injury to a blood vessel, platelets release *serotonin.* This chemical stimulates *vasoconstriction,* or narrowing of the blood vessel, to reduce blood loss. Platelets also adhere to the vessel wall and to each other, forming a sticky mass called a *platelet plug.* Platelet plugs temporarily seal breaks in small blood vessels. Platelets and injured tissues around the blood vessel also release *clotting factors.* Through a series of enzymatic reactions, clotting factors convert the plasma protein fibrinogen into the sticky protein *fibrin.* Fibrin adheres to the wall of the blood vessel, and as blood cells and platelets arrive, many of them stick to the fibrin like insects in a spider web. The resulting mass of fibrin, platelets, and blood cells (fig. 19.10) forms a clot that ideally seals the break in the blood vessel long enough for the vessel to heal.

Once the leak is sealed and the crisis has passed, platelets secrete *platelet-derived growth factor (PDGF),* a substance that stimulates fibroblasts and smooth muscle to proliferate and replace the damaged tissue of the blood vessel. When tissue repair is completed and the blood clot is no longer needed, the clot must be disposed of. Platelets then secrete *factor XII,* a protein that initiates a series of reactions leading to the formation of a fibrin-digesting enzyme called *plasmin.* Plasmin dissolves the old blood clot.

---

[14]*hemo* = blood + *stasis* = stability

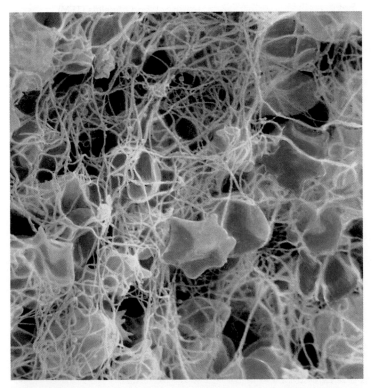

**Figure 19.10  A Blood Clot (SEM).** Platelets are seen trapped in a sticky protein mesh.
● *What is the name of this protein?*

Answer the following questions to test your understanding of the preceding section:

14. List several functions of blood platelets.
15. How are blood platelets produced? How long do they live?
16. Briefly describe the stages in which platelets help to stop bleeding and repair a damaged blood vessel.

# Clinical Perspectives

### *Objectives*
When you have completed this section, you should be able to
- describe changes that occur in the blood in old age; and
- describe some common abnormalities of RBC, WBC, and platelet count and morphology, and the consequences of these abnormalities.

## Hematology in Old Age

We have considered the embryonic origin and ongoing hemopoietic development of the blood in previous sections. At the other end of the life span, aging has multiple effects on the blood. Evidence suggests that the baseline rate of erythropoiesis does not change much with age; cell counts, hemoglobin concentration, and other variables are about the same among healthy people in their 70s as in the 30s. However, older people do not adapt well to stress on the hemopoietic system, perhaps because of the senescence of other organ systems. The stomach atrophies in old age, thus producing less of the *intrinsic factor* needed for the absorption of dietary vitamin $B_{12}$. A deficiency of vitamin $B_{12}$ causes *pernicious anemia.* Anemia can also stem from atrophy of the kidneys in old age, since the kidneys secrete erythropoietin, and erythropoietin is the principal stimulus for RBC production. There may also be a limit to how many times the hemopoietic stem cells can divide and continue producing new blood cells.

Anemia may also result from nutritional deficiencies, inadequate exercise, disease, and other causes. The factors that cause anemia in older people are very complicated and interrelated. It is almost impossible to determine whether aging alone causes anemia in the absence of other contributing factors such as poor exercise or nutritional habits.

Thrombosis, the abnormal clotting of blood in an unbroken blood vessel, becomes increasingly problematic in old age. Plaques of atherosclerosis in the blood vessels can act as sites of blood clotting. The blood clots especially easily in the veins, where blood flow is slowest. About 25% of people over age 50 experience venous blockage by thrombosis, especially people who do not exercise regularly and people confined to a bed or wheelchair.

## Disorders of the Blood

We conclude with a survey of some clinical aspects of hematology, especially disorders that affect the relative numbers of formed elements and thus the appearance of stained blood films, or that alter the appearance of the individual formed elements. Some common nonstructural blood disorders are described in table 19.5.

## Erythrocyte Disorders

The two principal RBC disorders are **anemia**[15] (an RBC or hemoglobin deficiency) and **polycythemia**[16] (an RBC excess). The latter is also known as *erythrocytosis.*

There are three fundamental causes of anemia:

1. Depressed erythropoiesis or hemoglobin synthesis, so erythropoiesis fails to keep pace with the normal death of RBCs. A lack of iron or certain vitamins in the diet can cause nutritional anemias (such as *iron-deficiency anemia*). Radiation, viruses, and some poisons cause anemia by destroying bone marrow. The role of gastric and renal atrophy in anemia of the elderly was discussed earlier.

2. Excess RBC destruction, exceeding the rate of erythropoiesis. Anemias in this category are called *hemolytic anemia,* and may result from a variety of poisons, drug reactions, sickle-cell disease, or blood-destroying parasitic infections such as malaria.

3. Blood loss, resulting in *hemorrhagic anemia.* This can be a consequence of trauma such as gunshot, automobile, or battlefield injuries; hemophilia; bleeding ulcers; ruptured aneurysms; or heavy menstruation.

While anemia most obviously affects the RBC count, it can also affect RBC morphology. *Thalassemia,* for example, is a hereditary blood disease among people of Mediterranean descent. It is characterized by deficient hemoglobin synthesis, and not only is the RBC count reduced but the existing RBCs are *microcytic* (abnormally small) and *hypochromic* (pale). Iron-deficiency anemia is characterized by these structural abnormalities as well as *poikilocytosis,*[17] in which RBCs assume teardrop, pencil, and other variable and abnormal shapes. Sickle-cell disease is another well-known hereditary anemia with abnormal RBC morphology (see Insight 19.3).

Polycythemia (POL-ee-sih-THEME-ee-uh), an excess RBC count, can result from cancer of the bone marrow (*primary polycythemia*) or from a multitude of other conditions (*secondary polycythemia*) such as an abnormally high oxygen demand (as in people who engage in overzealous aerobic exercise) or low oxygen supply (as in people who live at high altitudes or suffer lung diseases such as emphysema). RBC counts can rise as high as 11 million RBCs/$\mu$L and hematocrit as high as 80%. The thick blood "sludges" in the vessels, tremendously increases blood pressure, and puts a dangerous strain on the cardiovascular system that can lead to heart failure or stroke.

## Leukocyte Disorders

A WBC deficiency is called **leukopenia,** and can result from heavy metal poisoning, radiation exposure, and infectious diseases such as measles, chicken pox, polio, and AIDS. Such a deficiency of

---

[15]*an* = without + *emia* = blood
[16]*poly* = many + *cyt* = cells + *hemia* = blood condition

[17]*poikilo* = variable + *cyt* = cell + *osis* = condition

---

| TABLE 19.5 | Some Disorders of the Blood |
|---|---|
| **Disseminated intravascular coagulation (DIC)** | Widespread clotting within unbroken vessels, limited to one organ or occurring throughout the body. Usually triggered by septicemia but also occurs when blood circulation slows markedly (as in cardiac arrest). Marked by widespread hemorrhaging, congestion of the vessels with clotted blood, and tissue necrosis in blood-deprived organs. |
| **Embolism** | The presence of any abnormal object (*embolus*) traveling in the bloodstream, such as an air bubble (*air embolism*), agglutinated RBCs or bacteria, or traveling blood clot (*thromboembolism*). Presents a danger of blocking small blood vessels and shutting off the blood flow to vital tissues, thus causing stroke, heart failure, kidney failure, or pulmonary failure. |
| **Hemophilia** | Abnormally slow blood clotting as a result of the hereditary deficiency of a clotting factor, usually factor VIII (a liver product). Prolonged bleeding results in the painful pooling of clotted blood (*hematomas*) in such sites as the muscles and joints, or in fatal blood loss. Treatable with injections of the missing clotting factor. |
| **Infectious mononucleosis** | Infection of B lymphocytes with Epstein-Barr virus. Usually transmitted by exchange of saliva, as in kissing; most common in adolescents and young adults. Causes fever, fatigue, sore throat, inflamed lymph nodes, and leukocytosis. Usually self-limiting and resolves within a few weeks. |
| **Septicemia** | Bacteria in the bloodstream, stemming from infection elsewhere in the body. Often causes fever, chills, and nausea, and may cause septic shock. |
| **Thrombosis** | Abnormal clotting in unbroken blood vessels, triggered by atherosclerosis and other defects, or by immobility of people confined to bed or a wheelchair. Stationary blood clots can cause stroke, heart failure, etc. (see *embolism* in this table), and clots can break free and cause *thromboembolism*. |

### Disorders Described Elsewhere

## Clinical Application

### Sickle-cell Disease

Sickle-cell disease is a hereditary hemoglobin defect occurring mostly among people of African descent; its symptoms occur in about 1.3% of American blacks, and about 8.3% are asymptomatic carriers with the potential to pass it to their children. The disease is caused by a defective gene that results in the substitution of valine for a glutamic acid in each beta hemoglobin chain. The abnormal hemoglobin (HbS) turns to gel at low oxygen levels, as when blood passes through the oxygen-hungry skeletal muscles. The RBCs become elongated, stiffened, and pointed (sickle-shaped; fig 19.11). These deformed, inflexible cells cannot pass freely through the tiny blood capillaries, and they tend to adhere to each other and to the capillary wall. Thus, they congregate in the small blood vessels and block the circulation. Obstruction of the circulation produces severe pain and can lead to kidney or heart failure, stroke, or paralysis, among many other effects. The spleen removes defective RBCs faster than they can be replaced, thus leading to anemia and poor physical and mental development of the individual. Without treatment, a child with sickle-cell disease has little chance of living to age 2, and even with the best treatment, few victims live to an age of 50.

Sickle-cell disease originated in areas of Africa where millions of lives are lost to malaria. Malarial parasites normally invade and reproduce in RBCs, but they cannot survive in RBCs with HbS hemoglobin. Thus the sickle-cell gene confers resistance to malaria, even in individuals who are heterozygous for it (carry only one copy of the gene) and do not have sickle-cell disease. The lives saved by HbS in Africa far outnumber the deaths from sickle-cell disease, so natural selection favors the persistence of the gene rather than its elimination. But in North America, where malaria is not prevalent, the lost lives and suffering caused by the sickle-cell gene far outweigh any of its benefits.

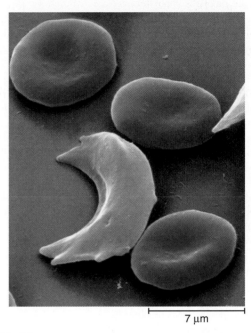

7 μm

**Figure 19.11** **Sickle-cell Disease.** The lower left RBC has become deformed into the pointed sickle shape diagnostic of this genetic disorder.

---

disease-fighting WBCs leaves a person susceptible to *opportunistic infections*, infections that a normal person could fight off. An abnormally high WBC count is called **leukocytosis.** It usually results from an infection or allergy, but can also stem from such causes as emotional stress and dehydration (WBCs become more concentrated when water is lost from the bloodstream). **Leukemia** is a cancer of the hemopoietic tissues that results in a high number of circulating WBCs. It, too, makes a person vulnerable to opportunistic infection, because even though the WBC count is high, these are immature WBCs incapable of performing their normal defensive roles. Leukemia tends to lead to anemia and thrombocytopenia (see the next section) because stem cells are diverted into the production of WBCs instead of RBC and platelet production.

### Platelet Disorders

**Thrombocytopenia,** a platelet count less than 100,000/μL, results from such causes as leukemia, radiation, or bone marrow poison-ing. It results not only in impaired clotting when a vessel is injured, but also in increased bleeding because of a loss of the normal blood vessel maintenance function of platelets.

Some other common blood disorders are briefly described in table 19.5.

## *Before You Go On*

*Answer the following questions to test your understanding of the preceding section:*

17. What are the terms for an excess and deficiency of RBCs? An excess and deficiency of WBCs?

18. What are the three basic categories of the causes of anemia?

19. In what way are leukocytosis and leukemia alike? What is the difference between them?

20. Describe some causes and effects of thrombocytopenia.

# CHAPTER REVIEW

## REVIEW OF KEY CONCEPTS

### Introduction (p. 552)

1. The *circulatory system* is composed of the heart, blood vessels, and blood; *cardiovascular system* refers to the heart and blood vessels only.

2. The circulatory system serves to transport $O_2$, $CO_2$, nutrients, wastes, hormones, and heat; it provides protection against infection and other pathogens; it includes mechanisms for minimizing blood loss from broken vessels; and it helps to stabilize the distribution and pH of the body fluids.

3. The blood is about 55% plasma and 45% formed elements.

4. Formed elements are cells and cell fragments; they include erythrocytes, platelets, and five kinds of leukocytes.

5. Blood plasma is a mixture of water, proteins, nutrients, electrolytes, nitrogenous wastes, hormones, and gases. Protein is the most abundant solute by weight. The three major plasma proteins are albumin, globulins, and fibrinogen.

6. The liver produces all the plasma proteins except gamma globulins (antibodies), which are produced by *plasma cells.*

### Erythrocytes (p. 555)

1. Erythrocytes (RBCs) serve to transport $O_2$ and $CO_2$. They are discoid cells with a sunken center and no organelles, but they do have a cytoskeleton of *spectrin* and *actin* that reinforces the plasma membrane.

2. The most important component of the cytoplasm is *hemoglobin (Hb).* Hb transports nearly all of the $O_2$ and some of the $CO_2$ in the blood.

3. RBC quantities are expressed as *RBC count* and *hematocrit (packed cell volume).* Collectively, the two sexes normally have RBC counts of 4.2 to 6.2 million RBCs/$\mu$L and hematocrits of 37% to 52%. The average values for women are somewhat lower than those for men.

4. Hemoglobin consists of four proteins *(globins)*—two alpha and two beta chains—each with a nonprotein *heme* group.

5. Oxygen binds to the $Fe^{2+}$ at the center of each heme. About 5% of the $CO_2$ in the blood binds to the globin component.

6. The hemoglobin concentration of the blood is normally 12 to 18 g/dL, averaging less in women than in men.

7. The production of the formed elements of blood is called *hemopoiesis.* The prenatal hemopoietic tissues and organs are the yolk sac, bone marrow, liver, spleen, and thymus; after birth, hemopoiesis is limited to the bone marrow and lymphatic organs and tissues.

8. *Erythropoiesis,* the production of RBCs, progresses through the following stages: *pluripotent stem cell → proerythroblast → erythroblast → reticulocyte → erythrocyte.* It is stimulated by the hormone *erythropoietin.*

9. An RBC lives for about 120 days, grows increasingly fragile, and then breaks apart, especially in the spleen.

10. There are multiple *blood types* based on genetically determined antigens on the RBC surface. The most familiar and clinically relevant are types in the ABO and Rh groups.

### Leukocytes (p. 558)

1. Leukocytes (WBCs) number 5,000 to 10,000 cells/$\mu$L. Leukocytes have nuclei and a full complement of cytoplasmic organelles.

2. WBCs play various roles in defending the body from pathogens.

3. Three types of WBCs—neutrophils, eosinophils, and basophils—are classified as *granulocytes* because of prominent **specific granules** in the cytoplasm. The other two types—lymphocytes and monocytes—are classified as *agranulocytes* because specific granules are absent. The identifying structural characteristics of the WBC types are shown in table 19.4.

4. *Neutrophils* act primarily to combat bacteria, which they destroy by phagocytosis and digestion and by producing a *killing zone* of toxic oxidizing agents.

5. *Eosinophils* secrete antiparasitic chemicals and phagocytize and dispose of allergens, inflammatory chemicals, and antigen–antibody complexes.

6. *Basophils* secrete the vasodilator histamine and the anticoagulant heparin, thus promoting increased blood flow to inflamed tissues.

7. *Monocytes* transform into a variety of *macrophages,* which phagocytize foreign and host cells and act as antigen-presenting cells.

8. *Lymphocytes* carry out nonspecific defense and specific immune reactions against cancer and various pathogens. The three families of lymphocytes—*B, T,* and *NK cells*—differ in function but are not microscopically distinguishable in blood films.

9. Leukocyte production is called *leukopoiesis.* It follows multiple pathways from pluripotent stem cells to the different types of mature WBCs.

10. Granulocytes, monocytes, and B lymphocytes mature in the red bone marrow. T lymphocytes are produced there but mature in the thymus. Both B and T lymphocytes then colonize various lymphatic organs and tissues throughout the body.

11. WBC life spans range from a few days for granulocytes to a few years for monocytes (after transformation to macrophages) and decades for some lymphocytes.

### Platelets (p. 564)

1. Platelets are not cells, but small, mobile, phagocytic fragments of cytoplasm from bone marrow cells called *megakaryocytes.* They have a variety of organelles but no nuclei.

2. Platelets function primarily to plug broken vessels and stop bleeding. They secrete vasoconstrictors, which cause spasmodic constriction of damaged vessels; form *platelet plugs,* which can temporarily seal a small break in a vessel; secrete clotting factors that lead to formation of blood clots; help to produce an enzyme that dissolves old blood clots; secrete chemicals that recruit WBCs to sites of inflammation; phagocytize bacteria; and secrete growth factors that promote repair and maintenance of blood vessels.

3. Platelet production, called *thrombopoiesis,* is stimulated by the hormone *thrombopoietin.* The stages in platelet production are *pluripotent stem cell → megakaryoblast → megakaryocyte → platelets.* Platelets are membrane-bounded fragments of cytoplasm that break away from the megakaryocyte surface.

### Clinical Perspectives (p. 565)

1. Healthy elderly people have blood values (hematocrit, hemoglobin, etc.) comparable to those of healthy young people. However, the hematologic system in old age is less responsive to stress, partly because of lower levels of intrinsic factor and erythropoietin. Thrombosis is also increasingly common in old age.

2. *Anemia* is a deficiency of erythrocytes or hemoglobin. The various causes of anemia relate to depressed erythropoiesis, excessive RBC destruction, or hemorrhage.

3. *Polycythemia* is an excessive RBC count. It results from bone marrow cancer or is secondary to causes such as zealous exercise, lung disease, or high-altitude living. It thickens the blood, stresses the heart, and may cause stroke or heart failure.

4. *Leukopenia* is a WBC deficiency. It can be caused by poisoning, radiation, or certain infections, and results in a reduction in immune defense and therefore vulnerability to *opportunistic infections.*

5. *Leukocytosis* is an elevated WBC count. It can result from infections, allergies, dehydration, stress, or cancer. In the last case, it is called *leukemia.* Leukemia is a cancer characterized by overproduction of WBCs that are functionally immature. It also presents a high risk of opportunistic infection. It leads as well to anemia and thrombocytopenia as stem cells are diverted to WBC production.

6. *Thrombocytopenia* is a platelet deficiency. It results in spontaneous bleeding and slow blood clotting.

## TESTING YOUR RECALL

1. Antibodies belong to a class of plasma proteins called
   a. albumins.
   b. gamma globulins.
   c. alpha globulins.
   d. procoagulants.
   e. agglutinins.

2. Serum is blood plasma minus its
   a. sodium ions.
   b. calcium ions.
   c. fibrinogen.
   d. albumin.
   e. cells.

3. The most abundant formed elements seen in most stained blood films are
   a. erythrocytes.
   b. neutrophils.
   c. lymphocytes.
   d. platelets.
   e. monocytes.

4. Heparin and histamine are secreted by
   a. plasma cells.
   b. basophils.
   c. B lymphocytes.
   d. platelets.
   e. neutrophils.

5. _____ have a finely granular cytoplasm and a nucleus typically divided into three to five lobes.
   a. Basophils
   b. Eosinophils
   c. Lymphocytes
   d. Monocytes
   e. Neutrophils

6. Platelets have all of the following functions *except*
   a. coagulation.
   b. plugging broken blood vessels.
   c. stimulating vasoconstriction.
   d. transporting oxygen.
   e. recruiting neutrophils.

7. Which of these is a granulocyte?
   a. a monocyte
   b. a lymphocyte
   c. a macrophage
   d. an eosinophil
   e. an erythrocyte

8. Allergies stimulate an increased _____ count.
   a. erythrocyte
   b. platelet
   c. eosinophil
   d. monocyte
   e. neutrophil

9. Which of the following leads to pernicious anemia?
   a. hypoxemia
   b. iron deficiency
   c. malaria
   d. lack of intrinsic factor
   e. lack of erythropoietin

10. Oxygen binds to the _____ of a hemoglobin molecule.
    a. valine
    b. $Fe^{2+}$
    c. globin
    d. spectrin
    e. beta chain

11. Production of all the formed elements of blood is called _____.

12. The percentage of blood volume composed of RBCs is called the _____.

13. Microglia and dendritic cells are two kinds of _____.

14. An excessively low WBC count is called _____.

15. _____ is the fluid that remains if all the formed elements and fibrinogen are removed from the blood.

16. The overall cessation of bleeding, involving several mechanisms, is called _____.

17. _____ results from a mutation that changes one amino acid in each beta chain of the hemoglobin molecule.

18. An excessively high RBC count is called _____.

19. Intrinsic factor enables the small intestine to absorb _____.

20. The kidney hormone _____ stimulates RBC production.

***Answers in the Appendix***

## TRUE OR FALSE

*Determine which five of the following statements are false, and briefly explain why.*

1. By volume, the blood usually contains more plasma than blood cells.

2. An increase in the albumin concentration of the blood tends to affect blood pressure.

3. Anemia is caused by a low oxygen concentration in the blood.

4. The most important WBCs in combating a bacterial infection are basophils.

5. Platelets and erythrocytes lack nuclei.

6. Lymphocytes are the most abundant WBCs in the blood.

7. Platelet count is often depressed in people with leukemia.

8. All formed elements of the blood come ultimately from pluripotent stem cells.

9. Since RBCs have no nuclei, they do not live as long as the granulocytes do.

10. Leukemia is a severe deficiency of white blood cells.

*Answers in the Appendix*

## TESTING YOUR COMPREHENSION

1. Considering the quantity of hemoglobin in an erythrocyte and the oxygen-binding properties of hemoglobin, calculate how many molecules of oxygen one erythrocyte could carry.

2. A patient is found to be seriously dehydrated and to have an elevated RBC count. Does the RBC count necessarily indicate a disorder of erythropoiesis? Why or why not?

3. Patients suffering from renal failure are typically placed on hemodialysis and erythropoietin (EPO) replacement therapy. Explain the reason for giving EPO, and predict what the consequences would be of not including this in the treatment regimen.

4. A leukemia patient exhibits minute hemorrhagic spots *(petechiae)* in her skin. Explain why leukemia could produce this effect.

5. Do you think platelets can synthesize proteins? Why or why not?

*Answers at aris.mhhe.com*

## ONLINE RESOURCES

Visit aprevealed.com to explore melt-away cadaver dissections, watch animations that clarify difficult concepts, review histological and radiological images, or take a quiz to assess your understanding of the material.

The Saladin *Human Anatomy,* 2e website at aris.mhhe.com features chapter-specific quizzes, labeling exercises, and other interactive tools to complement your study of human anatomy. If your instructor has provided an ARIS course code, you can also access assignments and information specific to your course.

# The Circulatory System II—The Heart

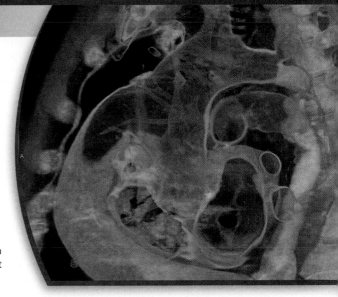

Three-dimensional CT scan
of the heart

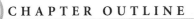

## CHAPTER OUTLINE

## INSIGHTS

## BRUSHING UP

To understand this chapter, you may find it helpful to review the following concepts:
- Thoracic cavity anatomy (p. 27)
- Desmosomes and gap junctions (pp. 59–61)
- Endothelium (p. 97)
- Ultrastructure of striated muscle (p. 263)
- Comparisons of cardiac and skeletal muscle (p. 284)
- Anatomy of the autonomic nervous system (chapter 16)

Anatomy & Physiology REVEALED®
aprevealed.com

**Cardiovascular System**

We are more conscious of our heart than we are of most organs, and more wary of its failure. Speculation about the heart is at least as old as written history. Some ancient Chinese, Egyptian, Greek, and Roman scholars correctly surmised that it was a pump for filling the vessels with blood. Aristotle's views, however, were a step backward. Perhaps because the heart quickens its pace when we are emotionally aroused and because grief causes "heartache," he thought it served primarily as the seat of emotion, but speculated that it might also be a source of heat to aid digestion. During the Middle Ages, Western medical schools clung dogmatically to Aristotle's ideas. In that era, perhaps the only significant advance came when thirteenth-century physician Ibn an-Nafis described the role of the coronary blood vessels in nourishing the heart. The sixteenth-century dissections and anatomical charts of Vesalius, however, greatly improved knowledge of cardiovascular anatomy and set the stage for a more scientific study of the heart and treatment of its disorders.

In the early decades of the twentieth century, little could be recommended for heart disease other than bed rest. Then nitroglycerin was found to improve coronary circulation and relieve the pain resulting from physical exertion; digitalis proved effective for treating abnormal heart rhythms; and diuretics were first used to reduce hypertension. In the last several decades, such advances as coronary bypass surgery, clot-dissolving enzymes, replacement of diseased valves, heart transplants, artificial pacemakers, and artificial hearts have made cardiology one of the most dramatic and attention-getting fields of medicine.

# Overview of the Cardiovascular System

## Objectives

When you have completed this section, you should be able to

- define and distinguish between the pulmonary and systemic circuits;
- describe the general location, size, and shape of the heart; and
- describe the pericardial sac that encloses the heart.

The **cardiovascular system** consists of the heart and blood vessels. The heart functions as a muscular pump that keeps blood flowing through the vessels. The vessels deliver the blood to all the body's organs and then return it to the heart. This chapter focuses on **cardiology**[1]—a field that embraces the study of the heart, clinical evaluation of its function and disorders, and treatment of cardiac diseases. The blood vessels are discussed in chapter 21.

## The Pulmonary and Systemic Circuits

The cardiovascular system has two major divisions: a **pulmonary circuit,** which carries blood to the lungs for gas exchange and returns it to the heart, and a **systemic circuit,** which supplies blood to every organ of the body (fig. 20.1), including other parts of the lungs and the wall of the heart itself.

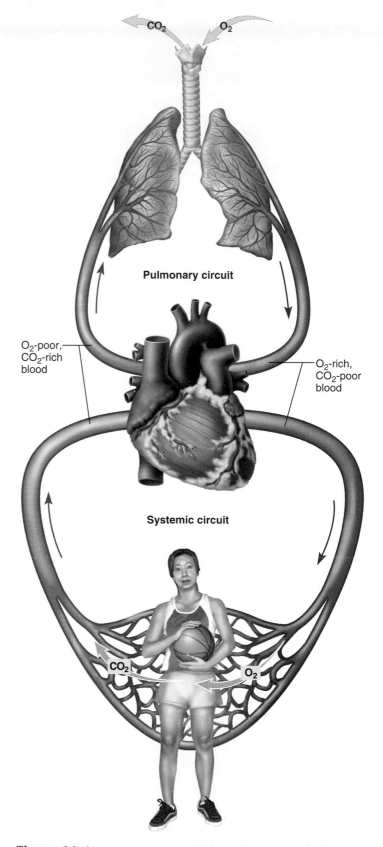

**Figure 20.1**  **General Schematic of the Cardiovascular System.**
● *Are the lungs supplied by the pulmonary circuit, the systemic circuit, or both? Explain.*

---

[1]*cardio* = heart + *logy* = study

The right side of the heart serves the pulmonary circuit. It receives blood that has circulated through the body and pumps it into a large artery, the *pulmonary trunk.* From there, the oxygen-poor blood is distributed to the lungs, where it unloads carbon dioxide and picks up a fresh load of oxygen. It then returns to the left side of the heart by way of the *pulmonary veins* (see fig. 20.3).

The left half of the heart serves the systemic circuit. It pumps blood into the body's largest artery, the *aorta.* The aorta gives off branches that ultimately deliver oxygen to every organ of the body and pick up their carbon dioxide and other wastes. After exchanging gases with the tissues, this blood returns to the heart by way of the body's two largest veins—the *superior vena cava,* which drains the upper body, and the *inferior vena cava,* which drains everything below the diaphragm. The pulmonary trunk,

pulmonary veins, aorta, and the two venae cavae are called the *great vessels* (*great arteries* and *veins*) because of their relatively large diameters.

## Position, Size, and Shape of the Heart

The heart is located in the thoracic cavity in the mediastinum, between the lungs and deep to the sternum. From its superior to inferior midpoints, it is tilted toward the left, so about two-thirds of the heart lies to the left of the median plane (fig. 20.2; see also fig. A.18, p. 39). The broad superior portion of the heart, called the **base,** is the point of attachment for the great vessels described previously. The inferior end tapers to a blunt point, the **apex** of the heart, immediately above the diaphragm (fig. 20.3).

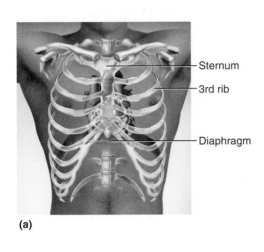

(a)

Sternum
3rd rib
Diaphragm

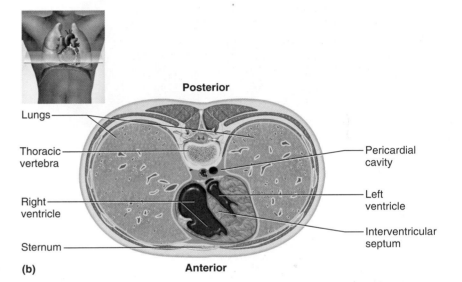

Posterior

Lungs
Thoracic vertebra
Right ventricle
Sternum

Pericardial cavity
Left ventricle
Interventricular septum

(b)

Anterior

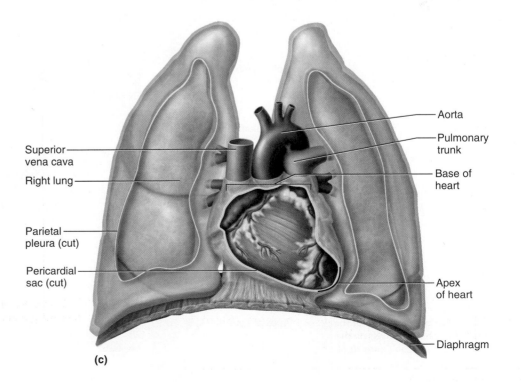

**Figure 20.2   Position of the Heart in the Thoracic Cavity.** (a) Relationship to the thoracic cage. (b) Cross section of the thorax at the level of the heart. (c) Frontal section of the thoracic cavity with the lungs slightly retracted and the pericardial sac opened.
● *Does most of the heart lie to the right or left of the median plane?*

Superior vena cava
Right lung
Parietal pleura (cut)
Pericardial sac (cut)

Aorta
Pulmonary trunk
Base of heart
Apex of heart
Diaphragm

(c)

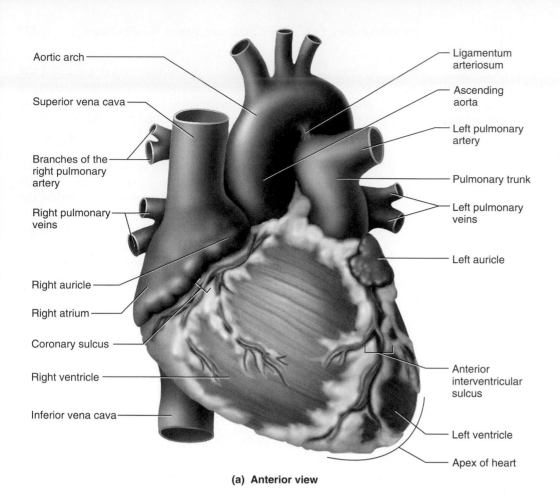

Aortic arch

Superior vena cava

Branches of the right pulmonary artery

Right pulmonary veins

Right auricle

Right atrium

Coronary sulcus

Right ventricle

Inferior vena cava

Ligamentum arteriosum

Ascending aorta

Left pulmonary artery

Pulmonary trunk

Left pulmonary veins

Left auricle

Anterior interventricular sulcus

Left ventricle

Apex of heart

**(a) Anterior view**

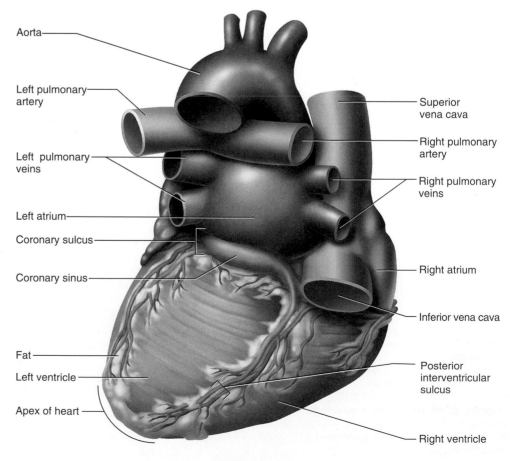

Aorta

Left pulmonary artery

Left pulmonary veins

Left atrium

Coronary sulcus

Coronary sinus

Fat

Left ventricle

Apex of heart

Superior vena cava

Right pulmonary artery

Right pulmonary veins

Right atrium

Inferior vena cava

Posterior interventricular sulcus

Right ventricle

**(b) Posterior view**

**Figure 20.3 Surface Anatomy of the Heart.** The coronary blood vessels on the heart surface are identified in figure 20.11.

The adult heart weighs about 300 g (10 oz) and measures about 9 cm (3.5 in.) wide at the base, 13 cm (5 in.) from base to apex, and 6 cm (2.5 in.) from anterior to posterior at its thickest point. Whatever one's body size, the heart is roughly the same size as the fist.

## The Pericardium

The heart is enclosed in a double-walled sac called the **pericardium.** The outer wall, called the **pericardial sac (parietal pericardium),** has a tough, superficial *fibrous layer* of dense irregular connective tissue and a deep, thin *serous layer.* The serous layer turns inward at the base of the heart and forms the **epicardium (visceral pericardium)** covering the heart surface (fig. 20.4); this is described later in the discussion of the heart wall. The pericardial sac is anchored by ligaments to the diaphragm below and the sternum anterior to it, and more loosely anchored by fibrous connective tissue to mediastinal tissue posterior to the heart.

The space between the parietal and visceral membranes is called the **pericardial cavity** (see figs. 20.2b and 20.4). It contains 5 to 30 mL of **pericardial fluid,** exuded by the serous pericardium. The fluid lubricates the membranes and allows the heart to beat with minimal friction. In *pericarditis*—inflammation of the pericardium—the membranes may become roughened and

produce a painful *friction rub* with each heartbeat. In addition to reducing friction, the pericardium isolates the heart from other thoracic organs and allows it room to expand, yet resists excessive expansion. (See *cardiac tamponade* in table 20.1, p. 591).

## *Before You Go On*

*Answer the following questions to test your understanding of the preceding section:*

1. Distinguish between the pulmonary and systemic circuits and state which part of the heart serves each one.

2. Make a two-color sketch of the pericardium, using one color for the pericardial sac and another for the epicardium. For the pericardial sac, label both the fibrous and serous layers. Show the relationship between the pericardium, pericardial cavity, and heart wall.

# Gross Anatomy of the Heart

### *Objectives*
When you have completed this section, you should be able to
- describe the three layers of the heart wall;
- identify the four chambers of the heart;
- identify the surface features of the heart and correlate them with its internal four-chambered anatomy;
- identify the four valves of the heart; and
- trace the flow of blood through the chambers and adjacent blood vessels.

## The Heart Wall

The heart wall consists of three layers—a thin epicardium covering its external surface, a thick muscular myocardium in the middle, and a thin endocardium lining the interior of the chambers (fig. 20.4).

The **epicardium**[2] is a serous membrane on the heart surface. It consists mainly of a simple squamous epithelium overlying a thin layer of areolar tissue. In some places, it also includes a thick layer of adipose tissue, whereas in other areas it is fat-free and translucent, so the muscle of the underlying myocardium shows through (fig. 20.5a). The largest branches of the coronary blood vessels travel through the epicardium. The **endocardium**[3] lines the interior of the heart chambers. Like the epicardium, it is composed of a simple squamous epithelium overlying a thin areolar tissue layer; however, it has no adipose tissue. The endocardium covers the valve surfaces and is continuous with the endothelium of the blood vessels.

The layer between these two, the **myocardium,**[4] is the thickest by far and performs the work of the heart. Its thickness is proportional

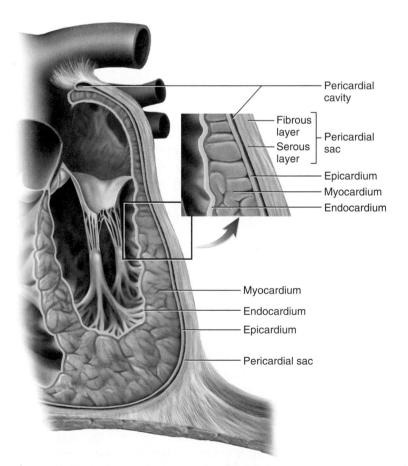

Pericardial cavity

Fibrous layer
Serous layer
} Pericardial sac

Epicardium
Myocardium
Endocardium

Myocardium
Endocardium
Epicardium
Pericardial sac

**Figure 20.4 The Pericardium and Heart Wall.** The inset shows the layers of the heart wall in relationship to the pericardium. The pericardium consists of the epicardium (visceral pericardium) and pericardial sac (parietal pericardium).

---

[2]*epi* = upon + *cardi* = heart
[3]*endo* = internal + *cardi* = heart
[4]*myo* = muscle + *cardi* = heart

**Figure 20.5** The Cadaver Heart.

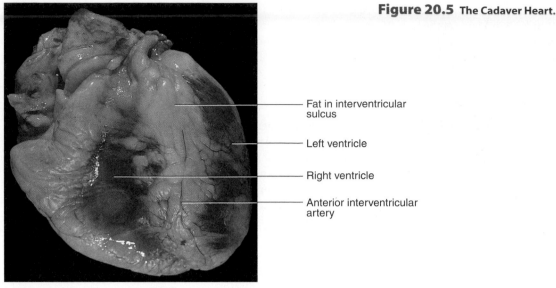

Fat in interventricular sulcus

Left ventricle

Right ventricle

Anterior interventricular artery

**(a) Anterior view, external anatomy**

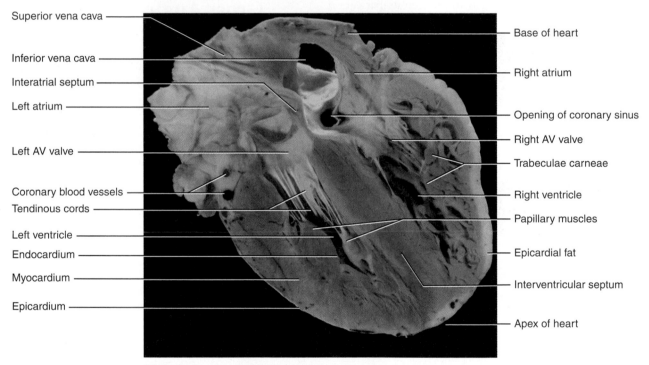

Superior vena cava

Inferior vena cava

Interatrial septum

Left atrium

Left AV valve

Coronary blood vessels

Tendinous cords

Left ventricle

Endocardium

Myocardium

Epicardium

Base of heart

Right atrium

Opening of coronary sinus

Right AV valve

Trabeculae carneae

Right ventricle

Papillary muscles

Epicardial fat

Interventricular septum

Apex of heart

**(b) Posterior view, internal anatomy**

to the workload on the individual heart chambers. It consists primarily of cardiac muscle, which spirals around the heart (fig. 20.6) in such a way that the heart contracts with a twisting or wringing motion. The microscopic structure of the cardiac muscle cells (*cardiac myocytes* or *cardiocytes*) is detailed later.

The heart also has a connective tissue meshwork of collagenous and elastic fibers called the **fibrous skeleton.** This tissue is especially concentrated in the walls between the heart chambers, in *fibrous rings (anuli fibrosi)* around the valves, and in sheets of tissue that interconnect these rings (see fig. 20.8). The fibrous skeleton has multiple functions: (1) It provides structural support for the heart,

especially around the valves and the openings of the great vessels; it holds these orifices open and prevents them from being excessively stretched when blood surges through them. (2) It anchors the myocytes and gives them something to pull against. (3) As a nonconductor of electricity, it serves as electrical insulation between the atria and the ventricles, so the atria cannot stimulate the ventricles directly. This insulation is important in the timing and coordination of electrical and contractile activity. (4) Some authorities think (while others disagree) that elastic recoil of the fibrous skeleton may aid in refilling the heart with blood after each beat, like a hollow rubber ball that expands when you relax your grip.

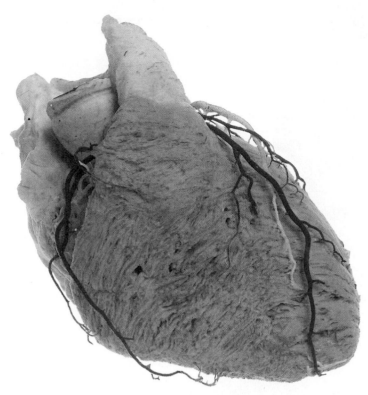

**Figure 20.6 Twisted Orientation of Myocardial Muscle.** A heart with the epicardium stripped off to expose the spiraling bundles of myocardial muscle.

**THINK ABOUT IT**

*Parts of the fibrous skeleton sometimes become calcified in old age. How would you expect this to affect cardiac function?*

## The Chambers

The heart has four chambers, best seen in a frontal section (fig. 20.7). The two at the superior pole (base) of the heart are the **right** and **left atria** (AY-tree-uh; singular *atrium*[5]). They are thin-walled receiving chambers for blood returning to the heart by way of the great veins. Most of the mass of each atrium is on the posterior side of the heart, so only a small portion is visible from an anterior view. Here, each atrium has a small earlike extension called an **auricle**[6] that slightly increases its volume.

The two inferior heart chambers, the **right** and **left ventricles,**[7] are the pumps that eject blood into the arteries and keep it flowing around the body. The right ventricle constitutes most of the anterior portion of the heart, while the left ventricle forms the apex and inferoposterior portion.

On the surface, the boundaries of the four chambers are marked by three sulci (grooves), which are largely filled with fat and the cor-

onary blood vessels (see fig. 20.5a). The **coronary**[8] (**atrioventricular) sulcus** encircles the heart near the base and separates the atria above from the ventricles below. It can be exposed by lifting the margins of the atria. The other two sulci extend obliquely down the heart from the coronary sulcus toward the apex—one on the front of the heart called the **anterior interventricular sulcus** and one on the back called the **posterior interventricular sulcus.** These sulci overlie an internal wall, the *interventricular septum,* that divides the right ventricle from the left. The coronary sulcus and two interventricular sulci harbor the largest of the coronary blood vessels.

The atria exhibit thin flaccid walls corresponding to their light workload—all they do is pump blood into the ventricles immediately below. They are separated from each other by a wall called the **interatrial septum.** The right atrium and both auricles exhibit internal ridges of myocardium called **pectinate**[9] **muscles.** The **interventricular septum** is a much more muscular, vertical wall between the ventricles. The right ventricle pumps blood only to the lungs and back, so its wall is only moderately muscular. The wall of the left ventricle is two to four times as thick because it bears the greatest workload of all four chambers, pumping blood through the entire body. Both ventricles exhibit internal ridges called **trabeculae carneae**[10] (trah-BEC-you-lee CAR-nee-ee).

## The Valves

To pump blood effectively, the heart needs valves that ensure a predominantly one-way flow. There is a valve between each atrium and the corresponding ventricle and another at the exit from each ventricle into its great artery (fig. 20.7), but there are no valves where the great veins empty into the atria. Each valve consists of two or three fibrous flaps of tissue called **cusps** or **leaflets,** covered with endocardium.

The **atrioventricular (AV) valves** regulate the openings between the atria and ventricles. The **right AV (tricuspid) valve** has three cusps, and the **left AV (bicuspid) valve** has two (fig. 20.8). The left AV valve is also known as the **mitral** (MY-trul) **valve** after its resemblance to a miter, the headdress of a church bishop. Stringlike **tendinous cords (chordae tendineae),** reminiscent of the shroud lines of a parachute, connect the valve cusps to conical **papillary muscles** on the floor of the ventricle.

The **semilunar**[11] **valves** (pulmonary and aortic valves) regulate the flow of blood from the ventricles into the great arteries. The **pulmonary valve** controls the opening from the right ventricle into the pulmonary trunk, and the **aortic valve** controls the opening from the left ventricle into the aorta. Each has three cusps shaped somewhat like shirt pockets. There are no tendinous cords on the semilunar valves.

The valves do not open and close by any muscular effort of their own. The cusps are simply pushed open and closed by changes in blood pressure (fig. 20.9). When the ventricles are relaxed and their pressure is low, the AV valve cusps hang down limply and both AV

---

[5]*atrium* = entryway
[6]*auricle* = little ear
[7]*ventr* = belly, lower part + *icle* = little

[8]*coron* = crown + *ary* = pertaining to
[9]*pectin* = comb + *ate* = like
[10]*trabecula* = little beam + *carne* = flesh, meat
[11]*semi* = half + *lunar* = like the moon

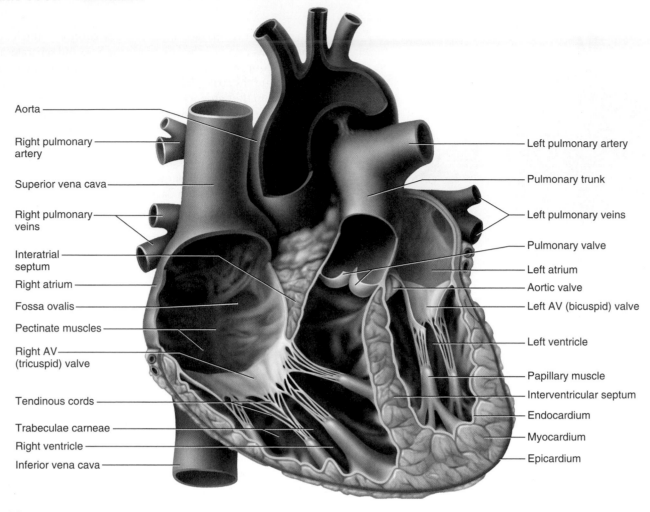

Aorta

Right pulmonary artery

Superior vena cava

Right pulmonary veins

Interatrial septum

Right atrium

Fossa ovalis

Pectinate muscles

Right AV (tricuspid) valve

Tendinous cords

Trabeculae carneae

Right ventricle

Inferior vena cava

Left pulmonary artery

Pulmonary trunk

Left pulmonary veins

Pulmonary valve

Left atrium

Aortic valve

Left AV (bicuspid) valve

Left ventricle

Papillary muscle

Interventricular septum

Endocardium

Myocardium

Epicardium

**Figure 20.7** **Internal Anatomy of the Heart.** Anterior view.

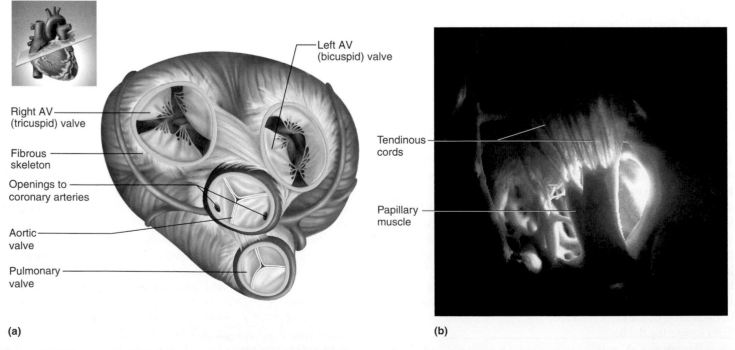

Left AV (bicuspid) valve

Right AV (tricuspid) valve

Fibrous skeleton

Openings to coronary arteries

Aortic valve

Pulmonary valve

Tendinous cords

Papillary muscle

**(a)**

**(b)**

**Figure 20.8** **The Heart Valves.** (a) Superior view of the heart with the atria removed. (b) Papillary muscle and tendinous cords seen from within the right ventricle.

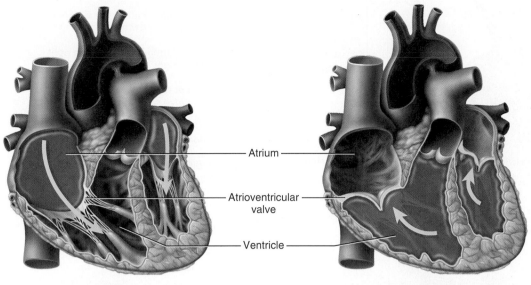

**Atrioventricular valves open**

**Atrioventricular valves closed**

Atrium

Atrioventricular valve

Ventricle

**(a)**

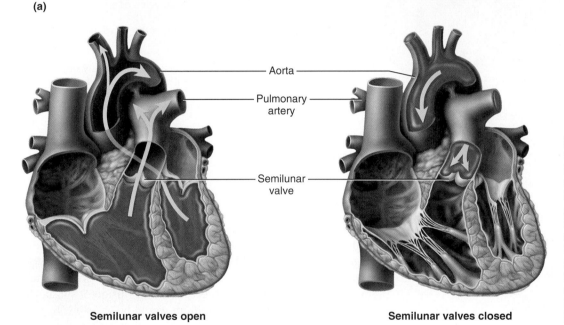

**Semilunar valves open**

**Semilunar valves closed**

Aorta

Pulmonary artery

Semilunar valve

**(b)**

**Figure 20.9** **Operation of the Heart Valves.** (a) The atrioventricular valves. When atrial pressure is greater than ventricular pressure, the valve opens and blood flows through. When ventricular pressure rises above atrial pressure, the blood in the ventricle pushes the valve cusps closed. (b) The semilunar valves. When the pressure in the ventricle is greater than the pressure in the artery, the valve is forced open and blood is ejected. When ventricular pressure is lower than arterial pressure, arterial blood holds the valve closed.
● *What role do the tendinous cords play?*

valves are open. Blood flows freely from the atria through the valves and into the ventricles below. When the ventricles have filled with blood, they begin to contract and force blood upward against the underside of these valves. This pushes the valve cusps together and closes the openings, so the blood is not simply squirted back into the atria.

At the same time, the rising pressure in the ventricles forces the pulmonary and aortic valves open, and blood is ejected from the heart. As the ventricles relax again and their pressure falls below that in the arteries, arterial blood briefly flows backward and fills the pocketlike cusps of each semilunar valve. The three cusps meet in the middle of the orifice, thereby sealing it and preventing blood from reentering the heart.

Although the AV valves are attached through their tendinous cords to papillary muscles in the floor of the heart, those muscles do not help the valves open. Rather, they contract along with the rest of the ventricular myocardium and tug on the tendinous cords. This prevents the AV valves from bulging excessively into the atria or flipping inside out like windblown umbrellas. Excessive bulging due to slack tendinous cords is called *valvular prolapse* (see table 20.1).

## Blood Flow Through the Chambers

Until the sixteenth century, anatomists thought that blood flowed directly from the right ventricle to the left through invisible pores in the septum. This is incorrect; blood in the right and left chambers of the heart is kept entirely separate. Figure 20.10 shows the pathway of the blood as it travels from the right atrium through the body and back to the starting point.

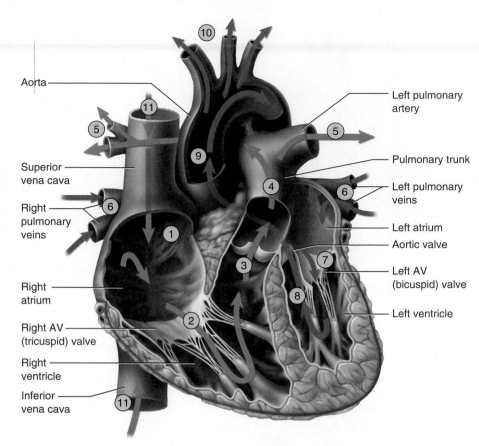

① Blood enters right atrium from superior and inferior venae cavae.

② Blood in right atrium flows through right AV valve into right ventricle.

③ Contraction of right ventricle forces pulmonary valve open.

④ Blood flows through pulmonary valve into pulmonary trunk.

⑤ Blood is distributed by right and left pulmonary arteries to the lungs, where it unloads $CO_2$ and loads $O_2$.

⑥ Blood returns from lungs via pulmonary veins to left atrium.

⑦ Blood in left atrium flows through left AV valve into left ventricle.

⑧ Contraction of left ventricle (simultaneous with step 3) forces aortic valve open.

⑨ Blood flows through aortic valve into ascending aorta.

⑩ Blood in aorta is distributed to every organ in the body, where it unloads $O_2$ and loads $CO_2$.

⑪ Blood returns to heart via venae cavae.

**Figure 20.10** **The Pathway of Blood Flow Through the Heart.** The pathway from 4 to 6 is the pulmonary circuit, and the pathway from 9 to 11 is the systemic circuit. Violet arrows indicate oxygen-poor blood, and orange arrows indicate oxygen-rich blood.

## *Before You Go On*

*Answer the following questions to test your understanding of the preceding section:*

3. Name the three layers of the heart and describe their structural differences.

4. What are the functions of the fibrous skeleton?

5. Trace the flow of blood through the heart, naming each chamber and valve in order.

# Coronary Circulation

### *Objectives*

When you have completed this section, you should be able to

• describe the arteries that nourish the myocardium and the veins that drain it; and

• define *myocardial infarction* and relate it to the coronary arteries.

If your heart lasts for 80 years and beats an average of 75 times a minute, it will beat more than 3 billion times and pump more than 200 million liters of blood. It is, in short, a remarkably hardworking organ, and understandably, it needs an abundant supply of oxygen and nutrients. These needs are not met to any appreciable extent by the blood in the chambers, because the diffusion of substances from there through the myocardium would be too slow. Instead, the myocardium has its own supply of arteries and capillaries that deliver blood to every myocyte. The blood vessels of the heart wall constitute the **coronary circulation.**

At rest, the coronary blood vessels supply the myocardium with about 250 mL of blood per minute. This constitutes about 5% of the circulating blood going to meet the metabolic needs of the heart alone, even though the heart is only 0.5% of the body's weight. It receives 10 times its "fair share" to sustain its strenuous workload.

## Arterial Supply

The coronary circulation is the most variable aspect of cardiac anatomy. The following description covers only the largest coronary blood vessels, and describes only the pattern seen in about 70% to 85% of persons.

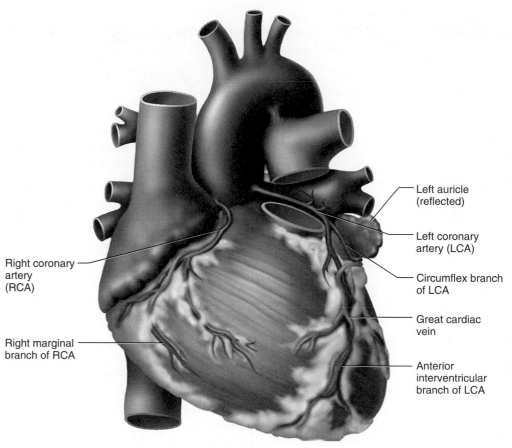

Left auricle (reflected)

Left coronary artery (LCA)

Circumflex branch of LCA

Great cardiac vein

Anterior interventricular branch of LCA

Right coronary artery (RCA)

Right marginal branch of RCA

**(a) Anterior view**

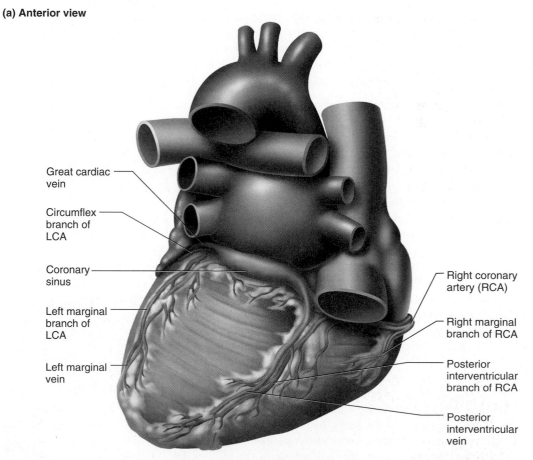

Great cardiac vein

Circumflex branch of LCA

Coronary sinus

Left marginal branch of LCA

Left marginal vein

Right coronary artery (RCA)

Right marginal branch of RCA

Posterior interventricular branch of RCA

Posterior interventricular vein

**Figure 20.11**  **The Principal Coronary Blood Vessels.**

**(b) Posterior view**

Immediately after the aorta leaves the left ventricle, it gives off a right and left coronary artery. The orifices of these two arteries lie deep in the pockets formed by two of the aortic valve cusps (see fig. 20.8a). The **left coronary artery (LCA)** travels through the coronary sulcus under the left auricle and divides into two branches (fig. 20.11):

1. The **anterior interventricular branch** travels down the anterior interventricular sulcus to the apex, rounds the bend, and travels a short distance up the posterior side of the heart. There it joins the posterior interventricular branch described shortly. Clinically, it is also called the *left anterior descending (LAD) branch.* This artery supplies blood to both ventricles and the anterior two-thirds of the interventricular septum.

2. The **circumflex branch** continues around the left side of the heart in the coronary sulcus. It gives off a **left marginal branch** that passes down the left margin of the heart and furnishes blood to the left ventricle. The circumflex branch then ends on the posterior side of the heart, where it supplies blood to the left atrium and posterior wall of the left ventricle.

The **right coronary artery (RCA)** supplies the right atrium and sinoatrial node (pacemaker), then continues along the coronary sulcus under the right auricle and gives off two branches of its own:

1. The **right marginal branch** runs toward the apex of the heart and supplies the lateral aspect of the right atrium and ventricle.

2. The RCA continues around the right margin of the heart to the posterior side, sends a small branch to the atrioventricular node, then gives off a large **posterior interventricular branch.** This branch travels down the corresponding sulcus and supplies the posterior walls of both ventricles as well as the posterior portion of the interventricular septum. It ends by joining the anterior interventricular branch of the LCA.

The energy demand of the cardiac muscle is so critical that an interruption of the blood supply to any part of the myocardium can cause necrosis within minutes. A fatty deposit or blood clot in a coronary artery can cause a **myocardial infarction**[12] **(MI),** the sudden death of a patch of tissue deprived of its blood flow (see Insight 20.1). Some protection from MI is provided by several **arterial anastomoses** (ah-NASS-tih-MO-seez), points where two arteries come together and combine their blood flow to points farther downstream. Anastomoses provide an alternative route, called **collateral circulation,** that can supply the heart tissue with blood if the primary route becomes obstructed.

In most organs, blood flow peaks when the ventricles contract and eject blood into the arteries, and diminishes when the ventricles relax and refill. The opposite is true in the coronary arteries. There are three reasons for this. (1) Contraction of the myocardium compresses the coronary arteries and obstructs blood flow. (2) During *ventricular systole* (contraction of the ventricles), the aortic valve is forced open and the valve cusps cover the openings to the coronary arteries, blocking blood from flowing into them. (3) During *ventricular diastole* (relaxation), blood in the aorta briefly surges back toward the heart. It fills the aortic valve cusps and some of it flows into the coronary arteries, like water pouring into a bucket and flowing out through a hole in the bottom. In

the coronary blood vessels, therefore, blood flow increases during ventricular relaxation.

## Venous Drainage

**Venous drainage** refers to the route by which blood leaves an organ. After flowing through capillaries of the heart wall, about 20% of the coronary blood empties directly from multiple small *thebesian*[13] *veins* into the heart chambers, especially the right ventricle. The other 80% returns to the right atrium by the following route (fig. 20.11):

- The **great cardiac vein** collects blood from the anterior aspect of the heart and travels alongside the anterior interventricular artery. It carries blood from the apex of the heart toward the coronary sulcus, then arcs around the left side of the heart and empties into the coronary sinus described below.

- The **posterior interventricular (middle cardiac) vein,** found in the posterior sulcus, collects blood from the posterior aspect of the heart. It, too, carries blood from the apex upward and drains into the same sinus.

- The **left marginal vein** travels from a point near the apex of the heart up the left margin and empties into the coronary sinus.

- The **coronary sinus,** a large transverse vein in the coronary sulcus on the posterior side of the heart, collects blood from all three of the aforementioned veins as well as some smaller ones. It empties blood into the right atrium.

### *Before You Go On*

*Answer the following questions to test your understanding of the preceding section:*

6. What are the three principal branches of the left coronary artery? Where are they located on the heart surface? What are the branches of the right coronary artery, and where are they located?

7. What is the medical significance of anastomoses in the coronary arterial system?

8. Why do the coronary arteries carry a greater blood flow during ventricular diastole than they do during ventricular systole?

9. What are the three major veins that empty into the coronary sinus?

## The Cardiac Conduction System and Cardiac Muscle

### *Objectives*
When you have completed this section, you should be able to

- describe the heart's electrical conduction system.

- contrast the structure of cardiac and skeletal muscle; and

- describe the types and significance of intercellular junctions between cardiac muscle cells.

---

[12]*infarct* = to stuff

[13]Adam Christian Thebesius (1686–1732), German physician

# INSIGHT 20.1

## Clinical Application

### Coronary Artery Disease

*Coronary artery disease (CAD)* is a narrowing of the coronary arteries resulting in insufficient blood flow to maintain the myocardium. It is usually caused by *atherosclerosis,* a vascular disorder in which fatty deposits form in an arterial wall, causing arterial degeneration and obstructed blood flow. The atherosclerotic *plaque (atheroma)* is composed of lipids, smooth muscle, and scar tissue, and may progress to a calcified *complicated plaque,* causing the arterial walls to become rigid. *Myocardial infarction* (heart attack) can occur when the artery becomes so occluded that cardiac muscle begins to die from lack of oxygen. Partial obstruction of an artery can cause a temporary sense of heaviness and chest pain called *angina pectoris* when the artery constricts.

There are multiple ways in which an atheroma can lead to heart attack. The atheroma itself may block so much of the artery that blood flow is insufficient to support the cardiac muscle (fig. 20.12), especially during exercise when the metabolic need of the myocardium increases sharply. Platelets often adhere to atheromas and produce blood clots. If the vessel space (lumen) is already largely closed off by the atheroma, a blood clot may finish the job. Furthermore, a clot can break free from the atheroma and block a smaller coronary artery downstream.

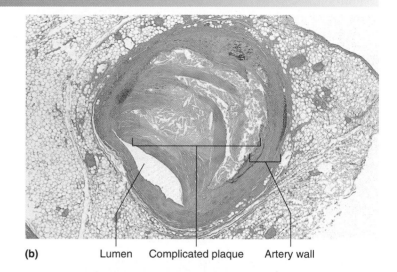

**(b)**    Lumen    Complicated plaque    Artery wall

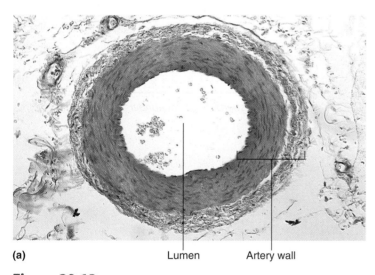

**(a)**    Lumen    Artery wall

**Figure 20.12** **Coronary Atherosclerosis.** (a) Cross section of a healthy artery. (b) Cross section of an artery with advanced atherosclerosis. The lumen is reduced to a small space that can easily be blocked by a stationary or traveling blood clot or by vasoconstriction. Most of the original lumen is obstructed by a plaque composed of calcified scar tissue. (c) Coronary arteriogram showing 60% obstruction of the anterior interventricular artery (arrow).

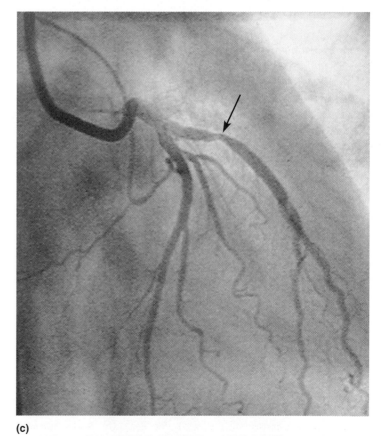

**(c)**

The most obvious physiological fact about the heart is its rhythmicity. It contracts at regular intervals, typically about 75 beats per minute (bpm) in a resting adult. Among invertebrates such as clams, crabs, and insects, each heartbeat is triggered by a pacemaker in the nervous system. The vertebrate heartbeat, however, is said to be *myogenic*[14] because the signal that triggers each heartbeat originates within the heart itself. Indeed, we can remove the heart from the body, keep it in aerated saline, and it will beat for hours. Cut the

---

[14]*myo* = muscle + *genic* = arising from

heart into little pieces, and each piece continues its own rhythmic pulsations. Thus, it obviously is not dependent on the nervous system for its rhythm. The heart has its own pacemaker and electrical conduction system, and it is to this system that we now turn our attention.

## The Conduction System

Cardiac myocytes are said to be **autorhythmic**[15] because they electrically discharge, or depolarize, spontaneously at regular time intervals. Some of the myocytes lose the ability to contract and become specialized, instead, for generating and conducting these electrical signals. These cells constitute the **cardiac conduction system,** which controls the route and timing of stimulation to ensure that the four heart chambers are coordinated with each other. Electrical signals arise and travel through the conduction system in the following order (fig. 20.13):

1. The **sinoatrial (SA) node.** This is a patch of modified myocytes in the right atrium, just under the epicardium near the superior vena cava. It serves as the **pacemaker** that initiates each heartbeat and determines the heart rate.

2. The **atrioventricular (AV) node.** This is a similar patch of modified myocytes located at the lower end of the interatrial septum near the right AV valve. It acts as an electrical gateway to the ventricles. All electrical signals traveling to the ventricles must pass through the AV node because the fibrous skeleton acts as an insulator that prevents currents from traveling to the ventricles by any other route.

---

[15]*auto* = self

3. The **atrioventricular (AV) bundle (bundle of His[16]).** This is a cord of modified myocytes that leaves the AV node and travels to the interventricular septum. It forks into **right** and **left bundle branches,** which enter the septum and descend toward the apex of the heart.

4. **Purkinje**[17] (pur-KIN-jee) **fibers.** These are nervelike processes that arise from the lower end of the bundle branches and turn upward to spread throughout the ventricular myocardium. Purkinje fibers distribute the electrical excitation to the myocytes of the ventricles. They form a more elaborate network in the left ventricle than in the right.

After we examine the structure of cardiac muscle, we will see how this conduction system relates to the heart's cycle of contraction and relaxation.

## Structure of Cardiac Muscle

The traveling electrical signal does not end with the Purkinje fibers, and Purkinje fibers do not reach every myocyte. Rather, the myocytes pass the signal from cell to cell. This is something that skeletal muscle cannot do, so to understand how the heartbeat is coordinated, one must understand the microscopic anatomy of cardiac myocytes and how they differ from skeletal muscle fibers.

Cardiac muscle is striated like skeletal muscle but otherwise differs from it in many structural and physiological ways. Cardiac myocytes, or *cardiocytes,* are relatively short, thick cells, typically 50 to 100 μm long and 10 to 20 μm wide (fig. 20.14). The ends of the cell are slightly branched, like a log with notches in the end. Through its different end branches, each cardiocyte contacts several other cells, so collectively they form a network throughout a heart chamber. A cardiocyte usually has only one, centrally placed nucleus, often surrounded by a mass of the energy-storage carbohydrate, glyco-

---

## INSIGHT 20.2
### Clinical Application

#### Heart Block

*Heart block* is a condition in which electrical signals cannot travel normally through the cardiac conduction system because of disease and degeneration of the conduction system fibers. A *bundle branch block* exists when one or both of the atrioventricular bundle branches are diseased. *Total heart block* results from disease of the AV node. Heart block is one of the causes of cardiac arrhythmia, an irregularity in the heartbeat (see fig. 20.15c). In total heart block, signals from the SA node stop at the diseased AV node and cannot reach the ventricular myocardium. The ventricles then beat at their own intrinsic rhythm of about 20 to 40 beats/min, out of synchrony with the atria and at a rate too slow to sustain life for very long.

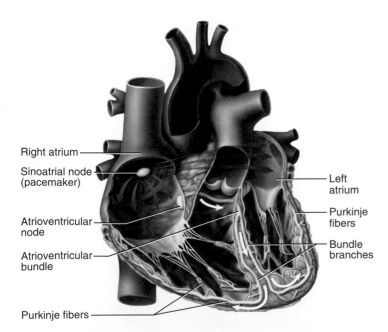

**Figure 20.13 The Cardiac Conduction System.** Electrical signals travel along the pathways indicated by the arrows.

Right atrium
Sinoatrial node (pacemaker)
Atrioventricular node
Atrioventricular bundle
Purkinje fibers
Left atrium
Purkinje fibers
Bundle branches

---

[16]Wilhelm His, Jr. (1863–1934), German physiologist
[17]Johannes E. Purkinje (1787–1869), Bohemian physiologist

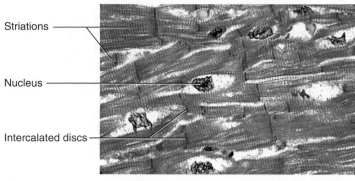

Striations

Nucleus

Intercalated discs

**(a)**

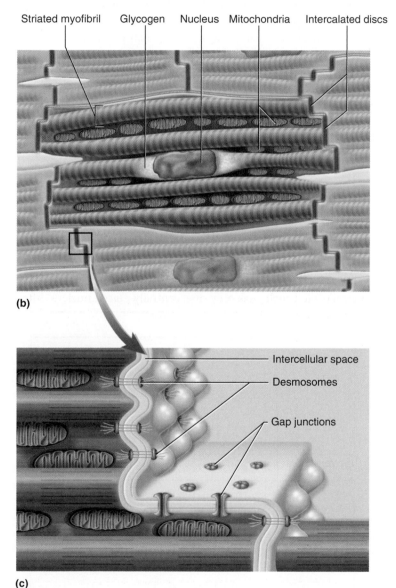

Striated myofibril    Glycogen    Nucleus    Mitochondria    Intercalated discs

**(b)**

Intercellular space

Desmosomes

Gap junctions

**(c)**

**Figure 20.14 Cardiac Muscle.** (a) Light micrograph. (b) Structure of a cardiocyte (center) and its relationship to adjacent cardiocytes. At each end, a cardiocyte is typically linked to two or more neighboring cells through the mechanical and electrical junctions of their intercalated discs. (c) Structure of an intercalated disc.
• *Which component of the intercalated disc allows a cardiocyte to electrically excite the neighboring cardiocytes?*

gen. The sarcoplasmic reticulum is less developed than in skeletal muscle; it lacks terminal cisternae, although it does have footlike sacs associated with the T tubules. The T tubules are much larger than in skeletal muscle. During excitation of the cell, they admit supplemental calcium ions from the extracellular fluid to activate muscle contraction. Cardiocytes have especially large mitochondria, which make up about 25% of the cell volume, compared to skeletal muscle mitochondria, which are much smaller and only 2% of the cell volume.

### THINK ABOUT IT

*Why should mitochondria be larger and more abundant in cardiac muscle than in skeletal muscle?*

Cardiocytes are joined end to end by thick connections called **intercalated** (in-TUR-ku-LAY-ted) **discs,** which appear as dark lines (thicker than the striations) in properly stained tissue sections. An intercalated disc is a complex steplike structure with three distinctive features not found in skeletal muscle:

1. **Interdigitating folds.** The plasma membrane at the end of the cell is folded somewhat like the bottom of an egg carton. The folds of adjoining cells interlock with each other and increase the surface area of intercellular contact.

2. **Mechanical junctions.** The cells are tightly joined by two types of mechanical junctions—the fascia adherens and desmosomes. The *fascia adherens*[18] (FASH-ee-ah ad-HEER-enz) is the most extensive. It is a broad band in which the actin of the thin myofilaments is anchored to the plasma membrane, and each cell is linked to the next by way of transmembrane proteins. Thus, the moving myofilaments of a contracting cell are able to pull indirectly on the neighboring cells. The fascia adherens is interrupted here and there by *desmosomes.* Described in more detail on page 59, desmosomes are weldlike mechanical junctions between cells. They prevent the contracting cardiocytes from pulling apart.

3. **Electrical junctions.** The intercalated discs also contain *gap junctions,* which form channels that allow ions to flow from the cytoplasm of one cell directly into the next (see p. 59 for their structure). These junctions enable each myocyte to electrically stimulate its neighbors. Thus, the entire myocardium of the two atria behaves almost as if it were a single cell, as does the entire myocardium of the two ventricles. This unified action is essential for the effective pumping of a heart chamber.

Skeletal muscle contains satellite cells that can divide and replace dead muscle fibers to some extent. Cardiac muscle lacks satellite cells, however, so the repair of damaged cardiac muscle is almost entirely by fibrosis (scarring). A limited capacity for myocardial mitosis and regeneration was discovered in 2001, raising some hope that this might one day be clinically enhanced to repair hearts damaged by myocardial infarction.

---

[18]*fascia* = band + *adherens* = adhering

## Nerve Supply to the Heart

Even though the heart has its own pacemaker, it also receives both sympathetic and parasympathetic nerves. They do not activate the heartbeat, but modify its rate and contraction strength. Sympathetic nerves can raise the heart rate to as high as 230 beats/min, while parasympathetic nerves can reduce it to as low as 20 beats/min or even stop the heart for a few seconds.

The sympathetic pathway to the heart originates with neurons in the lower cervical to upper thoracic spinal cord. Efferent fibers from these neurons pass from the spinal cord to the sympathetic chain and travel up the chain to the three cervical ganglia. **Cardiac nerves** arise from the cervical ganglia (see fig. 16.4, p. 472) and lead mainly to the ventricular myocardium, where they increase the force of contraction. Some fibers, however, innervate the atria. Sympathetic fibers to the coronary arteries dilate them and increase coronary blood flow during exercise.

The parasympathetic pathway to the heart is through the vagus nerves. The right vagus nerve innervates mainly the SA node, and the left vagus nerve innervates mainly the AV node, although there is some cross-innervation from each nerve to both nodes. The ventricles receive little or no vagal stimulation. The vagus nerves slow the heartbeat. Without this influence, the SA node would produce an average resting heart rate of about 100 beats/min, but steady background firing of the vagus nerves *(vagal tone)* normally holds the resting rate down to about 70 to 80 beats/min.

## The Cardiac Cycle

The foregoing anatomy should acquire more meaning if you can relate it to the **cardiac cycle**—one complete cycle of contraction and relaxation. This will show how the structures of the heart work together to achieve blood circulation.

---

## INSIGHT 20.3

### Clinical Application

### The Electrocardiogram

Next to listening to the heart sounds with a stethoscope *(auscultation)*, the most common clinical method of evaluating heart function is the *electrocardiogram (ECG* or *EKG)*—recording the electrical activity of the heart by means of electrodes applied to the skin. As the myocardium of the atria and ventricles electrically discharges *(depolarizes)* and recharges *(repolarizes),* it generates electrical currents that are conducted by electrolytes in the body fluids to the skin surface. Here the activity can be recorded as small voltage changes that show as upward and downward deflections of the ECG (fig. 20.15a).

Three major events are seen in the ECG, named the *P wave,* the *QRS complex,* and the *T wave.* (The letters are arbitrary; they do not stand for any words.) The P wave marks the depolarization of the atria; between then and the QRS complex, the atria are contracting and expelling blood into the ventricles. The QRS complex marks the depolarization of the ventricles. It is the largest wave of the ECG because the ventricles constitute the largest muscle mass of the heart and generate the greatest electrical current. The ventricles contract and expel blood from the heart in the interval between the QRS complex and the T wave. The atria also repolarize during the QRS complex, but this produces a smaller effect concealed by the large ventricular effect. The T wave marks the moment of ventricular repolarization. The ventricles relax and begin refilling with blood between then and the next P wave.

Irregularities in the ECG help to diagnose disorders such as ventricular fibrillation (fig. 20.15b), heart block (fig. 20.15c), and electrolyte imbalances.

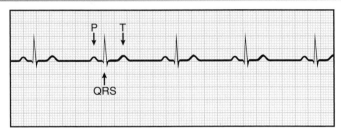

**(a) Normal electrocardiogram**

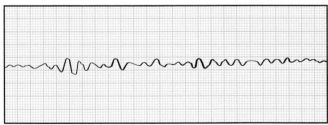

**(b) Ventricular fibrillation**

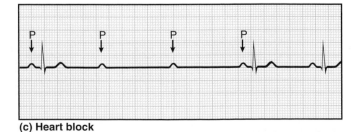

**(c) Heart block**

**Figure 20.15  The Electrocardiogram.**  (a) A normal ECG, showing the P wave, QRS complex, and T wave. (b) The abnormal ECG of ventricular fibrillation, with irregular electrical activity and squirming, uncoordinated contractions of the ventricular myocardium. This sort of ECG is typical of a heart attack. (c) The abnormal ECG of a heart block (see Insight 20.2).

The electrical events of the cardiac cycle can be recorded with skin electrodes as an **electrocardiogram (ECG)** (Insight 20.3 and fig. 20.15). Electrical excitation of a heart chamber induces contraction, or **systole** (SIS-toe-lee), which expels blood from the chamber. The relaxation of any chamber is called **diastole** (dy-ASS-toe-lee) and allows the chamber to refill. Figure 20.16 shows how the electrical and contractile activity of the heart relate to each other through the cardiac cycle.

① Initially, all four chambers are relaxed, in diastole. The AV valves are open, and as blood flows into the heart from the venae cavae and pulmonary veins, it flows through these valves and partially fills the ventricles.

② The sinoatrial (SA) node fires, exciting the atrial myocardium (see fig. 20.13), producing the P wave of the ECG, and initiating atrial systole. The contracting atria finish filling the ventricles.

③ The atrioventricular (AV) node fires and electrical excitation spreads throughout the ventricles, producing the QRS complex. This excitation sets off ventricular systole while the atria relax. Ventricular contraction forces the AV valves shut and the semilunar (aortic and pulmonary) valves open. The ventricles eject blood into the aorta and pulmonary trunk.

④ The ventricles repolarize (marked by the T wave) and relax; all four chambers are again in diastole. The semilunar

valves reclose because of back-pressure in the large arteries, the AV valves reopen, and the ventricles begin to refill in preparation for the next cycle.

This entire cycle repeats itself at intervals normally governed by the SA node—in a resting adult heart, typically every 0.8 sec or so, generating a heart rate of about 75 beats per minute. The normal heartbeat, timed by the sinoatrial node, is called a *sinus rhythm*. Figures 20.15b and c show some contrasting, abnormal records resulting from diseases of the myocardium or conduction system.

## *Before You Go On*

*Answer the following questions to test your understanding of the preceding section:*

10. Why is the human heart described as myogenic? Where is its pacemaker, and what is it called?

11. List the components of the cardiac conduction system in the order traveled by signals from the pacemaker.

12. What organelle(s) are less developed in cardiac muscle than in skeletal muscle? What organelle(s) are more developed? What is the functional significance of these differences?

13. Name two types of cell junctions in the intercalated discs and explain their functional importance.

14. Identify the nerve supplies to the SA node, AV node, and ventricular myocardium.

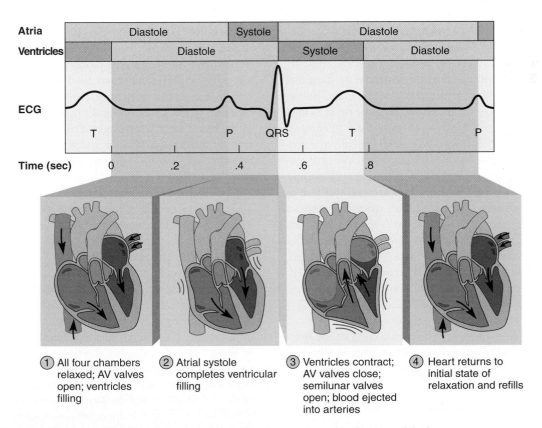

**Figure 20.16  The Cardiac Cycle.**  Major events in one complete cycle of contraction and relaxation of the heart.

# Developmental and Clinical Perspectives

### Objectives

When you have completed this section, you should be able to

- describe the embryonic development of the human heart;
- explain how and why the heart changes in old age; and
- define or briefly describe several of the most common heart diseases.

## Prenatal Development of the Heart

The heart is one of the earliest organs to begin functioning in the embryo. The first traces of it appear in week 3; by 22 to 23 days (usually before the mother is aware that she is pregnant), the heart is already beating; by day 24, it circulates blood throughout the embryo.

In week 3, a region of mesoderm at the far anterior end of the embryo condenses into a pair of longitudinal cellular cords. By day 19, these become hollow, parallel **endocardial heart tubes** (fig. 20.17a). As the embryo grows and the head region folds, these tubes are pushed closer together, the tissues dividing them break down, and they fuse into a single **heart tube** (fig. 20.17b). As the tubes are fusing, the surrounding mesoderm forms a primordial myocardium, responsible for the inception of the heartbeat just a few days later. The fetal heartbeat first becomes audible with a stethoscope at about 20 weeks.

With continued folding of the head region, the heart tube elongates and segments into five dilated spaces, some of them corresponding to future heart chambers. From rostral to caudal, these are the **truncus arteriosus,**[19] **bulbus cordis,**[20] **ventricle, atrium,** and **sinus venosus** (fig. 20.17c). Two of these, the ventricle and bulbus cordis, grow more rapidly than the others, causing the heart to loop into a U and then an S shape similar to a fish heart (fig. 20.17d, e). In the course of this looping, the bulbus cordis shifts caudally, the ventricle shifts to the left, and the atrium and sinus venosus shift rostrally, as indicated by the arrows in the figure. During this looping, the heart bulges into the pericardial cavity. Looping is completed by day 28 and results in the forerunners of the adult atria and ventricles assuming their final relationship to each other (the future atria are now superior, or rostral, to the future ventricles). The primordial ventricle seen at day 21 becomes the left ventricle of the adult heart, and the inferior part of the bulbus cordis becomes the right ventricle. The superior part of the bulbus cordis and the truncus arteriosus are now collectively called the **conotruncus** (fig. 20.17e). This passage soon gives rise to the aorta and pulmonary trunk.

The next phase of development is the partitioning of the heart tube into separate chambers (two atria and two ventricles) through the growth of the interatrial and interventricular septa. The interatrial septum begins to form at the end of week 4 and is well established by about 33 days, except for an opening between the atria called the *foramen ovale.* This foramen persists until after birth; its significance is discussed in the next section. The sinus venosus is initially a separate heart chamber, but it becomes extensively remodeled. Originally, it branches into a right and left horn at its inferior end. The right horn enlarges and receives systemic blood from the superior and inferior venae cavae. It eventually becomes part of the right atrium. The left horn shrinks. Parts of it become the coronary sinus, the sinoatrial node (pacemaker), and a portion of the atrioventricular node.

The interventricular septum begins to appear on the floor of the ventricle at the end of week 4 (fig. 20.17f) and increases in height as the two ventricles grow on either side of it. The septum is complete by the end of week 7. Meanwhile, the inner portion of the ventricular wall becomes honeycombed with cavities and differentiates into the trabeculae carneae, papillary muscles, and tendinous cords.

Yet another septum forms during week 5 within the bulbus cordis and truncus arteriosus, dividing this outflow passage in two along its length. The separate halves of the passage become the ascending aorta and pulmonary trunk. The passage twists about 180° as the septum forms. The evidence of this twisting shows in the way the adult pulmonary trunk twists around the aorta. This twisting must be closely coordinated with the closure of the interventricular septum so that the right ventricle will open into the pulmonary trunk and the left ventricle will open into the aorta. Developmental irregularities at this stage are responsible for many cardiac birth defects.

## Changes at Birth

There is little point to pumping all of the blood through the lungs of the fetus, because the fetal lungs are not yet inflated or functional. They receive enough blood to meet their metabolic and developmental needs, but most blood bypasses the pulmonary circuit by way of two anatomical shortcuts or *shunts* (fig. 20.18). One is the **foramen ovale,** the opening through the interatrial septum. Some of the blood entering the right atrium passes through this opening directly into the left atrium and from there into the left ventricle and systemic circuit. The other shunt is a short vessel, the **ductus arteriosus,** from the base of the left pulmonary artery to the aorta. Most of the blood that the right ventricle pumps into the pulmonary trunk takes this bypass directly into the aorta instead of following the usual path to the lungs.

At birth, the lungs inflate and their resistance to blood flow drops sharply. The sudden change in pressure gradients causes a flap of tissue to seal the foramen ovale. Blood in the right atrium is no longer able to flow directly into the left and bypass the lungs. In most people, the tissues grow together and permanently seal the foramen, leaving only a depression in the right atrial wall, the *fossa ovalis,* marking its former location. The foramen remains unsealed in about 15% of adults, but the tissue flap acts as a valve that prevents blood from passing through. The ductus arteriosus normally begins to constrict around 10 to 15 hours after birth. It is effectively closed to blood flow within 2 to 4 days, and becomes a permanently closed fibrous cord *(ligamentum arteriosum)* by the age of 2 to 3 weeks (but see Insight 20.4).

---

[19]*truncus* = trunk + *arteriosus* = arterial
[20]*bulbus* = bulb + *cordis* = of the heart

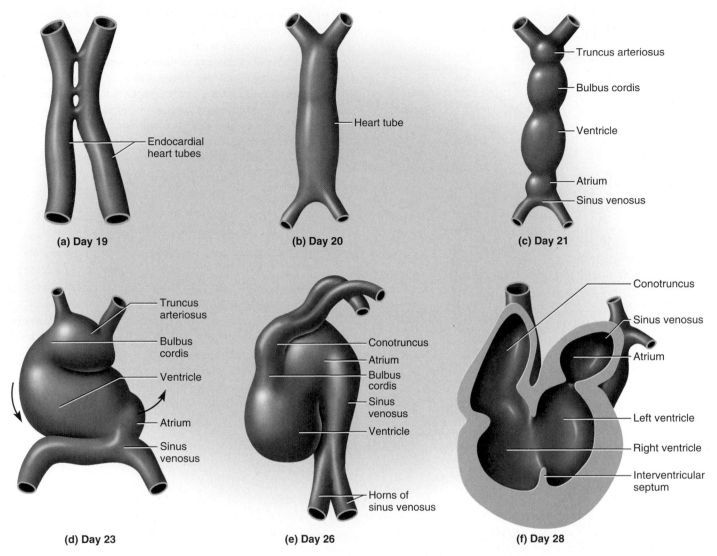

**(a) Day 19** — Endocardial heart tubes

**(b) Day 20** — Heart tube

**(c) Day 21** — Truncus arteriosus, Bulbus cordis, Ventricle, Atrium, Sinus venosus

**(d) Day 23** — Truncus arteriosus, Bulbus cordis, Ventricle, Atrium, Sinus venosus

**(e) Day 26** — Conotruncus, Atrium, Bulbus cordis, Sinus venosus, Ventricle, Horns of sinus venosus

**(f) Day 28** — Conotruncus, Sinus venosus, Atrium, Left ventricle, Right ventricle, Interventricular septum

**Figure 20.17 Embryonic Development of the Heart.** (a) The endocardial heart tubes beginning to fuse at day 19. (b) Complete fusion by day 20, forming the heart tube. (c) Division of the heart tube into five dilated segments by day 21. The heart begins beating about a day later. (d) The heart begins looping around day 23, with the bulbus cordis migrating caudally (left arrow) and the atrium and sinus venosus migrating rostrally (right arrow). Blood circulates throughout the embryo within a day of this stage. (e) Looping is nearly completed by day 26. (f) Frontal section of the heart at 28 days. As the interventricular septum develops, the conotruncus will divide longitudinally into the ascending aorta and pulmonary trunk, receiving blood from the left and right ventricles, respectively. The single atrium seen here divides into the right and left atria by day 33.

## The Aging Heart

The most noticeable effect of aging on the cardiovascular system is a stiffening of the arteries. While that itself is not a cardiac disease, it has important repercussions on the heart. Normally, when the ventricles eject blood, the arteries expand to accommodate the surge in pressure. When arteries are stiffened by age or calcified by arteriosclerosis, they cannot do so. They resist blood flow more than younger arteries, and the heart has to work harder to overcome this resistance. Like any other muscle, when the heart works harder, it grows. The ventricles enlarge, especially the left ventricle, which has to work the hardest to overcome the most resistance. In ventricular hypertrophy, the heart wall and interventricular septum can become so thick that the space within the ventricle is severely diminished. Cardiac output sometimes declines to the point of heart failure.

Many other changes are seen in the aging heart: The valve anuli become more fibrous or even calcified, and the AV valves (especially the mitral valve) thicken and tend to prolapse. The interventricular septum often deviates to the left and interferes with the ejection of blood into the aorta. The fibrous skeleton becomes less elastic, so it has less capacity to rebound in diastole and aid in the filling of the heart. There is a loss of cells from the SA node and conduction system, so impulse conduction is less efficient and more irregular. Degeneration of the conduction system increases the risk of cardiac arrhythmia or heart block. Myocytes die off in the myocardium, and the heart thus becomes weaker. Exercise tolerance is further diminished by decreasing sensitivity to sympathetic stimulation in the elderly heart.

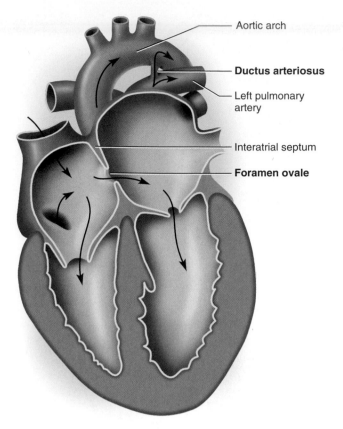

Aortic arch

**Ductus arteriosus**

Left pulmonary artery

Interatrial septum

**Foramen ovale**

**Figure 20.18** **The Fetal Heart.** Note the two shunts (foramen ovale and ductus arteriosus) that allow most blood to bypass the nonfunctional lungs.

## Heart Disease

Heart disease is the leading cause of death in the United States (about 30% of deaths per annum, averaged across all age groups). The most common form of heart disease is coronary atherosclerosis, often leading to myocardial infarction. However, there are a multitude of other heart diseases. The principal categories of heart disease are congenital defects in cardiac anatomy, myocardial hypertrophy or degeneration, inflammation of the pericardium and heart wall, valvular defects, and cardiac tumors. Several examples are described in the Insights in this chapter and in table 20.1.

## *Before You Go On*

*Answer the following questions to test your understanding of the preceding section:*

15. When does the embryonic heart begin to beat? At what gestational age does it become audible?

16. What are the five primitive chambers that develop from the heart tube? What becomes of each as the heart continues to develop?

17. Describe the two routes (shunts) by which fetal blood bypasses the lungs. What happens to each one shortly after birth?

18. Why does the heart tend to enlarge in old age? Why does the risk of cardiac arrhythmia increase?

# INSIGHT 20.4

## Clinical Application

### Patent Ductus Arteriosus

*Patent*[21] *ductus arteriosus (PDA)* is the failure of the ductus arteriosus to close. For a short time after birth, PDA causes no problems; but as the lungs become better inflated and more functional, pulmonary blood pressure drops below aortic blood pressure. Blood may then begin to flow from the aortic arch back into the pulmonary circuit for an immediate second trip through the lungs. Since this blood soon returns to the left ventricle, it adds markedly to the left ventricular workload. The lungs sometimes respond to the persistent high blood flow with vascular changes that increase pulmonary resistance and stress the right ventricle as well.

The signs of PDA include poor weight gain in early childhood, frequent respiratory illnesses, *dyspnea* (difficulty breathing) on exertion,

and *cardiomegaly* (enlargement of the heart). PDA is usually suspected at about 6 to 8 weeks of age because of a persistent "machinery-like" heart murmur; it is confirmed by X-ray and other cardiac imaging methods.

Usually, the ductus arteriosus can be stimulated to close with a prostaglandin inhibitor, but if this fails, surgery is required. Surgery is ideally performed between 1.5 and 2.5 years of age because there is a rising risk of *infective endocarditis* (see table 20.1) if it is delayed. The usual procedure is to tie off the DA with several ligatures. This is a low-risk surgery with almost no mortality. However, other methods are available for blocking blood flow through the DA that are less invasive and give an easier recovery for the young patient.

[21]*patent* = open

| TABLE 20.1 | Common Cardiac Pathologies |
|---|---|
| **Cardiac tamponade** | Compression of the heart by serous fluid or clotted blood in the pericardial cavity, rendering the heart unable to expand and fill completely during diastole, thus reducing systolic output. |
| **Cardiomyopathy** | Any disease of the myocardium from causes other than valvular dysfunction or vascular diseases. Can cause atrophy or hypertrophy of the heart wall and interventricular septum, or dilation and failure of the heart. |
| **Congestive heart failure (CHF)** | Failure of either ventricle to pump as much blood as the other one, resulting in accumulation of blood and edema (congestion) in peripheral tissues. Left ventricular failure results in pulmonary congestion and right ventricular failure in systemic congestion (once called *dropsy*). Failure of one ventricle stresses the other and may lead to its subsequent failure. |
| **Infective endocarditis** | Inflammation of the endocardium, usually due to bacterial infection with streptococci or staphylococci. |
| **Mitral valve prolapse (MVP)** | A valvular defect in which one or both mitral valve cusps balloon into the atrium during ventricular contraction. Often hereditary, affecting 1 out of 40 people overall, and young women especially. Causes significant illness in only 3% of cases, including chest pain, fatigue, shortness of breath, and occasionally infective endocarditis, arrhythmia, or stroke. |
| **Rheumatic fever** | Autoimmune disease triggered by a bacterial infection. Antibodies against streptococci or other bacteria attack tissues of the heart valves, causing scarring and constriction (stenosis) of the valves, especially the mitral valve. Regurgitation of blood through the incompetent valve causes turbulence heard as a *heart murmur.* |
| **Septal defects** | Abnormal openings in the interatrial or interventricular septum, allowing blood to flow directly between right and left heart chambers. Results in pulmonary hypertension, difficulty breathing, and fatigue. Often fatal in childhood if not corrected. |
| **Ventricular fibrillation** | Squirming, uncoordinated contractions of the ventricular myocardium with no effective ejection of blood. Often caused by myocardial infarction (MI); the usual cause of death in heart attack. |

### Disorders Described Elsewhere

# CHAPTER REVIEW

## REVIEW OF KEY CONCEPTS

### Overview of the Cardiovascular System (p. 572)

1. The cardiovascular system is divided into a pulmonary circuit served by the right side of the heart and a systemic circuit served by the left.

2. The pulmonary circuit serves only to exchange carbon dioxide for oxygen in the lungs. The systemic circuit serves to deliver oxygen and nutrients to all organs.

3. The heart is located in the mediastinum between the lungs, with about two-thirds of it to the left of the median plane.

4. The heart is enclosed in a fibrous, two-layered *pericardium*. The space between the pericardial sac and epicardium is the *pericardial cavity*, and contains lubricating *pericardial fluid*.

### Gross Anatomy of the Heart (p. 575)

1. The heart wall is composed of a thin outer *epicardium*, a thick muscular *myocardium*, and a thin inner *endocardium*.

2. The heart has a connective tissue *fibrous skeleton* that supports the myocardium and valves, anchors the myocytes, electrically insulates the ventricles from the atria, and may aid in ventricular filling by means of elastic recoil.

3. The two upper chambers of the heart are the *atria*, and serve to receive blood from the venae cavae and pulmonary veins. The two lower chambers are the *ventricles*, which eject blood into the pulmonary trunk and aorta. The ventricles are much more muscular than the atria. The atrioventricular and interventricular sulci on the heart surface mark the boundaries of these chambers.

4. The chambers are internally separated by an *interatrial septum* between the atria and *interventricular septum* between the ventricles.

5. The passages between the atria and ventricles are regulated by the atrioventricular valves (*tricuspid valve* on the right and *bicuspid*, or *mitral*, *valve* on the left). The cusps of these valves are connected by *tendinous cords* to *papillary muscles* on the floor of the ventricles.

6. The openings into the pulmonary trunk and aorta are regulated by the *semilunar* (*pulmonary* and *aortic*) *valves*. The opening and closing of the heart valves is caused by changes in the pressure difference on the two sides of a valve.

7. Systemic blood is received by the right atrium and flows into the right ventricle.

The right ventricle pumps it into the pulmonary trunk, from which it flows to the lungs. Pulmonary blood returning from the lungs is received by the left atrium and flows into the left ventricle. The left ventricle pumps it into the aorta, the beginning of the systemic circulation.

### Coronary Circulation (p. 580)

1. The myocardium has a high workload and metabolic rate and needs an abundant oxygen and nutrient supply. It gets this primarily from a system of blood vessels called the *coronary circulation*.

2. The *left coronary artery* arises behind an aortic valve cusp near the beginning of the aorta, and gives rise mainly to the *anterior interventricular* and *circumflex branches*. The circumflex gives off a *left marginal branch*.

3. The *right coronary artery* gives off mainly a *right marginal branch* and *posterior interventricular branch*.

4. The myocardium is drained mainly by the *great cardiac, posterior interventricular*, and *left marginal veins*, all of which empty into the *coronary sinus*. The coronary sinus and several small *thebesian veins* empty into the right atrium.

5. Obstruction of a coronary artery deprives the downstream myocardium of a blood supply and may cause *myocardial infarction* (heart attack). The risk of this is reduced to some extent by several *anastomoses* in the coronary circulation.

### The Cardiac Conduction System and Cardiac Muscle (p. 582)

1. The cardiac rhythm is set by its own internal pacemaker, the *sinoatrial (SA) node*. Electrical signals originating here spread through the atrial myocardium and then travel via the *atrioventricular (AV) node, AV bundle, bundle branches*, and *Purkinje fibers* to reach the ventricular myocytes.

2. Cardiac myocytes are striated muscle cells with a single nucleus, a poorly developed sarcoplasmic reticulum, very large T tubules, and large abundant mitochondria. They are joined end to end by *interdigitating folds* in their *intercalated discs*. The discs also include intercellular mechanical junctions (*fascia adherens* and *desmosomes*) and electrical (gap) junctions. The latter enable cardiocytes to electrically communicate directly with each other.

3. Although the heart can beat independently of the nervous system, it is innervated by the

autonomic nervous system, which modifies the heart rate and contraction force. Sympathetic nerves supply mainly the ventricular myocardium, and parasympathetic (vagus) nerves supply the SA and AV nodes. Sympathetic stimulation increases heart rate and contraction strength, and parasympathetic stimulation reduces the heart rate.

4. A cardiac cycle begins with all four chambers relaxed and blood flowing into the heart, through the atria to the ventricles. The SA node fires, and the two atria contract simultaneously and finish filling the ventricles. The AV node fires, and the two ventricles contract simultaneously and eject blood into the pulmonary artery and aorta.

### Developmental and Clinical Perspectives (p. 588)

1. Embryonic heart development begins when a pair of mesodermal *endothelial tubes* appear in the third week of gestation and fuse into a single median *heart tube*. The heart tube divides into five regions: the *truncus arteriosus, bulbus cordis, ventricle, atrium,* and *sinus venosus*. As the heart tube loops into U and S shapes around days 26 to 28, the truncus arteriosus and upper bulbus cordis divide longitudinally to become the pulmonary trunk and ascending aorta; the lower bulbus cordis becomes the right ventricle; the single embryonic ventricle develops into the mature left ventricle; the single atrium divides into the right and left atria; and the sinus venosus contributes to the right atrium, coronary sinus, sinoatrial node, and atrioventricular node.

2. In the fetal circulation, most blood bypasses the lungs by way of the *foramen ovale* between the right and left atria and the *ductus arteriosus* between the left pulmonary artery and the aortic arch. These passages close soon after birth so that all blood from the right ventricle is forced to flow through the lungs.

3. In old age, the heart has to work harder against increasing arterial resistance. This tends to lead to ventricular hypertrophy. The aged heart also exhibits fibrosis or calcification of the valve anuli, valvular dysfunction, deviation of the interventricular septum, stiffening of the fibrous skeleton, loss of cells from both the myocardium and the cardiac conduction system, and reduced sensitivity to sympathetic stimulation. These changes lead to weakening of the

myocardium, reduced cardiac output, less exercise tolerance, and increasing risk of ar-ryhthmia or heart block. Heart failure is the leading cause of death in the United States.

4. Heart diseases are very diverse and include congenital defects in anatomy, hypertrophy and atrophy of the myocardium,

inflammation of the pericardium and heart wall, valvular defects, and cardiac tumors.

## TESTING YOUR RECALL

1. The cardiac conduction system includes all of the following *except*
   a. the SA node.
   b. the AV node.
   c. the bundle branches.
   d. the tendinous cords.
   e. the Purkinje fibers.

2. To get from the right atrium to the right ventricle, blood flows through the right AV, or _____, valve.
   a. pulmonary
   b. tricuspid
   c. bicuspid
   d. aortic
   e. mitral

3. There is/are _____ pulmonary vein(s) emptying into the right atrium of the heart.
   a. no
   b. one
   c. two
   d. four
   e. more than four

4. The coronary blood vessels are part of the _____ circuit of the circulatory system.
   a. cardiac
   b. pulmonary
   c. systematic
   d. systemic
   e. cardiovascular

5. The outermost layer of the heart wall is known as
   a. the pericardial sac.
   b. the epicardium.
   c. the visceral pericardium.
   d. both *a* and *c*.
   e. both *b* and *c*.

6. These are some of the points that the blood passes as it circulates through the heart chambers, listed alphabetically: (1) left atrium, (2) left ventricle, (3) mitral valve, (4) pulmonary valve, (5) right atrium, (6) right ventricle, (7) tricuspid valve. Place these in the correct order from the time that blood enters the heart from the venae cavae to the time blood leaves the heart by way of the aorta.
   a. 1–3–2–4–5–7–6
   b. 1–2–3–5–7–6–4
   c. 5–3–6–4–1–2–7
   d. 6–7–5–4–2–3–1
   e. 5–7–6–4–1–3–2

7. The ascending aorta and pulmonary trunk develop from the embryonic
   a. bulbus cordis only.
   b. truncus arteriosus only.
   c. horns of the sinus venosus.
   d. conotruncus.
   e. ventricle.

8. The _____ prevent the AV valves from flipping inside out during ventricular systole.
   a. tendinous cords
   b. pectinate muscles
   c. trabeculae carneae
   d. AV nodes
   e. cusps

9. Blood in the anterior interventricular branch of the left coronary artery flows into myocardial blood capillaries and next drains into
   a. the superior vena cava.
   b. the great cardiac vein.
   c. the left atrium.
   d. the middle cardiac vein.
   e. the coronary sinus.

10. Which of these is *not* characteristic of the heart in old age?
    a. ventricular enlargement
    b. thickening of the atrial walls
    c. a less elastic fibrous skeleton
    d. fewer cells in the conduction system
    e. less sensitivity to norepinephrine

11. The contraction of any heart chamber is called _____, and its relaxation is called _____.

12. The circulatory route from aorta to the venae cavae is the _____ circuit.

13. The circumflex branch of the left coronary artery travels in a groove called the _____.

14. The finest passages through which electrical signals pass before reaching the ventricular myocytes are called _____.

15. Electrical signals pass quickly from one cardiac myocyte to another through the _____ of the intercalated discs.

16. The abnormal bulging of a bicuspid valve cusp into the atrium is called _____.

17. The _____ nerves innervate the heart and tend to reduce the heart rate.

18. The death of cardiac tissue from lack of blood flow is commonly known as a heart attack, but is clinically called _____.

19. Blood in the heart chambers is separated from the myocardium by a thin membrane called the _____.

20. The sinoatrial node develops from an embryonic heart tube chamber called the _____.

*Answers in the Appendix*

## TRUE OR FALSE

*Determine which five of the following statements are false, and briefly explain why.*

1. All blood that has circulated through the myocardium eventually flows into the coronary sinus and from there to the right atrium.

2. The aorta is the body's largest artery.

3. Normally, the only way electrical signals can get from the atria to the ventricles is to pass through the AV node and AV bundle.

4. The epicardium contains adipose tissue, but the endocardium does not.

5. If all nerves from the central nervous system to the heart were severed, the heart would stop beating.

6. The thickest myocardium is normally found in the left ventricle.

7. Many of the cardiac veins have anastomoses that ensure the myocardium will receive blood even if one of the veins becomes blocked.

8. During embryonic development, a ventricular septum grows and divides the single primordial ventricle into right and left ventricles.

9. Blood in the superior and inferior venae cavae flows through the semilunar valves as it enters the right atrium.

10. Cardiac myocytes transmit electrical signals to each other by way of their gap junctions.

*Answers in the Appendix*

## Testing Your Comprehension

1. Mr. Jones, 78, dies of a massive myocardial infarction triggered by coronary thrombosis. Upon autopsy, necrotic myocardium is found in the lateral and posterior right ventricle and posterior interventricular septum. Based on the information in this chapter, where in the coronary circulation do you think the thrombosis occurred?

2. Becky, age 2, was born with a hole in her interventricular septum (*ventricular septal defect,* or *VSD*). Considering that the blood pressure in the left ventricle is significantly higher than blood pressure in the right ventricle, predict the effect of the VSD on Becky's pulmonary blood pressure, systemic blood pressure, and long-term changes in the ventricular walls.

3. Marcus is born with *transposition* of the great arteries, in which the aorta arises from the right ventricle and the pulmonary artery arises from the left. Assuming no other anatomical abnormalities, trace the flow of blood through the pulmonary and systemic routes in his case. Predict the consequences, if any, for the ability of Marcus's cardiovascular system to deliver oxygen to the systemic tissues. Do you think Marcus would require immediate surgical correction in early infancy; correction at the age of 2 or 3 years; or that it could be left alone and not seriously affect his life expectancy?

4. Review the condition of heart block in Insight 20.2, and examine the electrocardiogram for this condition in figure 20.15c. Explain why the second P wave in the ECG is followed by another P instead of a QRS complex.

5. In dilated cardiomyopathy of the left ventricle, the ventricle can become enormously enlarged. Explain why this might lead to regurgitation of blood through the mitral valve (blood flowing from the ventricle back into the left atrium) during ventricular systole.

*Answers at aris.mhhe.com*

## Online Resources

Visit aprevealed.com to explore melt-away cadaver dissections, watch animations that clarify difficult concepts, review histological and radiological images, or take a quiz to assess your understanding of the material.

The Saladin *Human Anatomy,* 2e website at aris.mhhe.com features chapter-specific quizzes, labeling exercises, and other interactive tools to complement your study of human anatomy. If your instructor has provided an ARIS course code, you can also access assignments and information specific to your course.

21

# The Circulatory System III—Blood Vessels

Capillary beds

## BRUSHING UP

To understand this chapter, you may find it helpful to review the following concepts:
- Primary germ layers of the embryo (p. 109)
- Muscle compartments of the limbs (p. 325)
- The pulmonary and systemic circuits (p. 572)
- The great vessels associated with the heart (p. 573)
- Cardiac systole and diastole (p. 587)

**Cardiovascular System**

The route taken by the blood after it leaves the heart was a point of much confusion until the seventeenth century. Chinese emperor Huang Ti (2697–2597 BCE) correctly believed that it flowed in a complete circuit around the body and back to the heart. But in the second century, Roman physician Claudius Galen argued that it flowed back and forth in the veins, like air in the bronchial tubes. He believed that the liver received food from the small intestine and converted it to blood, the heart pumped the blood through the veins to all other organs, and those organs consumed it.

Huang Ti was right, but the first experimental demonstration of this did not come until the seventeenth century. English physician William Harvey (1578–1657) studied the filling and emptying of the heart in snakes, tied off the vessels above and below the heart to observe the effects on cardiac filling and output, and measured cardiac output in a variety of living animals. He concluded that (1) the heart pumps more blood in half an hour than there is in the entire body, (2) not enough food is consumed to account for the continual production of so much blood, and (3) since the planets orbit the sun and as he believed that the human body was modeled after the solar system, it follows that the blood orbits the body. So for a peculiar combination of experimental and superstitious reasons, Harvey argued that the blood must return to the heart rather than being consumed by the peripheral organs. He could not explain how, since the microscope had yet to be developed to the point that allowed Marcello Malpighi (1628–1694) and Antony van Leeuwenhoek (1632–1723) to discover the blood capillaries.

Harvey published his findings in 1628 in a short but elegant book entitled *Exercitio Anatomica de Motu Cordis et Sanguinis in Animalibus* (*Anatomical Studies on the Motion of the Heart and Blood in Animals*). This landmark in the history of biology and medicine was the first experimental study of animal physiology. But so entrenched were the ideas of Aristotle and Galen in the medical community, and so strange was the idea of doing experiments on living animals, that Harvey's contemporaries rejected his ideas. Indeed, some of them regarded him as a crackpot because his conclusion flew in the face of common sense—if the blood was continually recirculated and not consumed by the tissues, they reasoned, then what purpose could it possibly serve?

Harvey lived to a ripe old age, served as physician to the kings of England, and later did important work in embryology. His case is one of the most interesting in biomedical history, for it shows how empirical science overthrows old theories and spawns better ones, and how common sense and blind allegiance to authority can interfere with acceptance of the truth. But most importantly, Harvey's contributions represent the birth of experimental physiology.

# General Anatomy of the Blood Vessels

## Objectives
When you have completed this section, you should be able to
- describe the structure of a blood vessel;
- describe the different types of arteries, capillaries, and veins;
- trace the general route usually taken by the blood from the heart and back again; and
- describe some variations on this route.

There are three principal categories of blood vessels—arteries, veins, and capillaries. **Arteries** are the efferent vessels of the cardiovascular system—that is, vessels that carry blood away from the heart. **Veins** are the afferent vessels—vessels that carry blood back to the heart. **Capillaries** are microscopic, thin-walled vessels that connect the smallest arteries to the smallest veins. Aside from their general location and direction of blood flow, these three vessel types also differ in the histological structure of their walls.

## The Vessel Wall

The walls of arteries and veins are composed of three layers called *tunics* (figs. 21.1 and 21.2):

1. The **tunica interna (tunica intima)** lines the inside of the vessel and is exposed to the blood. It consists of a simple squamous epithelium called the **endothelium,** overlying a basement membrane and a sparse layer of loose connective tissue. The endothelium acts as a selectively permeable barrier to materials entering or leaving the bloodstream; it secretes chemicals that stimulate the muscle of the vessel wall to contract or relax, thus narrowing or widening the vessel; and it normally repels blood cells and platelets so that they flow freely without sticking to the vessel wall. Under special circumstances, however, platelets and blood cells do adhere to it. When the endothelium is damaged, platelets can adhere and form a blood clot; and when the tissue around a vessel is inflamed, the endothelial cells produce *cell-adhesion molecules* that induce leukocytes to adhere to the surface. This causes leukocytes to congregate in tissues where their defensive actions are needed.

2. The **tunica media,** the middle layer, is usually the thickest. It consists of smooth muscle, collagen, and in some cases, elastic tissue. The relative amounts of muscle and elastic tissue vary greatly from one vessel to another and form a basis for the classification of vessels described in the next section. The tunica media strengthens the vessels and prevents blood pressure from rupturing them, and it provides *vasomotion,* changes in vessel diameter. The widening of a vessel is called *vasodilation* and a narrowing is called *vasoconstriction.*

3. The **tunica externa (tunica adventitia[1])** is the outermost layer. It consists of loose connective tissue that often merges with that of neighboring blood vessels, nerves, or other organs. It anchors the vessel and allows small nerves, lymphatic vessels, and smaller blood vessels to reach and penetrate into a larger vessel. Small vessels called the **vasa vasorum[2]** (VAY-za vay-SO-rum)

---
[1]*advent* = added to
[2]*vasa* = vessels + *vasorum* = of the vessels

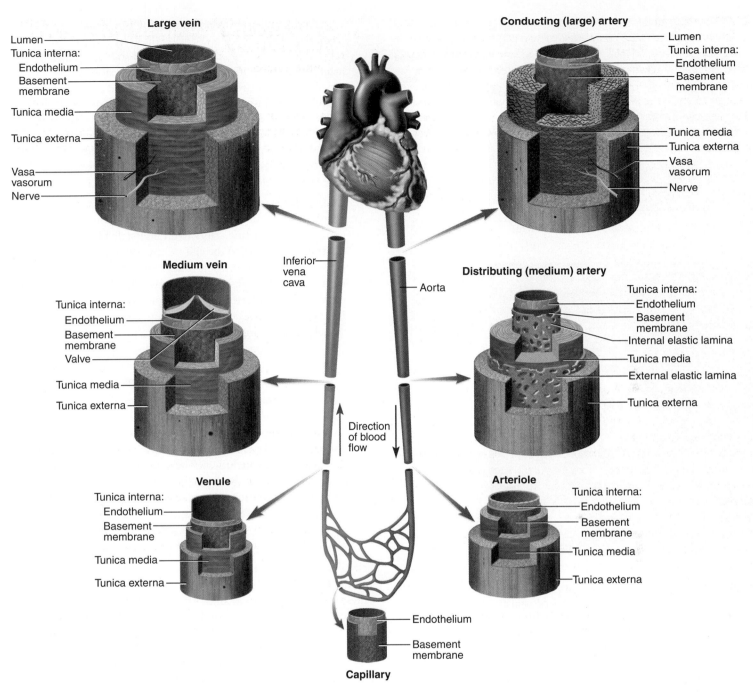

**Figure 21.1** Histological Structure of Blood Vessels.
● *Why do the arteries have so much more elastic tissue than the veins do?*

supply blood to at least the outer half of the vessel wall. Tissues of the inner half are thought to be nourished by diffusion from blood in the lumen.

## Arteries

Arteries are considered to be the *resistance vessels* of the cardiovascular system because they have a relatively strong, resilient tissue structure that resists the high blood pressure within. Each beat of

the heart creates a surge of pressure in the arteries as blood is ejected into them. Arteries are built to withstand these pressure surges. Being more muscular than veins, they retain their round shape even when empty, and they appear relatively circular in tissue sections. They are divided into three categories by size, but of course there is a smooth transition from one category to the next.

1. **Conducting (elastic** or **large) arteries** are the biggest arteries. The aorta, common carotid and subclavian arteries, pulmonary trunk, and common iliac arteries are examples

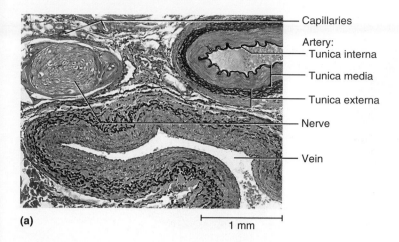

(a)

1 mm

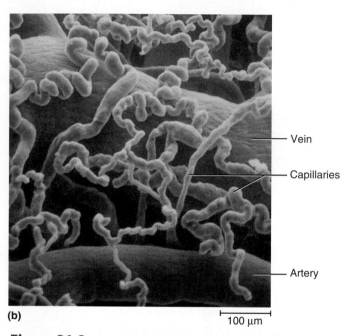

(b)

100 μm

**Figure 21.2 Micrographs of Blood Vessels.** (a) A neurovascular bundle, composed of a small artery, small vein, and nerve traveling together in a common sheath of connective tissue. The dark wavy line near the lumen of the artery is the internal elastic lamina. (b) A polymer cast of blood vessels of the eye (SEM).

of conducting arteries. They have a layer of elastic tissue called the *internal elastic lamina* at the border between the intima and media, but microscopically, it is incomplete and difficult to distinguish from the elastic tissue of the tunica media. The tunica media consists of 40 to 70 layers of elastic sheets, perforated like slices of Swiss cheese, alternating with thin layers of smooth muscle, collagen, and elastic fibers. In histological sections, the view is dominated by this elastic tissue. There is an *external elastic lamina* at the border between the media and externa, but it, too, is difficult to distinguish from the elastic sheets of the tunica media. The tunica externa is less than half as thick as the tunica media and relatively sparse in the largest arteries. It is well supplied with vasa vasorum.

Conducting arteries expand during ventricular systole to receive blood, and recoil during diastole. Their expansion takes some of the pressure off the blood so that smaller arteries downstream are subjected to less systolic stress. Their recoil between heartbeats prevents the blood pressure from dropping too low while the heart is relaxing and refilling. These effects lessen the fluctuations in blood pressure that would otherwise occur. Arteries stiffened by atherosclerosis cannot expand and recoil as freely. Consequently, the downstream vessels are subjected to greater stress and are more likely to develop aneurysms (see Insight 21.1).

2. **Distributing (muscular or medium) arteries** are smaller branches that distribute blood to specific organs. You could compare a conducting artery to an interstate highway and distributing arteries to the exit ramps and state highways that serve specific towns. Most arteries that have specific anatomical names are in these first two size classes. The brachial, femoral, renal, and splenic arteries are examples of distributing arteries. Distributing arteries typically have up to 40 layers of smooth muscle, constituting about three-quarters of the wall thickness. In histological sections, smooth muscle is more conspicuous than the elastic tissue. Both the internal and external elastic laminae, however, are thick and often conspicuous.

3. **Resistance (small) arteries** are usually too variable in number and location to be given individual names. They exhibit up to 25 layers of smooth muscle and relatively little elastic tissue. Compared to larger arteries, they have a thicker tunica media in proportion to the lumen. The smallest resistance arteries, about 40 to 200 μm in diameter and with only one to three layers of smooth muscle, are called **arterioles.** Arterioles have very little tunica externa.

**Metarterioles**[3] are short vessels that link arterioles and capillaries. Instead of a continuous tunica media, they have individual muscle cells spaced a short distance apart, each forming a **precapillary sphincter** that encircles the entrance to one capillary. Constriction of these sphincters reduces or shuts off blood flow through their respective capillaries and diverts blood to tissues or organs elsewhere.

## Arterial Sense Organs

Certain major arteries above the heart have sensory receptors in their walls that monitor blood pressure and chemistry (fig. 21.4). These receptors transmit information to the brainstem that serves to regulate the heartbeat, vasomotion, and respiration. They are of three kinds:

1. **Carotid sinuses.** These are *baroreceptors* (pressure sensors) that respond to changes in blood pressure. Ascending the neck on each side is a *common carotid artery* that branches near the angle of the mandible to form the *internal carotid artery* to the brain and *external carotid artery* to the face. The carotid sinuses are located in the wall of the internal carotid artery just above the branch point. The carotid sinus has a relatively thin tunica media and an abundance of glossopharyngeal

---

[3]*meta* = beyond, next in a series

INSIGHT 21.1 ●●●

## INSIGHT 21.1

### Clinical Application

## Aneurysm

An aneurysm is a weak point in an artery or in the heart wall. It forms a thin-walled, bulging sac that pulsates with each beat of the heart and may eventually rupture. In a *dissecting aneurysm*, blood accumulates between the tunics of an artery and separates them, usually because of degeneration of the tunica media. The most common sites of aneurysms are the abdominal aorta (fig. 21.3), renal arteries, and the arterial circle at the base of the brain. Even without hemorrhaging, aneurysms can cause pain or death by putting pressure on brain tissue, nerves, adjacent veins, pulmonary air passages, or the esophagus. Other consequences include neurological disorders, difficulty in breathing or swallowing, chronic cough, or congestion of the tissues with blood. Aneurysms sometimes result from congenital weakness of the blood vessels and sometimes from trauma or bacterial infections such as syphilis. The most common cause, however, is the combination of atherosclerosis and hypertension.

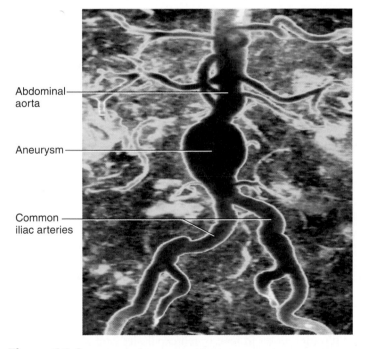

**Figure 21.3** **An Aortic Aneurysm.** This is a magnetic resonance angiogram (MRA) of the abdominal aorta of a patient with hypertension, showing a prominent bulge (aneurysm) of the aorta immediately superior to the common iliac arteries.

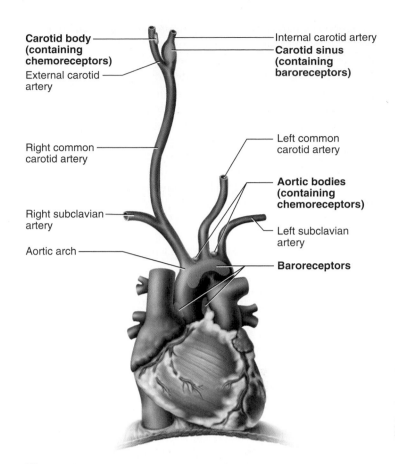

**Figure 21.4** **Baroreceptors and Chemoreceptors in the Arteries Superior to the Heart.** The structures shown here are repeated in the left carotid arteries.

2. **Carotid bodies.** Also located near the branch of the common carotid arteries, these are oval receptors about $3 \times 5$ mm, innervated by sensory fibers of the vagus and glossopharyngeal nerves. They are *chemoreceptors* that monitor changes in blood composition. They primarily transmit signals to the brainstem respiratory centers, which adjust breathing to stabilize the blood pH and its $CO_2$ and $O_2$ levels.

3. **Aortic bodies.** These are one to three chemoreceptors located in the aortic arch near the arteries to the head and arms. They are structurally similar to the carotid bodies and have the same function.

## Capillaries

For the blood to serve any purpose, materials such as nutrients, wastes, and hormones must pass between the blood and the tissue fluids, through the walls of the vessels. There are only two places in the circulation where this occurs—the capillaries and venules. We can think of these as the "business end" of the cardiovascular system, because all the rest of the system exists to serve the exchange processes that occur here. Since capillaries greatly outnumber venules, they are the more important of the two. Capillaries are sometimes called the *exchange vessels* of the cardiovascular system.

nerve fibers in the tunica externa. A rise in blood pressure easily stretches the thin media and stimulates these nerve fibers. The glossopharyngeal nerve then transmits signals to the vasomotor and cardiac centers of the brainstem, and the brainstem responds by lowering the heart rate and dilating the blood vessels, thereby lowering the blood pressure.

Blood capillaries (fig. 21.5) are composed of only an endothelium and basal lamina. Their walls are as thin as 0.2 to 0.4 μm. They average about 5 μm in diameter at the proximal end (where they receive arterial blood), they widen to about 9 μm at the distal end (where they empty into a small vein), and they often branch along the way. Since erythrocytes are about 7.5 μm in diameter, they often have to stretch into elongated shapes to squeeze through the smallest capillaries.

The number of capillaries has been estimated at a billion and their total surface area at 6,300 m². But a more important point is that scarcely any cell in the body is more than 60 to 80 μm (about four to six cell widths) away from the nearest capillary (see photo on p. 595). There are a few exceptions: Capillaries are scarce in tendons and ligaments, found only occasionally in cartilage, and absent from epithelia and the cornea and lens of the eye.

## Types of Capillaries

There are three types of capillaries, distinguished by the ease with which they allow substances to pass through their walls and by structural differences that account for their greater or lesser permeability.

1. **Continuous capillaries** (fig. 21.5) occur in most tissues, such as skeletal muscle. Their endothelial cells, held together by tight junctions, form a continuous tube. A thin protein–carbohydrate layer, the **basal lamina,** surrounds the endothelium and separates it from the adjacent connective tissues. The endothelial cells are usually separated by narrow **intercellular clefts** about 4 nm wide. Small solutes such as

glucose can pass through these clefts, but plasma proteins, other large molecules, and platelets and blood cells are held back. The continuous capillaries of the brain lack intercellular clefts and have more complete tight junctions that form the blood–brain barrier discussed in chapter 15 (p. 428).

Some continuous capillaries exhibit cells called **pericytes** that lie external to the endothelium. Pericytes have elongated tendrils that wrap around the capillary. They contain the same contractile proteins as muscle, and it is thought that they contract and regulate blood flow through the capillaries. They also can differentiate into endothelial and smooth muscle cells and thus contribute to vessel growth and repair.

2. **Fenestrated capillaries** have endothelial cells riddled with holes called **filtration pores (fenestrations**[4]**)** (fig. 21.6). These pores are about 20 to 100 nm in diameter, and are often spanned by a thin glycoprotein membrane. They allow for the rapid passage of small molecules but still retain most proteins and larger particles in the bloodstream. Fenestrated capillaries are important in organs that engage in rapid absorption or filtration—the kidneys, endocrine glands, small intestine, and choroid plexuses of the brain, for example.

3. **Sinusoids (discontinuous capillaries)** are irregular blood-filled spaces in the liver, bone marrow, spleen, and some other organs (fig. 21.7). They are twisted, tortuous passageways, typically 30 to 40 μm wide, that conform to the shape of the surrounding tissue. The endothelial cells are separated by wide gaps with no basal lamina, and the cells also frequently have especially large fenestrations through them. Even proteins and blood cells can pass through these pores; this is how albumin, clotting factors, and other proteins synthesized by the liver enter the blood, and how newly formed blood cells enter the circulation from the bone marrow and lymphatic organs. Some sinusoids contain macrophages or other specialized cells.

## Capillary Permeability

The structure of a capillary wall is closely related to its permeability, the ease with which substances pass through it from the blood to the tissue fluid, or vice versa. There are three routes that materials can travel through a capillary wall (fig. 21.8): (1) the intercellular clefts between endothelial cells; (2) the filtration pores in fenestrated capillaries; and (3) through the endothelial cell plasma membrane and cytoplasm. Nonpolar molecules such as $O_2$, $CO_2$, lipids, and thyroid hormone diffuse easily through the endothelial cells. Hydrophilic substances such as glucose, electrolytes, and large molecules such as insulin pass through the intercellular clefts and filtration pores, or cross through the endothelial cells by a process called *transcytosis:* The endothelial cell internalizes molecules or fluid droplets by endocytosis on one side of the capillary wall, transports the endocytotic vesicles to the other side of the cell, and releases the substances by exocytosis on that side.

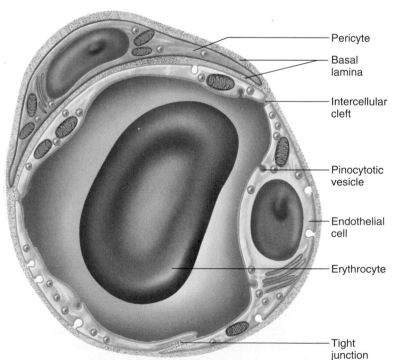

Pericyte

Basal lamina

Intercellular cleft

Pinocytotic vesicle

Endothelial cell

Erythrocyte

Tight junction

**Figure 21.5** **Structure of a Continuous Capillary.** Cross section.

[4]*fenestra* = window

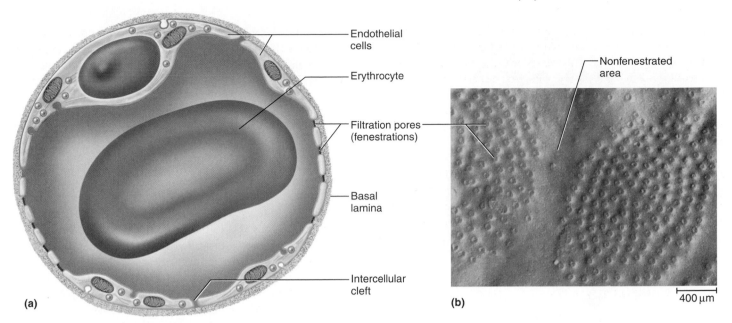

**(a)**

- Endothelial cells
- Erythrocyte
- Filtration pores (fenestrations)
- Basal lamina
- Intercellular cleft

**(b)**

- Nonfenestrated area

400 μm

**Figure 21.6** **Structure of a Fenestrated Capillary.** (a) Cross section of the capillary wall. (b) Surface view of a fenestrated endothelial cell (SEM). The cell has patches of filtration pores (fenestrations) separated by nonfenestrated areas.
● *Identify some organs that have this type of capillary rather than continuous capillaries.*

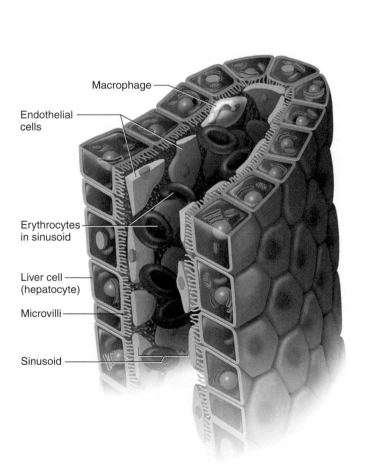

- Macrophage
- Endothelial cells
- Erythrocytes in sinusoid
- Liver cell (hepatocyte)
- Microvilli
- Sinusoid

**Figure 21.7** **A Sinusoid of the Liver.** Large gaps between the endothelial cells allow blood plasma to directly contact the liver cells, but retain blood cells in the lumen of the sinusoid.

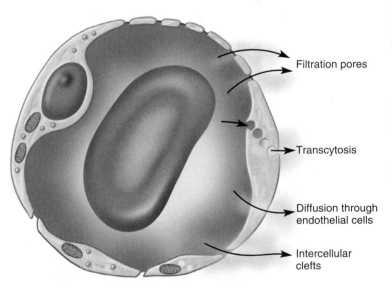

- Filtration pores
- Transcytosis
- Diffusion through endothelial cells
- Intercellular clefts

**Figure 21.8** **Pathways of Capillary Fluid Exchange.** Materials move through the capillary wall through filtration pores (in fenestrated capillaries only), by transcytosis, by diffusion through the endothelial cells, and through intercellular clefts. Although this figure depicts material leaving the bloodstream, material can also enter the bloodstream by the same methods.

## Capillary Beds

Capillaries are organized into groups called **capillary beds**—usually 10 to 100 capillaries supplied by a single metarteriole (fig. 21.9; see also photo on p. 595). Beyond the origins of the capillaries, the metarteriole continues as a **thoroughfare channel** leading directly to a venule. Capillaries empty into the distal end of the thoroughfare channel or directly into the venule.

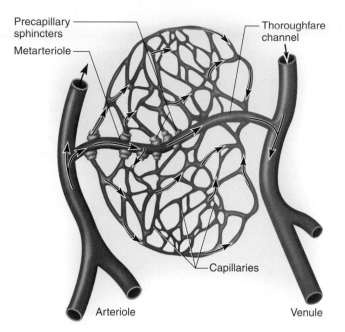

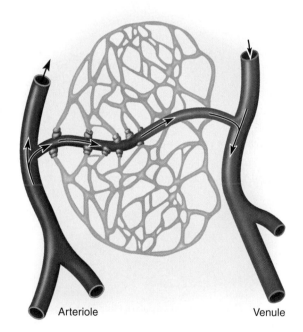

**(a) Sphincters open**

**(b) Sphincters closed**

**Figure 21.9** **Regulation of Capillary Blood Flow.** (a) Precapillary sphincters dilated and capillaries abundantly supplied with blood. (b) Precapillary sphincters closed, with blood bypassing the capillaries.

When the precapillary sphincters are open, the capillaries are well supplied with blood and engage in exchanges with the tissue fluid. When the sphincters are closed, blood bypasses the capillaries, flows through the thoroughfare channel to a venule, and engages in relatively little fluid exchange. There is not enough blood in the body to fill the entire vascular system at once; consequently, about three-quarters of the body's capillaries are shut down at any given time. In the skeletal muscles, for example, about 90% of them have little to no blood flow during periods of rest. During exercise, they receive an abundant flow, while capillary beds elsewhere—for example, in the skin and intestines—shut down to compensate for it.

## Veins

Veins are regarded as the *capacitance vessels* of the cardiovascular system because they are relatively thin-walled and flaccid, and expand easily to accommodate an increased volume of blood; that is, they have a greater capacity for blood containment than arteries do. At rest, about 54% of the blood is found in the systemic veins as compared to only 11% in the systemic arteries (fig. 21.10). The reason that veins are so thin-walled and accommodating is that, being distant from the ventricles of the heart, they are subjected to relatively low blood pressure. In large arteries, blood pressure averages 90 to 100 mm Hg (millimeters of mercury) and surges to 120 mm Hg during systole, whereas in veins, it averages about 10 mm Hg. Furthermore, the blood flow in the veins is steady, rather than pulsating with the heartbeat like the flow in the arteries. Veins therefore do not require thick, pressure-resistant walls. They collapse when empty and thus have relatively flattened, irregular shapes in histological sections (see fig. 21.2).

As we trace blood flow in the arteries, we find it splitting off repeatedly into smaller and smaller *branches* of the arterial system. In the venous system, conversely, we find small veins merging to form larger and larger ones as they approach the heart. We refer to the smaller veins as *tributaries,* by analogy to the streams that converge and act as tributaries to rivers. In examining the types of veins, we will follow the direction of blood flow, working up from the smallest to the largest vessels.

1. **Postcapillary venules** are the smallest of the veins, beginning with diameters of about 15 to 20 μm. They receive blood from capillaries directly or by way of the distal ends of the thoroughfare channels. They have a tunica interna with only

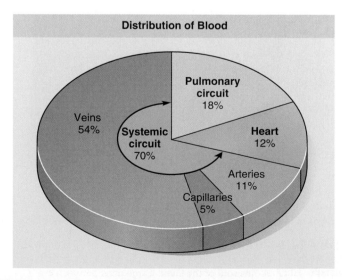

**Figure 21.10** **Typical Distribution of the Blood in a Resting Adult.**
● *What anatomical fact allows the veins to contain so much more blood than the arteries do?*

a few fibroblasts around it and no muscle. Like capillaries, they are often surrounded by pericytes. Postcapillary venules are even more porous than capillaries; therefore, venules also exchange fluid with the surrounding tissues. Most leukocytes emigrate from the bloodstream through the venule walls.

2. **Muscular venules** receive blood from the postcapillary venules. They are up to 1 mm in diameter. They have a tunica media of one or two layers of smooth muscle, and a thin tunica externa.

3. **Medium veins** range up to 10 mm in diameter. Most veins with individual names are in this category, such as the radial and ulnar veins of the forearm and the small and great saphenous veins of the leg. Medium veins have a tunica interna with an endothelium, basement membrane, loose connective tissue, and sometimes a thin internal elastic lamina. The tunica media is much thinner than it is in medium arteries; it exhibits bundles of smooth muscle, but not a continuous muscular layer as seen in arteries. The muscle is interrupted by regions of collagenous, reticular, and elastic tissue. The tunica externa is relatively thick.

Many medium veins, especially in the limbs, exhibit infoldings of the tunica interna that meet in the middle of the lumen, forming **venous valves** directed toward the heart (fig. 21.11). The pressure in the veins is not high enough to push all of the blood upward against the pull of gravity in a standing or sitting person. The upward flow of blood in these vessels depends partly on the massaging action of skeletal muscles and the ability of these valves to keep the blood from dropping down again when the muscles relax. When the muscles surrounding a vein contract, they force blood through the valves. The propulsion of venous blood

by muscular massaging, aided by the venous valves, is a mechanism of blood flow called the *skeletal muscle pump*. Varicose veins result in part from failure of the valves (see Insight 21.2). Such valves are absent from very small and large veins, veins of the abdominal cavity, and veins of the brain.

4. **Venous sinuses** are veins with especially thin walls, large lumens, and no smooth muscle. Examples include the coronary sinus of the heart and the dural sinuses of the brain. Unlike other veins, they are not capable of vasomotion.

5. **Large veins** have diameters greater than 10 mm. They have some smooth muscle in all three tunics. The tunica media is relatively thin with only a moderate amount of smooth muscle; the tunica externa is the thickest layer and contains longitudinal bundles of muscle. Large veins include the venae cavae, pulmonary veins, internal jugular veins, and renal veins.

## Circulatory Routes

The simplest and most common route of blood flow is heart → arteries → capillaries → veins → heart. Blood usually passes through only one network of capillaries from the time it leaves the heart until the time it returns (fig. 21.12a), but there are exceptions, notably portal systems and anastomoses.

In a **portal system** (fig. 21.12b), blood flows through two consecutive capillary networks before returning to the heart. Portal systems occur in the kidneys (chapter 25); connecting the hypothalamus and anterior pituitary gland (chapter 18); and connecting the intestines and liver (see table 21.7).

An **anastomosis** is a point where two veins or arteries merge with each other without intervening capillaries. In an **arteriovenous anastomosis (shunt),** blood flows from an artery directly into a vein (fig. 21.12c). Shunts occur in the fingers, palms, toes, and ears, where they reduce heat loss in cold weather by allowing warm blood to bypass these exposed surfaces. Unfortunately, this makes

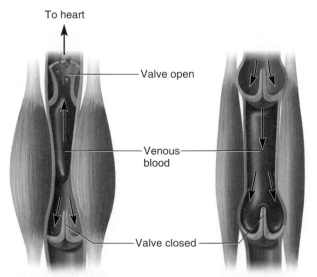

(a) **Contracted skeletal muscles**       (b) **Relaxed skeletal muscles**

**Figure 21.11** **The Skeletal Muscle Pump.** (a) Muscle contraction squeezes the deep veins and forces blood through the next valve in the direction of the heart. Valves below the point of compression prevent backflow. (b) When the muscles relax, blood flows back downward under the pull of gravity but can flow only as far as the nearest valve.

### INSIGHT 21.2

#### Clinical Application

### Varicose Veins

In people who stand for long periods, such as dentists and hairdressers, blood tends to pool in the lower limbs and stretch the veins. This is especially true of superficial veins, which are not surrounded by supportive tissue. Stretching pulls the cusps of the venous valves farther apart until they become incapable of sealing the vessel and preventing the backflow of blood. As the veins become further distended, their walls grow weak, and they develop into *varicose veins* with irregular dilations and twisted pathways. Obesity and pregnancy also promote development of varicose veins by putting pressure on large veins of the pelvic region and obstructing drainage from the limbs. Varicose veins sometimes develop because of hereditary weakness of the valves. With less drainage of blood, tissues of the leg and foot may become edematous and painful. *Hemorrhoids* are varicose veins of the anal canal.

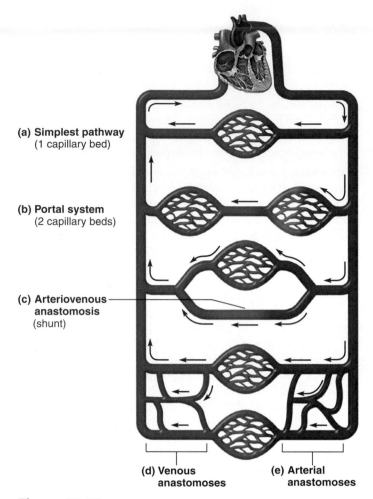

**(a) Simplest pathway**
(1 capillary bed)

**(b) Portal system**
(2 capillary beds)

**(c) Arteriovenous anastomosis**
(shunt)

**(d) Venous anastomoses**    **(e) Arterial anastomoses**

**Figure 21.12** Variations in Circulatory Pathways.
● *After studying tables 21.1 through 21.11, identify specific sites of three arterial anastomoses and three venous anastomoses.*

these blood-deprived areas more susceptible to frostbite. In an **arterial anastomosis,** two arteries merge, providing *collateral* (alternative) routes of blood supply to a tissue (fig. 21.12d). Those of the coronary circulation were mentioned in chapter 20 (page 582). They are also common around joints where movement may temporarily compress an artery and obstruct one pathway. **Venous anastomoses,** where one vein empties directly into another, are the most common. They provide several alternative routes of drainage from an organ, so blockage of a vein is rarely as life-threatening as blockage of an artery. Several arterial and venous anastomoses are described later in this chapter.

## Before You Go On

*Answer the following questions to test your understanding of the preceding section:*

1. Name the three tunics of a typical blood vessel, and explain how they differ from each other.

2. Contrast the tunica media of a conducting artery, arteriole, and venule, and explain how the histological differences are related to the functional differences between these vessels.

3. Describe the differences between a continuous capillary, a fenestrated capillary, and a sinusoid.

4. Describe the differences between a medium vein and a medium (distributing or muscular) artery. State the functional reasons for these differences.

5. Contrast an anastomosis and a portal system with the more typical pathway of blood flow.

6. Describe three routes by which blood-borne substances can pass through a capillary wall into the tissue fluid.

# The Pulmonary Circuit

*Objectives*
When you have completed this section, you should be able to

- trace the route of blood through the pulmonary circuit; and

- explain the anatomical and functional differences between the pulmonary and systemic blood supplies to the lungs.

The remainder of this chapter centers on the names and pathways of the principal arteries and veins. The pulmonary circuit is described here; the section after this concerns the systemic arteries and veins of the axial region (head, neck, thoracic, and abdominopelvic regions); and the section following that concerns the systemic arteries and veins of the appendicular region (the limbs).

The pulmonary circuit (fig. 21.13) begins with the **pulmonary trunk,** a large vessel that ascends diagonally from the right ventricle and branches into the right and left **pulmonary arteries.** As it approaches the lung, the right pulmonary artery branches in two, and both branches enter the lung at a medial indentation called the *hilum* (see fig. 23.9, p. 671). The upper branch is the **superior lobar artery,** serving the superior lobe of the lung. The lower branch divides again within the lung to form the **middle lobar** and **inferior lobar arteries,** supplying the lower two lobes of that lung. The left pulmonary artery is much more variable. It gives off several superior lobar arteries to the superior lobe before entering the hilum, then enters the lung and gives off a variable number of inferior lobar arteries to the inferior lobe.

In both lungs, these arteries lead ultimately to small basketlike capillary beds that surround the pulmonary alveoli (air sacs). This is where the blood unloads $CO_2$ and picks up $O_2$. After leaving the alveolar capillaries, the pulmonary blood flows into venules and veins, ultimately leading to the main **pulmonary veins** that exit the lung at the hilum. The left atrium of the heart receives two pulmonary veins on each side (see fig. 20.3b, p. 574).

The purpose of the pulmonary circuit is primarily to exchange $CO_2$ for $O_2$. The lungs also receive a separate systemic blood supply by way of the *bronchial arteries* (see part I.1 in table 21.4).

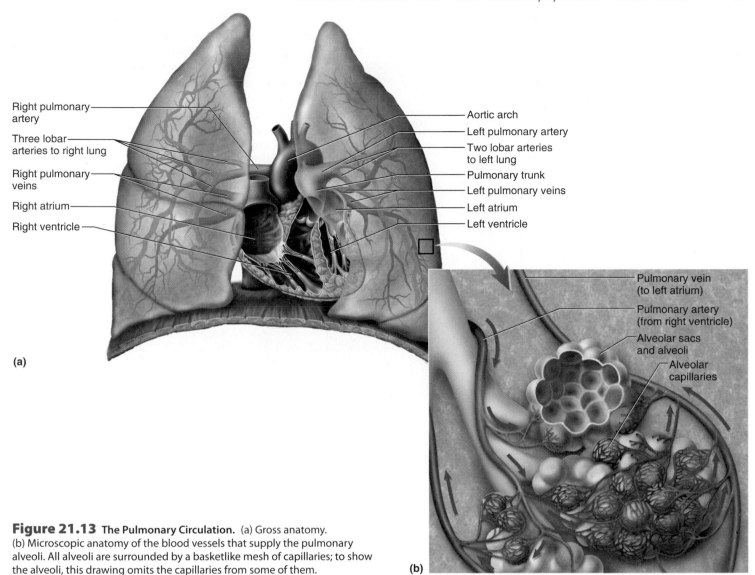

**Figure 21.13  The Pulmonary Circulation.** (a) Gross anatomy.
(b) Microscopic anatomy of the blood vessels that supply the pulmonary alveoli. All alveoli are surrounded by a basketlike mesh of capillaries; to show the alveoli, this drawing omits the capillaries from some of them.

## Before You Go On

*Answer the following questions to test your understanding of the preceding section:*

7. Trace the flow of an RBC from right ventricle to left atrium, naming the vessels along the way.

8. Each lung has two separate arterial supplies. Explain their functions.

## Systemic Vessels of the Axial Region

### Objectives
When you have completed this section, you should be able to

- identify the principal systemic arteries and veins of the axial region; and

- trace the flow of blood from the heart to any major organ of the axial region and back to the heart.

The systemic circuit (figs. 21.14 and 21.15) supplies oxygen and nutrients to all organs and removes their metabolic wastes. Part of it, the coronary circulation, was described in chapter 20. This section surveys the remaining arteries and veins of the axial region—the head, neck, and trunk. Tables 21.1 through 21.7 trace the arterial outflow and venous return, region by region. They outline only the most common circulatory pathways; there is a great deal of anatomical variation in the circulatory system from one person to another.

The names of the blood vessels often describe their location by indicating the body region traversed (as in the *axillary artery* and *brachial veins*), an adjacent bone (as in *temporal artery* and *ulnar vein*), or the organ supplied or drained by the vessel (as in *hepatic artery* and *renal vein*). In many cases, an artery and adjacent vein have similar names (*femoral artery* and *femoral vein,* for example).

As you trace blood flow in these tables, it is important to refer frequently to the illustrations. Verbal descriptions alone may often seem obscure if you do not make full use of the accompanying explanatory illustrations.

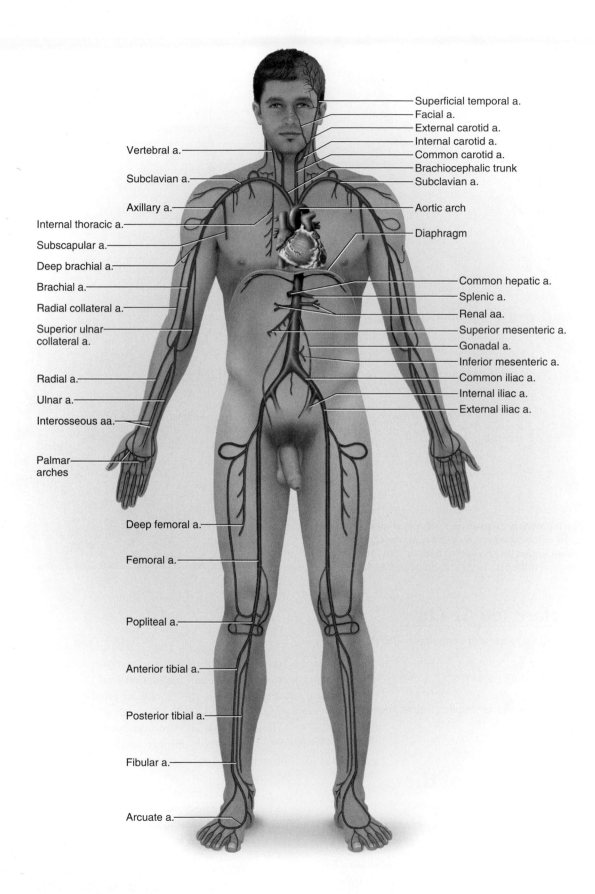

Superficial temporal a.
Facial a.
External carotid a.
Internal carotid a.
Common carotid a.
Brachiocephalic trunk
Subclavian a.
Aortic arch
Diaphragm
Common hepatic a.
Splenic a.
Renal aa.
Superior mesenteric a.
Gonadal a.
Inferior mesenteric a.
Common iliac a.
Internal iliac a.
External iliac a.

Vertebral a.
Subclavian a.
Axillary a.
Internal thoracic a.
Subscapular a.
Deep brachial a.
Brachial a.
Radial collateral a.
Superior ulnar collateral a.
Radial a.
Ulnar a.
Interosseous aa.
Palmar arches
Deep femoral a.
Femoral a.
Popliteal a.
Anterior tibial a.
Posterior tibial a.
Fibular a.
Arcuate a.

**Figure 21.14** **The Major Systemic Arteries.** Anterior view. Different arteries are illustrated on the left than on the right for clarity, but nearly all of those shown occur on both sides. (a. = artery; aa. = arteries)

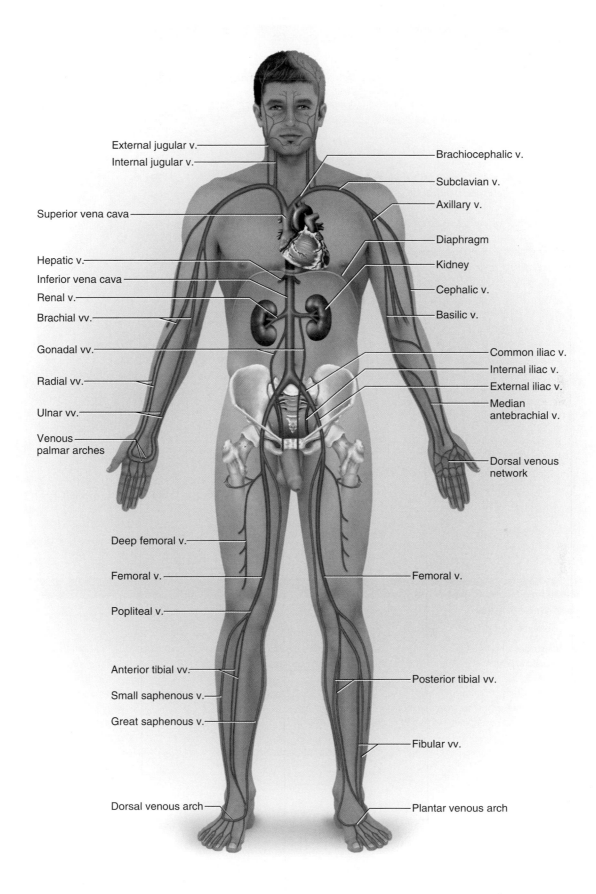

**Figure 21.15** **The Major Systemic Veins.** Anterior view. Different veins are illustrated on the left than on the right for clarity, but nearly all of those shown occur on both sides. (v. = vein; vv. = veins)

| TABLE 21.1 | The Aorta and Its Major Branches |
| --- | --- |

All systemic arteries arise from the aorta, which has three principal regions (fig. 21.16):

1. The **ascending aorta** rises for about 5 cm above the left ventricle. Its only branches are the coronary arteries, which arise behind two cusps of the aortic valve. They are the origins of the coronary circulation described in chapter 20.

2. The **aortic arch** curves to the left like an inverted U superior to the heart. It gives off three major arteries in this order: the **brachiocephalic**[5] (BRAY-kee-oh-seh-FAL-ic) **trunk, left common carotid** (cah-ROT-id) **artery,** and **left subclavian**[6] (sub-CLAY-vee-un) **artery.** These are further traced in tables 21.2 and 21.8.

3. The **descending aorta** passes downward dorsal to the heart, at first to the left of the vertebral column and then anterior to it, through the thoracic and abdominal cavities. It is called the *thoracic aorta* above the diaphragm and the *abdominal aorta* below it. It ends in the lower abdominal cavity by forking into the *right* and *left common iliac arteries* (see table 21.6, part IV).

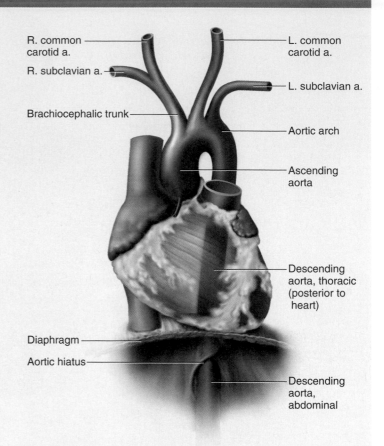

**Figure 21.16** The Thoracic Aorta.  (L. = left; R. = right; a. = artery)

| TABLE 21.2 | Arteries of the Head and Neck |
| --- | --- |

### I. Origins of the Head–Neck Arteries

The head and neck receive blood from four pairs of arteries (fig. 21.17):

1. The **common carotid arteries.** Shortly after leaving the aortic arch, the brachiocephalic trunk divides into the *right subclavian artery* (further traced in table 21.4) and **right common carotid artery.** A little farther along the aortic arch, the **left common carotid artery** arises independently. The common carotids pass up the anterolateral region of the neck, alongside the trachea (see part II of this table).

2. The **vertebral arteries.** These arise from the right and left subclavian arteries and travel up the neck through the transverse foramina of vertebrae C1 through C6. They enter the cranial cavity through the foramen magnum (see part III of this table).

3. The **thyrocervical**[7] **trunks.** These tiny arteries arise from the subclavian arteries lateral to the vertebral arteries; they supply the thyroid gland and some scapular muscles.

4. The **costocervical**[8] **trunks.** These arteries arise from the subclavian arteries a little farther laterally. They supply the deep neck muscles and some of the intercostal muscles of the superior rib cage.

---

[5]*brachio* = arm + *cephal* = head
[6]*sub* = below + *clavi* = clavicle, collarbone
[7]*thyro* = thyroid gland + *cerv* = neck
[8]*costo* = rib

**TABLE 21.2    Arteries of the Head and Neck (continued)**

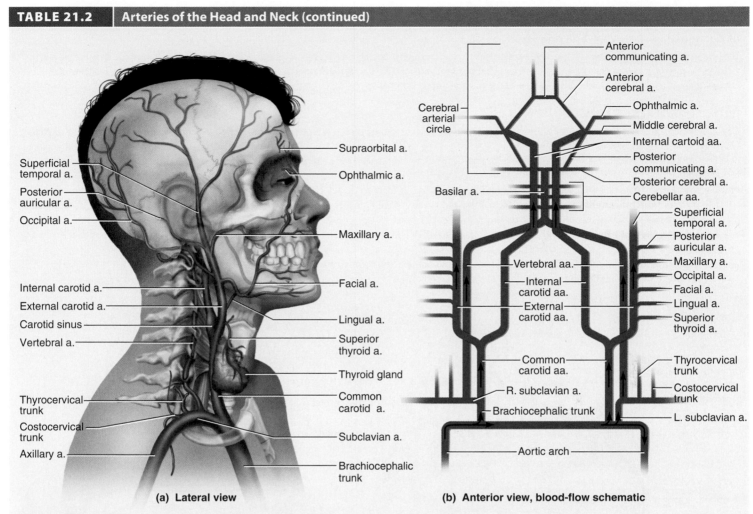

**(a) Lateral view**

**(b) Anterior view, blood-flow schematic**

**Figure 21.17  Superficial (Extracranial) Arteries of the Head and Neck.** The upper part of the schematic (b) depicts the cerebral circulation in figure 21.18. (a. = artery; aa. = arteries)

## II. Continuation of the Common Carotid Arteries

The common carotid arteries have the most extensive distribution of all the head–neck arteries. Near the laryngeal prominence ("Adam's apple"), each common carotid branches into an *external* and *internal carotid artery.*

1. The **external carotid artery** ascends the side of the head external to the cranium and supplies most external head structures except the orbits. It gives rise to the following arteries in ascending order:
    a. the **superior thyroid artery** to the thyroid gland and larynx;
    b. the **lingual artery** to the tongue;
    c. the **facial artery** to the skin and muscles of the face;
    d. the **occipital artery** to the posterior scalp;
    e. the **maxillary artery** to the teeth, maxilla, oral cavity, and external ear; and
    f. the **superficial temporal artery** to the chewing muscles, nasal cavity, lateral aspect of the face, most of the scalp, and the dura mater.
2. The **internal carotid artery** passes medial to the angle of the mandible and enters the cranial cavity through the carotid canal of the temporal bone. It supplies the orbits and about 80% of the cerebrum. Compressing the internal carotids near the mandible can therefore cause loss of consciousness. After entering the cranial cavity, each internal carotid gives rise to the following branches:
    a. the **ophthalmic artery** to the orbit, nose, and forehead;
    b. the **anterior cerebral artery** to the medial aspect of the cerebral hemisphere (see part IV of this table); and
    c. the **middle cerebral artery,** which travels in the lateral sulcus of the cerebrum, supplies the insula, and then issues numerous branches to the lateral region of the frontal, temporal, and parietal lobes of the brain.

## TABLE 21.2 | Arteries of the Head and Neck (continued)

### III. Continuation of the Vertebral Arteries

The vertebral arteries give rise to small branches that supply the spinal cord and its meninges, the cervical vertebrae, and deep muscles of the neck. They then enter the foramen magnum, supply the cranial bones and meninges, and converge to form a single **basilar artery** along the anterior aspect of the brainstem. Branches of the basilar artery supply the cerebellum, pons, and inner ear. At the pons–midbrain junction, the basilar artery divides and flows into the *cerebral arterial circle,* described next.

### IV. The Cerebral Arterial Circle

Blood supply to the brain is so critical that it is furnished by several arterial anastomoses, especially an array of arteries called the **cerebral arterial circle (circle of Willis[9]),** which surrounds the pituitary gland and optic chiasm (fig. 21.18). The circle receives blood from the internal carotid and basilar arteries. Most people lack one or more of its components; only 20% have a complete arterial circle. Knowledge of the distribution of the arteries arising from the circle is crucial for understanding the effects of blood clots, aneurysms, and strokes on brain function. The anterior and posterior cerebral arteries described here and the middle cerebral artery described in part II provide the most significant blood supplies to the cerebrum. Refer to chapter 15 for reminders of the relevant brain anatomy.

1. Two **posterior cerebral arteries** arise from the basilar artery and sweep posteriorly to the rear of the brain, serving the ventral and medial regions of the temporal and occipital lobes as well as the midbrain and thalamus.
2. Two **anterior cerebral arteries** arise from the internal carotids, travel anteriorly, and then arch posteriorly over the corpus callosum as far as the posterior limit of the parietal lobe. They give off extensive branches to the frontal and parietal lobes.
3. The single **anterior communicating artery** is a short anastomosis between the right and left anterior cerebral arteries.
4. The two **posterior communicating arteries** are small anastomoses between the posterior cerebral and internal carotid arteries.

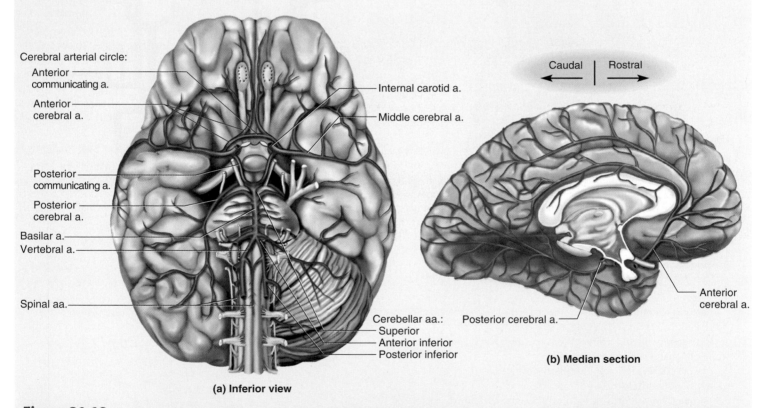

**(a) Inferior view**

**(b) Median section**

**Figure 21.18 Cerebral Circulation.** (a) Inferior view of the brain showing the blood supply to the brainstem, cerebellum, and cerebral arterial circle. (b) Medial section of the brain showing the more distal branches of the anterior and posterior cerebral arteries. Branches of the middle cerebral artery are distributed over the lateral surface of the cerebrum (not illustrated).

[9]Thomas Willis (1621–75), English anatomist

| TABLE 21.3 | Veins of the Head and Neck |
|---|---|

The head and neck are drained mainly by three pairs of veins—the *internal jugular, external jugular,* and *vertebral veins.* We will trace these from their origins to the *subclavian veins.*

## I. Dural Venous Sinuses

After blood circulates through the brain, it collects in large thin-walled veins called **dural venous sinuses**—blood-filled spaces between the layers of the dura mater (fig. 21.19a, b). A reminder of the structure of the dura mater will be helpful in understanding these sinuses. This tough membrane between the brain and cranial bone has a periosteal layer against the bone and a meningeal layer against the brain. In a few places, a space exists between these layers to accommodate a blood-collecting sinus. Between the two cerebral hemispheres is a vertical, sickle-shaped wall of dura called the *falx cerebri,* which contains two of the sinuses. There are about 13 dural venous sinuses in all; we survey only the few most prominent ones here.

1. The **superior sagittal sinus** is contained in the superior margin of the falx cerebri and overlies the longitudinal fissure of the brain (fig. 21.19a; see also figs. 15.3 and 15.5, pp. 426 and 429). It begins anteriorly near the crista galli of the skull and extends posteriorly to the very rear of the head, ending at the level of the posterior occipital protuberance of the skull. Here it bends, usually to the right, and drains into a *transverse sinus.*

2. The **inferior sagittal sinus** is contained in the inferior margin of the falx cerebri and arches over the corpus callosum, deep in the longitudinal fissure. Posteriorly, it joins the *great cerebral vein,* and their union forms the **straight sinus,** which continues to the rear of the head (see fig. 15.5). There, the superior sagittal and straight sinuses meet in a space called the **confluence of the sinuses.**

3. Right and left **transverse sinuses** lead away from the confluence and encircle the inside of the occipital bone, leading toward the ears (fig. 21.19b); their path is marked by grooves on the inner surface of the occipital bone (see fig. 7.5b, p. 182). The right transverse sinus receives blood mainly from the superior sagittal sinus, and the left one drains mainly the straight sinus. Laterally, each transverse sinus makes an S-shaped bend, the **sigmoid sinus,** then exits the cranium through the jugular foramen. From here, the blood flows down the internal jugular vein (see part II.1 of this table).

4. The **cavernous sinuses** are honeycombs of blood-filled spaces on each side of the body of the sphenoid bone (fig. 21.19b). They receive blood from the *superior ophthalmic vein* of the orbit and the *superficial middle cerebral vein* of the brain, among other sources. They drain through several outlets including the transverse sinus, internal jugular vein, and facial vein. They are clinically important because infections can pass from the face and other superficial sites into the cranial cavity by this route. Also, inflammation of a cavernous sinus can injure important structures that pass through it, including the internal carotid artery and cranial nerves III to VI.

## II. Major Veins of the Neck

Blood flows down the neck mainly through three veins on each side, all of which empty into the subclavian vein (fig. 21.19c).

1. The **internal jugular**[10] (JUG-you-lur) **vein** courses down the neck deep to the sternocleidomastoid muscle. It receives most of the blood from the brain, picks up blood from the **facial vein, superficial temporal vein,** and **superior thyroid vein** along the way, passes behind the clavicle, and joins the subclavian vein (which is further traced in table 21.5).

2. The **external jugular vein** courses down the side of the neck superficial to the sternocleidomastoid muscle and empties into the subclavian vein. It drains tributaries from the parotid gland, facial muscles, scalp, and other superficial structures. Some of this blood also follows venous anastomoses to the internal jugular vein.

3. The **vertebral vein** travels with the vertebral artery in the transverse foramina of the cervical vertebrae. Although the companion artery leads to the brain, the vertebral vein does not come from there. It drains the cervical vertebrae, spinal cord, and some of the small deep muscles of the neck, and empties into the subclavian vein.

Table 21.5 traces this blood flow the rest of the way to the heart.

---

[10]*jugul* = neck, throat

## TABLE 21.3 | Veins of the Head and Neck (continued)

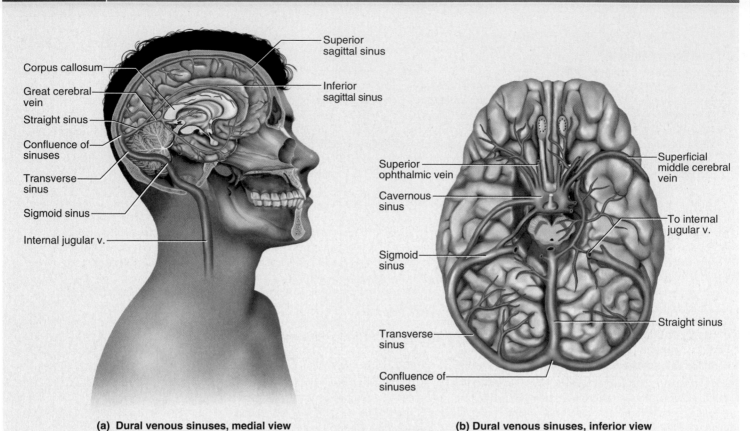

(a) **Dural venous sinuses, medial view**

(b) **Dural venous sinuses, inferior view**

(c) **Superficial veins of the head and neck**

**Figure 21.19** Veins of the Head and Neck. (a) Dural venous sinuses seen in a median section of the cerebrum. (b) Dural venous sinuses seen in an inferior view of the cerebrum. (c) Superficial (extracranial) veins of the head and neck.

| TABLE 21.4 | Arteries of the Thorax |
|---|---|

The thorax is supplied by several arteries arising directly from the aorta (parts I and II of this table) and from the subclavian and axillary arteries (part III). The thoracic aorta begins distal to the aortic arch and ends at the **aortic hiatus** (hy-AY-tus), a passage through the diaphragm. Along the way, it sends off numerous small branches to the thoracic viscera and the body wall (fig. 21.20).

### I. Visceral Branches of the Thoracic Aorta

These supply the viscera of the thoracic cavity:

1. **Bronchial arteries.** Although variable in number and arrangement, there are usually two of these on the left and one on the right. The right bronchial artery usually arises from one of the left bronchial arteries or from a *posterior intercostal artery* (see part II.1). The bronchial arteries supply the bronchi, bronchioles, and larger blood vessels of the lungs, the visceral pleura, the pericardium, and the esophagus.
2. **Esophageal arteries.** Four or five unpaired esophageal arteries arise from the anterior surface of the aorta and supply the esophagus.
3. **Mediastinal arteries.** Many small mediastinal arteries (not illustrated) supply structures of the posterior mediastinum.

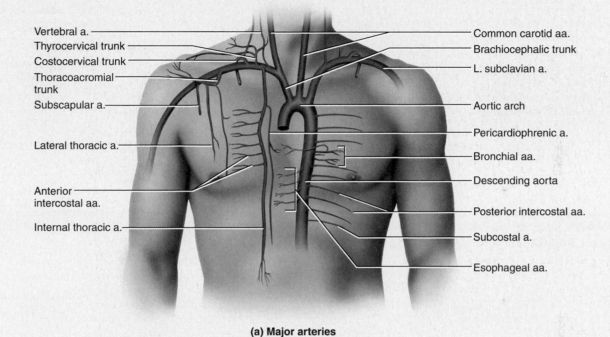

(a) Major arteries

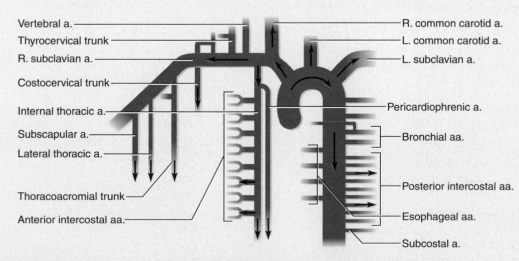

**Figure 21.20** Arteries of the Thorax.

(b) Blood-flow schematic

| **TABLE 21.4** | **Arteries of the Thorax (continued)** |
|---|---|

### II. Parietal Branches of the Thoracic Aorta

The following branches supply chiefly the muscles, bones, and skin of the chest wall; only the first are illustrated:

1. **Posterior intercostal arteries.** Nine pairs of these arise from the posterior surface of the aorta and course around the posterior side of the rib cage between ribs 3 through 12, then anastomose with the *anterior intercostal arteries* (see part III.1 in this table). They supply the intercostal, pectoralis, serratus anterior, and some abdominal muscles, as well as the vertebrae, spinal cord, meninges, breasts, skin, and subcutaneous tissue. They are enlarged in lactating women.

2. **Subcostal arteries.** A pair of these arise from the aorta inferior to the twelfth rib. They supply the posterior intercostal tissues, vertebrae, spinal cord, and deep muscles of the back.

3. **Superior phrenic**[11] (FREN-ic) **arteries** (not illustrated). These arteries, variable in number, arise at the aortic hiatus and supply the superior and posterior regions of the diaphragm.

### III. Branches of the Subclavian and Axillary Arteries

The thoracic wall is also supplied by the following arteries, which arise in the shoulder region—the first one from the subclavian artery and the other three from its continuation, the axillary artery:

1. The **internal thoracic (mammary) artery** supplies the breast and anterior thoracic wall and issues the following branches:
   a. The **pericardiophrenic artery** supplies the pericardium and diaphragm.
   b. The **anterior intercostal arteries** arise from the thoracic artery as it descends alongside the sternum. They travel between the ribs, supply the ribs and intercostal muscles, and anastomose with the posterior intercostal arteries. Each of these sends one branch along the lower margin of the rib above and another branch along the upper margin of the rib below.

2. The **thoracoacromial**[12] (THOR-uh-co-uh-CRO-me-ul) **trunk** provides branches to the superior shoulder and pectoral regions.

3. The **lateral thoracic artery** supplies the pectoral, serratus anterior, and subscapularis muscles. It also issues branches to the breast and is larger in females than in males.

4. The **subscapular artery** is the largest branch of the axillary artery. It supplies the scapula and the latissimus dorsi, serratus anterior, teres major, deltoid, triceps brachii, and intercostal muscles.

| **TABLE 21.5** | **Veins of the Thorax** |
|---|---|

### I. Tributaries of the Superior Vena Cava

The most prominent veins of the upper thorax are as follows. They carry blood from the shoulder region to the heart (fig. 21.21).

1. The **subclavian vein** drains the upper limb (see table 21.9). It begins at the lateral margin of the first rib and travels posterior to the clavicle. It receives the external jugular and vertebral veins, then ends where it receives the internal jugular vein.

2. The **brachiocephalic vein** is formed by union of the subclavian and internal jugular veins. The right brachiocephalic is very short, about 2.5 cm, and the left is about 6 cm long. They receive tributaries from the vertebrae, thyroid gland, and upper thoracic wall and breast, then converge to form the next vein.

3. The **superior vena cava** is formed by the union of the right and left brachiocephalic veins. It travels inferiorly for about 7 cm and empties into the right atrium of the heart. Its main tributary is the *azygos vein*. It drains all structures superior to the diaphragm except the pulmonary circuit and coronary circulation. It also receives drainage from the abdominal cavity by way of the azygos system, described next.

### II. The Azygos System

The principal venous drainage of the thoracic organs is by way of the *azygos* (AZ-ih-goss) *system* (fig. 21.21). The most prominent vein of this system is the **azygos**[13] **vein,** which ascends the right side of the posterior thoracic wall and is named for the lack of a mate on the left. It receives the following tributaries, then empties into the superior vena cava at the level of vertebra T4.

1. The right **ascending lumbar vein** drains the right abdominal wall, then penetrates the diaphragm and enters the thoracic cavity. The azygos vein begins where the ascending lumbar vein meets the right **subcostal vein** beneath rib 12.

2. The right **posterior intercostal veins** drain the intercostal spaces. The first (superior) one empties into the right brachiocephalic vein; intercostals 2 and 3 join to form a *right superior intercostal vein* before emptying into the azygos; and intercostals 4 through 11 each enter the azygos vein separately.

3. The right **esophageal, mediastinal, pericardial,** and **bronchial veins** (not illustrated) drain their respective organs into the azygos.

4. The **hemiazygos**[14] **vein** ascends the posterior thoracic wall on the left. It begins where the left ascending lumbar vein, having just penetrated the diaphragm, joins the subcostal vein below rib 12. The hemiazygos then receives the lower three posterior intercostal veins, esophageal veins, and mediastinal veins. At the level of vertebra T9, it crosses to the right and empties into the azygos.

5. The **accessory hemiazygos vein** descends the posterior thoracic wall on the left. It receives drainage from posterior intercostal veins 4 through 8 and sometimes the left bronchial veins. It crosses to the right at the level of vertebra T8 and empties into the azygos vein.

The left posterior intercostal veins 1 to 3 are the only ones on this side that do not ultimately drain into the azygos vein. They unite to form the *left superior intercostal vein,* which empties into the left brachiocephalic vein.

---

[11]*phren* = diaphragm
[12]*thoraco* = chest + *acr* = tip + *om* = shoulder

[13]unpaired; from *a* = without + *zygo* = union, mate
[14]*hemi* = half

**TABLE 21.5** | **Veins of the Thorax**

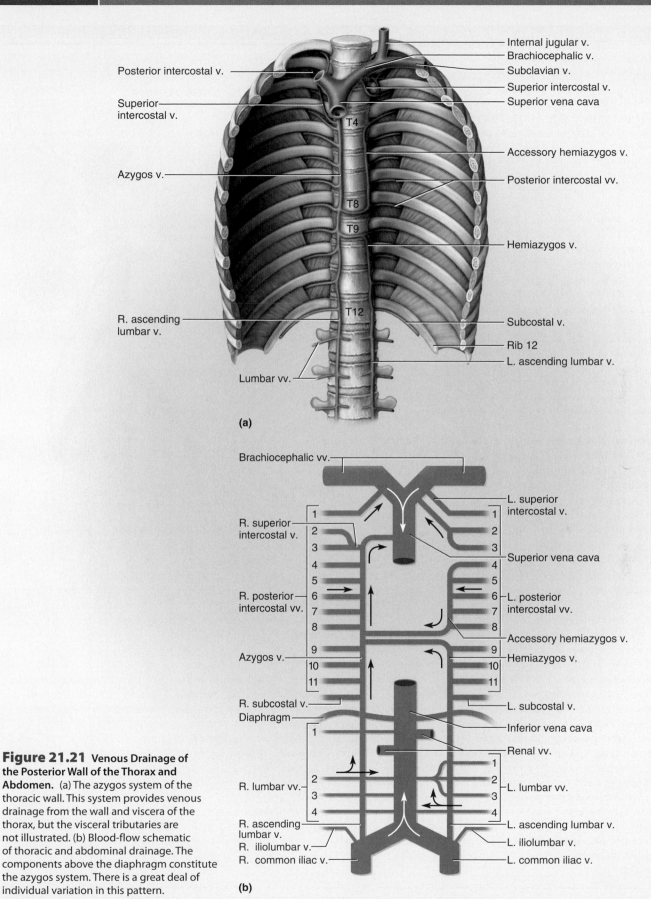

Posterior intercostal v.
Superior intercostal v.
Azygos v.
R. ascending lumbar v.
Lumbar vv.

Internal jugular v.
Brachiocephalic v.
Subclavian v.
Superior intercostal v.
Superior vena cava

T4
T8
T9
T12

Accessory hemiazygos v.
Posterior intercostal vv.
Hemiazygos v.
Subcostal v.
Rib 12
L. ascending lumbar v.

(a)

Brachiocephalic vv.

R. superior intercostal v.
R. posterior intercostal vv.
Azygos v.
R. subcostal v.
Diaphragm
R. lumbar vv.
R. ascending lumbar v.
R. iliolumbar v.
R. common iliac v.

L. superior intercostal v.
Superior vena cava
L. posterior intercostal vv.
Accessory hemiazygos v.
Hemiazygos v.
L. subcostal v.
Inferior vena cava
Renal vv.
L. lumbar vv.
L. ascending lumbar v.
L. iliolumbar v.
L. common iliac v.

(b)

**Figure 21.21** Venous Drainage of the Posterior Wall of the Thorax and Abdomen. (a) The azygos system of the thoracic wall. This system provides venous drainage from the wall and viscera of the thorax, but the visceral tributaries are not illustrated. (b) Blood-flow schematic of thoracic and abdominal drainage. The components above the diaphragm constitute the azygos system. There is a great deal of individual variation in this pattern.

**TABLE 21.6** | **Arteries of the Abdomen and Pelvic Region**

After passing through the aortic hiatus, the aorta descends through the abdominal cavity and ends at the level of vertebra L4, where it branches into right and left *common iliac arteries*. The abdominal aorta is retroperitoneal.

## I. Major Branches of the Abdominal Aorta

The abdominal aorta gives off arteries in the order listed here (fig. 21.22). Those indicated in the plural are paired right and left, and those indicated in the singular are solitary median arteries.

1. The **inferior phrenic arteries** supply the inferior surface of the diaphragm. They may arise from the aorta, celiac trunk, or renal artery. Each issues two or three small **superior suprarenal arteries** to the ipsilateral adrenal (suprarenal) gland.
2. The **celiac**[15] (SEE-lee-ac) **trunk** supplies the upper abdominal viscera (see part II of this table).
3. The **superior mesenteric artery** supplies the intestines (see part III).
4. The **middle suprarenal arteries** arise laterally from the aorta, usually at the same level as the superior mesenteric artery; they supply the adrenal glands.
5. The **renal arteries** supply the kidneys and issue a small **inferior suprarenal artery** to each adrenal gland.
6. The gonadal arteries (**ovarian arteries** in the female and **testicular arteries** in the male) are long, slender arteries that arise from the midabdominal aorta and descend along the posterior body wall to the female pelvic cavity or male scrotum. The gonads begin their embryonic development near the kidneys, and the gonadal arteries are then quite short. As the gonads descend to the pelvic cavity, these arteries grow and acquire their peculiar length and course.
7. The **inferior mesenteric artery** supplies the distal end of the large intestine (see part III).
8. The **lumbar arteries** arise from the lower aorta in four pairs. They supply the dorsal abdominal wall (muscles, joints, and skin) and the spinal cord and other tissues in the vertebral canal.
9. The **median sacral artery,** a tiny medial artery at the inferior end of the aorta, supplies the sacrum and coccyx.
10. The **common iliac arteries** arise as the aorta forks at its inferior end. They are further traced in part IV of this table.

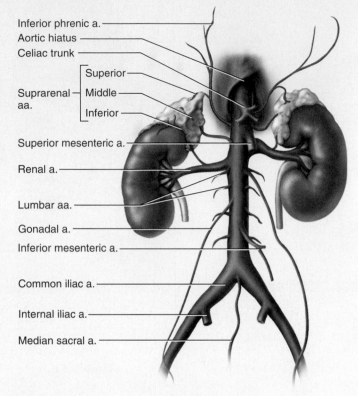

Inferior phrenic a.
Aortic hiatus
Celiac trunk
Suprarenal aa. — Superior / Middle / Inferior
Superior mesenteric a.
Renal a.
Lumbar aa.
Gonadal a.
Inferior mesenteric a.
Common iliac a.
Internal iliac a.
Median sacral a.

**Figure 21.22** **The Abdominal Aorta and Its Major Branches.**

## II. Branches of the Celiac Trunk

The celiac circulation to the upper abdominal viscera is perhaps the most complex route off the abdominal aorta. Because it has numerous anastomoses, the bloodstream does not follow a simple linear path but divides and rejoins itself at several points (fig. 21.23). As you study the following description, locate these branches in the figure and identify the points of anastomosis.

The short, stubby celiac trunk, barely more than 1 cm long, is a median branch of the aorta just below the diaphragm. It immediately gives rise to three branches—the *common hepatic, left gastric,* and *splenic arteries.*

1. The **common hepatic artery** passes to the right and issues two main branches—the gastroduodenal artery and the hepatic artery proper.
   a. The **gastroduodenal artery** gives off the **right gastro-omental (gastroepiploic**[16]) **artery** to the stomach. It then continues as the **superior pancreaticoduodenal** (PAN-cree-AT-ih-co-dew-ODD-eh-nul) **artery,** which splits into two branches that pass around the anterior and posterior sides of the head of the pancreas. These anastomose with the two branches of the *inferior pancreaticoduodenal artery,* discussed in part III.1.
   b. The **hepatic artery proper** ascends toward the liver. It gives off the **right gastric artery,** then branches into **right** and **left hepatic arteries.** The right hepatic artery issues a **cystic artery** to the gallbladder, then the two hepatic arteries enter the liver from below.
2. The **left gastric artery** supplies the stomach and lower esophagus, arcs around the *lesser curvature* (superomedial margin) of the stomach, and anastomoses with the right gastric artery (fig. 21.23b). Thus, the right and left gastric arteries approach from opposite directions and supply this margin of the stomach. The left gastric also has branches to the lower esophagus, and the right gastric also supplies the duodenum.
3. The **splenic artery** supplies blood to the spleen, but gives off the following branches on the way there:
   a. Several small **pancreatic arteries** supply the pancreas.
   b. The **left gastro-omental (gastroepiploic) artery** arcs around the *greater curvature* (inferolateral margin) of the stomach and anastomoses with the right gastro-omental artery. These two arteries stand off about 1 cm from the stomach itself and travel through the superior margin of the *greater omentum,* a fatty membrane suspended from the greater curvature (see figs. A.13, p. 34, and 24.3, p. 688). They furnish blood to both the stomach and omentum.
   c. The **short gastric arteries** supply the upper portion (fundus) of the stomach.

---

[15]*celi* = belly, abdomen
[16]*gastro* = stomach + *epi* = upon, above + *ploic* = pertaining to the greater omentum

**TABLE 21.6** | **Arteries of the Abdomen and Pelvic Region (continued)**

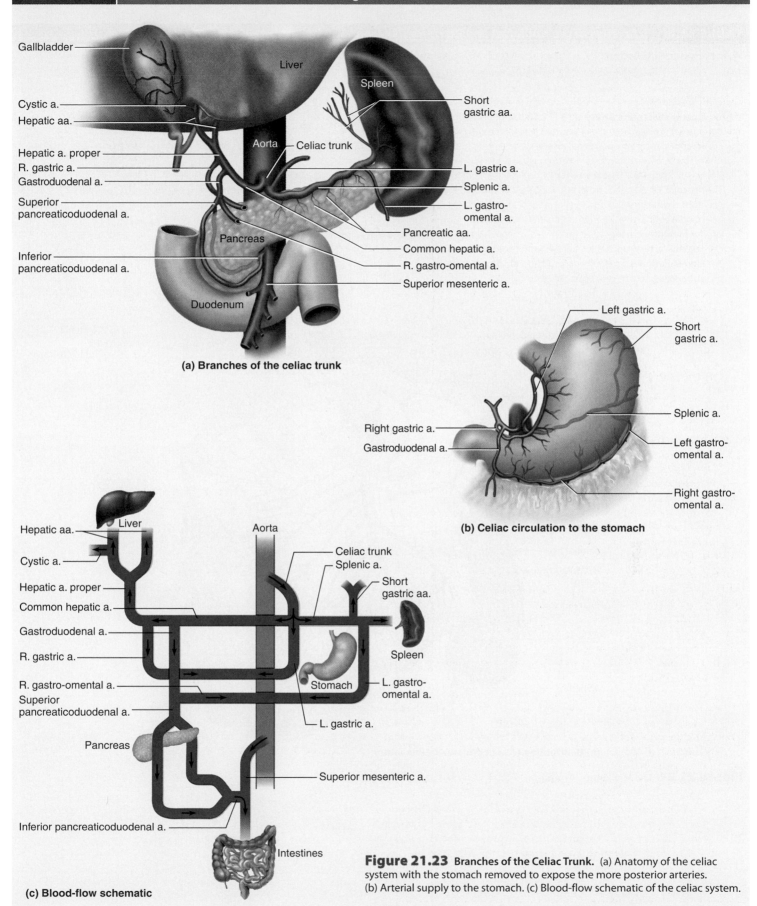

Gallbladder

Liver

Spleen

Short gastric aa.

Cystic a.

Hepatic aa.

Aorta — Celiac trunk

Hepatic a. proper

R. gastric a.

Gastroduodenal a.

L. gastric a.

Splenic a.

Superior pancreaticoduodenal a.

L. gastro-omental a.

Pancreatic aa.

Pancreas

Common hepatic a.

Inferior pancreaticoduodenal a.

R. gastro-omental a.

Superior mesenteric a.

Duodenum

**(a) Branches of the celiac trunk**

Left gastric a.

Short gastric a.

Right gastric a.

Gastroduodenal a.

Splenic a.

Left gastro-omental a.

Right gastro-omental a.

**(b) Celiac circulation to the stomach**

Hepatic aa.

Liver

Aorta

Cystic a.

Celiac trunk

Splenic a.

Hepatic a. proper

Short gastric aa.

Common hepatic a.

Gastroduodenal a.

R. gastric a.

Spleen

R. gastro-omental a.

Superior pancreaticoduodenal a.

Stomach

L. gastro-omental a.

Pancreas

L. gastric a.

Superior mesenteric a.

Inferior pancreaticoduodenal a.

Intestines

**Figure 21.23** **Branches of the Celiac Trunk.** (a) Anatomy of the celiac system with the stomach removed to expose the more posterior arteries. (b) Arterial supply to the stomach. (c) Blood-flow schematic of the celiac system.

**(c) Blood-flow schematic**

**TABLE 21.6** | **Arteries of the Abdomen and Pelvic Region (continued)**

### III. Mesenteric Circulation

The mesentery is a translucent sheet that suspends the intestines and other abdominal viscera from the posterior body wall (see figs. A.10, p. 30, and 24.3, p. 688). It contains numerous arteries, veins, and lymphatic vessels that supply and drain the intestines. The arterial supply arises from the *superior* and *inferior mesenteric arteries;* numerous anastomoses between these ensure adequate collateral circulation to the intestines even if one route is temporarily obstructed.

The **superior mesenteric artery** (fig. 21.24a) is the most significant intestinal blood supply, serving nearly all of the small intestine and the proximal half of the large intestine. It arises medially from the upper abdominal aorta and gives off the following branches:

1. The **inferior pancreaticoduodenal artery,** already mentioned, branches to pass around the anterior and superior sides of the pancreas and anastomose with the two branches of the superior pancreaticoduodenal artery.
2. Twelve to 15 **jejunal** and **ileal arteries** form a fanlike array that supplies nearly all of the small intestine (portions called the jejunum and ileum).
3. The **ileocolic** (ILL-ee-oh-CO-lic) **artery** supplies the ileum, appendix, and parts of the large intestine (cecum and ascending colon).
4. The **right colic artery** also supplies the ascending colon.
5. The **middle colic artery** supplies most of the transverse colon.

The **inferior mesenteric artery** arises from the lower abdominal aorta and serves the distal part of the large intestine (fig. 21.24b):

1. The **left colic artery** supplies the transverse and descending colon.
2. The **sigmoid arteries** supply the descending and sigmoid colon.
3. The **superior rectal artery** supplies the rectum.

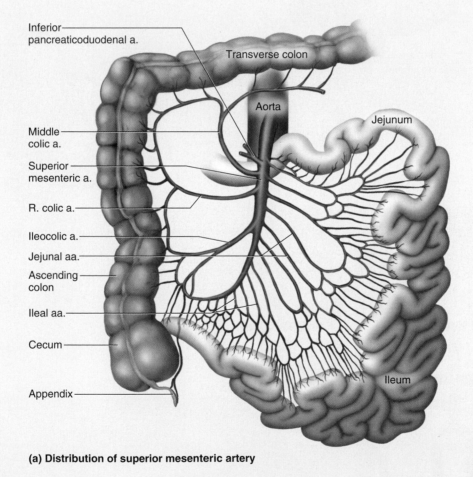

**(a) Distribution of superior mesenteric artery**

**Figure 21.24** The Mesenteric Arteries.

**TABLE 21.6** | **Arteries of the Abdomen and Pelvic Region (continued)**

### IV. Arteries of the Pelvic Region

The two common iliac arteries arise by branching of the aorta, descend for another 5 cm, and then, at the level of the sacroiliac joint, each divides into an external and internal iliac artery. The external iliac supplies mainly the lower limb (see table 21.10). The **internal iliac artery** supplies mainly the pelvic wall and viscera. Its branches are shown only in schematic form in figure 21.30.

Shortly after its origin, the internal iliac divides into anterior and posterior trunks. The anterior trunk produces the following branches:

1. The **superior vesical**[17] **artery** supplies the urinary bladder and distal end of the ureter. It arises indirectly from the anterior trunk by way of a short *umbilical artery*, a remnant of the artery that supplies the fetal umbilical cord. The rest of the umbilical artery becomes a closed fibrous cord after birth.
2. In men, the **inferior vesical artery** supplies the bladder, ureter, prostate gland, and seminal vesicle. In women, the corresponding vessel is the **vaginal artery,** which supplies the vagina and part of the bladder and rectum.
3. The **middle rectal artery** supplies the rectum.
4. The **obturator artery** exits the pelvic cavity through the obturator foramen and supplies the adductor muscles of the medial thigh.
5. The **internal pudendal**[18] (pyu-DEN-dul) **artery** serves the perineum and erectile tissues of the penis and clitoris; it supplies the blood for vascular engorgement during sexual arousal.
6. In women, the **uterine artery** is the main blood supply to the uterus and supplies some blood to the vagina. It enlarges substantially in pregnancy. It passes up the uterine margin, then turns laterally at the uterine tube and anastomoses with the *ovarian artery*, thus supplying blood to the ovary as well (see part I.6 of table 21.6, and fig. 26.19, p. 755).
7. The **inferior gluteal artery** supplies the gluteal muscles and hip joint.

The posterior trunk produces the following branches:

1. The **iliolumbar artery** supplies the lumbar body wall and pelvic bones.
2. The **lateral sacral arteries** lead to tissues of the sacral canal, skin, and muscles posterior to the sacrum. There are usually two of these, superior and inferior.
3. The **superior gluteal artery** supplies the skin and muscles of the gluteal region and the muscle and bone tissues of the pelvic wall.

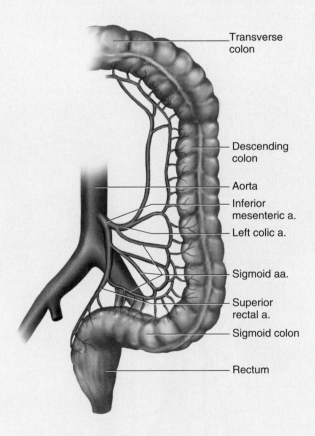

Transverse colon

Descending colon

Aorta

Inferior mesenteric a.

Left colic a.

Sigmoid aa.

Superior rectal a.

Sigmoid colon

Rectum

**(b) Distribution of inferior mesenteric artery**

---

[17]*vesic* = bladder
[18]*pudend* = literally "shameful parts"; the external genitals

| **TABLE 21.7** | Veins of the Abdomen and Pelvic Region |
|---|---|

## I. Tributaries of the Inferior Vena Cava

The **inferior vena cava (IVC)** is the body's largest blood vessel, having a diameter of about 3.5 cm. It forms by the union of the right and left common iliac veins at the level of vertebra L5 and drains many of the abdominal viscera as it ascends the posterior body wall. It is retroperitoneal and lies immediately to the right of the aorta. The IVC picks up blood from numerous tributaries in the following ascending order (fig. 21.25):

1. The **internal iliac veins** drain the gluteal muscles; the medial aspect of the thigh, the urinary bladder, rectum, prostate, and ductus deferens of the male; and the uterus and vagina of the female. They unite with the *external iliac veins,* which drain the lower limb and are described in table 21.11. Their union forms the **common iliac veins,** which then converge to form the IVC.
2. Four pairs of **lumbar veins** empty into the IVC, as well as into the ascending lumbar veins described in part II.
3. The gonadal veins (**ovarian veins** in the female and **testicular veins** in the male) drain the gonads. Like the gonadal arteries, and for the same reason (table 21.6, part I.6), these are long slender vessels that end far from their origins. The left gonadal vein empties into the left renal vein, whereas the right gonadal vein empties directly into the IVC.
4. The **renal veins** drain the kidneys into the IVC. The left renal vein also receives blood from the left gonadal and left suprarenal veins. It is up to three times as long as the right renal vein, since the IVC lies to the right of the median plane of the body.
5. The **suprarenal veins** drain the adrenal (suprarenal) glands. The right suprarenal empties directly into the IVC, and the left suprarenal empties into the left renal vein.
6. The **inferior phrenic veins** drain the inferior aspect of the diaphragm.
7. The **hepatic veins** drain the liver, extending a short distance from its superior surface to the IVC.

After receiving these inputs, the IVC penetrates the diaphragm and enters the right atrium of the heart from below. It does not receive any thoracic drainage.

## II. Veins of the Abdominal Wall

A pair of **ascending lumbar veins** receive blood from the common iliac veins below and the aforementioned lumbar veins of the posterior body wall (see fig. 21.21b). The ascending lumbar veins give off anastomoses with the inferior vena cava beside them as they ascend to the diaphragm. The left ascending lumbar vein passes through the diaphragm via the aortic hiatus and continues as the hemiazygos vein above. The right ascending lumbar vein passes through the diaphragm to the right of the vertebral column and continues as the azygos vein. The further paths of the azygos and hemiazygos veins are described in table 21.5.

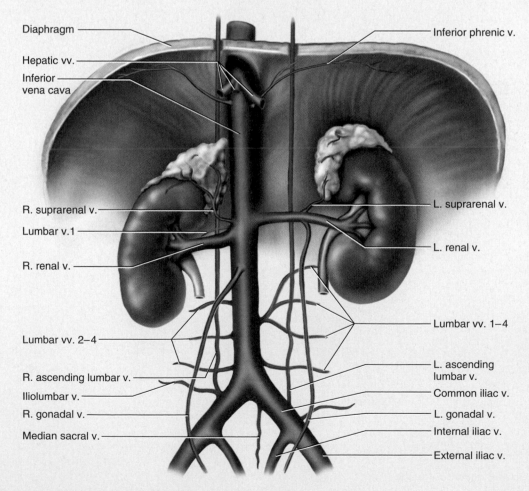

**Figure 21.25** **The Inferior Vena Cava and Its Tributaries.** Compare the blood-flow schematic in figure 21.21b.
● *Why do the veins that drain the ovaries and testes terminate so far away from the gonads?*

| TABLE 21.7 | Veins of the Abdomen and Pelvic Region (continued) |
|---|---|

### III. The Hepatic Portal System

The **hepatic portal system** receives all of the blood draining from the abdominal digestive tract, as well as from the pancreas, gallbladder, and spleen (fig. 21.26). It is called a portal system because it connects capillaries of the intestines and other digestive organs to modified capillaries (*hepatic sinusoids*) of the liver; thus, the blood passes through two capillary beds in series before it returns to the heart. Intestinal blood is richly laden with nutrients for a few hours following a meal. The hepatic portal system gives the liver first claim to these nutrients before the blood is distributed to the rest of the body. It also allows the blood to be cleansed of bacteria and toxins picked up from the intestines, an important function of the liver. Its principal veins are as follows:

1. The **inferior mesenteric vein** receives blood from the rectum and distal part of the colon. It converges in a fanlike array in the mesentery and empties into the splenic vein.

2. The **superior mesenteric vein** receives blood from the entire small intestine, ascending colon, transverse colon, and stomach. It, too, exhibits a fanlike arrangement in the mesentery and then joins the splenic vein to form the hepatic portal vein.

3. The **splenic vein** drains the spleen and travels across the abdominal cavity toward the liver. Along the way, it picks up **pancreatic veins** from the pancreas, then the inferior mesenteric vein, then ends where it meets the superior mesenteric vein.

4. The **hepatic portal vein** is the continuation beyond the convergence of the splenic and superior mesenteric veins. It travels about 8 cm upward and to the right, receives the **cystic vein** from the gallbladder, then enters the inferior surface of the liver. In the liver, it ultimately leads to the innumerable microscopic hepatic sinusoids. Blood from the sinusoids empties into the hepatic veins described earlier, and they empty into the IVC. Circulation within the liver is described in more detail in chapter 24 (p. 707).

5. The left and right **gastric veins** form an arch along the lesser curvature of the stomach and empty into the hepatic portal vein.

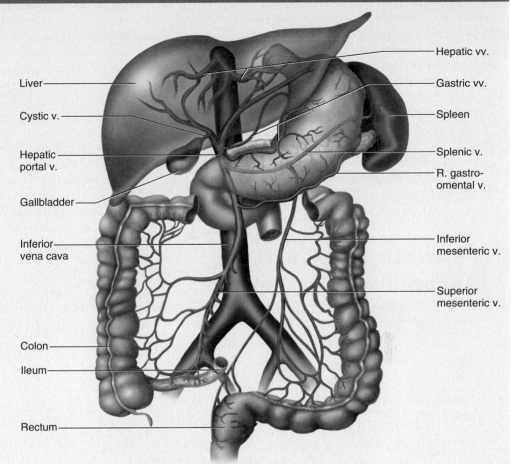

(a) Tributaries of the hepatic portal system

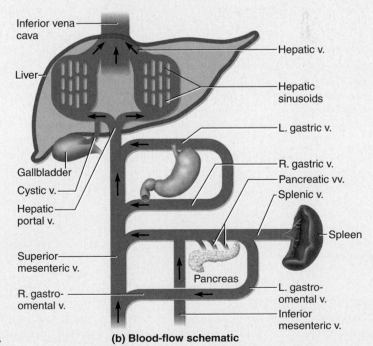

**Figure 21.26** The Hepatic Portal System.

(b) Blood-flow schematic

## Before You Go On

*Answer the following questions to test your understanding of the preceding section:*

9. Concisely contrast the destinations of the external and internal carotid arteries.

10. Briefly state the organs or parts of organs that are supplied with blood by (a) the cerebral arterial circle, (b) the celiac trunk, (c) the superior mesenteric artery, and (d) the internal iliac artery.

11. If you were dissecting a cadaver, where would you look for the internal and external jugular veins? What muscle would help you distinguish one from the other?

12. Trace a blood cell from the left lumbar body wall to the superior vena cava, naming the vessels through which it would travel.

# Systemic Vessels of the Appendicular Region

## Objectives

When you have completed this section, you should be able to

• identify the principal systemic arteries and veins of the limbs; and

• trace the flow of blood from the heart to any region of the upper or lower limb and back to the heart.

The principal vessels of the appendicular region are detailed in tables 21.8 through 21.11. While the appendicular arteries are usually deep and well protected, the veins occur in both deep and superficial groups; you may be able to see several of the superficial ones in your arms and hands. Deep veins run parallel to the arteries and often have similar names (*femoral artery* and *femoral vein*, for example). In several cases, the deep veins occur in pairs flanking the corresponding artery (such as the two *radial veins* traveling alongside the *radial artery*).

These blood vessels will be described in an order corresponding to the direction of blood flow. Thus, we will begin with the arteries in the shoulder and pelvic regions and progress to the hands and feet, whereas we will trace the veins beginning in the hands and feet and progressing toward the heart.

Venous pathways have more anastomoses than arterial pathways, so the route of flow is often not as clear. If all the anastomoses were illustrated, many of these venous pathways would look more like confusing networks than a clear route back to the heart. Therefore, most anastomoses—especially the highly variable and unnamed ones—are omitted from the figures to allow you to focus on the more general course of blood flow. The blood-flow schematics in several figures will also help to clarify these routes.

| TABLE 21.8 | Arteries of the Upper Limb |
|---|---|

The upper limb is supplied by a prominent artery that changes name along its course from *subclavian* to *axillary* to *brachial*, then issues branches to the arm, forearm, and hand (fig. 21.27).

### I. The Shoulder and Arm (Brachium)

1. The brachiocephalic trunk arises from the aortic arch and branches into the right common carotid artery and **left subclavian artery;** the **right subclavian artery** arises directly from the aortic arch. Each subclavian arches over the respective lung, rising as high as the base of the neck slightly superior to the clavicle. It then passes posterior to the clavicle, downward over the first rib, and ends in name only at the rib's lateral margin. In the shoulder, it gives off several small branches to the thoracic wall and viscera, described in table 21.4.

2. As the artery continues past the first rib, it is named the **axillary artery.** It continues through the axillary region, gives off small thoracic branches (see table 21.4), and ends, again in name only, at the neck of the humerus. Here, it gives off a pair of **circumflex humeral arteries,** which encircle the humerus, anastomose with each other laterally, and supply blood to the shoulder joint and deltoid muscle. Beyond this loop, the vessel is called the brachial artery.

3. The **brachial** (BRAY-kee-ul) **artery** continues down the medial and anterior sides of the humerus and ends just distal to the elbow, supplying the anterior flexor muscles of the brachium along the way. This artery is the most common site of blood pressure measurement, using an inflatable cuff that encircles the arm and compresses the artery.

4. The **deep brachial artery** arises from the proximal end of the brachial and supplies the humerus and triceps brachii muscle. About midway down the arm, it continues as the radial collateral artery.

5. The **radial collateral artery** descends in the lateral side of the arm and empties into the radial artery slightly distal to the elbow.

6. The **superior ulnar collateral artery** arises about midway along the brachial artery and descends in the medial side of the arm. It empties into the ulnar artery slightly distal to the elbow.

### II. The Forearm, Wrist, and Hand

Just distal to the elbow, the brachial artery forks into the *radial* and *ulnar arteries.*

1. The **radial artery** descends the forearm laterally, alongside the radius, nourishing the lateral forearm muscles. The most common place to take a pulse is at the radial artery just proximal to the thumb.

2. The **ulnar artery** descends medially through the forearm, alongside the ulna, nourishing the medial forearm muscles.

| TABLE 21.8 | Arteries of the Upper Limb (continued) |
|---|---|

3. The **interosseous**[19] **arteries** of the forearm lie between the radius and ulna. They begin with a short **common interosseous artery** branching from the upper end of the ulnar artery. The common interosseous quickly divides into anterior and posterior branches. The **anterior interosseous artery** travels down the anterior side of the interosseous membrane, nourishing the radius, ulna, and deep flexor muscles. It ends distally by passing through the interosseous membrane to join the posterior interosseous artery. The **posterior interosseous artery** descends along the posterior side of the interosseous membrane and nourishes mainly the superficial extensor muscles.

4. Two U-shaped **palmar arches** arise by anastomosis of the radial and ulnar arteries at the wrist. The **deep palmar arch** is fed mainly by the radial artery and the **superficial palmar arch** mainly by the ulnar artery. The arches issue arteries to the palmar region and fingers.

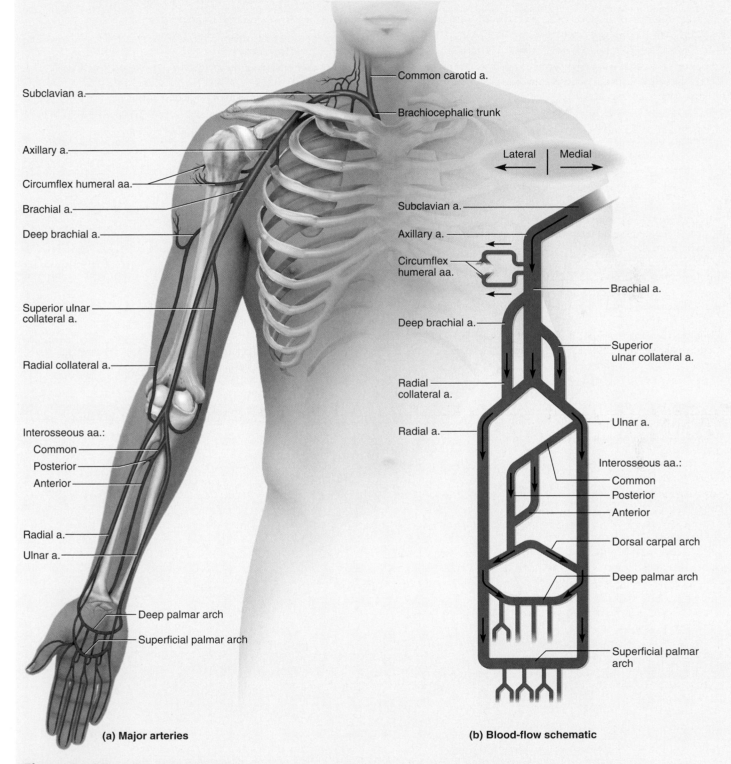

**(a) Major arteries**

**(b) Blood-flow schematic**

**Figure 21.27** Arteries of the Upper Limb.

• *Why are arterial anastomoses especially common at joints such as the shoulder and elbow?*

---

[19]*inter* = between + *osse* = bones

| **TABLE 21.9** | **Veins of the Upper Limb** |
|---|---|

Both superficial and deep veins drain the upper limb, ultimately leading to axillary and subclavian veins that parallel the arteries of the same names (fig. 21.28). The superficial veins are often externally visible and are larger in diameter and carry more blood than the deep veins.

### I. Superficial Veins

1. The **dorsal venous network** is a plexus of veins often visible through the skin on the back of the hand; it empties into the major superficial veins of the forearm, the cephalic and basilic.
2. The **cephalic**[20] (sef-AL-ic) **vein** arises from the lateral side of the network, travels up the lateral side of the forearm and arm to the shoulder, and joins the axillary vein there. Intravenous fluids are often administered through the distal end of this vein.
3. The **basilic**[21] (bah-SIL-ic) **vein** arises from the medial side of the network, travels up the posterior side of the forearm, and continues into the arm. It turns deeper about midway up the arm and joins the brachial vein at the axilla (see part II.4 of this table).

   As an aid to remembering which vein is cephalic and which is basilic, visualize your arm held straight away from the torso (abducted) with the thumb up, like the orientation of the embryonic limb bud. The cephalic vein runs along the upper side of the arm closer to the head (as suggested by *cephal,* "head"), and the name *basilic* is suggestive of the lower (basal) side of the arm (although not named for that reason).
4. The **median cubital vein** is a short anastomosis between the cephalic and basilic veins that obliquely crosses the cubital fossa (anterior bend of the elbow). It is often clearly visible through the skin and is the most common site for drawing blood.
5. The **median antebrachial vein** drains a network of blood vessels in the hand called the **superficial palmar venous network.** It travels up the medial forearm and terminates at the elbow, emptying variously into the basilic vein, median cubital vein, or cephalic vein.

### II. Deep Veins

1. The **deep** and **superficial venous palmar arches** receive blood from the fingers and palmar region. They are anastomoses that join the radial and ulnar veins.
2. Two **radial veins** arise from the lateral side of the palmar arches and course up the forearm alongside the radius. Slightly distal to the elbow, they converge and give rise to one of the brachial veins described shortly.
3. Two **ulnar veins** arise from the medial side of the palmar arches and course up the forearm alongside the ulna. They unite near the elbow to form the other brachial vein.
4. The two **brachial veins** continue up the brachium, flanking the brachial artery, and converge into a single vein just before the axillary region.
5. The **axillary vein** forms by the union of the brachial and basilic veins. It begins at the lower margin of the teres major muscle and passes through the axillary region, picking up the cephalic vein along the way. At the lateral margin of the first rib, it changes name to the subclavian vein.
6. The **subclavian vein** continues into the shoulder posterior to the clavicle and ends where it meets the internal jugular vein of the neck. There it becomes the brachiocephalic vein. The right and left brachiocephalics converge and form the superior vena cava, which empties into the right atrium of the heart.

---

[20]*cephalic* = related to the head
[21]*basilic* = royal, prominent, important

**TABLE 21.9** | **Veins of the Upper Limb (continued)**

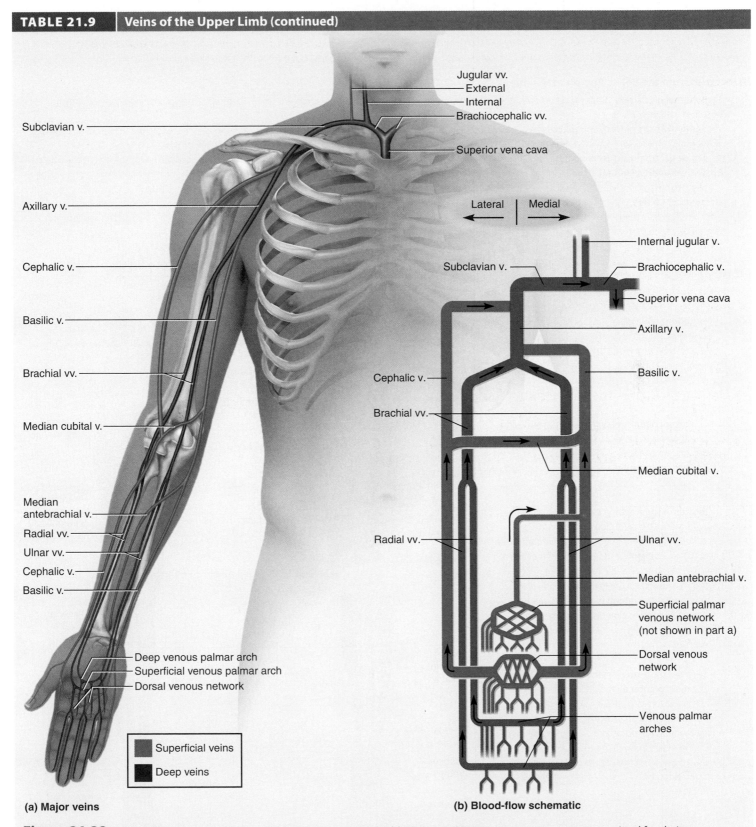

(a) Major veins

(b) Blood-flow schematic

**Figure 21.28 Veins of the Upper Limb.** Variations on this pattern are highly common. Many venous anastomoses are omitted for clarity.

## TABLE 21.10 | Arteries of the Lower Limb

As we have already seen, the aorta forks at its lower end into the right and left common iliac arteries, and each of these soon divides again into an internal and external iliac artery. We traced the internal iliac artery in table 21.6 (part IV), and we now trace the external iliac as it supplies the lower limb (figs. 21.29 and 21.30).

### I. Arteries from the Pelvic Region to the Knee

1. The **external iliac artery** sends small branches to the skin and muscles of the abdominal wall and pelvic girdle, then passes behind the inguinal ligament and becomes the femoral artery.
2. The **femoral artery** passes through the *femoral triangle* of the upper medial thigh, where its pulse can be palpated (see Insight 21.3). In the triangle, it gives off several small arteries to the skin and then produces the following branches before descending the rest of the way to the knee.
   a. The **deep femoral artery** arises from the lateral side of the femoral, within the triangle. It is the largest branch and is the major arterial supply to the thigh muscles.
   b. Two **circumflex femoral arteries** arise from the deep femoral, encircle the head of the femur, and anastomose laterally. They supply mainly the femur, hip joint, and hamstring muscles.
3. The **popliteal artery** is a continuation of the femoral artery in the popliteal fossa at the rear of the knee. It begins where the femoral artery emerges from an opening (*adductor hiatus*) in the tendon of the adductor magnus muscle and ends where it splits into the *anterior* and *posterior tibial arteries*. As it passes through the popliteal fossa, it gives off anastomoses called **genicular**[22] **arteries** that supply the knee joint.

### II. Arteries of the Leg and Foot

In the leg proper, the three most significant arteries are the anterior tibial, posterior tibial, and fibular arteries.

1. The **anterior tibial artery** arises from the popliteal artery and immediately penetrates through the interosseous membrane of the leg to the anterior compartment. There, it travels lateral to the tibia and supplies the extensor muscles. Upon reaching the ankle, it gives rise to the following dorsal arteries of the foot.
   a. The **dorsal pedal artery** traverses the ankle and upper medial surface of the foot and gives rise to the arcuate artery.
   b. The **arcuate artery** sweeps across the foot from medial to lateral and gives rise to vessels that supply the toes.
2. The **posterior tibial artery** is a continuation of the popliteal artery that passes down the leg, deep in the posterior compartment, supplying flexor muscles along the way. Inferiorly, it passes behind the medial malleolus of the ankle and into the plantar region of the foot. It gives rise to the following:
   a. The **medial** and **lateral plantar arteries** originate by bifurcation of the posterior tibial artery at the ankle. The medial plantar artery supplies mainly the great toe. The lateral plantar artery sweeps across the sole of the foot and becomes the deep plantar arch.
   b. The **deep plantar arch** gives off another set of arteries to the toes.
3. The **fibular (peroneal) artery** arises from the proximal end of the posterior tibial artery near the knee. It descends through the lateral side of the posterior compartment, supplying lateral muscles of the leg along the way, and ends in a network of arteries in the heel.

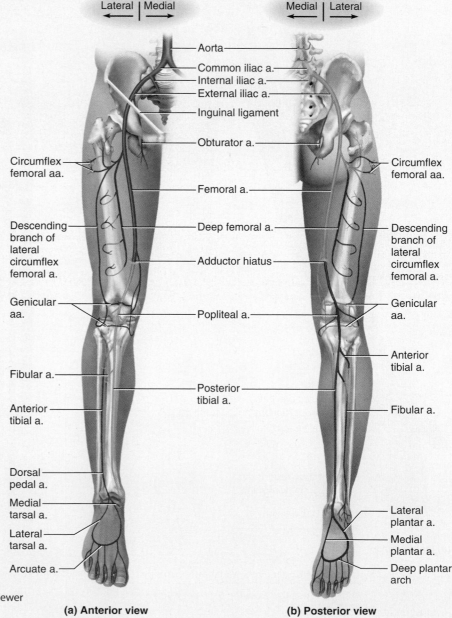

**Figure 21.29** **Arteries of the Lower Limb.** The foot is strongly plantar flexed with the dorsal surface facing the viewer in part (a) and the sole facing the viewer in part (b).

(a) Anterior view    (b) Posterior view

[Labels, left (lateral/medial):] Lateral | Medial

Aorta
Common iliac a.
Internal iliac a.
External iliac a.
Inguinal ligament
Obturator a.
Circumflex femoral aa.
Femoral a.
Descending branch of lateral circumflex femoral a.
Deep femoral a.
Adductor hiatus
Genicular aa.
Popliteal a.
Fibular a.
Posterior tibial a.
Anterior tibial a.
Dorsal pedal a.
Medial tarsal a.
Lateral tarsal a.
Arcuate a.

[Labels, right (medial/lateral):] Medial | Lateral

Circumflex femoral aa.
Descending branch of lateral circumflex femoral a.
Genicular aa.
Anterior tibial a.
Fibular a.
Lateral plantar a.
Medial plantar a.
Deep plantar arch

---

[22]*genic* = knee

**TABLE 21.10** | **Arteries of the Lower Limb (continued)**

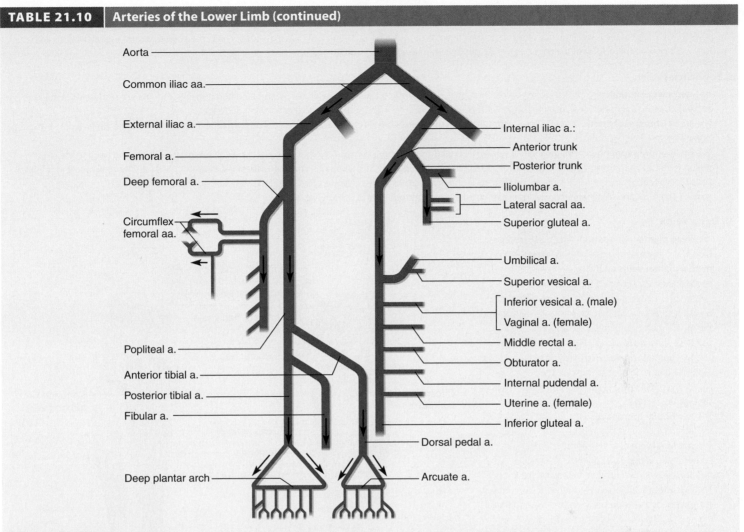

**Figure 21.30 Arterial Schematic of the Pelvic Region and Lower Limb.** The pelvic schematic on the right is stretched for clarity. These arteries are not located as far inferiorly as the limb arteries depicted on the left.

### THINK ABOUT IT

*There are certain similarities between the arteries of the hand and foot. What arteries of the wrist and hand are most comparable in arrangement and function to the arcuate artery and deep plantar arch of the foot?*

## TABLE 21.11 | Veins of the Lower Limb

We will follow drainage of the lower limb from the toes to the inferior vena cava (figs. 21.31 and 21.32). As in the upper limb, there are deep and superficial veins with anastomoses between them. Most of the anastomoses are omitted from the illustrations.

### I. Superficial Veins

1. The **dorsal venous arch** (fig. 21.31a) is often visible through the skin on the dorsum of the foot. It collects blood from the toes and more proximal part of the foot, and has numerous anastomoses similar to the dorsal venous network of the hand. It gives rise to the following two veins.
2. The **small (short) saphenous**[23] (sah-FEE-nus) **vein** arises from the lateral side of the arch and passes up that side of the leg as far as the knee. There, it drains into the popliteal vein.
3. The **great (long) saphenous vein,** the longest vein in the body, arises from the medial side of the arch and travels all the way up the leg and thigh to the inguinal region. It empties into the femoral vein slightly inferior to the inguinal ligament. It is commonly used as a site for the long-term administration of intravenous fluids; it is a relatively accessible vein in infants and in patients in shock whose veins have collapsed. Portions of this vein are commonly used as grafts in coronary bypass surgery. The great and small saphenous veins are among the most common sites of varicose veins.

### II. Deep Veins

1. The **deep plantar venous arch** (fig. 21.31b) receives blood from the toes and gives rise to **lateral** and **medial plantar veins** on the respective sides. The lateral plantar vein gives off the *fibular veins,* then crosses over to the medial side and approaches the medial plantar vein. The two plantar veins pass behind the medial malleolus of the ankle and continue as a pair of *posterior tibial veins.*
2. The two **posterior tibial veins** pass up the leg embedded deep in the calf muscles. They converge like an inverted Y into a single vein about two-thirds of the way up the tibia.
3. The two **fibular (peroneal) veins** ascend the back of the leg and similarly converge like a Y.
4. The **popliteal vein** begins near the knee by convergence of these two inverted Ys. It passes through the popliteal fossa at the back of the knee.
5. The two **anterior tibial veins** travel up the anterior compartment of the leg between the tibia and fibula (fig. 21.31a). They arise from the medial side of the dorsal venous arch, converge just distal to the knee, and then flow into the popliteal vein.
6. The **femoral vein** is a continuation of the popliteal vein into the thigh. It drains blood from the deep thigh muscles and femur.
7. The **deep femoral vein** drains the femur and muscles of the thigh supplied by the deep femoral artery. It receives four principal tributaries along the shaft of the femur and then a pair of **circumflex femoral veins** that encircle the upper femur, then finally drains into the upper femoral vein.
8. The **external iliac vein** is formed by the union of the femoral and great saphenous veins near the inguinal ligament.
9. The **internal iliac vein** follows the course of the internal iliac artery and its distribution. Its tributaries drain the gluteal muscles; the medial aspect of the thigh; the urinary bladder, rectum, prostate, and ductus deferens in the male; and the uterus and vagina in the female.
10. The **common iliac vein** is formed by the union of the external and internal iliac veins. The right and left common iliacs then unite to form the inferior vena cava.

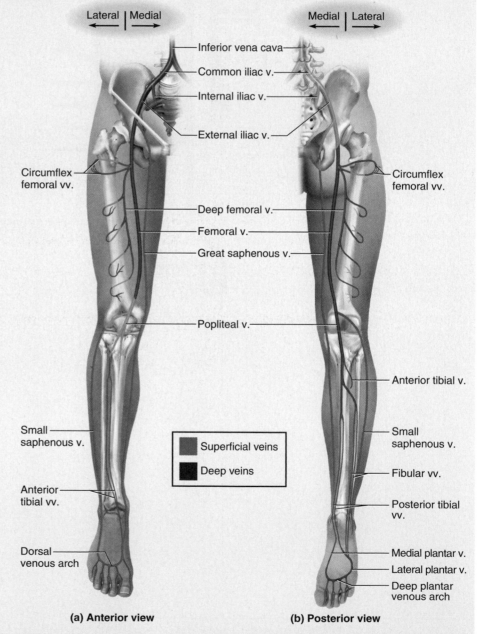

**(a) Anterior view**　　**(b) Posterior view**

**Figure 21.31** Veins of the Lower Limb. The foot is strongly plantar flexed with the dorsal surface facing the viewer in part (a) and the sole facing the viewer in part (b).

---

[23]*saphen* = standing

**TABLE 21.11**   **Veins of the Lower Limb (continued)**

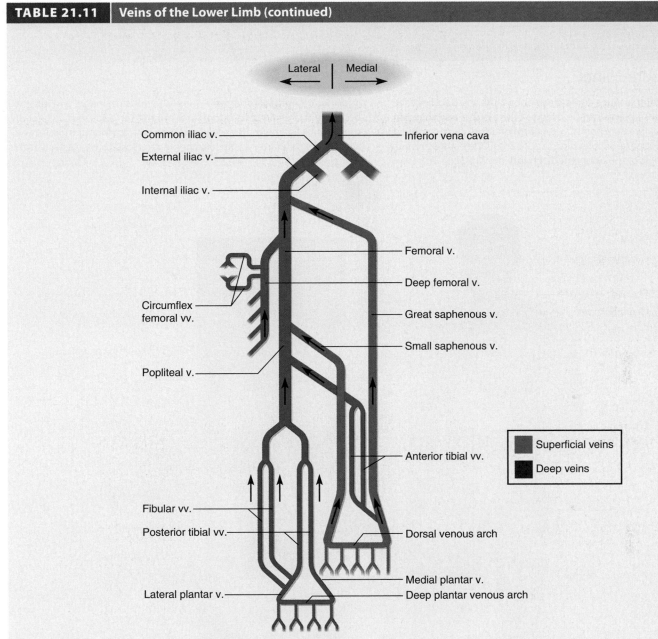

**Figure 21.32** **Venous Schematic of the Lower Limb.** Anterior view.

# INSIGHT 21.3

## Clinical Application

### Arterial Pressure Points

In some places, major arteries come close enough to the body surface to be palpated. These places can be used to take a pulse, and they can serve as emergency *pressure points,* where firm pressure can be applied to temporarily reduce arterial bleeding (fig. 21.33a). One of these points is the *femoral triangle* of the upper medial thigh (fig. 21.33b,c). This is an important landmark for arterial supply, venous drainage, and innervation of the lower limb. Its boundaries are the sartorius muscle laterally, the inguinal ligament superiorly, and the adductor longus muscle medially. The femoral artery, vein, and nerve run close to the surface at this point.

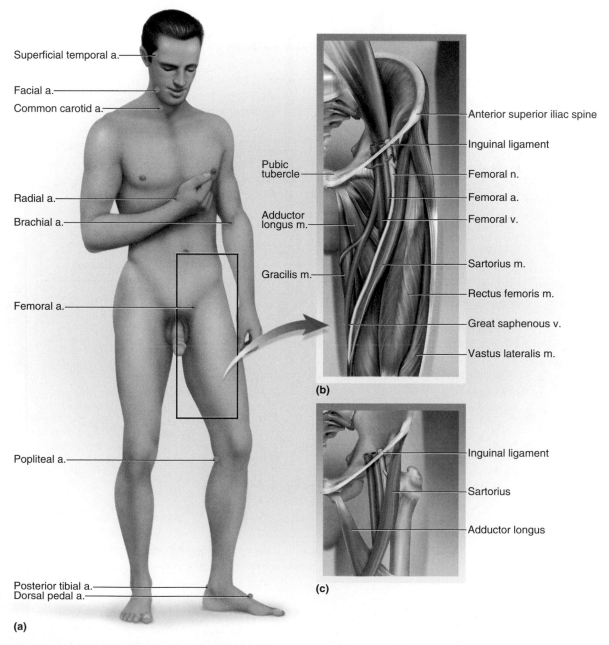

Superficial temporal a.

Facial a.

Common carotid a.

Radial a.

Brachial a.

Femoral a.

Popliteal a.

Posterior tibial a.
Dorsal pedal a.

(a)

Pubic tubercle

Adductor longus m.

Gracilis m.

Anterior superior iliac spine

Inguinal ligament

Femoral n.

Femoral a.

Femoral v.

Sartorius m.

Rectus femoris m.

Great saphenous v.

Vastus lateralis m.

(b)

Inguinal ligament

Sartorius

Adductor longus

(c)

**Figure 21.33** **Arterial Pressure Points.** (a) Areas where arteries lie close enough to the surface that a pulse can be palpated or pressure can be applied to reduce arterial bleeding. (b) Structures in the femoral triangle. (c) Boundaries of the femoral triangle.

## Before You Go On

*Answer the following questions to test your understanding of the preceding section:*

13. Trace one possible path of a red blood cell from the left ventricle to the toes.

14. Trace one possible path of a red blood cell from the fingers to the right atrium.

15. The subclavian, axillary, and brachial artery are really one continuous artery. What is the reason for giving it three different names along its course?

16. State two ways in which the great saphenous vein has special clinical significance. Where is this vein located?

# Developmental and Clinical Perspectives

### Objectives
When you have completed this section, you should be able to

- describe the embryonic development of the blood vessels;
- explain how the circulatory system changes at birth; and
- describe the changes that occur in the blood vessels in old age.

## Embryonic Development of the Blood Vessels

The development of blood vessels, both in the embryo and later in life, is called **angiogenesis.**[24] The first trace of embryonic angiogenesis appears at 13 to 15 days of gestation. At this time, the embryo is a three-layered disc of ectoderm, mesoderm, and endoderm, attached to the uterus by an *embryonic stalk* and associated with three membranes, the *chorion, amnion,* and *yolk sac* (see fig. 4.3, p. 110). In the yolk sac, groups of mesenchymal cells differentiate into cell masses called *blood islands.* Spaces open in the middle of a blood island, and cells in these spaces differentiate into *hemoblasts,* the forerunners of the first blood cells. Cells of the margin become *angioblasts,* which give rise to the endothelium of the future blood vessel (fig. 21.34).

As blood islands proliferate and grow, they begin to connect with each other, and their internal spaces form the lumens of the blood vessels. By the end of week 3, the yolk sac is fully vascularized. In subsequent weeks, blood islands begin to appear in the liver, spleen, and bone marrow, and those of the yolk sac and other sites external to the embryo disappear. Also during this time, the heart tube forms and links up with the blood vessels. Around the end of week 3, the heart begins beating (see chapter 20, p. 588), and a week later, a unidirectional blood flow is established. The blood vessels are not long uniform tubes at this time, but a network of irregularly shaped channels. Those that receive the greatest blood flow develop a tunica media and

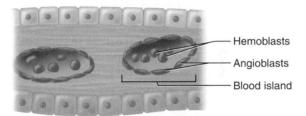

(a) **Early blood islands in yolk sac**

— Blood islands
— Yolk sac endoderm
— Yolk sac mesoderm

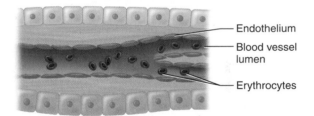

(b) **Differentiation of mesenchymal cells into angioblasts and hemoblasts**

— Hemoblasts
— Angioblasts
— Blood island

(c) **Merger of blood islands**

— Endothelium
— Blood vessel lumen
— Erythrocytes

**Figure 21.34** **Development of Blood Vessels and Erythrocytes from Embryonic Blood Islands.** (a) Early blood islands in the yolk sac. (b) Differentiation of mesenchymal cells into angioblasts and hemoblasts. (c) Merger of the lumens of the blood islands as a blood vessel begins to form and branch.

externa and become more tubular, thus becoming typical blood vessels. Those with a lesser flow either degenerate or remain composed of nothing but endothelium, thus becoming capillaries. Capillaries and the larger vessels sprout lateral branches, giving rise to the eventual anatomical circuitry of the mature cardiovascular system.

We will not examine the complex details of the embryonic development of all the major blood vessels, but primarily the major arteries and veins near the heart. Remember that the embryo forms five pairs of pharyngeal arches in weeks 4 to 5 (see chapter 4, p. 112). As these develop, a pouch called the *aortic sac* appears at the rostral end of the heart. An artery arises from each side of the sac, loops through the first pharyngeal arch, and ends in the dorsal aorta on that side. The loop is *aortic arch I.* Five more pairs of

---

[24]*angio* = vessel + *genesis* = origin

**aortic arches** (II–VI) later form between the pharyngeal pouches (fig. 21.35a). This reflects a primitive vertebrate pattern seen in fish, where the six aortic arches supply blood to the gills, but it becomes highly modified in humans and other mammals. The six arches actually never appear all at once as shown in the figure. Arches I and II degenerate before the most caudal arches appear, and arch V never develops to any great extent in mammals. Arches III, IV, and VI, however, play major roles in human development (fig. 21.35b). Arch III gives rise to the common carotid artery and the proximal

portion of the internal carotid artery; the external carotid artery buds from the common carotid. The common carotids are short at first, but elongate as the embryo grows and the heart moves caudally. Arch IV degenerates on the right, but on the left it produces the aortic arch. Arch VI gives rise to the pulmonary arteries.

Initially, the embryo has two *dorsal aortae* that pass side by side for the length of the body. Caudal to the pharyngeal arches, however, these soon fuse into a single **dorsal aorta,** the forerunner of the adult descending aorta (fig. 21.36). The dorsal aorta issues about

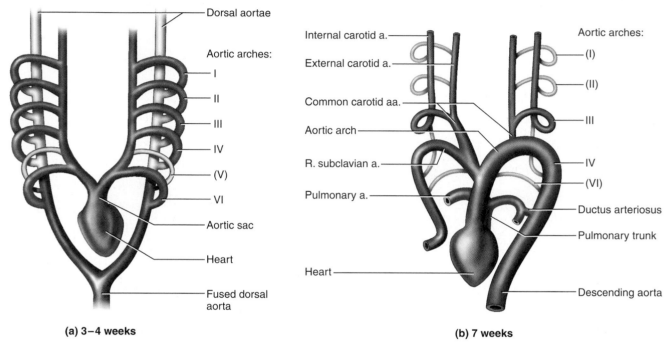

(a) 3–4 weeks  (b) 7 weeks

**Figure 21.35** **Development of Some Major Arteries from the Embryonic Aortic Arches.** (a) The six aortic arches, dorsal view. This is a composite diagram representing developments from day 22 through day 29. In reality, arch I degenerates as arches III and IV form, and arch II degenerates as arch VI forms. Aortic arch V develops very little, and sometimes not at all, in humans. (b) Remodeled arterial system at about 7 weeks. Pale colors and arch numbers in parentheses indicate the former positions of aortic arches that no longer exist at this time, for comparison to part (a). The left subclavian vein does not develop from an aortic arch and is not illustrated.

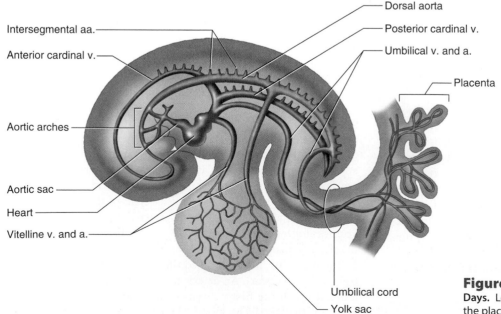

**Figure 21.36** **Major Embryonic Blood Vessels at 26 Days.** Left lateral view of the embryo, yolk sac, and part of the placenta.

30 pairs of *intersegmental arteries,* which supply blood to the somites and their derivatives. Most of these degenerate, but the adult intercostal arteries, lumbar arteries, and common iliac arteries are remnants of some of the embryonic intersegmental arteries.

The principal veins associated with the heart (fig. 21.36) are the *anterior cardinal vein,* which drains the head region; the *posterior cardinal vein,* which drains the body caudal to the heart; the *vitelline veins* from the yolk sac; and the *umbilical veins* from the placenta.

There are initially two umbilical veins, but only the left one persists until birth. The cardinal veins provide most of the venous drainage of the embryonic body. They meet at a *common cardinal vein* just before entering the heart. The future superior vena cava develops from the right anterior cardinal and common cardinal veins. The posterior cardinal veins largely degenerate, however, leaving only the common iliac veins and part of the azygos system as remnants. The inferior vena cava develops separately, not from the posterior cardinal veins.

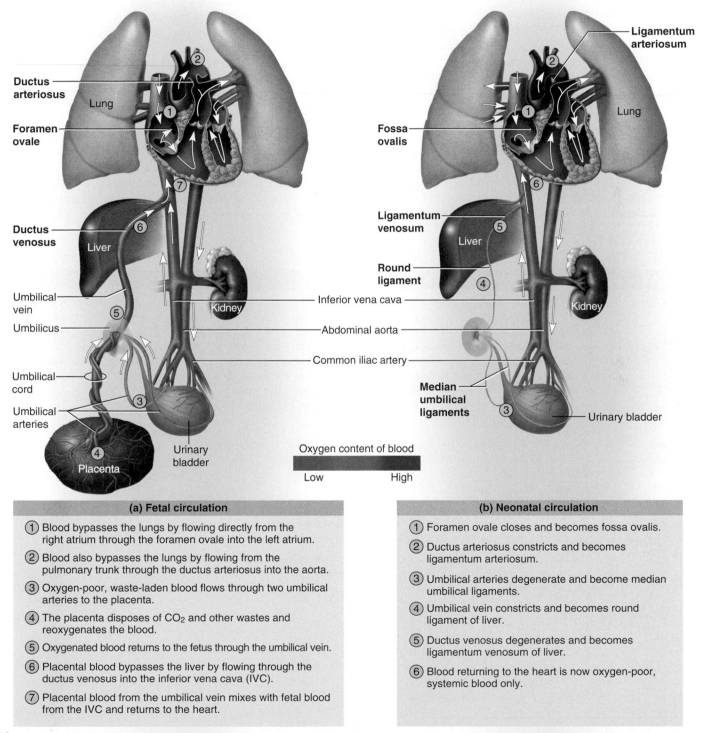

**(a) Fetal circulation**

①  Blood bypasses the lungs by flowing directly from the right atrium through the foramen ovale into the left atrium.

②  Blood also bypasses the lungs by flowing from the pulmonary trunk through the ductus arteriosus into the aorta.

③  Oxygen-poor, waste-laden blood flows through two umbilical arteries to the placenta.

④  The placenta disposes of $CO_2$ and other wastes and reoxygenates the blood.

⑤  Oxygenated blood returns to the fetus through the umbilical vein.

⑥  Placental blood bypasses the liver by flowing through the ductus venosus into the inferior vena cava (IVC).

⑦  Placental blood from the umbilical vein mixes with fetal blood from the IVC and returns to the heart.

**(b) Neonatal circulation**

①  Foramen ovale closes and becomes fossa ovalis.

②  Ductus arteriosus constricts and becomes ligamentum arteriosum.

③  Umbilical arteries degenerate and become median umbilical ligaments.

④  Umbilical vein constricts and becomes round ligament of liver.

⑤  Ductus venosus degenerates and becomes ligamentum venosum of liver.

⑥  Blood returning to the heart is now oxygen-poor, systemic blood only.

**Figure 21.37  Some Circulatory Changes Occurring at Birth.** (a) Circulatory system of the full-term fetus. (b) Circulatory system of the newborn.

## Changes at Birth

As we saw in chapter 20, page 588, the fetus has certain *shunts* that allow most blood to bypass the nonfunctional lungs: the *foramen ovale* and *ductus arteriosus*. After birth, when the lungs are functional, these shunts close, leaving a *fossa ovalis* in the interatrial septum and *ligamentum arteriosum* between the aortic arch and left pulmonary artery. Another fetal shunt called the *ductus venosus* bypasses the liver, which also is not very functional before birth. This is a vein; blood returning from the placenta enters the fetus through the umbilical vein and flows into the ductus venosus. The ductus venosus then empties into the inferior vena cava. After birth, the ductus venosus constricts, and blood is forced to flow through the liver. The ductus venosus leaves a fibrous remnant, the *ligamentum venosum*, on the inferior surface of the liver.

The two umbilical arteries become the *superior vesical arteries* to the urinary bladder. The umbilical vein becomes a fibrous cord, the *round ligament*, which attaches the liver to the ventral body wall (fig. 21.37).

## The Aging Vascular System

Atherosclerosis is the principal change seen in the blood vessels with advancing age. It is such a universal phenomenon that it is difficult to isolate and identify other age-related changes independent of atherosclerosis. However, even non-atherosclerotic vessels stiffen with age, owing to increasing deposition of collagen, cross-linking of collagen molecules (the same phenomenon that stiffens the skeletal joints, lens of the eye, and tissues elsewhere), and declining resilience of the elastic fibers. This arterial stiffening is less pronounced in elderly people who engage in routine vigorous exercise.

Another effect of aging is declining responsiveness of the baroreceptors, so vasomotor responses to changes in blood pressure are not as quick or efficient. Among some elderly people, the blunted response causes *orthostatic hypotension:* When one goes from a lying to a sitting or standing posture, blood is drawn away from the brain by gravity. Without a prompt corrective baroreflex, the drop in cerebral blood flow can cause dizziness or even fainting and falling, which in turn presents a risk of serious bone fractures.

## Vascular Diseases

Atherosclerosis, the most common vascular disease, can lead to stroke, renal failure, or heart failure—most notoriously the last of these. Therefore, it was described in chapter 20 in the context of coronary artery disease. Table 21.12 describes a few other vascular diseases. Some of the hematologic and cardiac pathologies in the preceding chapters also include aspects of vascular pathology.

| TABLE 21.12 | Some Vascular Pathologies |
|---|---|
| Hypertension | Abnormally high blood pressure. In a young adult, a BP up to 130/85 is considered normal, BP above 140/90 is considered hypertensive, and a BP between these ranges is borderline or "high normal." About 90% of cases of hypertension *(primary hypertension)* result from a poorly understood complex of hereditary, behavioral, and other factors. Risk factors include obesity, a sedentary lifestyle, diet, smoking, sex, and race. *Secondary hypertension* (10% of cases) results from other identifiable disorders such as renal insufficiency, atherosclerosis, hyperthyroidism, and polycythemia. Treated with dietary modification, weight loss, and drugs such as beta-blockers (which reduce responsiveness of the blood vessels to sympathetic stimulation), calcium channel blockers (which relax the vascular smooth muscle), diuretics (which reduce blood volume), and ACE inhibitors (which inhibit synthesis of the vasoconstrictor angiotensin II). |
| Phlebitis | Inflammation of a vein, causing pain, tenderness, edema, and skin discoloration along its course. Often of unknown cause, but may follow surgery, childbirth, or infections. |
| Raynaud[25] disease | Occasional spasmodic contractions of the digital arteries, causing pallor, numbness, and coldness of the fingers or toes. The digits may at first appear cyanotic, but then redden, with throbbing and paresthesia (tingling, burning, or itching sensations). Repeated and severe cases can lead to brittle nails and occasionally to gangrene and a necessity for amputation. Most common in young women and often triggered by emotional stress or brief exposure to cold. |
| Stroke (cerebrovascular accident) | The sudden death (infarction) of brain tissue occurring when cerebral atherosclerosis, thrombosis, or hemorrhage of a cerebral aneurysm cuts off blood flow to part of the brain. Effects range from unnoticeable to fatal, depending on the extent of tissue damage and function of the affected tissue. Blindness, paralysis, loss of speech, and loss of sensation are among the sublethal effects. |
| Vasculitis | Inflammation of any blood vessel (see also phlebitis in this table), usually caused by an immune response or infectious pathogen, but sometimes by radiation, trauma, or toxins. Produces a wide variety of symptoms, including muscle and joint pain, fever, headache, myocardial ischemia, numbness, and blindness. |

**Disorders Described Elsewhere**

Air embolism 566
Aneurysm 599
Atherosclerosis 583

Orthostatic hypotension 634
Patent ductus arteriosus 590
Varicose veins 603

---

[25]Maurice Raynaud (1834–81), French physician

## *Before You Go On*

Answer the following questions to test your understanding of the preceding section:

17. What do angioblasts develop from, and what do they develop into?

18. Describe, in humans, what becomes of the six pairs of aortic arches typical of vertebrate embryos.

19. Name two blood vessels that close off and become fibrous cords soon after birth.

20. Describe two changes that occur in the blood vessels in old age, other than specific vascular diseases.

# CHAPTER REVIEW

## REVIEW OF KEY CONCEPTS

### General Anatomy of the Blood Vessels (p. 596)

1. Blood normally circulates from the heart through arteries, z bed of capillaries, veins, and back to the heart.

2. Arteries and veins have three layers: an outer *tunica externa* of loose connective tissue; a middle *tunica media* of smooth muscle and connective tissue; and an inner *tunica interna* consisting of an *endothelium* overlying a basement membrane and thin connective tissue layer. In large and medium arteries, there is an *internal elastic lamina* at the boundary between the interna and media, and *external elastic lamina* at the boundary between media and externa.

3. Arteries are the efferent blood vessels. Although there is a gradual transition from one type to another, they can be classified into three general types: large *conducting arteries* with an abundance of elastic connective tissue in the tunica media, adapted to withstanding blood pressure surges; medium *distributing arteries* with a more muscular tunica media; and smaller *resistance arteries* with a thinner layer of smooth muscle in the media. The smallest resistance arteries are *arterioles.*

4. Metarterioles link arterioles to blood capillaries. They have no continuous tunica media, but have a circular cuff of smooth muscle, the *precapillary sphincter,* at the beginning of each capillary.

5. Some of the great arteries above the heart have special sense organs in their walls: a pair of baroreceptors (blood pressure monitors) called *carotid sinuses,* and chemoreceptors (blood chemistry monitors) called *carotid bodies* and *aortic bodies.* These receptors communicate with the brainstem by way of the glossopharyngeal and vagus nerves and trigger corrective responses in heartbeat, vasomotion, and breathing to maintain a normal blood pressure, pH, and $CO_2$ and $O_2$ levels.

6. Blood capillaries have only an endothelium and basal lamina (no tunica media or externa). They are the main point at which materials leave the bloodstream for the tissues, or return from the tissue fluid to the blood. Some capillaries are narrower than an RBC, and few cells in the body are more than four to six cell-widths away from the nearest capillary.

7. There are three types of capillaries: *continuous capillaries, fenestrated capillaries,* and *sinusoids.*

8. Capillaries are arranged in groups called *capillary beds,* supplied by a metarteriole and drained by venules and thoroughfare channels.

9. Veins are the afferent blood vessels. The smallest veins are *venules.* The smallest venules are very thin-walled and are another point of fluid exchange with the tissues. Even large veins have thinner, less muscular walls than arteries of comparable size. *Venous sinuses* have large lumens, thin walls, and no muscle.

10. Veins are under relatively low blood pressure. Consequently they are thin-walled, they stretch and accommodate more blood than any other vessels, and in the limbs, some of them have valves to help produce a one-way flow of blood.

11. Although systemic blood usually passes through one bed of capillaries in a single trip around the body, there are exceptions: *portal systems,* in which it passes through two consecutive capillary beds before returning to the heart, and *arteriovenous anastomoses,* in which it passes directly from an artery to a vein and returns to the heart without passing through any capillaries at all.

### The Pulmonary Circuit (p. 604)

1. The pulmonary circuit begins with the *pulmonary trunk,* which arises from the right ventricle of the heart and branches into the right and left *pulmonary arteries* to the lungs. These divide into one or more *lobar arteries* for each lobe of the respective lung. Finer branches lead to capillaries around the pulmonary alveoli, where gas exchange occurs.

2. Pulmonary blood empties into the left atrium of the heart by way of two pulmonary veins on each side.

3. The pulmonary circuit serves mainly for $CO_2$ unloading and $O_2$ loading. The lung tissue receives most nourishment and waste removal by a separate set of vessels, the *bronchial arteries* of the systemic circuit.

### Systemic Vessels of the Axial Region (p. 605)

1. The *ascending aorta* arises from the left ventricle and immediately gives off the two coronary arteries to the heart wall. It continues as the *aortic arch,* which gives off three large arteries to the neck, head, and upper limbs: the *brachiocephalic trunk, left common carotid artery,* and *left subclavian artery.* Beyond the arch, the aorta turns downward and continues as the *descending aorta,* divided into thoracic and abdominal regions (table 21.1).

2. Four arteries ascend each side of the neck: the *common carotid,* the *vertebral artery,* and branches of the *thyrocervical* and *costocervical trunks* (table 21.2, part I).

3. The common carotid arteries ascend beside the trachea and branch into an *external carotid artery,* supplying mainly head tissues external to the cranium, and *internal carotid artery,* supplying mainly the brain. The external carotid gives off *superior thyroid, lingual, facial, occipital, maxillary,* and *superficial temporal* arteries. The internal carotid gives off the *ophthalmic, anterior cerebral,* and *middle cerebral* arteries (table 21.2, part II).

4. The internal carotid and vertebral arteries converge on the *cerebral arterial circle* at the base of the brain, surrounding the pituitary gland. The arterial circle gives off *anterior*

and *posterior cerebral arteries* and often has short anastomoses called *anterior* and *posterior communicating arteries* that complete the circle (table 21.2, parts III, IV).

5. Blood from the brain drains into numerous *dural venous sinuses,* including the *superior sagittal, inferior sagittal, transverse,* and *cavernous sinuses.* The greatest outflow from these sinuses is via the *internal jugular vein,* which courses down the neck to the subclavian vein. The *external jugular* and *vertebral veins* drain more superficial structures of the head and neck and empty into the subclavian vein (table 21.3).

6. The thoracic aorta gives off *bronchial, esophageal,* and *mediastinal arteries* to the thoracic viscera; *posterior intercostal* and *subcostal arteries* to the skin, thoracic muscles, vertebrae, and other structures; and *superior phrenic arteries* to the diaphragm (table 21.4, parts I, II).

7. Continuing through the shoulder, the subclavian artery gives off the *internal thoracic artery, thoracoacromial trunk,* and *lateral thoracic artery* to the thoracic wall, then continues as the *axillary artery,* which gives off the *subscapular artery* to the scapula and numerous muscles of the thorax and arm (table 21.4, part III).

8. The thorax is drained in part by several small tributaries that flow into the *subclavian* and *brachiocephalic veins.* The right and left brachiocephalics join to form the *superior vena cava,* which empties into the right atrium of the heart (table 21.5, part I).

9. The thorax is also drained by the azygos system. The major veins of this system are the azygos vein on the right and the hemiazygos and accessory hemiazygos veins on the left. These veins receive blood from most of the posterior intercostal veins and carry it to the superior vena cava. They also receive blood from the subcostal veins, ascending lumbar veins of the abdomen, and esophageal, mediastinal, pericardial, and bronchial veins (table 21.5, part II).

10. As it descends through the abdominal cavity, the abdominal aorta gives off *inferior phrenic arteries,* the *celiac trunk,* and the *superior mesenteric, middle suprarenal, renal, ovarian* or *testicular, inferior mesenteric, lumbar,* and *median sacral* arteries. It ends by branching into two *common iliac arteries* (table 21.6, part I).

11. The celiac trunk provides a complex, anastomosing blood supply to the upper digestive and some other organs. Its three primary branches are the *common hepatic, left gastric,* and *splenic arteries.* The various subdivisions of these arteries supply the liver, gallbladder, pancreas, spleen, greater omentum, lower esophagus, stomach, and duodenum (table 21.6, part II).

12. The *superior mesenteric artery* gives rise to the *inferior pancreaticoduodenal, jejunal, ileal,* and *right* and *middle colic arteries.* It supplies nearly all of the small intestine and the proximal half of the large intestine. The *inferior mesenteric artery* gives off the *left colic, sigmoid,* and *superior rectal arteries,* serving the distal half of the large intestine (table 21.6, part III).

13. In the pelvic region, the common iliac artery branches into the *external* and *internal iliac arteries.* The internal iliac divides into *posterior* and *anterior trunks.* Subdivisions of these trunks supply the urinary bladder and ureters, rectum, penis and clitoris, and muscles, bones, and skin of the pelvic and femoral regions and contents of the lower vertebral canal (table 21.6, part IV).

14. Ascending the pelvic region, the *internal* and *external iliac veins* join to form the *common iliac vein,* and the two common iliacs merge to form the *inferior vena cava (IVC).* The IVC provides the major venous drainage of the pelvic region and abdomen. As it continues the ascent in the abdominal cavity, it receives the *lumbar veins, ovarian* or *testicular veins,* and the *renal, suprarenal, hepatic,* and *inferior phrenic veins.* It then enters the thorax and empties into the right atrium of the heart (table 21.7, part I).

15. Right and left *ascending lumbar veins* drain the abdominal wall, anastomose with the IVC, then penetrate the diaphragm and continue as the *azygos* and *hemiazygos veins,* respectively (table 21.7, part II).

16. Blood from the stomach, intestines, pancreas, gallbladder, and spleen flows to the liver by way of the *hepatic portal system.* The *splenic vein* receives the *pancreatic veins, inferior mesenteric vein,* and finally the *superior mesenteric vein.* From there it continues as the *hepatic portal vein,* which picks up the *cystic vein* and *gastric veins,* then enters the liver. This blood filters through the *hepatic sinusoids,* then exits the liver via the hepatic veins, which empty into the IVC (table 21.7, part III).

## Systemic Vessels of the Appendicular Region (p. 622)

1. Blood flow to the upper limb follows the *subclavian, axillary,* and *brachial arteries* into the arm, in that order. The brachial artery descends through the arm and gives off the *deep brachial* and *superior ulnar collateral arteries;* the deep brachial flows into the *radial collateral artery* (table 21.8, part I).

2. Near the elbow, the brachial artery branches into the *radial* and *ulnar arteries* of the fore-

arm. The ulnar artery gives rise (indirectly) to *anterior* and *posterior interosseous arteries.* The radial and ulnar arteries anastomose in a pair of *palmar arches* at the wrist, and these give off branches to the hand and fingers (table 21.8, part II).

3. Superficial venous drainage of the upper limb includes the *dorsal venous network* of the hand, flowing into the *cephalic* and *basilic veins* of the forearm. The *median antebrachial vein* drains the *superficial palmar venous network* of the hand and empties into the cephalic, basilic, or median cubital vein. The *median cubital vein* is a short anastomosis that joins the cephalic and basilic at the elbow (table 21.9, part I).

4. Deep venous drainage of the upper limb includes a pair of *venous palmar arches,* which drain into a pair of *radial veins* laterally and a pair of *ulnar veins* medially. These lead to two *brachial veins,* one formed by convergence of the radial veins and the other by convergence of the ulnar veins. The brachial veins join the basilic vein. This union forms the *axillary vein,* which continues into the shoulder and becomes the *subclavian vein* (table 21.9, part II).

5. Arterial flow to the lower limb comes from the *external iliac artery,* which supplies some structures of the pelvic region, then continues into the thigh as the *femoral artery.* The femoral artery gives off the *deep femoral* and two *circumflex femoral arteries,* then continues its descent, becoming the *popliteal artery* at the back of the knee and finally branching into the *anterior* and *posterior tibial arteries* just below the knee (table 21.10, part I).

6. The anterior tibial artery descends to the ankle and gives rise to the *dorsal pedal* and *arcuate artery* of the foot. The posterior tibial artery branches at the ankle to produce the *medial* and *lateral plantar arteries.* The lateral plantar leads to the *deep plantar arch,* which in turn gives off arteries to the toes. The *fibular artery* arises from the posterior tibial artery near the knee and ends in a network of small vessels in the heel (table 21.10, part II).

7. Blood from the toes and foot drains partly into a superficial *dorsal venous arch,* which drains on the lateral and medial sides into the *small saphenous* and *great saphenous veins,* respectively. The small saphenous ends at the knee by draining into the popliteal vein, whereas the great saphenous extends to the groin and empties into the femoral vein (table 21.11, part I).

8. The deep *plantar venous arch* of the foot drains the toes and gives rise to *lateral* and *medial plantar veins.* These, in turn, produce two *posterior tibial veins* and two *fibu-*

lar veins that ascend the leg and converge into a single posterior tibial and fibular vein higher up. Convergence of those two produces the *popliteal vein* of the knee. A pair of *anterior tibial veins* arise from the dorsal venous arch and empty into the popliteal vein (table 21.11, part II).

9. Above the knee, the popliteal vein continues as the *femoral vein.* The femoral receives the *deep femoral vein,* which drains the muscles and bone of the thigh, then joins the great saphenous vein to become the *external iliac vein.* In the pelvic region, the external iliac joins the internal iliac, and their union forms the *common iliac vein* (table 21.11).

### Developmental and Clinical Perspectives (p. 631)

1. The first indications of developing blood vessels in humans are the *blood islands* of the yolk sac. Cells in the middle of a blood island develop into *hemoblasts,* which give rise to blood cells, and cells on the periphery become *angioblasts,* which differentiate into the blood vessel endothelium. Convergence of blood islands gives rise to an irregular network of channels in the embryo that later become remodeled into tubular blood vessels.

2. Like other vertebrate embryos, the human embryo develops six pairs of *aortic arches* that connect the *aortic sac* of the heart with a pair of long *dorsal aortae.* Little becomes of arches I, II, and V in humans, but arch III becomes the common carotid artery and part of the internal carotid; IV on the right becomes the aortic arch; and VI gives rise to the pulmonary arteries.

3. The two dorsal aortae fuse into a single dorsal aorta, which gives off numerous *intersegmental arteries.* Most intersegmental arteries degenerate, but some remain as the adult intercostal, lumbar, and common iliac arteries.

4. Venous drainage of the embryonic body is mainly by way of the *anterior* and *posterior cardinal veins.* Other major veins are the *vitelline* and *umbilical veins,* draining the yolk sac and placenta, respectively. The anterior cardinal vein eventually contributes to the superior vena cava, whereas the posterior cardinal vein degenerates except for the common iliac veins and part of the azygos system.

5. In the fetus, two vascular shunts allow most blood to bypass the largely nonfunctional liver and lungs—the *ductus venosus* bypassing the liver and the *ductus arteriosus* bypassing the lungs. Shortly after birth, these shunts close and become fibrous cords called the *ligamentum venosum* and *ligamentum arteriosum,* respectively).

6. The aging vascular system exhibits stiffening of the vessels by deposition and cross-linking of collagen, and declining baroreflexes, resulting in less prompt adjustments to changes in posture and sometimes causing orthostatic hypotension.

7. Atherosclerosis is the most common disease of the aging blood vessels. Other disorders are described in table 21.12.

## TESTING YOUR RECALL

1. Blood normally flows into a capillary bed from
   a. a distributing artery.
   b. a conducting artery.
   c. a metarteriole.
   d. a thoroughfare channel.
   e. a venule.

2. Plasma solutes enter the tissue fluid most easily from
   a. continuous capillaries.
   b. fenestrated capillaries.
   c. arteriovenous anastomoses.
   d. collateral vessels.
   e. venous anastomoses.

3. A blood vessel adapted to withstand great fluctuations in blood pressure would be expected to have
   a. an elastic tunica media.
   b. a thick tunica interna.
   c. one-way valves.
   d. a flexible endothelium.
   e. a rigid tunica media.

4. A circulatory pathway in which the blood flows through two capillary beds in series before it returns to the heart is called
   a. an arteriovenous anastomosis.
   b. an arterial anastomosis.
   c. a venous anastomosis.
   d. a venous return pathway.
   e. a portal system.

5. Intestinal blood flows into the liver by way of
   a. the superior mesenteric vein.
   b. the hepatic portal vein.
   c. the abdominal aorta.
   d. the hepatic sinusoids.
   e. the hepatic veins.

6. Blood islands first form in the embryonic
   a. spleen.
   b. yolk sac.
   c. placenta.
   d. liver.
   e. red bone marrow.

7. Most blood flowing in all of the following arteries except _____ is destined to circulate through the brain before returning to the heart.
   a. the vertebral arteries
   b. the internal carotid arteries
   c. the basilar artery
   d. the superficial temporal artery
   e. the anterior communicating artery

8. All of the following blood vessels except _____ are located in the upper limb.
   a. the cephalic vein
   b. the small saphenous vein
   c. the brachial artery
   d. the circumflex humeral arteries
   e. the metacarpal arteries

9. The adult aortic arch develops from the embryonic
   a. right aortic arch IV.
   b. left aortic arch IV.
   c. right aortic arch V.
   d. conus arteriosus.
   e. dorsal aorta.

10. To get from the posterior tibial vein to the femoral vein, blood flows through
    a. the anterior tibial vein.
    b. the popliteal vein.
    c. the internal iliac vein.
    d. the great saphenous vein.
    e. the basilic vein.

11. Filtration pores are characteristic of _____ capillaries.

12. The capillaries of skeletal muscles are of the structural type called _____.

13. The epithelium that lines the inside of a blood vessel is called _____.

14. The two _____ veins unite like an upside-down Y to form the inferior vena cava.

15. Carotid and aortic bodies are called _____ because they respond to changes in blood chemistry.

16. Movement across the capillary endothelium by the uptake and release of fluid droplets is called _____.

17. The two largest veins that empty into the right atrium are the _____ and _____.

18. The pressure sensors in the major arteries near the head are called _____.

19. Most of the blood supply to the brain comes from a ring of arterial anastomoses called the _____.

20. The major superficial veins of the arm are the _____ on the medial side and _____ on the lateral side.

*Answers in the Appendix*

## TRUE OR FALSE

*Determine which five of the following statements are false, and briefly explain why.*

1. The lungs receive both a pulmonary and a systemic blood supply.

2. The pancreas and spleen receive their blood supply mainly from the superior mesenteric artery.

3. Veins anastomose more than arteries do.

4. From the time blood leaves the heart to the time it returns, it always passes through only one capillary bed.

5. The superior vena cava begins where the two subclavian veins meet.

6. Erythrocytes and endothelial cells arise from the same embryonic stem cells.

7. The smooth muscle of the tunica media of a large vessel is nourished mainly by the diffusion of nutrients from blood in the vessel lumen.

8. Venous blood from the intestines flows through the liver before it flows through the heart.

9. In a few unusual cases, one or more arteries of the cerebral arterial circle are lacking.

10. Arteries to the ovaries and testes originate relatively high in the abdominal cavity, near the kidneys.

*Answers in the Appendix*

## TESTING YOUR COMPREHENSION

1. Suppose a posterior tibial vein were obstructed by thrombosis. Describe one or more alternative routes by which blood from the foot could get to the common iliac vein.

2. Why would a ruptured aneurysm of the basilar artery be more serious than a ruptured aneurysm of the anterior communicating artery?

3. What differences would you expect between a sample of blood taken from the superior mesenteric vein and a sample taken from a hepatic vein? Consider, especially, differences in nutrient levels and bacterial count, and look forward in the book if necessary for a preview of liver functions.

4. Why could a choke hold (a tight grip around the neck) cause a person to pass out? What arteries would be involved?

5. Why is it better to have baroreceptors in the carotid sinus rather than in some other location such as the abdominal aorta or common iliac arteries?

*Answers at aris.mhhe.com*

## ONLINE RESOURCES

Visit aprevealed.com to explore melt-away cadaver dissections, watch animations that clarify difficult concepts, review histological and radiological images, or take a quiz to assess your understanding of the material.

The Saladin *Human Anatomy,* 2e website at aris.mhhe.com features chapter-specific quizzes, labeling exercises, and other interactive tools to complement your study of human anatomy. If your instructor has provided an ARIS course code, you can also access assignments and information specific to your course.

# The Lymphatic System and Immunity

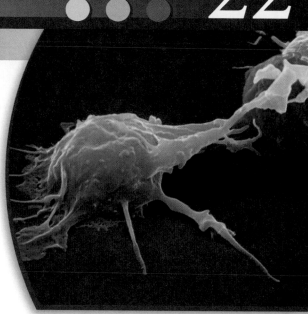

Natural killer cells (yellow) attacking a human cancer cell (red)

## BRUSHING UP

To understand this chapter, you may find it helpful to review the following concepts:
- General gland structure: capsule, septa, stroma, and parenchyma (pp. 95–96)
- Anatomy of the thymus (p. 535)
- Antigens and antibodies (p. 558)
- Leukocyte types, especially lymphocytes (pp. 558–562)

Anatomy & Physiology REVEALED®
aprevealed.com

**Lymphatic System**

The lymphatic system is a network of tissues, organs, and vessels that help to maintain the body's fluid balance, cleanse the body fluids of foreign matter, and provide immune cells for defense. Of all the body systems, it is perhaps the least familiar to most people. Yet without it, neither the circulatory system nor the immune system could function—circulation would shut down from fluid loss, and the body would be overrun by infection for lack of immunity. This chapter discusses the anatomy of the lymphatic system in relation to its roles in fluid recovery and immunity. The structure and function of the lymphatic system is so intimately tied to the immune system that this chapter will sometimes refer to them jointly as the *lymphatic–immune system*.

# Lymph and Lymphatic Vessels

## Objectives

When you have completed this section, you should be able to

- list the functions and basic components of the lymphatic system;
- explain how lymph is formed;
- describe the route that lymph takes to get into the bloodstream; and
- explain what makes lymph flow through the lymphatic vessels.

## Components and Functions of the Lymphatic System

The **lymphatic system** (fig. 22.1) consists of the following components: (1) *lymph,* the fluid the system collects from the interstitial spaces of the tissues and returns to the bloodstream; (2) *lymphatic vessels,* which transport the lymph; (3) *lymphatic tissue,* composed of aggregates of lymphocytes and macrophages that populate many organs of the body; and (4) *lymphatic organs,* in which these cells are especially concentrated and which are set off from surrounding organs by connective tissue capsules.

The functions of the lymphatic system include the following:

1. **Fluid recovery.** Fluid continually filters from the blood capillaries into the tissue spaces. The blood capillaries reabsorb about 85% of it, but the 15% they do not absorb would amount, over the course of a day, to 2 to 4 L of water and one-quarter to one-half of the plasma protein. One would die of circulatory failure within hours if this water and protein were not returned to the bloodstream. One task of the lymphatic system is to reabsorb this excess and return it to the blood. Even partial interference with lymphatic drainage can lead to severe edema and sometimes even more grotesque consequences (see Insight 22.1).

2. **Immunity.** As the lymphatic system recovers excess tissue fluid, it also picks up foreign cells and chemicals from the tissues. Some of these are **pathogens**[1]—agents with the potential to cause disease. On its way back to the bloodstream, the fluid passes through lymph nodes, where immune cells stand guard against pathogens and activate protective immune responses.

3. **Lipid absorption.** In the small intestine, special lymphatic vessels called *lacteals* absorb dietary lipids that cannot be absorbed by the intestinal blood capillaries (see p. 700).

## Lymph

**Lymph** is usually a clear, colorless fluid, similar to blood plasma but low in protein. It originates as tissue fluid that has been taken up by the lymphatic vessels. Its composition varies substantially from place to place. After a meal, for example, lymph draining from the small intestine has a milky appearance because of its high lipid content. This intestinal lymph is called *chyle*[2] (kile). Lymph leaving the lymph nodes contains a large number of lymphocytes—indeed, this is the main supply of lymphocytes to the bloodstream. Lymph can also contain macrophages, hormones, bacteria, viruses, cellular debris, and even traveling cancer cells.

## Lymphatic Vessels

Lymph flows through a system of **lymphatic vessels (lymphatics)** similar to blood vessels. These begin with microscopic **lymphatic capillaries (terminal lymphatics),** which penetrate nearly every tissue of the body but are absent from the central nervous system, cartilage, cornea, bone, and bone marrow. They are closely associated with blood capillaries, but unlike them, they are closed at one end (fig. 22.3). A lymphatic capillary consists of a sac of thin endothelial cells that loosely overlap each other like the shingles of a roof. The cells are tethered to surrounding tissue by protein filaments that prevent the sac from collapsing.

Unlike the endothelial cells of blood capillaries, lymphatic endothelial cells are not joined by tight junctions, nor do they have a continuous basement membrane; indeed, the gaps between them are so large that bacteria, lymphocytes, and other cells and particles can enter along with the tissue fluid. Thus, the composition of lymph arriving at a lymph node is like a report on the state of the upstream tissues.

The overlapping edges of the endothelial cells act as valvelike flaps that can open and close. When tissue fluid pressure is high, it pushes the flaps inward (open) and fluid flows into the capillary. When pressure is higher in the lymphatic capillary than in the tissue fluid, the flaps are pressed outward (closed).

### THINK ABOUT IT

*Contrast the structure of a lymphatic capillary with that of a continuous blood capillary. Explain why their structural difference is related to their functional difference.*

---

[1]*patho* = disease + *gen* = producing
[2]*chyle* = juice

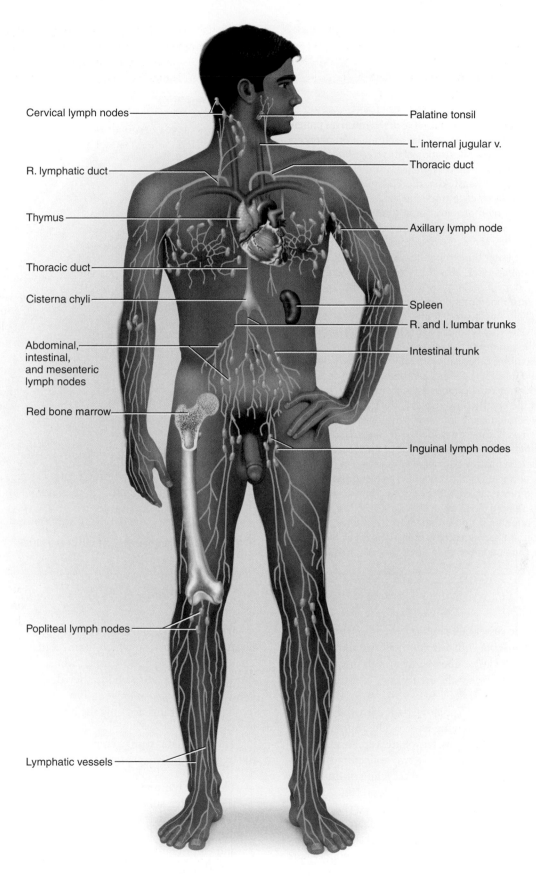

Cervical lymph nodes

Palatine tonsil

L. internal jugular v.

R. lymphatic duct

Thoracic duct

Thymus

Axillary lymph node

Thoracic duct

Cisterna chyli

Spleen

R. and l. lumbar trunks

Abdominal, intestinal, and mesenteric lymph nodes

Intestinal trunk

Red bone marrow

Inguinal lymph nodes

Popliteal lymph nodes

Lymphatic vessels

**Figure 22.1** The Lymphatic System.

# INSIGHT 22.1

## Clinical Application

### Elephantiasis

Any obstruction of the lymphatic vessels can block the return of fluid to the bloodstream and thus result in *edema,* the accumulation of excess tissue fluid. A particularly dramatic illustration of this is *elephantiasis* (fig. 22.2), a parasitic disease found in tropical climates worldwide, especially in Africa but also in India, southeast Asia, the Philippines, the Pacific Islands, and parts of South America (introduced by slave trading).

Elephantiasis is caused by mosquito-borne roundworms called *filariae* (fil-AIR-ee-ee), usually the species *Wuchereria bancrofti.* When an infected mosquito bites, tiny larvae escape from its proboscis, crawl into the bite wound, and enter the lymphatic vessels of the skin. They migrate to larger lymphatic vessels near the lymph nodes, where they mature into tightly coiled adults as large as 10 cm long and 0.3 cm wide. The worms cause intense inflammation of the lymphatic vessels and lymph nodes, especially in the lower half of the body. The vessels and nodes become swollen and painful, and infected males often suffer very painful edematous enlargement of the testes.

Infection with the worms, called *filariasis,* only occasionally leads to elephantiasis, but when it does, the effect can be horrible. The chronic blockage of lymph flow causes enormous enlargement and fibrosis of tissues upstream from the obstruction—notably the legs and arms, the scrotum of men *(lymph scrotum),* and sometimes the vulva and breasts of women. The skin becomes fibrotic, thickened, and cracked, so it comes to resemble an elephant's hide—hence the name of the disease.

Thousands of American military personnel who served in the Pacific theater in World War II contracted filariasis. Alarmed by pictures of extreme cases, some men feared having to carry their scrotum in a wheelbarrow. However, elephantiasis seldom develops in anyone whose first exposure to the filariae occurs in adulthood, and it requires many years of repetitive infection. Some servicemen had symptoms of filariasis for as long as 16 years after their return, but not one of them developed elephantiasis.

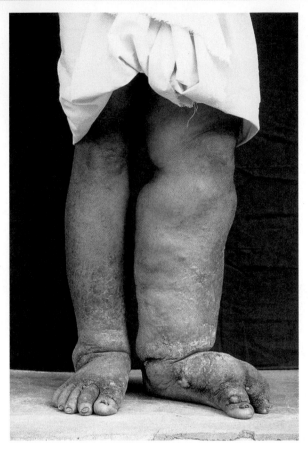

**Figure 22.2** Elephantiasis of the Lower Limb.

---

The larger lymphatic vessels are similar to veins in their histology. They have a *tunica interna* with an endothelium and valves (fig. 22.4), a *tunica media* with elastic fibers and smooth muscle, and a thin outer *tunica externa.* Their walls are thinner and their valves are closer together than those of the veins.

As the lymphatic vessels converge along their path, they become larger and larger vessels with changing names. The route from the tissue fluid back to the bloodstream is: lymphatic capillaries → collecting vessels → six lymphatic trunks → two collecting ducts → subclavian veins. Thus, there is a continual recycling of fluid from blood to tissue fluid to lymph and back to the blood (fig. 22.5).

The lymphatic capillaries converge to form **collecting vessels.** These often travel alongside veins and arteries and share a common connective tissue sheath with them. At irregular intervals, they empty into lymph nodes. The lymph trickles slowly through the node, where bacteria are phagocytized and immune cells monitor the fluid for foreign antigens. It leaves the other side of the node through another collecting vessel, traveling on and often encountering additional lymph nodes before it finally returns to the bloodstream.

Eventually, the collecting vessels converge to form larger **lymphatic trunks,** each of which drains a major portion of the body. There are six lymphatic trunks, whose names indicate their locations and parts of the body they drain: the *jugular, subclavian, bronchomediastinal, intercostal, intestinal,* and *lumbar trunks.* The lumbar trunk drains not only the lumbar region but also the lower limbs.

The lymphatic trunks converge to form two **collecting ducts,** the largest of the lymphatic vessels (fig. 22.6):

1. The **right lymphatic duct** is formed by the convergence of the right jugular, subclavian, and bronchomediastinal trunks in the right thoracic cavity. It receives lymphatic drainage from the right upper limb and right side of the thorax and head, and empties into the right subclavian vein.

2. The **thoracic duct,** on the left, is larger and longer. It begins just below the diaphragm, anterior to the vertebral column at the level of the second lumbar vertebra. Here, the two lumbar trunks and the intestinal trunk join and form a prominent

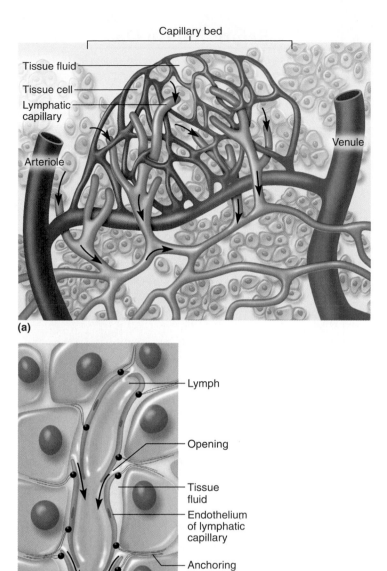

**(a)**

Capillary bed

Tissue fluid

Tissue cell

Lymphatic capillary

Arteriole

Venule

**(b)**

Lymph

Opening

Tissue fluid

Endothelium of lymphatic capillary

Anchoring filaments

**Figure 22.3** Lymphatic Capillaries. (a) Relationship of the lymphatic capillaries to a bed of blood capillaries. (b) Uptake of tissue fluid by a lymphatic capillary.
● *Why can traveling (metastasizing) cancer cells get into the lymphatic system more easily than they can enter the bloodstream?*

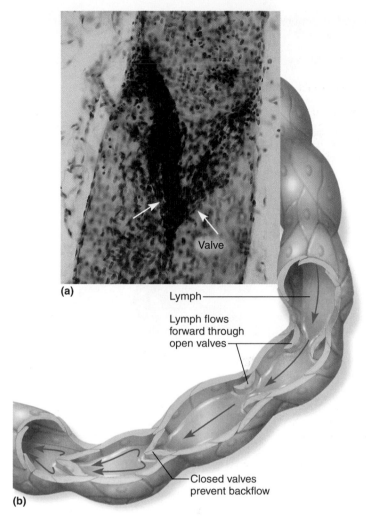

**(a)**

Valve

Lymph

Lymph flows forward through open valves

Closed valves prevent backflow

**(b)**

**Figure 22.4** Valves in the Lymphatic Vessels. (a) Photograph of a lymphatic valve. (b) Operation of the valves to ensure a one-way flow of lymph.

sac called the **cisterna chyli** (sis-TUR-nuh KY-lye), named for the large amount of chyle that it collects after a meal. The thoracic duct then passes through the diaphragm with the aorta and ascends the mediastinum, adjacent to the vertebral column. As it passes through the thorax, it receives additional lymph from the left bronchomediastinal, left subclavian, and left jugular trunks, then empties into the left subclavian vein. Collectively, this duct therefore drains all of the body below the diaphragm, and the left upper limb and left side of the head, neck, and thorax.

## The Flow of Lymph

Lymph flows under forces similar to those that govern venous return, except that the lymphatic system has no pump like the heart, and it flows at even lower pressure and speed than venous blood. The primary mechanism of flow is rhythmic contractions of the lymphatic vessels themselves, induced when the flowing lymph stretches them. The valves of lymphatic vessels, like those of veins, prevent the fluid from flowing backward. Lymph flow is also produced by skeletal muscles squeezing the lymphatic vessels, like the skeletal muscle pump that moves venous blood. Since lymphatic vessels are often wrapped with an artery in a common connective tissue sheath, arterial pulsation may also rhythmically squeeze the lymphatic vessels and contribute to lymph flow. A thoracic (respiratory) pump promotes the flow of lymph from the abdominal to the thoracic cavity as one inhales. During inhalation, pressure in the thoracic cavity falls below the pressure in the abdominal cavity. Abdominal pressure squeezing on the abdominal lymphatic trunks and cisterna chyli causes lymph to flow upward into the thoracic

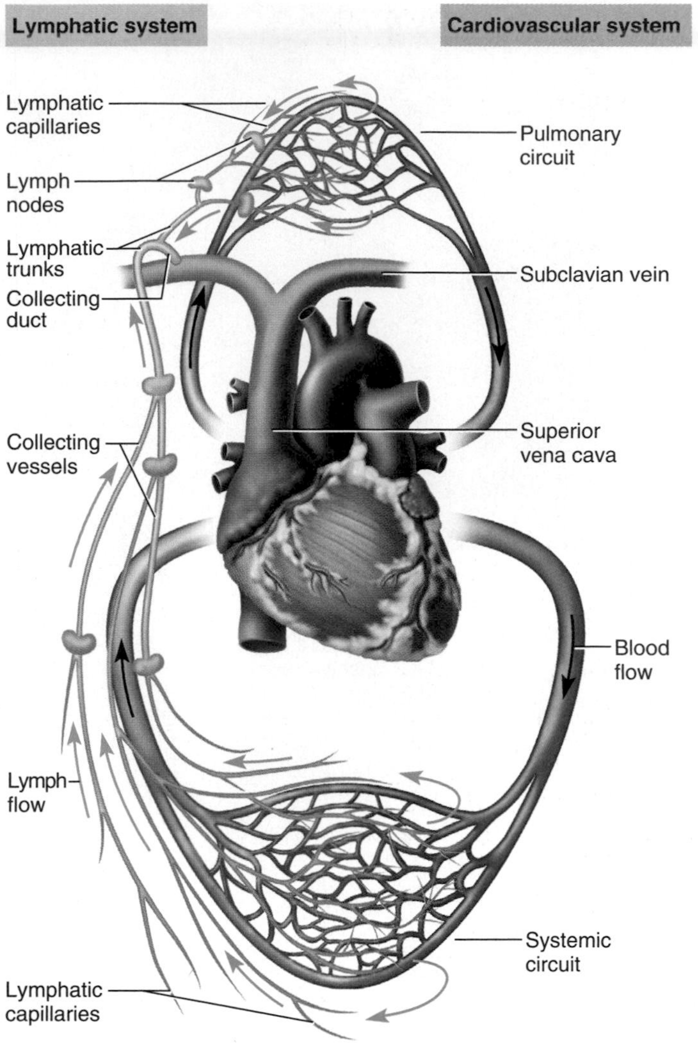

**Lymphatic system**   **Cardiovascular system**

**Figure 22.5** **Fluid Exchange Between the Cardiovascular and Lymphatic Systems.** Blood capillaries lose fluid to the tissue spaces. The lymphatic system picks up excess tissue fluid and returns it to the bloodstream. The lymph flows from lymphatic capillaries through collecting vessels, lymphatic trunks, and collecting ducts, and is filtered through multiple lymph nodes before reentering the bloodstream at the subclavian veins.
● *Identify two benefits in having lymphatic capillaries pick up tissue fluid that is not reclaimed by the blood capillaries.*

lymphatics. Finally, at the point where the collecting ducts empty into the subclavian veins, the rapidly flowing bloodstream draws the lymph into it.

**THINK ABOUT IT**

*Why does it make more functional sense for the collecting ducts to connect to the subclavian veins than it would for them to connect to the subclavian arteries?*

*Before You Go On*

Answer the following questions to test your understanding of the preceding section:

1. List the primary functions of the lymphatic system.
2. How does fluid get into the lymphatic system? What prevents it from draining back out?
3. Where does this fluid (lymph) go once it enters the lymphatic vessels? What makes it flow?

# Lymphatic Cells, Tissues, and Organs

### Objectives
When you have completed this section, you should be able to
- name the major types of cells in the lymphatic system and state their functions;
- describe the types of lymphatic tissue; and
- describe the anatomy and lymphatic–immune function of the red bone marrow, thymus, lymph nodes, tonsils, and spleen.

In addition to lymphatic vessels, another component of the lymphatic system is the lymphatic tissues. These range from loosely scattered cells in the mucous membranes of the digestive, respiratory, reproductive, and urinary tracts, to compact cell populations encapsulated in lymphatic organs. These tissues are composed of a variety of lymphocytes and other cells with various roles in defense and immunity.

## Lymphatic Cells

The principal cell types of the lymphatic system are as follows:

1. **Natural killer (NK) cells.** These are large lymphocytes that attack and lyse bacteria, transplanted tissue cells, and *host cells* (cells of one's own body) that have either become infected with viruses or turned cancerous (see photo on p. 639). Their continual patrolling of the body "on the lookout" for abnormal cells is called *immunological surveillance,* and is one of the body's most important defenses against cancer.

2. **T lymphocytes (T cells).** These are so-named because they develop for a time in the thymus and later depend on thymic hormones to regulate their activity. The *T* stands for *thymus-dependent.* There are three subclasses of T cells:
   - *Cytotoxic T ($T_C$) cells* are the only T lymphocytes that directly attack and kill other cells. They are especially responsive to cells of transplanted tissues and organs, cancer cells, and host cells infected with viruses, bacteria, or intracellular parasites. They are also called T8, CD8, or

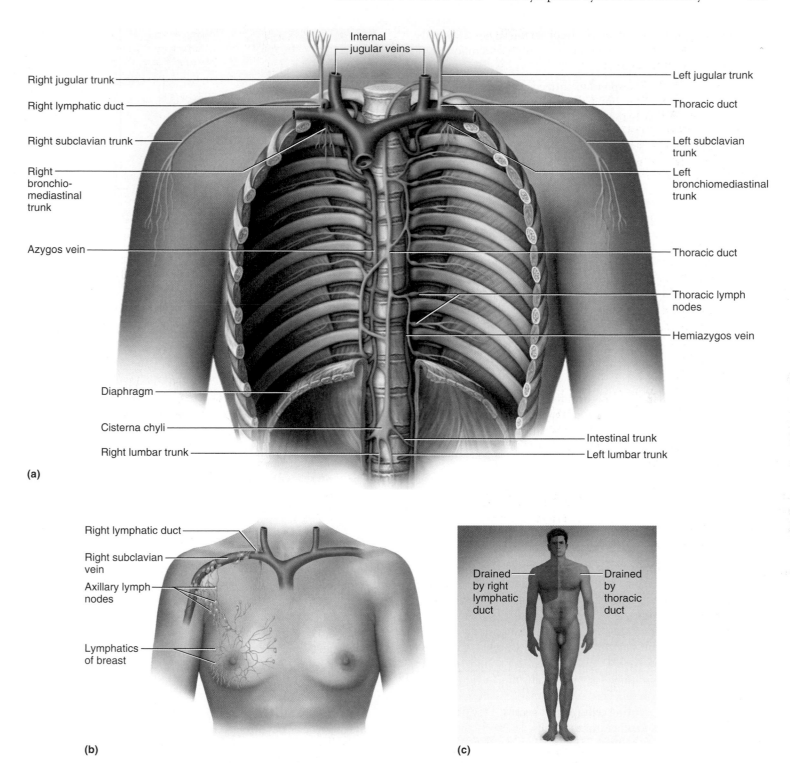

**Figure 22.6** **Lymphatics of the Thoracic Region.** (a) Lymphatics of the thorax and upper abdomen and their relationship to the subclavian veins, where the lymph returns to the bloodstream. (b) Lymphatic drainage of the right mammary and axillary regions. (c) Regions of the body drained by the right lymphatic duct and thoracic duct.

• *Why are the axillary lymph nodes often biopsied in cases of suspected breast cancer?*

CD8+ cells for their surface glycoprotein, CD8. (*CD* stands for *cluster of differentiation,* a classification system for many cell-surface molecules.)

- *Helper T ($T_H$) cells* respond to antigens and activate various defense mechanisms, but do not carry out the attack themselves; instead, they help other immune cells respond to the threat. $T_H$ cells play a central coordinating role in multiple forms of defense. They are also called T4, CD4, or CD4+ cells because of a surface glycoprotein called CD4.

- *Memory T ($T_M$) cells* provide long-lasting memory of an antigen. Upon reexposure, the immune system neutralizes the antigen so quickly that it causes no disease symptoms. This is what we mean by being immune to a disease.

3. **B lymphocytes (B cells).** These lymphocytes differentiate into *plasma cells*—connective tissue cells that secrete the antibodies of the immune system. They were named for an organ in chickens (the *bursa of Fabricius*[3]) in which they were first discovered; however, you may find it more helpful to think of *B* for *bone marrow,* the site where these cells mature. Some B cells become memory B cells instead of plasma cells, functioning like memory T cells to confer long-lasting immunity.

In stained blood films, the different types of lymphocytes are not morphologically distinguishable, but they are about 80% T cells, 15% B cells, and 5% NK and stem cells.

### THINK ABOUT IT

*Suppose a new virus emerged that selectively destroyed memory T and B cells. What would be the pathological effect of such a virus?*

4. **Macrophages.** These cells develop from monocytes that have emigrated from the bloodstream. Macrophages are very large, avidly phagocytic cells. They phagocytize tissue debris, dead neutrophils, bacteria, and other foreign matter (fig. 22.7). They also process foreign matter and transport antigenically active fragments of it *(antigenic determinants)* to the cell surface, where they "display" it to $T_C$ and $T_H$ cells. This stimulates the T cells to launch an immune response against the foreign invader. Macrophages, B lymphocytes, and reticular cells are collectively called **antigen-presenting cells (APCs)** because they display antigen fragments to other immune cells.

5. **Dendritic cells.** These are branched macrophages found in the epidermis, mucous membranes, and lymphatic organs. (In the skin, they are often called *Langerhans*[4] *cells.*) They engulf foreign matter by receptor-mediated endocytosis rather than phagocytosis, but they otherwise function like macrophages.

*The macrophage system* includes all of the body's phagocytic cells except leukocytes. Some of these phagocytes are wandering cells that actively seek pathogens; others are fixed in place and phagocytize only those pathogens that

**Figure 22.7** **Macrophages Attacking Bacteria.** Filamentous pseudopods of the macrophages snare the rod-shaped bacteria and draw them to the cell surface, where they are phagocytized.

come to them—although they are strategically positioned for this to occur. Cells of the macrophage system include the macrophages of the loose connective tissue, *microglia* of the central nervous system, *alveolar macrophages* in the lungs, *hepatic macrophages* in the liver, and dendritic cells. Alveolar and hepatic macrophages are described in chapters 23 and 24.

6. **Reticular cells.** These are branched stationary cells that contribute to the stroma of the lymphatic organs and act as APCs in the thymus (see fig. 22.10). (They should not be confused with reticular *fibers,* which are fine branched collagen fibers common in lymphatic organs.)

## Lymphatic Tissues

**Lymphatic (lymphoid) tissues** are aggregations of lymphocytes in the connective tissues of mucous membranes and various organs. The simplest form is **diffuse lymphatic tissue,** in which the lymphocytes are scattered rather than densely clustered. It is particularly prevalent in body passages that are open to the exterior—the respiratory, digestive, urinary, and reproductive tracts—where it is called **mucosa-associated lymphatic tissue (MALT).** (In the respiratory and digestive tracts, it is sometimes called bronchus-associated and gut-associated lymphatic tissue, BALT and GALT, respectively).

In some places, lymphocytes and macrophages congregate in dense masses called **lymphatic nodules (follicles)** (fig. 22.8), which come and go as pathogens invade the tissues and the immune system answers the challenge. Abundant lymphatic nodules are, however, a relatively constant feature of the lymph nodes, tonsils, and appendix. In the ileum, the distal portion of the small intestine, they form clusters called **Peyer**[5] patches.

## Overview of Lymphatic Organs

In contrast to the diffuse lymphatic tissue, **lymphatic (lymphoid) organs** have well-defined anatomical sites and at least partial

---

[3]Hieronymus Fabricius (Girolamo Fabrizzi) (1537–1619), Italian anatomist
[4]Theodor Langerhans (1839–1915), German pathologist

[5]Johann Conrad Peyer (1653–1712), Swiss anatomist

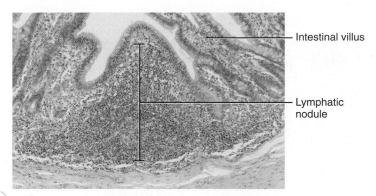

**Figure 22.8** Lymphatic Nodule in the Mucous Membrane of the Small Intestine.

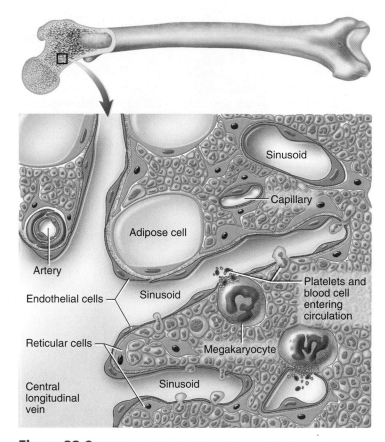

**Figure 22.9** Histology of the Red Bone Marrow. The formed elements of blood squeeze through the endothelial cells into the sinusoids, which converge on the central longitudinal vein at the lower left.

connective tissue capsules that separate the lymphatic tissue from neighboring tissues. These organs include the red bone marrow, thymus, lymph nodes, tonsils, and spleen. The red bone marrow and thymus are regarded as *primary lymphatic organs* because they are the sites where B and T lymphocytes, respectively, become *immunocompetent*—that is, able to recognize and respond to antigens. The lymph nodes, tonsils, and spleen are called *secondary lymphatic organs* because they are populated with immunocompetent lymphocytes only after the cells have matured in the primary lymphatic organs.

## Red Bone Marrow

As discussed in chapter 6, there are two kinds of bone marrow—red and yellow. Red bone marrow is involved in hemopoiesis (blood formation) and immunity; yellow bone marrow can be disregarded for our present purposes. In children, red bone marrow occupies the medullary spaces of nearly the entire skeleton. In adults, it is limited to parts of the axial skeleton and the proximal heads of the humerus and femur (see fig. 6.7, p. 161). Red bone marrow is an important supplier of lymphocytes to the immune system. Its role in the life history of lymphocytes is described later.

Red bone marrow is a soft, loosely organized, highly vascular material, separated from osseous tissue by the endosteum of the bone. It produces all classes of formed elements of the blood; its red color comes from the abundance of erythrocytes. Numerous small arteries enter *nutrient foramina* on the bone surface, penetrate the bone, and empty into large *sinusoids* (45 to 80 μm wide) in the marrow (fig. 22.9). The sinusoids drain into a *central longitudinal vein* that exits the bone via the same route that the arteries entered it. The sinusoids are lined by endothelial cells, like other blood vessels, and are surrounded by reticular cells and reticular fibers. The reticular cells secrete colony-stimulating factors that induce the formation of various leukocyte types. In the long bones of the limbs, aging reticular cells accumulate fat and transform into adipose cells, eventually replacing red bone marrow with yellow bone marrow.

The spaces between the sinusoids are occupied by *islands (cords)* of hemopoietic cells, composed of macrophages and blood cells in all stages of development. The macrophages destroy malformed blood cells and the nuclei discarded by developing erythrocytes. As blood cells mature, they push their way through the reticular and endothelial cells to enter the sinus and flow away in the bloodstream.

### THINK ABOUT IT

*If we regard red bone marrow as a lymphatic organ and define lymphatic organs partly by the presence of a connective tissue capsule, what could we regard as the capsule of red bone marrow?*

## The Thymus

The **thymus** was introduced in chapter 18 because it is a member of both the endocrine and lymphatic systems. It is a bilobed organ located in the mediastinum between the heart and the base of the neck (fig. 22.10). The two lobes are connected by a median bridge of tissue. In children, the organ is relatively firm and conical, much larger than it is in adults, and deep red due to its rich supply of blood vessels. After age 15 or so, it shrinks and contains less and less lymphatic tissue, and its color changes to gray and then yellowish as it becomes infiltrated with fat (see fig. 18.7, p. 536). In old age, it is barely distinguishable from the surrounding fat and fibrous tissue of the mediastinum.

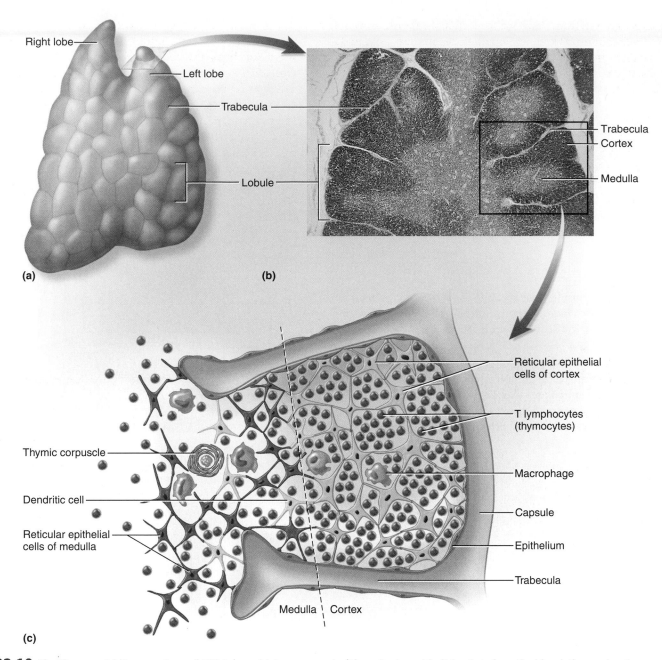

**Figure 22.10** **The Thymus.** (a) Gross anatomy. (b) Histology. (c) Arrangement of the reticular epithelial cells to form the blood–thymus barrier separating the cortex from the medulla of one lobule.
● *Which of the cells in this organ secretes hormones?*

The fibrous capsule of the thymus gives off trabeculae (septa) that penetrate into the gland and divide it into several angular lobules. Each lobule has a dense, dark-staining *cortex* and a lighter *medulla* inhabited by T lymphocytes (fig. 22.10b). **Reticular epithelial cells** seal off the cortex from the medulla and surround the blood vessels and lymphocyte clusters in the cortex. They thereby form a *blood–thymus barrier* that isolates developing lymphocytes from blood-borne antigens. In the medulla, the reticular epithelial cells form whorls called

*thymic (Hassall[6]) corpuscles,* which are useful for identifying the thymus histologically.

Besides forming the blood–thymus barrier, reticular epithelial cells secrete hormones called *thymosins, thymulin,* and *thymopoietin,* which promote the development and action of T cells. If the

---

[6]Arthur H. Hassall (1817–94), British chemist and physician

thymus is removed from newborn mammals, they waste away and never develop immunity. Other lymphatic organs also seem to depend on thymosins or T cells and develop poorly in thymectomized animals. The relationship of T cell maturation to thymic histology is discussed later in this chapter.

## Lymph Nodes

**Lymph nodes** are the most numerous lymphatic organs, numbering in the hundreds. They serve two functions: to cleanse the lymph and to act as a site of T and B cell activation. A lymph node is an elongated or bean-shaped structure, usually less than 3 cm long, often with an indentation called the *hilum* on one side (fig. 22.11). It is enclosed in a fibrous capsule with trabeculae that partially divide the interior of the node into compartments. Between the capsule and parenchyma is a narrow, relatively clear space called the *subcapsular sinus,* which contains reticular fibers, macrophages, and dendritic cells. Deep to this, the gland consists mainly of a stroma of reticular connective tissue (reticular fibers and reticular cells) and a parenchyma of lymphocytes and antigen-presenting cells.

The parenchyma is divided into an outer C-shaped **cortex** that encircles about four-fifths of the organ, and an inner **medulla** that extends to the surface at the hilum. The cortex consists mainly of ovoid to conical lymphatic nodules. When the lymph node is fighting a pathogen, these nodules acquire light-staining **germinal centers** where B cells multiply and differentiate into plasma cells.

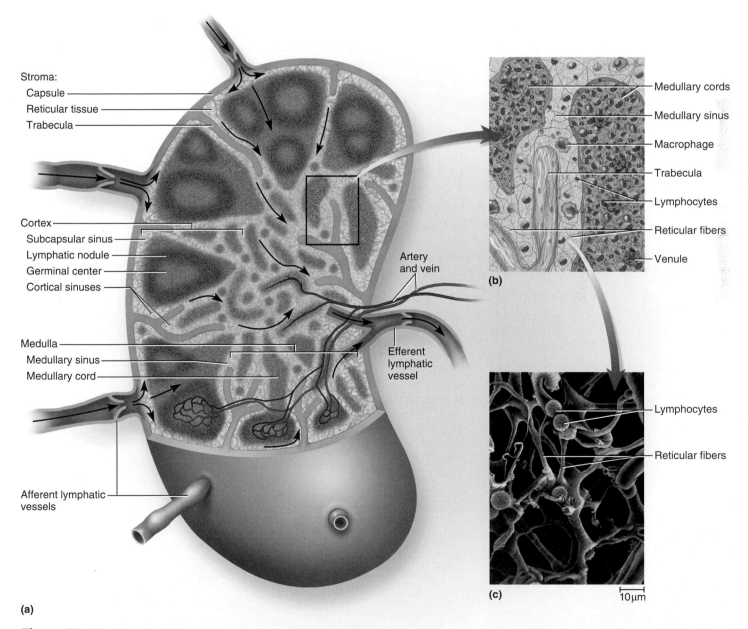

**Figure 22.11 Anatomy of a Lymph Node.** (a) Partially bisected lymph node showing pathway of lymph flow. (b) Detail of the boxed region in part (a). (c) Reticular fiber stroma and immune cells in a medullary sinus (SEM).

The medulla consists largely of a branching network of *medullary cords* composed of lymphocytes, plasma cells, macrophages, reticular cells, and reticular fibers. The cortex and medulla also contain lymph-filled sinuses continuous with the subcapsular sinus.

Several **afferent lymphatic vessels** lead into the node along its convex surface. Lymph flows from these vessels into the subcapsular sinus, percolates slowly through the sinuses of the cortex and medulla, and leaves the node through one to three **efferent lymphatic vessels** that emerge from the hilum. No other lymphatic organs have afferent lymphatic vessels; lymph nodes are the only organs that filter lymph as it flows along its course. The lymph node is a bottleneck that slows down lymph flow and allows time for cleansing it of foreign matter. The macrophages and reticular cells of the sinuses remove about 99% of the impurities before the lymph leaves the node. On its way to the bloodstream, lymph flows through one lymph node after another and thus becomes quite thoroughly cleansed of most impurities.

Blood vessels also penetrate the hilum of a lymph node. Arteries follow the medullary cords and give rise to capillary beds in the medulla and cortex. In the *deep cortex* near the junction with the medulla, lymphocytes can emigrate from the bloodstream into the parenchyma of the node. Most lymphocytes in the deep cortex are T cells.

Lymph nodes are widespread but especially concentrated in the following locations:

- *Cervical lymph nodes* occur in deep and superficial groups in the neck, and monitor lymph coming from the head and neck.

- *Axillary lymph nodes* are concentrated in the armpit (axilla) and receive lymph from the upper limb and the female breast (see fig. 22.6b).

- *Thoracic lymph nodes* occur in the thoracic cavity and receive lymph from the lungs, airway, and mediastinum.

- *Abdominal lymph nodes* monitor lymph from the urinary and reproductive systems.

- *Intestinal* and *mesenteric lymph nodes* monitor lymph from the digestive tract (fig. 22.12a).

- *Inguinal lymph nodes* occur in the groin (fig. 22.12b) and receive lymph from the entire lower limb.

- *Popliteal lymph nodes* occur at the back of the knee and receive lymph from the leg proper.

Physicians routinely palpate the superficial lymph nodes of the cervical, axillary, and inguinal regions for swelling *(lymphadenitis)*. Lymph nodes are common sites of metastatic cancer (see Insight 22.2).

## Tonsils

The **tonsils** are patches of lymphatic tissue located at the entrance to the pharynx, where they guard against ingested and inhaled pathogens. Each is covered by an epithelium and has deep pits called **tonsillar crypts** lined by lymphatic nodules (fig. 22.13). The crypts often contain food debris, dead leukocytes, bacteria, and antigenic chemicals. Below the crypts, the tonsils are partially separated from underlying connective tissue by an incomplete fibrous capsule.

## INSIGHT 22.2 ● ● ●

### Clinical Application

### Lymph Nodes and Metastatic Cancer

*Metastasis* is a phenomenon in which cancerous cells break free of the original *primary tumor,* travel to other sites in the body, and establish new tumors. Because of the high permeability of lymphatic capillaries, metastasizing cancer cells easily enter them and travel in the lymph. They tend to lodge in the first lymph node they encounter and multiply there, eventually destroying the node. Cancerous lymph nodes are swollen but relatively firm and usually painless. Cancer of a lymph node is called *lymphoma.*

Once a tumor is well established in one node, cells may emigrate from there and travel to the next. However, if the metastasis is detected early enough, cancer can sometimes be eradicated by removing not only the primary tumor, but also the nearest lymph nodes downstream from that point. For example, breast cancer is often treated with a combination of lumpectomy or mastectomy along with removal of the nearby axillary lymph nodes.

There are three main sets of tonsils: (1) a single median **pharyngeal tonsil (adenoids)** on the wall of the pharynx just behind the nasal cavity, (2) a pair of **palatine tonsils** at the posterior margin of the oral cavity, and (3) numerous **lingual tonsils,** each with a single crypt, concentrated in a patch on each side of the root of the tongue (see fig. 24.5, p. 690).

The palatine tonsils are the largest and most often infected. *Tonsillitis* is an acute inflammation of the palatine tonsils, usually caused by a *Streptococcus* infection. Their surgical removal, called *tonsillectomy,* used to be one of the most common surgical procedures performed on children, but it is done less often today. Tonsillitis is now usually treated with antibiotics.

### THINK ABOUT IT

*Which tonsil(s) is or are most likely to be affected by an inhaled pathogen?*

## The Spleen

The **spleen** is the body's largest lymphatic organ, measuring up to 12 cm long and weighing up to 160 g. It is located in the left hypochondriac region, just inferior to the diaphragm and dorsolateral to the stomach (fig. 22.14; see also fig. A.15, p. 36). It is protected by ribs 10 through 12. The spleen fits snugly between the diaphragm, stomach, and kidney and has indentations called the *gastric area* and *renal area* where it presses against these adjacent viscera. It has a medial hilum penetrated by the splenic artery, splenic vein, and lymphatic vessels.

The parenchyma exhibits two types of tissue named for their appearance in fresh specimens (not in stained sections): **red pulp,** which consists of sinuses gorged with concentrated erythrocytes, and **white pulp,** which consists of lymphocytes and macrophages aggregated

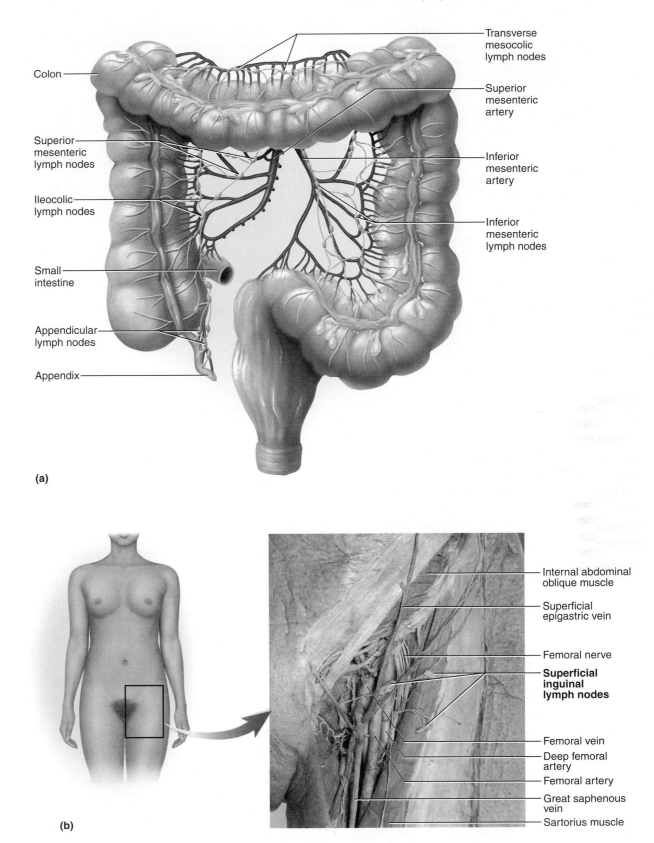

Colon

Superior mesenteric lymph nodes

Ileocolic lymph nodes

Small intestine

Appendicular lymph nodes

Appendix

Transverse mesocolic lymph nodes

Superior mesenteric artery

Inferior mesenteric artery

Inferior mesenteric lymph nodes

(a)

Internal abdominal oblique muscle

Superficial epigastric vein

Femoral nerve

**Superficial inguinal lymph nodes**

Femoral vein

Deep femoral artery

Femoral artery

Great saphenous vein

Sartorius muscle

(b)

**Figure 22.12** **Some Areas of Lymph Node Concentration.** (a) Mesenteric lymph nodes associated with the large intestine. (b) Inguinal lymph in a female cadaver.

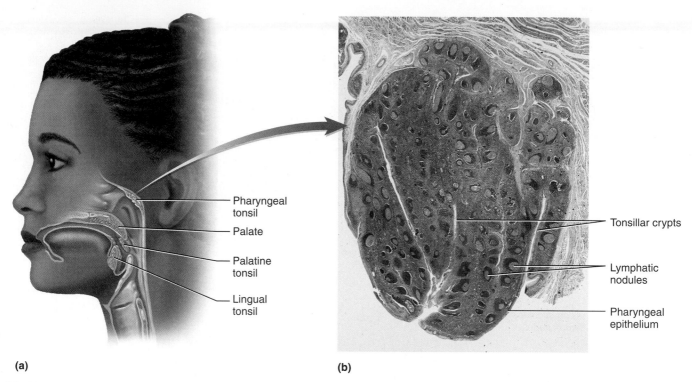

**Figure 22.13** **The Tonsils.** (a) Locations of the tonsils. (b) Histology of the pharyngeal tonsil.

INSIGHT 22.3
Clinical Application

## Splenectomy

A ruptured spleen is one of the most common consequences of blows to the left thoracic or abdominal wall, as in sports injuries and automobile accidents. It is especially likely to rupture if the lower ribs are fractured, and sometimes it is nicked during abdominal surgery. The spleen is such a pulpy and vascular organ that it bleeds profusely, and its capsule is so thin and delicate that it is difficult to repair surgically. To prevent fatal hemorrhaging, it is often necessary to quickly remove the spleen and tie off the splenic artery. This procedure is called *splenectomy.*

The loss of splenic function, called *hyposplenism,* is usually not serious; its functions are adequately carried out by hepatic and bone marrow macrophages. However, it does leave a person somewhat more at risk of septicemia (bacteria in the blood) and pneumococcal infections. Therefore, if possible, surgeons try to leave some of the spleen in place; the spleen regenerates rapidly in such cases.

Some people have overactive spleens (*hypersplenism*), in which excessive phagocytosis of the formed elements of blood can lead to anemia, leukopenia, or thrombocytopenia (see chapter 19). This can be another reason for performing a splenectomy.

like sleeves along small branches of the splenic artery. In tissue sections, white pulp appears as an ovoid mass of lymphocytes with an arteriole passing through it. However, it is important to bear in mind that its three-dimensional shape is not egglike but cylindrical.

These two tissue types reflect the multiple functions of the spleen. It produces blood cells in the fetus and may resume this role in adults in the event of extreme anemia. Lymphocytes and macrophages of the white pulp monitor the blood for foreign antigens, much like the lymph nodes do the lymph. The splenic blood capillaries are very permeable; they allow RBCs to leave the bloodstream, accumulate in the sinuses of the red pulp, and reenter the bloodstream later. The spleen is an "erythrocyte graveyard"—old, fragile RBCs rupture as they squeeze through the capillary walls into the sinuses. Macrophages phagocytize their remains, just as they dispose of blood-borne bacteria and other cellular debris. The spleen also helps to stabilize blood volume by transferring excess plasma from the bloodstream into the lymphatic system.

### THINK ABOUT IT

*From an anatomical perspective, why are lymph nodes the only lymphatic organs that can filter the lymph?*

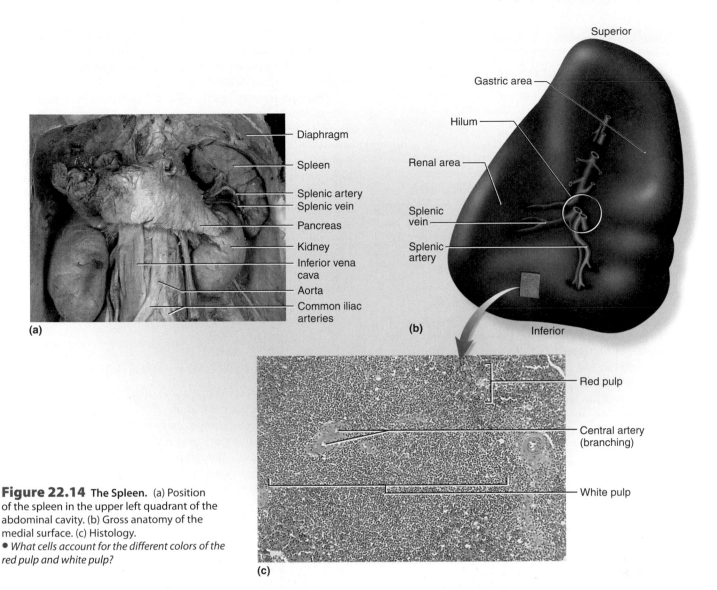

Figure 22.14 **The Spleen.** (a) Position of the spleen in the upper left quadrant of the abdominal cavity. (b) Gross anatomy of the medial surface. (c) Histology.
● *What cells account for the different colors of the red pulp and white pulp?*

## Before You Go On

*Answer the following questions to test your understanding of the preceding section:*

4. What do T, B, and NK cells have in common? How do NK cells functionally differ from the other two? How do T and B cells functionally differ from each other?

5. What is the function of an antigen-presenting cell (APC)? Name three kinds of APCs.

6. What is a lymphatic nodule? Describe three places where lymphatic nodules can be found.

7. What are the two primary lymphatic organs? Why are they called that? Describe their collaborative relationship in producing the lymphocytes that populate other organs.

8. Describe the structural and functional differences between the cortex and medulla of a lymph node.

9. Name the three kinds of tonsils and state how they differ in number and location.

10. What are the two types of "pulp" in the spleen? What are their respective functions?

11. In what sense does the spleen serve the blood in the same way that the lymph nodes serve the lymph?

## The Lymphatic System in Relation to Immunity

### Objectives

When you have completed this section, you should be able to

• define *immune system* and explain its relationship to the lymphatic system;

• identify the body's three lines of defense against pathogens;

- distinguish between nonspecific defense and specific immunity;
- distinguish between humoral and cellular immunity; and
- describe the life histories and immune functions of B cells and T cells, and how these relate to the anatomy of the lymphatic organs.

The **immune system** is not an organ system, but rather a population of disease-fighting cells that reside in the mucous membranes, lymphatic organs, and other localities in the body. Although it does not have a specific anatomy distinct from what we have already studied in this chapter, a brief survey of immune function will enhance your understanding of the defensive role of the lymphatic system.

## Modes of Defense

We have three lines of defense against pathogens: (1) a system of physical barriers to invasion, chiefly the skin and mucous membranes; (2) a system of nonspecific actions against pathogens that get past the first defense; and (3) the immune system, which not only defeats the pathogen but "remembers" it, enabling the body to defeat it so quickly in future encounters that we never notice any symptoms of disease.

The first two defenses lack the capacity to remember a particular pathogen and react to it differently in the future. Furthermore, they defend equally against a broad range of pathogens; thus they are called **nonspecific defenses.** In addition to the skin and mucous membranes, these nonspecific defenses include neutrophils, macrophages, natural killer (NK) cells, various antimicrobial proteins such as interferons, and such processes as inflammation, fever, and immunological surveillance. The third defense confers a protection called **specific immunity**—*specific* because the body must develop a separate immunity to each pathogen. For example, immunity to one disease, such as chicken pox, does not confer immunity against another, such as measles. The ability to distinguish one pathogen from another is based on their **antigens**—complex molecules such as proteins and glycoproteins that genetically distinguish organisms, and even different members of the same species, from each other and that trigger the immune response. The agents that carry out specific immune responses are T and B lymphocytes.

Some cells play roles in both specific and nonspecific defense—notably macrophages and helper T cells. Macrophages are fairly undiscriminating in the microbes they attack, but they also act to present foreign antigens to activate the lymphocytes of specific immunity. Helper T ($T_H$) cells activate not only the B and $T_c$ cells of specific immunity, but also help to mediate the nonspecific inflammatory response.

There are two forms of specific immunity called *humoral* and *cellular immunity.* **Humoral (antibody-mediated) immunity** is carried out by B lymphocytes and antibodies. It is called *humoral* because the antibodies circulate freely in the body fluids; *humor* is an archaic term for a body fluid. **Cellular (cell-mediated) immunity** is carried out by cytotoxic T cells. We will not delve into the

details of these defenses, but we will take a look at how the activities of B and T cells are related to the anatomy of the lymphatic organs. These lymphocytes are the most abundant cells of the lymphatic organs.

There are some things that B and T cells have in common, and we can address these before examining the differences in their life histories. Both types begin their development as *pluripotent stem cells* (PPSCs) in the red bone marrow. PPSCs divide and give rise to *lymphocyte colony-forming units,* which ultimately produce B and T lymphocytes (see fig. 19.8, p. 563). Before they can take part in immune reactions, both types of lymphocytes must develop antigen receptors on their surfaces, giving them **immunocompetence**—the ability to recognize, bind, and respond to an antigen. In addition, the body must get rid of lymphocytes that react against its own (host) antigens so that the immune system will not attack our own organs. The destruction or deactivation of self-reactive lymphocytes is called **negative selection.** Only about 2% of the lymphocytes survive this culling process. The developmental histories of B and T cells are contrasted in figure 22.15.

## B Cells and Humoral Immunity

B cells achieve immunocompetence and go through negative selection in the red bone marrow. Many of the mature immunocompetent B cells remain there, while many more disperse and populate other sites such as the mucous membranes, spleen, and especially the cortical nodules of the lymph nodes, where they can sit and await the arrival of antigens in the incoming lymph.

When one of these B cells encounters an antigen, it internalizes and digests it, and presents fragments of the antigen to a helper T cell. The helper T cell secretes chemical *helper factors* that stimulate the B cell to divide still more. Most of its daughter cells differentiate into **plasma cells,** which are larger than B cells and have an abundance of rough endoplasmic reticulum (fig. 22.16)—as well they might, for plasma cells secrete antibodies at the astounding rate of up to 2,000 molecules per second for a life span of 4 or 5 days. Plasma cells develop mainly in the germinal centers of the nodules of the lymph nodes. About 10% of them remain there, while the rest emigrate from the lymph nodes and populate the bone marrow and other lymphatic organs and tissues. Their antibodies travel throughout the body in the blood and other fluids and react in various ways against antigens that they encounter.

Instead of becoming plasma cells, some B cells become memory cells. These live for months to years, and respond very quickly if they ever encounter the same antigen again. This provides long-lasting immunity to that pathogen.

## T Cells and Cellular Immunity

T lymphocytes leave the bone marrow before reaching maturity. They migrate to the fetal thymus and colonize the cortex, where the blood–thymus barrier isolates them from premature exposure to blood-borne antigens. Reticular epithelial cells secrete thymic hormones that stimulate these T cells to develop antigen receptors, thus becoming immunocompetent. Following negative selection,

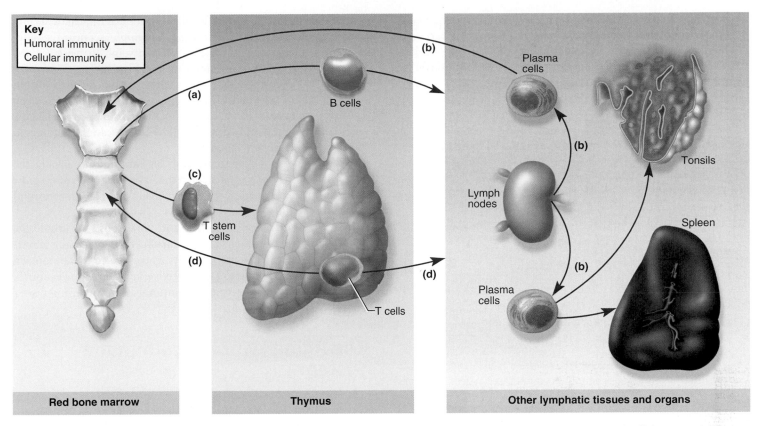

**Figure 22.15  The Life History and Migrations of B and T Cells.** Humoral immunity is represented by the violet pathways and cellular immunity by the red. (a) B cells achieve immunocompetence in the red bone marrow (left), and many emigrate to a variety of lymphatic tissues and organs, including the lymph nodes, tonsils, and spleen (right). (b) Plasma cells develop in the lymph nodes (among other sites) and emigrate to the bone marrow and other lymphatic organs, where they spend a few days secreting antibodies. (c) T stem cells emigrate from the bone marrow and attain immunocompetence in the thymus. (d) Immunocompetent T cells leave the thymus and recolonize the bone marrow or colonize varied lymphatic organs (right).

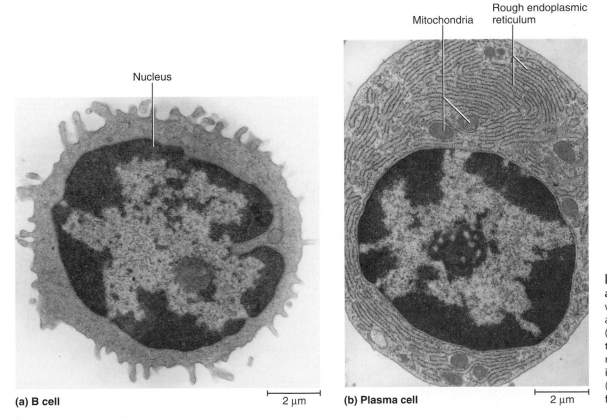

**Figure 22.16  A B Cell and Plasma Cell.** (a) A B cell, with a nucleus occupying almost the entire cell volume. (b) A plasma cell, showing the extreme proliferation of rough endoplasmic reticulum in keeping with its protein- (antibody-) synthesizing function.

the surviving T cells migrate into the medulla of the thymus, where they spend another 3 weeks. There is no blood–thymus barrier in the medulla, so T cells here can easily enter the blood and lymphatic vessels and disperse throughout the body. They colonize the same sites as B cells do, including recolonizing the red bone marrow. They become especially concentrated in the deep cortex of the lymph nodes.

When cytotoxic ($T_C$) cells encounter an enemy cell, they attack it directly and destroy it with a *lethal hit* of toxic chemicals. This is why immunity carried out by T cells is called *cellular (cell-mediated) immunity*. As in humoral immunity, some T cells remain as memory T cells that live as long as a few decades and thus confer long-lasting protection.

## Before You Go On

*Answer the following questions to test your understanding of the preceding section:*

12. What are the three lines of defense against pathogens?

13. How does specific immunity differ from nonspecific defense?

14. What is the difference between humoral and cellular immunity?

15. Where do B cells acquire immunocompetence? Where do T cells do so?

16. What are the structural and functional differences between a B cell and a plasma cell?

# Developmental and Clinical Perspectives

### Objectives

When you have completed this section, you should be able to

- describe the embryonic origins of the lymphatic organs;
- describe changes in the lymphatic system that occur with old age; and
- describe some common disorders of the lymphatic–immune system.

## Embryonic Development

Embryonic development of the thymus was described in chapter 18, page 544. Here we will examine the development of the lymphatic vessels, lymph nodes, and spleen.

Lymphatic vessels begin as endothelium-lined channels in the mesoderm called **lymph sacs.** Some of these originate by budding from the blood vessels and then detaching from them; others originate as isolated mesodermal channels that fuse with each other and ultimately link up with the venous system. In a manner similar to the development of blood vessels (see chapter 21, p. 631), lymph sacs proliferate, enlarge, and merge with each other to form larger and larger channels in the mesoderm (fig. 22.17a).

Those with the greatest fluid flow later develop a tunica media and externa. The first to form are the *jugular lymph sacs* near the junction of the internal jugular and subclavian veins. By week 7, these sacs join the primitive veins and thus form the forerunners of the thoracic and right lymphatic ducts. The cisterna chyli arises from a *median lymph sac* that initially grows from the primitive vena cava and then breaks away from it. Smaller lymphatic vessels grow outward from the lymph sacs and follow blood vessels growing into the developing limbs.

Lymph nodes begin to develop as lymphocytes invade the lymph sacs and form cell clusters in the lumens. Blood vessels grow into these clusters, while a connective tissue capsule forms around them (fig. 22.17b).

The spleen develops from mesenchymal cells that invade the dorsal mesentery leading to the stomach. Thus it remains enveloped in this mesentery and permanently connected to the stomach by a *gastrosplenic ligament*. The spleen is poorly developed at birth. Invasion of the splenic tissue by immunocompetent lymphocytes stimulates its postnatal development.

## The Aging Lymphatic–Immune System

The effects of old age on the lymphatic system are seen not so much in anatomical changes as in declining immune function. There are several reasons for the reduced immune responsiveness. The quantities of red bone marrow and lymphatic tissue decline, so there are fewer hemopoietic stem cells, leukocytes, and antigen-presenting cells. As the thymus shrinks, the level of thymic hormones declines. Perhaps because of this, an increasing percentage of lymphocytes fail to mature and achieve immunocompetence. There are fewer helper T cells, so both humoral and cellular immunity suffer from their absence. $T_C$ cells are less responsive to antigens, and even antibody levels rise more slowly in response to infection. With fewer NK cells, immunological surveillance is weaker—one of multiple reasons that cancer becomes more common in old age. Paradoxically, while normal antibody responses are weaker in old age, the level of circulating *autoantibodies* rises. These are antibodies that fail to distinguish between host and foreign antigens, and therefore attack the body's own tissues, causing a variety of *autoimmune*[7] *diseases* such as rheumatoid arthritis.

With reduced immunity in old age, infectious diseases can be not only more common but also more serious. Epidemics of influenza (flu), for example, take a disproportionate toll of lives among the elderly. It becomes increasingly important in old age to be vaccinated against such acute seasonal diseases.

## Lymphatic–Immune Disorders

It is a delicate balancing act for the body to discriminate between foreign and host antigens, ward off foreign pathogens, and mount immune responses that are not too weak, not too strong, and not misdirected. It comes as no surprise, therefore, that many

---

[7]*auto* = self

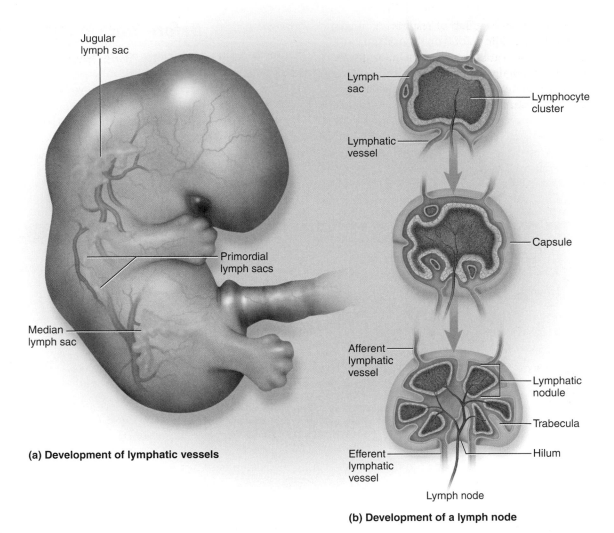

**(a) Development of lymphatic vessels**

**(b) Development of a lymph node**

**Figure 22.17** **Embryonic Development of the Lymphatic Vessels and Lymph Nodes.** (a) A 7-week embryo showing the right jugular lymph sac, which connects to the future subclavian vein; the primordial lymph sacs, which will merge to form the thoracic duct; and the median lymph sac, which will become the cisterna chyli. (b) Stages in the development of a lymph node. Top: Lymphocytes aggregate in a lymph sac, and blood vessels grow into the cluster. Middle: A fibrous capsule then forms around the sac as blood vessels proliferate. Bottom: Ingrowths of the capsule form trabeculae that partially subdivide the interior as the lymph node takes shape.

things can go wrong. Most immune disorders can be classified into three categories: autoimmune diseases, hypersensitivity, and immunodeficiency.

**Autoimmune diseases,** as already mentioned, are diseases resulting from an immune attack misdirected against one's own tissues. Insulin-dependent diabetes mellitus, rheumatic fever, rheumatoid arthritis, and systemic lupus erythematosus are some examples.

**Hypersensitivity** is an exaggerated, harmful immune response to antigens. The most prevalent examples are *allergies*—excessive reactions to environmental antigens *(allergens)* that most people tolerate. Allergens are found in a broad range of substances such as bee and wasp venoms; toxins from poison ivy and other plants; mold; dust; pollen; animal dander; foods such as nuts, milk, eggs, and shellfish; cosmetics; latex; vaccines; and drugs such as penicillin, tetracycline, and insulin. In many cases, an allergen stimulates basophils and mast cells to release histamine and other chemicals that cause a broad range of symptoms: edema, congestion, watery eyes, runny nose, hives, cramps, diarrhea, vomiting, and sometimes catastrophic circulatory failure *(anaphylactic shock).*

**Immunodeficiency diseases** are failures of the immune system to respond strongly enough to ward off disease. One of these is a congenital (inborn) condition—*severe combined immunodeficiency disease (SCID),* in which an infant is born without a functional immune system and must live in a sterile enclosure to avoid fatal infections. The most notorious immunodeficiency disease, of course, is AIDS *(acquired immunodeficiency syndrome).* Unlike SCID, this is not inborn but results from an infection with the human immunodeficiency virus (HIV), usually acquired by sexual intercourse or use of contaminated needles for drug injection. HIV targets especially the helper T (CD4) cells. When the $T_H$ count drops from its normal level of 600 to 1,200 cells/$\mu$L of blood to less than 200 cells/$\mu$L, a person has "full-blown AIDS" and is highly susceptible to *opportunistic infections*—infections that become established and produce disease only in people with weakened immune systems. In AIDS, some common examples are *Toxoplasma* (a protozoan that infects brain tissue), *Pneumocystis* (a group of respiratory fungi), *Candida* (a fungus that grows in white patches on the oral mucosa), herpes simplex, cytomegalovirus, and tuberculosis. Opportunistic infection is the principal cause of death in AIDS.

More specific to the lymphatic system, this chapter has already discussed filariasis and elephantiasis, lymph node cancer, tonsillitis, and ruptured spleen. A few more lymphatic disorders are briefly described in table 22.1.

## Before You Go On

*Answer the following questions to test your understanding of the preceding section:*

17. How do lymph sacs form in the embryo? How do lymph nodes form?

18. Describe some reasons for the declining efficiency of the immune system in old age.

19. What are the three principal categories of immune system disorders? Give an example of each.

| **TABLE 22.1** | **Some Disorders of the Lymphatic System** |
|---|---|
| **Lymphadenitis**[8] (lim-FAD-en-EYE-tis) | Inflammation of a lymph node in response to challenge from a foreign antigen; marked by swelling and tenderness. |
| **Lymphadenopathy**[9] (lim-FAD-en-OP-a-thee) | Collective term for all diseases of the lymph nodes |
| **Lymphangitis**[10] (LIM-fan-JY-tis) | Inflammation of a lymphatic vessel, as in filariasis (see Insight 22.1); marked by redness and pain along the course of the vessel. |
| **Hodgkin**[11] **disease** | A lymph node malignancy, with early symptoms including enlarged painful lymph nodes, especially in the neck, and fever, anorexia, weight loss, night sweats, and severe itching. Diagnosis is confirmed by finding characteristic *Reed–Sternberg* cells in a lymph node biopsy. Often progresses to neighboring lymph nodes. Radiation and chemotherapy cure about three out of four patients. |
| **Splenomegaly**[12] | Enlargement of the spleen, sometimes without underlying disease but often indicating infections, autoimmune diseases, heart failure, cirrhosis, Hodgkin disease, and other cancers. The enlarged spleen may "hoard" erythrocytes, causing anemia, and it may become fragile and subject to rupture. |
| **Non-Hodgkin lymphoma** | A lymphoma similar to Hodgkin disease, but more common, with more widespread distribution in the body (including axillary, inguinal, and femoral lymph nodes), and without Reed–Sternberg cells. Has a higher mortality rate than Hodgkin disease. |

### Disorders Described Elsewhere

AIDS 657
Allergy 657
Autoimmune diseases 657
Cancer of lymph nodes 650
Elephantiasis 642

Filariasis 642
Opportunistic infection 657
Ruptured spleen 652
Severe combined immunodeficiency disease 657
Tonsillitis 650

---

[8]*lymph* + *adeno* = gland + *itis* = inflammation
[9]*lymph* + adeno = gland + *pathy* = disease
[10]*lymph* + *ang* = vessel + *itis* = inflammation
[11]Thomas Hodgkin (1798–1866), British physician
[12]*megaly* = enlargement

# CHAPTER REVIEW

## REVIEW OF KEY CONCEPTS

### Lymph and Lymphatic Vessels (p. 640)

1. The lymphatic system consists of *lymph* and lymphatic vessels, tissues, and organs.

2. The system serves to recover tissue fluid and maintain fluid balance; provide immune cells and monitor the body fluids for foreign matter; and transport dietary lipids from the small intestine to the blood.

3. Lymph is usually a colorless liquid similar to blood plasma, but is milky when absorbing digested lipids. It contains lymphocytes, macrophages, and hormones, and may contain metastasizing cancer cells, cellular debris, bacteria, and viruses.

4. Lymph originates in blind *lymphatic capillaries* that pick up tissue fluid throughout the body. The endothelial cells of lymphatic capillaries have large gaps between them that permit cells and other large particles to enter the lymph stream.

5. Lymphatic capillaries converge to form larger *collecting vessels* with a histology similar to that of blood vessels. Lymph nodes lie at irregular intervals along the collecting vessels and filter the lymph on its way back to the blood.

6. Collecting vessels converge to form six *lymphatic trunks* that drain specific regions of the body. The lymphatic trunks then converge to form two *collecting ducts*—the *right lymphatic duct* and *thoracic duct*—which empty lymph into the subclavian veins.

7. There is no heartlike pump to move the lymph; lymph flows under forces similar to those that drive venous blood flow, and like some veins, lymphatic vessels have valves to ensure a one-way flow.

### Lymphatic Cells, Tissues, and Organs (p. 644)

1. The cells of lymphatic tissue are natural killer (NK) cells, T lymphocytes, B lymphocytes, macrophages, dendritic cells, and reticular cells.

2. *NK cells* provide a nonspecific defense against bacteria, viruses, tissue transplants, and cancer. Their constant patrolling of the body for infected, cancerous, or defective cells is called *immunological surveillance.*

3. *T lymphocytes* are named for their development in the thymus. The types of T cells are *cytotoxic T ($T_C$) cells,* which directly attack and destroy enemy cells; *helper T ($T_H$) cells,* which stimulate other lymphocytes as well as inflammation; and *memory T ($T_M$) cells,* which provide lasting immunity after the initial exposure to an antigen.

4. *B lymphocytes* attain maturity in the bone marrow. Upon exposure to an antigen, some of them develop into *plasma cells,* which secrete protective antibodies, and others into *memory B cells.*

5. *Macrophages* are large, highly phagocytic cells that develop from monocytes. They engulf and destroy foreign matter and dead host cells, and act as *antigen-presenting cells (APCs)* to activate immune responses. There are several kinds of macrophages, including microglia, dendritic cells, and alveolar and hepatic macrophages.

6. *Dendritic cells* are macrophages of the skin, mucous membranes, and lymphatic organs. They engulf foreign matter by receptor-mediated endocytosis rather than phagocytosis, but otherwise act like any other macrophage.

7. *Reticular cells* are branched stationary cells that make up part of the stroma of lymphatic organs and act as APCs in the thymus.

8. *Diffuse lymphatic tissue* is an aggregation of lymphatic cells in the walls of other organs, especially in the mucous membranes of the respiratory, digestive, urinary, and reproductive tracts—where it is called mucosa-associated lymphatic tissue (MALT). In some places, lymphocytes and macrophages form dense masses called *lymphatic nodules,* such as the *Peyer patches* of the ileum.

9. Lymphatic organs have well-defined anatomical locations and have a fibrous capsule that at least partially separates them from adjacent organs and tissues. Two of these, the red bone marrow and thymus, are called *primary lymphatic organs* because lymphocytes mature here before colonizing the other sites. The other sites, called *secondary lymphatic organs,* are the lymph nodes, tonsils, and spleen.

10. Red bone marrow is a hemopoietic tissue and the point of origin of all immune cells of the lymphatic system. It consists of *islands* of hemopoietic tissue composed of macrophages and developing blood cells, separated by *sinusoids* that converge on a *central longitudinal vein.* Lymphocytes and other formed elements pass from the islands into the sinusoids and enter the bloodstream.

11. The *thymus* is located in the mediastinum above the heart. It is divided into numerous polygonal lobules, each with a dense cortex and lighter medulla. Reticular epithelial cells separate the cortex from the medulla and surround the blood vessels, forming a blood thymus barrier that isolates developing lymphocytes from blood-borne antigens. These cells also secrete thymic hormones that regulate T cell development and activity.

12. *Lymph nodes* are numerous small, bean-shaped organs that receive lymph through *afferent lymphatic vessels,* filter it, and pass it along via *efferent lymphatic vessels* that exit the hilum. They monitor the lymph for foreign antigens, remove impurities before it returns to the bloodstream, contribute lymphocytes to the lymph and blood, and mount immune responses to foreign antigens.

13. The parenchyma of a lymph node exhibits an outer cortex composed mainly of lymphatic nodules, and a deeper medulla with a network of *medullary cords.* B cells multiply and differentiate into plasma cells in the germinal centers of the nodules. T cells are very concentrated in the *deep cortex* next to the medulla.

14. Lymph nodes are widespread but especially concentrated in cervical, axillary, thoracic, abdominal, intestinal, mesenteric, inguinal, and popliteal groups.

15. The *tonsils* encircle the pharynx and guard against inhaled and ingested pathogens. They include a medial *pharyngeal tonsil* in the nasopharynx, a pair of *palatine tonsils* at the rear of the oral cavity, and numerous *lingual tonsils* clustered in the root of the tongue. Their superficial surface is covered with epithelium and their deep surface with a fibrous partial capsule. They have deep pits called *tonsillary crypts* bordered by rows of lymphatic follicles.

16. The *spleen* lies in the left hypochondriac region between the diaphragm, stomach, and kidney. Its parenchyma is composed of *red pulp* containing concentrated RBCs and *white pulp* composed of lymphocytes and macrophages.

17. The spleen monitors the blood for foreign antigens, activates immune responses to them, disposes of old RBCs, and helps to regulate blood volume.

### The Lymphatic System in Relation to Immunity (p. 653)

1. The immune system is a population of disease-fighting cells (mainly lymphocytes

and macrophages) that inhabit the mucous membranes, connective tissues, and lymphatic organs among other sites.

2. The three lines of defense against pathogens are surface barriers to invasion (skin and mucous membranes); various additional forms of *nonspecific defense* against pathogens that breach the surface; and *specific immunity.*

3. Nonspecific defense includes the surface barriers, neutrophils and macrophages, NK cells, immunological surveillance, inflammation, fever, and antimicrobial proteins. It does not provide a mechanism for remembering a particular pathogen.

4. Specific immunity is a rapid response to a particular pathogen remembered from a previous encounter. The two forms of specific immunity are *humoral immunity,* carried out by B cells and antibodies, and *cellular immunity,* carried out by cytotoxic T cells.

5. Both B and T cells arise from bone marrow pluripotent stem cells through *lymphocyte colony-forming units.* Before participating in immune reactions, they must become *immunocompetent* and survive the process of *negative selection,* which eliminates lymphocytes that would attack the body's own tissues.

6. B cells achieve immunocompetence in the red bone marrow. The few that survive negative selection emigrate to colonize the lymph nodes and other sites, where they multiply and stand guard against pathogens.

7. Upon encountering an antigen, a B cell displays fragments of it on its surface. $T_H$ cells respond by secreting *helper factors,* which stimulate B cell multiplication. Most of the daughter B cells become antibody-secreting *plasma cells,* while some become the *memory B cells* that confer lasting immunity to that antigen.

8. T cells originate in the red bone marrow but achieve immunocompetence and undergo selection in the thymic cortex. Mature T cells then pass into the medulla, emigrate from the thymus via blood and lymphatic vessels, and colonize the various lymphatic organs. $T_C$ cells directly attack enemy cells and destroy them with a *lethal hit* of toxic chemicals. Some T cells remain as *memory T cells* that produce lasting immunity.

### Developmental and Clinical Perspectives (p. 656)

1. Lymphatic ducts begin as *lymph sacs,* which are endothelium-lined channels in the mesoderm. Some of these arise by budding from the blood vessels and then detaching from them, and some as isolated mesodermal channels that fuse with each other and then (in the case of the two collecting ducts) join the venous system.

2. Embryonic lymph sacs are infiltrated with lymphocytes, which form dense clusters, become encapsulated, and develop into lymph nodes.

3. The spleen develops from a mass of mesenchymal cells in the dorsal mesentery leading to the stomach. Most of its development is postnatal.

4. In old age, the lymphatic system itself shows little anatomical change, but the quantity of lymphatic tissue and numbers of lymphocytes decline, and immune responses become less efficient. Elderly people are thus more susceptible to infectious diseases and cancer. Autoantibody levels rise in old age and cause such autoimmune diseases as rheumatoid arthritis.

5. There are three principal classes of immune system disorders: misdirected immune attacks (autoimmune diseases), hypersensitivity disorders such as allergy, and immunodeficiency diseases such as SCID and AIDS. AIDS, the most notorious immune disease, is caused by destruction of $T_H$ cells by HIV, leaving a person susceptible to cancer and a variety of opportunistic infections.

6. Table 22.1 describes some disorders of the lymphatic system. Lymph node diseases in general are called *lymphadenopathy.* Inflammation of lymph nodes and lymphatic vessels, respectively, is called *lymphadenitis* and *lymphangitis.* Lymph node tumors are called *lymphomas.* Two categories of lymphoma are Hodgkin disease and non-Hodgkin lymphoma. *Splenomegaly* is enlargement of the spleen.

## TESTING YOUR RECALL

1. The only lymphatic organ with both afferent and efferent lymphatic vessels is
   a. the spleen.
   b. a lymph node.
   c. a tonsil.
   d. a Peyer patch.
   e. the thymus.

2. Which of the following cells are involved in nonspecific defense but not in specific immunity?
   a. helper T cells
   b. cytotoxic T cells
   c. natural killer cells
   d. B cells
   e. plasma cells

3. The lethal hit is used by ___ to kill enemy cells.
   a. neutrophils
   b. basophils
   c. mast cells
   d. NK cells
   e. cytotoxic T cells

4. Which of these is a macrophage?
   a. microglia
   b. a plasma cell
   c. a reticular cell
   d. a helper T cell
   e. a mast cell

5. Which of these lymphatic organs has a cortex and medulla: (I) spleen; (II) lymph node; (III) thymus; (IV) red bone marrow?
   a. II only
   b. III only
   c. II and III only
   d. III and IV only
   e. I, II, and III

6. What cells form the blood–thymus barrier?
   a. astrocytes
   b. Hassall corpuscles
   c. T cells
   d. dendritic cells
   e. reticular epithelial cells

7. Where do B cells attain immunocompetence?
   a. in the red bone marrow
   b. in the germinal centers of the lymph nodes
   c. in the thymic cortex
   d. in the thymic medulla
   e. in the splenic white pulp

8. If it were not for the process of negative selection, we would expect to see more
   a. allergies.
   b. lymphatic nodules in the MALT.
   c. antigen-presenting cells.
   d. immunodeficiency diseases.
   e. autoimmune diseases.

9. Lymph nodes tend to be especially concentrated in all of these sites *except*
   a. the cervical region.
   b. the popliteal region.
   c. the carpal region.
   d. the inguinal region.
   e. the mesenteries.

10. All lymph ultimately reenters the bloodstream at what point?
    a. the right atrium
    b. the common carotid arteries
    c. the internal iliac veins
    d. the subclavian veins
    e. the inferior vena cava

11. Any organism or substance capable of causing disease is called a/an _____.

12. The milky lymph, rich in fat, absorbed from the small intestine is called _____.

13. Lymphatic vessels called _____ carry lymph from one lymph node to the next.

14. The two lymphatics that empty into the subclavian veins are the _____ on the right and the _____ on the left.

15. The latter duct in question 14 begins with a sac called the _____ below the diaphragm.

16. B cells become _____ cells before they begin to secrete antibodies.

17. Any cells that process antigens and display fragments of them to activate immune reactions are called _____.

18. The _____ is a lymphatic organ composed mainly of hemopoietic islands and sinusoids.

19. The ovoid masses of lymphocytes that line the tonsillar crypts are called _____.

20. Any disease in which antibodies attack one's own tissues is called a/an _____ disease.

*Answers in the Appendix*

---

## TRUE OR FALSE

*Determine which five of the following statements are false, and briefly explain why.*

1. B cells play roles in both nonspecific defense and specific immunity.

2. T lymphocytes undergo negative selection in the thymus.

3. Lymphatic capillaries are more permeable than blood capillaries.

4. T lymphocytes are involved only in cellular immunity.

5. The white pulp of the spleen gets its color mainly from lymphocytes and macrophages.

6. Obstruction of a major lymphatic vessel is likely to cause edema.

7. Lymph nodes are populated by B cells but not T cells.

8. Lymphatic nodules are permanent structures enclosed in fibrous capsules.

9. Tonsillectomy is regarded as the current treatment of choice for most cases of tonsillitis.

10. Most plasma cells form in the germinal centers of the lymph nodes.

*Answers in the Appendix*

---

## TESTING YOUR COMPREHENSION

1. About 10% of people have one or more *accessory spleens,* typically about 1 cm in diameter and located near the hilum of the main spleen or embedded in the tail of the pancreas. If a surgeon is performing a splenectomy as a treatment for hypersplenism (see Insight 22.3), why would it be important to search for and remove any accessory spleens? What might be the consequences of overlooking one of these?

2. In treating a woman for malignancy in the right breast, the surgeon removes some of her axillary lymph nodes. Following surgery, the patient experiences edema of her right arm. Explain why.

3. Explain why a detailed knowledge of the pathways of lymphatic drainage is important to the clinical management of cancer.

4. A burn research center uses mice for studies of skin grafting. To prevent graft rejection, the mice are thymectomized at birth. Even though B cells do not develop in the thymus, these mice show no humoral immune response and are very susceptible to infection. Explain why the removal of the thymus would improve the success of skin grafts but adversely affect humoral immunity.

5. Contrast the structure of a B cell with that of a plasma cell, and explain how their structural difference relates to their functional difference.

*Answers at aris.mhhe.com*

---

## ONLINE RESOURCES

 Visit aprevealed.com to explore melt-away cadaver dissections, watch animations that clarify difficult concepts, review histological and radiological images, or take a quiz to assess your understanding of the material.

 The Saladin *Human Anatomy,* 2e website at aris.mhhe.com features chapter-specific quizzes, labeling exercises, and other interactive tools to complement your study of human anatomy. If your instructor has provided an ARIS course code, you can also access assignments and information specific to your course.

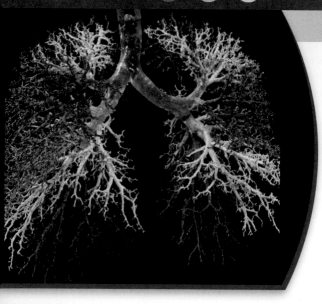

# The Respiratory System

The bronchial trees, with each bronchopulmonary segment shown in a different color (resin cast)

## CHAPTER OUTLINE

## INSIGHTS

## BRUSHING UP

To understand this chapter, you may find it helpful to review the following concepts:
- Serous and mucous membranes (p. 97)
- The ethmoid bone, maxilla, nasal bones, and vomer (pp. 187–190)
- The muscles of respiration (p. 310)
- Basic brainstem anatomy (pp. 430–433)
- Divisions of the autonomic nervous system (p. 469)
- Pulmonary blood circulation (p. 604)

**Anatomy & Physiology | REVEALED®**
aprevealed.com

**Respiratory System**

Breath represents life. The first breath of a baby and the last gasp of a dying person are two of the most dramatic moments of human experience. The need to breathe is driven by cellular demands for energy in the form of ATP; most ATP synthesis requires oxygen and generates carbon dioxide. The respiratory system consists essentially of tubes that deliver air to the lungs, where oxygen diffuses into the blood and carbon dioxide is removed from it.

The respiratory and cardiovascular systems have such a close functional and spatial relationship that a disorder of the lungs often has direct effects on the heart, and vice versa. The two systems are often considered jointly as the *cardiopulmonary system.*

The principal organs of the respiratory system are the nose, pharynx, larynx, trachea, bronchi, and lungs (fig. 23.1). Within the lungs, air flows along a dead-end pathway consisting essentially of bronchi → bronchioles → alveoli (with some refinements to be introduced later). Incoming air stops in the *alveoli* (millions of thin-walled, microscopic air sacs), exchanges gases with the bloodstream across the alveolar wall, and then flows back out.

The **conducting division** of the respiratory system consists of those passages that serve only for airflow, essentially from the nostrils through the bronchioles. The **respiratory division** consists of the alveoli and other distal gas-exchange regions. The airway from the nose through the larynx is often called the **upper respiratory tract** (that is, the respiratory organs in the head and neck), and the regions from the trachea through the lungs compose the **lower respiratory tract** (the respiratory organs of the thorax). However, these are inexact terms and various authorities place the dividing line between the upper and lower tracts at different points.

## Overview of the Respiratory System

### Objectives
When you have completed this section, you should be able to

- state the functions of the respiratory system;
- name the principal organs of this system;
- distinguish between the conducting and respiratory divisions; and
- distinguish between the upper and lower respiratory tract.

The **respiratory system** is an organ system specialized primarily to provide oxygen to the blood and remove carbon dioxide from it. It has a broader range of functions than are commonly supposed:

1. It provides for oxygen and carbon dioxide exchange between the blood and air.

2. It serves for speech and other vocalizations (laughing, crying).

3. It provides the sense of smell, which is important in social interactions, food selection, and avoiding danger (such as a gas leak or spoiled food).

4. By eliminating $CO_2$, it helps to control the pH of the body fluids. Excess $CO_2$ reacts with water and releases hydrogen ions ($CO_2 + H_2O \rightarrow H_2CO_3 \rightarrow HCO_3^- + H^+$); therefore, if the respiratory system does not keep pace with the rate of $CO_2$ production, $H^+$ accumulates and the body fluids have an abnormally low pH *(acidosis).*

5. The lungs carry out a step in the synthesis of a vasoconstrictor called *angiotensin II,* which helps to regulate blood pressure.

6. Breathing creates pressure gradients between the thorax and abdomen that promote the flow of lymph and venous blood.

7. Taking a deep breath and holding it while contracting the abdominal muscles (the *Valsalva*[1] *maneuver*) helps to expel abdominal contents during urination, defecation, and childbirth.

[1]Antonio Maria Valsalva (1666–1723), Italian anatomist

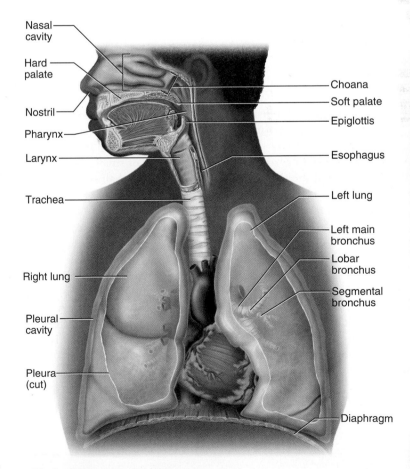

**Figure 23.1** The Respiratory System.

## Before You Go On

*Answer the following questions to test your understanding of the preceding section:*

1. What are some functions of the respiratory system other than supplying $O_2$ to the body and removing $CO_2$?

2. Which portions of the respiratory tract belong to the conducting division? What portions belong to the respiratory division? How do the two divisions differ functionally?

3. What is the distinction between the upper and lower respiratory tract?

# The Upper Respiratory Tract

## Objectives

When you have completed this section, you should be able to

- trace the flow of air from the nose through the larynx;
- describe the anatomy of these passages;
- relate the anatomy of any portion of the upper respiratory tract to its function; and
- describe the action of the vocal cords in speech.

## The Nose

The **nose** has several functions: it warms, cleanses, and humidifies inhaled air; it detects odors in the airstream; and it serves as a resonating chamber that amplifies the voice. It extends from a pair of anterior openings called the **nostrils,** or **nares** (NAIR-eze), to a pair of posterior openings called the **choanae**[2] (co-AH-nee), or **posterior nasal apertures** (fig. 23.2b).

The facial part of the nose is shaped by bone and hyaline cartilage. Its superior half is supported by a pair of small nasal bones medially and the maxillae laterally. The inferior half is supported by the **lateral** and **alar cartilages** (fig. 23.3). By palpating your own nose, you can easily find the boundary between the bone and cartilage. The flared portion at the lower end of the nose, called the **ala nasi**[3] (AIL-ah NAZE-eye), is shaped by the alar cartilages and dense connective tissue.

The **nasal cavity** begins with a small dilated chamber called the **vestibule** just inside the nostril, bordered by the ala nasi. This space is lined with stratified squamous epithelium like the facial skin and has stiff **guard hairs,** or **vibrissae** (vy-BRISS-ee), that block insects and large airborne particles from the nose. The nasal cavity is divided into right and left halves called **nasal fossae** (FAW-see) by a wall of bone and hyaline cartilage, the **nasal septum.** The septum has three components: the bony *vomer* forming the inferior part, the perpendicular plate of the *ethmoid bone* forming the superior part, and a hyaline *septal nasal cartilage* forming the anterior part.

The roof of the nasal cavity is formed by the ethmoid and sphenoid bones, and the hard palate forms its floor. The palate separates the nasal cavity from the oral cavity and allows you to breathe while chewing food (see Insight 7.2, p. 189). The nasal cavity receives drainage from the paranasal sinuses (see p. 179) and the nasolacrimal ducts of the orbits (see p. 506).

There is not much space in the nasal cavity. Most of it is occupied by three folds of tissue—the **superior, middle,** and **inferior nasal conchae**[4] (CON-kee)—that project from the lateral walls toward the septum (see fig. 23.2). Beneath each concha is a narrow air passage called a **meatus** (me-AY-tus). The narrowness of these passages and the turbulence caused by the conchae ensure that most air contacts the mucous membrane on its way through. As it does, most dust in the air sticks to the mucus, and the air picks up moisture and heat from the mucosa. The conchae thus enable the nose to cleanse, warm, and humidify the air more effectively than if the air had an unobstructed flow through a cavernous space.

Odors are detected by sensory cells in the **olfactory epithelium,** which covers a small area of the roof of the nasal fossa and adjacent parts of the septum and superior concha (see fig. 17.7, p. 495). The rest of the nasal cavity, except for the vestibule, is lined with **respiratory epithelium.** Both of these are ciliated pseudostratified columnar epithelia. However, in the olfactory epithelium, the cilia are immobile and serve to bind odor molecules. In the respiratory epithelium, they are mobile. The respiratory epithelium is similar to the one seen in figure 3.7 (p. 80). Its wineglass-shaped goblet cells secrete mucus, and its ciliated cells propel the mucus posteriorly toward the pharynx. The nasal mucosa also contains mucous glands, located in the lamina propria (the connective tissue layer beneath the epithelium). They supplement the mucus produced by the goblet cells. Inhaled dust, pollen, bacteria, and other foreign matter stick to the mucus and are swallowed; they are either digested or pass through the digestive tract rather than contaminating the lungs. The lamina propria is also well populated by lymphocytes that mount immune defenses against inhaled pathogens, and by plasma cells that secrete antibodies into the tissue fluid.

The lamina propria contains large blood vessels that help to warm the air. The inferior concha has an especially extensive venous plexus called the **erectile tissue (swell body).** Every 30 to 60 minutes, the erectile tissue on one side becomes engorged with blood and restricts airflow through that fossa. Most air is then directed through the other nostril and fossa, allowing the engorged side time to recover from drying. Thus, the preponderant flow of air shifts between the right and left nostrils once or twice each hour.

## The Pharynx

The **pharynx** (FAIR-inks) is a muscular funnel extending about 13 cm (5 in.) from the choanae to the larynx. It has three regions: the *nasopharynx, oropharynx,* and *laryngopharynx* (fig. 23.2c).

The **nasopharynx** lies posterior to the choanae and soft palate. It receives the auditory (eustachian) tubes from the middle ears and houses the pharyngeal tonsil. Inhaled air turns 90° downward

---

[2]*choana* = funnel
[3]*ala* = wing + *nasi* = of the nose

[4]*concha* = seashell

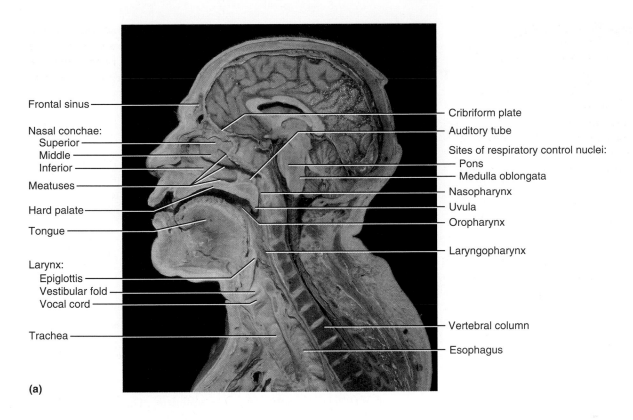

Frontal sinus — Cribriform plate

Nasal conchae:
  Superior — Auditory tube
  Middle — Sites of respiratory control nuclei:
  Inferior — Pons
Meatuses — Medulla oblongata
 — Nasopharynx
Hard palate — Uvula
Tongue — Oropharynx

 — Laryngopharynx

Larynx:
  Epiglottis
  Vestibular fold
  Vocal cord — Vertebral column

Trachea — Esophagus

**(a)**

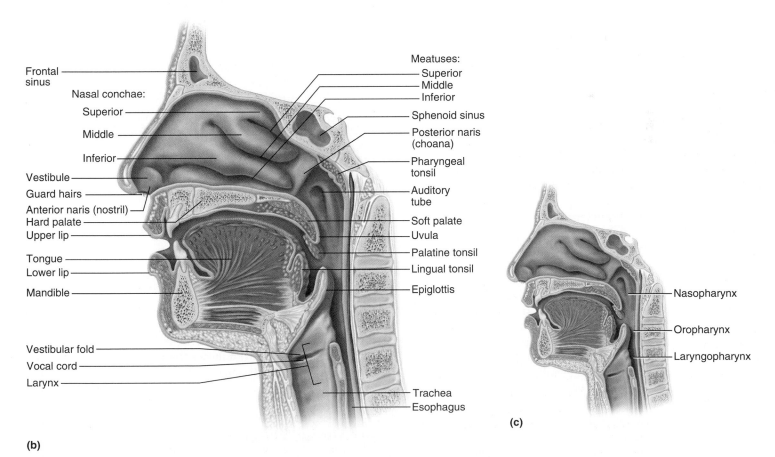

Frontal sinus — Meatuses:
 — Superior
 — Middle
Nasal conchae: — Inferior
  Superior — Sphenoid sinus
  Middle — Posterior naris (choana)
  Inferior — Pharyngeal tonsil
Vestibule — Auditory tube
Guard hairs
Anterior naris (nostril) — Soft palate
Hard palate — Uvula
Upper lip — Palatine tonsil
Tongue — Lingual tonsil
Lower lip — Epiglottis
Mandible

Vestibular fold
Vocal cord
Larynx — Trachea
 — Esophagus

**(b)**

 — Nasopharynx
 — Oropharynx
 — Laryngopharynx

**(c)**

**Figure 23.2** **Anatomy of the Upper Respiratory Tract.** (a) Median section of the head. (b) Internal anatomy. (c) Regions of the pharynx.
• *Draw a line across part (b) of this figure to indicate the boundary between the upper and lower respiratory tract.*

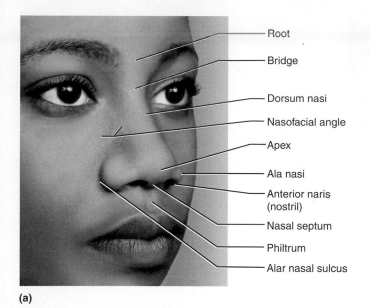

- Root
- Bridge
- Dorsum nasi
- Nasofacial angle
- Apex
- Ala nasi
- Anterior naris (nostril)
- Nasal septum
- Philtrum
- Alar nasal sulcus

(a)

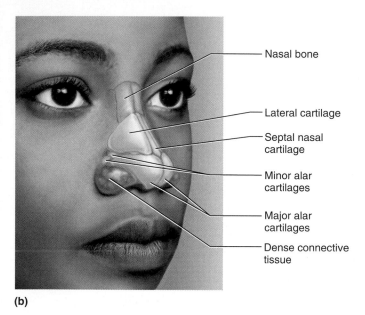

- Nasal bone
- Lateral cartilage
- Septal nasal cartilage
- Minor alar cartilages
- Major alar cartilages
- Dense connective tissue

(b)

**Figure 23.3** **Anatomy of the Nasal Region.** (a) External anatomy. (b) Connective tissues that shape the nose.

● *Which of the cartilages in part (b) extends most deeply into the face?*

as it passes through the nasopharynx. Relatively large particles (>10 μm) generally cannot make the turn because of their inertia. They collide with the posterior wall of the nasopharynx and stick to the mucosa near the tonsil, which is well positioned to respond to airborne pathogens.

The **oropharynx** is a space between the soft palate and root of the tongue. It extends inferiorly as far as the hyoid bone, and contains the palatine and lingual tonsils. Its anterior border is formed by the base of the tongue and the *fauces* (FAW-seez), the opening of the oral cavity into the pharynx.

The **laryngopharynx** (la-RIN-go-FAIR-inks) begins with the union of the nasopharynx and oropharynx at the level of the hyoid bone. It passes downward, posterior to the larynx, and ends

where the esophagus begins at the level of the *cricoid cartilage* of the larynx (described next). The nasopharynx passes only air and is lined by pseudostratified columnar epithelium, whereas the oropharynx and laryngopharynx pass air, food, and drink and are lined by stratified squamous epithelium.

## The Larynx

The **larynx** (LAIR-inks), or "voice box" (fig. 23.4), is a cartilaginous chamber about 4 cm (1.5 in.) long. Its primary function is to keep food and drink out of the airway, but it evolved the additional role of sound production *(phonation)* in many animals and achieved its highest vocal sophistication in humans.

The superior opening of the larynx is guarded by a flap of tissue called the **epiglottis**[5] (figs. 23.4c and 23.5a). At rest, the epiglottis usually stands almost vertically. During swallowing, however, *extrinsic muscles* of the larynx pull the larynx upward toward the epiglottis, the tongue pushes the epiglottis downward to meet it, and the epiglottis closes the airway and directs food and drink into the esophagus behind it.

In infants, the larynx is relatively high in the throat, and the epiglottis touches the soft palate. This creates a more or less continuous airway from the nasal cavity to the larynx and allows an infant to breathe continually while swallowing. The epiglottis deflects milk away from the airstream, like rain running off a tent while it remains dry inside. By age 2, the root of the tongue becomes more muscular and forces the larynx to descend to a lower position. It then becomes impossible to breathe and swallow at the same time without choking.

The framework of the larynx consists of nine cartilages. The first three are solitary and relatively large. The most superior one, the **epiglottic cartilage,** is a spoon-shaped supportive plate in the epiglottis. The largest, the **thyroid**[6] **cartilage,** is named for its shieldlike shape. It broadly covers the anterior and lateral aspects of the larynx. The "Adam's apple" is an anterior peak of the thyroid cartilage called the *laryngeal prominence.* Testosterone stimulates the growth of this prominence, which is therefore larger in males than in females. Inferior to the thyroid cartilage is a ringlike **cricoid**[7] (CRY-coyd) **cartilage,** which connects the larynx to the trachea. The thyroid and cricoid cartilages essentially constitute the "box" of the "voice box."

The remaining cartilages are smaller and occur in three pairs. Posterior to the thyroid cartilage are the two **arytenoid**[8] (AR-ih-TEE-noyd) **cartilages,** and attached to their upper ends are a pair of little horns, the **corniculate**[9] (cor-NICK-you-late) **cartilages.** The arytenoid and corniculate cartilages function in speech, as explained shortly. A pair of **cuneiform**[10] (cue-NEE-ih-form) **cartilages** support the soft tissues between the arytenoids and the epiglottis. The thyroid and cricoid cartilages and inferior part of the arytenoids are

---

[5]*epi* = above, upon + *glottis* = back of the tongue
[6]*thyr* = shield + *oid* = resembling
[7]*crico* = ring + *oid* = resembling
[8]*aryten* = ladle + *oid* = resembling
[9]*corni* = horn + *cul* = little + *ate* = possessing
[10]*cune* = wedge + *form* = shape

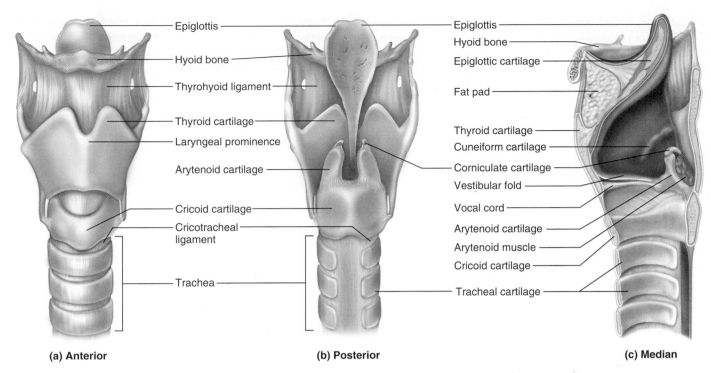

**(a) Anterior**          **(b) Posterior**          **(c) Median**

**Figure 23.4  Anatomy of the Larynx.** Most muscles are removed in order to show the cartilages.
● *What three cartilages in this figure are more mobile than any other?*

hyaline cartilage; the epiglottic, corniculate, and cuneiform cartilages and superior part of the arytenoids are elastic cartilage.

A group of fibrous ligaments bind the cartilages of the larynx together and to adjacent structures in the neck. Superiorly, a broad sheet called the **thyrohyoid ligament** joins the thyroid cartilage to the hyoid bone, and inferiorly, the **cricotracheal ligament** joins the cricoid cartilage to the trachea. These are collectively called the *extrinsic ligaments* because they link the larynx to other organs. The *intrinsic ligaments* are contained entirely within the larynx and link its nine cartilages to each other.

The walls of the larynx are also quite muscular. The deep *intrinsic muscles* operate the vocal cords, and the superficial *extrinsic muscles* connect the larynx to the hyoid bone and elevate the larynx during swallowing. The extrinsic muscles, also called the *infrahyoid group,* are named and described in chapter 11 (table 11.3, p. 306).

Two pairs of intrinsic ligaments, the **vestibular** and **vocal ligaments,** extend from the thyroid cartilage in front to the arytenoid cartilages in back, and support the vestibular folds and vocal cords, respectively. The superior **vestibular folds** (fig. 23.5a) play no role in speech but close the glottis during swallowing. The inferior **vocal cords (vocal folds)** produce sound when air passes between them. They are covered with stratified squamous epithelium, best suited to endure vibration and contact between the cords. The vocal cords and the opening between them are collectively called the **glottis** (fig. 23.5a).

The intrinsic muscles control the vocal cords by pulling on the corniculate and arytenoid cartilages, causing the cartilages to pivot.

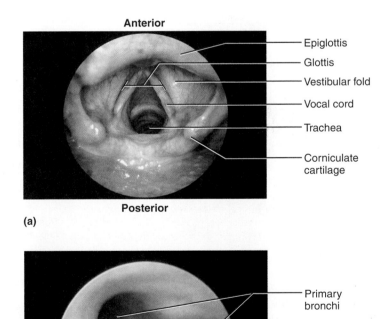

**Figure 23.5  Endoscopic Views of the Respiratory Tract.** (a) Superior view of the larynx, seen with a laryngoscope. (b) Lower end of the trachea, where it forks into the two primary bronchi, seen with a bronchoscope.

Depending on their direction of rotation, the arytenoid cartilages abduct or adduct the vocal cords (fig. 23.6). Air forced between the adducted vocal cords vibrates them, producing a high-pitched sound when the cords are relatively taut and a lower-pitched sound when they are more relaxed. In adult males, the vocal cords are longer and thicker, vibrate more slowly, and produce lower-pitched sounds than in females. Loudness is determined by the force of the air passing between the vocal cords. Although the vocal cords alone produce sound, they do not produce intelligible speech. The crude sounds coming from the larynx are formed into words by actions of the pharynx, oral cavity, tongue, and lips.

## *Before You Go On*

*Answer the following questions to test your understanding of the preceding section:*

4. Describe the histology of the mucous membrane of the nasal cavity and the functions of the cell types present.

5. Name the anterior and posterior openings that mark the beginning and end of the nasal cavity.

6. What are the right and left halves of the nasal cavity called? What are the three scroll-like folds on the wall of each nasal fossa called? What is their function?

7. Palpate two of your laryngeal cartilages and name them. Name the ones that are impossible to palpate on a living person.

8. Describe the roles of the intrinsic muscles, corniculate cartilages, and arytenoid cartilages in speech.

# The Lower Respiratory Tract

### *Objectives*
When you have completed this section, you should be able to

• trace the flow of air from the trachea to the pulmonary alveoli;

• describe the anatomy of these passages;

• relate the gross anatomy of any portion of the lower respiratory tract to its function;

• relate the microscopic anatomy of the pulmonary alveoli to their role in gas exchange; and

• describe the relationship of the pleurae to the lungs.

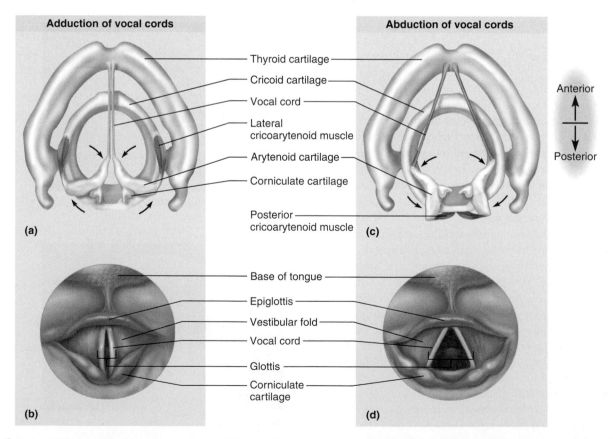

**Figure 23.6** **Action of Some of the Intrinsic Laryngeal Muscles on the Vocal Cords.** (a) Adduction of the vocal cords by the lateral cricoarytenoid muscles. (b) Adducted vocal cords seen with the laryngoscope. (c) Abduction of the vocal cords by the posterior cricoarytenoid muscles. (d) Abducted vocal cords seen with the laryngoscope.

If you palpate your larynx, you will find the laryngeal prominence of the thyroid cartilage only slightly above your sternum. All the rest of the respiratory tract is in the thorax rather than the head and neck, and is thus called the lower respiratory tract. This portion extends from the trachea to the pulmonary alveoli.

## The Trachea and Bronchi

The **trachea** (TRAY-kee-uh), or "windpipe," is a tube about 12 cm (4.5 in.) long and 2.5 cm (1 in.) in diameter, lying anterior to the esophagus (fig. 23.7a). It is supported by 16 to 20 C-shaped rings of hyaline cartilage, some of which you can palpate between your larynx and sternum. The inner lining of the trachea is a pseudostratified columnar epithelium composed mainly of mucus-secreting goblet cells, ciliated cells, and short basal stem cells (figs. 23.7b and 23.8). The mucus traps inhaled particles, and the upward beating of the cilia drives the debris-laden mucus toward the pharynx, where it is swallowed. This mechanism of debris removal is called the **mucociliary escalator.**

The connective tissue beneath the tracheal epithelium contains lymphatic nodules, mucous and serous glands, and the tracheal cartilages. Like the wire spiral in a vacuum cleaner hose, the cartilage rings reinforce the trachea and keep it from collapsing when you inhale. The open part of the C faces posteriorly and allows room for the esophagus to expand as swallowed food passes by. The gap is spanned by smooth muscle tissue called the **trachealis** (fig. 23.7c). Contraction of this muscle narrows or widens the trachea to adjust airflow. The outermost layer of the trachea, called the **adventitia,** is fibrous connective tissue that blends into the adventitia of other organs of the mediastinum.

At the level of the sternal angle and the superior margin of vertebra T5, the trachea forks into right and left *main bronchi*. The lowermost tracheal cartilage has an internal median ridge called the **carina**[11] (ca-RY-na) that directs the airflow to the right and left (see fig. 23.5b). The bronchi are further traced in the discussion of the *bronchial tree* of the lungs.

## The Lungs

Each **lung** (fig. 23.9) is a somewhat conical organ with a broad, concave **base** resting on the diaphragm and a blunt peak called the **apex** projecting slightly above the clavicle. The broad **costal surface** is pressed against the rib cage, and the smaller concave **mediastinal surface** faces medially. The mediastinal surface exhibits a slit called the **hilum** through which the lung receives the main bronchus, blood vessels, lymphatic vessels, and nerves. These structures constitute the **root** of the lung.

[11]*carina* = keel

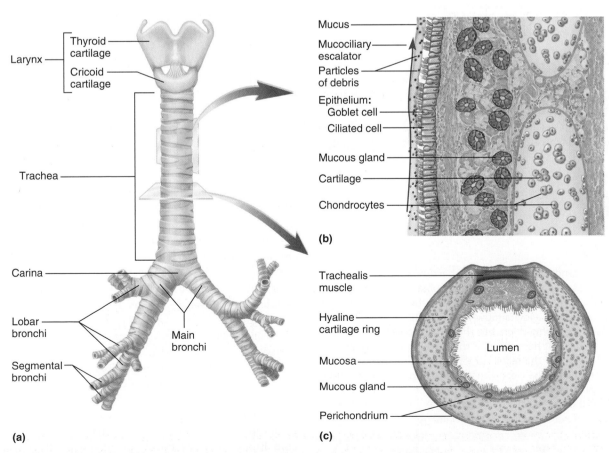

**Figure 23.7** **Anatomy of the Lower Respiratory Tract.** (a) Anterior view. (b) Longitudinal section of the trachea showing the action of the mucociliary escalator. (c) Cross section of the trachea showing the C-shaped tracheal cartilage.

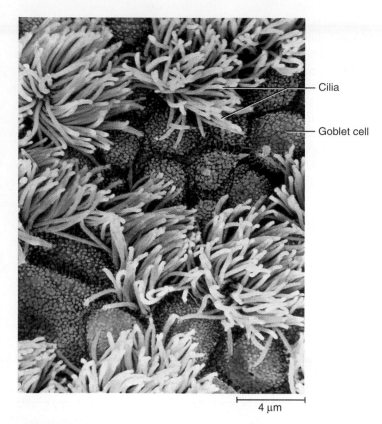

Cilia

Goblet cell

4 μm

**Figure 23.8** **The Tracheal Epithelium Showing Ciliated Cells and Nonciliated Goblet Cells.** The small bumps on the goblet cells are microvilli.
● *What is the function of the goblet cells?*

The lungs are crowded by adjacent viscera and therefore neither fill the entire rib cage, nor are they symmetric. Inferior to the lungs and diaphragm, much of the space within the rib cage is occupied by the liver, spleen, and stomach (see fig. A.14, p. 35). The right lung is shorter than the left because the liver rises higher on the right.

# INSIGHT 23.1

## Clinical Application

### Tracheostomy

The functional importance of the nasal cavity becomes especially obvious when it is bypassed. If the upper airway is obstructed, it may be necessary to make a temporary opening in the trachea inferior to the larynx and insert a tube to allow airflow—a procedure called *tracheostomy.*[12] This prevents *asphyxiation,* but the inhaled air bypasses the nasal cavity and thus is not humidified. If the opening is left for long, the mucous membranes of the respiratory tract dry out and become encrusted, interfering with the clearance of mucus from the tract and promoting infection. When a patient is on a ventilator and air is introduced directly into the trachea, the air must be filtered and humidified by the apparatus to prevent respiratory tract damage.

---

[12]*tracheo* = trachea + *stom* = hole

The left lung, while taller, is narrower than the right because the heart tilts toward the left and occupies more space on this side of the mediastinum. On the medial surface, the left lung has an indentation called the **cardiac impression** where the heart presses against it. The right lung has three lobes—**superior, middle,** and **inferior.** A deep groove called the **horizontal fissure** separates the superior lobe from the middle lobe, and a similar groove called the **oblique fissure** separates the middle and inferior lobes. The left lung has only a superior and inferior lobe and a single oblique fissure.

## The Bronchial Tree

Each lung contains a branching system of air tubes called the **bronchial tree,** extending from the main bronchus to the *terminal bronchioles.* From the fork in the trachea, the right **main (primary) bronchus** (BRON-cus) measures about 2 to 3 cm long. It is slightly wider and more vertical than the left one; consequently, inhaled (aspirated) foreign objects lodge more often in the right bronchus than in the left. Just before entering the lung, the right main bronchus gives off a **superior lobar (secondary) bronchus.** The main and lobar bronchi enter the hilum of the lung together. The superior lobar bronchus projects into the superior lobe of the lung, and the main bronchus continues a little farther and branches into **middle** and **inferior lobar bronchi** to the lower two lobes of the lung. The left main bronchus is about 5 cm long and is narrower and more horizontal than the right. It enters the hilum of the left lung before branching, then gives off superior and inferior lobar bronchi to the two lobes of that lung.

In both lungs, each lobar bronchus branches into **segmental (tertiary) bronchi.** Each of these ventilates one functionally independent unit of lung tissue called a **bronchopulmonary segment.** There are 10 of these in the right lung and 8 in the left (see photo on p. 662).

The main bronchi are supported, like the trachea, by C-shaped hyaline cartilages, whereas the lobar and segmental bronchi are supported by overlapping crescent-shaped cartilaginous plates. All of the bronchi are lined by a ciliated pseudostratified columnar epithelium, but the cells grow shorter and the epithelium thinner as we progress distally. The lamina propria beneath the epithelium exhibits mucous glands and many aggregations of lymphocytes (*bronchus-associated lymphatic tissue, BALT),* favorably positioned to respond to inhaled pathogens. All divisions of the bronchial tree also have a substantial amount of elastic connective tissue, which contributes to the recoil that expels air from the lungs in each respiratory cycle. The mucosa also has a well-developed layer of smooth muscle, the *muscularis mucosae,* which regulates airway diameter and airflow.

**Bronchioles** are continuations of the airway that lack supportive cartilage and are 1 mm or less in diameter. The portion of the lung ventilated by one bronchiole is called a **pulmonary lobule.** The epithelium of the bronchioles starts out as ciliated pseudostratified columnar in the larger, more proximal passages. As we progress distally, it gets thinner (the cells do not grow as tall) and grades into simple columnar and finally simple cuboidal epithelium. Bronchioles lack mucous glands and goblet cells, but they are ciliated throughout. It is an important point that the cilia continue more deeply into the airway than the mucous glands and goblet

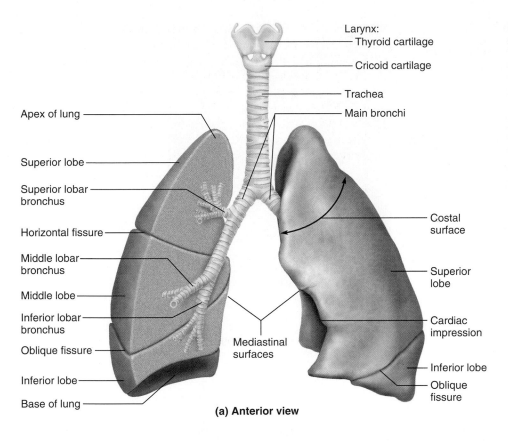

**(a) Anterior view**

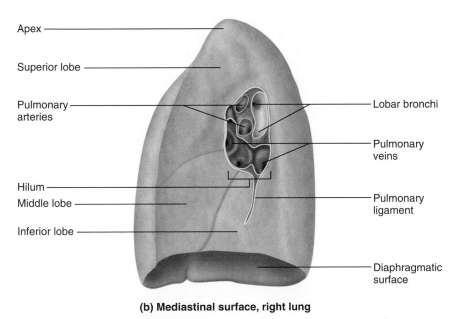

**(b) Mediastinal surface, right lung**

**Figure 23.9** Gross Anatomy of the Lungs.

Each bronchiole divides into 50 to 80 **terminal bronchioles,** the final branches of the conducting division; there are about 65,000 of these in each lung. They measure 0.5 mm or less in diameter. Each terminal bronchiole gives off two or more smaller **respiratory bronchioles,** which have alveoli budding from their walls. Respiratory bronchioles are the beginning of the respiratory division. Their walls have scanty smooth muscle, and the smallest of them are nonciliated. Each respiratory bronchiole divides into 2 to 10 elongated, thin-walled passages called **alveolar ducts,** which also have alveoli along their walls (fig. 23.10). The alveolar ducts and smaller divisions have nonciliated simple squamous epithelia. The ducts end in **alveolar sacs,** which are grapelike clusters of alveoli arrayed around a central space called the **atrium** (fig. 23.10a). The distinction between an alveolar duct and atrium is their shape—an elongated passage or a space with about equal length and width. It is sometimes a subjective judgment whether to regard a space as an alveolar duct or atrium.

Air in the conducting division of the respiratory tract cannot exchange gases with the blood; it is therefore called *dead air,* and the lumen of the conducting division is called the *anatomic dead space.* In a state of relaxation, parasympathetic nerve fibers (from the vagus nerve) stimulate the muscularis mucosae and keep the airway partially constricted. This minimizes the dead space so that a greater percentage of the inhaled air goes to the alveoli, where it can oxygenate the blood. In exercise, the sympathetic nerves relax the smooth muscle and dilate the airway. Even though this increases the dead space, it enables air to flow more easily and rapidly so the alveoli can be ventilated in proportion to the demands of exercise. The increased airflow more than compensates for the increased dead space. The bronchioles exert the greatest control over airflow for two reasons: (1) they are the most numerous components of the conducting division, and (2) with their well-developed smooth muscle and lack of confining cartilage, they can change relative diameter more than the larger air passages can. Narrowing of the bronchioles is called *bronchoconstriction,* and widening is called *bronchodilation.*

As described in chapter 20, the lungs receive a blood supply from both the pulmonary arteries and bronchial arteries. Branches of the pulmonary artery closely follow the bronchial tree on their way to capillaries surrounding the alveoli (fig. 23.11), where gas exchange occurs. Branches of the bronchial arteries service the bronchi, bronchioles, and some other pulmonary tissues (see p. 604). The lungs are the only organs to receive both a pulmonary and a systemic blood supply.

cells do. This ensures that mucus draining distally from those gland cells can still be captured by the beating cilia and cleared from the airway. Aside from the epithelium, the mucosa of the bronchioles consists mainly of smooth muscle. Spasmodic contractions of this muscle at death cause the bronchioles to exhibit a wavy lumen in most histological sections (fig. 23.10a).

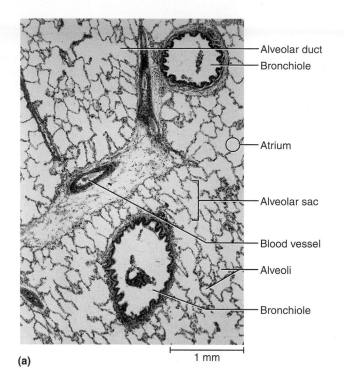

Alveolar duct
Bronchiole
Atrium
Alveolar sac
Blood vessel
Alveoli
Bronchiole

**(a)**

1 mm

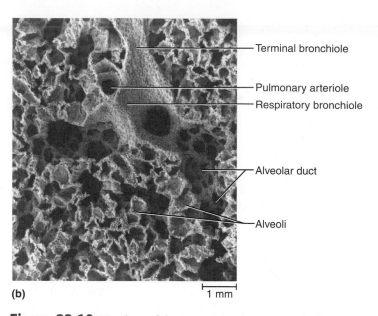

Terminal bronchiole
Pulmonary arteriole
Respiratory bronchiole
Alveolar duct
Alveoli

**(b)**

1 mm

**Figure 23.10** **Histology of the Lung.** (a) Light micrograph. (b) Scanning electron micrograph. Note the spongy texture of the lung.
● *Histologically, how can we tell the two largest passages in part (a) are bronchioles and not bronchi?*

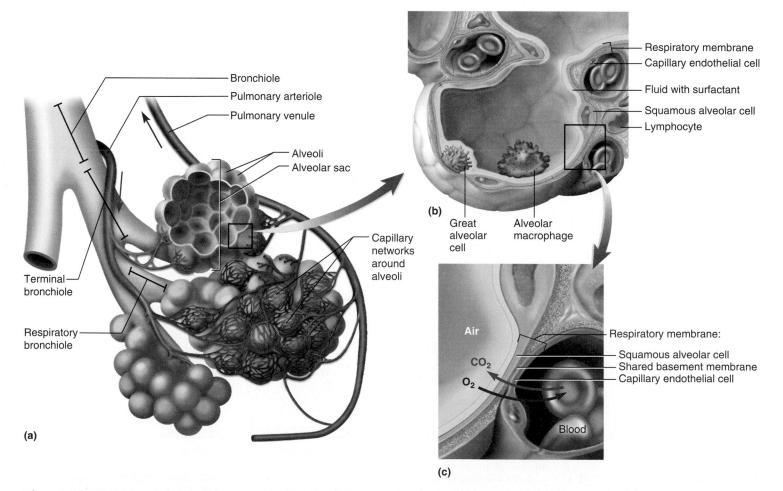

Bronchiole
Pulmonary arteriole
Pulmonary venule
Alveoli
Alveolar sac
Capillary networks around alveoli
Terminal bronchiole
Respiratory bronchiole

**(a)**

Respiratory membrane
Capillary endothelial cell
Fluid with surfactant
Squamous alveolar cell
Lymphocyte

**(b)** Great alveolar cell
Alveolar macrophage

Air
$CO_2$
$O_2$

Respiratory membrane:
Squamous alveolar cell
Shared basement membrane
Capillary endothelial cell
Blood

**(c)**

**Figure 23.11** **Pulmonary Alveoli.** (a) Clusters of alveoli and their blood supply. (b) Structure of an alveolus. (c) Structure of the respiratory membrane.

## Alveoli

Each human lung is a spongy mass with about 150 million little sacs, the alveoli, which provide about 70 m² of surface for gas exchange. An **alveolus** (AL-vee-OH-lus) is a pouch about 0.2 to 0.5 mm in diameter (fig. 23.11). Thin, broad cells called **squamous (type I) alveolar cells** cover about 95% of the alveolar surface area. Their thinness allows for rapid gas diffusion between the alveolus and bloodstream. The other 5% is covered by round to cuboidal **great (type II) alveolar cells.** Even though they cover less surface area, great alveolar cells considerably outnumber the squamous alveolar cells. Great alveolar cells have two functions: (1) they repair the alveolar epithelium when the squamous alveolar cells are damaged, and (2) they secrete *pulmonary surfactant*, a mixture of phospholipids and protein that coats the alveoli and smallest bronchioles and prevents them from collapsing when one exhales. Without surfactant, the walls of a deflating alveolus would tend to cling together like sheets of wet paper, and it would be very difficult to reinflate them on the next inhalation (see Insight 23.4).

The most numerous of all cells in the lung are **alveolar macrophages (dust cells),** which wander the lumens of the alveoli and the connective tissue between them. These cells keep the alveoli free of debris by phagocytizing dust particles that escape entrapment by mucus in the higher parts of the respiratory tract. In lungs that are infected or bleeding, the macrophages also phagocytize bacteria and loose blood cells. As many as 100 million alveolar macrophages perish each day as they ride up the mucociliary escalator to be swallowed and digested, thus ridding the lungs of their load of debris.

Each alveolus is surrounded by a basket of blood capillaries supplied by the pulmonary artery. The barrier between the alveolar air and blood, called the **respiratory membrane,** consists only of the squamous alveolar cell, the squamous endothelial cell of the capillary, and their shared basement membrane (fig. 23.11b). These have a total thickness of only 0.5 μm, in contrast to the 7 μm diameter of the erythrocytes passing through the capillaries.

It is very important to prevent fluid from accumulating in the alveoli, because gases diffuse too slowly through liquid to sufficiently aerate the blood. Except for the film of moisture on the alveolar wall, the alveoli are kept dry by the absorption of excess liquid by the blood capillaries and abundant lymphatic capillaries of the lungs. The lungs have a more extensive lymphatic drainage than any other organ in the body.

## The Pleurae

The surface of the lung is covered by a serous membrane, the **visceral pleura** (PLOOR-uh), which extends into the fissures. At the hilum, the visceral pleura turns back on itself and forms the **parietal pleura,** which adheres to the mediastinum, inner surface of the rib cage, and superior surface of the diaphragm (fig. 23.12). An extension of the parietal pleura, the *pulmonary ligament,* connects it to the diaphragm.

The space between the parietal and visceral pleurae is called the **pleural cavity.** The two membranes are normally separated only by a film of slippery **pleural fluid;** thus, the pleural cavity is only a *potential space,* meaning there is normally no room between the membranes. Under pathological conditions, however, this space can fill with air or liquid (see Insight 23.2).

The pleurae and pleural fluid have three functions:

1. **Reduction of friction.** Pleural fluid acts as a lubricant that enables the lungs to expand and contract with minimal friction.

2. **Creation of a pressure gradient.** During inspiration (inhalation), the rib cage expands and draws the parietal pleura outward along with it. The visceral pleura clings to the parietal pleura, and since the visceral pleura is the lung surface, its outward movement expands the lung. The air pressure within the lung thus drops below the atmospheric pressure outside the body, and outside air flows down its pressure gradient into the lung.

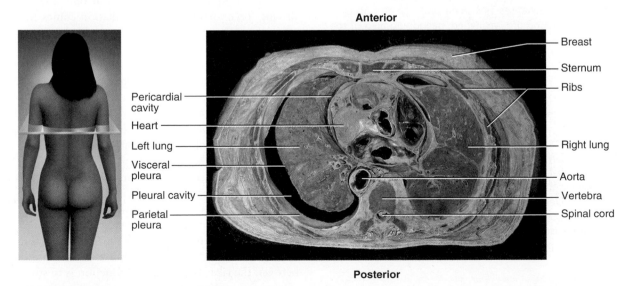

**Figure 23.12 Cross Section Through the Thoracic Cavity.** This photograph is oriented the same way as the reader's body. The pleural cavity is especially evident where the left lung has shrunken away from the thoracic wall, but in a living person, the lung fully fills this space, the parietal and visceral pleurae are pressed together, and the pleural cavity is only a potential space between the membranes, as on the left side of this photograph.

3. **Compartmentalization.** The pleurae, mediastinum, and pericardium compartmentalize the thoracic organs and prevent infections of one organ from spreading easily to neighboring organs.

### THINK ABOUT IT

*In what ways do the structure and function of the pleurae resemble the structure and function of the pericardium?*

---

## INSIGHT 23.2

### Clinical Application

## Pulmonary Collapse

*Pulmonary collapse (collapsed lung),* or *atelectasis*[13] (AT-eh-LEC-ta-sis), is a state in which part or all of a lung is devoid of air. It is the normal state of a fetus and a newborn that has not drawn the first breath. After breathing begins, cases of pulmonary collapse fall into two categories: compression and absorption atelectasis.

*Compression atelectasis* is due to external pressure on the lung preventing its complete expansion. The pressure may come from blood, serous fluid, or air in the pleural cavity. Air in the pleural cavity, a state called *pneumothorax,* often results from "sucking wounds" to the chest—for example, when the thoracic wall is punctured by a knife or a broken rib and inspiration sucks air through the opening. The visceral pleura (lung surface) and parietal pleura separate, and the lung recoils from the thoracic wall and collapses. Pneumothorax can also occur in the absence of a chest wound if a weakened, ballooning area of the lung surface (called a *bleb*) ruptures and air flows from the lung into the pleural cavity.

*Absorption atelectasis* occurs when gases are absorbed into the blood and not replaced by fresh air, resulting in collapse of the alveoli. It can occur when the airway is obstructed by a mucous plug or an aspirated foreign object such as a bite of food, or when it is compressed by an adjacent tumor or pulmonary aneurysm. It also frequently occurs after surgery, especially if a patient is in pain and is reluctant to breathe deeply or change position in bed. Postoperative patients are encouraged to breathe deeply because it promotes the clearance of secretions from the lungs, the even distribution of surfactant, and the flow of air from better-ventilated alveoli into less-ventilated ones.

When one lung collapses, the positive pressure in that pleural cavity can shift the entire mediastinum (including the heart and major blood vessels) toward the other pleural cavity, compressing and partially collapsing that lung as well.

[13]*atel* = imperfect + *ectasis* = expansion

---

## Before You Go On

*Answer the following questions to test your understanding of the preceding section:*

9. A dust particle is inhaled and gets into an alveolus without being trapped along the way. Describe the path it takes, naming all air passages from nostrils to alveoli. What would happen to it after arrival in an alveolus?

10. Contrast the epithelium of the bronchioles with that of the alveoli and explain how the structural difference is related to their functional differences.

11. Describe the relationship of the parietal and visceral pleurae to the lungs and thoracic wall.

## Neuromuscular Aspects of Respiration

### Objectives

When you have completed this section, you should be able to
- identify the muscles that ventilate the lungs and describe their respective roles;
- describe the brainstem centers and peripheral nerves that control breathing, and explain their functions; and
- identify the inputs that influence the activity of those brainstem centers.

## The Respiratory Muscles

The lungs do not ventilate themselves. The only muscle they contain is smooth muscle in the walls of the bronchi and bronchioles, which does not create the airflow but only affects its speed. The driving force for pulmonary ventilation comes from the skeletal muscles of the trunk, especially the diaphragm and intercostal muscles (fig. 23.13).

The prime mover of pulmonary ventilation is the **diaphragm,** the muscular dome that separates the thoracic cavity from the abdominal cavity. It alone accounts for about two-thirds of the pulmonary airflow. When relaxed, it bulges upward to its farthest extent, pressing against the base of the lungs. The lungs are then at their minimum volume. When the diaphragm contracts, it tenses and flattens somewhat, dropping about 1.5 cm in relaxed inspiration and as much as 7 cm in deep breathing. This enlarges the thoracic cavity and lungs and causes an inflow of air. When the diaphragm relaxes, it bulges upward again, compresses the lungs, and expels air.

Several other muscles aid the diaphragm as synergists. Chief among these are the **internal** and **external intercostal muscles** between the ribs. Their primary function is to stiffen the thoracic cage during respiration and prevent it from caving inward when the diaphragm descends. However, they also contribute to enlargement and contraction of the thoracic cage and add about one-third of

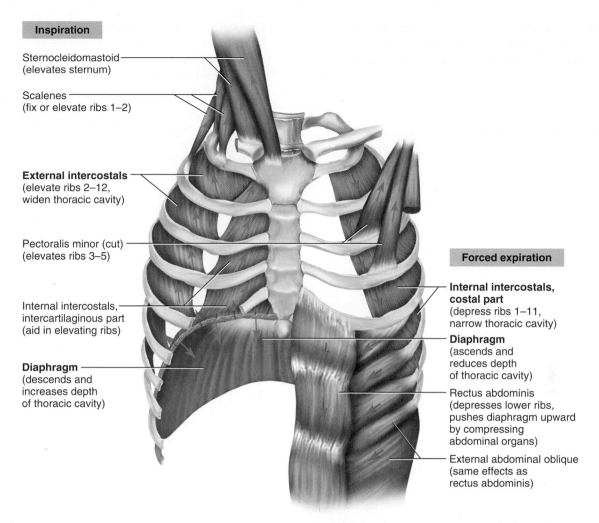

**Inspiration**

Sternocleidomastoid
(elevates sternum)

Scalenes
(fix or elevate ribs 1–2)

**External intercostals**
(elevate ribs 2–12,
widen thoracic cavity)

Pectoralis minor (cut)
(elevates ribs 3–5)

Internal intercostals,
intercartilaginous part
(aid in elevating ribs)

**Diaphragm**
(descends and
increases depth
of thoracic cavity)

**Forced expiration**

**Internal intercostals,
costal part**
(depress ribs 1–11,
narrow thoracic cavity)

**Diaphragm**
(ascends and
reduces depth
of thoracic cavity)

Rectus abdominis
(depresses lower ribs,
pushes diaphragm upward
by compressing
abdominal organs)

External abdominal oblique
(same effects as
rectus abdominis)

**Figure 23.13** **The Respiratory Muscles.** Boldface indicates the principal respiratory muscles; the others are accessory. Arrows indicate the direction of muscle pull. Muscles listed on the left are active during inspiration, and those on the right are active during forced expiration. Note that the diaphragm is active in both phases, and different parts of the internal intercostals serve for inspiration and expiration. Some other accessory muscles not shown here are discussed in the text.

the air that ventilates the lungs. During quiet breathing, the scalene muscles of the neck fix (hold stationary) ribs 1 and 2, while the external intercostal muscles pull the other ribs upward. Since most ribs are anchored at both ends—by their attachment to the vertebral column at the proximal end and their attachment through the costal cartilage to the sternum at the distal end—they swing upward like the handle on a bucket and thrust the sternum forward. These actions increase both the transverse (left to right) and anteroposterior (AP) diameters of the chest. In deep breathing, the AP diameter increases by as much as 20%.

Other muscles of the chest and abdomen also aid in breathing, especially during forced respiration—that is, taking deeper breaths than normal. These are considered the *accessory muscles* of respiration. Deep inspiration is aided by the *erector spinae,* which arches the back and increases AP chest diameter, and by several muscles that elevate the upper ribs: the *sternocleidomastoids* and *scalenes* of the neck; the *pectoralis minor, pectoralis major,* and *serratus anterior* of the chest; and the *intercartilaginous (interchondral) part* of the internal intercostal muscles (the anterior part of the muscles

between the costal cartilages). Although the scalenes merely fix the upper ribs during quiet respiration, they elevate them during forced inspiration.

Normal expiration (exhalation) is an energy-saving passive process. It is normally achieved by the elasticity of the lungs and thoracic cage. The bronchial tree, the attachments of the ribs to the spine and sternum, and the tendons of the diaphragm and other respiratory muscles all have a degree of elasticity that causes them to spring back when the muscles relax. As these structures recoil, the thoracic cage diminishes in size, the air pressure in the lungs rises above the atmospheric pressure, and the air flows out. The only muscular effort involved in normal expiration is a braking action—that is, the muscles relax gradually rather than abruptly, thus preventing the lungs from recoiling too suddenly. This makes the transition from inspiration to expiration smoother.

But during forced expiration—for example, when singing or shouting, coughing or sneezing, or playing a wind instrument—the *rectus abdominis* pulls down on the sternum and lower ribs, while the *interosseous (costal) part* of the internal intercostal muscles (the part between the ribs proper) pull the other ribs downward. These actions reduce the chest diameter and help to expel air more rapidly and thoroughly than usual. Other muscles that contribute to forced expiration are the *latissimus dorsi* of the lower back, the *transverse* and *oblique abdominal muscles,* and even some muscles of the pelvic floor. They raise the pressure in the abdominal cavity and push some of the viscera, such as the stomach and liver, up against the diaphragm. This increases the pressure in the thoracic cavity and thus helps to expel air. Abdominal control of airflow is particularly important in singing, public speaking, coughing, and sneezing.

## Respiratory Neuroanatomy

The heartbeat and breathing are the two most conspicuously rhythmic processes of the body, but while the heart contains its own pacemaker, the lungs do not. As we have just seen, breathing requires the coordinated action of numerous skeletal muscles. These must be under centralized control; therefore, they depend on output from the brain. Breathing is controlled at two levels of the brain. One is cerebral and conscious, enabling us to inhale or exhale at will. Most of the time, however, we breathe without thinking about it—fortunately, for we otherwise could not go to sleep without fear of respiratory arrest (see Insight 23.3). The automatic, unconscious cycle of breathing is controlled by three paired respiratory centers in the medulla oblongata and pons (fig. 23.14):

1. The **dorsal respiratory group (DRG)** is an elongated mass of neurons that extends for much of the length of the medulla near the central canal. It is responsible for inspiration. The neurons here issue axons that decussate to the contralateral spinal cord and terminate in integrating centers of the cervical and thoracic regions. Lower motor neurons in these centers issue axons via the *phrenic nerves* to the diaphragm and via the *intercostal nerves* to the external intercostal muscles. They stimulate contraction of the muscles of inspiration, causing the chest to expand and take in air.

2. The **ventral respiratory group (VRG)** is another elongated neural network just anterior to the DRG. It is active during both inspiration and expiration. It shows little activity in quiet respiration, but comes into play in heavy breathing, such as during exercise. The VRG is especially important in stimulating the abdominal and other accessory muscles that produce deep breaths.

3. The **pneumotaxic center** is a nucleus in the pons that regulates the shift from inspiration to expiration. Its output inhibits the DRG and terminates inspiration. Therefore, strong output from the pneumotaxic center makes each breath shorter and the respiratory rate faster. Weak output results in long, slow breaths.

These respiratory centers receive input from multiple sources:

- **Central chemoreceptors** are brainstem neurons that respond especially to changes in the pH of the cerebrospinal fluid. They are concentrated on each side of the medulla oblongata about 0.2 mm beneath its anterior surface.

- **Peripheral chemoreceptors** occur in the aortic arch and carotid bodies (fig. 23.15). They respond to the $O_2$ and $CO_2$ content and pH of the blood. The aortic bodies communicate with the medulla by way of the vagus nerves and the carotid bodies by way of the glossopharyngeal nerves.

- **Stretch receptors** are found in the smooth muscle of the bronchi and bronchioles and in the visceral pleura. They communicate with the DRG via the vagus nerves and respond to inflation of the lungs. Excessive inflation triggers a protective reflex that strongly inhibits inspiration.

- **Irritant receptors** are nerve endings in the epithelia of the airway. They respond to smoke, dust, pollen, chemical fumes, cold air, and excess mucus. They transmit signals to the DRG via the vagus nerves, and the DRG responds with protective reflexes such as coughing, bronchoconstriction, shallower breathing, or breath holding.

- Higher brain centers including the limbic system, hypothalamus, and cerebral cortex also influence the respiratory nuclei. This input allows for conscious control over breathing (as in holding one's breath) and for emotions to affect respiration—for example, in gasping, crying, and laughing and when anxiety provokes a bout of hyperventilation (rapid breathing in excess of physiological need). Signals for voluntary control over breathing travel down the corticospinal tracts to the respiratory neurons in the spinal cord, thus bypassing the brainstem respiratory centers.

### THINK ABOUT IT

*Some authorities refer to the respiratory rhythm as an* autonomic *function. Discuss whether you think this is an appropriate word for it. What are the effectors of the autonomic nervous system? (See chapter 16.) What are the effectors that ventilate the lungs? What bearing might this have on the question?*

## INSIGHT 23.3

### Clinical Application

### Ondine's Curse

In German legend, there was a water nymph named Ondine who took a mortal lover. When he was unfaithful to her, the king of the nymphs put a curse on him that took away his automatic physiological functions. Consequently, he had to remember to take each breath, and he could not go to sleep or he would die of suffocation—which, as exhaustion overtook him, was indeed his fate.

Some people suffer a disorder called *Ondine's curse,* in which the automatic respiratory functions are disabled—usually as a result of brainstem damage from poliomyelitis or as an accident of spinal cord surgery. Victims of Ondine's curse must remember to take each breath and cannot sleep without using a mechanical ventilator or being awakened repeatedly by episodes of *apnea* (temporary cessation of breathing).

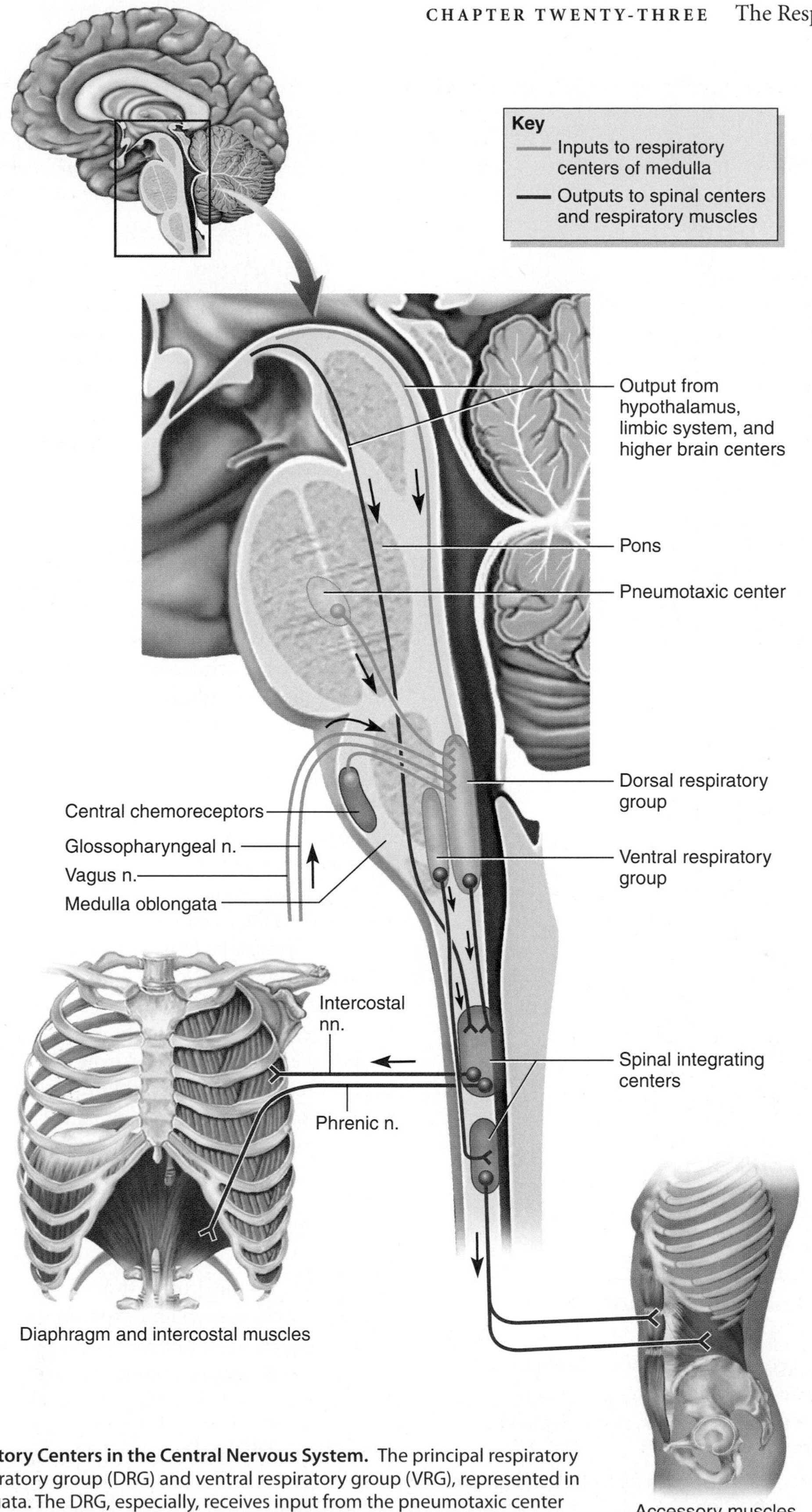

**Key**
— Inputs to respiratory centers of medulla
— Outputs to spinal centers and respiratory muscles

Output from hypothalamus, limbic system, and higher brain centers

Pons

Pneumotaxic center

Dorsal respiratory group

Central chemoreceptors

Glossopharyngeal n.

Vagus n.

Medulla oblongata

Ventral respiratory group

Intercostal nn.

Phrenic n.

Spinal integrating centers

Diaphragm and intercostal muscles

Accessory muscles of respiration

**Figure 23.14** **Respiratory Centers in the Central Nervous System.** The principal respiratory centers are the dorsal respiratory group (DRG) and ventral respiratory group (VRG), represented in blue in the medulla oblongata. The DRG, especially, receives input from the pneumotaxic center (green) in the pons, from the central chemoreceptors (red) in the medulla, from higher brain centers involved in emotional and voluntary influences on respiration, and from peripheral chemoreceptors and stretch receptors by way of the vagus and glossopharyngeal nerves (see fig. 23.15). Output from the DRG goes especially to integrating centers in the spinal cord (violet), which stimulate the intercostal muscles and diaphragm. Output from the VRG goes especially to spinal cord centers that stimulate abdominal and other accessory muscles of respiration.

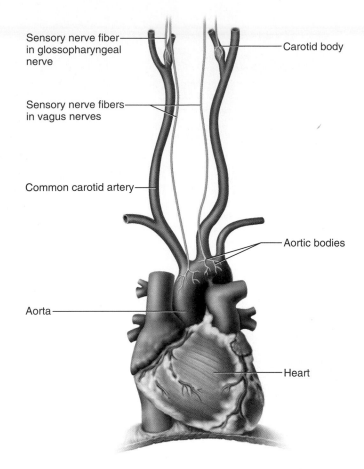

Sensory nerve fiber in glossopharyngeal nerve

Carotid body

Sensory nerve fibers in vagus nerves

Common carotid artery

Aortic bodies

Aorta

Heart

**Figure 23.15** The Peripheral Chemoreceptors of Respiration.

## *Before You Go On*

*Answer the following questions to test your understanding of the preceding section:*

12. Explain why breathing is not controlled by a pacemaker in the lungs.

13. What is the prime mover of respiration? What muscle group acts as the most important synergist? What nerves innervate each of these?

14. Name some other synergists that act during forced inspiration and some that act during forced expiration.

15. State the names and locations of the brainstem nuclei that regulate the respiratory rhythm. What role does each one play?

16. From what sources do the respiratory nuclei receive input that influences respiration?

# Developmental and Clinical Perspectives

### *Objectives*

When you have completed this section, you should be able to

- describe the prenatal development of the respiratory system;
- describe the changes that occur in the respiratory system in old age; and
- describe some common respiratory disorders.

## Prenatal and Neonatal Development

The first embryonic trace of the respiratory system is a small pouch in the floor of the pharynx called the **pulmonary groove,** appearing at about 3.5 weeks. The groove grows down the mediastinum as an elongated tube, the future trachea, and branches into two **lung buds** by week 4 (fig. 23.16). The lung buds branch repeatedly and grow laterally and posteriorly, occupying the space posterior to the heart. Repeated branching of the lung buds produces the bronchial tree, which is completed as far as the bronchioles by the end of month 6. For the remainder of gestation and after birth, the bronchioles bud off alveoli. The adult number of alveoli is attained around the age of 10 years.

By week 8, the lungs are isolated from the heart by the growth of the pericardium, and by week 9, the diaphragm forms and separates the lungs and pleurae from the abdominal cavity. At 28 weeks, the respiratory system is usually adequately developed to support independent life (see Insight 23.4).

By 11 weeks, the fetus begins respiratory movements called **fetal breathing,** in which it rhythmically inhales and exhales amniotic fluid for as much as 8 hours per day. Fetal breathing stimulates lung development and conditions the respiratory muscles for life outside the womb. It ceases during labor. When the newborn infant begins breathing air, the fluid in the lungs is quickly absorbed by the pulmonary blood and lymphatic capillaries.

For the newborn infant, breathing is very laborious at first. The fetal lungs are collapsed and airless, and the neonate must take very strenuous first breaths to pop the alveoli open. Once they are fully inflated, the alveoli normally never collapse again. Even the pulmonary blood vessels are collapsed in the fetus, but as the infant takes its first breaths, the drop in thoracic pressure draws blood into the pulmonary circulation and expands the vessels. As pulmonary resistance drops, the foramen ovale and ductus arteriosus close (see p. 588), and pulmonary blood flow increases to match the airflow.

### THINK ABOUT IT

*In a certain criminal investigation, the pathologist performing an autopsy on an infant removes the lungs, places them in a pail of water, and concludes that the infant was live-born. What do you think the pathologist saw that led to this conclusion? What contrasting observation would suggest that an infant had been stillborn?*

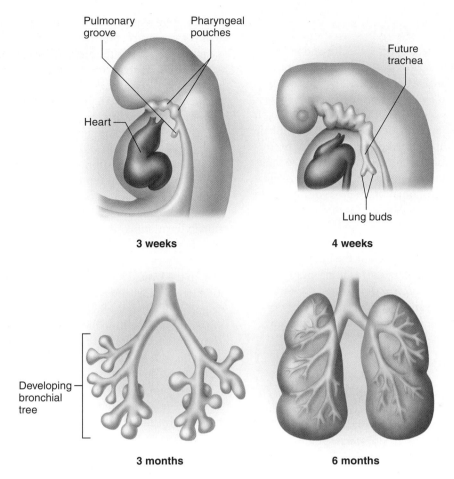

**Figure 23.16** Embryonic Development of the Respiratory System.

## INSIGHT 23.4

### Clinical Application

## Premature Birth and Respiratory Distress Syndrome

Premature infants often suffer from *respiratory distress syndrome (RDS)*, also called *hyaline membrane disease* (compare adult respiratory distress syndrome, table 23.1). They have not yet produced enough pulmonary surfactant to keep the alveoli open between inspirations. Consequently, the alveoli collapse during expiration, and a great effort is required to reinflate them. The infant becomes exhausted by the effort to breathe, and becomes progressively *cyanotic* (blue) because of the deficiency of oxygen in the blood *(hypoxemia)*. Progressive destruction of the alveolar epithelium and capillary walls leads to leakage of plasma into the alveolar air spaces and connective tissue between the alveoli. The plasma coagulates, and the alveoli fill with stiff clear "membranes" of fibrin, fibrinogen, and cell debris. Eventually, the infant cannot inhale forcefully enough to inflate the alveoli again, and without treatment, death ensues from hypoxemia and carbon dioxide retention *(hypercapnia)*.

RDS occurs in about 60% of infants born before 28 weeks of gestation, and 15% to 20% of those born between 32 and 36 weeks. It is the most common cause of neonatal death, with about 60,000 cases and 5,000 deaths per year in the United States. In addition to premature birth, some risk factors for RDS include maternal diabetes, oversedation of the mother during labor, aspiration of blood or amniotic fluid, and prenatal hypoxia caused by winding of the umbilical cord around the neck.

RDS can be treated with a ventilator that forces air into the lungs and keeps the alveoli inflated *(positive end-expiratory pressure, PEEP)* until the infant's lungs produce their own surfactant, and by giving a mist of surfactant from external sources such as calf lungs or genetically engineered bacteria. The infant may also be given oxygen therapy, but this is a limited and risky treatment because oxygen generates damaging free radicals that can cause blindness and severe bronchial problems. Oxygen toxicity can be minimized by a technique called *extracorporeal membrane oxygenation (ECMO)*, which is similar to the heart–lung bypass procedure used in surgery. Blood flows from catheters in the baby's neck to a machine that oxygenates it, warms it, and returns it to the body.

# The Aging Respiratory System

Pulmonary ventilation declines steadily after the 20s and is one of several factors in a person's gradual loss of stamina. The costal cartilages and joints of the thoracic cage become less flexible, the lungs have less elastic tissue, and there are fewer alveoli in old age. There is a corresponding decline in the volume of air inhaled in each breath (*tidal volume*), the maximum amount of air a person can inhale (*vital capacity*), and the maximum speed of airflow (*forced expiratory volume*). The elderly are also less capable of clearing the lungs of irritants and pathogens, and therefore are increasingly susceptible to respiratory infections. Pneumonia causes more deaths in old age than any other communicable disease and is often contracted in hospitals and nursing homes.

*Chronic obstructive pulmonary diseases* (see next section) are more common in old age since they represent the cumulative effects of a lifetime of degenerative change. Declining pulmonary function also contributes to cardiovascular disease and hypoxemia, and the latter is a factor in degenerative disorders of all other organ systems. Respiratory health is therefore a major concern in aging.

# Respiratory Pathology

Many of the respiratory disorders can be classified as *restrictive* or *obstructive disorders*. **Restrictive disorders** stiffen the lungs and reduce their *compliance* (ease of inflation) and vital capacity. An example is pulmonary fibrosis, in which much of the normal respiratory tissue of the lung is replaced by fibrous scar tissue. Fibrosis is an effect of such diseases as *tuberculosis* and the *black lung disease* of coal miners. **Obstructive disorders** narrow the airway and interfere with airflow, so expiration requires more effort and may be less complete than normal. Airway obstructions, bronchoconstriction, and tumors or aneurysms that compress the airways can cause obstructive disorders.

**Chronic obstructive pulmonary diseases (COPDs)** are disorders in which there is a long-term obstruction of airflow and a substantial reduction in pulmonary ventilation. The major COPDs are chronic bronchitis, emphysema, and asthma. The first two of these, usually caused by cigarette smoking, are among the few leading causes of death in old age. **Chronic bronchitis** is characterized by airway congestion with *sputum*, a mixture of thick mucus and cellular debris, accompanied by chronic respiratory infection and bronchial inflammation. **Emphysema**[14] (EM-fih-SEE-muh) is characterized by a breakdown of alveolar walls, resulting in a reduction in the number of alveoli and a reduced ability to oxygenate the blood. **Asthma** is the most common chronic illness of children and the leading cause of school absenteeism and childhood hospitalization in the United States. About half of all cases develop before age 10 and only 15% after age 40. Asthma takes about 5,000 lives per year. It is an allergic reaction to airborne antigens (allergens) that stimulate intense bronchoconstriction and airway inflammation, sometimes to the point of suffocation. Any COPD can also lead to *cor pulmonale*—enlargement and potential failure of the right side of the heart due to obstruction of the pulmonary circulation.

**Lung cancer** accounts for more deaths than any other form of cancer. The most important cause is cigarette smoking, distantly followed by air pollution. Lung cancer commonly follows or accompanies COPD. It begins with uncontrolled proliferation of cells

---

[14]*emphys* = inflamed

---

| TABLE 23.1 | Some Disorders of the Respiratory System |
|---|---|
| **Acute rhinitis** | The common cold. Caused by many types of viruses that infect the upper respiratory tract. Symptoms include congestion, increased nasal secretion, sneezing, and dry cough. Transmitted especially by contact of contaminated hands with mucous membranes; not transmitted orally. |
| **Adult respiratory distress syndrome** | Acute lung inflammation and alveolar injury stemming from trauma, infection, burns, aspiration of vomit, inhalation of noxious gases, drug overdoses, and other causes. Alveolar injury is accompanied by severe pulmonary edema and hemorrhage, followed by fibrosis that progressively destroys lung tissue. Fatal in about 40% of cases under age 60 and in 60% of cases over age 65. |
| **Pneumonia** | A lower respiratory infection caused by any of several viruses, fungi, or protozoans (most often the bacterium *Streptococcus pneumoniae*). Causes filling of alveoli with fluid and dead leukocytes and thickening of the respiratory membrane, which interferes with gas exchange and causes hypoxemia. Especially dangerous to infants, the elderly, and people with compromised immune systems, such as AIDS and leukemia patients. |
| **Sleep apnea** | Cessation of breathing for 10 seconds or longer during sleep; sometimes occurs hundreds of times per night, often accompanied by restlessness and snoring. Can result from altered function of CNS respiratory centers, airway obstruction, or both. Over time, may lead to daytime drowsiness, hypoxemia, polycythemia, pulmonary hypertension, congestive heart failure, and cardiac arrhythmia. Most common in obese people and in men. |
| **Tuberculosis (TB)** | Pulmonary infection with the bacterium *Mycobacterium tuberculosis*, which invades the lungs by way of air, blood, or lymph. Stimulates the lung to form fibrous nodules called tubercles around the bacteria. Progressive fibrosis compromises the elastic recoil and ventilation of the lungs. Especially common among impoverished and homeless people and becoming increasingly common among people with AIDS. |

## Disorders Described Elsewhere

of the surface epithelium or mucous glands of the bronchi. As the dividing epithelial cells invade the underlying tissues of the bronchial wall, the bronchus develops bleeding lesions. Dense masses of keratin and malignant cells appear in the lung parenchyma and replace functional respiratory tissue. Because of the extensive lymphatic drainage of the lungs, lung cancer quickly metastasizes to other organs—especially the pericardium, heart, bones, liver, lymph nodes, and brain. The chance of recovery is poor, with only 7% of patients surviving for 5 years after diagnosis.

Some other disorders of the respiratory system are briefly described in table 23.1.

## Before You Go On

*Answer the following questions to test your understanding of the preceding section:*

17. When and where does the pulmonary groove appear? Concisely describe its further development.

18. What changes in the lungs occur at birth? What corresponding changes occur in the cardiovascular system?

19. Identify some reasons why a person's vital capacity declines in old age.

20. Name and compare two COPDs and describe some pathological effects they have in common.

21. In what lung tissue does lung cancer originate? How does it kill?

# CHAPTER REVIEW

## REVIEW OF KEY CONCEPTS

### Overview of the Respiratory System (p. 663)

1. The respiratory system enables the blood to exchange gases with the air; serves for vocalization; provides a sense of smell; regulates blood pH and blood pressure; and creates pressure gradients that aid in the flow of lymph and blood and in expelling the contents of some abdominal organs.

2. The *conducting division* of the respiratory system consists of the nose, pharynx, larynx, trachea, bronchi, and most bronchioles; it serves only for airflow.

3. The *respiratory division* consists of *respiratory bronchioles, alveoli,* and other distal gas-exchange regions of the lungs.

4. The *upper respiratory tract* consists of the respiratory organs of the head and neck, extending from the nose through the larynx. The *lower respiratory tract* consists of the respiratory organs of the thorax, including the trachea, bronchi, and lungs.

### The Upper Respiratory Tract (p. 664)

1. The nose serves to warm and cleanse inhaled air, detect odors, and amplify the voice.

2. The nose extends from the nostrils to the *choanae* and is internally divided by the nasal septum into right and left *nasal fossae*. The facial part of the nose is shaped by the maxillae, nasal bones, and the lateral and alar cartilages.

3. The nasal septum consists of the perpendicular plate of the ethmoid bone superiorly, the vomer inferiorly, and the *septal nasal cartilage* anteriorly. The roof of the nasal cavity is formed by parts of the ethmoid and sphenoid bones, and the floor by the hard palate.

4. Each fossa has three scroll-like *nasal conchae* covered with a ciliated mucous membrane.

Air flows through narrow spaces called the *meatuses* between the conchae. The conchae warm, humidify, and cleanse the air flowing over them.

5. The nasal cavity is lined with a sensory *olfactory epithelium* high in each fossa, and with a ciliated pseudostratified *respiratory epithelium* throughout the rest of the cavity. The respiratory epithelium traps airborne particles in its mucus and propels the mucus to the pharynx to be swallowed.

6. Erectile tissues of the inferior nasal concha swell and shrink, usually in one fossa at a time, to periodically shift airflow from one fossa to the other. This allows the less-ventilated fossa a chance to periodically recover from drying.

7. The *pharynx* is a muscular passage divided into *nasopharynx, oropharynx,* and *laryngopharynx*.

8. The *larynx* is a cartilaginous chamber beginning superiorly at the *glottis* and ending about 4 cm lower at the trachea. It is supported by nine cartilages bound to each other by intrinsic ligaments, and two extrinsic ligaments attach the larynx to the hyoid bone above and the trachea below.

9. The larynx has a pair of superior *vestibular folds* that exclude food and drink from the airway, and a pair of inferior *vocal cords* that function in speech. *Extrinsic muscles* of the larynx help to close it during swallowing, and its *intrinsic muscles* operate the vocal cords during speech.

### The Lower Respiratory Tract (p. 668)

1. The *trachea* is a 12 cm tube, supported by cartilaginous rings, that extends from the larynx above to the two main bronchi below. The ciliated mucosa of the trachea acts as a *mucociliary escalator* to remove inhaled debris, stuck in the tracheal mucus, from the respiratory tract. The C-shaped cartilage rings hold the trachea open during inspiration. The gap on the posterior side of the C allows for expansion of the esophagus during swallowing.

2. Each lung is a conical organ extending from the superior *apex* to the inferior, broad *base*. Its extensive *costal surface* lies against the rib cage, and its indented *mediastinal surface* faces the heart. The mediastinal surface has a *hilum* through which it receives the main bronchi, pulmonary blood vessels, nerves, and lymphatics.

3. The right lung is shorter but broader than the left and is divided by two deep fissures into superior, middle, and inferior lobes. The left lung is taller but narrower and has only a superior and inferior lobe, separated by a single fissure.

4. The bronchial tree is a branching system of air passages extending from one *main bronchus* supplying each lung to *lobar bronchi* (2 in the left lung and 3 in the right), *segmental bronchi* (8 in the left lung and 10 in the right), *bronchioles, terminal bronchioles,* and *respiratory bronchioles*. Each lobar bronchus supplies one lobe of the lung; each segmental bronchus supplies one *bronchopulmonary segment*. The terminal bronchioles are the end of the conducting division; all branches beyond this have *alveoli* and belong to the respiratory division.

5. Respiratory bronchioles branch into 2 to 10 thin-walled *alveolar ducts*. Alveolar ducts end in grapelike clusters of alveoli called *alveolar sacs*.

6. *Bronchoconstriction* narrows the bronchioles and reduces airflow; *bronchodilation* widens them and increases airflow.

7. Each lung receives a pulmonary blood supply from the pulmonary artery and a systemic blood supply from the bronchial arteries.

8. An alveolus is a thin-walled sac surrounded by a basket of blood capillaries. It is composed of *squamous* and *great alveolar cells* and contains *alveolar macrophages,* the last line of defense against inhaled debris. The great alveolar cells secrete *pulmonary surfactant,* which prevents the alveoli from collapsing during expiration.

9. Gases are exchanged through the thin *respiratory membrane* composed of the capillary endothelial cells, the squamous alveolar cells, and their shared basement membrane.

10. The surface of each lung is a serous membrane called the *visceral pleura.* It continues as the *parietal pleura,* which lines the inside of the rib cage. The space between the pleurae is the *pleural cavity,* and is lubricated with *pleural fluid.* The pleurae reduce friction during breathing, contribute to the pressure gradients that move air into and out of the lungs, and help compartmentalize the thoracic cavity.

## Neuromuscular Aspects of Respiration (p. 674)

1. The diaphragm is the prime mover of pulmonary ventilation and accounts for about two-thirds of the airflow. The other one-third is due mainly to the external and internal intercostal muscles. Many other neck, thoracic, and abdominal muscles (accessory muscles of respiration) contribute to deep breathing.

2. Quiet inspiration is achieved mainly by contraction of the diaphragm and elevation of the ribs by the external intercostals.

These actions enlarge the thoracic cavity in the vertical, transverse, and anteroposterior dimensions, causing an inflow of air.

3. Forced (deep) inspiration is aided by muscles that elevate the upper ribs (sternocleidomastoids, scalenes, pectoralis minor and major, serratus anterior, and part of the internal intercostals).

4. Quiet expiration is achieved when the inspiratory muscles relax and the thoracic structures recoil because of their own elasticity.

5. Forced expiration is aided by muscles that depress the ribs and sternum (internal intercostals, rectus abdominis) and compress the abdominal cavity (latissimus dorsi, transverse abdominal, oblique abdominals).

6. The respiratory rhythm is set by respiratory centers in the brainstem.

7. The medulla oblongata contains a nucleus called the *dorsal respiratory group* that produces inspiration and one called the *ventral respiratory group* with both inspiratory and expiratory roles in heavy breathing. The pons contains a *pneumotaxic center* that governs the rate and depth of breathing.

8. These respiratory centers are influenced by input from central chemoreceptors in the brainstem, peripheral chemoreceptors in the aorta and carotid arteries, stretch and irritant receptors in the lungs, and higher brain centers.

## Developmental and Clinical Perspectives (p. 678)

1. The respiratory system begins development as a *pulmonary groove* that grows from the floor of the pharynx around 3.5 weeks of gestation. This groove grows into a tube than forks into two *lung buds,* then branches extensively to form the bronchial trees. By weeks 8 to 9, the pericardium and diaphragm isolate the lungs and pleural cavities from the heart and abdominal cavity.

2. The neonate's first breaths are very strenuous because of the need to inflate the alveoli. The pulmonary blood vessels also expand during these breaths, and the foramen ovale and ductus arteriosus gradually close to direct blood to the lungs.

3. With advancing age, the thoracic cage becomes less flexible, and the depth and rate of breathing decline. Irritants and pathogens cannot be cleared from the lungs as easily, so elderly people become more susceptible to respiratory infections. Pneumonia is a common cause of death in old age.

4. *Restrictive disorders* of the lung interfere with their inflation. Pulmonary fibrosis is an example. *Obstructive disorders* narrow the airway and interfere with the ease and speed of airflow. This can be caused by tumors, aneurysms, or bronchial congestion.

5. The *chronic obstructive pulmonary diseases (COPDs)* are *chronic bronchitis, emphysema,* and *asthma.* The first two of these, usually caused by tobacco smoke, are among the few leading causes of death in old age. Chronic bronchitis entails congestion of the airway with thick mucus and susceptibility to respiratory infection. Emphysema entails destruction of pulmonary alveoli. Asthma is an allergic disease involving intense inflammation and constriction of the bronchioles, sometimes severe enough to cause suffocation. The COPDs also frequently lead to right-sided heart failure.

6. Lung cancer also is usually caused by tobacco smoke. Tumors replace functional respiratory tissue, cause bleeding lesions of the lung, and metastasize quickly to adjacent thoracic organs.

# TESTING YOUR RECALL

1. The nasal cavity is divided by the nasal septum into right and left
   a. nares.
   b. vestibules.
   c. fossae.
   d. choanae.
   e. conchae.

2. The intrinsic laryngeal muscles regulate speech by rotating
   a. the extrinsic laryngeal muscles.
   b. the thyroid cartilage.
   c. the arytenoid cartilages.
   d. the hyoid bone.
   e. the vocal cords.

3. The largest air passages that engage in gas exchange with the blood are
   a. the respiratory bronchioles.
   b. the terminal bronchioles.
   c. the primary bronchi.
   d. the alveolar ducts.
   e. the alveoli.

4. Respiratory arrest would most likely result from a tumor of the
   a. pons.
   b. midbrain.
   c. thalamus.
   d. cerebellum.
   e. medulla oblongata.

5. A deficiency of pulmonary surfactant is most likely to cause
   a. chronic obstructive pulmonary disease.
   b. atelectasis.
   c. pneumothorax.
   d. chronic bronchitis.
   e. asthma.

6. The source of pulmonary surfactant is
   a. the visceral pleura.
   b. tracheal glands.
   c. alveolar capillaries.
   d. squamous alveolar cells.
   e. great alveolar cells.

7. Which of the following are fewest in number but largest in diameter?
   a. alveoli
   b. terminal bronchioles
   c. alveolar ducts
   d. tertiary bronchi
   e. respiratory bronchioles

8. The rhythm of breathing is set by neurons in
   a. the medulla oblongata.
   b. the pons.
   c. the midbrain.
   d. the hypothalamus.
   e. the cerebral cortex.

9. Which of the following muscles aids in deep expiration?
   a. the scalenes
   b. the sternocleidomastoids
   c. the rectus abdominis
   d. the external intercostals
   e. the diaphragm

10. All regions of the respiratory division are characterized by the presence of
    a. mucous glands.
    b. ciliated cells.
    c. alveoli.
    d. cartilage rings.
    e. goblet cells.

11. The digestive and respiratory tracts share a segment of the pharynx called the _____.

12. Within each lung, the airway forms a branching complex called the _____.

13. The flared areas of the nose lateral to the nostrils are shaped by _____ cartilages.

14. The three folds on the lateral walls of the nasal cavity are called _____.

15. _____ disorders reduce the speed of airflow through the airway.

16. Some inhaled air does not participate in gas exchange because it fills the _____ of the respiratory tract.

17. The largest cartilage of the larynx is the _____ cartilage.

18. Inspiration is caused by the firing of inspiratory neurons in the _____ of the medulla oblongata.

19. The primary bronchi and pulmonary blood vessels penetrate the lung at a medial slit called the _____.

20. The last line of defense against inhaled particles are phagocytic cells called _____.

*Answers in the Appendix*

## TRUE OR FALSE

*Determine which five of the following statements are false, and briefly explain why.*

1. The glottis is the opening from the larynx to the trachea.

2. The lungs contain more respiratory bronchioles than terminal bronchioles.

3. The lungs occupy the spaces between the parietal and visceral pleurae.

4. Expiration is normally caused by contraction of the internal intercostal muscles.

5. Atelectasis can result from causes other than pneumothorax.

6. Alveoli continue to be produced after birth.

7. Unlike bronchi, bronchioles have no cartilage.

8. Blood gases are monitored by the aortic and carotid sinuses.

9. The respiratory system begins its development by budding from the posterior side of the esophagus.

10. Extrinsic ligaments link the larynx to adjacent nonlaryngeal structures.

*Answers in the Appendix*

## TESTING YOUR COMPREHENSION

1. Discuss how the different functions of the conducting division and respiratory division relate to differences in their histology.

2. From the upper to the lower end of the trachea, the ratio of goblet cells to ciliated cells gradually changes. Would you expect the highest ratio of ciliated cells to goblet cells to be in the upper trachea or the lower trachea? Give a functional rationale for your answer.

3. The bronchioles are to the airway and airflow what the arterioles are to the circulatory system and blood flow. Explain or elaborate on this comparison.

4. A patient has suffered damage to the left phrenic nerve, resulting in paralysis of the left side of the diaphragm but not the right. X-rays show that during inspiration, the right side of the diaphragm descends as normal, but the left side *rises*. Explain the unusual motion of the left diaphragm.

5. An 83-year-old woman is admitted to the hospital, where a critical care nurse attempts to insert a nasoenteric tube ("stomach tube") for feeding. The patient begins to exhibit dyspnea, and a chest X-ray reveals air in the right pleural cavity and a collapsed right lung. The patient dies 5 days later from respiratory complications. Name the conditions revealed by the X-ray and explain how they could have resulted from the nurse's procedure.

*Answers at aris.mhhe.com*

## ONLINE RESOURCES

Visit aprevealed.com to explore melt-away cadaver dissections, watch animations that clarify difficult concepts, review histological and radiological images, or take a quiz to assess your understanding of the material.

The Saladin *Human Anatomy,* 2e website at aris.mhhe.com features chapter-specific quizzes, labeling exercises, and other interactive tools to complement your study of human anatomy. If your instructor has provided an ARIS course code, you can also access assignments and information specific to your course.

# 24

# The Digestive System

Filiform papillae of the human tongue
(SEM)

## INSIGHTS

## BRUSHING UP

To understand this chapter, you may find it helpful to review the following concepts:
- Brush borders and microvilli (pp. 56–57)
- The embryonic disc and germ layers (pp. 108–109)
- The autonomic nervous system (chapter 16)
- The celiac and mesenteric blood circulation (pp. 616–619)

Anatomy & Physiology | REVEALED®
aprevealed.com

**Digestive System**

Some of the most fundamental facts we know about digestion date to a grave accident that occurred in 1822. A Canadian fur trapper, Alexis St. Martin, was accidentally hit by a shotgun blast while standing outside a trading post on Mackinac Island, Michigan. An Army doctor summoned to the scene, William Beaumont, found part of St. Martin's lung protruding through the wound, and a hole in the stomach "large enough to receive my forefinger." Surprisingly, St. Martin survived, but the wound left a permanent opening (fistula) into his stomach, covered for the rest of his life by only a loose fold of tissue.

Beaumont saw this as an opportunity to learn something about digestion. Now disabled from hunting, St. Martin agreed to participate in Beaumont's experiments in exchange for room and board. Working under crude frontier conditions with little idea of scientific methods, Beaumont nevertheless performed more than 200 experiments on St. Martin over a period of several years. He placed food into the stomach through the fistula and removed it hourly to observe the progress of digestion. He sent vials of gastric juice to chemists for analysis. He proved that digestion required hydrochloric acid and an unknown agent we now know to be the enzyme pepsin. St. Martin had a short temper, and during his outbursts, Beaumont observed that little digestion occurred; we now know this to be due to the inhibitory effect of the sympathetic nervous system on digestion.

In 1833, Beaumont published a book on his results that laid a foundation for modern *gastroenterology,*[1] the scientific study and medical treatment of the digestive system. Many authorities continued to believe, for a time, that the stomach acted essentially as a grinding chamber, fermentation vat, or cooking pot. Some of them even attributed digestion to a supernatural spirit in the stomach. Beaumont was proven right, however, and his work had no equal until Russian physiologist Ivan Pavlov built upon it, receiving a Nobel Prize in 1904 for his studies of digestion.

# Digestive Processes and General Anatomy

## *Objectives*

When you have completed this section, you should be able to

- identify the functions and major processes of the digestive system;

- list the regions and accessory organs of the digestive system;

- identify the layers of the wall of the digestive tract;

- describe the enteric nervous system; and

- name the mesenteries and describe their relationship to the digestive system.

The digestive system is essentially a disassembly line—its primary purpose is to break nutrients down into forms that can be used by the body, and to absorb them so they can be distributed to the tissues. Most of what we eat cannot be used in the form found in the food. Nutrients must be broken down into smaller components, such as amino acids and monosaccharides, that are universal to all species. Consider what happens if you eat a piece of beef, for example. The myosin of beef differs very little from that of your own muscles, but the two are not identical, and even if they were, beef myosin could not be absorbed, transported in the blood, and incorporated into your muscles. Like any other dietary protein, it must be broken down into amino acids before it can be used. Since beef and human proteins are made of the same 20 amino acids, those of beef proteins might indeed become part of your own myosin but could equally well wind up in your insulin, fibrinogen, collagen, or any other protein.

## Digestive System Functions

The **digestive system** is the organ system that processes food, extracts nutrients from it, and eliminates the residue. It does this in five stages:

1. **ingestion,** the selective intake of food;
2. **digestion,** the mechanical and chemical breakdown of food into a form usable by the body;
3. **absorption,** the uptake of nutrients into the blood and lymph;
4. **compaction,** absorbing water and consolidating the indigestible residue into feces; and finally
5. **defecation,** the elimination of feces.

## General Anatomy

The digestive system has two anatomical subdivisions, the digestive tract and the accessory organs (fig. 24.1). The **digestive tract** is a muscular tube extending from mouth to anus, measuring about 9 m (30 ft) long in the cadaver. It is also known as the *alimentary*[2] *canal* or *gut.* It includes the mouth, pharynx, esophagus, stomach, small intestine, and large intestine. Part of it, the stomach and intestines, constitutes the *gastrointestinal (GI) tract.* The **accessory organs** are the teeth, tongue, salivary glands, liver, gallbladder, and pancreas.

The digestive tract is open to the environment at both ends. Most of the material in it has not entered any body tissues and is considered to be external to the body until it is absorbed by epithelial cells of the alimentary canal. In the strict sense, defecated food residue was never in the body.

Most of the digestive tract follows the basic structural plan shown in figure 24.2, with a wall composed of the following tissue layers, in order from the inner to the outer surface:

Mucosa

    Epithelium

    Lamina propria

    Muscularis mucosae

Submucosa

Muscularis externa

    Circular layer

    Longitudinal layer

---

[1]*gastro* = stomach + *entero* = intestine + *logy* = study of

[2]*aliment* = food

Serosa

    Areolar tissue

    Mesothelium

Slight variations on this theme are found in different regions of the tract.

The **mucosa (mucous membrane),** which lines the lumen, consists of an inner epithelium, a loose connective tissue layer called the **lamina propria,** and a thin layer of smooth muscle called the **muscularis mucosae** (MUSS-cue-LAIR-is mew-CO-see). The epithelium is simple columnar in most of the digestive tract, but the mouth, pharynx, esophagus, and anal canal differ. These upper and lower ends of the digestive tract are subject to more abrasion than the stomach and intestines, and thus have a stratified squamous epithelium. The muscularis mucosae tenses the mucosa, creating grooves and ridges that enhance its surface area and contact with food. This improves the efficiency of digestion and nutrient absorption. The mucosa often exhibits an abundance of lymphocytes and lymphatic nodules—the *mucosa-associated lymphatic tissue (MALT)* (see p. 646).

The **submucosa** is a thicker layer of loose connective tissue containing blood vessels, lymphatic vessels, a nerve plexus, and in some places, mucous glands. The MALT also extends into the submucosa in some parts of the GI tract.

The **muscularis externa** consists of usually two layers of smooth muscle near the outer surface. Cells of the inner layer encircle the tract and those of the outer layer run longitudinally. In some places, the circular layer is thickened to form valves (sphincters) that regulate the passage of material through the digestive tract. The muscularis externa is responsible for the motility that propels food and residue through the tract.

The **serosa** is composed of a thin layer of areolar tissue topped by a simple squamous mesothelium. It begins in the lower 3 to 4 cm of the esophagus and ends just before the rectum. The pharynx, most of the esophagus, and the rectum are surrounded by a fibrous connective tissue layer called the **adventitia** (AD-ven-TISH-ah), which blends into the adjacent connective tissues of other organs.

## Innervation

Tongue movements, mastication, and the initial actions of swallowing employ skeletal muscles innervated by somatic motor fibers from six of the cranial nerves (V, VII, and IX–XII) and from the ansa cervicalis; these muscles and their innervation are detailed in table 11.3 (p. 304). The salivary glands are innervated by sympathetic fibers from the superior cervical ganglion and parasympathetic fibers from cranial nerves VII and IX (see figs. 15.31, p. 457; 15.33, p. 458; and 16.4, p. 472).

From the lower esophagus to the anal canal, most of the muscle is smooth muscle (the external anal sphincter is the only exception), and therefore receives only autonomic innervation. Parasympathetic innervation dominates the digestive tract and comes mainly from the vagus nerves, which supply all of the tract from esophagus to transverse colon. The descending colon and rectum receive their parasympathetic innervation from pelvic nerves arising from the inferior hypogastric plexus (see fig. 16.7, p. 476). The parasympathetic nervous system relaxes sphincter muscles and stimulates gastrointestinal motility and secretion. Thus, in general, it promotes digestion.

The sympathetic nervous system plays a lesser role, but in general it inhibits motility and secretion and keeps the GI sphincters contracted and closed. Thus, it inhibits digestion. Sympathetic efferent pathways travel through the celiac ganglion to the stomach, liver, and pancreas; through the superior mesenteric ganglion to the small intestine and most of the large intestine; and through the inferior mesenteric ganglion to the rectum (see fig. 16.4, p. 472).

Even though the digestive tract receives such extensive innervation from the CNS, it can function independently even if these nerves are severed. This is because the esophagus, stomach, and intestines have their own extensive nervous network called the **enteric**[3] **nervous system,** which is thought to have over 100

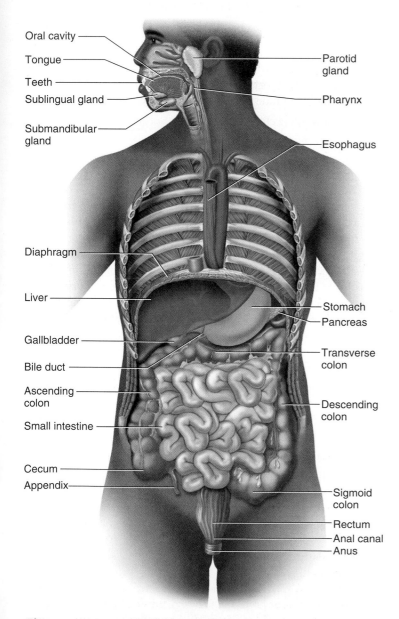

Oral cavity

Tongue

Teeth

Sublingual gland

Submandibular gland

Diaphragm

Liver

Gallbladder

Bile duct

Ascending colon

Small intestine

Cecum

Appendix

Parotid gland

Pharynx

Esophagus

Stomach

Pancreas

Transverse colon

Descending colon

Sigmoid colon

Rectum

Anal canal

Anus

**Figure 24.1** The Digestive System.

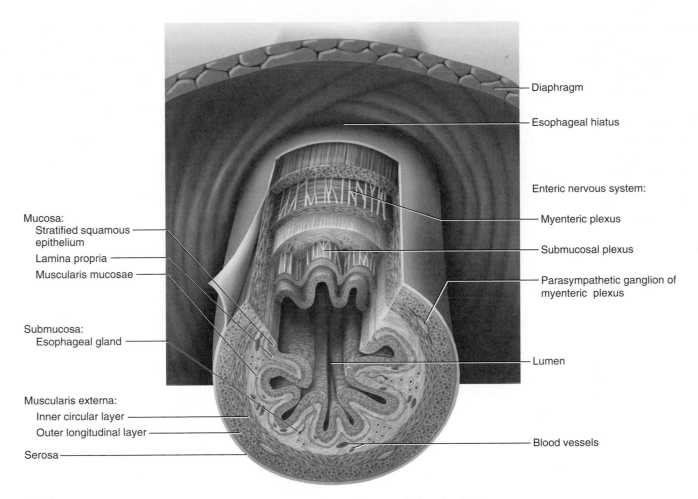

Mucosa:
    Stratified squamous epithelium
    Lamina propria
    Muscularis mucosae

Submucosa:
    Esophageal gland

Muscularis externa:
    Inner circular layer
    Outer longitudinal layer
    Serosa

Diaphragm

Esophageal hiatus

Enteric nervous system:
    Myenteric plexus
    Submucosal plexus
    Parasympathetic ganglion of myenteric plexus

Lumen

Blood vessels

**Figure 24.2** **Tissue Layers of the Digestive Tract.** Cross section of the esophagus just below the diaphragm.

million neurons—more than the spinal cord! These include sensory neurons that monitor tension in the gut wall; interneurons; and motor neurons that activate such effectors as smooth muscle and gland cells of the gut. It also contains clusters of parasympathetic postganglionic neurons that act essentially as autonomic ganglia.

Neurons of the enteric nervous system are distributed in two networks: the **submucosal (Meissner[4]) plexus** in the submucosa and the **myenteric (Auerbach[5]) plexus** between the two layers of the muscularis externa. Parasympathetic preganglionic fibers terminate in the ganglia of the myenteric plexus. Postganglionic fibers arising in this plexus not only innervate the muscularis externa, but also pass through its inner circular layer and contribute to the submucosal plexus. The myenteric plexus controls peristalsis and other contractions of the muscularis externa, while the submucosal plexus controls movements of the muscularis mucosae and glandular secretion of the mucosa.

Sensory nerve fibers monitor stretching of the GI wall and chemical conditions in the lumen. These fibers carry signals to adjacent regions of the GI tract in **short (myenteric) reflex arcs** contained in the myenteric plexus, and to the central nervous system by way of **long (vagovagal) reflex arcs,** predominantly in the vagus nerves. These visceral reflex arcs enable different regions of the GI tract to regulate each other over both short and long distances.

## Circulation

We will see near the end of this chapter that the embryonic digestive tract forms in three segments: the foregut, midgut, and hindgut. These segments are defined by their arterial blood supply (see table 21.6, pp. 616–619).

- The **foregut** includes the mouth, pharynx, esophagus, stomach, and the beginning of the duodenum (to the point where the bile duct empties into it). Above the diaphragm, the thoracic aorta gives off a series of **esophageal arteries** to the esophagus. Below the diaphragm, the foregut components receive their blood from branches of the **celiac trunk.**

- The **midgut** begins at the opening of the bile duct and includes the rest of the duodenum, the jejunum and ileum (the second and third portions of the small intestine), and the large intestine as far as the first two-thirds of the transverse colon. It receives blood from the **superior mesenteric artery** (fig. 21.24a, p. 619).

---

[3]*enter* = intestine
[4]Georg Meissner (1829–1905), German histologist
[5]Leopold Auerbach (1828–97), German anatomist

- The **hindgut** includes the remainder of the large intestine, from the end of the transverse colon through the anal canal. It is supplied by branches of the **inferior mesenteric artery** (fig. 21.24b, p. 619).

The most noteworthy general point about the venous drainage of the GI tract is that blood from the entire tract below the diaphragm ultimately drains into the **hepatic portal vein,** which enters the liver. The system of vessels connecting the lower digestive tract to the liver is the **hepatic portal system** (table 21.7, p. 620). It routes all blood from the stomach and intestines, as well as from some other abdominal viscera, through the liver before returning it to the general circulation. Like other portal systems, this one has two capillary networks in series. Capillaries in the small intestine receive digested nutrients, and capillaries in the liver (the *hepatic sinusoids* described later) deliver these nutrients to the liver cells. This gives the liver a chance to process most nutrients and cleanse the intestinal blood of bacteria.

## Relationship to the Peritoneum

In processing food, the stomach and intestines undergo such strenuous contractions that they need freedom to move in the abdominal cavity. Thus, they are not tightly bound to the abdominal wall, but over most of its length, the tract is loosely suspended from it by connective tissue sheets called the **mesenteries** (see figs. A.9 and A.10, pp. 29, 30). The mesenteries also hold the abdominal viscera in their proper relationship to each other and prevent the small intestine, especially, from becoming twisted and tangled by changes in body position and by its own contractions. Furthermore, the mesenteries provide passage for the blood vessels and nerves that supply the digestive tract, and contain many lymph nodes and lymphatic vessels.

The parietal peritoneum is a serous membrane that lines the wall of the abdominal cavity (see p. 000). Along the posterior (dorsal) midline of the body, it turns inward and forms the **dorsal mesentery,** a translucent two-layered membrane extending to the digestive tract. Upon reaching an organ such as the stomach or small intestine, the two layers of the mesentery separate and pass around opposite sides of the organ, forming the serosa. In some places, the two layers come together again on the far side of that organ and continue as another sheet of tissue, the **ventral mesentery.** The ventral mesentery may hang freely in the abdominal cavity or attach to the ventral abdominal wall or other organs. The relationship between the dorsal and ventral mesenteries and the serosa are shown in figure A.9.

Along the right superior margin (*lesser curvature*) of the stomach, a ventral mesentery called the **lesser omentum** extends from the stomach to the liver (fig. 24.3). Another membrane, a fatty **greater omentum,** hangs from the left inferior margin (*greater curvature*) of the stomach and loosely covers the small intestine like an apron. At its inferior margin, the greater omentum turns back on itself and passes upward, thus forming a deep pouch between its deep and superficial layers. At its inner superior margin, it continues as a serosa enclosing the spleen and transverse colon, then continues still farther as the **mesocolon,** which anchors the transverse colon to the dorsal abdominal wall. The omenta have a loosely organized, lacy appearance due partly to many holes or gaps in the membranes and partly to an irregular distribution of adipose tissue. They adhere to perforations or inflamed areas of the stomach or intestines, contribute immune cells to the site, and isolate infections that might otherwise give rise to peritonitis.

When an organ is enclosed by mesentery (serosa) on both sides, it is considered to be within the peritoneal cavity, or **intraperito-**

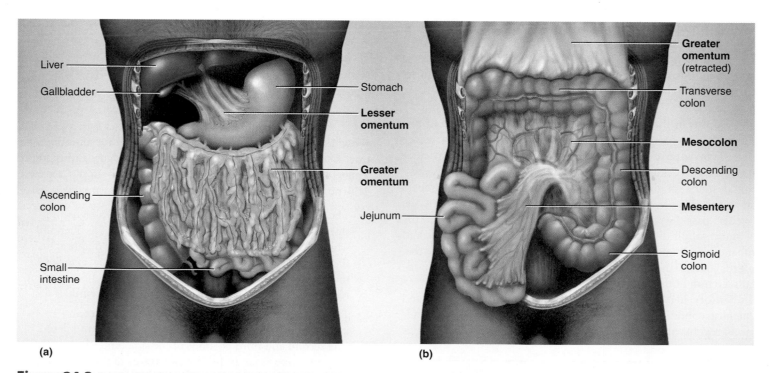

(a)                                                                 (b)

**Figure 24.3** **Serous Membranes Associated with the Digestive Tract.** (a) The greater and lesser omenta. (b) Greater omentum and small intestine retracted to show the mesocolon and mesentery. These membranes contain the mesenteric arteries and veins.

**neal.**[6] When an organ lies against the dorsal body wall and is covered by peritoneum on the ventral side only, it is said to be outside the peritoneal cavity, or **retroperitoneal.**[7] The duodenum, most of the pancreas, and parts of the large intestine are retroperitoneal. The stomach, liver, and other parts of the small and large intestines are intraperitoneal.

## Before You Go On

*Answer the following questions to test your understanding of the preceding section:*

1. Name the principal regions of the digestive tract in order from mouth to anus.

2. What are the similarities and differences between the lamina propria and the submucosa?

3. What are the two components of the enteric nervous system? How do they differ in location and function?

4. What three major branches of the aorta supply the digestive tract? What is the relationship between these three arterial supplies and the embryonic development of the digestive tract?

5. Name the serous membranes that suspend the intestines from the dorsal body wall. Name the external layer of the intestines formed by an extension of this membrane.

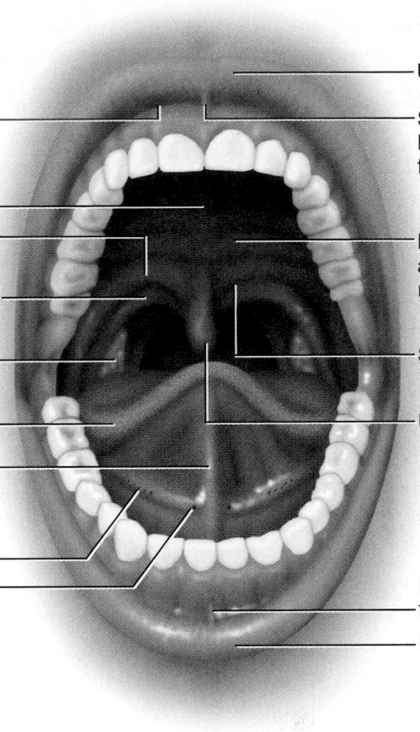

**Figure 24.4  The Mouth.** For a photographic medial view, see figure A.17 (p. 38).

# The Mouth Through Esophagus

### Objectives
When you have completed this section, you should be able to

- describe the teeth, tongue, and other organs of the oral cavity;
- state the names and locations of the salivary glands;
- describe the location and function of the pharyngeal constrictor muscles; and
- describe the gross anatomy and histology of the esophagus.

## The Mouth

The **mouth** is also known as the **oral (buccal**[8]**) cavity.** Its functions include ingestion (food intake), taste and other sensory responses to food, chewing, chemical digestion, swallowing, speech, and respiration. The mouth is enclosed by the cheeks, lips, palate, and tongue (fig. 24.4). Its anterior opening between the lips is the **oral fissure,** and its posterior opening into the throat is the **fauces**[9] (FAW-seez).

The mouth is lined with stratified squamous epithelium. It is keratinized in areas subject to the greatest abrasion, such as the gums and hard palate, and nonkeratinized in other areas such as the floor of the mouth, the soft palate, and the inside of the cheeks and lips.

## The Cheeks and Lips

The cheeks and lips retain food and push it between the teeth for mastication, and are essential for articulate speech and for sucking and blowing actions, including suckling by infants. Their fleshiness is due mainly to subcutaneous fat, the buccinator muscles of the cheeks, and the orbicularis oris muscle of the lips. A median fold called the **labial frenulum**[10] attaches each lip to the gum, between the anterior incisors. The **vestibule** is the space between the cheeks or lips and the teeth—the space where you insert your toothbrush when brushing the outer surfaces of the teeth.

The lips are divided into three areas: (1) The *cutaneous area* is colored like the rest of the face and has hair follicles and sebaceous glands; on the upper lip, this is where a mustache grows. (2) The *red area (vermilion),* is the hairless region where the lips meet (where some people apply lipstick). It has unusually tall dermal papillae, which allow blood capillaries and nerve endings to come closer to the epidermal surface. Thus, this area is redder and more sensitive than the cutaneous area. (3) The *labial mucosa* is the inner surface of the lip, facing the gums and teeth.

---

[6]*intra* = within
[7]*retro* = behind
[8]*bucca* = cheek
[9]*fauces* = throat

[10]*labi* = lip + *frenulum* = little bridle

## The Tongue

The tongue (fig. 24.5), although muscular and bulky, is an agile and sensitive organ with several functions: it aids in food intake; it has sensory receptors for taste, texture, and temperature that are important in the acceptance or rejection of food; it compresses and breaks up food; it maneuvers food between the teeth for mastication; it secretes mucus and enzymes; it compresses the chewed food into a soft mass, or *bolus,* that is easier to swallow; it initiates swallowing; and it is necessary for articulate speech. Its surface is covered with nonkeratinized stratified squamous epithelium and exhibits bumps and projections called **lingual papillae,** the site of the taste buds. The types of papillae and sense of taste are discussed in chapter 17.

The anterior two-thirds of the tongue, called the **body,** occupies the oral cavity; the posterior one-third, the **root,** occupies the oropharynx. The boundary between the body and root is marked by a V-shaped row of *vallate papillae* and, behind these, a groove called the **terminal sulcus.** A ventral median fold called the **lingual frenulum** attaches the body of the tongue to the floor of the mouth. The root of the tongue contains the lingual tonsils. Amid the tongue muscles are serous and mucous **lingual glands,** which secrete a portion of the saliva.

The muscles of the tongue, which compose most of its mass, are described in chapter 11. The **intrinsic muscles,** contained entirely within the tongue, produce the relatively subtle tongue movements of speech. The **extrinsic muscles,** with origins elsewhere and insertions in the tongue, produce the stronger movements of food manipulation. The extrinsic muscles include the *genioglossus, hyoglossus, styloglossus,* and *palatoglossus* (see table 11.3, p. 304).

## The Palate

The palate, separating the oral cavity from the nasal cavity, makes it possible to breathe while chewing food. Its anterior portion, the **hard (bony) palate,** is supported by the palatine processes of the maxillae and by the smaller palatine bones. It has transverse ridges called *palatine rugae* that aid the tongue in holding and manipulating food. Posterior to this is the **soft palate,** which has a more spongy texture and is composed mainly of skeletal muscle and glandular tissue, but no bone. It has a conical medial projection, the **uvula,**[11] visible at the rear of the mouth. The uvula helps to retain food in the mouth until one is ready to swallow.

A pair of muscular arches on each side of the oral cavity begin dorsally near the uvula and follow the wall of the cavity to its floor. The anterior one is the **palatoglossal arch** and the posterior one is the **palatopharyngeal arch.** The latter arch marks the beginning of the pharynx. The palatine tonsils are located on the wall between the arches.

## The Teeth

The teeth are collectively called the **dentition.** They serve to *masticate* the food, breaking it into smaller pieces. This not only makes the food easier to swallow, but also exposes more surface area to the action of digestive enzymes and thus speeds up chemical digestion. Adults normally have 16 teeth in the mandible and 16 in the maxilla. From the midline to the rear of each jaw, there are two incisors,

---

[11]*uvula* = little grape

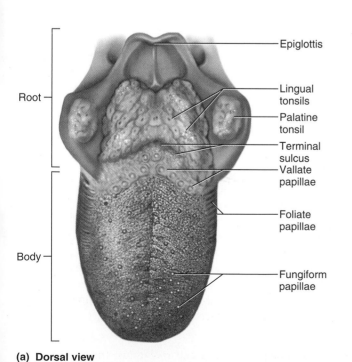

Root

Body

Epiglottis

Lingual tonsils

Palatine tonsil

Terminal sulcus

Vallate papillae

Foliate papillae

Fungiform papillae

**(a) Dorsal view**

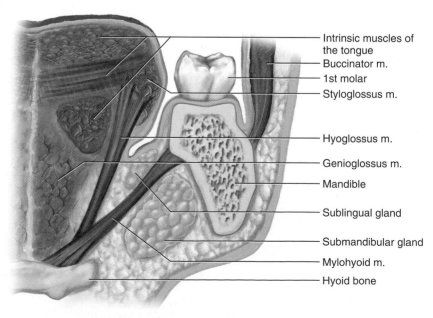

Intrinsic muscles of the tongue

Buccinator m.

1st molar

Styloglossus m.

Hyoglossus m.

Genioglossus m.

Mandible

Sublingual gland

Submandibular gland

Mylohyoid m.

Hyoid bone

**(b) Frontal section, anterior view**

**Figure 24.5** **The Tongue.** For a sagittal section, see figure A.17 (p. 38).

a canine, two premolars, and up to three molars (fig. 24.6a). The **incisors** are chisel-like cutting teeth used to bite off a piece of food. The **canines** are more pointed and act to puncture and shred it. They serve as weapons in many mammals but became reduced in the course of human evolution until they now project barely beyond the other teeth. The **premolars** and **molars** have relatively broad surfaces adapted for crushing and grinding.

Each tooth is embedded in a socket called an **alveolus,** forming a joint called a *gomphosis* between the tooth and bone (fig. 24.7). The alveolus is lined by a **periodontal** (PERR-ee-oh-DON-tul) **ligament,** a modified periosteum whose collagen fibers penetrate into the bone on one side and into the tooth on the other. This anchors the tooth firmly in the alveolus, but allows for a slight amount of movement

under the pressure of chewing. The gum, or **gingiva** (JIN-jih-vuh), covers the alveolar bone. Regions of a tooth are defined by their relationship to the gingiva: the **crown** is the portion above the gum, the **root** is the portion inserted into the alveolus below the gum, and the **neck** is the line where the crown, root, and gum meet. The space between the tooth and gum is the **gingival sulcus.** The hygiene of this sulcus is especially important to dental health (see Insight 24.1).

Most of a tooth consists of hard yellowish tissue called **dentine,** covered with **enamel** in the crown and **cementum** in the root. Dentine and cementum are living connective tissues with cells or cell processes embedded in a calcified matrix. Cells of the cementum *(cementocytes)* are scattered more or less randomly and occupy tiny cavities similar to the lacunae of bone. Cells of the dentine *(odontoblasts)* line the pulp cavity and have slender processes that travel through tiny parallel tunnels in the dentine. Enamel is not a tissue but a cell-free secretion produced before the tooth emerges above the gum. Damaged dentine and cementum can regenerate, but damaged enamel cannot—it must be artificially repaired.

Internally, a tooth has a dilated **pulp cavity** in the crown and upper root, and a narrow **root canal** in the lower root. These spaces are occupied by **pulp**—a mass of loose connective tissue, blood and lymphatic vessels, and nerves. These nerves and vessels enter the tooth through a pore, the **apical foramen,** at the inferior end of each root canal.

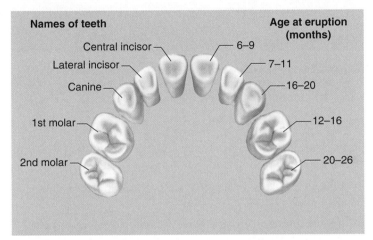

**(a) Deciduous (baby) teeth**

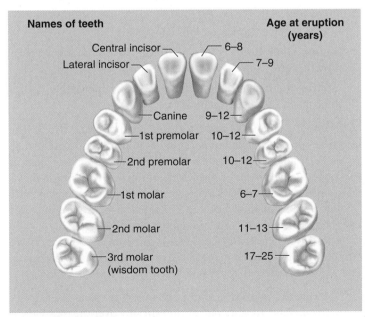

**(b) Permanent teeth**

**Figure 24.6** **The Dentition.** Each figure shows only the upper teeth. The ages at eruption are composite ages for the corresponding upper and lower teeth. Generally, the lower (mandibular) teeth erupt somewhat earlier than their upper (maxillary) counterparts.
● *Which teeth are absent from a 3-year-old child?*

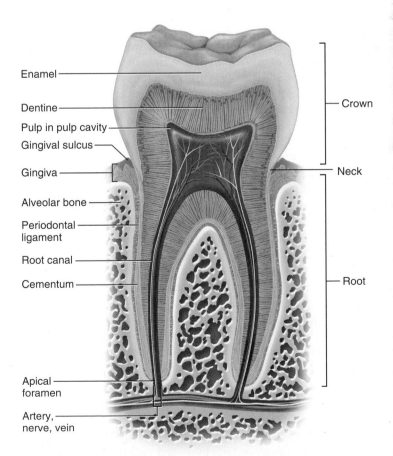

**Figure 24.7** **Structure of a Tooth and Its Alveolus.** This particular example is a molar.
● *Of all the components shown here, which is or are not living tissue(s)?*

INSIGHT 24.1

## Clinical Application

### Tooth and Gum Disease

Food leaves a sticky residue on the teeth called *plaque*, composed mainly of bacteria and sugars. If plaque is not thoroughly removed by brushing and flossing, bacteria accumulate, metabolize the sugars, and release lactic acid and other acids. These acids dissolve the minerals of enamel and dentine, and the bacteria enzymatically digest the collagen and other organic components. The eroded "cavities" of the tooth are known as *dental caries*.[12] If not repaired, caries may fully penetrate the dentine and spread to the pulp cavity. This requires either extraction of the tooth or *root canal therapy*, in which the pulp is removed and replaced with inert material.

When plaque calcifies on the tooth surface, it is called *calculus (tartar)*. Calculus in the gingival sulcus wedges the tooth and gum apart and allows bacterial invasion of the sulcus. This leads to *gingivitis*, or gum inflammation. Nearly everyone has gingivitis at some time. In some cases, bacteria spread from the sulcus into the alveolar bone and begin to dissolve it, producing *periodontal disease*. About 86% of people over age 70 have periodontal disease, and many suffer tooth loss as a result. This accounts for 80% to 90% of adult tooth loss.

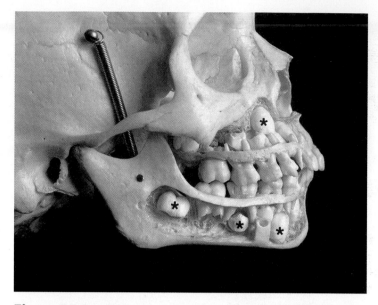

**Figure 24.8** **Permanent and Deciduous Teeth in a Child's Skull.** This dissection shows erupted deciduous teeth and, deep to them and marked with asterisks, the permanent teeth waiting to erupt.

The meeting of the teeth when the mouth closes is called *occlusion* (ah-CLUE-zhun), and the surfaces where they meet are called the **occlusal surfaces.** The occlusal surface of a premolar has two rounded bumps called **cusps;** thus the premolars are also known as **bicuspids.** The molars have four to five cusps. Cusps of the upper and lower premolars and molars mesh when the jaws are closed and slide over each other as the jaw makes lateral chewing motions. This grinds and tears food more effectively than if the occlusal surfaces were flat.

Teeth develop beneath the gums and **erupt** (emerge) in predictable order. Twenty **deciduous teeth** ("milk teeth" or "baby teeth") erupt from the ages of 6 to 30 months, beginning with the incisors (fig. 24.6a). Between 6 and 25 years of age, these are replaced by 32 **permanent teeth.** As a permanent tooth grows deep to a deciduous tooth (fig. 24.8), the root of the deciduous tooth dissolves and leaves little more than the crown by the time it falls out. The third molars (wisdom teeth) erupt around ages 17 to 25, if at all. Over the course of human evolution, the face became flatter and the jaws shorter, leaving little room for the third molars. Thus, they often remain below the gum and become *impacted*—so crowded against neighboring teeth and bone that they cannot erupt.

## The Salivary Glands

Saliva moistens the mouth, digests a small amount of starch and fat, cleanses the teeth, inhibits bacterial growth, dissolves molecules so they can stimulate the taste buds, and moistens food and binds particles together to aid in swallowing. It is a solution of 97.0% to 99.5% water and the following solutes:

- **salivary amylase,** an enzyme that begins starch digestion in the mouth;
- **lingual lipase,** an enzyme that is activated by stomach acid and digests fat after the food is swallowed;
- **mucus,** which binds and lubricates the food mass and aids in swallowing;
- **lysozyme,** an enzyme that kills bacteria;
- **immunoglobulin A (IgA),** an antibody that inhibits bacterial growth; and
- **electrolytes,** including sodium, potassium, chloride, phosphate, and bicarbonate salts.

There are two kinds of salivary glands, intrinsic and extrinsic. The **intrinsic salivary glands** are an indefinite number of small glands dispersed amid the other oral tissues. They include *lingual glands* in the tongue, *labial glands* on the inside of the lips, and *buccal glands* on the inside of the cheeks. They secrete saliva at a fairly constant rate whether we are eating or not, but in relatively small amounts. This saliva keeps the mouth moist and inhibits bacterial growth.

The **extrinsic salivary glands** are three pairs of larger, more discrete organs located outside of the oral mucosa. They communicate with the oral cavity by way of ducts (fig. 24.9). They are:

1. The **parotid**[13] **gland,** located just beneath the skin anterior to the earlobe. Its duct passes superficially over the masseter, pierces the buccinator, and opens into the mouth opposite the second upper molar tooth. *Mumps* is an inflammation and swelling of the parotid gland caused by a virus.

---

[12]*caries* = rottenness

[13]*par* = next to + *ot* = ear

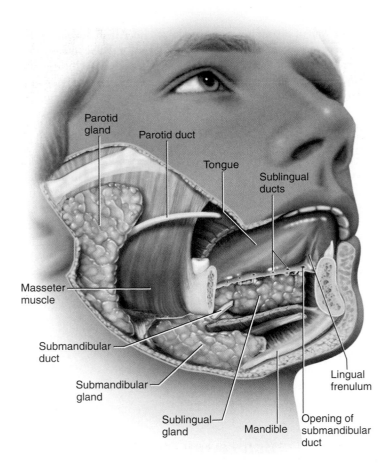

**Figure 24.9** **The Extrinsic Salivary Glands.** Half of the mandible has been removed to expose the sublingual gland medial to it.

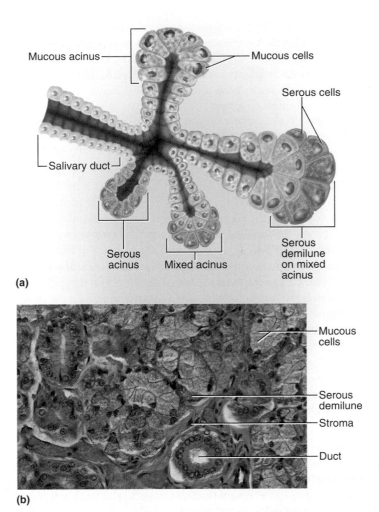

(a)

(b)

**Figure 24.10** **Microscopic Anatomy of the Salivary Glands.** (a) Duct and acini of a generalized salivary gland with a mixture of mucous and serous cells. Serous cells often form crescent-shaped caps called serous demilunes over the ends of mucous acini. No one salivary gland shows all the features shown here. (b) Histology of the sublingual salivary gland.

2. The **submandibular gland,** located halfway along the body of the mandible, medial to its margin, just deep to the mylohyoid muscle. Its duct empties into the mouth at a papilla on the side of the lingual frenulum, near the lower central incisors.

3. The **sublingual gland,** located in the floor of the mouth. It has multiple ducts that empty into the mouth posterior to the papilla of the submandibular duct.

These are all compound tubuloacinar glands with a treelike arrangement of branching ducts ending in acini (see p. 96). Some acini have only mucous cells, some have only serous cells, and some have a mixture of both (fig. 24.10). Mucous cells secrete salivary mucus, and serous cells secrete a thinner fluid rich in amylase and electrolytes.

Salivation is controlled by groups of neurons called **salivatory nuclei** in the medulla oblongata and pons. They receive signals from sensory receptors in the mouth as well as from higher brain centers that respond to the odor, sight, or thought of food. Efferent nerve pathways to the salivary glands were described earlier (p. 686). Salivation is mostly under the control of parasympathetic fibers in cranial nerves VII and IX, which stimulate the secretion of watery, enzyme-rich saliva. Sympathetic fibers from cervical ganglia stimulate the secretion of thicker, mucus-rich saliva.

### THINK ABOUT IT

*Explain why the mouth may feel dry or sticky when one is nervous. (Hint: Draw on information about the autonomic nervous system in chapter 16.)*

## The Pharynx

The pharynx, as described in chapter 23, consists of three regions called the nasopharynx, oropharynx, and laryngopharynx (fig. 23.2c, p. 665). The first is exclusively respiratory and is lined with pseudostratified columnar epithelium; the last two are shared by the respiratory and digestive tracts and are lined with nonkeratinized stratified squamous epithelium, an adaptation to withstanding abrasion by passing food.

The pharynx has a deep layer of longitudinally oriented skeletal muscle and a superficial layer of circular skeletal muscle. The circular muscle is divided into **superior, middle,** and **inferior pharyngeal constrictors,** which force food downward during swallowing. When one is not swallowing, the inferior constrictor remains contracted to exclude air from the esophagus. This constriction is regarded as the **upper esophageal sphincter,** although it is not an anatomical feature of the esophagus. It disappears at the time of death when the muscle relaxes. Thus it is regarded as a *physiological sphincter* rather than a constant anatomical structure.

## The Esophagus

The **esophagus** is a straight muscular tube 25 to 30 cm long, posterior to the trachea (see figs. 24.1 and 24.2). Its superior opening lies between vertebra C6 and the cricoid cartilage of the larynx. After passing downward through the mediastinum, the esophagus penetrates the diaphragm at an opening called the **esophageal hiatus,** continues another 3 to 4 cm, and meets the stomach at the level of vertebra T7. Its opening into the stomach is called the **cardiac orifice** (for its proximity to the heart). Food pauses briefly at this point before entering the stomach because of a constriction called the **lower esophageal sphincter (LES).** The LES is also a physiological rather than an anatomical sphincter, and thus is not found in the cadaver. It is thought to be either a constriction of the diaphragm surrounding the esophageal hiatus, or muscle tone in the smooth muscle of the esophagus. The LES prevents stomach contents from regurgitating into the esophagus, thus protecting the esophageal mucosa from the corrosive effect of the stomach acid (see Insight 24.2).

# INSIGHT 24.2

## Clinical Application

### Gastroesophageal Reflux Disease

It would seem that churning of the stomach would drive its contents back up the esophagus. Such backflow, or *gastroesophageal reflux,* is normally prevented, however, by the lower esophageal sphincter. Weakening of the LES leads to repetitive or chronic backflow, called *gastroesophageal reflux disease (GERD).* Stomach acid and sometimes bile acids and pancreatic enzymes regurgitate into the esophagus and irritate the mucosa. This causes the sensation of "heartburn," so named for its location although it has nothing to do with the heart. GERD affects as much as 50% of the population in the United States, especially white males. Beside sex and race, risk factors include age (middle-aged or beyond), being overweight, and going to bed too soon after eating.

The heartburn sensation can often be managed with antacids and is commonly dismissed by physicians and patients as merely a nuisance. However, in a few cases, GERD can lead to more serious complications such as scarring and narrowing of the esophagus *(stricture),* erosion and inflammation of the esophageal wall *(erosive esophagitis),* a transformation (metaplasia) of esophageal epithelium to an intestinal-type columnar epithelium (*Barrett*[14] *esophagus*), and a form of esophageal cancer called *adenocarcinoma.* Although most people with Barrett esophagus and adenocarcinoma have a long-term history of GERD, only 5% to 15% of those with GERD progress to Barrett esophagus and fewer than 0.1% to adenocarcinoma.

[14]Norman R. Barrett (1903–79), British surgeon

The wall of the esophagus is organized into the tissue layers described earlier, with some regional specializations. The mucosa has a nonkeratinized stratified squamous epithelium. The submucosa contains **esophageal glands,** which secrete lubricating mucus into the lumen. When the esophagus is empty, the mucosa and submucosa are deeply folded into longitudinal ridges, giving the lumen a starlike shape in cross section.

The muscularis externa is composed of skeletal muscle in the upper one-third of the esophagus, a mixture of skeletal and smooth muscle in the middle one-third, and only smooth muscle in the lower one-third. This transition corresponds to a shift from voluntary to involuntary phases of swallowing as food passes down the esophagus.

Most of the esophagus is in the mediastinum. Here, it is covered with a connective tissue adventitia that merges into the adventitias of the trachea and thoracic aorta. The short segment below the diaphragm is covered by a serosa.

Swallowing, or *deglutition* (DEE-glu-TISH-un), is a complex action involving over 22 muscles in the mouth, pharynx, and esophagus, coordinated by the **swallowing center,** a pair of nuclei in the medulla oblongata. This center communicates with muscles of the pharynx and esophagus by way of the trigeminal, facial, glossopharyngeal, and hypoglossal nerves (cranial nerves V, VII, IX, and XII), and coordinates a complex series of muscle contractions to produce swallowing without choking.

## Before You Go On

Answer the following questions to test your understanding of the preceding section:

6. List as many functions of the tongue as you can.

7. Name the four types of teeth in order from the midline to the rear of the jaw. How do they differ in function?

8. What is the difference in function and location between intrinsic and extrinsic salivary glands? Name the extrinsic salivary glands and describe their locations.

9. The upper and lower esophageal sphincters cannot be found in the cadaver. Why not? What forms these sphincters, and what purpose does each one serve?

# The Stomach

### Objectives

When you have completed this section, you should be able to

- describe the gross and microscopic anatomy of the stomach;
- describe the nerve and blood supply to the stomach;
- state the function of each type of epithelial cell in the gastric mucosa; and
- explain how the stomach is protected from digesting itself.

The stomach is a muscular sac in the upper left abdominal cavity immediately inferior to the diaphragm (see fig. 24.1). It functions primarily as a food storage organ, with an internal volume of about 50 mL when empty and 1.0 to 1.5 L after a typical meal. When extremely full, it may hold up to 4 L and extend nearly as far as the pelvis. The stomach mechanically breaks up food particles, liquefies the food, and begins the chemical digestion of proteins and a small amount of fat. This produces a soupy or pasty mixture of semidigested food called **chyme**[15] (pronounced "kime"). Most digestion occurs after the chyme passes on to the small intestine.

## Gross Anatomy

The stomach is somewhat J-shaped (fig. 24.11) and vertical in tall people, whereas in short people it is more nearly horizontal. The **lesser curvature** of the stomach extends the short distance (about 10 cm) from esophagus to duodenum along the medial to superior aspect, facing the liver, and the **greater curvature** extends the longer distance (about 40 cm) from esophagus to duodenum on the lateral to inferior aspect. As described earlier, the lesser omentum extends from the lesser curvature to the liver, and the greater omentum is suspended from the greater curvature and overhangs the intestines below.

The stomach is divided into four regions: (1) The **cardiac region (cardia)** is the small area within about 3 cm of the cardiac orifice. (2) The **fundic region (fundus)** is the dome-shaped portion superior to the esophageal attachment. (3) The **body (corpus)** makes up the greatest part of the stomach distal to the cardiac orifice. (4) The **pyloric region** is a slightly narrower pouch at the distal end; it is subdivided into a funnel-like **antrum**[16] and a narrower **pyloric canal.** The latter terminates at the **pylorus,**[17] a narrow passage into the duodenum. The pylorus is surrounded by a thick ring of smooth muscle, the **pyloric (gastroduodenal) sphincter,** which regulates the passage of chyme into the duodenum.

## Microscopic Anatomy

The stomach wall has tissue layers similar to those of the esophagus, with some variations. The surface of the mucosa is a simple columnar glandular epithelium (fig. 24.12). The apical regions of its surface cells are filled with mucin. After it is secreted, mucin swells with water and becomes mucus. When the stomach is full, the mucosa and submucosa are flat and smooth, but as it empties, these layers fold into longitudinal wrinkles called **gastric rugae**[18] (ROO-gee). The lamina propria is almost entirely occupied by tubular glands, to be described shortly. The muscularis externa has three layers, rather than two—an outer longitudinal, middle circular, and inner oblique layer (see fig. 24.11a).

> ### THINK ABOUT IT
> *Contrast the epithelium of the esophagus with that of the stomach. Why is each epithelial type best suited to the function of its respective organ?*

[15]*chyme* = juice
[16]*antrum* = cavity
[17]*pylorus* = gatekeeper
[18]*ruga* = fold, crease

The gastric mucosa is pocked with depressions called **gastric pits** lined with the same columnar epithelium as the mucosal surface. Two or three tubular glands open into the bottom of each gastric pit and span the rest of the lamina propria. The glands are simple wavy or coiled tubes of more or less uniform diameter, except for a constriction called the **neck** at the point where the gland opens into the pit. In the cardiac and pyloric regions, they are called **cardiac glands** and **pyloric glands,** respectively. In the rest of the stomach, they are called **gastric glands** (fig. 24.12b, c). Collectively, the glands have the following cell types:

- **Mucous cells,** which secrete mucus, predominate in the cardiac and pyloric glands. In gastric glands, they are called *mucous neck cells* and are concentrated in the neck of the gland.

- **Regenerative (stem) cells,** found in the base of the pit and neck of the gland, divide rapidly and produce a continual supply of new cells. Newly generated cells migrate upward to the gastric surface as well as downward into the glands to replace cells that die and fall off into the lumen of the stomach.

- **Parietal cells,** found mostly in the upper half of the gland, secrete hydrochloric acid (HCl) and intrinsic factor. They are found mostly in the gastric glands, but a few occur in the pyloric glands.

- **Chief cells,** so named because they are the most numerous, secrete chymosin (formerly called rennin) and lipase in infancy and pepsinogen throughout life. They dominate the lower half of the gastric glands but are absent from cardiac and pyloric glands.

- **Enteroendocrine cells,** concentrated especially in the lower end of a gland, secrete hormones and paracrine messengers that regulate digestion. They are found in all regions of the stomach, but are most numerous in the gastric and pyloric glands. There are at least eight different kinds in the stomach, each of which produces a different chemical messenger. **G cells,** for example, secrete a hormone called *gastrin,* which stimulates the exocrine cells of the gastric glands to secrete acid and enzymes.

In general, the cardiac and pyloric glands secrete mainly mucus; acid and enzyme secretion occur predominantly in the gastric glands; and hormones are secreted throughout the stomach. Table 24.1 describes the functions of the gastric gland secretions.

It may seem that the stomach would digest itself; we can, after all, digest tripe (animal stomachs) as readily as any other meat. The living stomach, however, is protected from self-digestion in three ways:

1. **Mucous coat.** A thick, highly alkaline mucus resists the action of acid and enzymes.

2. **Tight junctions.** The epithelial cells are joined by tight junctions that prevent gastric juice from seeping between them and digesting the connective tissue of the lamina propria or beyond.

3. **Epithelial cell replacement.** In spite of these other protections, the stomach's epithelial cells live only 3 to 6 days and are then sloughed off into the chyme and digested with the food. They are replaced just as rapidly, however, by the division of stem cells in the gastric pits.

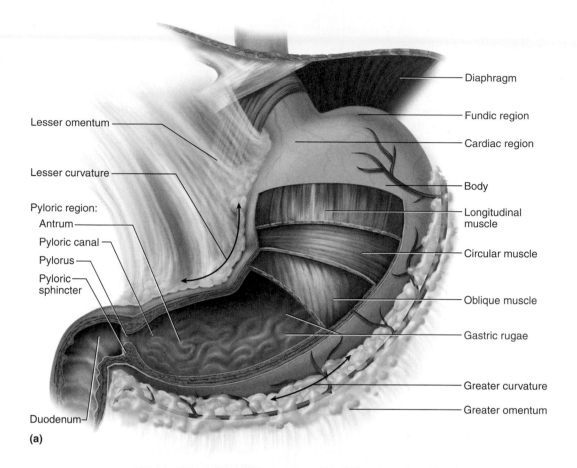

Lesser omentum

Lesser curvature

Pyloric region:
Antrum
Pyloric canal
Pylorus
Pyloric sphincter

Duodenum

**(a)**

Diaphragm

Fundic region

Cardiac region

Body

Longitudinal muscle

Circular muscle

Oblique muscle

Gastric rugae

Greater curvature

Greater omentum

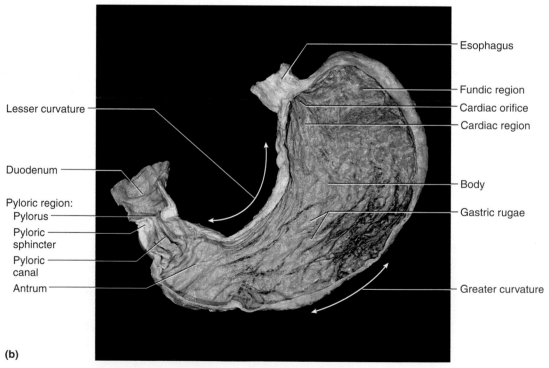

Lesser curvature

Duodenum

Pyloric region:
Pylorus
Pyloric sphincter
Pyloric canal
Antrum

**(b)**

Esophagus

Fundic region
Cardiac orifice
Cardiac region

Body

Gastric rugae

Greater curvature

**Figure 24.11** **The Stomach.** (a) Gross anatomy. (b) Photograph of the internal surface.
● *How does the muscular wall of the stomach differ from that of the esophagus?*

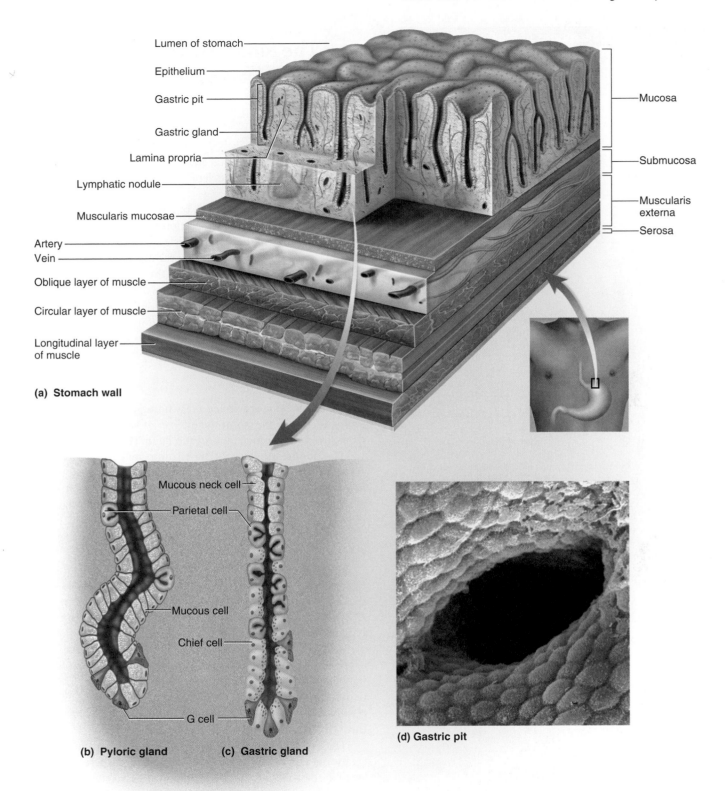

Lumen of stomach

Epithelium

Gastric pit

Gastric gland

Lamina propria

Lymphatic nodule

Muscularis mucosae

Artery

Vein

Oblique layer of muscle

Circular layer of muscle

Longitudinal layer of muscle

**(a) Stomach wall**

Mucosa

Submucosa

Muscularis externa

Serosa

Mucous neck cell

Parietal cell

Mucous cell

Chief cell

G cell

**(b) Pyloric gland**

**(c) Gastric gland**

**(d) Gastric pit**

**Figure 24.12** **Microscopic Anatomy of the Stomach Wall.** (a) A block of tissue showing all layers from the mucosa (top) to the serosa (bottom). (b) A pyloric gland from the inferior end of the stomach. Note the absence of chief cells and relatively few parietal cells. (c) A gastric gland, the most widespread type in the stomach. (d) The opening of a gastric pit into the stomach, surrounded by the rounded apical surfaces of the columnar epithelial cells of the mucosa (SEM).

| TABLE 24.1 | Major Secretions of the Gastric Glands | |
|---|---|---|
| **Secretory Cells** | **Secretion** | **Function** |
| Mucous neck cells | Mucus | Protects mucosa from HCl and enzymes |
| Parietal cells | Hydrochloric acid | Activates pepsin and lingual lipase; helps liquefy food; reduces dietary iron to usable form ($Fe^{2+}$); destroys ingested pathogens |
| | Intrinsic factor | Enables small intestine to absorb vitamin $B_{12}$ |
| Chief cells | Pepsinogen | Converted to pepsin, which digests protein |
| | Chymosin | Coagulates milk proteins in infant stomach; not secreted in adults |
| | Gastric lipase | Digests fats in infant stomach; not secreted in adults |
| Enteroendocrine cells | Gastrin | Stimulates gastric glands to secrete HCl and enzymes; stimulates intestinal motility; relaxes ileocecal valve |
| | Serotonin | Stimulates gastric motility |
| | Histamine | Stimulates HCl secretion |
| | Somatostatin | Inhibits gastric secretion and motility; delays emptying of stomach; inhibits secretion by pancreas; inhibits gallbladder contraction and bile secretion; reduces blood circulation and nutrient absorption in small intestine |

The breakdown of these protective mechanisms can result in inflammation and peptic ulcer (see Insight 24.3).

## *Before You Go On*

*Answer the following questions to test your understanding of the preceding section:*

10. Distinguish between the cardiac region, fundic region, body, and pyloric region of the stomach.

11. Name the cell types in the gastric and pyloric glands and state what each one secretes.

12. Explain why the stomach does not digest itself.

# The Small Intestine

## *Objectives*

When you have completed this section, you should be able to

• describe the gross and microscopic anatomy of the small intestine; and

• describe the structural adaptations of the small intestine for digestion and nutrient absorption.

The stomach "spits" about 3 mL of chyme at a time into the small intestine. Nearly all chemical digestion and nutrient absorption occur here. To perform these roles efficiently, the small intestine must have a large surface area exposed to the chyme. This surface area is imparted to it by extensive folding of the mucosa, and by the great length of the small intestine. It measures about 2.7 to 4.5 m long in a living person, but in the cadaver, where there is no muscle tone, it is 4 to 8 m long. The expression *small* intestine refers not to its length but to its diameter—about 2.5 cm (1 in.).

## Gross Anatomy

The small intestine is a coiled mass filling most of the abdominal cavity inferior to the stomach and liver. It is divided into three regions: the duodenum, jejunum, and ileum (fig. 24.14).

The **duodenum** (dew-ODD-eh-num or DEW-oh-DEE-num) constitutes the first 25 cm (10 in.). It begins at the pyloric sphincter, arcs around the head of the pancreas and passes to the left, and ends at a sharp bend called the **duodenojejunal flexure.** Its name refers to its length, about equal to the width of 12 fingers.[19] The first 2 cm of the duodenum is intraperitoneal, but the rest is retroperitoneal, along with the pancreas.

Internally, the duodenum exhibits transverse to spiral ridges, up to 10 mm high, called **circular folds (plicae circulares)** (see fig. 24.20). They cause the chyme to flow on a spiral path along the mucosa, slowing its progress, causing more contact with the mucosa, and promoting thorough mixing, digestion, and nutrient absorption.

Adjacent to the head of the pancreas, the duodenal wall has a prominent wrinkle called the **major duodenal papilla** where the bile and pancreatic ducts open into the intestine. This papilla marks the boundary between the foregut and midgut. In most people, there is a smaller **minor duodenal papilla** a little proximal to this, which receives an *accessory pancreatic duct.*

The duodenum receives and mixes the stomach contents, pancreatic juice, and bile. Stomach acid is neutralized here by bicarbonate in the pancreatic juice, fats are physically broken up (emulsified) by the bile, pepsin is inactivated by the rise in pH, and pancreatic enzymes take over the job of chemical digestion.

The **jejunum** (jeh-JOO-num) is the next 2.5 m (8 ft), or by definition, the first 40% of the small intestine beyond the duodenum. Its name refers to the fact that early anatomists typically found it to

---

[19]*duoden* = 12

# INSIGHT 24.3

## Clinical Application

### Peptic Ulcer

Inflammation of the stomach, called *gastritis,* can lead to a *peptic ulcer* as pepsin and hydrochloric acid erode the stomach wall (fig. 24.13). Peptic ulcers occur even more commonly in the duodenum and occasionally in the esophagus. If untreated, they can perforate the organ and cause fatal hemorrhaging or peritonitis. Most such fatalities occur in people over age 65.

There is no evidence to support the popular belief that peptic ulcers result from psychological stress. Hypersecretion of acid and pepsin is sometimes involved, but even normal secretion can cause ulceration if the mucosal defense is compromised by other causes. Many or most ulcers involve an acid-resistant bacterium, *Helicobacter pylori,* that invades the mucosa of the stomach and duodenum and opens the way to chemi-cal damage to the tissue. Other risk factors include smoking and the use of aspirin and other nonsteroidal anti-inflammatory drugs (NSAIDs). NSAIDs suppress the synthesis of prostaglandins, which normally stimulate the secretion of protective mucus and acid-neutralizing bicarbonate. Aspirin itself is an acid that directly irritates the gastric mucosa.

Until recently, the most widely prescribed drug in the United States was Cimetidine (Tagamet), which was designed to treat peptic ulcers by reducing acid secretion. Histamine stimulates acid secretion by binding to sites on the parietal cells called $H_2$ receptors; Cimetidine, an $H_2$ blocker, prevents this binding. Lately, however, ulcers have been treated more successfully with antibiotics against *Helicobacter* combined with bismuth suspensions such as Pepto-Bismol. This is a much shorter and less expensive course of treatment and permanently cures about 90% of peptic ulcers, as compared with a cure rate of only 20% to 30% for $H_2$ blockers.

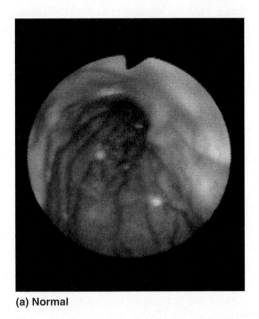

**(a) Normal**

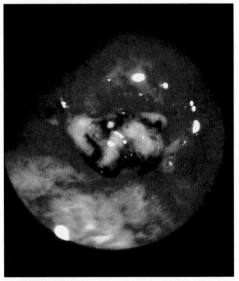

**(b) Peptic ulcer**

**Figure 24.13 Endoscopic Views of the Gastroesophageal Junction.** The esophagus can be seen opening into the cardiac stomach. (a) A view of the cardiac orifice from above, showing a healthy esophageal mucosa. The small white spots are reflections of light from the endoscope. (b) A bleeding peptic ulcer. A peptic ulcer typically has an oval shape and yellow-white color. Here the yellowish floor of the ulcer is partially obscured by black blood clots, and fresh blood is visible around the margin.

be empty.[20] The jejunum begins in the upper left quadrant of the abdomen but lies mostly within the umbilical region (see fig. A.6, p. 27). It has large, tall, closely spaced circular folds. Most digestion and nutrient absorption occur here. Its wall is relatively thick and muscular, and it has an especially rich blood supply that gives it a relatively red color.

The **ileum**[21] forms the last 3.6 m (12 ft), or 60% of the postduodenal small intestine. (The lengths given here are for the cadaver.) The ileum occupies mainly the hypogastric region and part of the pelvic cavity. Compared to the jejunum, its wall is thinner, less muscular, and less vascular, and it has a paler pink color. Its circular folds are smaller and more sparse, and are lacking from the distal end. On the side opposite from its mesenteric attachment, the ileum has prominent lymphatic nodules in clusters called **Peyer**[22] **patches,** which are readily visible to the naked eye and become progressively larger approaching the large intestine.

The end of the small intestine is the **ileocecal** (ILL-ee-oh-SEE-cul) **junction,** where the ileum joins the *cecum* of the large intestine. The muscularis of the ileum is thickened at this point to form

---

[20]*jejun* = empty, dry
[21]from *eilos* = twisted

[22]Johann K. Peyer (1653–1712), Swiss anatomist

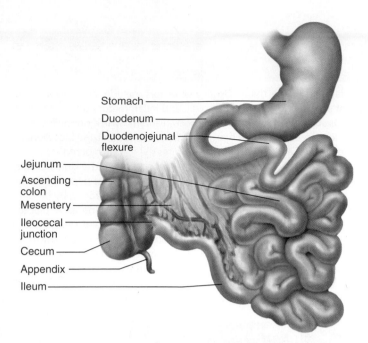

Stomach
Duodenum
Duodenojejunal flexure
Jejunum
Ascending colon
Mesentery
Ileocecal junction
Cecum
Appendix
Ileum

**Figure 24.14 Gross Anatomy of the Small Intestine.** The intestine is pulled aside to expose the mesentery and ileocecal junction.

a sphincter, the **ileocecal** (ILL-ee-oh-SEE-cul) **valve,** which protrudes into the cecum and regulates the passage of food residue into the large intestine. Both the jejunum and ileum are intraperitoneal and thus covered with a serosa, which is continuous with the complex, folded mesentery that suspends the small intestine from the dorsal abdominal wall.

## Microscopic Anatomy

The tissue layers of the small intestine are reminiscent of those in the esophagus and stomach with modifications appropriate for nutrient digestion and absorption. The lumen is lined with simple columnar epithelium. The muscularis externa is notable for a thick inner circular layer and a thinner outer longitudinal layer.

Effective digestion and nutrient absorption require that the small intestine have a large internal surface area. This is provided by its relatively great length and by three kinds of internal folds or projections: the circular folds, villi, and microvilli. If the mucosa of the small intestine were smooth, like the inside of a hose, it would have a surface area of about 0.3 to 0.5 m$^2$, but with these surface elaborations, its actual surface area is about 200 m$^2$—clearly a great advantage for nutrient absorption. The circular folds increase the surface area by a factor of 2 to 3; the villi by a factor of 10; and the microvilli by a factor of 20.

The largest of these elaborations, the circular folds, were described earlier. They occur from the duodenum to the middle of the ileum. They involve only the mucosa and submucosa; they are not visible on the external surface, which is smooth.

If the mucosa is examined more closely, it appears fuzzy, like a terrycloth towel. This is due to the **villi** (VIL-eye; singular, *villus*), tongue- to finger-shaped projections about 0.5 to 1.0 mm high (fig. 24.15). The villi are largest in the duodenum and become

progressively smaller in more distal regions of the small intestine. A villus is covered with two kinds of epithelial cells—columnar **absorptive cells** and mucus-secreting goblet cells. Like epithelial cells of the stomach, those of the small intestine are joined by tight junctions that prevent digestive enzymes from seeping between them.

The core of a villus is filled with areolar tissue of the lamina propria. Embedded in this tissue are an arteriole, a bed of blood capillaries, a venule, and a lymphatic capillary called a **lacteal** (LAC-tee-ul) (fig. 24.15c). Blood capillaries of the villus absorb most nutrients, but the lacteal absorbs most dietary lipid. The reason for this difference is that when lipids pass through the intestinal absorptive cells, the Golgi complex packages them into protein- and phospholipid-coated droplets called *chylomicrons,* then releases them from the base of the epithelium into the core of the villus. Chylomicrons are too large (60 to 750 nm) to pass into the bloodstream through the blood capillary walls, but they can pass through the larger gaps between the cells of lymphatic capillaries and thus enter the lymph. The lymphatic system, of course, eventually delivers the chylomicrons to the bloodstream. The fatty lymph in the lacteal is called *chyle.* It has a milky appearance for which the lacteal is named.[23] The core of the villus also has a few smooth muscle cells that contract periodically. This enhances mixing of the chyme in the intestinal lumen and milks lymph down the lacteal to the larger lymphatic vessels of the submucosa.

### THINK ABOUT IT

*Identify the exact place in the body where chylomicrons enter the blood. (Hint: see chapter 22.)*

Each absorptive cell of a villus has a fuzzy brush border of microvilli about 1 μm high. The brush border not only increases the absorptive surface area of the intestinal cells, but also contains *brush border enzymes,* proteins of the plasma membrane. One of these, *enterokinase,* activates pancreatic enzymes. Others carry out some of the final stages in the enzymatic digestion of small carbohydrates and peptides. These enzymes are not released into the lumen; instead, the chyme must contact the brush border for digestion to occur. This process, called *contact digestion,* is one reason that thorough mixing of the chyme is so important.

On the floor of the small intestine, between the bases of the villi, there are numerous pores that open into tubular glands called **intestinal crypts** (**crypts of Lieberkühn;**[24] LEE-ber-koohn). These crypts, similar to the gastric glands, extend as far as the muscularis mucosae. In the upper half, they consist of absorptive and goblet cells like those of the villi. The lower half is dominated by dividing epithelial cells. In its life span of 3 to 6 days, an epithelial cell migrates up the crypt to the tip of the villus, where it is sloughed off and digested. Also seen deep in the crypts are enteroendocrine cells and **Paneth**[25] **cells.** Paneth cells secrete the antimicrobial enzyme *lysozyme* and other defensive proteins that resist bacterial invasion of the mucosa.

[23]*lact* = milk
[24]Johann N. Lieberkühn (1711–56), German anatomist
[25]Josef Paneth (1857–90), Austrian physician

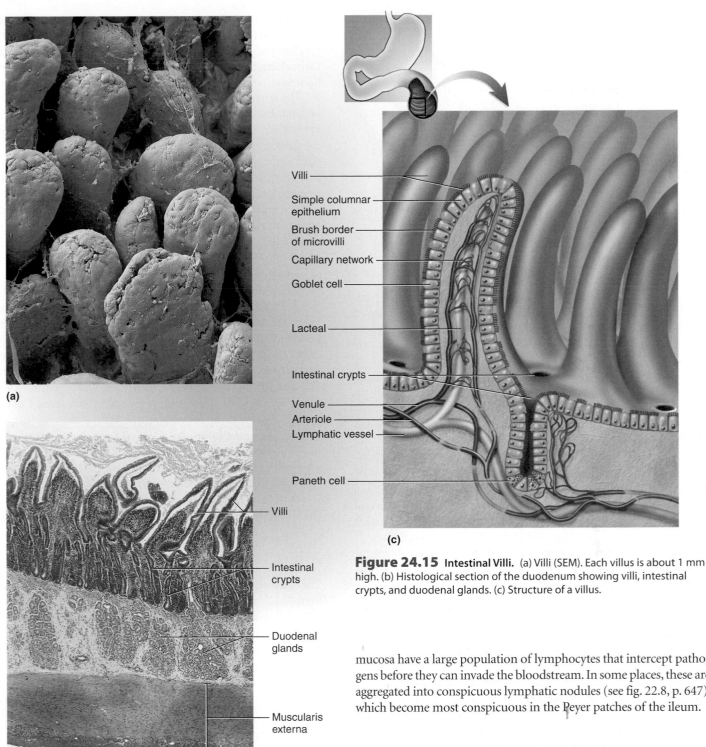

(a)

(b)

0.5 mm

Villi

Intestinal
crypts

Duodenal
glands

Muscularis
externa

Serosa

Villi

Simple columnar
epithelium

Brush border
of microvilli

Capillary network

Goblet cell

Lacteal

Intestinal crypts

Venule

Arteriole

Lymphatic vessel

Paneth cell

(c)

**Figure 24.15**  **Intestinal Villi.**  (a) Villi (SEM). Each villus is about 1 mm high. (b) Histological section of the duodenum showing villi, intestinal crypts, and duodenal glands. (c) Structure of a villus.

mucosa have a large population of lymphocytes that intercept pathogens before they can invade the bloodstream. In some places, these are aggregated into conspicuous lymphatic nodules (see fig. 22.8, p. 647), which become most conspicuous in the Peyer patches of the ileum.

## *Before You Go On*

*Answer the following questions to test your understanding of the preceding section:*

13. Name the three regions of the small intestine and describe the distinctive features of each one.

14. Name the sphincters at the beginning and end of the small intestine.

15. What three structures increase the absorptive surface area of the small intestine?

16. Sketch a villus and label its epithelium, brush border, lamina propria, blood capillaries, and lacteal.

The duodenum has prominent **duodenal (Brunner[26]) glands** in the submucosa. They secrete an abundance of alkaline mucus, which neutralizes stomach acid and shields the mucosa from its corrosive effects. Throughout the small intestine, the lamina propria and sub-

[26]Johann C. Brunner (1653–1727), Swiss anatomist

# The Large Intestine

### Objectives
When you have completed this section, you should be able to

- describe the gross and microscopic anatomy of the large intestine; and
- contrast the mucosa of the colon with that of the small intestine.

The large intestine (fig. 24.16) receives about 500 mL of indigestible food residue per day, reduces it to about 150 mL of feces by absorbing water and salts, and eliminates the feces by defecation.

## Gross Anatomy

The large intestine measures about 1.5 m (5 ft) long and 6.5 cm (2.5 in.) in diameter in the cadaver. It begins with the **cecum,**[27] a pouch in the lower right abdominal quadrant inferior to the ileocecal valve. Attached to the lower end of the cecum is the **appendix,** a blind tube 2 to 7 cm long. The mucosa of the appendix is densely populated with lymphocytes and is a significant source of immune cells. Herbivorous primates such as gorillas and orangutans have an enormous cecum, packed with bacteria that digest the plant fiber in their coarse diet. Humans, with more mixed and easily digested diet, have only the appendix as a vestige of the larger cecum.

The **colon** is that portion of the large intestine between the ileocecal junction and the rectum (not including the cecum, rectum, or anal canal). It is divided into the ascending, transverse, descending, and sigmoid regions. The **ascending colon** begins at the ileocecal valve and passes up the right side of the abdominal cavity. It makes a 90° turn at the **right colic (hepatic) flexure,** near the right lobe of the liver, and becomes the **transverse colon.** This passes horizontally across the upper abdominal cavity and turns 90° downward at the **left colic (splenic) flexure** near the spleen. Here it becomes the **descending colon,** which passes down the left side of the abdominal cavity. Ascending, transverse, and descending colons thus form a squarish, three-sided frame around the small intestine.

The pelvic cavity is narrower than the abdominal cavity, so at the pelvic inlet the colon turns medially and downward, forming a roughly S-shaped portion called the **sigmoid**[28] **colon.** (Visual examination of this region is performed with an instrument called a *sigmoidoscope.*) In the pelvic cavity, the large intestine continues as the **rectum,**[29] about 15 cm long. In spite of its name, the rectum is not straight but has three lateral curves as well as a dorsoventral curve. The rectal mucosa is smoother than that of the colon. It has three internal **transverse rectal folds (rectal valves)** that enable it to retain feces while passing gas. The large intestine contains about 7 to 10 L of gas per day, expelling about 500 mL/day anally as *flatus* and reabsorbing the rest through the colonic wall.

The final 3 cm of the large intestine is the **anal canal** (fig. 24.16b), which passes through the levator ani muscle of the pelvic floor and terminates at the anus. The mucosa of the anal canal forms longitudinal ridges called **anal columns** with depressions between them called **anal sinuses.** As feces pass through the canal, they press against the sinuses and cause them to exude extra mucus, which lubricates the canal during defecation. Large **hemorrhoidal veins** form superficial plexuses in the anal columns and around the orifice. Unlike veins in the limbs, they lack valves and are particularly subject to distension and venous pooling. *Hemorrhoids* are permanently distended veins that protrude into the anal canal or form bulges external to the anus.

The muscularis externa of the colon is unusual. Although it completely encircles the colon just as it does the small intestine, its longitudinal fibers are especially concentrated in three thickened, ribbonlike strips called the **taeniae coli** (TEE-nee-ee CO-lye). The muscle tone of the taeniae coli contracts the colon lengthwise and causes its wall to bulge, forming pouches called **haustra**[30] (HAW-stra; singular, *haustrum*). In the rectum and anal canal, however, the longitudinal muscle forms a continuous sheet and haustra are absent. The anus is normally held shut by two muscular rings—an **internal anal sphincter** composed of smooth muscle of the muscularis externa, and an **external anal sphincter** composed of skeletal muscle of the pelvic diaphragm. The internal anal sphincter is under involuntary control and relaxes automatically when the rectum is distended with feces. The external anal sphincter is under voluntary control and enables one to postpone defecation when appropriate.

The ascending and descending colon are retroperitoneal, whereas the transverse and sigmoid colon are covered with serosa and anchored to the dorsal abdominal wall by the mesocolon. The serosa of these regions often has **epiploic**[31] **(omental) appendages,** clublike fatty pouches of peritoneum of unknown function.

## Microscopic Anatomy

The mucosa of the large intestine has a simple columnar epithelium in all regions except the lower half of the anal canal, where it has a nonkeratinized stratified squamous epithelium. The latter provides more resistance to the abrasion caused by the passage of feces. There are no circular folds or villi in the large intestine, but there are intestinal crypts. They are deeper than in the small intestine and have a greater density of goblet cells; mucus is their only significant secretion. The lamina propria and submucosa have an abundance of lymphatic tissue, providing protection from the bacteria that densely populate the large intestine.

The mucosa of the ascending and transverse colon is specialized for fluid and electrolyte absorption. During the process of digestion, a great deal of water is secreted by the salivary glands, stomach, and small intestine. Almost all of this is reabsorbed by the large intestine. When absorption is hindered, as in some bacterial infections, the result is diarrhea—an increase in the liquid eliminated with the feces. Severe diarrhea can lead to serious and sometimes fatal dehydration and electrolyte imbalances.

---

[27]*cec* = blind
[28]*sigm* = sigma or S + *oid* = resembling
[29]*rect* = straight

[30]*haustr* = to draw
[31]*epiploic* = pertaining to an omentum

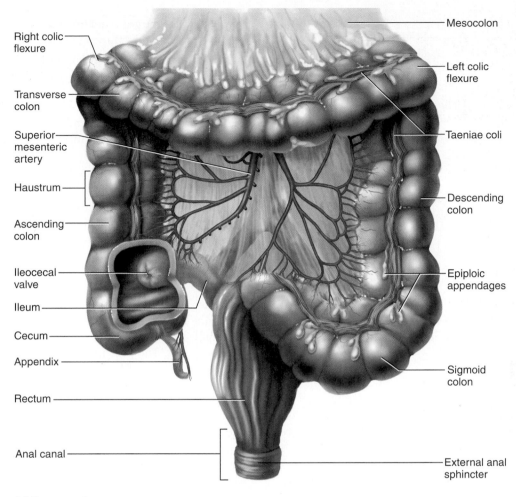

Right colic flexure

Transverse colon

Superior mesenteric artery

Haustrum

Ascending colon

Ileocecal valve

Ileum

Cecum

Appendix

Rectum

Anal canal

Mesocolon

Left colic flexure

Taeniae coli

Descending colon

Epiploic appendages

Sigmoid colon

External anal sphincter

**(a) Gross anatomy**

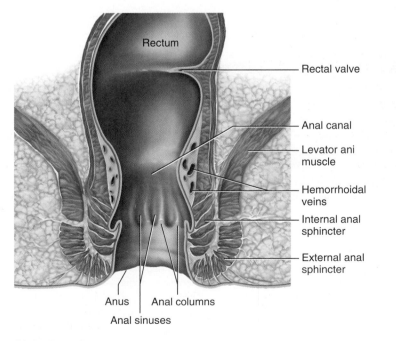

Rectum

Rectal valve

Anal canal

Levator ani muscle

Hemorrhoidal veins

Internal anal sphincter

External anal sphincter

Anus

Anal columns

Anal sinuses

**(b) Anal canal**

**Figure 24.16** The Large Intestine.

• *Which anal sphincter is controlled by the autonomic nervous system? Which is controlled by the somatic nervous system? Explain the basis for your answers.*

## Before You Go On

*Answer the following questions to test your understanding of the preceding section:*

17. Name the regions of the large intestine in order from cecum to anus.

18. How does the mucosa of the large intestine differ from that of the small intestine? How does the muscularis externa differ?

19. How do the two anal sphincters differ in location, tissue composition, and function?

# Accessory Glands of Digestion

### Objectives

When you have completed this section, you should be able to

- describe the gross and microscopic anatomy of the liver, gallbladder, and bile duct system;

- describe the functions of the liver and bile;

- describe the gross and microscopic anatomy of the pancreas; and

- list the digestive secretions of the pancreas and their functions.

The small intestine receives not only chyme from the stomach but also secretions from the liver and pancreas, which enter the digestive tract near the junction of the stomach and small intestine.

## The Liver

The liver (fig. 24.17) is a reddish brown gland located immediately inferior to the diaphragm, filling most of the right hypochondriac and epigastric regions. It is the body's largest gland, weighing about 1.4 kg (3 lb). The liver has numerous functions (table 24.2). From their variety and importance, it is not hard to understand why such liver diseases as cirrhosis, hepatitis, and liver cancer are so serious and often fatal. Only one of these functions contributes to digestion—the secretion of bile. **Bile** is a yellow-green fluid containing minerals, cholesterol, neutral fats, phospholipids, bile pigments, and bile acids. The principal pigment is *bilirubin,* derived from the decomposition of hemoglobin. Bacteria of the large intestine metabolize bilirubin to *urobilinogen,* which is responsible for the brown color of feces. In the absence of bile secretion, the feces are grayish white and marked with streaks of undigested fat *(acholic feces). Bile acids (bile salts)* are steroids synthesized from cholesterol. Bile acids and *lecithin,* a phospholipid, emulsify fat—breaking globules of dietary fat into smaller droplets with more surface area exposed to enzyme action. Emulsification greatly enhances the efficiency of fat digestion.

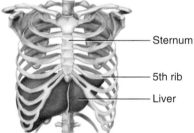

**(a) Location**

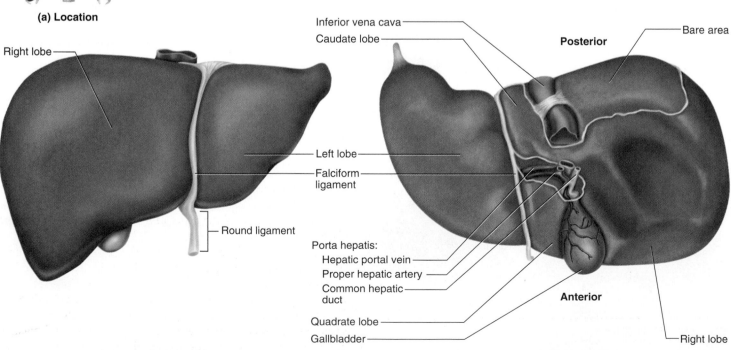

**(b) Anterior view**

**(c) Inferior view**

**Figure 24.17** Gross Anatomy of the Liver.

| TABLE 24.2 | Functions of the Liver |
|---|---|
| **Digestion** | Synthesizes bile acids and lecithin, which emulsify fat and promote its digestion. |
| **Carbohydrate metabolism** | Converts dietary fructose and galactose to glucose. Stabilizes blood glucose concentration by storing excess glucose as glycogen (glycogenesis), releasing glucose from glycogen when needed (glycogenolysis), and synthesizing glucose from fats and amino acids (gluconeogenesis) when glucose demand exceeds glycogen reserves. Receives lactic acid generated by anaerobic fermentation in skeletal muscle and other tissues and converts it to pyruvic acid or glucose 6-phosphate for storage or energy-releasing metabolism. |
| **Lipid metabolism** | Degrades chylomicron remnants. Carries out most of the body's fat synthesis (lipogenesis) and synthesizes cholesterol and phospholipids. Produces very low-density lipoproteins (VLDLs) to transport lipids to adipose tissue and other tissues for storage or use, and stores fat in its own cells. Carries out most fatty acid oxidation. Produces protein shells of high-density lipoproteins (HDLs), which pick up excess cholesterol from other tissues and return it to the liver; liver excretes the excess cholesterol in bile. |
| **Protein and amino acid metabolism** | Metabolizes amino acids; removes their $-NH_2$ and converts the resulting ammonia to urea, the major nitrogenous waste in the urine. Synthesizes some amino acids. |
| **Vitamin and mineral metabolism** | Converts vitamin $D_3$ to calcidiol, a step in the synthesis of the hormone calcitriol; stores a 3- to 4-month supply of vitamin D. Stores a 10-month supply of vitamin A and enough vitamin $B_{12}$ to last one to several years. Stores iron in ferritin and releases it as needed. Excretes excess calcium by way of the bile. |
| **Synthesis of plasma proteins** | Synthesizes nearly all the proteins of blood plasma, including albumin, $\alpha$ and $\beta$ globulins, fibrinogen, prothrombin, and several other clotting factors. (Does not synthesize plasma enzymes, peptide hormones, or gamma globulins.) |
| **Disposal of drugs, toxins, and hormones** | Detoxifies alcohol, antibiotics, and many other drugs. Metabolizes bilirubin from RBC breakdown and excretes it as bile pigments. Deactivates thyroxine and steroid hormones and excretes them or converts them to a form more easily excreted by the kidneys. |
| **Phagocytosis** | Hepatic macrophages cleanse the blood of bacteria and other foreign matter. |

## Gross Anatomy

The liver is enclosed in a fibrous capsule and, external to this, most of it is covered by serosa. The serosa is absent from the *bare area* where its superior surface is attached to the diaphragm.

The liver is superficially subdivided into the right, left, quadrate, and caudate lobes. From an anterior view, we see only the large **right lobe** and smaller **left lobe.** They are separated from each other by the **falciform**[32] **ligament,** a sheet of mesentery that attaches the liver to the anterior abdominal wall. Superiorly, the falciform ligament forks into right and left **coronary**[33] **ligaments,** which suspend the liver from the diaphragm. The **round ligament (ligamentum teres),** visible anteriorly at the inferior end of the falciform, is a fibrous remnant of the umbilical vein, which carries blood from the umbilical cord to the liver of a fetus.

From the inferior view, we also see a squarish anterior **quadrate lobe** next to the gallbladder and a tail-like **caudate**[34] **lobe** posterior to that. An irregular opening between these lobes, the **porta hepatis,**[35] is a point of entry for the hepatic portal vein and hepatic arter-ies and a point of exit for the bile passages. All of these blood vessels and bile passages travel in the lesser omentum. The gallbladder adheres to a depression on the inferior surface of the liver between the right and quadrate lobes. The posterior aspect of the liver has a deep groove (sulcus) occupied by the inferior vena cava.

## Microscopic Anatomy

The interior of the liver is filled with an enormous number of tiny cylinders called **hepatic lobules,** about 2 mm long by 1 mm in diameter. A lobule consists of a **central vein** passing down its core, surrounded by radiating sheets of cuboidal cells called **hepatocytes** (fig. 24.18). Imagine spreading a book wide open until its front and back covers touch. The pages of the book would fan out around the spine somewhat like the plates of hepatocytes fan out from the central vein of a liver lobule.

Each plate of hepatocytes is an epithelium one or two cells thick. The spaces between the plates are blood-filled channels called **hepatic sinusoids.** The sinusoids are lined by a fenestrated epithelium that separates the hepatocytes from the blood cells. There is a space between the hepatocytes and endothelial cells, however, where the hepatocytes are in direct contact with the blood plasma and have abundant microvilli that enable them to rapidly absorb blood-borne substances. After a meal, as blood from the intestines

---

[32]*falci* = sickle + *form* = shape
[33]*coron* = crown + *ary* = like, resembling
[34]*caud* = tail
[35]*porta* = gateway, entrance + *hepatis* = of the liver

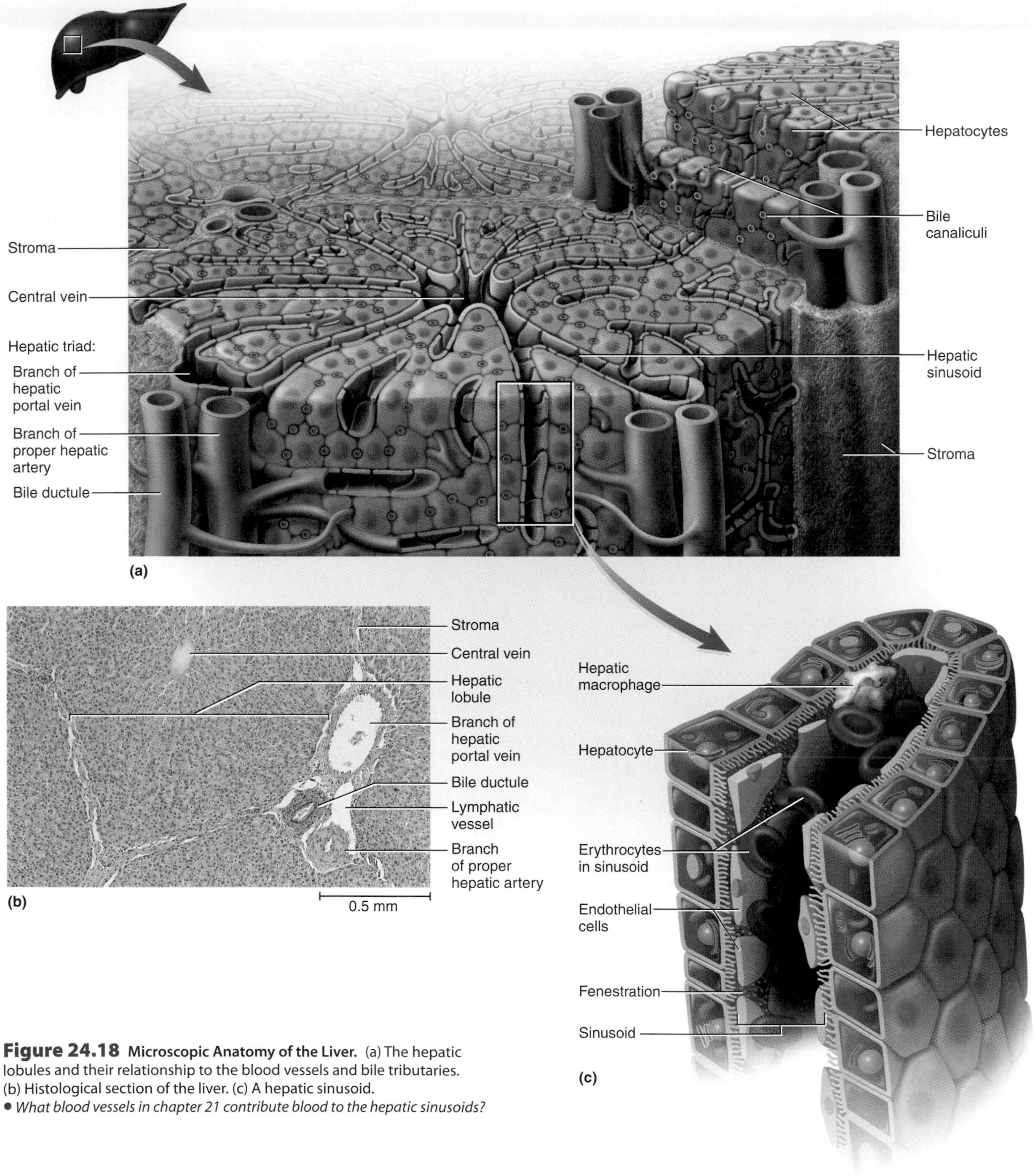

(a)

(b)

0.5 mm

(c)

Stroma

Central vein

Hepatic triad:

Branch of hepatic portal vein

Branch of proper hepatic artery

Bile ductule

Hepatocytes

Bile canaliculi

Hepatic sinusoid

Stroma

Stroma

Central vein

Hepatic lobule

Branch of hepatic portal vein

Bile ductule

Lymphatic vessel

Branch of proper hepatic artery

Hepatic macrophage

Hepatocyte

Erythrocytes in sinusoid

Endothelial cells

Fenestration

Sinusoid

**Figure 24.18** **Microscopic Anatomy of the Liver.** (a) The hepatic lobules and their relationship to the blood vessels and bile tributaries. (b) Histological section of the liver. (c) A hepatic sinusoid.

● *What blood vessels in chapter 21 contribute blood to the hepatic sinusoids?*

circulates through the hepatic sinusoids, the hepatocytes rapidly remove glucose, amino acids, iron, vitamins, and other nutrients for metabolism or storage. They also remove and degrade hormones, toxins, bile pigments, and drugs. Conversely, they secrete albumin, lipoproteins, clotting factors, glucose, and other products into the blood. The sinusoids also contain phagocytic cells called **hepatic macrophages** (**Kupffer**[36] **cells**), which remove bacteria and debris from the blood.

The hepatocytes secrete bile into narrow channels, the **bile canaliculi,** between the plates of the lobules. Bile passes from there into the small **bile ductules** between lobules. These ductules lead ultimately to the **right** and **left hepatic ducts,** which exit the inferior surface of the liver at the porta hepatis.

The hepatic lobules are separated by a sparse connective tissue stroma. In cross sections, the stroma is especially visible in the triangular areas where three or more lobules meet. Here, there is often a **hepatic triad** of two blood vessels and a bile ductule. The blood vessels are small branches of the hepatic arteries and hepatic portal vein.

---

[36]Karl W. von Kupffer (1829–1902), German anatomist

## Circulation

The liver receives blood from two sources: about 70% from the **hepatic portal vein** and 30% from the **hepatic arteries.** The hepatic portal vein delivers blood received from the stomach, intestines, pancreas, and spleen, and carries nutrients from the intestines to the liver. The hepatic arteries arise from the aorta (via the celiac trunk and common hepatic artery) and deliver oxygen to the liver. The arterial and venous bloodstreams mix in the hepatic sinusoids. After processing by the hepatocytes, the blood collects in the central vein at the core of the lobule. Blood from the central veins ultimately converges in the right and left **hepatic veins,** which exit the superior surface of the liver and empty into the nearby inferior vena cava.

## The Gallbladder and Bile Passages

Since the only digestive role of the liver is bile secretion, we will further trace the flow of bile through organs associated with the liver. The most conspicuous of these organs is the **gallbladder,** a pear-shaped sac on the underside of the liver that serves to store and concentrate the bile (fig. 24.19). It is about 10 cm long and internally lined by a highly folded mucosa with a simple columnar epithelium. Its head *(fundus)* usually projects slightly beyond the

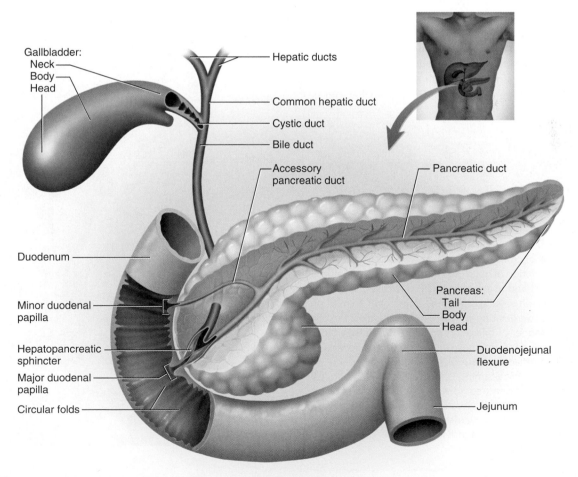

**Figure 24.19 Gross Anatomy of the Gallbladder, Pancreas, and Bile Passages.** The liver is omitted to show the gallbladder, which adheres to its inferior surface, and to show the hepatic ducts, which emerge from the liver tissue.

inferior margin of the liver. Its neck *(cervix)* leads into the **cystic duct,** through which bile enters and leaves the gallbladder.

When the two hepatic ducts leave the porta hepatis, they converge almost immediately to form the **common hepatic duct.** This duct goes only a short distance before joining the cystic duct. Their union forms the **bile duct,** which descends through the lesser omentum to the duodenum. The bile duct and main pancreatic duct both approach the major duodenal papilla. Usually, just before emptying into the duodenum, the two ducts join each other and form an expanded chamber called the **hepatopancreatic ampulla.** A muscular **hepatopancreatic sphincter (sphincter of Oddi[37])** regulates the release of bile and pancreatic juice from the ampulla into the duodenum.

## The Pancreas

Most digestion is carried out by pancreatic enzymes. The **pancreas** (fig. 24.19) is a spongy digestive gland posterior to the greater curvature of the stomach. It is about 15 cm long and divided into a globose *head* encircled on the right by the duodenum, a midportion called the *body,* and a blunt, tapered *tail* on the left near the spleen. It has a very thin connective tissue capsule and a nodular surface. It is retroperitoneal; its anterior surface is covered by parietal peritoneum, whereas its posterior surface contacts the aorta, left kidney, left adrenal gland, and other viscera on the posterior body wall.

The pancreas is both an endocrine and exocrine gland. Its endocrine part is the pancreatic islets, which secrete the hormones insulin and glucagon (see chapter 18, p. 539). Ninety-nine percent of the pancreas is exocrine tissue, which secretes enzymes and sodium bicarbonate. The exocrine pancreas is a compound tubuloacinar gland—that is, it has a system of branching ducts whose finest branches end in

sacs of secretory cells, the acini. The cells of the acini exhibit a high density of rough ER and *zymogen granules,* which are vesicles filled with secretion (fig. 24.20). The smaller ducts converge on a main **pancreatic duct,** which runs lengthwise through the middle of the gland and joins the bile duct at the hepatopancreatic ampulla. Usually, there is a smaller **accessory pancreatic duct** that branches from the main pancreatic duct and opens independently into the duodenum at the minor duodenal papilla, proximal to the major papilla. The accessory duct bypasses the hepatopancreatic sphincter and allows pancreatic juice to be released into the duodenum even when bile is not.

The pancreas secretes 1,200 to 1,500 mL of *pancreatic juice* per day. This fluid is an alkaline mixture of water, sodium bicarbonate, other electrolytes, enzymes, and zymogens (table 24.3). Zymogens are inactive precursors of enzymes that are activated after they are secreted.

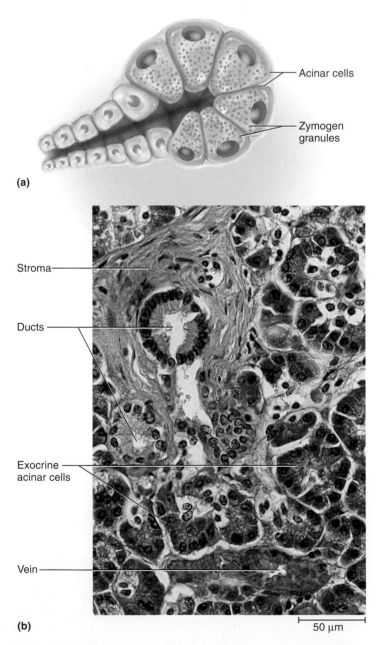

(a)

(b)                                    50 μm

**Figure 24.20** **Microscopic Anatomy of the Pancreas.** (a) An acinus. (b) Histological section of the exocrine tissue and some of the connective tissue stroma.

*Labels:* Acinar cells · Zymogen granules · Stroma · Ducts · Exocrine acinar cells · Vein

# INSIGHT 24.4

## Clinical Application

### Gallstones

*Gallstones (biliary calculi)* are hard masses in the gallbladder or bile ducts, usually composed of cholesterol, calcium carbonate, and bilirubin. *Cholelithiasis,* the formation of gallstones, is most common in obese women over the age of 40 and usually results from excess cholesterol. The gallbladder may contain several gallstones, some over 1 cm in diameter. Gallstones cause excruciating pain when they obstruct the bile ducts or when the gallbladder or bile ducts contract. When they block the flow of bile into the duodenum, they cause jaundice (yellowing of the skin due to bile pigment accumulation), poor fat digestion, and impaired absorption of fat-soluble vitamins. Once treated only by surgical removal, gallstones are now often treated with stone-dissolving drugs or by *lithotripsy,* the use of ultrasonic vibration to pulverize them without surgery. Reobstruction can be prevented by inserting a stent (tube) into the bile duct, which keeps it distended and allows gallstones to pass while they are still small.

[37]Ruggero Oddi (1864–1913), Italian physician

| TABLE 24.3 | Exocrine Secretions of the Pancreas |
|---|---|
| **Secretion** | **Function** |
| **Sodium bicarbonate** | Neutralizes HCl |
| **Zymogens** | Converted to active digestive enzymes after secretion |
| Trypsinogen | Becomes trypsin, which digests protein |
| Chymotrypsinogen | Becomes chymotrypsin, which digests protein |
| Procarboxypeptidase | Becomes carboxypeptidase, which hydrolyzes the terminal amino acid from the carboxyl (–COOH) end of small peptides |
| **Enzymes** | |
| Pancreatic amylase | Digests starch |
| Pancreatic lipase | Digests fat |
| Ribonuclease | Digests RNA |
| Deoxyribonuclease | Digests DNA |

## *Before You Go On*

*Answer the following questions to test your understanding of the preceding section:*

20. What does the liver contribute to digestion? List several of its non-digestive functions.

21. Describe the structure of a hepatic lobule and the blood flow through a lobule.

22. Describe the pathway that bile takes from a hepatocyte that secretes it to the point where it enters the duodenum.

23. Describe the pathway taken by pancreatic juice from a gland acinus to the duodenum.

24. Explain why the pancreas is considered to be both an endocrine and an exocrine gland. How does the pancreas contribute to digestion?

# Developmental and Clinical Perspectives

### *Objectives*
When you have completed this section, you should be able to

- describe the prenatal development of the digestive tract, liver, and pancreas;

- describe the structural and functional changes in the digestive system in old age; and

- define and describe some common disorders of the digestive system.

## Prenatal Development

The digestive system is one of the earliest organ systems to appear in the embryonic stage of development. Shortly after the three-layered embryonic disc is formed at 2 weeks, it elongates in the cephalocaudal (head-to-tail) direction. Endodermal pockets form at each end which become the foregut and hindgut (fig. 24.21a). Initially, there is a wide opening between the embryo and the yolk sac, but as the embryo continues to grow, the passage between them becomes constricted and a distinct tubular midgut appears. Temporarily, the midgut continues to communicate with the yolk sac through a narrow **vitelline duct.** In week 4, the anterior end of the digestive tract breaks through to form the mouth, and 3 weeks later, the posterior end breaks through to form the anus.

Growth of the embryonic body segments (*somites*) causes the lateral margins of the embryo to fold inward, changing the flat embryonic disc into a more cylindrical body and separating the embryonic body cavity from the yolk sac. By week 5, the gut is an elongated tube suspended from the body wall by the dorsal mesentery (fig. 24.21b). Although the inner epithelial lining of the gut is endoderm, the tube is covered by a layer of mesoderm that gives rise to all other tissue layers of the digestive tract: the lamina propria, submucosa, muscle layers, and serosa.

At 4 weeks, the foregut exhibits a dilation that is the first sign of the future stomach (fig. 24.22). Further development of the digestive tract entails elongation, rotation, and differentiation of its regions into the esophagus, stomach, and small and large intestines. At 6 weeks, the body cavity is crowded by the rapidly growing liver and the intestine is so long and crowded that a loop of it herniates into the umbilical cord. This loop normally withdraws back into the enlarged body cavity in week 10, but in some tragic cases it fails to do so, resulting in severely deformed infants with part of the bowel outside the body (*omphalocele*[38]).

The liver appears in the middle of week 3 as a **liver bud,** a pocketlike outgrowth of the endodermal tube at the junction of the foregut and midgut. Its connection to the gut narrows and becomes the bile duct. A small outgrowth from the ventral side of the bile duct becomes the gallbladder and cystic duct. By week 12, the liver secretes bile into the gut, so the gut contents become dark green. The liver produces blood cells throughout most of fetal development, but this function gradually subsides in the last 2 months.

The pancreas originates as two buds, a **dorsal** and **ventral pancreatic bud,** around week 4. The ventral bud eventually rotates dorsally and merges with the dorsal bud. Pancreatic islets appear in the third month and begin secreting insulin at 5 months.

At birth, the digestive tract contains dark, sticky feces called **meconium,** which is discharged in the first few bowel movements of the neonate.

## The Aging Digestive System

Like most other organ systems, the digestive system shows significant degenerative change (*senescence*) in old age. Less saliva is secreted in old age, making food less flavorful, swallowing more difficult, and

---

[38]*omphalo* = navel, umbilicus + *cele* = swelling, herniation

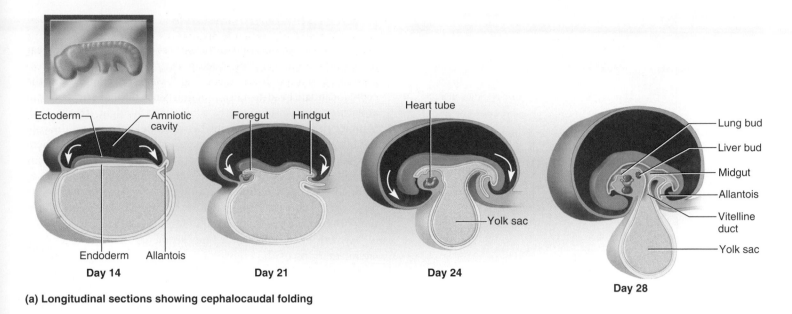

**(a) Longitudinal sections showing cephalocaudal folding**

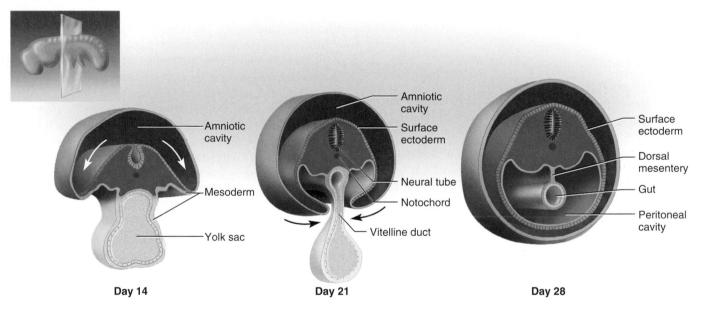

**(b) Cross sections showing lateral folding**

**Figure 24.21** **Embryonic Development of the Digestive Tract.** (a) Cephalocaudal (head-to-tail) folding from days 14 to 28 produces the foregut and hindgut. The connection between the midgut and yolk sac grows progressively narrower. (b) Lateral folding over the same time period encloses the tubular gut and reduces the yolk sac connection to a narrow vitelline duct. The 28-day embryo in (b) is sectioned a little farther caudally than the 28-day embryo in (a) to show a region of hindgut already fully enclosed within the peritoneal cavity.

the teeth more prone to caries. Nearly half of people over age 65 wear dentures because they have lost their teeth to caries and periodontal disease. The stratified squamous epithelium of the oral cavity and esophagus is thinner and more vulnerable to abrasion.

The gastric mucosa atrophies and secretes less acid and intrinsic factor. Acid deficiency reduces the absorption of calcium, iron, zinc, and folic acid. The declining level of intrinsic factor reduces the absorption of vitamin $B_{12}$. Since this vitamin is needed for hemopoiesis, the deficiency can lead to a form of anemia called *pernicious anemia.*

Heartburn becomes more common in old age as the weakening lower esophageal sphincter fails to prevent reflux into the esophagus. The most common digestive complaint of older people is constipation, which results from the reduced muscle tone and weaker peristalsis of the colon. This seems to stem from a combination of factors: atrophy of the muscularis externa, reduced sensitivity to neurotransmitters, less fiber and water in the diet, and less exercise. The liver, gallbladder, and pancreas show only slightly reduced function in old age. Any drop in liver function, however, makes it harder to detoxify drugs and can contribute to overmedication.

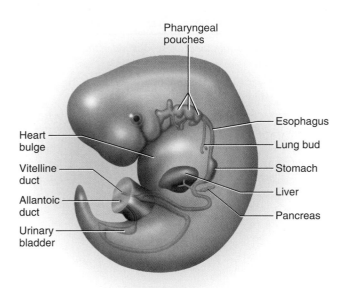

**Figure 24.22   Lateral View of the 5-week Embryo.** The primordial stomach is present as a foregut dilation, and the liver and pancreatic buds are present. The loop of midgut approaching the vitelline duct herniates into the umbilical cord within the next week.

Many older people reduce their food intake because of lower energy demand and appetite, because declining sensory functions make food less appealing, and because reduced mobility makes it more difficult to shop and prepare meals. However, they need fewer calories than younger people because they have lower basal metabolic rates and tend to be less physically active. Protein, vitamin, and mineral requirements remain essentially unchanged, although vitamin and mineral supplements may be needed to compensate for reduced food intake and intestinal absorption. Malnutrition is common among older people and is an important factor in anemia and reduced immunity.

## Digestive Disorders

The digestive system is subject to a wide variety of disorders. Disorders of motility include difficulty swallowing *(dysphagia)*, gastroesophageal reflux disease (GERD), and pyloric obstruction. Inflammatory diseases include esophagitis, gastritis, appendicitis, colitis, diverticulitis, pancreatitis, hepatitis, and cirrhosis. Cancer can occur in virtually every part of the digestive system: oral, esophageal, gastric, colon, rectal, hepatic, and pancreatic. Colon and pancreatic cancer are among the leading causes of cancer deaths in the United States.

| TABLE 24.4 | Some Digestive System Diseases |
|---|---|
| **Acute pancreatitis** | Severe pancreatic inflammation, perhaps caused by trauma, leading to leakage of pancreatic enzymes into parenchyma, where they digest tissue and cause inflammation and hemorrhage. |
| **Appendicitis** | Inflammation of the appendix, with swelling, pain, and a threat of gangrene, perforation, and peritonitis. |
| **Ascites** | Accumulation of serous fluid in the peritoneal cavity, often causing extreme distension of the abdomen. Most often caused by cirrhosis of the liver and frequently associated with alcoholism. The diseased liver "weeps" fluid into the abdomen. |
| **Cirrhosis[39] of the liver** | An irreversible inflammatory disease of the liver often caused by alcoholism. Gives the liver a "cobbly" appearance and hard consistency due to fibrosis and nodular regeneration of damaged tissue. Obstruction of bile ducts causes jaundice, and obstruction of the circulation causes new vessels to grow and bypass the liver, leaving the liver subject to hypoxia, further necrosis, and failure. |
| **Crohn[40] disease** | Inflammation of small and large intestines, similar to ulcerative colitis in symptoms and hereditary predisposition. Produces granular lesions and fibrosis of intestine; diarrhea; and lower abdominal pain. |
| **Diverticulitis** | Presence of inflamed herniations (outpocketings, diverticula) of the colon, associated especially with low-fiber diets. Diverticula may rupture, leading to peritonitis. |
| **Dysphagia[41]** | Difficulty swallowing. Can result from esophageal obstructions (tumors, constrictions) or impaired peristalsis (due to neuromuscular disorders). |
| **Hiatal hernia** | Protrusion of part of the stomach into the thoracic cavity, where the negative thoracic pressure may cause it to balloon. Often causes gastroesophageal reflux (especially when a person is supine). |
| **Ulcerative colitis** | Chronic inflammation resulting in ulceration of the large intestine, especially the sigmoid colon and rectum. Tends to be hereditary but exact causes are not well known. |

### Disorders Described Elsewhere

| | | |
|---|---|---|
| Constipation 710 | Gastroesophageal reflux disease 694 | Mumps 692 |
| Dental caries 692 | Gingivitis 692 | Omphalocele 709 |
| Diarrhea 702 | Hemorrhoids 702 | Peptic ulcer 699 |
| Gallstones 708 | Impacted molars 692 | Periodontal disease 692 |

---

[39]*cirrho* = orange-yellow + *osis* = condition
[40]Burrill B. Crohn (1884–1983), American gastroenterologist
[41]*dys* = bad, difficult, abnormal + *phag* = eat, swallow

Digestive disorders can be manifested in a variety of signs and symptoms: anorexia (loss of appetite), vomiting, constipation, diarrhea, abdominal pain, or gastrointestinal bleeding. Many of these are nonspecific; they do not by themselves identify a particular digestive disorder. Gastrointestinal bleeding, for example, can result from *varices* (varicose veins) in the digestive tract wall, intestinal polyps, GI inflammation, hemorrhoids, peptic ulcers, parasitic infections, or cancer. Nausea is even less specific; it may result not only from nondigestive disorders but also from such causes as tumors in the abdomen or brainstem, trauma to the urogenital organs, or inner-ear dysfunction.

It was remarked earlier that the foregut, midgut, and hindgut are defined by differences in arterial blood supply. This embryonic division also extends to the nerve supply and to the perception of pain from the digestive tract. Gastrointestinal pain is often perceived as if it were coming from the abdominal wall (see *referred pain*, p. 491). Pain arising from the foregut is referred to the epigastric region, midgut pain to the umbilical region, and hindgut pain to the hypogastric region.

Table 24.4 lists and describes some common digestive disorders.

## *Before You Go On*

*Answer the following questions to test your understanding of the preceding section:*

25. Explain why the foregut and hindgut appear in the embryo earlier than the midgut.

26. What accessory digestive gland arises as a single bud from the embryonic gut? What gland arises as a pair of buds that later merge?

27. Explain why dental caries, constipation, and heartburn become more common as the digestive system ages.

28. Explain why gastrointestinal bleeding and nausea provide only inconclusive evidence for the existence and location of a digestive system disorder.

# CHAPTER REVIEW

## REVIEW OF KEY CONCEPTS

### Digestive Processes and General Anatomy (p. 685)

1. The digestive system processes food, extracts nutrients, and eliminates the residue. It does this in five stages: ingestion, digestion, absorption, compaction, and defecation.

2. The *digestive tract* is a tube consisting of the mouth, pharynx, esophagus, stomach, and small and large intestines. The *accessory organs* are the teeth, tongue, salivary glands, liver, gallbladder, and pancreas.

3. In most areas, the wall of the digestive tract consists of an inner *mucosa,* a *submucosa,* a *muscularis externa,* and an outer *serosa.* The mucosa is usually composed of an epithelium, *lamina propria,* and *muscularis mucosae.* In some areas a connective tissue *adventitia* replaces the serosa.

4. The upper digestive system is innervated by somatic motor fibers from several cranial nerves and the ansa cervicalis. Autonomic fibers innervate the salivary glands and most of the digestive tract from esophagus to rectum. In general, parasympathetic stimulation promotes digestion, and sympathetic stimulation inhibits it.

5. The *enteric nervous system* regulates most digestive activity and consists of two nerve networks in the wall of the digestive tract: the *submucosal plexus* and the *myenteric plexus.*

6. The foregut receives blood from esophageal arteries above the diaphragm and the celiac trunk below. The midgut is supplied by the superior mesenteric artery and the hindgut by the inferior mesenteric artery.

7. Veins from all of the digestive tract below the diaphragm drain into the hepatic portal system, which routes blood to the liver. The liver thus has opportunity to extract nutrients from the intestinal blood before the blood flows to any other organ.

8. In the abdominal cavity, the *dorsal mesentery* suspends the digestive tract from the body wall, wraps around it to form the serosa, and in some places continues as a *ventral mesentery.* The ventral mesentery includes the *greater* and *lesser omenta.*

9. Digestive organs completely enclosed in a serosa are *intraperitoneal.* Organs that lie against the abdominal wall and are covered by a serosa only anteriorly are *retroperitoneal.*

### The Mouth Through Esophagus (p. 689)

1. The *mouth (oral cavity)* serves for ingestion, sensory responses to food, mastication, chemical digestion, swallowing, speech, and respiration.

2. The mouth extends from the *oral fissure* anteriorly to the *fauces* posteriorly. Its anatomical elements include the lips, cheeks, tongue, hard and soft palates, teeth, and salivary glands.

3. The tongue functions in ingestion, the manipulation and physical breakdown of food, the sense of taste, mucus and enzyme secretion, and swallowing. It exhibits surface projections called *lingual papillae,* many of them with taste buds. *Intrinsic* and *extrinsic muscles* control tongue movements.

4. The bony *hard palate* separates the oral cavity from the nasal cavity. Posterior to this, the fleshy *soft palate* separates the oropharynx from the nasopharynx.

5. The adult teeth *(dentition)* include two incisors, one canine, two premolars, and up to three molars on each side of each jaw. A tooth is composed mainly of dentine, covered with cementum on the root and enamel on the crown. It encloses a *pulp cavity* and *root canal* occupied by blood vessels, nerves, and loose connective tissue.

6. Mastication breaks food into pieces small enough to be swallowed and exposes more food surface to the action of digestive enzymes, making digestion more efficient.

7. Saliva moistens the mouth, digests starch and fat, cleanses the teeth, inhibits bacterial growth, dissolves taste molecules, and binds food into a soft *bolus* to facilitate swallowing. It contains amylase, lipase, mucus, lysozyme, IgA, and electrolytes.

8. Saliva is produced by *intrinsic salivary glands* in the tongue, lips, and cheeks, and *extrinsic salivary glands* (the *parotid, submandibular,* and *sublingual glands*) with ducts leading to the oral cavity.

9. Salivation is controlled by *salivatory nuclei* in the medulla oblongata and pons, and occurs in response to the thought, odor, sight, taste, or oral feel of food.

10. The pharynx is a muscular funnel in the throat where the respiratory and digestive tracts meet. Its wall contains three sets of *pharyngeal constrictor* muscles that aid in swallowing.

11. The esophagus is a muscular tube from the pharynx to the *cardiac orifice* of the stomach. It is lined with a nonkeratinized stratified squamous epithelium, has a mixture of skeletal muscle (dominating the upper esophagus) and smooth muscle (dominating the lower), and is lubricated by mucous *esophageal glands* in the submucosa.

12. The upper end of the esophagus is normally held closed by the *upper esophageal sphincter,* a constriction maintained by muscle tone in the inferior pharyngeal constrictor. This sphincter prevents air from entering the esophagus during breathing.

13. The lower end of the esophagus is held closed by the *lower esophageal sphincter,* a constriction maintained by muscle tone around the esophageal hiatus of the diaphragm or in the esophageal smooth muscle. This sphincter protects the esophagus from regurgitation of stomach acid.

14. *Deglutition* (swallowing) requires the coordinated action of numerous muscles and is integrated by the *swallowing center* of the medulla oblongata.

## The Stomach (p. 694)

1. The stomach is primarily a food-storage organ, with a capacity of 4 L. It mechanically breaks up food, begins the chemical digestion of proteins and fat, and converts ingested food to soupy *chyme.*

2. The stomach extends from the *cardiac orifice* proximally to the *pylorus* distally. Its subdivisions are the *cardiac region, fundic region, body,* and *pyloric region.* The pylorus is regulated by the *pyloric sphincter.*

3. The gastric mucosa has a simple columnar epithelium of mucous cells and is marked by *gastric pits.* Two or three tubular glands open into the bottom of each pit. Most of the stomach has digestive *gastric glands,* whereas the cardiac and pyloric regions have mucous *cardiac glands* and *pyloric glands,* respectively. These glands contain mucous, regenerative, parietal, chief, and enteroendocrine cells.

4. The stomach is protected from self-digestion by its mucous coat, tight junctions between the epithelial cells, and a high rate of cell replacement.

## The Small Intestine (p. 698)

1. The small intestine carries out most digestion and nutrient absorption. Efficient and thorough digestion and absorption require a large surface area, which is provided by its great length and by its internal *circular folds, villi,* and *microvilli.*

2. The *duodenum* begins at the pylorus and extends for about 12 cm to the *duodenojejunal flexure.* It receives the stomach contents and secretions of the liver and pancreas. The submucosa contains mucous *duodenal glands.*

3. The *jejunum* extends for the next 2.5 m. Most digestion and nutrient absorption occur here. It has high, closely spaced circular folds and a relatively thick, muscular wall with a high density of blood vessels, giving it a reddish color.

4. The *ileum* is the final 3.6 m, ending at the *ileocecal junction* (gateway to the large intestine). It has a thinner wall and is paler in color; it has lower circular folds but more lymphocytes, with lymphatic nodules clustered in *Peyer patches.*

5. Villi are tongue- to finger-shaped projections of the mucosal surface. They are covered with a columnar epithelium of absorptive cells and goblet cells. The absorptive cells have a brush border of microvilli on their surface. The core of a villus contains blood capillaries, which absorb most nutrients, and a *lacteal* (lymphatic capillary), which absorbs lipids.

6. The brush border bears enzymes that carry out the terminal *contact digestion* of carbohydrates and peptides, and an enzyme, *enterokinase,* that activates the pancreatic enzyme trypsin.

7. Glandular *intestinal crypts* open onto the floor of the intestine between the villi. The crypt epithelium is composed of absorptive and goblet cells, stem cells, enteroendocrine cells, and antibacterial *Paneth cells.*

## The Large Intestine (p. 702)

1. The large intestine receives the indigestible residue of food, absorbs water and salts, consolidates the residue into feces, and eliminates the feces by defecation.

2. The large intestine is about 1.5 m long and consists of the *cecum;* the *ascending, transverse, descending,* and *sigmoid colon; rectum;* and *anal canal.* The *colon* is the region from the ascending through sigmoid colon.

3. The longitudinal layer of the muscularis externa exhibits three strips of muscle, the *taeniae coli,* whose muscle tone folds the wall of the colon into pouches called *haustra.*

4. The anal canal has an involuntary *internal anal sphincter* of smooth muscle and a voluntary *external anal sphincter* of skeletal muscle.

5. The mucosa is mostly simple columnar epithelium except for the lower half of the anal canal, which is stratified squamous. The mucosa has intestinal crypts but lacks villi and circular folds. Mucus is the only substance secreted by the large intestine.

## Accessory Glands of Digestion (p. 704)

1. The liver is the body's largest gland and has a broad range of metabolic functions (table 24.2). Its one digestive function is to secrete *bile acids* and *lecithin,* which emulsify dietary fats and facilitate their digestion by pancreatic lipase.

2. The liver is divided into four lobes: the right, left, caudate, and quadrate. An opening on the inferior surface, the *porta hepatis,* receives the hepatic portal vein and hepatic artery, and is the exit for the bile duct system.

3. The liver parenchyma is composed of microscopic, cylindrical *hepatic lobules.* Each lobule has sheets of *hepatocytes* (liver cells) that fan out around a *central vein.* Blood filters through narrow spaces called *hepatic sinusoids* between the sheets of hepatocytes.

4. The liver receives nutrient-rich intestinal blood from the hepatic portal vein and oxygen-rich arterial blood from the hepatic arteries. The two bloodstreams mix in the sinusoids. The sinusoids converge on the central vein of the lobule. These ultimately lead to two *hepatic veins* that exit the superior surface of the liver and lead to the inferior vena cava.

5. Hepatocytes secrete bile into channels called the *bile canaliculi.* Bile exits the liver via the *right* and *left hepatic ducts.* These join to form the *common hepatic duct.* This, in turn, joins the *cystic duct* from the gallbladder to form the *bile duct.* The bile duct leads to the duodenum, usually joining the pancreatic duct just before emptying into the duodenum.

6. The gallbladder is a sac on the inferior surface of the liver that stores and concentrates the bile.

7. The pancreas produces the hormones insulin and glucagon, and about 1,200 to 1,500 mL of pancreatic juice per day. The pancreatic juice passes through a *pancreatic duct,* which joins the bile duct before emptying into the duodenum at the *major duodenal papilla.* Usually a smaller *accessory pancreatic duct* opens independently into the duodenum, at the *minor duodenal papilla* proximal to the major papilla.

8. The pancreatic secretions are summarized in table 24.3.

## Developmental and Clinical Perspectives (p. 709)

1. As the embryonic disc begins to elongate at 2 weeks, the foregut and hindgut appear. The midregion becomes an enclosed midgut as the opening between the embryo and yolk sac constricts. The digestive mucosal epithelium forms from the embryonic

endoderm, and the other layers of the GI tract from mesoderm.

2. The liver bud appears at 3.5 weeks, and the stomach and two pancreatic buds at 4 weeks. The GI tract continues its development by elongation, rotation, and differentiation of its regions. Between weeks 6 and 10, the body cavity is so crowded that a loop of intestine herniates into the umbilical cord.

3. In old age, declining salivation makes food less appealing and dental caries and periodontal disease more common. Gastric atrophy promotes poorer nutrient absorption. Heartburn (gastroesophageal reflux) is increasingly common, and reduced GI motility tends to cause constipation. Malnutrition in old age is common and has causes ranging from the difficulty of shopping and cooking to declining nutrient absorption by the intestinal mucosa.

4. The digestive system is subject to a wide range of disorders including abnormalities in motility, inflammatory diseases, and several kinds of cancer. Digestive disorders can be manifested in anorexia, vomiting, constipation, diarrhea, pain, or bleeding. GI pain is referred to different regions of the anterior abdominal wall correlated with the foregut, midgut, or hindgut origin of the pain.

# TESTING YOUR RECALL

1. All of the following are retroperitoneal *except*
   a. the liver.
   b. the pancreas.
   c. the duodenum.
   d. the ascending colon.
   e. the descending colon.

2. The falciform ligament attaches the _____ to the abdominal wall.
   a. colon
   b. liver
   c. spleen
   d. pancreas
   e. stomach

3. A brush border is found on the
   a. goblet cells.
   b. intestinal absorptive cells.
   c. enteroendocrine cells.
   d. parietal cells.
   e. chief cells.

4. The yolk sac is connected to the embryonic _____ by way of the vitelline duct.
   a. liver bud
   b. stalk
   c. foregut
   d. midgut
   e. hindgut

5. Lacteals absorb dietary
   a. proteins.
   b. carbohydrates.
   c. enzymes.
   d. vitamins.
   e. lipids.

6. All of the following contribute to the absorptive surface area of the small intestine *except*
   a. its length.
   b. the brush border.
   c. haustra.
   d. circular folds.
   e. villi.

7. Which of the following is a periodontal tissue?
   a. gingiva
   b. enamel
   c. cementum
   d. pulp
   e. dentine

8. The _____ of the stomach most closely resemble the _____ of the small intestine.
   a. gastric pits, intestinal crypts
   b. pyloric glands, intestinal crypts
   c. rugae, Peyer patches
   d. parietal cells, goblet cells
   e. gastric glands, duodenal glands

9. Which of the following cells secrete digestive enzymes?
   a. chief cells
   b. mucous neck cells
   c. parietal cells
   d. goblet cells
   e. enteroendocrine cells

10. The tissue layer between the muscularis mucosae and muscularis externa of the digestive tract is
    a. the mucosa.
    b. the lamina propria.
    c. the submucosa.
    d. the serosa.
    e. the adventitia.

11. The alimentary canal has an extensive nervous network called the _____.

12. The passage of chyme from the stomach into the duodenum is controlled by a muscular ring called the _____.

13. The _____ salivary gland is named for its location near the ear.

14. The _____ is a complex of veins that carry blood from the stomach and intestines to the liver.

15. Nervous stimulation of gastrointestinal activity is mediated mainly through the parasympathetic fibers of the _____ nerves.

16. Hydrochloric acid is secreted by _____ cells of the stomach.

17. Hepatic macrophages occur in blood-filled spaces of the liver called _____.

18. The superior opening into the stomach is called the _____.

19. The root of a tooth is covered with a calcified tissue called _____.

20. Protrusions of the tongue surface, some of which bear taste buds, are called _____.

*Answers in the Appendix*

## TRUE OR FALSE

*Determine which five of the following statements are false, and briefly explain why.*

1. The liver and pancreas are retroperitoneal.

2. A tooth is composed mostly of enamel.

3. Hepatocytes secrete bile into the hepatic sinusoids.

4. The small intestine is much shorter in a living person than it is after death.

5. Peristalsis is controlled by the myenteric nerve plexus.

6. The pylorus is a gateway from the stomach to the duodenum.

7. The greater omentum suspends the stomach from the body wall.

8. Salivary acini can be composed of mucous cells, serous cells, or both.

9. In all parts of the digestive tract, the muscularis externa has two layers.

10. The external anal sphincter is under voluntary control; the internal sphincter is not.

*Answers in the Appendix*

## TESTING YOUR COMPREHENSION

1. People who suffer from GERD (see Insight 24.2) when they lie down often find their heartburn is worse when they lie on the right side than when they lie on the left. Give an anatomical explanation for this effect.

2. Cystic fibrosis (CF) is characterized by unusually thick, sticky mucus that obstructs the respiratory tract and pancreatic duct. Predict the effect of CF on digestion, nutrition, and growth in childhood.

3. Explain why the small intestine would function poorly if it had the same type of mucosal epithelium as the esophagus.

4. News reports of patients (especially children) in need of organ transplants often prompt people to call and offer to donate one of their organs, such as a kidney, to save the patient's life. If you worked in an organ donor program, what would you say to a well-meaning volunteer offering to donate a liver?

5. The hyposecretion of pancreatic bicarbonate and the hyposecretion of mucus by duodenal goblet cells could both contribute to the same pathological result. What would that result be, and why would it occur?

*Answers at aris.mhhe.com*

## ONLINE RESOURCES

  Visit aprevealed.com to explore melt-away cadaver dissections, watch animations that clarify difficult concepts, review histological and radiological images, or take a quiz to assess your understanding of the material.

The Saladin *Human Anatomy,* 2e website at aris.mhhe.com features chapter-specific quizzes, labeling exercises, and other interactive tools to complement your study of human anatomy. If your instructor has provided an ARIS course code, you can also access assignments and information specific to your course.

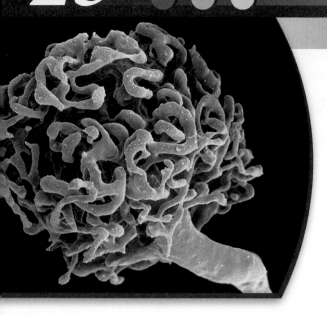

# The Urinary System

The renal glomerulus, a mass of capillaries where the kidney filters the blood (SEM of a polymer cast)

## CHAPTER OUTLINE

## INSIGHTS

## BRUSHING UP

To understand this chapter, you may find it helpful to review the following concepts:
• Transitional epithelium (p. 82)
• General exocrine gland architecture (pp. 95–96)
• Fenestrated capillaries (p. 600)

Anatomy & Physiology | REVEALED®
aprevealed.com

**Urinary System**

Metabolism produces a variety of waste products that cannot be allowed to accumulate in the body, for if they do, the body is quickly poisoned. The respiratory and digestive systems and the sweat glands eliminate some metabolic wastes, but the urinary system is the principal means of excretion. Its functions go far beyond that, however. It also collaborates with the endocrine, circulatory, and respiratory systems to regulate many aspects of homeostasis such as blood pressure, erythrocyte count, blood gases, and electrolyte and acid–base balance.

Anatomically, the urinary system is closely associated with the reproductive system. In many animals the eggs and sperm are emitted through the urinary tract, and the two systems share some aspects of evolutionary history, embryonic development, and adult anatomy. This is reflected in humans, where the systems develop together in the embryo and, in the male, the urethra continues to serve as a passage for both urine and sperm. Thus, the urinary and reproductive systems are often collectively called the *urogenital (U-G)* or *genitourinary (G-U) system,* and *urologists* treat both urinary and reproductive disorders. Because of their anatomical and developmental relationship, we consider the urinary and reproductive systems in these last two chapters.

# Functions of the Urinary System

## Objectives

When you have completed this section, you should be able to

- name and locate the organs of the urinary system;
- list several functions of the kidneys in addition to urine formation;
- define *excretion;* and
- identify the major nitrogenous waste excreted by the kidneys.

The **urinary system** serves primarily to cleanse the blood of metabolic wastes and eliminate them in the urine. A branch of medicine called **urology** is concerned with the diagnosis and treatment of disorders of the urinary system in both sexes and with the male reproductive system. The urinary system consists of six organs: two **kidneys,** two **ureters,** the **urinary bladder,** and the **urethra.** Figure 25.1 shows these organs in anterior and posterior views. The urinary tract has especially important relationships with the uterus and vagina in females and the

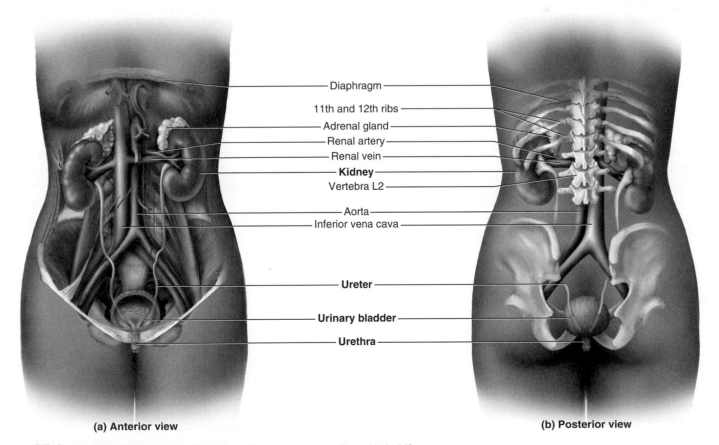

Diaphragm
11th and 12th ribs
Adrenal gland
Renal artery
Renal vein
**Kidney**
Vertebra L2
Aorta
Inferior vena cava
**Ureter**
**Urinary bladder**
**Urethra**

**(a) Anterior view**          **(b) Posterior view**

**Figure 25.1** **The Urinary System.** Organs of the urinary system are indicated in boldface.
• *On yourself or another person, palpate the location of the kidneys. What landmark can be used to locate them?*

prostate gland in males. These relationships are best appreciated from the sagittal views in figures 26.9 (male) and 26.11 (female) (pp. 745 and 749). Most of the focus of the present chapter is on the kidneys.

Although the primary function of this system is excretion, the kidneys play more roles than are commonly realized:

- They filter blood plasma, separate wastes from the useful chemicals, and eliminate the wastes while returning the rest to the bloodstream.
- They regulate the osmolarity of the body fluids by controlling the relative amounts of water and solutes eliminated.
- They regulate blood volume and pressure by eliminating or conserving water as necessary.
- They also help in the hormonal regulation of blood pressure. They secrete the enzyme *renin,* which catalyzes a step in the synthesis of the hormone angiotensin II. Angiotensin II raises blood pressure by stimulating widespread vasoconstriction. It also stimulates the adrenal cortex to secrete aldosterone, the "salt-retaining hormone," which causes the kidneys to retain sodium and water.
- They secrete the hormone *erythropoietin,* which stimulates the production of red blood cells and therefore helps regulate the oxygen-carrying capacity of the blood.
- They carry out the final step in synthesizing the hormone *calcitriol* (vitamin D), and thereby contribute to calcium homeostasis.
- They collaborate with the lungs to regulate the $CO_2$ and acid–base balance of the body fluids.
- They detoxify free radicals and drugs.
- In times of starvation, they convert amino acids to glucose (a process called *gluconeogenesis*) and thus help to support blood glucose level.

**Excretion,** the most obvious function of the urinary system, is the process of extracting wastes from the body fluids and eliminating them, thus preventing metabolic poisoning of the body. Among other things, the kidneys excrete organic nitrogen-containing molecules called **nitrogenous wastes.** The most abundant of these is **urea,** a product of protein metabolism. If the kidneys do not function adequately, one develops a condition called **azotemia**[1] (AZ-oh-TEE-me-uh), in which the blood urea concentration (or *blood-urea nitrogen, BUN*) is abnormally high. In severe renal failure, azotemia progresses to **uremia** (you-REE-me-uh), a syndrome of diarrhea, vomiting, dyspnea (labored breathing), and cardiac arrhythmia. Convulsions, coma, and death can follow within a few days, underscoring the importance of adequate renal function.

### Before You Go On

*Answer the following questions to test your understanding of the preceding section:*

1. State four functions of the kidneys other than forming urine.
2. What is the most abundant nitrogenous waste in the urine? What terms describe an abnormally high level of this waste in the blood, and poisoning by this waste?

---

[1]*azot* = nitrogen + *emia* = blood condition

# Anatomy of the Kidney

### Objectives
When you have completed this section, you should be able to
- describe the location and general appearance of the kidney, and its relationship to neighboring organs;
- identify the major external and internal features of the kidney;
- trace the flow of blood through the kidney;
- describe the nerve supply to the kidney;
- trace the flow of fluid through the renal tubules; and
- state the function of each segment of a renal tubule.

## Position and Associated Structures

The kidneys lie against the posterior abdominal wall at the level of vertebrae T12 to L3. Rib 12 crosses the approximate middle of the kidney. The right kidney is slightly lower than the left because of the space occupied by the large right lobe of the liver above it. The kidneys are retroperitoneal, along with the ureters, urinary bladder, renal artery and vein, and the adrenal[2] glands (fig. 25.2). The left adrenal gland rests on the superior pole of that kidney, and the right adrenal gland lies against the superomedial surface of its kidney. Their functions (see chapter 18, p. 537–539) are not as directly related to the kidneys as their spatial relationship might suggest, although the kidneys and adrenals do influence each other.

## Gross Anatomy

The kidney is a compound tubular gland containing about 1.2 million functional excretory units called **nephrons**[3] (NEF-rons). Each kidney weighs about 150 g and measures about 11 cm long, 6 cm wide, and 3 cm thick—about the size of a bar of bath soap. The lateral surface is convex, whereas the medial surface is concave and has a slit, the **hilum,** where it receives the renal nerves, blood vessels, lymphatics, and ureter.

The kidney is protected by three layers of connective tissue (fig. 25.2): (1) A fibrous **renal fascia,** immediately deep to the parietal peritoneum, binds the kidney and associated organs to the abdominal wall; (2) a layer of **perirenal fat** cushions the kidney and holds it in place; and (3) the **renal capsule,** a fibrous sac, encloses the kidney like a cellophane wrapper anchored at the hilum, and protects it from trauma and infection. Collagen fibers extend from the renal capsule, through the fat, to the renal fascia. The renal fascia is fused with the peritoneum anteriorly and with the deep fascia of the lumbar muscles posteriorly. Thus the kidneys are suspended in place. Nevertheless, they drop about 3 cm when one goes from a supine to a standing position, and under some circumstances, they become detached and drift even lower, with pathological results (see nephroptosis, or "floating kidney," in table 25.1 at the end of this chapter).

---

[2]*ad* = to, toward, near + *ren* = kidney + *al* = pertaining to
[3]*nephro* = kidney

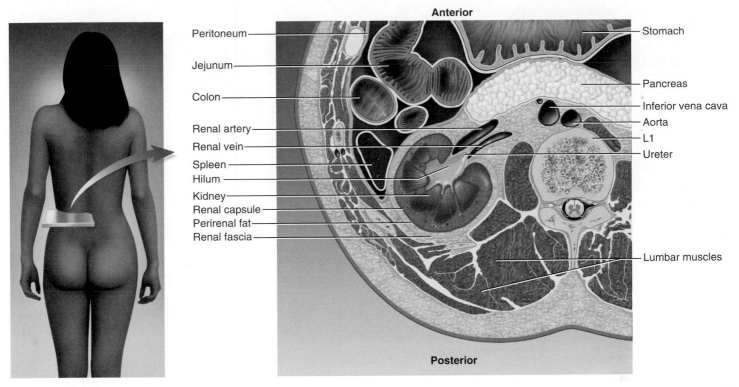

**Figure 25.2** **Location of the Kidney.** Cross section of the abdomen at the level of vertebra L1, showing the relationship of the kidney to the body wall and peritoneum.
● *If the kidney was not retroperitoneal, where on this figure would you have to relocate it?*

The renal parenchyma—the glandular tissue that forms the urine—appears C-shaped in frontal section. It encircles a medial space, the **renal sinus,** occupied by blood and lymphatic vessels, nerves, and urine-collecting structures. Adipose tissue fills the remaining space in the sinus and holds these structures in place.

The parenchyma is divided into two zones: an outer **renal cortex** about 1 cm thick and an inner **renal medulla** facing the sinus (fig. 25.3). Extensions of the cortex called **renal columns** project toward the sinus and divide the medulla into 6 to 10 **renal pyramids.** Each pyramid is conical, with a broad base facing the cortex and a blunt point called the **renal papilla** facing the sinus. One pyramid and the overlying cortex constitute one *lobe* of the kidney.

The papilla of each renal pyramid is nestled in a cup called a **minor calyx**[4] (CAY-lix), which collects its urine. Two or three minor calyces (CAY-lih-seez) converge to form a **major calyx,** and two or three major calyces converge in the sinus to form the funnel-like **renal pelvis.**[5] The ureter is a tubular continuation of the renal pelvis that drains the urine down to the urinary bladder.

## Circulation

Although the kidneys account for only 0.4% of the body weight, they receive about 21% of the cardiac output (the *renal fraction*). This is a hint of how important the kidneys are in regulating blood volume and composition.

The larger divisions of the renal circulation are shown in figure 25.4. Each kidney is supplied by a **renal artery** arising from the aorta. Just before or after entering the hilum, the renal artery divides into a few **segmental arteries,** and each of these gives rise to a few **interlobar arteries.** An interlobar artery penetrates each renal column and travels between the pyramids toward the *corticomedullary junction,* the boundary between the cortex and medulla. Along the way, it branches again to form **arcuate arteries,** which make a sharp 90° bend and travel along the base of the pyramid. Each arcuate artery gives rise to several **interlobular arteries,** which pass upward into the cortex.

The finer branches of the renal circulation are shown in figure 25.5. As an interlobular artery ascends through the cortex, a series of **afferent arterioles** arise from it at nearly right angles like the limbs of a pine tree. Each afferent arteriole supplies one nephron. It leads to a spheroidal mass of capillaries called a **glomerulus**[6] (glo-MERR-you-lus), enclosed in a nephron structure called the *glomerular capsule,* to be discussed later. The glomerulus is drained by an **efferent arteriole.** The efferent arteriole usually leads to a plexus of **peritubular capillaries,** named for the fact that they form a network around the tubules of the nephron. These capillaries pick up the water and solutes reabsorbed by the tubules.

From the peritubular capillaries, blood flows to **interlobular veins, arcuate veins, interlobar veins,** and the **renal vein,** in that order. These veins travel parallel to the arteries of the same names. (There are, however, no segmental veins corresponding to the segmental arteries.) The renal vein leaves the hilum and drains into the inferior vena cava.

[4]*calyx* = cup
[5]*pelvis* = basin

[6]*glomer* = ball + *ulus* = little

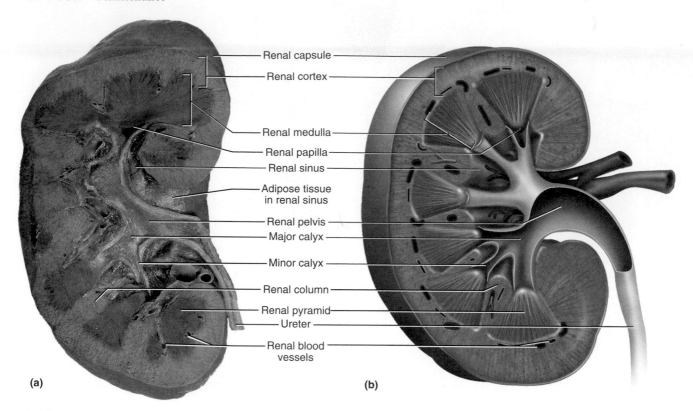

Renal capsule
Renal cortex
Renal medulla
Renal papilla
Renal sinus
Adipose tissue in renal sinus
Renal pelvis
Major calyx
Minor calyx
Renal column
Renal pyramid
Ureter
Renal blood vessels

(a)

(b)

**Figure 25.3  Gross Anatomy of the Kidney.**  Posterior views. (a) Photograph of a frontal section. (b) Major anatomical features.

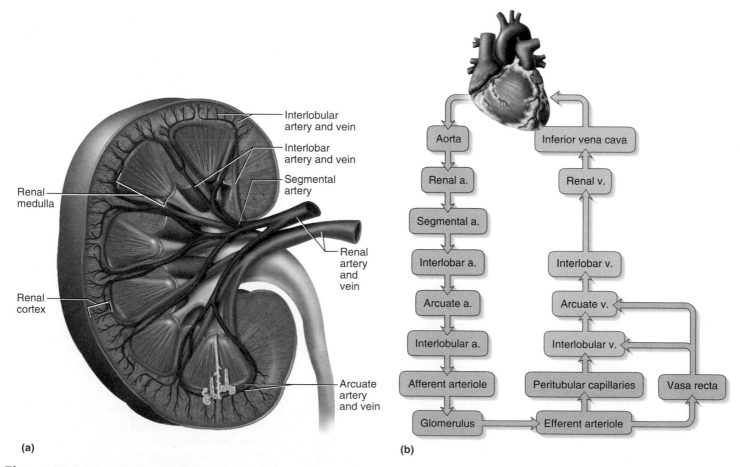

Interlobular artery and vein
Interlobar artery and vein
Segmental artery
Renal medulla
Renal cortex
Renal artery and vein
Arcuate artery and vein

Aorta — Inferior vena cava
Renal a. — Renal v.
Segmental a.
Interlobar a. — Interlobar v.
Arcuate a. — Arcuate v.
Interlobular a. — Interlobular v.
Afferent arteriole — Peritubular capillaries — Vasa recta
Glomerulus — Efferent arteriole

(a)

(b)

**Figure 25.4  Renal Circulation.**  (a) The larger blood vessels of the kidney. (b) Flow chart of renal circulation. The pathway through the vasa recta (instead of peritubular capillaries) applies only to the juxtamedullary nephrons.

● *Is the kidney in this figure shown from an anterior or posterior view? How can you tell?*

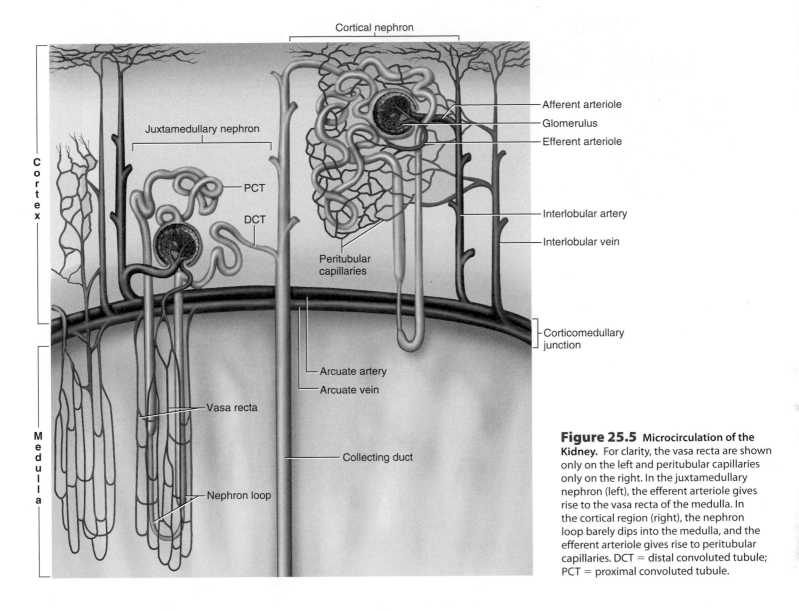

**Figure 25.5** **Microcirculation of the Kidney.** For clarity, the vasa recta are shown only on the left and peritubular capillaries only on the right. In the juxtamedullary nephron (left), the efferent arteriole gives rise to the vasa recta of the medulla. In the cortical region (right), the nephron loop barely dips into the medulla, and the efferent arteriole gives rise to peritubular capillaries. DCT = distal convoluted tubule; PCT = proximal convoluted tubule.

The renal medulla receives only 1% to 2% of the total renal blood flow, supplied by a network of vessels called the **vasa recta.**[7] These arise from the nephrons in the deep cortex, closest to the medulla *(juxtamedullary nephrons).* Here, the efferent arterioles descend immediately into the medulla and give rise to the vasa recta instead of peritubular capillaries. The capillaries of the vasa recta lead into venules that ascend and empty into the arcuate and interlobular veins. Capillaries of the vasa recta are wedged into the tight spaces between the medullary parts of the renal tubule, and carry away water and solutes reabsorbed by those sections of the tubule. Figure 25.4b summarizes the route of renal blood flow.

### THINK ABOUT IT

*Can you identify a portal system in the renal circulation?*

[7]*vasa* = vessels + *recta* = straight

## Innervation

**Renal nerves** arise from the superior mesenteric ganglion (see p. 474) and enter the hilum of each kidney. They follow branches of the renal artery and innervate the afferent and efferent arterioles. These nerves consist mostly of sympathetic fibers that regulate the blood flow into and out of each glomerulus, and thus control the rate of filtration and urine formation. If the blood pressure falls, they also stimulate the nephron to secrete renin, an enzyme that activates hormonal mechanisms for restoring the blood pressure.

## The Nephron

A nephron (fig. 25.6) consists of two principal parts: a *renal corpuscle,* which filters the blood plasma, and a long *renal tubule,* which converts the filtrate to urine.

Before we embark on the microscopic anatomy of the nephron, it will be helpful to have a broad overview of the process of urine production. This knowledge will lend functional meaning to

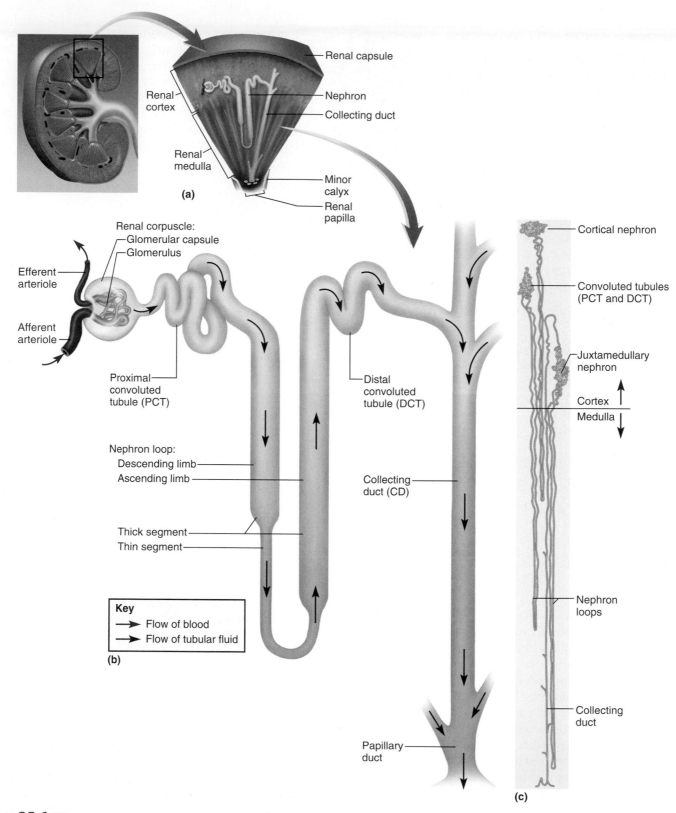

**Figure 25.6 Microscopic Anatomy of the Nephron.** (a) Location of the nephrons in one wedge-shaped lobe of the kidney. (b) Structure of a nephron. The nephron is stretched out to separate the convoluted tubules and is greatly shortened for the purpose of illustration. (c) The true proportions of the nephron loops relative to the convoluted tubules. Three nephrons are shown. Their proximal and distal convoluted tubules are commingled in a single mass in each nephron. Note the extreme lengths of the nephron loops.

the structural details of the nephron. The kidney converts blood plasma to urine in three stages (fig. 25.7):

1. **Glomerular filtration** is the passage of fluid from the bloodstream into the nephron, carrying not only wastes but also chemicals useful to the body. The fluid filtered from the blood is called *glomerular filtrate.* In contrast to the blood, it is free of cells and very low in protein. After it passes into the renal tubule, its composition is quickly modified by the following processes, and we call it *tubular fluid.*

2. **Tubular reabsorption** and **tubular secretion** are two simultaneous processes that alter the composition of the tubular fluid. Substances useful to the body, such as glucose, are reabsorbed from it and returned to the blood. Blood-borne substances such as hydrogen ions and some drugs, conversely, are extracted from the peritubular capillaries and secreted into the tubular fluid, thus becoming part of the urine.

3. **Water conservation** is achieved by reabsorbing variable amounts of water from the fluid so the body can eliminate metabolic wastes without losing excess water. If reabsorption did not occur, a typical adult hypothetically would produce

180 liters of urine per day—although in reality, this would be an impossible feat considering that we have only about 5 liters of blood and about 40 liters of total body water. Usually, the kidneys excrete urine that is **hypertonic** to the blood plasma—that is, it has a higher ratio of waste solutes to water than the plasma does. Water reabsorption occurs in all parts of the renal tubule, but is the final change occurring in the urine as it passes through the collecting duct. The fluid is regarded as urine once it has entered this duct.

We can now examine the individual segments of the nephron, their contribution to the foregoing processes, and how their structures are adapted to their individual roles.

## The Renal Corpuscle

The **renal corpuscle** (fig. 25.8) consists of the glomerulus and, enclosing it, a two-layered **glomerular (Bowman[8]) capsule.** The inner, or visceral, layer of the glomerular capsule consists of elaborate cells called *podocytes* wrapped around the capillaries. The parietal (outer) layer is a simple squamous epithelium. The two layers are separated by a filtrate-collecting **capsular space.** In tissue sections, the capsular space appears as an empty circular or C-shaped space around the glomerulus.

Opposite sides of the renal corpuscle are called the vascular pole and urinary pole. At the **vascular pole,** the afferent arteriole enters the capsule, bringing blood to the glomerulus, and the efferent arteriole exits the capsule and carries blood away. The afferent arteriole is conspicuously larger than the efferent arteriole. Thus, the glomerulus has a large inlet and small outlet. This gives its capillaries an unusually high blood pressure, which is the driving force of glomerular filtration. At the **urinary pole,** the parietal wall of the capsule turns away from the corpuscle and gives rise to the renal tubule. The simple squamous epithelium of the capsule becomes simple cuboidal in the renal tubule.

A **podocyte**[9] is shaped somewhat like an octopus, with a bulbous cell body and several thick arms (fig. 25.9). Each arm has numerous little extensions called **foot processes (pedicels**[10]) that wrap around the glomerular blood capillaries and interdigitate with each other, like wrapping your hands around a pipe and lacing your fingers together. The foot processes have narrow **filtration slits** between them.

The job of the renal corpuscle is glomerular filtration: blood cells and plasma proteins are retained in the bloodstream because they are too large to pass through the barriers described below. Water, however, freely passes through and carries along small solute particles such as urea, glucose, amino acids, and electrolytes. The high blood pressure in the glomerulus drives the water and small solutes out through the capillary walls, into the capsular space. Pressure in the capsular space drives the filtrate into the renal tubule and ultimately all the way to the calyces and renal pelvis.

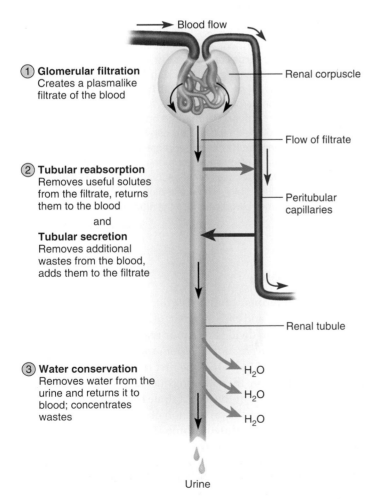

① **Glomerular filtration**
Creates a plasmalike filtrate of the blood

Blood flow

Renal corpuscle

Flow of filtrate

② **Tubular reabsorption**
Removes useful solutes from the filtrate, returns them to the blood
and
**Tubular secretion**
Removes additional wastes from the blood, adds them to the filtrate

Peritubular capillaries

Renal tubule

③ **Water conservation**
Removes water from the urine and returns it to blood; concentrates wastes

$H_2O$

$H_2O$

$H_2O$

Urine

**Figure 25.7** Basic Steps in the Formation of Urine.

---

[8]Sir William Bowman (1816–92), British physician
[9]*podo* = foot + *cyte* = cell
[10]*pedi* = foot + *cel* = little

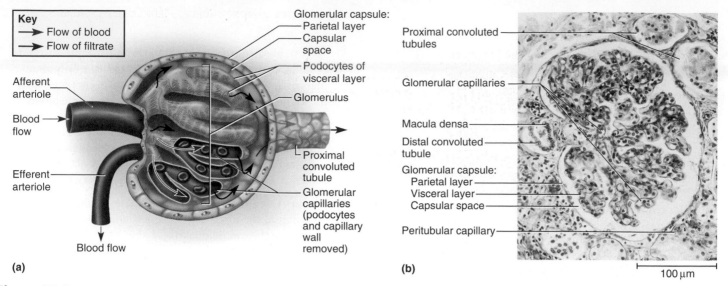

**Figure 25.8** **The Renal Corpuscle.** (a) Anatomy of the corpuscle. (b) Light micrograph of the renal corpuscle and sections of the surrounding renal tubule.

Anything leaving the bloodstream must pass through a barrier called the **filtration membrane,** composed of three layers (fig. 25.9c):

1. **Capillary endothelium.** Glomerular capillaries have a fenestrated endothelium (see fig. 21.6, p. 601) honeycombed with large filtration pores about 70 to 90 nm in diameter. They are much more permeable than capillaries elsewhere, although the filtration pores are small enough to hold back blood cells.

2. **Basement membrane.** This is a layer of proteoglycan gel (a protein–carbohydrate complex) beneath the endothelial cells. For large molecules to pass through it is like trying to pass sand through a kitchen sponge. A few particles may penetrate its small spaces, but most are held back. On the basis of size alone, the basement membrane excludes any molecules larger than 8 nm. Some smaller molecules, however, are also held back by a negative electrical charge on the proteoglycans. Blood albumin is slightly less than 7 nm in diameter, but it is also negatively charged and thus repelled by the basement membrane. Therefore, the protein concentration is about 7% in the blood plasma but only 0.03% in the glomerular filtrate. The filtrate contains traces of albumin and smaller polypeptides, including some hormones.

3. **Filtration slits.** The slits between the podocyte foot processes are about 30 nm wide and are also negatively charged. This charge is a final barrier to large anions such as proteins.

Almost any molecule smaller than 3 nm passes freely through the filtration membrane. This includes water, electrolytes, glucose, fatty acids, amino acids, nitrogenous wastes, and vitamins. Such substances have about the same concentration in the filtrate as in the blood plasma. Some substances of low molecular weight are retained in the bloodstream because they are bound to plasma proteins that cannot get through the membrane. For example, most calcium, iron, and thyroid hormone in the blood are bound to plasma proteins that retard their filtration by the kidneys. The small fraction that is unbound, however, passes freely through the membrane and appears in the urine.

**INSIGHT 25.1**

## Clinical Application

### Blood and Protein in the Urine

*Urinalysis,* one of the most routine procedures performed upon patient admission and in routine medical examinations, is an analysis of the physical and chemical properties of the urine. It includes tests for blood and protein, both of which are normally lacking from urine. Damage to the filtration membrane, however, can result in blood or protein in the urine, called *hematuria*[11] and *proteinuria (albuminuria),* respectively. These can be signs of kidney infections, trauma, and other kidney diseases (see table 25.1 at the end of the chapter). They can be temporary conditions of little concern, or they can be chronic and gravely serious. Long-distance runners and swimmers often show temporary proteinuria and hematuria. Strenuous exercise reduces renal circulation as blood shifts to the muscles. With a reduced blood flow, the glomeruli deteriorate and leak protein and sometimes blood cells into the filtrate.

### The Renal Tubule

The **renal (uriniferous**[12]**) tubule** is a duct that leads away from the glomerular capsule and ends at the tip of a medullary pyramid. It is about 3 cm long and divided into four major regions: the *proximal convoluted tubule, nephron loop, distal convoluted tubule,* and *collecting duct* (see fig. 25.6). Only the first three of these are parts of an individual nephron; the collecting duct receives fluid from many nephrons. Each region of the renal tubule has unique physiological properties and roles in the production of urine.

The **proximal convoluted tubule (PCT)** arises from the glomerular capsule. It is the longest and most coiled of the four regions and thus dominates histological sections of renal cortex. The PCT has a simple cuboidal epithelium with prominent microvilli (a

---

[11]*hemat* = blood + *uria* = urine condition
[12]*urin* = urine + *fer* = to carry

724

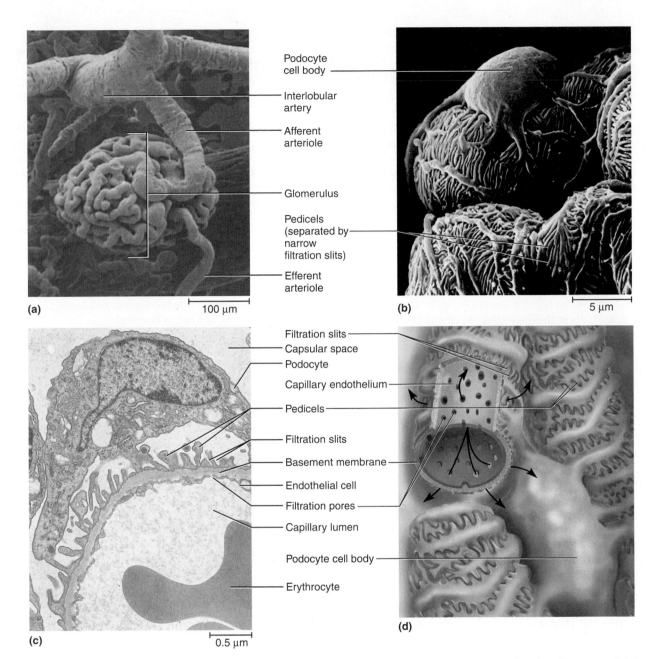

**Figure 25.9** **Structure of the Glomerulus.** (a) A polymer cast of the glomerulus and nearby arteries (SEM). Note that the efferent arteriole is much narrower than the afferent arteriole, which causes blood pressure in the glomerulus to be unusually high. (b) Blood capillaries of the glomerulus closely wrapped in the spidery podocytes that form the visceral layer of the glomerular capsule (SEM). (c) A blood capillary and podocyte showing filtration pores of the capillary and filtration slits of the podocyte (TEM). (d) The production of glomerular filtrate by the passage of fluid through the endothelium and filtration slits. [Part (a) from R. G. Kessel and R. H. Kardon, *Tissues and Organs: A Text-Atlas of Scanning Electron Microscopy*, W. H. Freeman, 1979]

● *Which is larger, the efferent arteriole or afferent arteriole? How does this affect the function of the glomerulus?*

brush border), which attests to the great deal of absorption that occurs here. The microvilli give the epithelium a distinctively shaggy look in tissue sections.

The PCT carries out both tubular reabsorption and tubular secretion. It reabsorbs about 65% of the glomerular filtrate, and consumes about 6% of one's daily ATP expenditure in doing so. On the surface facing the tubular fluid, the epithelial cells have a variety of membrane transport proteins that carry solutes into the cells by active transport and facilitated diffusion. These solutes and water pass

through the cell cytoplasm (the **transcellular**[13] **route**) and either diffuse out or are actively pumped out the basal and lateral cell surfaces, adjacent to peritubular blood capillaries waiting to receive them. Water and solutes also take a **paracellular**[14] **route** between the epithelial cells. Even though the cells are joined by tight junctions, these are quite leaky and allow a substantial amount of fluid to pass through.

---

[13]*trans* = across
[14]*para* = next to

Among the solutes reabsorbed by the PCT are sodium, potassium, magnesium, phosphate, chloride, bicarbonate, glucose, amino acids, lactate, protein, smaller peptides, amino acids, urea, and uric acid. Water follows by osmosis.

By tubular secretion, the PCT extracts solutes from the peritubular capillaries and secretes them into the tubular fluid, so they can be passed in the urine. Secreted solutes include hydrogen and bicarbonate ions, ammonia, urea, uric acid, creatinine, bile acids, pollutants, and some drugs (aspirin, penicillin, and morphine, for example). Notice that urea and uric acid go both ways between the blood and tubular fluid, transported by both tubular reabsorption and tubular secretion. The kidneys do not completely cleanse the blood of these wastes; indeed, they remove only about half of the urea, but this is sufficient to keep the blood urea concentration down to a safe level.

### THINK ABOUT IT

*The proximal convoluted tubule exhibits some of the same structural adaptations as the small intestine, and for the same reason. Discuss what they have in common, and the reason for it.*

The **nephron loop** (**loop of Henle**[15]) is a long U-shaped portion of the renal tubule found mostly in the medulla. It begins where the PCT straightens out and dips toward or into the medulla, forming the **descending limb** of the loop. At its deep end, the loop turns 180° and forms the **ascending limb,** which returns to the cortex, traveling parallel and close to the descending limb. The loop is divided into thick and thin segments. The **thick segments** have a simple cuboidal epithelium. They form the initial part of the descending limb and part or all of the ascending limb. The cells here are heavily engaged in active transport of salts, so they have very high metabolic activity and are loaded with mitochondria. The **thin segment** has a simple squamous epithelium. It forms the lower part of the descending limb, and in some nephrons, it rounds the bend and continues partway up the ascending limb. The cells here have low metabolic activity but are very permeable to water.

The nephron loop reabsorbs about 25% of the sodium, potassium, and chloride and 15% of the water that was in the glomerular filtrate. Its primary function, however, is to maintain a gradient of salinity in the renal medulla. It does this by pumping $Na^+$, $K^+$, and $Cl^-$ from the ascending limb into the medullary tissue fluid. At the corticomedullary junction, the tissue fluid is isotonic with the blood plasma (300 milliosmoles/liter), but deep in the medulla, it is four times as concentrated. The significance of this is explained later.

The nephron loops are not identical in all nephrons. Nephrons just beneath the renal capsule, close to the kidney surface, are called **cortical nephrons.** They have relatively short nephron loops that dip only slightly into the outer medulla before turning back (see fig. 25.6), or turn back even before leaving the cortex. Some cortical nephrons have no nephron loops at all. Nephrons close to the medulla are called **juxtamedullary**[16] **nephrons.** They have very long nephron loops that extend nearly to the apex of the renal pyramid. Only 15% of the nephrons are juxtamedullary, but these are almost solely responsible for maintaining the salinity gradient of the medulla.

### INSIGHT 25.2

### Evolutionary Medicine

## The Kidney and Life on Dry Land

Physiologists first suspected that the nephron loop plays a role in water conservation because of their studies of a variety of animal species. Animals that must conserve water have longer, more numerous nephron loops than animals with little need to conserve it. Fish and amphibians lack nephron loops and produce urine that is isotonic to their blood plasma. Aquatic mammals such as beavers have short nephron loops and only slightly hypertonic urine.

But the kangaroo rat, a desert rodent, provides an instructive contrast. It lives on seeds and other dry foods and can live without drinking any water at all. The water produced by its aerobic respiration is enough to meet its needs because its kidneys are extraordinarily efficient at conserving it. They have extremely long nephron loops and produce urine that is 10 to 14 times as concentrated as their blood plasma (compared with about 4 times, at most, in humans).

Comparative studies thus suggested a hypothesis for the function of the nephron loop that was confirmed through a long line of ensuing research. This shows how comparative anatomy provides suggestions and insights into function and why physiologists do not study human function in isolation from other species.

The **distal convoluted tubule (DCT)** is a coiled part of the renal tubule located in the cortex beyond the nephron loop. It is the end of the nephron. The DCT is shorter and less convoluted than the PCT, so fewer sections of it are seen in histological sections. It has a simple cuboidal epithelium with smooth-surfaced cells nearly devoid of microvilli. It absorbs variable amounts of sodium, calcium, chloride, and water, and secretes potassium and hydrogen into the tubular fluid. Unlike the PCT, which absorbs solutes and water at a constant rate, the DCT reabsorbs these at variable rates determined by the hormone *aldosterone,* which regulates sodium and potassium excretion. *Parathyroid hormone* acts on both the PCT and DCT to regulate calcium and phosphate excretion.

The initial portion of the DCT, before it coils, contacts the afferent and efferent arterioles adjacent to the renal corpuscle, and the three structures form the **juxtaglomerular** (JUX-tuh-glo-MER-you-lur) **apparatus** (fig. 25.10). This is a device for monitoring the fluid entering the DCT and adjusting the performance of the nephron. Three specialized cell types are found here:

1. The **macula densa**[17] is a patch of slender, closely spaced epithelial cells in the DCT on the side facing the afferent arteriole. Much is still unknown about their physiology, but they apparently act as sensory cells that monitor the flow or composition of the tubular fluid and communicate with the cells described next.

2. **Juxtaglomerular (JG) cells** are enlarged smooth muscle cells found in the afferent arteriole and in smaller numbers in the efferent arteriole. When stimulated by the macula densa, they

---

[15]Friedrich G. J. Henle (1809–85), German anatomist
[16]*juxta* = next to

[17]*macula* = spot, patch + *densa* = dense

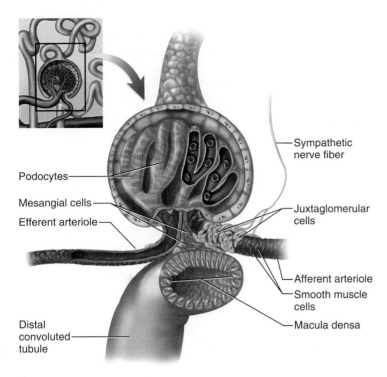

**Figure 25.10** The Juxtaglomerular Apparatus.

dilate or constrict the arterioles. JG cells also secrete renin, the enzyme mentioned earlier that triggers corrective changes in blood pressure.

3. **Mesangial**[18] (mez-AN-jee-ul) **cells** occupy the cleft between the afferent and efferent arterioles and the spaces between the capillaries of the glomerulus. Their role is not yet clearly understood, but they are connected to the macula densa and JG cells by gap junctions and perhaps mediate communication between those cells.

The **collecting duct** is a straight tubule that passes down into the medulla. It is part of the renal tubule but not part of the nephron; the nephron and collecting duct have separate embryonic origins. The cortical part of the collecting duct receives fluid from the DCTs of several nephrons. The duct then continues into the medulla, where the greater part of it lies. Near the renal papilla, several collecting ducts converge to form a larger, short stretch called the **papillary duct.** About 30 papillary ducts drain from each papilla into a minor calyx. Once the urine drains into a minor calyx, it undergoes no further change in composition or concentration.

The collecting duct is lined with a simple cuboidal epithelium with two types of cells—intercalated ("in between") cells and principal cells. **Intercalated cells** play a role in regulating the body's acid–base balance by secreting either $H^+$ or bicarbonate ions ($HCO_3^-$) into the urine. **Principal cells** reabsorb $Na^+$ and water and secrete $K^+$ into the urine. They represent the kidney's last chance to adjust the water content and thus the osmolarity of the urine. The principal cells also have water channels called *aquaporins* in their membranes. As the tubular fluid descends through the

collecting duct, water passes by osmosis through these channels, out of the tubule and into the increasingly salty tissue fluid of the medulla. The salinity gradient created by the nephron loop makes this osmotic reabsorption of water possible. The reabsorbed water is carried away by the blood capillaries of the vasa recta.

The collecting duct is influenced by two hormones: *atrial natriuretic peptide,* which increases sodium excretion in the urine, and *antidiuretic hormone,* which promotes water retention and reduces urine volume.

To summarize, the flow of fluid from the point where the glomerular filtrate is formed to the point where urine leaves the kidney is glomerular capsule → proximal convoluted tubule → nephron loop → distal convoluted tubule → collecting duct → papillary duct → minor calyx → major calyx → renal pelvis → ureter.

## *Before You Go On*

*Answer the following questions to test your understanding of the preceding section:*

3. Arrange the following in order from the most numerous to the least numerous structures in a kidney: glomeruli, major calyces, minor calyces, interlobular arteries, interlobar arteries.

4. Trace the path taken by one red blood cell from the renal artery to the renal vein.

5. Concisely state the functions of the glomerulus, PCT, nephron loop, DCT, and collecting duct.

6. Describe the location and appearance of podocytes and explain their function.

7. Consider one molecule of urea in the urine. Trace the route that it took from the bloodstream to the point where it left the body.

## Anatomy of the Ureters, Urinary Bladder, and Urethra

### *Objectives*

When you have completed this section, you should be able to

• describe the functional anatomy of the ureters, urinary bladder, and male and female urethra.

Urine is produced continually, but fortunately, it does not drain continually from the body. Urination *(micturition)* is episodic—occurring when we allow it. This is made possible by an apparatus for storing urine and by neural controls for its timely release.

### The Ureters

The renal pelvis funnels urine into the ureter, a retroperitoneal, muscular tube that extends to the urinary bladder. The ureter is about 25 cm long and reaches a maximum diameter of about 1.7 cm near the bladder. The ureters pass posterior to the bladder and enter it from below, penetrating obliquely through its muscular

---

[18]*mes* = in the middle + *angi* = vessel

# INSIGHT 25.3

## Clinical Application

### Kidney Stones

A *renal calculus*[19] (kidney stone) is a hard granule of calcium, phosphate, uric acid, and protein. Renal calculi form in the renal pelvis and are usually small enough to pass unnoticed in the urine flow. Some, however, grow as large as several centimeters and block the renal pelvis or ureter, which can lead to the destruction of nephrons as pressure builds in the kidney. A large, jagged calculus passing down the ureter stimulates strong contractions that can be excruciatingly painful. It can also damage the ureter and cause hematuria. Causes of renal calculi include hypercalcemia (excess calcium in the blood), dehydration, pH imbalances, frequent urinary tract infections, or an enlarged prostate gland causing urine retention. Calculi are sometimes treated with stone-dissolving drugs, but often they require surgical removal. A nonsurgical technique called *lithotripsy*[20] uses ultrasound to pulverize the calculi into fine granules easily passed in the urine.

wall and opening onto its floor. A small flap of bladder mucosa acts as a valve at the opening of each ureter to keep urine from backing up into the ureter when the bladder contracts.

The ureter has three layers: an adventitia, muscularis, and mucosa. The adventitia is a connective tissue layer that binds it to the surrounding tissues. It blends with the capsule of the kidney at the superior end and with the connective tissue of the bladder wall at the inferior end. The muscularis consists of two layers of smooth muscle over most of its length, but a third layer appears in the lower ureter. The inner muscular layer consists of longitudinal muscle cells; the cells in the next layer superficial to this have a circular arrangement; and the third and outermost layer in the lower ureter is again longitudinal. Peristaltic waves of contraction in the muscularis "milk" urine from the renal pelvis down to the bladder. The mucosa of the ureter has a transitional epithelium that begins in the minor calyces of the kidney and extends through the urinary bladder. The lumen is very narrow and is easily obstructed by kidney stones (see Insight 25.3).

## The Urinary Bladder

The urinary bladder (fig. 25.11) is a muscular sac on the floor of the pelvic cavity, inferior to the peritoneum and posterior to the pubic symphysis. It is covered by parietal peritoneum on its flattened superior surface and by a fibrous adventitia elsewhere. Its muscular layer, called the **detrusor**[21] (deh-TROO-zur) **muscle,** consists of three indistinctly separated layers of smooth muscle. The mucosa has a transitional epithelium. When the bladder is empty, this epithelium is five or six cells thick, and the mucosa has conspicuous wrinkles called **rugae**[22] (ROO-gee). When the bladder fills, the

stretching smooths out the rugae, and the epithelium thins to about two or three cells thick. The bladder is a highly distensible organ, capable of holding up to 800 mL of urine.

The openings of the two ureters and the urethra mark a smooth-surfaced triangular area called the **trigone**[23] on the bladder floor. This is a common site of bladder infection (see Insight 25.4). For photographs of the relationship of the bladder and urethra to other pelvic organs in both sexes, see figure A.22 (p. 41).

## The Urethra

The urethra conveys urine out of the body. In the female, it is a tube 3 to 4 cm long bound to the anterior wall of the vagina by fibrous connective tissue (fig. 25.11a). Its opening, the **external urethral orifice,** lies between the vaginal orifice and clitoris. The male urethra (fig. 25.11b) is about 18 cm long and has three regions: (1) The **prostatic urethra** begins at the urinary bladder and passes for about 2.5 cm through the prostate gland. During orgasm, it receives semen from the reproductive glands. (2) The **membranous urethra** is a short (0.5 cm), thin-walled portion where the urethra passes through the muscular floor of the pelvic cavity. (3) The **spongy (penile) urethra** is about 15 cm long and passes through the penis to the external urethral orifice. It is named for the *corpus spongiosum,* an erectile tissue that surrounds the penile urethra (see p. 747). The male urethra assumes an S-shape: it passes downward from the bladder, turns anteriorly as it enters the root of the penis, and then turns about 90° downward again as it enters the external, pendant part of the penis. The mucosa has a transitional epithelium near the bladder, a pseudostratified columnar epithelium for most of its length, and finally a stratified squamous epithelium near the external urethral orifice. There are mucous **urethral glands** in the wall of the penile urethra.

In both sexes, the detrusor muscle is thickened near the urethra to form an **internal urethral sphincter,** which compresses the urethra and retains urine in the bladder. Since this sphincter is composed of

# INSIGHT 25.4

## Clinical Application

### Urinary Tract Infections

Infection of the urinary bladder is called *cystitis.*[24] It is especially common in females because bacteria such as *Escherichia coli* can travel easily from the perineum up the short urethra. Because of this risk, young girls should be taught never to wipe the anus in a forward direction. If cystitis is untreated, bacteria can spread up the ureters and cause *pyelitis,*[25] infection of the renal pelvis. If it reaches the renal cortex and nephrons, it is called *pyelonephritis.* Kidney infections can also result from invasion by blood-borne bacteria. Urine stagnation due to renal calculi or prostate enlargement increases the risk of infection.

---

[19]*calc* = calcium, stone + *ul* = little
[20]*litho* = stone + *tripsy* = crushing
[21]*de* = down + *trus* = push
[22]*ruga* = fold, wrinkle

[23]*tri* = three + *gon* = angle
[24]*cyst* = bladder + *itis* = inflammation
[25]*pyel* = pelvis

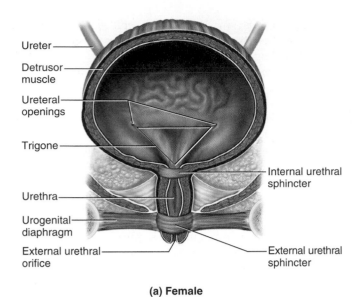

**(a) Female**

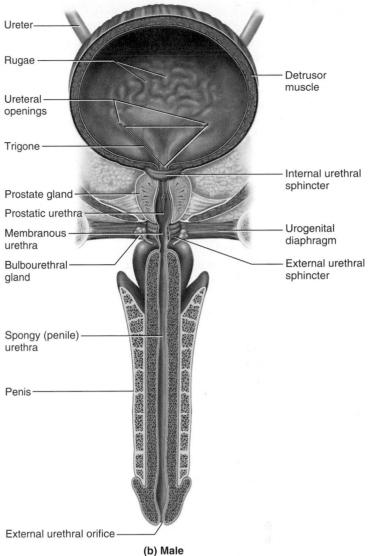

**Figure 25.11 The Urinary Bladder and Urethra.** Frontal sections.
● *Why would an enlarged prostate gland make it more difficult to empty the bladder?*

**(b) Male**

smooth muscle, it is under involuntary control. Where the urethra passes through the pelvic floor, it is encircled by an **external urethral sphincter** of skeletal muscle, which provides voluntary control over the voiding of urine.

## *Before You Go On*

*Answer the following questions to test your understanding of the preceding section:*

8. Describe the anatomical relationship of the ureter to the renal pelvis and to the bladder wall.

9. Compare and contrast the structure and function of the internal and external urethral sphincters.

10. Contrast the structure of the bladder wall when the bladder is empty with when it is full.

11. Name and define the three segments of the male urethra.

# Developmental and Clinical Perspectives

### *Objectives*
When you have completed this section, you should be able to
- describe the embryonic development of the urinary system;
- describe the degenerative changes that occur in old age;
- describe the causes and effects of renal failure; and
- briefly define or describe several urinary system diseases.

## Prenatal Development

Perhaps surprisingly, the embryonic urinary system develops two pairs of primitive, temporary kidneys before "settling down" and producing the permanent pair. The system develops as if replaying the evolutionary history of the vertebrate urinary system. Early in week 4, a rudimentary kidney called the *pronephros*[26] appears in the cervical region, resembling the kidneys of many fish and amphibian embryos and larvae. The pronephros disappears by the end of that week. As it degenerates, a second kidney, the *mesonephros*,[27] appears in the thoracic to lumbar region. The mesonephros functions in the embryos of all vertebrates, but is of minor importance in most mammals, where wastes are eliminated via the placenta. Most of the mesonephros disappears by the end of month 2, but its collecting duct, the *mesonephric duct,* remains and contributes

---
[26]*pro* = first + *nephros* = kidney
[27]*meso* = middle + *nephros* = kidney

importantly to the male reproductive tract (see p. 760). This duct opens into an embryonic *cloaca,* a temporary rectumlike receiving chamber for the digestive, urinary, and reproductive systems. The final kidney, the *metanephros,*[28] appears in week 5 and thus overlaps the existence of the mesonephros.

The permanent urinary tract begins with a pouch called the **ureteric bud** growing from the lower end of each mesonephric duct. The closed, upper end of the bud dilates and branches to form the renal pelvis, then the major and minor calyces, and finally the collecting ducts (fig. 25.12). Each collecting duct has a cap of metanephric kidney tissue over its tip. The duct induces this cap to differentiate into an S-shaped tubule (fig. 25.13a). Blood capillaries grow into one end of the tubule and form a glomerulus as the tubule grows around it to form the double-walled glomerular capsule. The other end of the tubule breaks through to become continuous with the collecting duct. The tubule gradually lengthens and differentiates into the proximal convoluted tubule, nephron loop, and distal convoluted tubule. By the time of birth, each kidney will have formed over 1 million nephrons in this manner. No more nephrons form after birth, but the existing ones continue to grow. The kidney surface is lumpy at birth but smooths out because of nephron growth.

The kidneys originate in the pelvic region and later migrate superiorly—a movement called **ascent of the kidney.** Initially, the kidney is supplied by a pelvic branch of the aorta, but as it ascends, new arteries higher and higher on the aorta take over the job of supplying the kidney, while the lower arteries degenerate.

In weeks 4 to 7, the cloaca divides into an anterior *urogenital (U-G) sinus* and a posterior *anal canal.* The superior part of the U-G sinus forms the urinary bladder, and the inferior part forms the urethra. In infants and children, the urinary bladder is located in the abdomen. It begins to drop into the greater pelvis at about 6 years of age, but does not enter the lesser pelvis and become a true pelvic organ until after puberty. Early in its development, the bladder is connected to the allantois, an extraembryonic sac described in chapter 4 (p. 116). This connection eventually becomes a constricted passage, the *urachus* (yur-AY-kus), connecting the bladder to the umbilicus. In the adult, the urachus is reduced to a fibrous cord, the *median umbilical ligament.*

Urine production begins around week 12 of fetal development, but metabolic wastes are cleared by the placenta, not by the fetal urinary system. Fetal urine is continually recycled as the fetus voids it into the amniotic fluid, swallows it, and then excretes it again.

## The Aging Urinary System

The kidneys exhibit a striking degree of atrophy in old age. From ages 25 to 85, the number of nephrons declines by 30% to 40%, and up to one-third of the remaining glomeruli become atherosclerotic, bloodless, and nonfunctional. The kidneys of a 90-year-old are 20% to 40% smaller than those of a 30-year-old and receive only half as much blood. They are proportionately less efficient at clearing wastes from the blood. Although baseline renal function

[28]*meta* = beyond, next in a series + *nephros* = kidney

## INSIGHT 25.5

### Clinical Application

#### Developmental Abnormalities of the Kidney

Several anomalies can occur during the embryonic development of the kidneys (see fig. 1.7c). *Pelvic kidney* is a condition in which the kidney fails to ascend and remains in the pelvic cavity for life. *Horseshoe kidney* is a single C-shaped kidney formed when the ascending kidneys are crowded together and merge into one. The C typically snags on the inferior mesenteric artery, preventing the horseshoe kidney from ascending any farther. Some people have two ureters arising from a single kidney, resulting from a splitting of the ureteric bud in early embryonic development. Usually the two ureters empty into the bladder, but in rare cases, one of them empties into the uterus, vagina, urethra, or elsewhere. This requires surgical correction so that urine does not dribble continually from the urethra or vagina. Some kidneys have an *accessory renal artery* resulting from failure of one of the early, temporary renal arteries to degenerate as the permanent renal artery forms. Most such irregularities cause no functional problems and usually go unnoticed, but they may be discovered in surgery, radiography, or cadaver dissection.

is adequate even in old age, the kidneys have little reserve capacity; thus, other diseases can lead to surprisingly rapid renal failure. Drug doses often need to be reduced for the elderly because the kidneys cannot clear drugs from the blood as rapidly. Reduced renal function is a significant factor in overmedication of the aged.

Water balance becomes more precarious in old age because the kidneys are less responsive to antidiuretic hormone and because the sense of thirst is blunted. Even with free access to water, many elderly people do not drink enough to maintain normal blood osmolarity, and dehydration is common.

Voiding and bladder control become a problem for both men and women. About 80% of men over the age of 80 are affected by *benign prostatic hyperplasia,* a noncancerous growth of the prostate gland that compresses the urethra, reduces the force of the urine stream, and makes it harder to empty the bladder. Urine retention can cause pressure to back up in the kidneys, aggravating the failure of the nephrons. Older women become increasingly subject to *urinary incontinence* (see table 25.1), especially if their history of pregnancy and childbearing has weakened the pelvic muscles and urethral sphincters. Senescence of the sympathetic nervous system and nervous disorders such as stroke and Alzheimer disease can also cause incontinence.

## Urinary System Disorders

The most serious disorder of the urinary system is renal failure. *Acute renal failure* is an abrupt decline in kidney function, often caused by trauma or by a hemorrhage or thrombosis cutting off blood flow to the nephrons. *Chronic renal failure* is a long-term, progressive, irreversible loss of functional nephrons. It can result from such causes as prolonged or repetitive kidney infections, trauma, poisoning, atherosclerosis of the renal arteries (often in

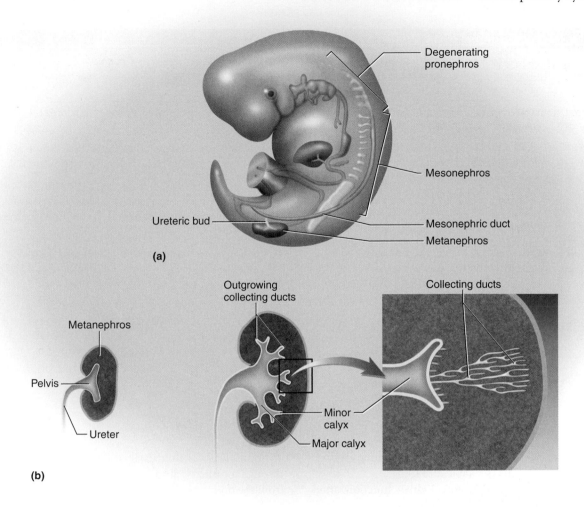

(a)

(b)

**Figure 25.12** **Embryonic Development of the Urinary Tract.**  (a) Relationship of the early ureteric bud and metanephros to the lower mesonephric duct. (b) Progression in the development of the ureter, renal pelvis, calyces, and collecting ducts, all of which arise from the ureteric bud.

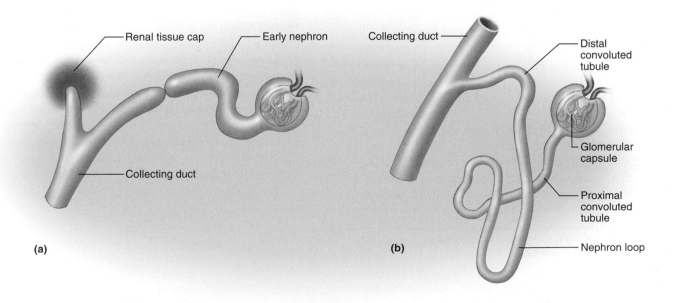

(a)                                                      (b)

**Figure 25.13** **Embryonic Development of the Nephron.**  (a) The collecting duct induces mesoderm to differentiate into a renal (metanephric) tissue cap, as shown at the far left. This cap differentiates into an S-shaped tube that will become the nephron, as shown on the right fork of the duct (representing a later stage of development). (b) The renal tubule has begun to differentiate into proximal and distal convoluted tubules and nephron loop.

| TABLE 25.1 | Some Disorders of the Urinary System |
|---|---|
| **Acute glomerulonephritis** | An autoimmune inflammation of the glomeruli, often following a streptococcus infection. Results in destruction of glomeruli leading to hematuria, proteinuria, edema, reduced glomerular filtration, and hypertension. Can progress to chronic glomerulonephritis and renal failure, but most individuals recover from acute glomerulonephritis without lasting effect. |
| **Hydronephrosis**[29] | Increase in fluid pressure in the renal pelvis and calyces owing to obstruction of the ureter by kidney stones, nephroptosis, or other causes. Can progress to complete cessation of glomerular filtration and atrophy of nephrons. |
| **Nephroptosis**[30] (NEFF-rop-TOE-sis) | Slippage of the kidney to an abnormally low position *(floating kidney)*. Occurs in people with too little body fat to hold the kidney in place, and in people who subject the kidneys to prolonged vibration, such as truck drivers, equestrians, and motorcyclists. Can twist or kink the ureter, which causes pain, obstructs urine flow, and potentially leads to hydronephrosis. |
| **Nephrotic syndrome** | Excretion of large amounts of protein in the urine ($\geq$ 3.5 g/day) due to glomerular injury. Can result from trauma, drugs, infections, cancer, diabetes mellitus, lupus erythematosus, and other diseases. Loss of plasma protein leads to edema, ascites (pooling of fluid in the abdominal cavity), hypotension, and susceptibility to infection (because of immunoglobulin loss). |
| **Urinary incontinence** | Inability to hold the urine; involuntary leakage from the bladder. Can result from incompetence of the urinary sphincters; bladder irritation; pressure on the bladder in pregnancy; an obstructed urinary outlet so that the bladder is constantly full and dribbles urine *(overflow incontinence)*; uncontrollable urination due to brief surges in bladder pressure, as in laughing or coughing *(stress incontinence)*; and neurological disorders such as spinal cord injuries. |

### Disorders Described Elsewhere

| | | |
|---|---|---|
| Azotemia 718 | Kidney stones 728 | Pyelonephritis 728 |
| Cystitis 728 | Proteinuria 724 | Uremia 718 |
| Hematuria 724 | Pyelitis 728 | |

conjunction with diabetes mellitus), or an autoimmune disease called acute glomerulonephritis (see table 25.1).

Nephrons can regenerate and restore kidney function after short-term injuries, and even when some nephrons are irreversibly destroyed, others can hypertrophy and compensate for their lost function. Indeed, a person can survive on as little as one-third of one kidney. When 75% of the nephrons are lost, however, the remaining ones cannot maintain homeostasis. The result is azotemia and acidosis, and if 90% of renal function is lost, uremia is likely. Loss of nephron function also leads to anemia, because erythrocyte production depends on the hormone *erythropoietin*, which is secreted mainly by the kidneys.

Renal insufficiency or failure must be treated either with a kidney transplant or with *hemodialysis*. The latter is a procedure in which, usually, arterial blood is pumped through a *dialysis machine*. In the machine, the blood passes through tubes of dialysis membrane immersed in dialysis fluid. Wastes and excess water diffuse from the blood into the fluid, which is discarded, and drugs can be added to the dialysis fluid to diffuse into the blood. Another method called *continuous ambulatory peritoneal dialysis (CAPD)* frees the patient from the dialysis machine and can be carried out at home. Dialysis fluid is introduced into the peritoneal cavity through a catheter, absorbs metabolic wastes, and then is drained from the body and discarded.

Some other urinary system disorders are briefly described in Table 25.1.

## *Before You Go On*

*Answer the following questions to test your understanding of the preceding section:*

12. Explain why the nephron has a different embryonic origin than the passages from collecting duct to urethra.

13. How does the number of functional nephrons change in old age? What are the implications of this change for homeostasis and medication dosages?

14. What are some causes of renal failure? Describe some clinical signs of renal failure.

15. Cover the right side of table 25.1 and define or describe the disorders on the left from memory.

---

[29]*hydro* = water + *nephr* = kidney + *osis* = medical condition
[30]*nephro* = kidney + *ptosis* = sagging, falling

# CHAPTER REVIEW

## REVIEW OF KEY CONCEPTS

### Functions of the Urinary System (p. 717)

1. The urinary system consists of two kidneys, two ureters, the urinary bladder, and the urethra.

2. The kidneys filter blood plasma; separate wastes from useful chemicals; regulate blood volume and pressure; control blood osmolarity; secrete renin, erythropoietin, and calcitriol; regulate blood pH; detoxify free radicals and drugs; and carry out gluconeogenesis in times of starvation.

3. Excretion is the process of isolating wastes from the body fluids and eliminating them.

4. The kidneys excrete nitrogenous wastes, among other waste products. The most abundant nitrogenous waste in the urine is *urea*.

5. An elevated level of blood urea is called *azotemia*, and may progress to a serious syndrome called *uremia*.

### Anatomy of the Kidney (p. 718)

1. The kidneys are located retroperitoneally against the upper posterior abdominal wall. Each is provided with a renal artery and renal vein. The adrenal glands lie against the superior to medial aspects of the kidneys.

2. Each kidney contains about 1.2 million functional units called *nephrons*.

3. The kidney has a slit called the *hilum* on its concave side, where it receives renal nerves, blood and lymphatic vessels, and the ureter.

4. From superficial to deep, the kidney is enclosed by the *renal fascia, adipose capsule,* and *renal capsule.*

5. The renal parenchyma is a C-shaped tissue enclosing a space called the *renal sinus.* The parenchyma is divided into an outer *renal cortex* and inner *renal medulla.* The medulla is divided into 6 to 10 *renal pyramids.*

6. The apex, or *papilla,* of each pyramid projects into a receptacle called a *minor calyx,* which collects the urine from that lobe. Minor calyces converge to form *major calyces,* and these converge on the *renal pelvis,* where the ureter arises.

7. The renal artery branches and gives rise to *segmental arteries, interlobar arteries, arcuate arteries,* and then *interlobular arteries,* which penetrate into the cortex. For each nephron, an *afferent arteriole* arises from the interlobular artery and supplies the capillaries of the *glomerulus.* An *efferent arteriole* leaves the glomerulus and usually gives rise to a bed of *peritubular capillaries* around the renal tubules. Blood then flows through a series of *interlobular, arcuate,* and *interlobar veins,* before leaving the kidney by way of the *renal vein.*

8. The renal medulla is supplied by vessels called the *vasa recta,* which arise from the efferent arterioles of juxtamedullary nephrons and empty into arcuate and interlobular veins.

9. *Renal nerves* follow the renal artery and innervate the afferent and efferent arterioles. They provide sympathetic control over blood flow to the glomerulus, and thus regulate the rate of glomerular filtration and urine formation. They also stimulate renin secretion.

10. A nephron produces urine in three stages: *glomerular filtration, tubular reabsorption* and *secretion,* and *water conservation.*

11. A nephron begins with a double-walled *glomerular capsule* enclosing the glomerulus; the glomerulus and capsule constitute the *renal corpuscle.* The capsule consists of a parietal layer with a simple squamous epithelium and a visceral layer composed of *podocytes.* Podocytes have numerous *foot processes* that wrap around the glomerular capillaries.

12. To leave the blood and enter the glomerular capsule, water and solutes must pass through the filtration pores of the capillary endothelium, the basement membrane, and the *filtration slits* between the podocyte foot processes. The small sizes and negative charges on these barriers prevent blood cells and most protein from leaving the capillaries.

13. Filtrate collects in the *capsular space* between the capsule layers and then flows into the *renal tubule* leading away from the capsule.

14. The renal tubule consists of a highly coiled *proximal convoluted tubule (PCT),* a U-shaped *nephron loop,* a coiled *distal convoluted tubule (DCT),* and a *collecting duct.* The first three of these belong to a single nephron; the collecting duct receives fluid from many nephrons.

15. The proximal convoluted tubule (PCT) is the longest part of the renal tubule, and has a brush border of prominent microvilli. It reabsorbs about 65% of the glomerular filtrate and returns it to the peritubular capillaries. Materials pass through its epithelium by both *transcellular* and *paracellular routes.*

16. The PCT reabsorbs electrolytes, glucose, amino acids, lactate, protein and other peptides, amino acids, urea, uric acid, and water. It secretes urea, uric acid, creatinine, ammonia, bile acids, $H^+$, $HCO_3^-$, drugs, and other solutes into the tubular fluid.

17. The nephron loop reabsorbs $Na^+$, $K^+$, $Cl^-$, and water, and serves mainly to maintain a gradient of salinity in the tissue fluid of the renal medulla. In conjunction with the collecting duct, this makes it possible to excrete hypertonic urine, thus to eliminate wastes without excessive water loss.

18. The distal convoluted tubule (DCT) reabsorbs $Na^+$, $Ca^{2+}$, $Cl^-$, phosphate, and water, and secretes $K^+$ and $H^+$, all at variable rates depending on the influence of aldosterone, atrial natriuretic peptide, and parathyroid hormone.

19. The *juxtaglomerular apparatus* is a junction of the DCT with the afferent and efferent arterioles near the glomerular capsule. It is a feedback device for monitoring the flow and composition of the tubular fluid and adjusting glomerular filtration.

20. The *collecting duct* receives filtrate from nephrons in the cortex and passes down through the medulla to the renal papilla. It secretes variable amounts of $H^+$, $K^+$, and $HCO_3^-$ into the tubular fluid and reabsorbs $Na^+$. Most importantly, it reabsorbs variable amounts of water according to the influence of antidiuretic hormone, thus adjusting the osmolarity of the urine and regulating the body's water balance.

### Anatomy of the Ureters, Urinary Bladder, and Urethra (p. 727)

1. The ureter is a muscular tube from the renal pelvis to the floor of the urinary bladder. It drives urine to the bladder by means of peristalsis.

2. The urinary bladder has a smooth muscle layer called the *detrusor muscle* with a thickened ring, the *internal urethral sphincter,* around the origin of the urethra. Most of its mucosa exhibits folds called *rugae* when the bladder is empty. The *trigone,* a smooth triangular area between the openings of the ureters and urethra, is the most common site of bladder infections.

3. The urethra is 3 to 4 cm long in the female, but in the male, it is 18 cm long and divided into *prostatic, membranous,* and *spongy (penile)* segments. An *external urethral sphincter* of skeletal muscle encircles the urethra in both sexes where it passes through the pelvic floor.

**Developmental and Clinical Perspectives**
**(p. 729)**

1. Temporary embryonic kidneys called the *pronephros* and *mesonephros* develop and degenerate before the permanent kidney, the *metanephros,* appears early in week 5.

2. At this time, a pouch called the *ureteric bud* arises from the lower end of the mesonephric duct. It elongates and branches, eventually giving rise to the ureter, renal pelvis and calyces, and collecting ducts.

3. As the ureteric bud penetrates into the mesonephric kidney tissue, it induces the formation of nephrons. These start as S-shaped tubules that eventually enfold glomerular capillaries at one end, connect with the collecting duct at the other end, and differentiate into PCT, nephron loop, and DCT.

4. The embryonic urinary tract initially opens into a cloaca that also receives the digestive and reproductive tracts, but in weeks 4 to 7, the cloaca divides into an anal canal and a urogenital sinus. The upper part of the urogenital sinus differentiates into the urinary bladder, and the lower end into the urethra.

5. In old age, the kidneys atrophy markedly and become less efficient at clearing wastes and drugs from the blood. Elderly women often experience urinary incontinence due to weakening of the pelvic muscles and urethral sphincters, whereas elderly men often experience urine retention and reduced flow during urination because of pressure on the urethra from an enlarged prostate gland.

6. Renal failure can have numerous causes ranging from atherosclerosis to poisoning and trauma. It presents a danger of azotemia or uremia, and may require hemodialysis or a kidney transplant.

# TESTING YOUR RECALL

1. Which of these is *not* a function of the kidneys?
   a. to secrete hormones
   b. to excrete nitrogenous wastes
   c. to store urine
   d. to control blood volume
   e. to control acid–base balance

2. The compact ball of capillaries in a nephron is called
   a. the nephron loop.
   b. the peritubular plexus.
   c. the renal corpuscle.
   d. the glomerulus.
   e. the vasa recta.

3. Which of these is *not* true of the position of the kidneys in the body?
   a. They are medial to the aorta.
   b. They are retroperitoneal.
   c. The right kidney is lower than the left.
   d. They are inferior to the liver and spleen.
   e. They lie partially within the rib cage.

4. Which of these lies closest to the renal cortex?
   a. the parietal peritoneum
   b. the renal fascia
   c. the renal capsule
   d. the perirenal fat
   e. the renal pelvis

5. The water that is reabsorbed by the collecting duct enters
   a. the nephron loop.
   b. the minor calyx.
   c. the ureter.
   d. the efferent arteriole.
   e. the vasa recta.

6. A glomerulus and glomerular capsule make up one
   a. renal capsule.
   b. renal corpuscle.
   c. kidney lobule.
   d. kidney lobe.
   e. nephron.

7. The kidney has more _____ than any of the other structures listed.
   a. arcuate arteries
   b. minor calyces
   c. medullary pyramids
   d. afferent arterioles
   e. collecting ducts

8. The _____ arises from the embryonic ureteric bud.
   a. nephron
   b. renal pelvis
   c. glomerulus
   d. urinary bladder
   e. proximal convoluted tubule

9. The ___ absorbs variable amounts of water depending on the level of antidiuretic hormone present.
   a. proximal convoluted tubule
   b. nephron loop
   c. distal convoluted tubule
   d. collecting duct
   e. urinary bladder

10. In cortical nephrons, blood of the efferent arteriole flows next into
    a. the peritubular capillaries.
    b. the arcuate artery.
    c. the arcuate vein.
    d. the vasa recta.
    e. the glomerulus.

11. The most abundant nitrogenous waste in the urine is _____.

12. The ureter, renal pelvis, calyces, and collecting duct arise from an embryonic pouch called the _____.

13. The openings of the two ureters and the urethra form the boundaries of a smooth area called the _____ on the floor of the urinary bladder.

14. The _____ is a group of epithelial cells of the distal convoluted tubule that monitors the flow or composition of the tubular fluid.

15. To enter the capsular space, filtrate must pass between foot process of the _____, which are cells that form the visceral layer of the glomerular capsule.

16. What part of the nephron is characterized by a brush border and especially great length?

17. Epithelial cells in the _____ of the nephron loop have few mitochondria and low metabolic activity, but they are very permeable to water.

18. The smooth muscle of the bladder wall is called the _____.

19. Each renal pyramid drains into a separate cuplike urine receptacle called a _____.

20. Blood flows through the _____ arteries just before entering the interlobular arteries.

*Answers in the Appendix*

## TRUE OR FALSE

*Determine which five of the following statements are false, and briefly explain why.*

1. The ureters open through pores in the roof of the urinary bladder.

2. The kidneys secrete antidiuretic hormone to promote water retention and prevent dehydration.

3. The kidney has more distal convoluted tubules than collecting ducts.

4. Tight junctions prevent material from leaking between the epithelial cells of the renal tubule.

5. Many collecting ducts empty into each minor calyx.

6. The glomerulus is a complex of blood capillaries located in the capsular space of the glomerular capsule.

7. Each interlobular artery serves multiple nephrons.

8. Blood-borne solutes can become incorporated into the urine by either glomerular filtration or tubular secretion.

9. The kidneys are normally located in the pelvic cavity.

10. The kidneys develop in the pelvic region and ascend to a higher location in the abdominal cavity during fetal development.

*Answers in the Appendix*

## TESTING YOUR COMPREHENSION

1. What function could the collecting duct *not* perform if there were no nephron loops? Why?

2. Why would a simple squamous epithelium function poorly as an inner lining of the urinary bladder?

3. In some infants, the urachus fails to close; it remains as an open passage *(urachal fistula)* from the urinary bladder to the umbilicus. What would you expect to be the most obvious sign of a urachal fistula?

4. Suppose the ureters entered the bladder from above instead of from below. Which disorder in table 25.1 would you expect to result from this? Explain why.

5. In what ways do the proximal and distal convoluted tubules differ in structure? How is this related to their functional difference?

*Answers at aris.mhhe.com*

## ONLINE RESOURCES

 Visit aprevealed.com to explore melt-away cadaver dissections, watch animations that clarify difficult concepts, review histological and radiological images, or take a quiz to assess your understanding of the material.

 The Saladin *Human Anatomy,* 2e website at aris.mhhe.com features chapter-specific quizzes, labeling exercises, and other interactive tools to complement your study of human anatomy. If your instructor has provided an ARIS course code, you can also access assignments and information specific to your course.

# The Reproductive System

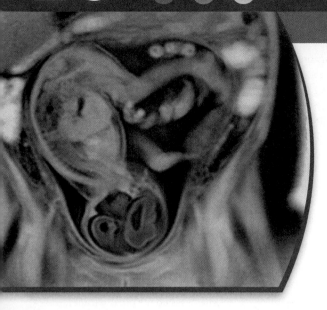

MRI scan of a fetus in the uterus at the 36th week of pregnancy

## BRUSHING UP

To understand this chapter, you may find it helpful to review the following concepts:
- Chromosome structure (p. 67)
- Mitosis (p. 67)
- Muscles of the pelvic floor (p. 318)
- Hypothalamic releasing factors and pituitary gonadotropins (p. 530)
- Androgens (p. 539)
- Embryology of the mesonephric duct (p. 729)

Anatomy & Physiology REVEALED®
aprevealed.com

**Reproductive System**

From all we have learned of the structure and function of the human body, it seems a wonder that it works at all! The fact is, however, that even with modern medicine we can't keep it working forever. The body inevitably suffers degenerative changes as we age, and eventually we expire. Yet our genes live on in new containers—our offspring. This final chapter concerns the means of their production—the male and female reproductive systems.

# Sexual Reproduction

### Objectives
When you have completed this section, you should be able to
- define *sexual reproduction;*
- identify the most fundamental biological distinction between male and female; and
- define *primary sex organs, secondary sex organs,* and *secondary sex characteristics.*

## The Two Sexes

The essence of sexual reproduction is that it is biparental—the offspring receive genes from two parents and therefore are not genetically identical to either one. To achieve this, the parents must produce **gametes**[1] (sex cells) that meet and combine their genes in a **zygote**[2] (fertilized egg). The gametes must have two properties for reproduction to be successful: motility so they can achieve contact, and nutrients for the developing embryo. A single cell cannot perform both of these roles optimally, because to contain ample nutrients means to be relatively large and heavy, and this is inconsistent with the need for motility. Therefore, these tasks are usually apportioned to two kinds of gametes. The small motile one—little more than DNA with a propeller—is the **sperm (spermatozoon)**, and the large nutrient-laden one is the **egg (ovum).**

In any sexually reproducing species, by definition, an individual that produces eggs is female and one that produces sperm is male. This criterion is not always that simple, as we see in certain abnormalities in sexual development. Genetically, however, any human with a Y sex chromosome is classified as male and anyone lacking a Y is classified as female. Normally, a male inherits an X from the mother and Y from the father, and his sex chromosomes are thus designated XY. A female inherits an X from each parent, and therefore has an XX chromosome pair.

In mammals, the female is also the parent that provides a sheltered internal environment for the development and prenatal nutrition of the embryo. For fertilization and development to occur in the female, the male must have a copulatory organ, the penis, for introducing his gametes into the female reproductive tract and the female must have a copulatory organ, the vagina, for receiving the sperm. This is the most obvious difference between the sexes, but appearances can be deceiving (see fig. 18.16, p. 547).

[1]*gam* = marriage, union
[2]*zygo* = yoke, union

## Overview of the Reproductive System

The **reproductive system** in the male serves to produce sperm and introduce them into the female body. The female reproductive system produces eggs, receives the sperm, provides for the union of these gametes, harbors the fetus, gives birth, and nourishes the offspring.

In both sexes, the reproductive system consists of primary and secondary sex organs, or **genitalia.** The **primary sex organs,** or **gonads,**[3] are the organs that produce gametes—testes of the male and ovaries of the female. The **secondary sex organs** are organs other than gonads that are necessary for reproduction. In the male, they constitute a system of ducts, glands, and the penis, concerned with the storage, survival, and conveyance of sperm. In the female, they include the uterine tubes, uterus, and vagina, concerned with uniting the sperm and egg and harboring the fetus.

According to location, the reproductive organs are classified as **external** and **internal genitalia** (table 26.1). The external genitalia are located in the perineum—the diamond-shaped region marked by the pubic symphysis anteriorly, the coccyx posteriorly, and the ischial tuberosities laterally (fig. 26.1; see also fig. 11.17, p. 319). Most of them are externally visible, except for the accessory glands of the female perineum (see fig. 26.21). The internal genitalia are located mainly in the pelvic cavity, except for the male testes and some associated ducts contained in the scrotum.

**Secondary sex characteristics** are features that develop in adolescence, further distinguish the sexes, and play a role in mate attraction. From the call of a bullfrog to the tail of a peacock, these are well known in the animal kingdom. In humans, the identification of secondary sex characteristics rests on somewhat subjective and culturally variable judgments of what is sexually attractive. Commonly

[3]*gon* = seed

| TABLE 26.1 | The External and Internal Genitalia |
| --- | --- |
| **External Genitalia** | **Internal Genitalia** |
| **Male** | |
| Penis | Testes (s. testis) |
| Scrotum | Epididymides (s. epididymis) |
| | Ductus deferentes (s. ductus deferens) |
| | Seminal vesicles |
| | Prostate |
| | Bulbourethral glands |
| **Female** | |
| Mons pubis | Ovaries |
| Labia majora (s. labium majus) | Uterine tube |
| Labia minora (s. labium minus) | Uterus |
| Clitoris | Vagina |
| Vaginal orifice | |
| Vestibular bulbs | |
| Vestibular glands | |
| Paraurethral glands | |

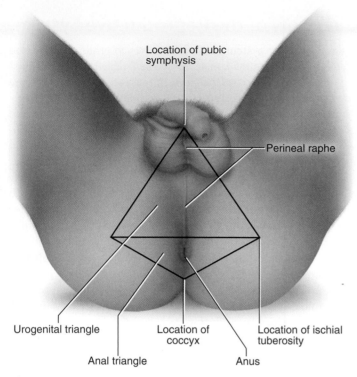

Location of pubic symphysis

Perineal raphe

Urogenital triangle

Location of coccyx

Location of ischial tuberosity

Anal triangle

Anus

**Figure 26.1** The Male Perineum.

considered among the secondary sex characteristics are the pubic, axillary, and male facial hair; apocrine scent glands associated with these patches of hair; differences in the texture and visibility of the hair on the limbs and trunk; the female breasts; differences in muscularity and the quantity and distribution of body fat; and differences in the pitch of the voice.

## *Before You Go On*

*Answer the following questions to test your understanding of the preceding section:*

1. Define *gonad* and *gamete*. Explain the relationship between the terms.

2. Define *male, female, sperm,* and *egg*.

# Male Reproductive Anatomy

## *Objectives*
When you have completed this section, you should be able to

• describe the anatomy of the scrotum, testes, spermatic ducts, accessory glands, and penis;

• describe the stages in spermatogenesis, the production of sperm; and

• describe the structure of a sperm cell and the composition of semen.

We will survey the male reproductive system beginning with the scrotum and testes and following the direction of sperm transport, thus ending with the penis.

## The Scrotum

The testes are contained in the **scrotum,**[4] a pouch of skin, muscle, and fibrous connective tissue (fig. 26.2). The left testis is usually suspended lower than the right so the two are not compressed against each other between the thighs. The skin of the scrotum has sebaceous glands, sparse hair, rich sensory innervation, and somewhat darker pigmentation than skin elsewhere. The scrotum is divided into right and left compartments by an internal **median septum,** which protects each testis from infections of the other one. The location of the septum is externally marked by a seam called the **perineal raphe**[5] (RAY-fee), which also extends anteriorly along the ventral side of the penis and posteriorly as far as the margin of the anus (see fig. 26.1).

Posteriorly, the scrotum contains the **spermatic cord,** a bundle of fibrous connective tissue containing the *ductus deferens* (a sperm duct), blood and lymphatic vessels, and testicular nerves. It passes upward behind and superior to the testis, where it is easily palpated through the skin of the scrotum. It continues across the anterior side of the pubis and into a 4-cm-long **inguinal canal,** which leads through the muscles of the groin and emerges into the pelvic cavity. The inferior entrance into the inguinal canal is called the *external inguinal ring,* and its superior exit into the pelvic cavity is the *internal inguinal ring.*

The original reason that a scrotum evolved is a subject of debate among reproductive biologists. For whatever reason human testes reside in the scrotum, however, they have adapted to this cooler environment and cannot produce sperm at the core body temperature of 37°C; they must be held at about 35°C. The scrotum has three mechanisms for regulating the temperature of the testes:

1. The **cremaster**[6] **muscle**—strips of the internal abdominal oblique muscle that enmesh the spermatic cord. When it is cold, the cremaster contracts and draws the testes closer to the body to keep them warm. When it is warm, the cremaster relaxes and the testes are suspended farther from the body.

2. The **dartos**[7] **muscle**—a subcutaneous layer of smooth muscle. It, too, contracts when cold, making the scrotum taut and wrinkled. This reaction holds the testes snugly against the warm body and reduces the surface area of the scrotum, thus reducing heat loss.

3. The **pampiniform**[8] **plexus**—an extensive network of veins from the testis that surround the testicular artery in the spermatic cord. The plexus prevents warm arterial blood from overheating the testis, which would inhibit sperm production. It acts as a *countercurrent heat exchanger.* Blood ascending

---

[4]*scrotum* = bag
[5]*raphe* = seam
[6]*cremaster* = suspender
[7]*dartos* = skinned
[8]*pampin* = tendril + *form* = shape

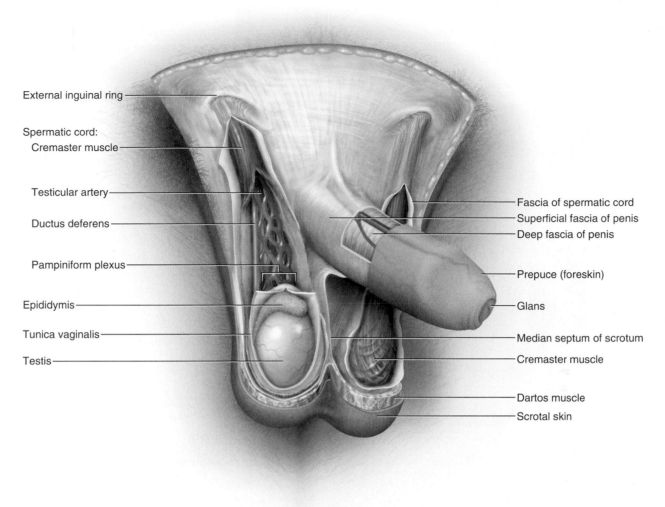

External inguinal ring

Spermatic cord:
  Cremaster muscle

Testicular artery

Ductus deferens

Pampiniform plexus

Epididymis

Tunica vaginalis

Testis

Fascia of spermatic cord
Superficial fascia of penis
Deep fascia of penis

Prepuce (foreskin)

Glans

Median septum of scrotum

Cremaster muscle

Dartos muscle
Scrotal skin

**Figure 26.2** The Scrotum and Spermatic Cord.

through the plexus is relatively cool (about 35°C) and absorbs heat from the warmer (37°C) blood descending through the testicular artery. By the time the arterial blood reaches the testis, it is 1.5° to 2.5°C cooler than it was when it left the pelvic cavity.

## The Testes

The **testes (testicles)** are the male gonads—combined endocrine and exocrine glands that produce sex hormones and sperm. Each testis is oval and slightly flattened, about 4 cm long, 3 cm from anterior to posterior, and 2.5 cm from left to right (fig. 26.3). Its anterior and lateral surfaces are covered by the **tunica vaginalis,**[9] a saccular extension of the peritoneum. The testis itself has a white fibrous capsule called the **tunica albuginea**[10] (TOO-nih-ca AL-byu-JIN-ee-uh). Connective tissue septa extend from the capsule into the parenchyma of the testis, dividing it into 200 to 300 wedge-shaped lobules. Each lobule contains one to three **seminiferous**[11] (SEM-ih-

NIF-er-us) **tubules**—slender ducts up to 70 cm long in which the sperm are produced. Between the seminiferous tubules are clusters of **interstitial (Leydig**[12]**) cells,** the source of testosterone.

A seminiferous tubule has a narrow lumen lined by a thick **germinal epithelium** (fig. 26.4). The epithelium consists of several layers of **germ cells** in the process of becoming sperm, and a much smaller number of tall **sustentacular**[13] (**Sertoli**[14]) **cells,** which protect the germ cells and promote their development. The germ cells depend on the sustentacular cells for nutrients, waste removal, growth factors, and other needs. The sustentacular cells also secrete a hormone, *inhibin,* which regulates the rate of sperm production.

A sustentacular cell is shaped a little like a tree trunk whose roots spread out over the basement membrane, forming the boundary of the tubule, and whose thick trunk reaches to the tubule lumen. Tight junctions between adjacent sustentacular cells form a **blood–testis barrier (BTB),** which prevents antibodies and other large molecules in the blood and intercellular fluid from getting to the germ cells. This is important because the germ cells, being genetically different from other cells of the body, would otherwise be

[9]*tunica* = coat + *vagina* = sheath
[10]*alb* = white
[11]*semin* = seed, sperm + *fer* = to carry

[12]Franz von Leydig (1821–1908), German anatomist
[13]*sustentacul* = support
[14]Enrico Sertoli (1842–1910), Italian histologist

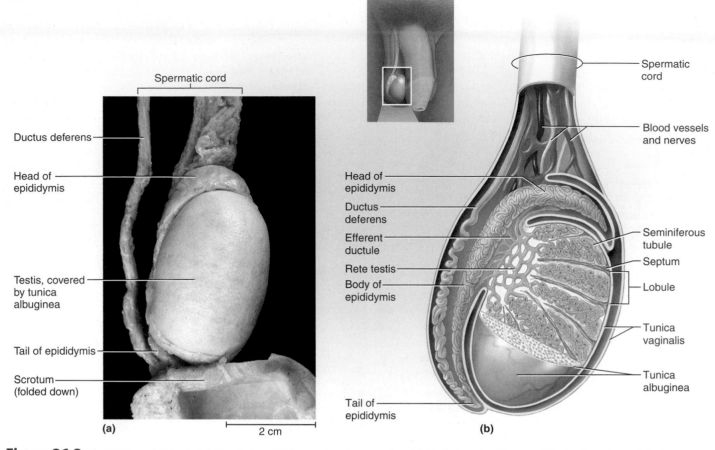

**Figure 26.3** **The Testis and Associated Structures.** (a) The scrotum is opened and folded downward to reveal the testis and associated organs. (b) Anatomy of the testis, epididymis, and spermatic cord.

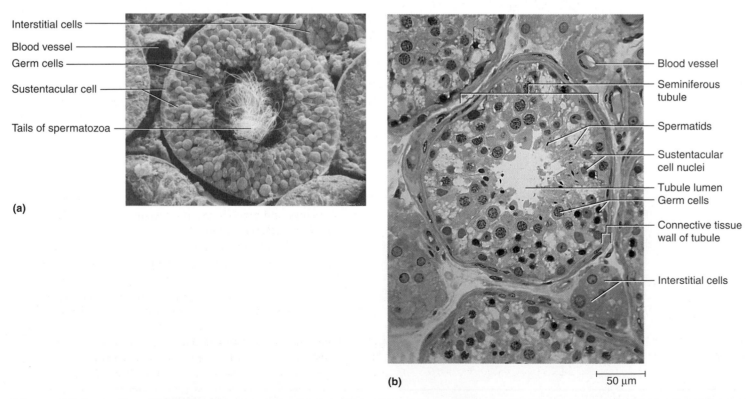

**Figure 26.4** **Histology of the Testis.** (a) Scanning electron micrograph. (b) Light micrograph. Part (b) is from a region of the tubule that did not have mature sperm at the time. [Part (a) from R. G. Kessel and R. H. Kardon, Tissues and Organs: A Text-Atlas of Scanning Electron Microscopy, W. H. Freeman, 1979.]

attacked by the immune system. Some cases of sterility occur when the BTB fails to form adequately in adolescence and the immune system produces autoantibodies against the germ cells.

### THINK ABOUT IT

*Would you expect to find blood capillaries in the walls of the seminiferous tubules? Why or why not?*

The seminiferous tubules lead into a network called the **rete**[15] (REE-tee) **testis,** embedded in the capsule on the posterior side. Sperm partially mature in the rete. They are moved along by the flow of fluid secreted by the sustentacular cells and by the cilia on some rete cells. Sperm do not swim while they are in the male.

Each testis is supplied by a **testicular artery,** which arises from the abdominal aorta just below the renal artery. This is a very long, slender artery that winds its way down the posterior abdominal wall before passing through the inguinal canal into the scrotum. Its blood pressure is very low, and this is one of the few arteries to have no pulse. Consequently, blood flow to the testes is quite meager and they receive a poor oxygen supply. The sperm appear to compensate by developing unusually large mitochondria, which may precondition them for survival in the hypoxic environment of the female reproductive tract.

Blood leaves the testis by way of a the pampiniform plexus of veins. As these veins pass through the inguinal canal, they converge and form the **testicular vein.** The right testicular vein drains into the inferior vena cava and the left one drains into the left renal vein. Lymphatic vessels also drain each testis. They travel through the inguinal canal with the veins and lead to lymph nodes adjacent to the lower aorta. Lymph from the penis and scrotum, however, travels to lymph nodes adjacent to the iliac arteries and veins and in the inguinal region.

**Testicular nerves** lead to the gonads from spinal cord segments T10 and T11. They are mixed sensory and motor nerves containing predominantly sympathetic but also some parasympathetic fibers. The sensory fibers are concerned primarily with pain and the autonomic fibers are predominantly vasomotor, for regulation of blood flow.

## Spermatogenesis and Sperm

**Spermatogenesis** is the process of sperm production. It occurs in the seminiferous tubules and involves three principal events: (1) remodeling of a relatively large germ cell into small, mobile cells with flagella; (2) reduction of the chromosome number by one-half, so that when the sperm and egg combine, we do not get a doubling of chromosome number in every generation; and (3) a shuffling of the genes so that each chromosome of the sperm carries new gene combinations that did not exist in the chromosomes received from the parents. This ensures genetic variety in the offspring. The genetic recombination and reduction in chromosome number are achieved through a form of cell division called **meiosis,** which produces four daughter cells that subsequently differentiate into sperm (fig. 26.5).

Early in prenatal development, **primordial germ cells** form in the yolk sac, migrate by ameboid motion into the embryo itself, and colonize the *gonadal ridges* (see p. 760). Here they become stem cells called **spermatogonia.** These cells remain dormant through childhood, lying along the periphery of the seminiferous tubules near the basement membrane, outside the blood–testis barrier (BTB). These cells are **diploid**[16]—they have 46 chromosomes (23 pairs) and are genetically identical to most other cells of the body, so they require no protection from the immune system.

At puberty, testosterone secretion rises, reactivates the spermatogonia, and brings on spermatogenesis. The essential steps of spermatogenesis are as follows; see the same-numbered steps in figure 26.6.

1. Spermatogonia divide by mitosis. One daughter cell from each division remains near the tubule wall as a stem cell called the *type A spermatogonium.* Type A spermatogonia serve as a lifetime supply of stem cells, so men normally remain fertile throughout old age. The other daughter cell, called the *type B spermatogonium,* migrates slightly away from the wall on its way to becoming sperm.

2. The type B spermatogonium enlarges and becomes a **primary spermatocyte.** Since this cell is about to undergo meiosis and become genetically different from other cells of the body, it must be protected from the immune system. Ahead of the primary spermatocyte, the tight junction between two sustentacular cells is dismantled, while a new tight junction forms behind the spermatocyte. The spermatocyte moves forward toward the lumen, like passing through the double-doored airlock of a spaceship, and is now protected by the BTB.

3. The primary spermatocyte undergoes *meiosis I,* a cell division that reduces the chromosome number by half. The daughter cells, called **secondary spermatocytes,** are therefore **haploid**[17]—they have 23 unpaired chromosomes, although each chromosome consists of two genetically identical strands called chromatids (see fig. 2.21, p. 69).

4. The secondary spermatocytes undergo another division, *meiosis II,* in which each chromosome splits into separate chromatids. The result is four daughter cells (two from each spermatocyte) called **spermatids,** each with 23 single-stranded chromosomes.

5. A spermatid divides no further, but undergoes a process called **spermiogenesis,** in which it differentiates into a single spermatozoon (sperm). The fundamental changes in spermiogenesis are a loss of excess cytoplasm and the growth of a tail (flagellum), making the sperm a lightweight, mobile cell (fig. 26.7).

---

[15]*rete* = network

[16]*diplo* = double
[17]*haplo* = half

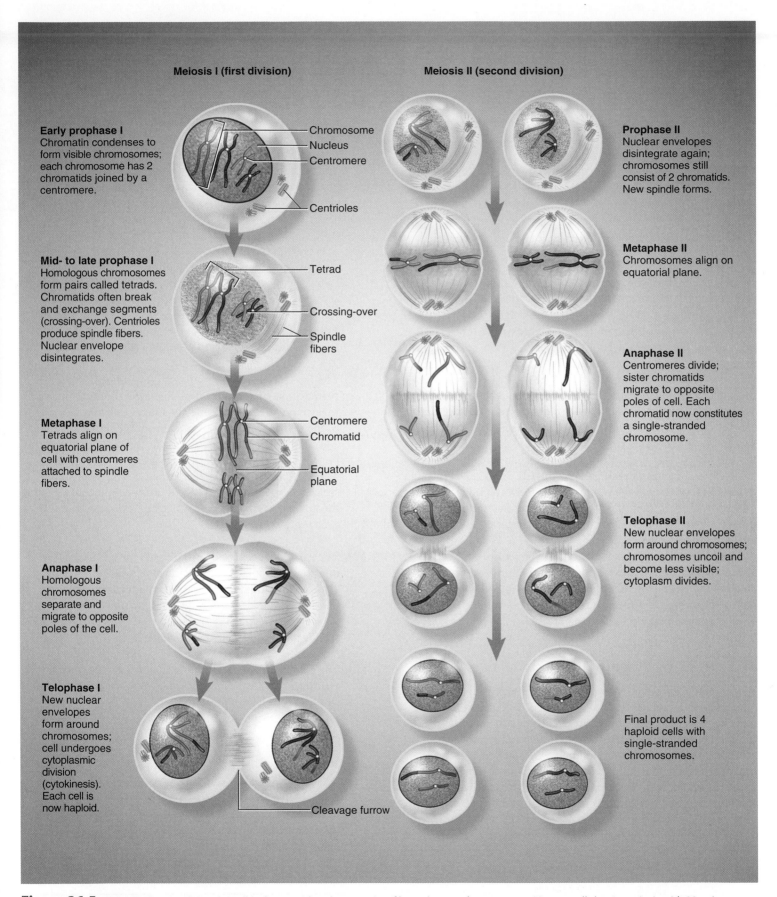

**Meiosis I (first division)**

**Meiosis II (second division)**

**Early prophase I**
Chromatin condenses to form visible chromosomes; each chromosome has 2 chromatids joined by a centromere.

— Chromosome
— Nucleus
— Centromere
— Centrioles

**Mid- to late prophase I**
Homologous chromosomes form pairs called tetrads. Chromatids often break and exchange segments (crossing-over). Centrioles produce spindle fibers. Nuclear envelope disintegrates.

— Tetrad
— Crossing-over
— Spindle fibers

**Metaphase I**
Tetrads align on equatorial plane of cell with centromeres attached to spindle fibers.

— Centromere
— Chromatid
— Equatorial plane

**Anaphase I**
Homologous chromosomes separate and migrate to opposite poles of the cell.

**Telophase I**
New nuclear envelopes form around chromosomes; cell undergoes cytoplasmic division (cytokinesis). Each cell is now haploid.

— Cleavage furrow

**Prophase II**
Nuclear envelopes disintegrate again; chromosomes still consist of 2 chromatids. New spindle forms.

**Metaphase II**
Chromosomes align on equatorial plane.

**Anaphase II**
Centromeres divide; sister chromatids migrate to opposite poles of cell. Each chromatid now constitutes a single-stranded chromosome.

**Telophase II**
New nuclear envelopes form around chromosomes; chromosomes uncoil and become less visible; cytoplasm divides.

Final product is 4 haploid cells with single-stranded chromosomes.

**Figure 26.5  Meiosis.**  For simplicity, the cell is shown with only two pairs of homologous chromosomes. Human cells begin meiosis with 23 pairs.

Cross section of
seminiferous tubules

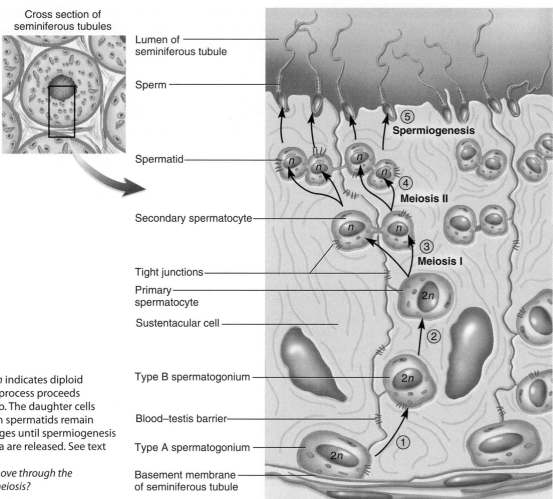

Lumen of seminiferous tubule

Sperm

⑤ Spermiogenesis

Spermatid

Meiosis II ④

Secondary spermatocyte

③ Meiosis I

Tight junctions

Primary spermatocyte

Sustentacular cell

Type B spermatogonium

Blood–testis barrier

Type A spermatogonium

Basement membrane of seminiferous tubule

**Figure 26.6** **Spermatogenesis.** 2*n* indicates diploid cells, and *n* indicates haploid cells. The process proceeds from the bottom of the figure to the top. The daughter cells from secondary spermatocytes through spermatids remain connected by slender cytoplasmic bridges until spermiogenesis is complete and individual spermatozoa are released. See text for explanation of steps 1 through 5.

● *Why must the primary spermatocyte move through the blood–testis barrier before undergoing meiosis?*

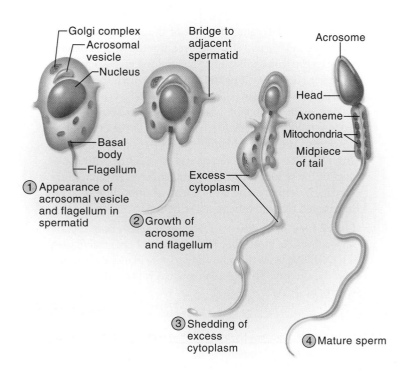

Golgi complex
Acrosomal vesicle
Nucleus

Bridge to adjacent spermatid

Acrosome

Head
Axoneme
Mitochondria
Midpiece of tail

Basal body
Flagellum

Excess cytoplasm

① Appearance of acrosomal vesicle and flagellum in spermatid

② Growth of acrosome and flagellum

③ Shedding of excess cytoplasm

④ Mature sperm

**Figure 26.7** **Spermiogenesis.** In this process, the spermatids discard excess cytoplasm, grow tails, and become spermatozoa.

All stages from primary spermatocyte to spermatozoon are enfolded in tendrils of the sustentacular cells and bound to them by tight junctions and gap junctions. In addition, the daughter cells do not completely separate from each other in meiosis I and II, but remain joined to each other by narrow cytoplasmic bridges. They do not completely separate until the very end of spermiogenesis.

At the conclusion of spermiogenesis, the spermatozoa are released and washed down the tubule by fluid from the sustentacular cells. It takes about 74 days for a spermatogonium to become mature sperm. A young adult male produces about 300,000 sperm per minute, or 400 million per day.

## The Spermatozoon

The spermatozoon has two parts: a pear-shaped head and a long tail (fig. 26.8). The **head,** about 4 to 5 μm long and 3 μm wide at its broadest part, contains three structures: a nucleus, acrosome, and flagellar basal body. The most important of these is the nucleus, which fills most of the head and contains a haploid set of condensed, genetically inactive chromosomes. The **acrosome**[18] is a lysosome in the form of a thin cap covering the apical half of the nucleus. It contains enzymes that are later used to penetrate the egg if the sperm is successful. The basal body of the tail flagellum is nestled in an indentation at the posterior end of the nucleus.

---

[18]*acro* = tip, peak + *some* = body

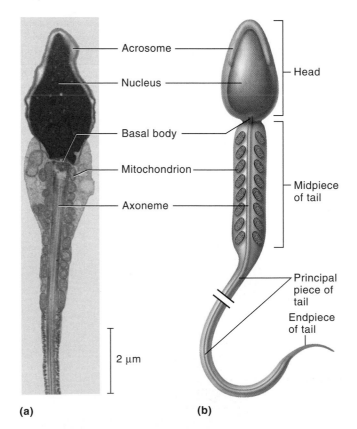

Acrosome

Nucleus

Basal body

Mitochondrion

Axoneme

Head

Midpiece of tail

Principal piece of tail

Endpiece of tail

2 μm

**(a)**  **(b)**

**Figure 26.8** The Mature Spermatozoon. (a) Head and part of the tail of a spermatozoon (TEM). (b) Sperm structure.

The **tail** is divided into three regions called the midpiece, principal piece, and endpiece. The **midpiece,** a cylinder about 5 to 9 μm long and half as wide as the head, is the thickest part. It contains numerous large mitochondria that spiral tightly around the axoneme of the flagellum. They produce the ATP needed for the beating of the tail when the sperm migrates up the female reproductive tract. The **principal piece,** 40 to 45 μm long, constitutes most of the tail and consists of the axoneme surrounded by a sheath of supportive fibers. The **endpiece,** 4 to 5 μm long, consists of the axoneme only and is the narrowest part of the sperm.

## The Spermatic Ducts

After leaving the testis, the sperm travel through a series of *spermatic ducts* to reach the urethra. These include the following (fig. 26.9):

- **Efferent ductules.** About 12 small efferent ductules arise from the posterior side of each testis and carry sperm to the epididymis (see fig. 26.3b). They have clusters of ciliated cells that help drive the sperm along.

- **Duct of the epididymis.** The **epididymis**[19] (EP-ih-DID-ih-miss; plural, *epididymides*) is a site of sperm maturation and storage. It adheres to the posterior side of the testis, measures about 7.5 cm long, and consists of a clublike *head* at the superior end, a long middle *body,* and a slender *tail* at its inferior end. It contains a single coiled duct, about 6 m (18 ft) long, embedded in connective tissue. This duct reabsorbs about 90% of the fluid secreted by the testis. Sperm are physiologically immature (incapable of fertilizing an egg) when they leave the testis, but mature as they travel through the head and body of the epididymis. In 20 days or so, they reach the tail. They are stored here and in the adjacent portion of the ductus deferens. Stored sperm remain fertile for 40 to 60 days, but if they become too old without being ejaculated, they disintegrate and the epididymis reabsorbs them.

- **Ductus (vas) deferens.** The duct of the epididymis straightens out at the tail, turns 180°, and becomes the ductus deferens. This is a muscular tube about 45 cm long and 2.5 mm in diameter (fig. 26.9). It passes upward through the spermatic cord and inguinal canal, and enters the pelvic cavity. There, it turns medially and approaches the urinary bladder. After passing between the bladder and ureter, the duct turns downward behind the bladder and widens into a terminal **ampulla.** The ductus deferens ends by uniting with the duct of the seminal vesicle, a gland considered later. It has a very narrow lumen and a thick wall of smooth muscle well innervated by sympathetic nerve fibers.

- **Ejaculatory duct.** Where the ductus deferens and duct of the seminal vesicle meet, they form a short (2 cm) ejaculatory duct, which passes through the prostate gland and empties into the urethra. The ejaculatory duct is the last of the spermatic ducts.

---

[19]*epi* = upon + *didym* = twins, testes

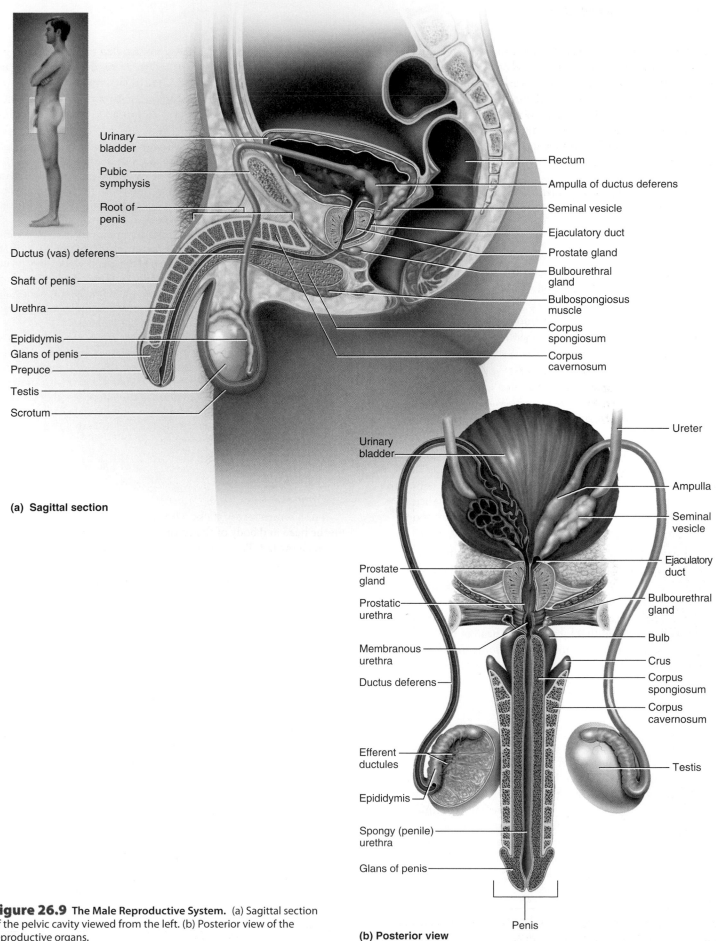

Urinary
bladder

Pubic
symphysis

Root of
penis

Ductus (vas) deferens

Shaft of penis

Urethra

Epididymis

Glans of penis

Prepuce

Testis

Scrotum

Rectum

Ampulla of ductus deferens

Seminal vesicle

Ejaculatory duct

Prostate gland

Bulbourethral
gland

Bulbospongiosus
muscle

Corpus
spongiosum

Corpus
cavernosum

**(a) Sagittal section**

Urinary
bladder

Prostate
gland

Prostatic
urethra

Membranous
urethra

Ductus deferens

Efferent
ductules

Epididymis

Spongy (penile)
urethra

Glans of penis

Ureter

Ampulla

Seminal
vesicle

Ejaculatory
duct

Bulbourethral
gland

Bulb

Crus

Corpus
spongiosum

Corpus
cavernosum

Testis

Penis

**(b) Posterior view**

**Figure 26.9** **The Male Reproductive System.** (a) Sagittal section
of the pelvic cavity viewed from the left. (b) Posterior view of the
reproductive organs.

The male urethra is shared by the reproductive and urinary systems. It is about 20 cm long and consists of three regions: the *prostatic, membranous,* and *spongy (penile) urethra.* Although it serves both urinary and reproductive roles, it cannot pass urine and semen simultaneously. During ejaculation, the internal urethral sphincter contracts to prevent the voiding of urine and keep semen out of the urinary bladder.

## The Accessory Glands

There are three sets of *accessory glands* in the male reproductive system (fig. 26.9):

- **Seminal vesicles.** These are a pair of glands posterior to the urinary bladder; one is associated with each ductus deferens. A seminal vesicle is about 5 cm long, or approximately the dimensions of one's little finger. It has a connective tissue capsule and underlying layer of smooth muscle. The secretory portion is a very convoluted duct with numerous branches that form a complex labyrinth. The duct empties into the ejaculatory duct.
- **Prostate**[20] (PROSS-tate) **gland.** This is a median structure that surrounds the urethra and ejaculatory duct immediately inferior to the urinary bladder. It measures about 3 cm in diameter. It is actually a composite of 30 to 50 compound tubuloacinar glands enclosed in a single fibrous capsule. These glands empty into the urethra through about 20 pores in the urethral wall. The stroma of the prostate consists of connective tissue and smooth muscle, like that of the seminal vesicles. The prostate gland is the source of the two most common urogenital dysfunctions in older men (see Insight 26.1).
- **Bulbourethral (Cowper**[21]**) glands.** These are named for their position near a dilated bulb at the inner end of the penis and their association with the penile urethra. They are brownish, spherical glands about 1 cm in diameter, with a 2.5 cm duct to the urethra. During sexual arousal, they produce a clear slippery fluid that lubricates the head of the penis in preparation for intercourse. Perhaps more importantly, though, the fluid protects the sperm by neutralizing the acidity of residual urine in the urethra.

### Semen

A typical ejaculation discharges 2 to 5 mL of **semen**[22] (**seminal fluid),** a complex mixture of sperm and glandular secretions. About 10% of it consists of sperm and fluids from the spermatic ducts; 30% is a thin, milky fluid from the prostate; and 60% is a viscous, yellowish fluid from the seminal vesicles. The bulbourethral glands contribute a trace of fluid. Normal semen contains about 50 to 120 million sperm per milliliter—the sperm count. A count lower than 20 to 25 million/mL is usually associated with *infertility (sterility),* the inability to fertilize an egg (see table 26.2).

# INSIGHT 26.1
## Clinical Application

### Prostate Diseases

The prostate gland weighs about 20 g by age 20, remains at that weight until age 45 or so, and then begins to grow slowly again. By age 70, over 90% of men show some degree of *benign prostatic hyperplasia (BHP)*—noncancerous enlargement of the gland. The major complication of BHP is that it compresses the urethra, slows the flow of urine, and sometimes promotes bladder and kidney infections.

*Prostate cancer* is the second most common cancer in men (after lung cancer); it affects about 9% of men over the age of 50. Prostate tumors tend to form near the periphery of the gland, where they do not obstruct urine flow; therefore, they often go unnoticed until they cause pain. Prostate cancer often metastasizes to nearby lymph nodes and then to the lungs and other organs. It is more common among American blacks than whites and is rare among the Japanese.

The position of the prostate immediately anterior to the rectum allows it to be palpated through the rectal wall to check for tumors. This procedure is called *digital rectal examination (DRE)*. Prostate cancer can also be diagnosed from elevated levels of *serine protease* (also known as *prostate specific antigen, PSA*) and *acid phosphatase* (another prostatic enzyme) in the blood. Up to 80% of men with prostate cancer survive when it is detected and treated early, but only 10% to 50% survive if it spreads beyond the prostatic capsule.

Fresh semen is very sticky. This results from the action of a clotting enzyme in the prostatic fluid on a protein, *proseminogelin,* in the seminal vesicle fluid. The enzyme converts this to *seminogelin,* an adhesive protein very similar to the fibrin of a blood clot. The functional advantage of this seems to be that it ensures semen will adhere to the cervix and vagina rather than draining back out. Twenty to 30 minutes later, another prostatic enzyme, *serine protease,* breaks down seminogelin and liquifies the semen, liberating the sperm for their migration up the female reproductive tract. Sperm motility requires energy, which they get from fructose and other sugars provided by the seminal vesicles. The seminal vesicles also contribute lipids called *prostaglandins*—named for their discovery in the prostatic fluid of bulls, but later found to be even more abundant in the seminal vesicle fluid. Prostaglandins may contribute to the passage of sperm from the vagina into the uterus by thinning the mucus in the *cervical canal* (see p. 754) and perhaps inducing peristaltic contractions that suck semen into the uterus.

## The Penis

The **penis**[23] serves to deposit semen in the vagina. Half of it is an internal **root** and half is the externally visible **shaft** and **glans**[24] (see figs. 26.9 and 26.10). The glans is the expanded head at the distal end of the penis with the external urethral orifice at its tip. The

---

[20]*pro* = before + *stat* = to stand; commonly misspelled and mispronounced "prostrate"
[21]William Cowper (1666–1709), British anatomist
[22]*semen* = seed

[23]*penis* = tail
[24]*glans* = acorn

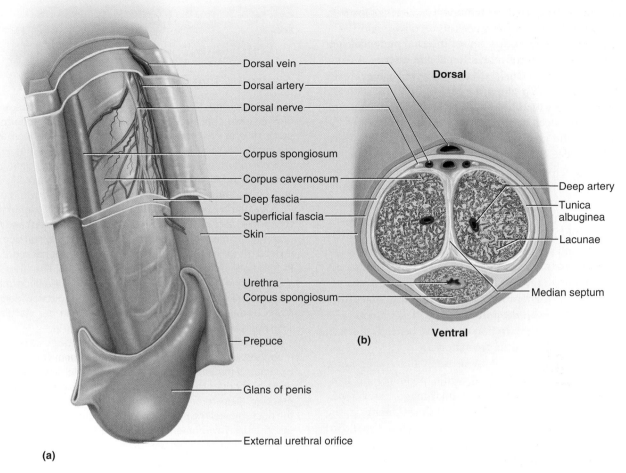

Dorsal vein
Dorsal artery
Dorsal nerve
Corpus spongiosum
Corpus cavernosum
Deep fascia
Superficial fascia
Skin
Urethra
Corpus spongiosum
Prepuce
Glans of penis
External urethral orifice

(a)

Dorsal
Deep artery
Tunica albuginea
Lacunae
Median septum
Ventral

(b)

**Figure 26.10  Anatomy of the Penis.**  (a) Superficial dissection of shaft, lateral view. (b) Cross section at midshaft.
● *What is the functional benefit of the corpus spongiosum not having a tunica albuginea?*

external portion is about 8 to 10 cm (3–4 in.) long and 3 cm in diameter when flaccid (nonerect); the typical dimensions of an erect penis are 13 to 18 cm (5–7 in.) long and 4 cm in diameter.

The skin is loosely attached to the shaft, allowing for expansion during erection. It continues over the glans as the **prepuce,** or foreskin, which is often removed by circumcision. A ventral fold of tissue called the *frenulum* attaches the skin to the proximal margin of the glans. The skin of the glans itself is thinner and firmly attached to the underlying erectile tissue. The glans and facing surface of the prepuce have sebaceous glands that produce a waxy secretion called **smegma.**[25]

Directional terminology may be a little confusing in the penis, because the *dorsal* side is the one that faces anteriorly, at least when the penis is flaccid, whereas the *ventral* side of the penis faces posteriorly. This is because in most mammals, the penis is horizontal, held against the abdomen by skin, and points anteriorly. The urethra passes through its lower, more obviously ventral, half. Directional terminology in the human penis follows the same convention as for other mammals, even though our bipedal posture and more pendulous penis change these anatomical relationships.

The penis consists mainly of three cylindrical bodies called **erectile tissues,** which fill with blood during sexual arousal and account for its enlargement and erection. A single erectile body, the **corpus spongiosum,** passes along the ventral side of the penis and encloses the penile urethra. It expands at the distal end to fill the entire glans. Proximal to the glans, the dorsal side of the penis has a **corpus cavernosum** (plural, *corpora cavernosa*) on each side. Each is ensheathed in a tight fibrous sleeve called the **tunica albuginea,** and they are separated from each other by a **median septum.** (Note that the testes also have a tunica albuginea and the scrotum also has a median septum.)

All three cylinders of erectile tissue are spongy in appearance and contain numerous tiny blood sinuses called **lacunae.** The partitions between lacunae, called **trabeculae,** are composed of connective tissue and smooth **trabecular muscle.** In the flaccid penis, trabecular muscle tone collapses the lacunae, which appear as slits in the tissue.

At the body surface, the penis turns 90° posteriorly and continues inward as the root. The corpus spongiosum terminates at the internal end of the root as a dilated **bulb,** which is ensheathed in the bulbospongiosus muscle and attached to the lower surface of the perineal membrane in the urogenital triangle (see p. 318). The corpora cavernosa diverge like the arms of a Y. Each arm, called a **crus** (pronounced "cruss"; plural, *crura*), attaches the penis to the pubic

---

[25]*smegma* = unguent, ointment, soap

arch of the pelvis and to the perineal membrane on its respective side. Each crus is enveloped by an ischiocavernosus muscle.

The penis receives blood from a pair of **internal pudendal (penile) arteries,** which branch from the internal iliac arteries. As each artery enters the root of the penis, it divides in two. One branch, the **dorsal artery,** travels dorsally along the penis not far beneath the skin, supplying blood to the skin, fascia, and corpus spongiosum. The other branch, the **deep artery,** travels through the core of the corpus cavernosum and gives off smaller **helicine**[26] **arteries,** which penetrate the trabeculae and empty into the lacunae. There are numerous anastomoses between the dorsal and deep arteries, so neither of them is the exclusive source of blood to any one erectile tissue.

When the deep arteries dilate, the lacunae fill with blood and the erectile tissues swell. The tunica albuginea around the corpora cavernosa cannot expand much, so pressure builds especially in these two erectile tissues and the penis becomes elongated and erect. The corpus spongiosum becomes less engorged, but swells and becomes more visible as a cordlike ridge along the ventral surface of the penis. When the penis is flaccid, most of its blood supply comes from the dorsal arteries. A median **deep dorsal vein** drains blood from the penis. It runs between the two dorsal arteries beneath the deep fascia and empties into a plexus of prostatic veins.

The penis is richly innervated by sensory and motor nerve fibers. The glans has an abundance of tactile, pressure, and temperature receptors, especially on its proximal margin and frenulum. They lead by way of a pair of prominent **dorsal nerves** to the **internal pudendal nerves,** then via the sacral plexus to spinal cord segments S2 to S4. Sensory fibers of the shaft, scrotum, perineum, and elsewhere are also highly important to erotic stimulation.

Both autonomic and somatic motor fibers carry signals from integrating centers in the spinal cord to the penis and other pelvic organs. Sympathetic nerve fibers arise from levels T12 to L2, pass through the hypogastric and pelvic nerve plexuses, and innervate the penile arteries, trabecular muscle, spermatic ducts, and accessory glands. They dilate the penile arteries and can induce erection even when the sacral region of the spinal cord is damaged. They also initiate erection in response to input from the special senses and to sexual thoughts.

Parasympathetic fibers extend from segments S2 to S4 of the spinal cord through the pudendal nerves to the arteries of the penis. They are involved in an autonomic reflex arc that causes erection in response to direct stimulation of the penis and other perineal organs.

---

[26]*helic* = coil, helix

---

## INSIGHT 26.2

### Clinical Application

### Reproductive Effects of Pollution

In recent decades, wildlife biologists have noticed increasing numbers of male birds, fish, and alligators with a variety of abnormalities in reproductive development. These deformities have been attributed to chemical pollutants called *endocrine disruptors* or *estrogen mimics.* Evidence is mounting that humans, too, are showing declining fertility and increasing anatomical abnormalities due to pollutants in water, meat, vegetables, and even breast milk and the uterine environment.

Over the last several decades, there has been an alarming increase in the incidence of *cryptorchidism* (undescended testes) and *hypospadias* (a condition in which the urethra opens on the ventral side of the penis instead of at the tip). The rate of testicular cancer has more than tripled in that time. Data on 15,000 men from several countries also show a sharp drop in average sperm count—from 113 million/mL in 1940 to only 66 million/mL in 1990. Total sperm production decreased even more, because the average volume of semen per ejaculate dropped 19% over this period.

The pollutants implicated in this trend include a wide array of common herbicides, insecticides, industrial chemicals, and breakdown products of materials ranging from plastics to dishwashing detergents. Some authorities think these chemicals act by mimicking estrogens or blocking testosterone receptors. Other scientists, however, question the data and feel the issue may be overstated. While the debate continues, the U.S. Environmental Protection Agency is screening thousands of industrial chemicals for endocrine effects.

## *Before You Go On*

*Answer the following questions to test your understanding of the preceding section:*

3. Name the stages of spermatogenesis from spermatogonium to spermatozoon. How do they differ in the number of chromosomes per cell and chromatids per chromosome?

4. Name two types of cells in the testis other than the germ cells, and describe their locations and functions.

5. Describe the three major parts of a spermatozoon and state what organelles or cytoskeletal components are contained in each.

6. Name all the ducts the sperm follow, in order, from the time they form in the testis to the time of ejaculation.

7. Describe the locations and functions of the seminal vesicles, prostate, and bulbourethral glands.

8. Name the erectile tissues of the penis, and describe their locations relative to each other.

# Female Reproductive Anatomy

### Objectives
When you have completed this section, you should be able to
- describe the structure of the ovary;
- describe the stages of oogenesis and how these relate to changes in histology of the ovarian follicles;
- trace the female reproductive tract and describe the gross anatomy and histology of each organ;
- describe changes in the uterine lining through the menstrual cycle;
- identify the ligaments that support the female reproductive organs;
- describe the blood supply to the female reproductive tract;
- identify the external genitalia of the female; and
- describe the structure of the nonlactating breast and lactating mammary gland.

Figure 26.11 shows the female reproductive tract. The principal reproductive organs of the pelvic cavity are the *ovaries, uterine tubes, uterus,* and *vagina,* which will be described in that order.

## The Ovaries

The female gonads are the **ovaries,**[27] which produce egg cells (ova) and sex hormones. The ovary is an almond-shaped organ nestled in a depression of the posterior pelvic wall called the *ovarian fossa.* It measures about 3 cm long, 1.5 cm wide, and 1 cm thick. Its capsule, like that of the testis, is called the **tunica albuginea.** The interior of the ovary is indistinctly divided into a central **medulla** and an outer **cortex** (fig. 26.12). The medulla is a zone of fibrous connective tissue occupied by the principal arteries and veins of the

---

[27]*ov* = egg + *ary* = place for

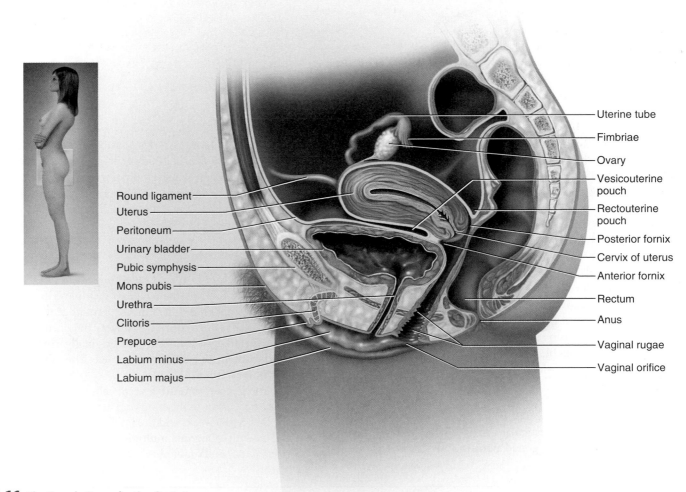

**Figure 26.11** The Female Reproductive System.

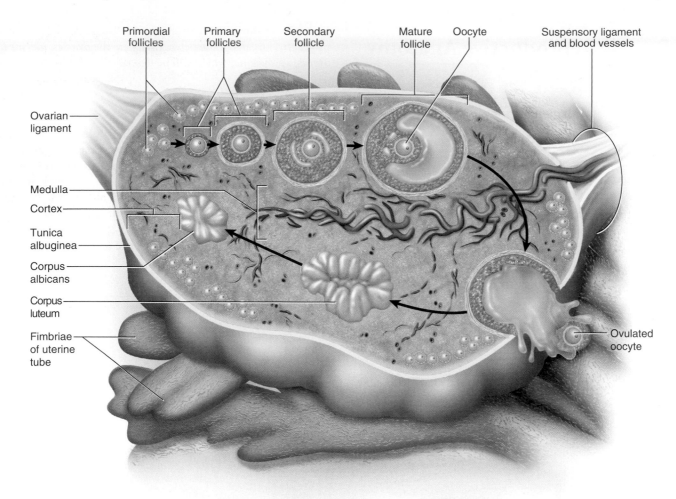

**Figure 26.12** Structure of the Ovary. Arrows indicate the developmental sequence of the ovarian follicles.

ovary. The cortex is the site of the ovarian **follicles,** each of which consists of one developing ovum surrounded by numerous small follicular cells. The ovary does not have a system of tubules like the testis; eggs are released one at a time by the bursting of the follicles (*ovulation*).

The ovaries and other internal genitalia are held in place by several connective tissue ligaments (fig. 26.13). The medial pole of the ovary is attached to the uterus by the **ovarian ligament** and its lateral pole is attached to the pelvic wall by the **suspensory ligament.** The anterior margin of the ovary is anchored by a peritoneal fold called the **mesovarium.**[28] This ligament extends to a sheet of peritoneum called the **broad ligament,** which flanks the uterus and encloses the uterine tube in its superior margin.

The ovary receives blood from two arteries: the **ovarian branch of the uterine artery,** which passes through the mesovarium and approaches the medial pole of the ovary, and the **ovarian artery,** which passes through the suspensory ligament and approaches the lateral pole (see fig. 26.19). The ovarian artery is the female equivalent of the male testicular artery, arising high on the aorta and traveling down to the gonad along the posterior body wall. The

ovarian and uterine arteries anastomose along the margin of the ovary and give off multiple small arteries that enter the ovary on that side. Ovarian veins, lymphatics, and nerves also travel through the suspensory ligament. The veins and lymphatics follow a course similar to those of the testes described earlier.

## Oogenesis and Ova

The production of eggs is called **oogenesis**[29] (OH-oh-JEN-eh-sis) (fig. 26.14). Like spermatogenesis, it employs meiosis and produces haploid gametes. It differs from spermatogenesis in other respects, however: It is not a continual process, but occurs in a rhythm called the **ovarian cycle,** and for each original germ cell (oogonium), it produces only one functional gamete. The other daughter cells are tiny **polar bodies** that soon die.

The female primordial germ cells arise, like those of the male, from the yolk sac of the embryo. They colonize the gonadal ridges in the first 5 to 6 weeks and then differentiate into **oogonia** (OH-oh-GO-nee-uh). Oogonia multiply until the fifth month of gestation, reach 6 to 7 million in number, and then go into a state of arrested

---

[28]*mes* = middle + *ovari* = ovary

[29]*oo* = egg + *genesis* = production

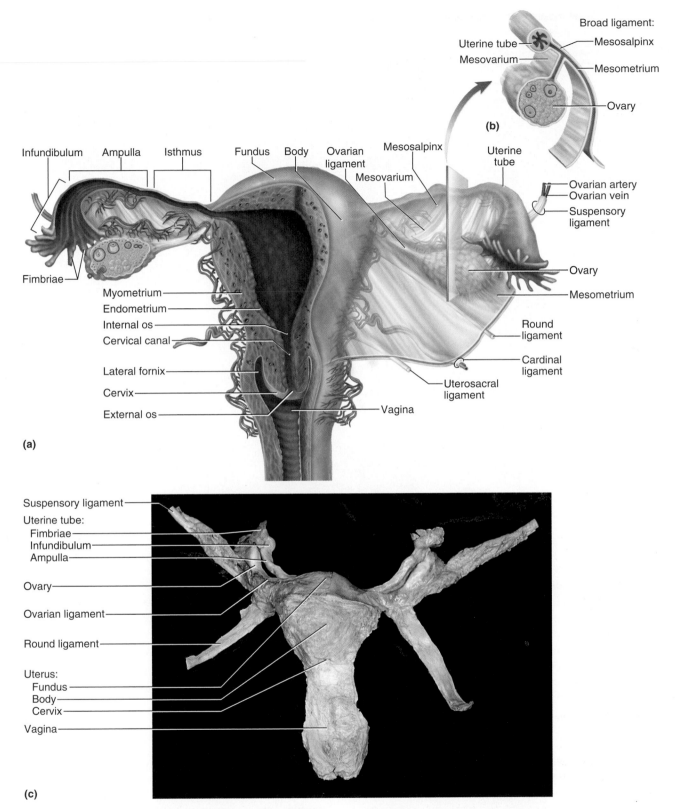

**Figure 26.13** **The Female Reproductive Tract and Supportive Ligaments.** (a) Posterior view of the reproductive tract. (b) Relationship of the uterine tube and ovary to the supporting ligaments. (c) Anterior view of the major female reproductive organs from a cadaver.

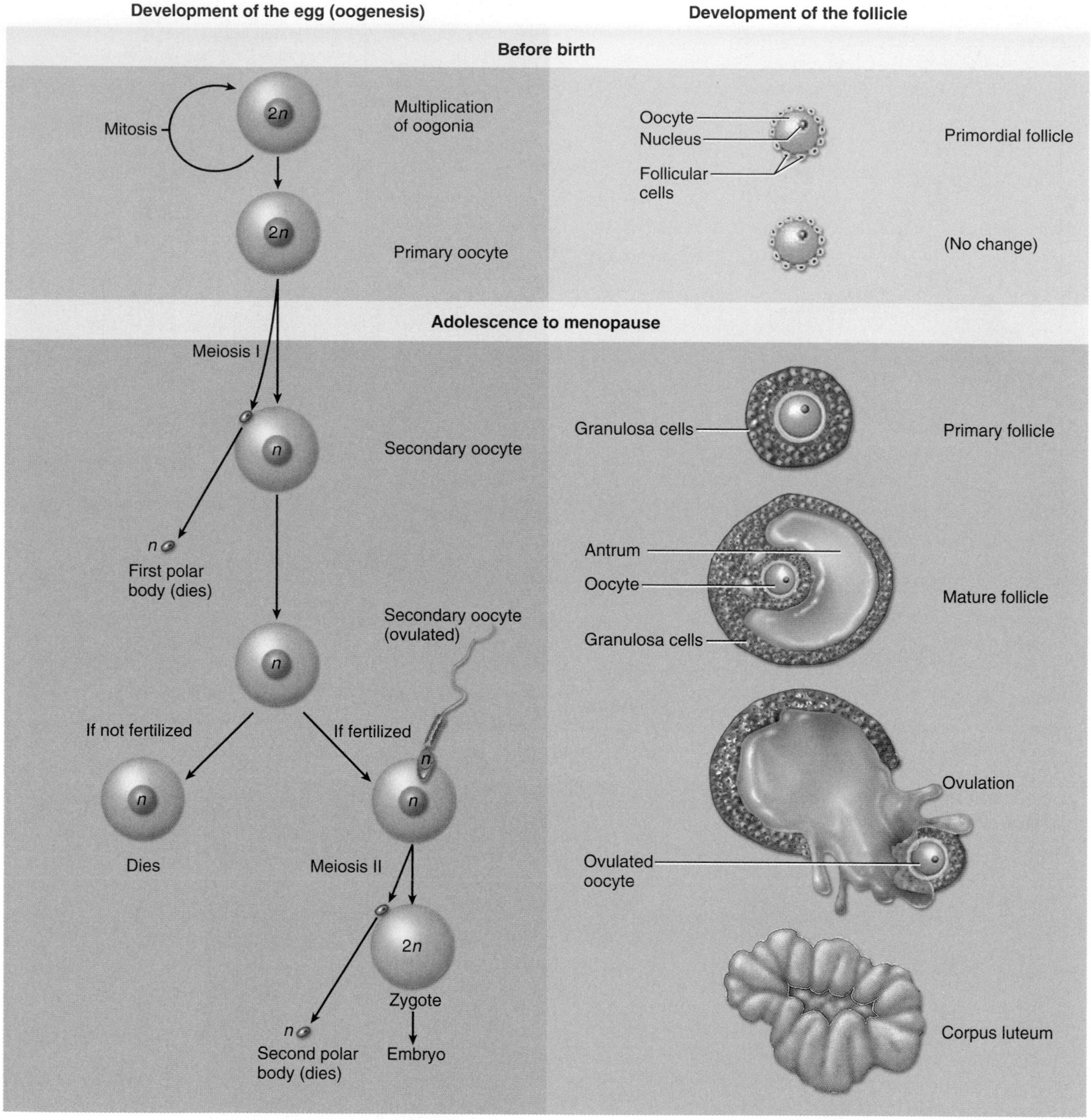

**Development of the egg (oogenesis)**          **Development of the follicle**

**Before birth**

Mitosis — Multiplication of oogonia

2n

Primary oocyte

2n

Oocyte
Nucleus
Follicular cells

Primordial follicle

(No change)

**Adolescence to menopause**

Meiosis I

Secondary oocyte

n

First polar body (dies)

n

Secondary oocyte (ovulated)

n

If not fertilized          If fertilized

Dies          Meiosis II

n          n

2n

Zygote

Second polar body (dies)          Embryo

Granulosa cells          Primary follicle

Antrum
Oocyte
Granulosa cells          Mature follicle

Ovulation

Ovulated oocyte

Corpus luteum

**Figure 26.14** Oogenesis (left) and Corresponding Development of the Follicle (right).

development until shortly before birth. At that time, some of them transform into **primary oocytes** and go as far as early meiosis I. Any stage from the primary oocyte to the time of fertilization can be called an egg, or **ovum.**

Most primary oocytes degenerate even before a girl is born; only 2 million remain at birth. Furthermore, most of these degenerate during childhood, and by the onset of puberty, only about 400,000 remain. This is generally thought to be the female's lifetime supply of germ cells. The degeneration of oocytes and follicles without maturation is called *atresia* (ah-TREE-zhee-uh).

During a woman's reproductive years, about 20 to 25 oocytes and follicles begin to develop each month. Normally just one of these reaches maturity and ovulates, and the rest degenerate. The stages of oogenesis are accompanied by pronounced changes in the follicle.

The primary oocyte is initially enclosed in a **primordial follicle,** composed of a single layer of squamous follicular cells applied tightly to the oocyte (fig. 26.15a). About 3 days before the menstrual period begins, pituitary secretion of follicle-stimulating hormone (FSH) stimulates several primordial follicles to develop into **primary follicles.** The follicular cells thicken into a cuboidal

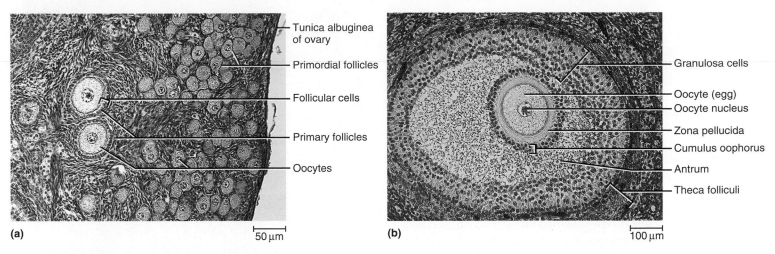

(a)                                                                  50 µm

- Tunica albuginea of ovary
- Primordial follicles
- Follicular cells
- Primary follicles
- Oocytes

(b)                                                                  100 µm

- Granulosa cells
- Oocyte (egg)
- Oocyte nucleus
- Zona pellucida
- Cumulus oophorus
- Antrum
- Theca folliculi

**Figure 26.15** Ovarian Follicles. (a) Primordial and primary follicles. Note the very thin layer of squamous cells around the oocyte in a primordial follicle, and the single layer of cuboidal cells in a primary follicle. (b) A mature (graafian) follicle. Just before ovulation, this follicle will grow to as much as 2.5 cm (1 in.) in diameter.

epithelium, multiply, and become stratified. They are now called **granulosa cells.** The ovarian stroma adjacent to the follicle condenses into a fibrous capsule called the **theca**[30] **folliculi** (THEE-ca fol-IC-you-lye). The theca and granulosa cells collaborate to synthesize *estrogens.* Among other effects, estrogens stimulate regrowth of the uterine lining (endometrium) after menstruation.

Most primary follicles degenerate with no further development. In a few, however, the granulosa cells secrete pools of estrogen-rich **follicular fluid.** These pools grow and merge until they form a single fluid-filled cavity, the **antrum.** The follicle is now called a **secondary (antral) follicle.** This is the state of development when menstruation ends around day 5. (Day 1 of the cycle is regarded as the first day of menstruation.)

By day 10 or so, all but one of the developing follicles usually degenerate. That one enlarges to as much as 2.5 cm in diameter and bulges like a balloon from the surface of the ovary. This **mature (graafian**[31]**) follicle** (fig. 26.15b) is the one destined to ovulate. The oocyte in this follicle is held against the follicular wall by a mound of granulosa cells called the **cumulus oophorus**[32] (CUE-mew-lus oh-OFF-or-us). A layer of glycoprotein gel called the **zona pellucida**[33] separates the granulosa cells from the oocyte and appears as a clear space in histological sections. The innermost layer of cumulus cells is called the **corona radiata.**[34] Microvilli from the corona cells and the oocyte span the zona pellucida.

The primary oocyte, suspended in prophase I of meiosis, now completes its division. It divides into a large **secondary oocyte** and a small *first polar body* (see fig. 26.14). Meiosis I reduces the chromosome number by half, so the secondary oocyte is haploid. It retains as much of the cytoplasm as possible, so that if it is fertilized, it can divide repeatedly and produce numerous daughter cells. Splitting each oocyte into four equal but small parts would run counter

to this purpose. The first polar body is simply a way of discarding the other haploid set of chromosomes; it soon dies. The secondary oocyte begins meiosis II and then goes into developmental arrest again until after ovulation. If this egg is fertilized, it completes meiosis II and produces a *second polar body.* If not fertilized, it dies and never finishes meiosis.

**Ovulation,** the release of an oocyte, typically occurs on day 14, the midpoint of the average cycle. As ovulation approaches, the oocyte and cumulus oophorus become detached from the follicular wall and drift in the antrum. Ovulation takes only 2 or 3 minutes. A nipplelike **stigma** appears on the ovarian surface over the follicle. Follicular fluid seeps from the stigma for 1 or 2 minutes, and then the follicle ruptures. The remaining follicular fluid oozes out, carrying the oocyte and cumulus cells (fig. 26.16).

Infundibulum of uterine tube       Fimbriae

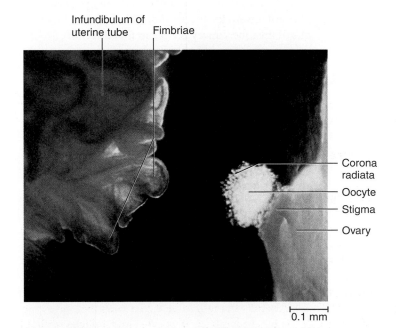

- Corona radiata
- Oocyte
- Stigma
- Ovary

0.1 mm

**Figure 26.16** Endoscopic View of Human Ovulation.

---

[30]*theca* = box, case
[31]Reijnier de Graaf (1641–73), Dutch physiologist and histologist
[32]*cumulus* = little mound + *oo* = egg + *phor* = to carry
[33]*zona* = zone + *pellucid* = clear, transparent
[34]*corona* = crown + *radiata* = radiating

When the oocyte is expelled, the follicle collapses and bleeds into the antrum. As the clotted blood is slowly absorbed, granulosa and theca interna cells multiply and fill the antrum, and a dense bed of blood capillaries grows amid them. The ovulated follicle has now become a structure called the **corpus luteum**,[35] named for a yellow lipid that accumulates in the theca interna cells (see fig. 26.12). These cells are now called **lutein cells.** The corpus luteum secretes a large amount of progesterone, which stimulates the uterus to prepare for possible pregnancy.

If pregnancy does not occur, the corpus luteum atrophies from days 24 to 26—a process called *involution.* As it does, the level of circulating progesterone declines, and this brings about menstruation. By day 26 or so, involution is complete and the corpus luteum becomes an inactive scar, the **corpus albicans.**[36] If pregnancy occurs, however, the corpus luteum remains active for about 3 months. Its progesterone is necessary to sustain the early pregnancy. Eventually the placenta takes over the role of progesterone secretion, among other functions, and the corpus luteum is no longer needed.

These events in the ovarian cycle are correlated with changes in uterine histology, which we will examine later.

## The Uterine Tubes

An ovulated oocyte is received into the **uterine tube,** also called the **oviduct** or **fallopian**[37] **tube** (see fig. 26.11). The tube is a ciliated canal about 10 cm long leading from the ovary to the uterus. At the distal (ovarian) end, it flares into a trumpet-shaped **infundibulum**[38] with feathery projections called **fimbriae**[39] (FIM-bree-ee); the middle and longest part of the tube is the **ampulla;** and the segment near the uterus is a narrower **isthmus.** The uterine tube is enclosed in the **mesosalpinx**[40] (MEZ-oh-SAL-pinks), which is the superior margin of the broad ligament.

The wall of the uterine tube is well endowed with smooth muscle. Its mucosa is highly folded into longitudinal ridges. It has an epithelium of ciliated cells and a smaller number of secretory **peg cells** (fig. 26.17). The cilia beat toward the uterus and, with the help of muscular contractions of the tube, convey the egg in that direction.

## The Uterus

The **uterus**[41] is a thick muscular chamber that opens into the roof of the vagina and usually tilts forward over the urinary bladder (see figs. 26.11 and 26.13). Its function is to harbor the fetus, provide it with a source of nutrition (the placenta, composed partially of uterine tissue), and expel the fetus at the end of gestation (pregnancy). It is somewhat pear-shaped, with a broad superior curvature called the **fundus,** a midportion called the **body (corpus),** and a narrow inferior end called the **cervix.** The uterus measures about

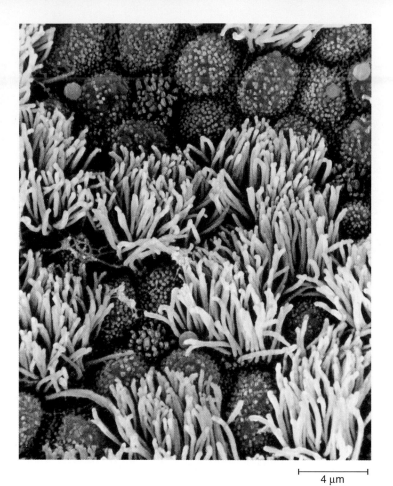

$\vdash\!\!\!-\!\!\!-\!\!\!\dashv$ 4 μm

**Figure 26.17** Epithelial Lining of the Uterine Tube. Secretory cells are shown in red and green, and cilia of the ciliated cells in yellow (SEM).

7 cm from cervix to fundus, 4 cm wide at its broadest point on the fundus, and 2.5 cm thick, but it is somewhat larger in women who have been pregnant.

The lumen of the uterus is roughly triangular, with its two upper corners opening into the uterine tubes. In the nonpregnant uterus, the lumen is not a hollow cavity but rather a *potential space* (see p. 30); the mucous membranes of the opposite walls are pressed together with little room between them. The lumen communicates with the vagina by way of a narrow passage through the cervix called the **cervical canal.** The superior opening of this canal into the body of the uterus is the *internal os*[42] (pronounced "oss"), and its opening into the vagina is the *external os.* The canal contains **cervical glands** that secrete mucus, thought to prevent the spread of microorganisms from the vagina into the uterus. Near the time of ovulation, the mucus becomes thinner than usual and allows easier passage for sperm.

### The Uterine Wall

The uterine wall consists of an external serosa called the *perimetrium,* a middle muscular layer called the *myometrium,* and an inner mucosa called the *endometrium.* The **perimetrium** is composed of simple squamous epithelium overlying a thin layer of areolar

---

[35]*corpus* = body + *lute* = yellow
[36]*corpus* = body + *alb* = white
[37]Gabriele Fallopio (1528–62), Italian anatomist and physician
[38]*infundibulum* = funnel
[39]*fimbria* = fringe
[40]*meso* = mesentery + *salpin* = trumpet
[41]*uterus* = womb

[42]*os* = mouth

tissue. The **myometrium,**[43] about 1.25 cm thick in the nonpregnant uterus, constitutes most of the wall. It is composed mainly of bundles of smooth muscle that sweep downward from the fundus and spiral around the body of the uterus. The myometrium is less muscular and more fibrous near the cervix; the cervix itself is almost entirely collagenous. The muscle cells of the myometrium are about 40 μm long immediately after menstruation, twice this long at the middle of the menstrual cycle, and up to 10 times as long in pregnancy. The function of the myometrium is to produce the labor contractions that help to expel the fetus.

The inner lining of the uterus, or mucosa, is called the **endometrium.**[44] It has a simple columnar epithelium, compound tubular glands, and a stroma populated by leukocytes, macrophages, and other cells (fig. 26.18). The superficial half to two-thirds of it, called the **stratum functionalis,** is shed in each menstrual period. The deeper layer, called the **stratum basalis,** stays behind and regenerates a new functionalis in the next cycle. When pregnancy occurs, the endometrium is the site of attachment of the embryo and forms the maternal part of the placenta.

## Ligaments

The uterus is supported by the muscular floor of the pelvic outlet and folds of peritoneum that form supportive ligaments around the organ, as they do for the ovary and uterine tube (see fig. 26.13). The

---

[43]*myo* = muscle + *metr* = uterus
[44]*endo* = inside + *metr* = uterus

**broad ligament** has two parts: the *mesosalpinx* mentioned earlier and the *mesometrium* on each side of the uterus. The cervix and superior part of the vagina are supported by **cardinal (lateral cervical) ligaments** extending to the pelvic wall. A pair of **uterosacral ligaments** attach the posterior surface of the uterus to the sacrum, and a pair of **round ligaments** arise from the anterior surface of the uterus, pass through the inguinal canals, and terminate in the labia majora.

As the peritoneum folds around the various pelvic organs, it creates several dead-end recesses and pouches (extensions of the peritoneal cavity). Two major ones are the **vesicouterine**[45] **pouch,** which forms the space between the uterus and urinary bladder, and the **rectouterine pouch** between the uterus and rectum (see fig. 26.11).

## Blood Supply

The uterine blood supply is particularly important to the menstrual cycle and pregnancy. A **uterine artery** arises from each internal iliac artery and travels through the broad ligament to the uterus (fig. 26.19). It gives off several branches that penetrate into the myometrium and lead to **arcuate arteries.** Each arcuate artery travels in a circle around the uterus and anastomoses with the arcuate artery on the other side. Along its course, it gives rise to smaller arteries that penetrate the rest of the way through the myometrium, into the endometrium, and produce the **spiral arteries.** The spiral arteries coil between the endometrial glands toward the surface of the mucosa. They rhythmically constrict and dilate, making the mucosa alternately blanch and flush with blood.

## Cyclic Changes in Uterine Histology

Uterine histology is not constant. In fertile women, it changes throughout the **menstrual cycle,** the monthly rhythm of endometrial buildup, breakdown, and discharge. This cycle averages 28 days long, with day 1 considered to be the first day of visible vaginal

---

[45]*vesico* = bladder

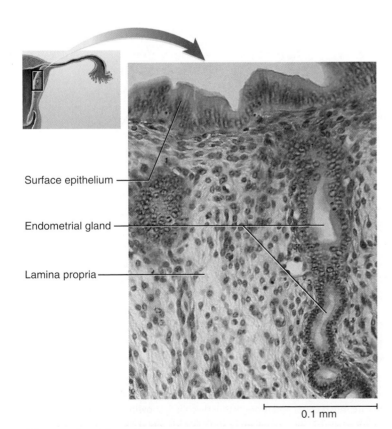

Surface epithelium

Endometrial gland

Lamina propria

0.1 mm

**Figure 26.18** Histology of the Endometrium.

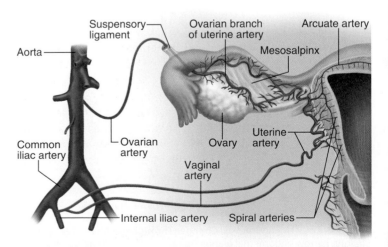

Aorta

Suspensory ligament

Ovarian branch of uterine artery

Arcuate artery

Mesosalpinx

Common iliac artery

Ovarian artery

Ovary

Uterine artery

Vaginal artery

Internal iliac artery

Spiral arteries

**Figure 26.19** Blood Supply to the Female Reproductive Tract. The vaginal, uterine, and ovarian arteries are exaggerated in length by the perspective of the drawing, moving the aorta away from the uterus for clarity.

discharge of menstrual fluid. Why that discharge occurs is best understood by first considering the histological changes leading up to it.

The **proliferative phase** is a time of rebuilding of endometrial tissue lost at the last menstruation. At the end of menstruation, around day 5, the endometrium is about 0.5 mm thick and consists only of the stratum basalis. The stratum functionalis is rebuilt by mitosis from day 6 to day 14, under the influence of estrogen from the growing ovarian follicles. By day 14, the endometrium is about 2 to 3 mm thick (fig. 26.20a).

The **secretory phase** is a period of further endometrial thickening, but results from secretion and fluid accumulation rather than mitosis. It extends from day 15 (after ovulation) to day 26 of a typical cycle, and is stimulated by progesterone from the corpus luteum. In this phase, the endometrial glands grow wider, longer, and more coiled. As a result of the coiling, a vertical section through the endometrium shows these glands with a sawtooth or zigzag appearance (fig. 26.20b). Endometrial cells and the uterine stroma

accumulate glycogen during this phase. By the end of the secretory phase, the endometrium is about 5 to 6 mm thick—a soft, wet, nutritious bed available for embryonic development in the event of pregnancy.

The **premenstrual phase** is a period of endometrial degeneration occuring in the last 2 days or so of the menstrual cycle. When the corpus luteum involutes, the spiral arteries exhibit spasmodic contractions that cause endometrial ischemia (interrupted blood flow). The premenstrual phase is therefore also called the **ischemic** (iss-KEE-mic) **phase.** Ischemia leads to tissue necrosis. As the endometrial glands, stroma, and blood vessels degenerate, pools of blood accumulate in the stratum functionalis. Necrotic endometrium falls away from the uterine wall, mixes with blood and serous fluid in the lumen, and forms the **menstrual fluid** (fig. 26.20c).

The **menstrual phase (menses)** begins when enough menstrual fluid has accumulated in the uterus that it begins to be discharged vaginally. The first day of external discharge marks day 1 of a new cycle.

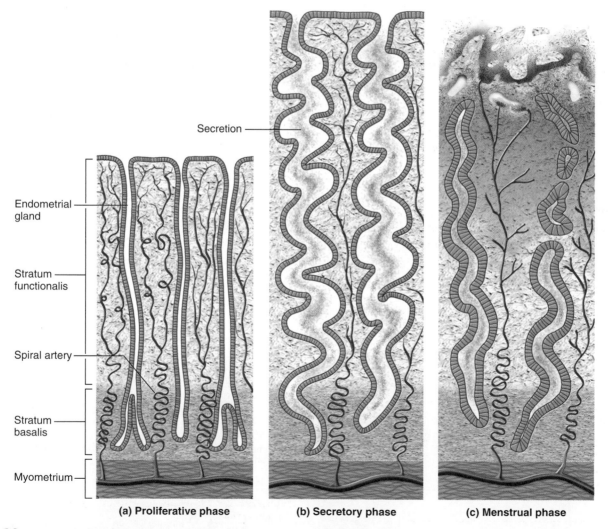

**Figure 26.20** **Endometrial Changes Through the Menstrual Cycle.**  (a) Late proliferative phase. The endometrium is 2 to 3 mm thick and has relatively straight, narrow endometrial glands. Spiral arteries penetrate upward between the endometrial glands. (b) Secretory phase. The endometrium has thickened to 5 to 6 mm thick by accumulation of glycogen and mucus. The endometrial glands are much wider and more distinctly coiled, showing a zigzag or "sawtooth" appearance in histological sections. (c) Menstrual phase. Ischemic tissue has begun to die and fall away from the uterine wall, with bleeding from broken blood vessels and pooling of blood within the tissue and in the uterine cavity.

## The Vagina

The **vagina,**[46] or birth canal, is a tube about 8 to 10 cm long that allows for the discharge of menstrual fluid, receipt of the penis and semen, and birth of a baby. The vaginal wall is thin but very distensible. It consists of an outer adventitia, a middle muscularis, and an inner mucosa. The vagina tilts posteriorly between the urethra and rectum; the urethra is bound to its anterior wall. The vagina has no glands, but it is lubricated by the *transudation* ("vaginal sweating") of serous fluid through its walls and by mucus from the cervical glands above it. The vagina extends slightly beyond the cervix and forms blind spaces called **fornices**[47] (FOR-nih-sees; singular, *fornix*) surrounding it (see fig. 26.11).

The lower end of the vagina has transverse friction ridges, or **vaginal rugae,** which stimulate the penis and help induce ejaculation. At the vaginal orifice, the mucosa folds inward and forms a membrane, the **hymen,** which stretches across the opening. The hymen has one or more openings to allow menstrual fluid to pass, but it usually must be ruptured to allow for intercourse. A little bleeding often accompanies the first act of intercourse; however, the hymen is commonly ruptured before then by tampons, medical examinations, or strenuous exercise.

The vaginal epithelium is simple cuboidal in childhood, but the estrogens of puberty transform it into a stratified squamous epithelium. This is an example of *metaplasia,* the transformation of one tissue type to another. The epithelial cells are rich in glycogen. Bacteria ferment this to lactic acid, which produces a low vaginal pH (about 3.5–4.0) that inhibits the growth of pathogens. The mucosa also has antigen-presenting cells called **dendritic cells,** which are a route by which HIV invades the female body.

### THINK ABOUT IT

*Why do you think the vaginal epithelium changes type at puberty? Of all types of epithelium it might become, why stratified squamous?*

## The External Genitalia

The external genitalia of the female occupy most of the perineum, and are collectively also known as the **vulva**[48] or **pudendum**[49] (fig. 26.21). The perineum has the same skeletal landmarks in the female as in the male.

The **mons**[50] **pubis** (see fig. A.5a, p. 26) consists mainly of an anterior mound of adipose tissue overlying the pubic symphysis, covered with skin and bearing pubic hair. The **labia majora**[51] (singular, *labium majus*) are a pair of thick folds of skin and adipose tissue inferior to the mons, between the thighs; the slit between them is the *pudendal cleft.* Pubic hair grows on the lateral surfaces of the labia majora at puberty, but the medial surfaces remain hairless.

---

[46]*vagina* = sheath
[47]*fornix* = arch, vault
[48]*vulva* = covering
[49]*pudend* = shameful
[50]*mons* = mountain
[51]*labi* = lip + *major* = larger, greater

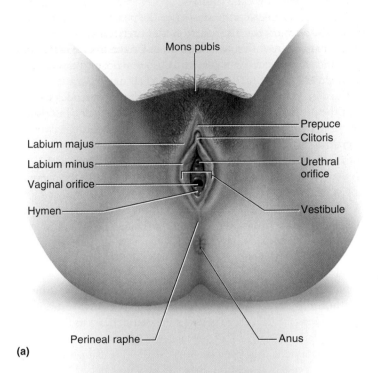

(a)

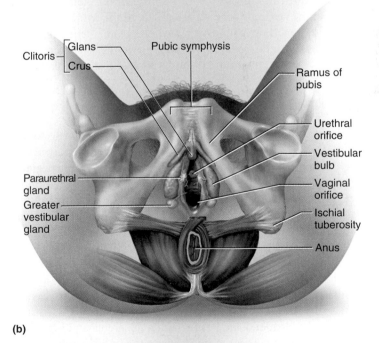

(b)

**Figure 26.21   The Female Perineum.** (a) Surface anatomy. (b) Subcutaneous structures.
● *Which of the glands in (b) is homologous to the male prostate gland?*

Medial to the labia majora are the much thinner, entirely hairless **labia minora**[52] (singular, *labium minus*). The area enclosed by them, called the **vestibule,** contains the urinary and vaginal orifices. At the anterior margin of the vestibule, the labia minora meet and form a hoodlike **prepuce** over the clitoris.

The **clitoris** is structured much like the penis in many respects, but has no urinary role. Its function is entirely sensory, serving as the primary center of erotic stimulation. Unlike the penis, it is almost entirely internal, it has no corpus spongiosum, and it does not enclose the urethra. Essentially, it is a pair of corpora cavernosa enclosed in connective tissue. Its head, the **glans,** protrudes slightly from the prepuce. The **body (corpus)** passes internally, inferior to the pubic symphysis (see fig. 26.11). At its internal end, the corpora cavernosa diverge like a Y as a pair of **crura,** which, like those of the penis, attach the clitoris to each side of the pubic arch. The circulation and innervation of the clitoris are largely the same as for the penis.

Just deep to the labia majora, a pair of subcutaneous erectile tissues called the **vestibular bulbs** bracket the vagina like parentheses. They become congested with blood during sexual excitement and cause the vagina to tighten somewhat around the penis, enhancing sexual stimulation.

Next to the vagina are a pair of pea-sized **greater vestibular (Bartholin**[53]**) glands** with short ducts opening into the vestibule or lower vagina (fig. 26.21b). These are the counterpart to the bulbourethral glands of the male. They keep the vulva moist, and during sexual excitement they provide most of the lubrication for intercourse. The vestibule is also lubricated by a number of **lesser vestibular glands.** A pair of mucous **paraurethral (Skene**[54]**) glands** open into the vestibule near the external urethral orifice. They may eject fluid, sometimes abundantly, during orgasm ("female ejaculation"). These glands arise from the same embryonic structure as the male prostate, and their fluid is similar to the prostatic secretion.

## The Breasts and Mammary Glands

The **breast** (fig. 26.22) is a mound of tissue overlying the pectoralis major. It develops at puberty and remains for life, but most of this time it contains very little mammary gland. The **mammary gland** develops within the breast during pregnancy, remains active in the lactating breast, and atrophies when a woman ceases to nurse.

The breast has two principal regions: the conical to pendulous **body,** with the nipple at its apex, and an extension toward the armpit called the **axillary tail.** Lymphatics of the axillary tail are especially important as a route of breast cancer metastasis.

The nipple is surrounded by a circular colored zone, the **areola.** Dermal blood capillaries and nerves come closer to the surface here than in the surrounding skin and make the areola more sensitive and more reddish in color. In pregnancy, the areola and nipple often darken, making them more visible to the indistinct vision of a nursing infant. Sensory nerve fibers of the areola are important in triggering a *milk ejection reflex* when an infant nurses. The areola has sparse hairs and **areolar glands,** visible as small bumps on the surface. These glands are intermediate between sweat glands and mammary glands in their degree of development. When a woman is nursing, the areola is protected from chapping and cracking by secretions of the areolar glands and sebaceous glands. The dermis of the areola has smooth muscle fibers that contract in response to cold, touch, and sexual arousal, wrinkling the skin and erecting the nipple.

Internally, the nonlactating breast consists mostly of adipose and collagenous tissue (fig. 26.22). Breast size is determined by the amount of adipose tissue and has no relationship to the amount of milk the mammary gland can produce. **Suspensory ligaments** attach the breast to the dermis of the overlying skin and to the fascia of the pectoralis major. The nonlactating breast contains very little glandular tissue, but it does have a system of ducts branching through its connective tissue stroma and converging on the nipple.

When the mammary gland develops during pregnancy, it exhibits 15 to 20 lobes arranged radially around the nipple, separated from each other by fibrous stroma. Each lobe is drained by a **lactiferous**[55] **duct,** which dilates to form a **lactiferous sinus** opening onto the nipple. Internally, this duct branches repeatedly with the finest branches ending in secretory acini. The acini are organized into grapelike clusters (lobules) within each lobe of the breast. Each acinus consists of pyramidal secretory cells arranged around a central lumen, and a network of contractile **myoepithelial cells** around the secretory cells (fig. 26.22d). When a woman nurses, stimulation of the nipple induces the posterior lobe of the pituitary gland to secrete oxytocin. Oxytocin stimulates the myoepithelial cells to contract, squeezing milk from the acini into the lactiferous ducts.

## *Before You Go On*

*Answer the following questions to test your understanding of the preceding section:*

9. What are the stages of oogenesis? Describe all the ways in which it differs from spermatogenesis.

10. Describe the changes that occur in the ovarian follicles and uterine endometrium over the course of the ovarian and menstrual cycle.

11. How does the structure of the uterine tube mucosa relate to its function?

12. What structures are externally visible in the vulva? Describe their anatomical arrangement.

13. Name the accessory glands of the vulva and state their locations and functions.

14. How does the structure of the nonlactating breast differ from that of the lactating breast? What is the difference between a breast and a mammary gland?

---

[52]*minor* = smaller, lesser
[53]Caspar Bartholin (1655–1738), Danish anatomist
[54]Alexander J. C. Skene (1838–1900), American gynecologist

[55]*lact* = milk + *fer* = to carry

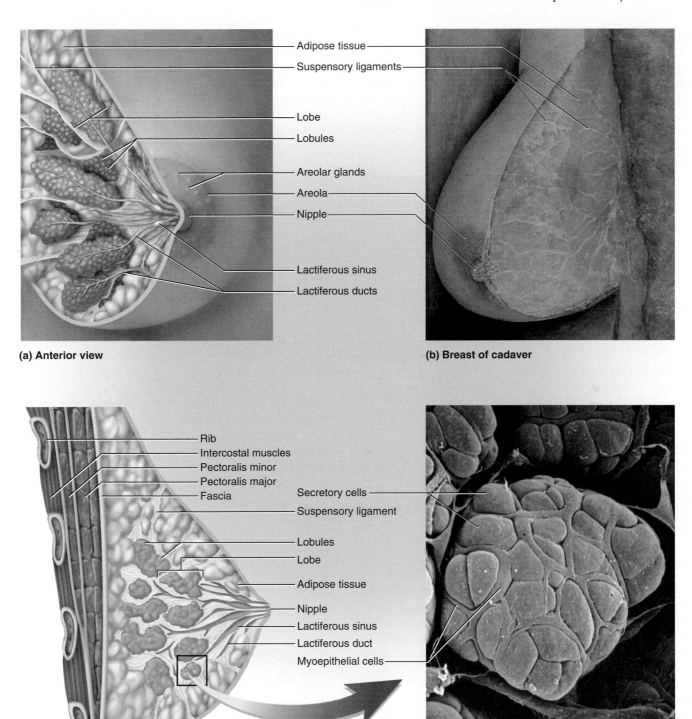

(a) Anterior view

- Adipose tissue
- Suspensory ligaments
- Lobe
- Lobules
- Areolar glands
- Areola
- Nipple
- Lactiferous sinus
- Lactiferous ducts

(b) Breast of cadaver

(c) Sagittal section

- Rib
- Intercostal muscles
- Pectoralis minor
- Pectoralis major
- Fascia
- Secretory cells
- Suspensory ligament
- Lobules
- Lobe
- Adipose tissue
- Nipple
- Lactiferous sinus
- Lactiferous duct
- Myoepithelial cells

(d) Mammary acinus

**Figure 26.22** **The Breast.** Parts (a), (c), and (d) depict the breast in a lactating state. Some of the features in (a) and (c) are absent from the nonlactating breast in part (b). The cluster of lobules boxed in (c) would contain numerous microscopic acini like the one in (d). Part (d) is not to be construed as an enlargement of the entire boxed area of (c).

• *What is the function of the myoepithelial cells in (d)?*

# Developmental and Clinical Perspectives

### Objectives

When you have completed this section, you should be able to

- explain how sexual differentiation is determined by the sex chromosomes and prenatal hormones;
- describe the embryonic development of the reproductive system;
- describe what aspects of anatomical development the male and female have in common, and how they become differentiated from each other;
- summarize the changes in reproductive function that occur in old age; and
- describe some reproductive disorders of each sex.

## Prenatal Development and Sexual Differentiation

The male and female reproductive systems begin with embryonic sex organs that are anatomically "indifferent," yet genetically destined to differentiate into the genitalia of one sex or the other. Thus, the testes and ovaries develop from an initially indistinguishable *indifferent gonad,* the glans of the penis and clitoris develop from a single embryonic *genital tubercle,* and the scrotum and labia majora develop from the embryonic *labioscrotal folds.* Organs that develop from the same embryonic precursor are said to be **homologous** to each other.

### The Internal Genitalia

The gonad appears at 5 to 6 weeks as a **gonadal ridge** near the mesonephros, the primitive kidney. Adjacent to each gonadal ridge are two ducts, the **mesonephric**[56] (**wolffian**[57]) **duct** described in chapter 25 (p. 729), and the **paramesonephric**[58] (**müllerian**[59]) **duct.** In males, the mesonephric ducts develop into parts of the reproductive tract, and the paramesonephric ducts degenerate. In females, the opposite occurs (fig. 26.23).

The differentiation of these ducts into the organs of one sex or the other is determined by an interaction between genes and hormones. If the zygote has sex chromosomes X and Y, it is normally destined to develop into a male; if it has two X chromosomes and no Y, it will develop into a female. Thus the sex of a child is determined at conception (fertilization), depending on whether the egg (always X) is fertilized by an X- or a Y-bearing sperm.

But why? The answer lies in the Y chromosome, where a gene called **SRY** (sex-determining region of the Y) codes for a protein called **testis-determining factor** (**TDF**). TDF then interacts with genes on some of the other chromosomes, including a gene on the X chromosome for androgen receptors and genes that initiate the development of male anatomy. By 8 to 9 weeks, the male gonadal ridge has become a rudimentary testis whose interstitial cells begin to secrete testosterone. Testosterone stimulates the mesonephric duct to develop into the system of male reproductive ducts. Sustentacular cells of the fetal testis secrete a hormone called **müllerian-inhibiting factor** (**MIF**), which causes atrophy of the paramesonephric duct. Even an adult male, however, retains a tiny Y-shaped vestige of the paramesonephric ducts, like a vestigial uterus and uterine tubes, in the area of the prostatic urethra. It is named the *prostatic utricle.*[60]

In a female fetus, the absence of testosterone causes the mesonephric ducts to degenerate, and in the absence of MIF, the paramesonephric ducts develop "by default" into a female reproductive tract. Each duct differentiates into one of the uterine tubes. At their inferior end, the ducts fuse to form the single uterus and the upper one-third of the vagina. The lower two-thirds of the vagina develops as an outgrowth of the urogenital sinus described in chapter 25 (p. 730).

It may seem as if androgens should induce the formation of a male reproductive tract and estrogens induce a female reproductive tract. However, estrogen levels are always high during pregnancy, so if this mechanism were the case, it would feminize all fetuses. Thus, the development of a female results from the low level of androgens, not the presence of estrogens.

### The External Genitalia

At 8 weeks, the external genitalia are represented by the following sexually undifferentiated structures (fig. 26.24):

- the **genital tubercle,** an anterior bud destined to become the glans of the penis or clitoris;
- **urogenital folds,** a pair of medial tissue folds slightly posterior to the genital tubercle; and
- **labioscrotal folds,** a larger pair of tissue folds lateral to the urogenital folds.

These organs begin to show sexual differentiation by the end of week 9, and either male or female genitalia are distinctly identifiable by the end of week 12. In the female, the three structures just listed become the clitoral glans, labia minora, and labia majora, respectively. In the male, the genital tubercle elongates to form the *phallus;* the urogenital folds fuse to enclose the urethra, and join the phallus to form the penis; and the labioscrotal folds fuse to form the scrotum.

The homology of the male and female genitalia becomes strikingly evident in certain abnormalities of sexual development. In the presence of excess androgen, the clitoris may enlarge and the labioscrotal folds fuse, so closely resembling a penis and scrotum

---

[56]*meso* = middle + *nephr* = kidney; named for a temporary embryonic kidney, the mesonephros
[57]Kaspar F. Wolff (1733–94), German anatomist
[58]*para* = next to
[59]Johannes P. Müller (1801–58), German physician

[60]*utricle* = little bag

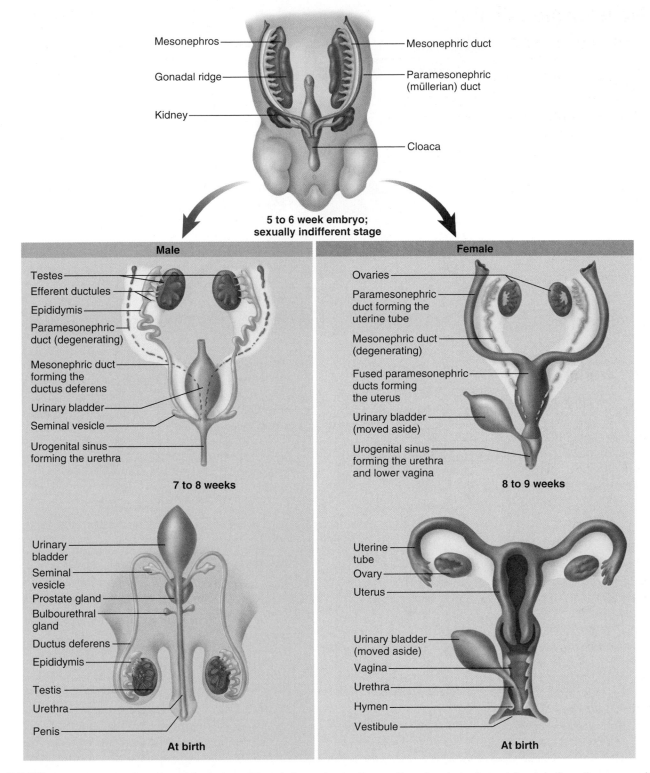

**Figure 26.23  Embryonic Development of the Male and Female Reproductive Tracts.** Note that the male tract develops from the mesonephric duct and the female tract from the paramesonephric duct; the other duct in each sex degenerates.

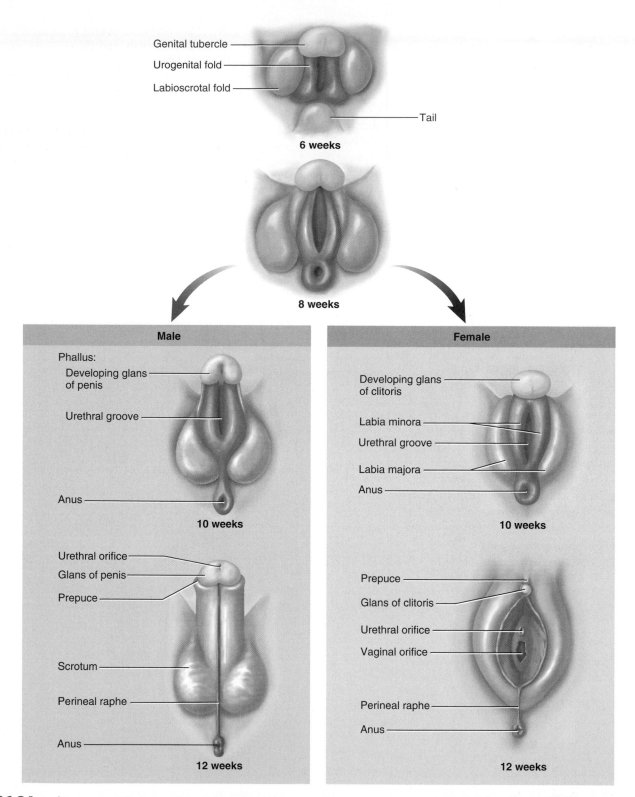

**Figure 26.24  Development of the External Genitalia.**  By 6 weeks, the embryo has three primordial structures—the genital tubercle, urogenital folds, and labioscrotal folds—which will become the male or female genitalia. At 8 weeks, these structures have grown, but the sexes are still indistinguishable. Slight sexual differentiation is noticeable at 10 weeks. The sexes are fully distinguishable by 12 weeks. Matching colors identify homologous structures of the male and female.

that a newborn girl can be misidentified as a boy. In other cases, the ovaries descend into the labia majora as if they were testes descending into a scrotum.

## Descent of the Gonads

Both male and female gonads initially develop high in the abdominal cavity and migrate into the pelvic cavity (ovaries) or scrotum (testes). The most pronounced migration is the **descent of the testes** (fig. 26.25). In the embryo, a connective tissue cord called the **gubernaculum**[61] (GOO-bur-NACK-you-lum) extends from the gonad to the floor of the abdominopelvic cavity. As it continues to grow, it passes between the internal and external abdominal oblique muscles and into the scrotal swelling. Independently of any migration of the testis, the peritoneum also develops a fold that extends into the scrotum as the *vaginal process.* The gubernaculum and the vaginal process create a path of low resistance through the groin, the inguinal canal—the most common site of herniation in boys and men (*inguinal hernia;* see Insight 11.3, p. 320).

The descent of the testes begins as early as week 6. The superior part of the embryonic gonad degenerates, and its inferior part migrates downward, guided by the gubernaculum. In the seventh month, the testes abruptly passes through the inguinal canals, anterior to the pubic symphysis, into the scrotum. As they descend, they are accompanied by ever-elongating testicular arteries and veins and by lymphatic vessels, nerves, sperm ducts, and extensions of the internal abdominal oblique muscle that become the cremaster muscle. The vaginal process becomes separated from the peritoneal cavity and persists as a sac, the *tunica vaginalis,* enfolding the anterior side of the testis. Although multiple hypotheses have been offered, the actual mechanism of descent remains obscure. Testosterone stimulates the descent, but it is unknown how. About 3% of boys, however, are born with undescended testes, or *cryptorchidism* (see table 26.2).

The ovaries also descend, but to a much lesser extent. A gubernaculum extends from the inferior pole of the ovary to the labioscrotal fold. The ovaries eventually lodge just inferior to the brim of the lesser pelvis. The inferior part of the gubernaculum becomes the round ligament of the uterus, and the superior part becomes the ovarian ligament.

## Puberty

Unlike any other organ system, the reproductive system remains dormant for several years after birth. Around age 10 to 12 in most boys and 8 to 10 in most girls, however, the hypothalamus begins to secrete gonadotropin-releasing hormone (GnRH), and the pituitary responds by secreting the two gonadotropins, follicle-stimulating hormone (FSH) and luteinizing hormone (LH). These hormones, in turn, stimulate the gonads to secrete estrogens, progesterone, and testosterone. Combined with surges in the secretion of growth hormone and other hormones, the adolescent body exhibits pronounced anatomical changes. **Puberty,**[62] the first few years of **adolescence,**[63] has begun.

In boys, the earliest sign of puberty is usually enlargement of the testes and scrotum, and in girls, it is breast development, called **thelarche**[64] (thee-LAR-kee). These changes are soon followed by **pubarche** (pyu-BAR-kee), the growth of pubic and axillary hair, sebaceous glands, and apocrine glands. In girls, the third principal event is **menarche**[65] (men-AR-kee), the first menstrual period. Menarche does not immediately signify fertility. A girl's first few menstrual cycles are typically *anovulatory* (no egg is ovulated). Most girls begin ovulating regularly about a year after they begin menstruating. The male counterpart to menarche is the onset of ejaculation. Puberty ends when an individual is fully capable of reproducing, while adolescence extends until a person reaches full height in the late teens to early twenties.

Puberty entails many other changes too numerous for the scope of this book. The internal and external genitalia enlarge. Changes in muscularity and fat deposition bring about some of the male–female differences known as the secondary sex characteristics. The

---

[61]*gubern* = rudder, to steer, guide

[62]*puber* = grown up
[63]*adolesc* = to grow up
[64]*thel* = breast, nipple + *arche* = beginning
[65]*men* = monthly

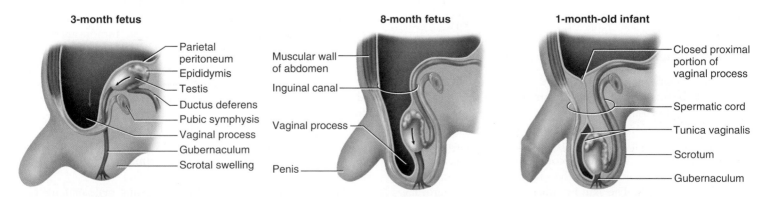

**Figure 26.25 Descent of the Testis.** Note that the testis and spermatic ducts are retroperitoneal. An extension of the peritoneum called the *vaginal process* follows the testis through the inguinal canal and becomes the tunica vaginalis.
• *Why is this structure of male anatomy called the tunica vaginalis?*

male voice deepens as the larynx enlarges. Testosterone, estrogens, and growth hormone cause rapid elongation of the long bones, and thus the adolescent growth in stature. And to the great anxiety of the parents of adolescents, the anatomical readiness for reproduction is accompanied by psychological interest in sex, the *libido,* elicited in both sexes by testosterone. (Testosterone is produced not only by the testes but also, in small amounts, by the ovaries and adrenal cortex.)

## The Aging Reproductive System

Fertility and sexual function decline in and beyond middle age, owing to declining levels of testosterone and estrogen. Around ages 50 to 55, both men and women go through a period of physical and psychological change called **climacteric,** although (jokes about "male menopause" aside) only women experience *menopause,* the cessation of menses.

### Male Climacteric

In males, testosterone secretion peaks at about 7 mg/day at age 20 and then declines steadily to as little as one-fifth of this level by age 80. There is a corresponding decline in the number and secretory activity of the interstitial cells (the source of testosterone) and sustentacular cells (the source of inhibin). Along with the declining testosterone level, the sperm count and libido diminish. By age 65, sperm count is typically about one-third of what it was in a man's 20s. Nevertheless, men remain capable of fathering a child throughout old age.

Male climacteric is brought on by falling levels of testosterone and inhibin. When the pituitary is less inhibited by these hormones, it secretes elevated levels of FSH and LH. In some cases, these gonadotropins cause mood changes, hot flashes, or even illusions of suffocation—symptoms similar to those that occur in perimenopausal women. Most men, however, pass through climacteric with little or no effect.

About 20% of men in their 60s and 50% of men in their 80s experience *erectile dysfunction (impotence),* the frequent inability to maintain a sufficient erection for intercourse. Erectile dysfunction can also result from hypertension, atherosclerosis, medication, diabetes mellitus, and psychological causes. Over 90% of men with erectile dysfunction nevertheless remain able to ejaculate.

### Female Climacteric and Menopause

Female climacteric is brought on by declining ovarian function. It generally begins when the ovaries are down to their last 1,000 eggs or so, and the follicles and ova that remain are less responsive to gonadotropins. Consequently, the follicles secrete less estrogen and progesterone. Without these steroids, the uterus, vagina, and breasts atrophy. Intercourse may become uncomfortable, and vaginal infections more common, as the vagina becomes thinner, less distensible, and drier. The skin becomes thinner, cholesterol levels rise (increasing the risk of cardiovascular disease), and bone mass declines (increasing the risk of osteoporosis). Blood vessels constrict and dilate in response to shifting hormone balances, and the sudden dilation of cutaneous arteries may cause *hot flashes*—a spreading sense of heat from the abdomen to the thorax, neck, and face. Hot flashes may occur several times a day, sometimes accompanied by headaches resulting from the sudden vasodilation of arteries in the head. In some people, the changing hormonal profile also causes mood changes.

Female climacteric is accompanied by **menopause,** the cessation of menstruation and end of fertility. Menopause usually occurs between the ages of 45 and 55. The average age has increased steadily in the last century and is now about 52. It is difficult to precisely establish the time of menopause because the menstrual periods can stop for several months and then begin again. Menopause is generally considered to have occurred when there has been no menstruation for a year or more.

## Reproductive Disorders of the Male

Prostate cancer (see Insight 26.1) is the most common cancer of the male reproductive system, but not the only one. Men are also subject to testicular, penile, and breast cancer. Testicular cancer is the most common of these three and often strikes at a relatively young age compared to prostate cancer. Testicular self-examination combined with regular physical examinations are important preventive measures. Some additional facts about these cancers and other male reproductive disorders are given in table 26.2.

## Reproductive Disorders of the Female

The most important malignancies of the female reproductive system are breast and cervical cancer, although the increase in cigarette smoking has caused lung cancer to surpass both of these as a cause of female mortality in the United States. Breast cancer occurs in one out of every eight or nine American women. Breast tumors originate in cells of the mammary ducts and may metastasize to other organs by way of mammary and axillary lymphatics. Although some breast cancer is genetic, many nonhereditary risk factors are also known, including age, early menarche and late menopause, high alcohol or fat consumption, and smoking. Over 70% of cases of breast cancer, however, lack any identifiable risk factor. Early detection through regular breast X-rays (mammograms) are currently regarded as the best protection. Breast self-examination (BSE) may also be helpful, but recent research has cast doubt on whether tumors are detected early enough by BSE to significantly reduce female mortality.

Uterine cancer is of two kinds, endometrial and cervical. Cervical cancer is a slow-growing neoplasia of the lower cervical canal and can be detected by microscopic examination of squamous cells from the cervix (a Pap smear; Insight 26.3).

There are many other disorders of female reproductive function, too numerous to discuss here. Pregnancy adds its own risks to women's health. Table 26.3 describes some of the more common complications of pregnancy.

More common than any of the foregoing male or female reproductive disorders are the **sexually transmitted diseases (STDs),** caused by infectious microorganisms transmitted by intercourse

| TABLE 26.2 | Some Male Reproductive Disorders |
|---|---|
| Breast cancer | Accounts for 0.2% of male cancers in the United States, usually seen after age 60 but sometimes in children and adolescents. About 175 females get breast cancer for every male who does so. Usually felt as a lump near the nipple, often with crusting and discharge from the nipple. Often quite advanced by the time of diagnosis, with poor prospects for recovery, because of denial and delay in seeking treatment. |
| Cryptorchidism[66] (crip-TOR-ki-dizm) | Failure of one or both testes to descend completely into the scrotum. Leads to infertility if not corrected, because undescended testes are too warm for spermatogenesis. In most cases, the testes descend spontaneously in the first year of infancy; otherwise, the condition can be corrected with hormone injections or surgery. |
| Hypospadias[67] (HY-po-SPAY-dee-us) | A congenital defect in which the urethra opens on the ventral side or base of the penis rather than at the tip; usually corrected surgically at about 1 year of age. |
| Infertility | Inability to fertilize an egg because of a low sperm count (lower than 20–25 million/mL), poor sperm motility, or a high percentage of deformed sperm (two heads, defective tails, etc.). May result from malnutrition, gonorrhea and other infections, toxins, or testosterone deficiency. |
| Penile cancer | Accounts for 1% of male cancers in the United States; most common in black males aged 50 to 70 and of low income. Most often seen in men with nonretractable foreskins (phimosis) combined with poor penile hygiene; least common in men circumcised at birth. |
| Testicular cancer | The most common solid tumor in men 15 to 34 years old, especially white males of middle to upper economic classes. Typically begins as a painless lump or enlargement of the testis. Highly curable if detected early. Men should routinely palpate the testes for normal size and smooth texture. |
| Varicocele (VAIR-ih-co-seal) | Abnormal dilation of veins of the spermatic cord, so they resemble a "bag of worms." Occurs in 10% of males in the United States. Caused by absence or incompetence of venous valves. Reduces testicular blood flow and often causes infertility. |

### Disorders Described Elsewhere

Androgen-insensitivity syndrome  546
Benign prostatic hyperplasia  746

Erectile dsyfunction  764
Prostate cancer  746

and other sexual activity, and to infants during or before birth. Most of these are caused by viruses and bacteria. Currently the most serious viral STDs are **AIDS** (caused by the human immunodeficiency virus, HIV) and **hepatitis C.** HIV infects helper T lymphocytes among other cells, thus exerting a devastating effect on the immune system and leaving a person susceptible to certain forms of cancer and opportunistic infection (see p. 657). The hepatitis C virus (HCV) is a common cause of liver failure and is the leading reason for liver transplants in the United States. Other viral STDs include genital herpes (usually caused by herpes simplex virus type 2, HSV-2) and genital warts (caused by 60 or more human papillomaviruses, HPVs). Some forms of HPV are associated with cervical, vaginal, penile, and anal cancer.

Bacterial STDs include gonorrhea and syphilis, caused by the bacteria *Neisseria gonorrhoeae* and *Treponema pallidum,* respectively. Cases of these two diseases are outnumbered, however, by chlamydia (caused by *Chlamydia trachomatis*), which affects 3 to 5 million people per year in the United States.

## Before You Go On

*Answer the following questions to test your understanding of the preceding section:*

15. What are mesonephric and paramesonephric ducts? What factors determine which one develops and which one regresses in the fetus?

16. What male structures develop from the genital tubercle and labio-scrotal folds?

17. Define the *gubernaculum* and describe its function.

18. Which of the following occur in both men and women—thelarche, pubarche, climacteric, menopause, breast cancer, and cryptorchidism? Explain.

---

[66]*crypt* = hidden + *orchid* = testes
[67]*hypo* = below + *spad* = to draw off (the urine)

# INSIGHT 26.3

## Clinical Application

### Cervical Cancer and Pap Smears

Cervical cancer is common among women between the ages of 30 and 50, especially those who smoke, who began sexual activity at an early age, and who have histories of frequent sexually transmitted diseases or cervical inflammation. It is often caused by the human papillomavirus (HPV), a sexually transmitted pathogen. Cervical cancer usually begins in the epithelial cells of the lower cervix, develops slowly, and remains a local, easily removed lesion for several years. If the cancerous cells spread to the subepithelial connective tissue, however, the cancer is said to be *invasive* and is much more dangerous and potentially fatal.

The best protection against cervical cancer is early detection by means of a *Pap*[68] *smear*—a procedure in which loose cells are removed from the cervix and vagina with a small flat stick and cervical brush, then microscopically examined. The pathologist looks for cells with signs of *dysplasia* (abnormal development) or carcinoma (fig. 26.26). One system of grading Pap smears classifies abnormal results in three grades of *cervical intraepithelial neoplasia (CIN)*. Findings are rated on the following scale, and further vigilance or treatment planned accordingly:

ASCUS—atypical squamous cells of undetermined significance

CIN I—mild dysplasia with cellular changes typically associated with HPV

CIN II—moderate dysplasia with precancerous lesions

CIN III—severe dysplasia, *carcinoma in situ* (preinvasive carcinoma of surface cells)

A rating of ASCUS or CIN I calls for a repeat Pap smear and visual examination of the cervix (*colposcopy*[69]) in 3 to 6 months. CIN II calls for a biopsy, often done with an "electric scalpel" in a procedure called LEEP (loop electrosurgical excision procedure). A cone of tissue is removed to evaluate the depth of invasion by the malignant or premalignant cells. This in itself may be curative if all margins of the specimen are normal, indicating all normal cells were removed. CIN III may be cause for *hysterectomy*[70] or radiation therapy.

An average woman is typically advised to have annual Pap smears for 3 years and may then have them less often at the discretion of her physician. Women with any of the risk factors listed may be advised to have more frequent examinations.

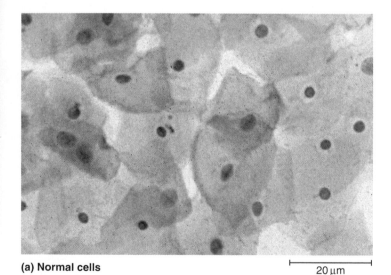

**(a) Normal cells**  20 µm

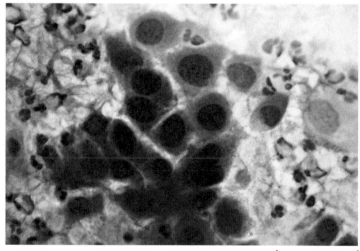

**(b) Malignant (CIN III) cells**  20 µm

**Figure 26.26** **Pap Smears.** These are smears of squamous epithelial cells scraped from the cervix. In the malignant (cancerous) cells, note the loss of cell volume and the greatly enlarged nuclei.

---

[68]George N. Papanicolaou (1883–1962), Greek–American physician and cytologist

[69]*colpo* = vagina + *scopy* = viewing
[70]*hyster* = uterus + *ectomy* = cutting out

| TABLE 26.3 | Some Female Reproductive Disorders |
|---|---|

### Disorders of Pregnancy

| | |
|---|---|
| Abruptio placentae[71] | Premature separation of the placenta from the uterine wall, often associated with preeclampsia or cocaine use. May require birth by cesarian section. |
| Ectopic[72] pregnancy | Implantation of the conceptus anywhere other than the normal location in the uterus, such as the uterine tube (over 90% of cases), cervix, or abdominal cavity; usually must be surgically terminated to prevent serious and potentially fatal hemorrhage. |
| Gestational diabetes | A form of diabetes mellitus that develops in about 1% to 3% of pregnant women, characterized by insulin insensitivity, hyperglycemia, glycosuria, and a risk of excessive fetal size and birth trauma. Glucose metabolism usually returns to normal after delivery of the infant, but 40% to 60% of women with gestational diabetes develop diabetes mellitus within 15 years after the pregnancy. |
| Hyperemesis gravidarum[73] | Prolonged vomiting, dehydration, alkalosis, and weight loss in early pregnancy, often requiring hospitalization to stabilize fluid, electrolyte, and acid–base balance; sometimes associated with liver damage. |
| Placenta previa[74] | Blockage of the cervical canal by the placenta, preventing birth of the infant before the placenta separates from the uterus. Requires birth by cesarian section. |
| Preeclampsia[75] (toxemia of pregnancy) | Rapid onset of hypertension and edema, with swelling especially of the face and hands; proteinuria and reduced glomerular filtration rate; increased blood clotting; sometimes with headaches, visual disturbances, and small cerebral infarctions. Seen in about 4% of pregnancies, especially in the third trimester of women pregnant for the first time. Can progress to *eclampsia,* with seizures and widespread vascular spasms that are sometimes fatal to the mother, fetus, or both. Eclampsia usually occurs shortly before or after childbirth. |
| Spontaneous abortion | Occurs in 10% to 15% of pregnancies, usually because of fetal deformities or chromosomal abnormalities incompatible with survival, but may also result from maternal abnormalities, infectious disease, and drug abuse. |

### Other Reproductive Disorders

| | |
|---|---|
| Amenorrhea[76] | Absence of menstruation. Normal in pregnancy, lactation, early adolescence, and perimenopausal years, but can also result from gonadotropin hyposecretion, genetic disorders, CNS disorders, or excessively low body fat content. |
| Dysmenorrhea[77] | Painful menstruation in the absence of pelvic disease, caused by excessive endometrial prostaglandin secretion. Prostaglandins stimulate painful contractions of myometrium and uterine blood vessels. Usually begins around age 15 or 16 and affects up to 75% of women from 15 to 25 years old. |
| Endometriosis | Growth of endometrial tissue in any site other than the uterus, including the uterine tubes, ovaries, urinary bladder, vagina, pelvic cavity, small or large intestine, or even the lungs or pleural cavity. May cause dysmenorrhea, abnormal vaginal bleeding, and infertility. |
| Leiomyomas[78] (uterine fibroids) | Benign tumors of uterine smooth muscle. Usually small and asymptomatic, but may cause abnormal uterine bleeding and pain or heavy menstruation. |
| Pelvic inflammatory disease (PID) | Acute, painful inflammation due to infection of the uterus, uterine tubes, or ovaries, usually with the organisms of sexually transmitted diseases. Causes abdominopelvic pain, pain on urination, and irregular bleeding. |

### Disorders Described Elsewhere

---

[71]*ab* = away + *rupt* = to tear + *placentae* = of the placenta
[72]*ec* = out of + *top* = place
[73]*hyper* = excessive + *emesis* = vomiting + *gravida* = pregnant woman
[74]*pre* = before + *via* = the way (obstructing the way)
[75]*ec* = forth + *lampsia* = shining
[76]*a* = without + *meno* = monthly + *rrhea* = flow
[77]*dys* = painful, abnormal + *meno* = monthly + *rrhea* = flow
[78]*leio* = smooth + *myo* = muscle + *oma* = tumor

# CHAPTER REVIEW

## REVIEW OF KEY CONCEPTS

### Sexual Reproduction (p. 737)

1. Sexual reproduction is the production of offspring that combine genes from two parents.

2. Sexual reproduction entails the union of two *gametes* to form a *zygote* (fertilized egg). The gametes are a small motile *sperm* produced by the male and a large, immobile, nutrient-laden *egg (ovum)* produced by the female.

3. The sexes are genetically defined by their sex chromosomes. Normally, males have an X and a Y chromosome, and females have two X chromosomes.

4. The *gonads* (testes and ovaries) are the *primary sex organs*. Secondary sex organs are other anatomical structures needed to produce offspring, such as the male glands, ducts, and penis and the female uterine tubes, uterus, and vagina. *Secondary sex characteristics* are features not essential to reproduction but which help to attract mates.

### Male Reproductive Anatomy (p. 738)

1. The *scrotum* contains the testes and the *spermatic cord*—a bundle of connective tissue, testicular blood and lymphatic vessels, nerves, and a sperm duct, the *ductus deferens*. The spermatic cord passes up the back of the scrotum and through the external inguinal ring into the inguinal canal.

2. Sperm cannot develop at the core body temperature of 37°C. The testes are kept about 2°C cooler than this by three structures in the scrotum: the *cremaster muscle* of the spermatic cord, which relaxes when it is warm and contracts when it is cool, thus lowering or raising the scrotum and testes; the *dartos muscle* in the scrotal wall, which contracts and tautens the scrotum when it is cool; and the *pampiniform plexus* of veins in the spermatic cord, which acts as a *countercurrent heat exchanger* to cool the blood on its way to the testis.

3. The testis has a fibrous capsule, the *tunica albuginea*. Fibrous septa divide the interior of the testis into 250 to 300 compartments called *lobules*. Each lobule contains 1 to 3 sperm-producing *seminiferous tubules*. Testosterone-secreting *interstitial cells* lie in clusters between the tubules.

4. The epithelium of a seminiferous tubule consists of *germ cells* and *sustentacular cells*. The germ cells develop into sperm. The sustentacular cells support and nourish the germ cells, form a *blood–testis barrier* between them and the nearest blood supply,

and secrete *inhibin*, which regulates the rate of sperm production.

5. Each testis is supplied by a long, slender *testicular artery* and drained by veins of the pampiniform plexus, which converge to form the *testicular vein*. It is also supplied with *testicular nerves* and lymphatic vessels.

6. Sperm formation, or *spermatogenesis*, begins with primordial germ cells that migrate from the embryonic yolk sac into the gonad and become *spermatogonia*. Beginning at puberty, spermatogonia give rise to a series of cells called *primary spermatocytes, secondary spermatocytes, spermatids,* and finally *spermatozoa (sperm)*.

7. The sperm consists of a head containing the nucleus and *acrosome*, and a tail composed of a mitochondria-stuffed *midpiece*, a long *principal piece*, and a short *endpiece*.

8. *Spermatic ducts* carry sperm from the testis to the urethra. They include *efferent ductules* leaving the testis; the *duct of the epididymis*, a highly coiled structure adhering to the posterior side of the testis; a muscular *ductus deferens* that travels through the spermatic cord and inguinal canal into the pelvic cavity; and a short *ejaculatory duct* that carries sperm and seminal vesicle secretions the last 2 cm to the urethra. The urethra completes the path of the sperm to the outside of the body.

9. The male has three sets of accessory glands: a pair of *seminal vesicles* posterior to the urinary bladder; a single *prostate gland* inferior to the bladder, enclosing the prostatic urethra; and a pair of small *bulbourethral glands* that secrete into the proximal end of the penile urethra. The seminal vesicles and prostate secrete most of the semen. The bulbourethral glands produce a small amount of clear slippery fluid that lubricates the urethra and neutralizes its pH.

10. *Semen* is a mixture of sperm (10% of the volume) and fluids from the prostate (30%) and seminal vesicles (60%). It contains about 50 to 120 million sperm/mL, as well as seminogelin, serine protease (prostate-specific antigen), fructose, prostaglandins, and other chemicals.

11. The *penis* is divided into an internal *root* and an external *shaft* and *glans*. It is covered with loose skin that extends over the glans as the *prepuce*, or foreskin.

12. Internally, the penis consists mainly of three long *erectile tissues*—a pair of dorsal *corpora cavernosa*, which engorge with blood and

produce most of the effect of erection, and a single ventral *corpus spongiosum*, which contains the urethra. All three tissues have blood sinuses called *lacunae* separated by *trabeculae* composed of connective tissue and smooth muscle (*trabecular muscle*).

13. At the proximal end of the penis, the corpus spongiosum dilates into a *bulb* that receives the urethra and ducts of the bulbourethral glands, and the corpora cavernosa diverge into a pair of *crura* that anchor the penis to the pubic arch and perineal membrane.

14. The penis is supplied by a pair of internal pudendal arteries. Each branches into a *dorsal artery*, which travels dorsally under the skin of the penis, and a *deep artery*, which travels through the corpus cavernosum and supplies blood to the lacunae. The dorsal arteries supply most of the blood when the penis is flaccid, and the deep arteries during erection.

15. Nerves of the penis converge on a pair of *dorsal nerves*, which lead via the *internal pudendal nerves* to the sacral plexus and then the spinal cord. The penis receives sympathetic, parasympathetic, and somatic motor nerve fibers.

### Female Reproductive Anatomy (p. 749)

1. The ovary has a central *medulla*; a surface *cortex*; and an outer fibrous capsule, the *tunica albuginea*.

2. Each egg develops in its own bubblelike *follicle*. Follicles are located primarily in the cortex.

3. The ovary is supported by a medial *ovarian ligament*, lateral *suspensory ligament*, and anterior *mesovarium*. It receives blood from a branch of the *uterine artery* medially and from the *ovarian artery* laterally.

4. *Oogenesis* is the production of eggs. Unlike spermatogenesis, it occurs in a monthly rhythm (the *ovarian cycle*) and usually produces only one gamete (egg) per month.

5. Oogenesis begins with primordial germ cells, which colonize the fetal gonad and become *oogonia*. These multiply until the fifth month of fetal development. Some of these develop into *primary oocytes* and begin meiosis I before birth. Most primary oocytes undergo *atresia* during childhood, leaving about 400,000 at puberty.

6. Each month, about 20 to 25 *primordial follicles* begin to develop. The single layer of squamous follicular cells around the oocyte thicken into cuboidal cells, then mul-

tiply and become stratified *granulosa cells.* The follicle is then a *primary follicle.* The granulosa cells secrete *follicular fluid,* which forms small pools amid the granulosa cells. These pools eventually coalesce to form a single cavity, the *antrum,* and the follicle is then called a *secondary (antral) follicle.* Normally only one of these secondary follicles becomes a fully *mature (graafian) follicle,* destined to ovulate.

7. At the secondary follicle stage, the primary oocyte completes meiosis I and becomes a *secondary oocyte.* This is the stage that ovulates. It never develops further unless it is fertilized.

8. After ovulation, the remnant of the follicle becomes a *corpus luteum,* which secretes progesterone. If pregnancy does not occur, the corpus luteum undergoes involution (degenerates) from days 24 to 26 of an average 28-day cycle. It persists for about 3 months if pregnancy does occur.

9. The *uterine (fallopian) tube* is a ciliated duct that extends from the ovary to the uterus. Its flared distal end, near the ovary, is called the *infundibulum* and has feathery projections called *fimbriae* to receive the ovulated egg. Its long midportion is the *ampulla,* and the short constricted zone near the uterus is the *isthmus.*

10. The uterus is a thick muscular chamber superior to the urinary bladder. It consists of an upper *fundus,* middle *corpus* (body), and lower *cervix* (neck), where it meets the vagina.

11. The uterine wall is three-layered: an outer serosa called the *perimetrium,* a thick muscular *myometrium,* and an inner mucosa called the *endometrium.* The endometrium contains numerous tubular glands and is divided into two layers—a thick superficial *stratum functionalis,* which is shed in each menstrual period, and a thinner basal *stratum basalis,* which is retained from cycle to cycle.

12. The uterus is supported by a pair of lateral winglike *broad ligaments* and cordlike *cardinal, uterosacral,* and *round ligaments.* It receives blood from a pair of *uterine arteries.*

13. The endometrium undergoes cyclic histological changes called the *menstrual cycle,* governed by the shifting hormonal secretions of the ovaries. The *proliferative phase* of the menstrual cycle consists of mitotic rebuilding of tissue lost in the previous menstrual period. The *secretory phase* consists of further thickening of the endometrium by accumulation of secretions, not

by mitosis. The *premenstrual phase* is characterized by ischemia and necrosis of the endometrium. The *menstrual phase* begins when endometrial tissue and blood is first discharged from the vagina, and marks day 1 of a new cycle.

14. The *vagina* tilts dorsally between the urethra and rectum. It has no glands but is moistened by transudation of serous fluid through the vaginal wall and by mucus from glands in the cervical canal. The adult vagina is lined with a stratified squamous epithelium populated by antigen-presenting *dendritic cells.*

15. The *vulva* (*pudendum* or *external genitalia*) include the *mons pubis, labia majora* and *minora, clitoris,* vaginal orifice, accessory glands (*greater* and *lesser vestibular glands* and *paraurethral glands*), and erectile tissues (*vestibular bulbs*). The urethra also opens into the vulva.

16. The breast is internally divided into lobes, each with a *lactiferous duct* that conveys milk to the nipple. Outside of pregnancy or lactation, the breast contains only small traces of mammary gland. During pregnancy, the ducts grow and branch, and secretory acini develop at the ends of the smallest branches.

### Developmental and Clinical Perspectives (p. 760)

1. Many organs of the male and female reproductive systems develop from the same embryonic organs. Organs with the same embryonic precursor are said to be *homologous* to each other—for example, the scrotum and labia majora are homologous because both develop from the labioscrotal folds.

2. Both sexes initially exhibit a pair of *gonadal ridges, mesonephric ducts,* and *paramesonephric ducts.*

3. In an XY (male) fetus, the *SRY gene* codes for a protein called *testis-determining factor,* which initiates the development of male genitalia. The gonadal ridge becomes a testis, which secretes testosterone and müllerian-inhibiting factor. These hormones cause the paramesonephric (müllerian) duct to degenerate, while the mesonephric duct develops into the male reproductive tract.

4. In a female fetus, where there is no Y chromosome, the gonads become ovaries, the mesonephric ducts degenerate, and the paramesonephric ducts develop into a female reproductive tract.

5. The external genitalia of both sexes begin as a *genital tubercle,* a pair of *urogenital folds,* and a pair of *labioscrotal folds.* By week 12 of prenatal development, the genital tubercle differentiates into the glans of the penis or clitoris; the urogenital folds enclose the urethra of the male or become the labia minora of a female; and the labioscrotal folds become the scrotum of a male or labia majora of a female.

6. During male development, the fetal testes descend through the inguinal canal into the scrotum; this is called *descent of the testes.* In the female fetus, the ovaries also descend to a point just below the brim of the lesser pelvis.

7. Puberty is initiated by the secretion of GnRH by the hypothalamus, inducing secretion of FSH and LH by the anterior pituitary. The visible changes at puberty result from many hormones including testosterone, estrogens, growth hormone, and others. Puberty is at an end when the individual attains fertility. Adolescence continues until full adult height is attained.

8. The earliest visible sign of male puberty is enlargement of the testes and scrotum; the completion of puberty is marked by the ejaculation of fertile sperm.

9. Female puberty is marked by *thelarche* (breast development), *pubarche* (growth of pubic and axillary hair, also occurring in males), and *menarche* (the onset of menstruation). Regular ovulation and fertility are attained about a year after menarche.

10. At midlife, both sexes go through a period of hormonal and physical change called *climacteric.* This is marked by a decline in testosterone or estrogen secretion, and a rise in the secretion of FSH and LH. In females, climacteric is accompanied by *menopause,* the cessation of ovarian function and fertility.

11. Among the important issues for male reproductive health are prostate, testicular, penile, and breast cancer. Other reproductive disorders are described in table 26.2.

12. The most important diseases of the female reproductive system are uterine and breast cancer. Pregnancy also carries a risk of varied complications described in table 26.3.

13. The most common reproductive disorders in both sexes are sexually transmitted diseases. Most of these are caused by viruses (HIV, HCV, HSV, HPV) and bacteria (*Neisseria, Treponema,* and *Chlamydia*).

## TESTING YOUR RECALL

1. The ductus deferens develops from the
   _____ of the embryo.
   a. mesonephric duct
   b. paramesonephric duct
   c. phallus
   d. labioscrotal folds
   e. urogenital folds

2. Descent of the testes includes their passage
   through
   a. the inguinal canal.
   b. the spermatic cord.
   c. the ductus deferens.
   d. the seminiferous tubule.
   e. the ampulla.

3. Four spermatozoa arise from each
   a. primordial germ cell.
   b. type A spermatogonium.
   c. type B spermatogonium.
   d. secondary spermatocyte.
   e. spermatid.

4. Prior to ejaculation, sperm are stored
   primarily in
   a. the seminiferous tubules.
   b. the epididymis.
   c. the seminal vesicles.
   d. the bulb of the penis.
   e. the ejaculatory ducts.

5. The principal source of testosterone is (are)
   a. the seminiferous tubules.
   b. the sustentacular cells.
   c. the interstitial cells.
   d. the seminal vesicles.
   e. the prostate gland.

6. The fluid-filled central cavity of a mature
   ovarian follicle is
   a. the antrum.
   b. the zona pellucida.
   c. the theca folliculi.
   d. the granulosa.
   e. the stigma.

7. The tissue lost in menstruation is
   a. perimetrium.
   b. myometrium.
   c. stratum basalis.
   d. stratum functionalis.
   e. stratum corneum.

8. The male scrotum is homologous to the
   female
   a. ovaries.
   b. vagina.
   c. labia majora.
   d. vestibular bulbs.
   e. clitoris.

9. The narrowest part of the uterus is
   a. the fundus.
   b. the infundibulum.
   c. the body.
   d. the ampulla.
   e. the cervix.

10. The vesicouterine pouch is a space in the
    peritoneal cavity between the uterus and
    a. the fornices.
    b. the uterine tube.
    c. the sacrum.
    d. the urinary bladder.
    e. the rectum.

11. Under the influence of androgens, the
    embryonic _____ duct develops into the
    male reproductive tract.

12. Spermatozoa obtain energy for locomotion
    from _____ in the semen.

13. The _____, a network of veins in the
    spermatic cord, helps keep the testes cooler
    than the core body temperature.

14. Each egg cell develops in its own fluid-filled
    space called a/an _____.

15. The mucosa of the uterus is called the
    _____.

16. Over half of the semen consists of
    secretions from a pair of glands called the
    _____.

17. The blood–testis barrier is formed by tight
    junctions between the _____ cells.

18. The male organ(s) homologous to the
    female's paraurethral glands is (are) the
    _____.

19. A yellowish structure called the _____
    secretes progesterone during the secretory
    phase of the menstrual cycle.

20. The funnel-like distal end of the uterine
    tube is called the _____ and has feathery
    processes called _____.

*Answers in the Appendix*

## TRUE OR FALSE

*Determine which five of the following statements
are false, and briefly explain why.*

1. After ovulation, a follicle begins to move
   down the uterine tube to the uterus.

2. The uterine tubes develop from the
   embryonic mesonephric ducts.

3. Thelarche normally precedes menarche in
   female puberty.

4. The follicle that ovulates is called the
   primary follicle.

5. Sperm cannot develop at the core body
   temperature.

6. A high testosterone level makes a fetus
   develop a male reproductive system, and
   a high estrogen level makes it develop a
   female reproductive system.

7. Most ovarian follicles degenerate before a
   girl reaches puberty.

8. The pampiniform plexus serves to keep
   the testes warm.

9. Prior to ejaculation, sperm are stored
   mainly in the epididymis.

10. The thickest layer of the uterine wall is the
    myometrium.

*Answers in the Appendix*

## TESTING YOUR COMPREHENSION

1. The most common method of male sterilization is vasectomy, in which the ductus (vas) deferens is tied, cut, or both. What is the equivalent method of female sterilization? Why are the difficulty and risks of that procedure greater than for a vasectomy?

2. *Uterus bicornis* (*bicorn* = two horns) is a rare condition in which a woman has two separate uteri, each opening by its own cervix into the vagina. What abnormal event of embryonic development do you think could account for this?

3. Suppose the corpus spongiosum became as engorged with blood as the corpora cavernosa do during erection of the penis. What problem would this create for sexual function? In light of this, why is it beneficial that the corpus spongiosum is not enclosed in a tunica albuginea?

4. What male structure(s) do you think is (are) homologous to the vestibular bulbs of the female? Explain your reasoning.

5. An oocyte lives for only 24 hrs after ovulation if it is not fertilized. The trip down the uterine tube, from infundibulum to uterus, takes about 72 hrs. In light of this, where do you think fertilization normally occurs?

*Answers at aris.mhhe.com*

## ONLINE RESOURCES

Visit aprevealed.com to explore melt-away cadaver dissections, watch animations that clarify difficult concepts, review histological and radiological images, or take a quiz to assess your understanding of the material.

The Saladin *Human Anatomy,* 2e website at aris.mhhe.com features chapter-specific quizzes, labeling exercises, and other interactive tools to complement your study of human anatomy. If your instructor has provided an ARIS course code, you can also access assignments and information specific to your course.

# Answers to Chapter Review Questions

Answers are provided here for the end-of-chapter Testing Your Recall, True or False questions, and the questions in the figure legends. Answers to Think About It and Testing Your Comprehension questions are available on the Saladin ARIS website at aris.mhhe.com.

## Chapter 1

### Testing Your Recall

| | | | | | |
|---|---|---|---|---|---|
| 1. | a | 8. | d | 15. | functional morphology |
| 2. | b | 9. | c | 16. | palpation |
| 3. | c | 10. | b | 17. | computed tomography |
| 4. | a | 11. | dissection | 18. | organ |
| 5. | e | 12. | Robert Hooke | 19. | stereoscopic |
| 6. | c | 13. | metabolism | 20. | prehensile, opposable |
| 7. | a | 14. | homeostasis | | |

### True or False

(These items are false for the reasons given; all others are true.)

3. Auscultation is listening to sounds made by the body.
4. Radiology is concerned with all methods of medical imaging.
6. Nearly every cell contains many organelles.
7. Leeuwenhoek was a textile merchant by trade.
9. Stereoscopic vision was probably an adaptation to the arboreal habitat.

### Figure Legend Questions

1.2 MRI is better than X-ray at showing soft tissues such as the eye and its muscles and the brain tissue. X-ray is better than PET at showing hard, dense structures such as the bones and teeth.

1.3 Radiography can CT use X-rays, which have the potential to cause mutations and birth defects; sonography uses no harmful radiation.

1.4 Physicians and surgeons could make many errors if they assumed that every human body has exactly the same structure. Physicians in training must become aware of human anatomical variation.

1.9 The embryonic tail suggests that *Homo sapiens* arose, ultimately, from ancestors with tails and still possess the genes for the formation of a tail.

1.12 A gorilla. About 4.5 million years.

## Atlas A

### Testing Your Recall

| | | | | | |
|---|---|---|---|---|---|
| 1. | d | 8. | d | 15. | hand, foot |
| 2. | c | 9. | b | 16. | meninges |
| 3. | e | 10. | e | 17. | retroperitoneal |
| 4. | d | 11. | supinated | 18. | medial |
| 5. | d | 12. | parietal | 19. | inferior |
| 6. | a | 13. | mediastinum | 20. | cubital, popliteal |
| 7. | a | 14. | occipital, nuchal | | |

### True or False

(These items are false for the reasons given; all others are true.)

4. The diaphragm is inferior to the lungs.
5. No organs are contained between the parietal and visceral pleurae; the pleurae adhere to each other with only a potential space between them.
6. The liver is in the right hypochondriac and epigastric regions.
9. The peritoneum lines the abdominal cavity and external surfaces of the stomach and intestines.
10. The sigmoid colon is in the lower left quadrant.

### Figure Legend Questions

A.3 Median or midsagittal
A.4 A frontal (coronal) section
A.6 The upper right quadrant
A.10 No, it is in the pelvic cavity, inferior to the peritoneum. Note that the peritoneum is seen passing over the superior surface of the bladder.
A.13 The transverse abdominal muscle. The external abdominal oblique.
A.14 The heart, lungs, livers, spleen, and stomach, among others
A.15 The bronchus, esophagus, and thoracic aorta are medial to the lungs. The adrenal gland, spleen, esophagus, diaphragm, and all of the thoracic organs seen here are superior to the kidneys.
A.16 Superior. Lateral.
A.17 Posterior or dorsal. Superior.
A.18 Pleural and pericardial.
A.19 Posterior
A.21 Fat (adipose tissue)

## Chapter 2

### Testing Your Recall

| | | | | | |
|---|---|---|---|---|---|
| 1. | e | 8. | a | 15. | tight junctions |
| 2. | d | 9. | d | 16. | squamous |
| 3. | b | 10. | b | 17. | mitochondrion, nuclear envelope |
| 4. | b | 11. | micrometers (μm) | 18. | peroxisomes, smooth ER |
| 5. | e | 12. | receptor | 19. | cell-adhesion molecules |
| 6. | a | 13. | gates | 20. | phagocytosis |
| 7. | d | 14. | mitochondria | | |

### True or False

(These items are false for the reasons given; all others are true.)

2. Proteins are only 1% to 10% of the molecules of a plasma membrane.
6. Movement down a gradient does not employ ATP.
7. Osmosis is a case of simple diffusion.
9. Desmosomes provide no channels from one cell to another.
10. The nucleolus is not an organelle.

### Figure Legend Questions

2.2 The cells are thinner here than around the rim, so more light shines through.
2.8 The region that projects into the cytoplasm. Amphiphilic.
2.12 To stiffen and support the microvillus, anchor it to the cell, and produce contractions of the microvillus that milk its contents into the cell

2.13    Microvilli are much smaller than cilia, they lack axonemes, and they have a supportive core of actin.

2.14    Gap junctions

2.15    Microfilaments have a supportive role in microvilli, and microtubules form the axonemes of cilia and flagella.

2.17    The nucleus

# Chapter 3

## Testing Your Recall

| | | |
|---|---|---|
| 1. a | 8. e | 14. fibers |
| 2. b | 9. b | 15. collagen |
| 3. c | 10. b | 16. multipotent |
| 4. e | 11. apoptosis (pro- | 17. basement membrane |
| 5. d | grammed cell death) | 18. matrix |
| 6. a | 12. mesothelium | 19. holocrine |
| 7. b | 13. lacunae | 20. simple |

## True or False

(These items are false for the reasons given; all others are true.)

2.  The noncellular components include ground substance and fibers.
5.  The tongue epithelium is nonkeratinized.
6.  Macrophages develop from monocytes.
8.  Brown fat produces no ATP.
9.  In metaplasia, one mature tissue type transforms into another.

## Figure Legend Questions

3.1     The microtubule could be drawn roughly as two parallel bars, like the upper right diagram of figure 3.2, but if the globular tubulin molecules were taken into account (see fig. 2.16), each bar could be shown as a linear chain of spherical tubulin molecules.

3.13    Dense regular connective tissue

3.28    Exocytosis

3.30    The trachea, for example, is lined with a ciliated pseudostratified columnar epithelium like this one.

# Chapter 4

## Testing Your Recall

| | | |
|---|---|---|
| 1. b | 8. a | 14. implantation |
| 2. b | 9. e | 15. chorionic villi |
| 3. d | 10. d | 16. acrosome |
| 4. c | 11. teratogens | 17. uterine tube |
| 5. a | 12. nondisjunction | 18. somites |
| 6. e | 13. neural groove or | 19. polyspermy |
| 7. c | neural tube | 20. embryo |

## True or False

(These items are false for the reasons given; all others are true.)

1.  Sperm must undergo capacitation first.
2.  Fertilization occurs in the uterine tube.
3.  Several sperm must digest a path for the one that fertilizes the egg.
8.  Oogenesis produces one large oocyte and small discarded polar bodies.
10.  The energy comes from the midpiece mitochondria.

## Figure Legend Questions

4.2     An egg will already have died by the time it reaches the uterus if it was not already fertilized.

4.10    At about 8 weeks

4.11    There are two arteries and one vein. Blood in the vein is more oxygenated than blood in the arteries.

4.13    If an XX egg was fertilized by a Y-bearing sperm, the result would be Klienfelter syndrome (XXY). If the egg with no sex chromosome was fertilized by a Y-bearing sperm, the resulting YO zygote would soon die for lack of critical genes found only on X chromosomes; no birth would result.

4.14    It was a female, as we can tell from the two X chromosomes at the lower right.

# Chapter 5

## Testing Your Recall

| | | |
|---|---|---|
| 1. d | 8. a | 15. dermal papillae |
| 2. c | 9. a | 16. earwax |
| 3. d | 10. d | 17. sebaceous glands |
| 4. b | 11. dermato-, cutane- | 18. cuticle |
| 5. a | 12. piloerector (arrector pili) | 19. dermal papilla |
| 6. e | 13. keratin, collagen | 20. second-degree |
| 7. c | 14. cyanosis | |

## True or False

(These items are false for the reasons given; all others are true.)

3.  The dermis is mainly collagen.
4.  Vitamin D synthesis begins in the keratinocytes and is completed in the liver and kidneys.
7.  The hypodermis is not part of the skin.
8.  People of all colors have similar densities of melanocytes.
9.  Malignant melanoma is the most deadly but least common form of skin cancer.

## Figure Legend Questions

5.5     Keratinocytes

5.7     The cuticle

5.10    Terminal hair; they are connected to the follicles of the coarse hairs of the pubic, axillary, and beard regions.

5.13    Asymmetry (A), border irregularity (B), and color (C). The photograph does not provide enough information to judge diameter (D).

# Chapter 6

## Testing Your Recall

| | | |
|---|---|---|
| 1. e | 8. e | 15. parathyroid |
| 2. a | 9. b | 16. articular cartilage |
| 3. d | 10. d | 17. osteoblasts |
| 4. c | 11. hydroxyapatite | 18. osteoporosis |
| 5. d | 12. canaliculi | 19. metaphysis |
| 6. c | 13. appositional | 20. intramembranous ossification |
| 7. d | 14. osteons | |

## True or False

(These items are false for the reasons given; all others are true.)

3.  The most common bone disorder is osteoporosis.
4.  The growth zone is the epiphyseal plate.
5.  Osteoclasts develop from stem cells related to monocytes.
7.  The protein of the bone matrix is collagen.
9.  Only the red bone marrow is hemopoietic.

## Figure Legend Questions

6.2     The wide epiphyses provide expanded surface area for bone articulation and for tendon and ligament attachments. Joints would be very unstable if they were as narrow as the diaphysis.

6.5     Spongy bone

6.7     The crest of the hip and the sternum

6.8     The parietal and frontal bones (answers may vary)

6.10    The humerus, radius, ulna, femur, tibia, and fibula (any two)

6.12    The zones of cell proliferation and hypertrophy (2 and 3)

# Chapter 7

## Testing Your Recall

| | | |
|---|---|---|
| 1. b | 8. a | 15. anulus fibrosus |
| 2. e | 9. a | 16. dens |
| 3. a | 10. c | 17. auricular |
| 4. d | 11. fontanels | 18. false, floating |
| 5. a | 12. temporal | 19. costal cartilages |
| 6. b | 13. sutures | 20. xiphoid process |
| 7. a | 14. sphenoid | |

*True or False*

(These items are false for the reasons given; all others are true.)
1. The vertebral bodies are derived from the sclerotomes.
2. Adults have fewer bones than children do.
4. The zygomatic processes of the temporal bone and maxilla also contribute to the arch.
5. The dura mater lies loosely against most of the cranium.
10. Lumbar vertebrae have transverse processes, but not transverse costal facets.

*Figure Legend Questions*

7.7 They produce turbulence in the airflow and support the mucous membranes that warm, cleanse, and humidify inhaled air.
7.8 If these spaces were solid bone instead of filled with air, the anterior portion of the skull would be much heavier, and the skull would tend to tip forward. More effort would be required to oppose this.
7.9 The cerebellum
7.10 The occipital, parietal, sphenoid, and zygomatic bone and the mandible
7.12 The frontal, sphenoid, lacrimal, and nasal bones and the vomer and maxilla (any five)
7.13 The vomer and the perpendicular plate of the ethmoid.
7.16 The hyoid is a delicate, easily broken bone, and its location subjects it to fracture by a rope, hands, or other means of strangulation applied around the neck.
7.17 The front of the human skull is flatter and lighter, and the skull is better balanced on the occipital condyles. Therefore, it does not require such strong muscles pulling back on the head (on the supraorbital ridges) to hold it erect.
7.23 They allow passage of the spinal nerves connected to the spinal cord.
7.24 The dens could shift forward and severely damage the spinal cord.
7.30 Most joints of an infant are still cartilaginous and therefore not very resistant to stress.
7.31 The last fontanel closes at 18 to 24 months.
7.36 The lumbar vertebrae and discs must bear more weight from the body and from heavy objects that one lifts, and are therefore the most likely ones to herniate. The cervical vertebrae and discs bear very little weight.

## Chapter 8

*Testing Your Recall*

| | | | |
|---|---|---|---|
| 1. a | 8. b | 15. hamate |
| 2. e | 9. e | 16. interpubic disc |
| 3. c | 10. b | 17. crural |
| 4. b | 11. pollex, hallux | 18. styloid |
| 5. a | 12. scapula | 19. trochanters |
| 6. d | 13. 56 | 20. medial longitudinal |
| 7. c | 14. epicondyles | |

*True or False*

(These items are false for the reasons given; all others are true.)
2. Each hand and foot has 14 phalanges.
3. The upper limb is attached at the glenohumeral joint.
5. The arm contains only the humerus, but the leg contains the tibia and fibula.
7. The most frequently broken bone is the clavicle.
10. That opening is the pelvic inlet.

*Figure Legend Questions*

8.1 See Insight 8.1 for the reasons.
8.2 It is attached at the glenoid cavity to the humerus and attached to the clavicle at the acromion.
8.6 During birth, the fetal head must pass through the narrow pelvic inlet. It could not do so if the cranial bones were immovably fused; the infant must be born before the bones fuse at the sutures and fontanels.
8.10 Four: the head, the medial condyle, the lateral condyle, and the patellar surface

## Chapter 9

*Testing Your Recall*

| | | | |
|---|---|---|---|
| 1. c | 8. d | 15. gomphosis |
| 2. b | 9. b | 16. serrate |
| 3. a | 10. b | 17. extension |
| 4. e | 11. synovial fluid | 18. range of motion |
| 5. c | 12. bursa | 19. rheumatologist |
| 6. c | 13. pivot | 20. menisci |
| 7. c | 14. kinesiology | |

*True or False*

(These items are false for the reasons given; all others are true.)
1. Osteoarthritis is much more common than rheumatoid arthritis.
2. A doctor who treats arthritis is a rheumatologist.
3. Synovial joints are diarthroses
5. This action hyperextends the shoulder; the elbow cannot be hyperextended.
9. Synovial fluid fills the bursae but is secreted by the synovial membrane of the joint capsule.

*Figure Legend Questions*

9.1 A gomphosis is a joint between a bone and a tooth; teeth are not bones.
9.3 The pubic disc is only the fibrocartilage pad; the pubic symphysis is the disc plus the adjacent areas of the pubic bones.
9.4 Interphalangeal joints are not subject to routine compression.
9.9 The clavicles are also elevated and depressed at their distal (acromioclavicular) ends. The mandible also exhibits elevation and depression during speech and eating.
9.14 The atlas
9.17 Variable answers; for example, changing direction when walking or running, or walking on a rocky trail
9.19 The glenoid labrum
9.22 False; this ligament is relatively slack. Other ligaments of the hip are more important in securing the femur in the acetabulum.

## Chapter 10

*Testing Your Recall*

| | | | |
|---|---|---|---|
| 1. e | 9. d | 15. fasciae |
| 2. c | 10. b | 16. myoglobin |
| 3. c | 11. synaptic vesicles | 17. Z discs |
| 4. a | 12. neuromuscular | 18. sphincter |
| 5. a | junction or motor | 19. myoblasts |
| 6. e | end plate | 20. peristalsis |
| 7. e | 13. terminal cisternae | |
| 8. c | 14. myosin | |

*True or False*

(These items are false for the reasons given; all others are true.)
4. The expression *slow oxidative* refers to skeletal muscle fibers.
5. One motor neuron can supply from a few to a thousand muscle fibers.
6. Calcium binds to troponin, not to myosin.
9. The blood vessels become wavy when the muscle shortens.
10. Muscle growth involves an increase in muscle fiber thickness, not in their number.

*Figure Legend Questions*

10.1 Unlike the other muscle types, the skeletal muscle here exhibits long parallel fibers with no branching or tapering, and many nuclei in each fiber. Its striations also distinguish it from smooth muscle.
10.3 Strength depends on both fascicle arrangement and muscle diameter. A large parallel muscle could be stronger than a small fusiform muscle.
10.4 The biceps brachii and distal end of the triceps brachii (both heads) exhibit indirect attachments. The brachialis and lateral head of the triceps brachii exhibit direct attachments.
10.5 It is a first-class lever because the fulcrum lies between the effort and resistance.

10.8   The function of the T tubule is to stimulate the opening of calcium gates in the terminal cisternae.

10.11   The neuromuscular junction is a region containing multiple neuromuscular synapses.

# Chapter 11

## Testing Your Recall

| | | | |
|---|---|---|---|
| 1. b | 8. a | 14. | hypoglossal |
| 2. c | 9. c | 15. | digastric |
| 3. a | 10. d | 16. | urogenital triangle |
| 4. c | 11. erector spinae | 17. | linea alba |
| 5. e | 12. bulbospongiosus | 18. | larynx |
| 6. e | 13. levator palpebrae | 19. | sternocleidomastoid |
| 7. a | superioris | 20. | trapezius |

## True or False

(These items are false for the reasons given; all others are true.)

1.  The mastoid process is the insertion, not the origin.
5.  Normal exhalation is passive and does not employ the internal intercostals.
6.  The floor of the mouth is formed by the mylohyoid muscle.
7.  The scalenes are deep to the trapezius.
10.  Only cranial nerves III, V, VII, XI, and XII innervate head and neck muscles.

## Figure Legend Questions

11.4   Zygomaticus major, levator palpebrae superioris, orbicularis oris. (Answers may vary.)

11.6   If the mandible were already at its farthest right lateral excursion, the right medial pterygoid would help draw it back to the zero position or midline (medial excursion), or it could contract still more to cause left lateral excursion.

11.8   Compare figure 11.7b. A1 contains the sternohyoid and superior belly of the omohyoid; A4 contains the mylohyoid and anterior belly of the digastric; and P1 contains the scalenes, levator scapulae, and splenius capitis. (Answers may vary.)

11.13   The pectoralis minor, subclavius, and the upper intercostal and serratus anterior muscles

# Chapter 12

## Testing Your Recall

| | | | |
|---|---|---|---|
| 1. c | 8. a | 15. | retinacula |
| 2. e | 9. d | 16. | adductor pollicis |
| 3. b | 10. a | 17. | quadriceps femoris |
| 4. d | 11. deltoid | 18. | coracobrachialis |
| 5. d | 12. great toe | 19. | gracilis |
| 6. e | 13. teres, quadratus | 20. | iliacus, psoas major |
| 7. b | 14. hamstring | | |

## True or False

(These items are false for the reasons given; all others are true.)

1.  The plantaris muscle inserts on the foot by a tendon of its own.
5.  The interosseous muscles are pennate.
7.  The psoas major and rectus femoris are synergists in flexing the hip
8.  Hamstring injuries usually result from rapid extension of the knee, not flexion.
10.  These muscles are on opposite sides of the tibia and act as antagonists.

## Figure Legend Questions

12.3   The deltoid

12.6   *Teres* indicates that muscle's rounded, cordlike shape; *quadratus* indicates that muscle's angular, four-sided shape.

12.7   Those two muscles are found in the distal half of the forearm, whereas this section represents the more proximal muscles.

12.12   Lifting the body to the next higher step when climbing stairs; the backswing of the lower limb when walking or running. (Answers may vary.)

12.15   The rectus abdominis

12.17   The soleus

# Atlas B

## Muscle Test (fig. B.15)

| | | | | |
|---|---|---|---|---|
| 1. f | 7. z | 13. n | 19. x | 25. a |
| 2. b | 8. w | 14. e | 20. w | 26. u |
| 3. k | 9. c | 15. g | 21. k | 27. j |
| 4. p | 10. a | 16. v | 22. d | 28. i |
| 5. h | 11. x | 17. f | 23. s | 29. g |
| 6. y | 12. m | 18. c | 24. b | 30. q |

## Figure Legend Questions

B.1   The orbicularis oris. The trapezius.
B.2   The sternocleidomastoids
B.7   Four
B.8   At the base of the first metacarpal bone, between the two "Flexion lines" leaders in (a)
B.9   Deep to the rectus femoris
B.10   The fibula
B.13   There is no such bone; the great toe has only two phalanges, proximal and distal.

# Chapter 13

## Testing Your Recall

| | | | |
|---|---|---|---|
| 1. e | 8. d | 15. | oligodendrocytes |
| 2. e | 9. a | 16. | axosomatic |
| 3. d | 10. c | 17. | peripheral nervous system |
| 4. a | 11. afferent | 18. | neurilemma, endoneurium |
| 5. e | 12. reverberating | 19. | ganglia |
| 6. d | 13. anencephaly | 20. | postsynaptic |
| 7. a | 14. dendrites | | |

## True or False

(These items are false for the reasons given; all others are true.)

4.  Sensory (afferent) neurons connect sense organs to the CNS.
6.  The myelin sheath is deep to the neurilemma.
7.  Nodes of Ranvier also exist in the CNS.
8.  Interneurons are contained entirely within the CNS.
9.  Unipolar neurons have an axon and produce action potentials.

## Figure Legend Questions

13.1   The PNS, because it is more exposed to trauma than the CNS. The CNS is protected by the cranial and vertebral bones.

13.3   *Afferent* is derived from *af (ad)*, meaning "toward," and *fer*, meaning "to carry." Afferent neurons carry signals toward the CNS. *Efferent* is derived from *ef (ex)*, meaning "out." Efferent neurons carry signals out of the CNS.

13.4   The presence of multiple dendrites

13.8   Unmyelinated fibers conduct signals relatively slowly, but they occupy less space.

13.9   Axosomatic

# Chapter 14

## Testing Your Recall

| | | | |
|---|---|---|---|
| 1. e | 8. a | 15. | central pattern generators |
| 2. c | 9. e | 16. | phrenic |
| 3. d | 10. b | 17. | decussation |
| 4. d | 11. ganglia | 18. | proprioception |
| 5. e | 12. rami | 19. | dorsal root |
| 6. c | 13. spinocerebellar | 20. | tibial, common fibular |
| 7. c | 14. sacral | | |

## True or False

(These items are false for the reasons given; all others are true.)

1.  The gracile fasciculus is a sensory (ascending) tract.
4.  All spinal nerves are mixed nerves.
5.  The dura mater is set off from the vertebral bone by the epidural space.

8. Dermatomes overlap each other by as much as 50%.
9. Many somatic reflexes involve the brain.

### Figure Legend Questions

14.3    It would have to be T4 because the cuneate fasciculus does not exist below level T6.
14.4    Heat and cold stimuli are carried to the opposite side of the spinal cord before ascending the spinothalamic tract to the brain. The phenomenon is called decussation.
14.8    Unipolar (or pseudounipolar)
14.11   It would result in a loss of sensation within the corresponding region on that side of the body.
14.13   Respiratory arrest would occur if both the right and left phrenic nerves were severed; severing only one of them paralyzes half of the diaphragm and severely diminishes ventilation of the ipsilateral lung.
14.19   If the hamstrings contracted, they would promote flexion of the knee and thus oppose the knee-extending patellar tendon reflex.

## Chapter 15

### Testing Your Recall

| | | |
|---|---|---|
| 1. c | 8. d | 15. choroid plexus |
| 2. d | 9. e | 16. precentral |
| 3. e | 10. e | 17. frontal |
| 4. a | 11. corpus callosum | 18. association cortex |
| 5. e | 12. ventricles, cerebrospinal | 19. categorical |
| 6. c | 13. arbor vitae | 20. Broca area |
| 7. a | 14. hippocampus | |

### True or False

(These items are false for the reasons given; all others are true.)

1. The longitudinal fissure separates the cerebral hemispheres, not cerebellar hemispheres.
2. Degeneration of the substantia nigra causes Parkinson disease.
5. The choroid plexuses produce only 30% of the CSF.
6. Hearing is a temporal lobe function.
10. The optic nerve carries visual signals, not motor signals.

### Figure Legend Questions

15.1    The dura mater
15.7    (To be answered by pointing out or marking structures in the illustration.)
15.8    (To be answered by pointing out or marking structures in the illustration.)
15.14   Dendrites
15.19   Those with many small muscles
15.22   No; everyone makes extensive use of both hemispheres.

## Chapter 16

### Testing Your Recall

| | | |
|---|---|---|
| 1. b | 8. d | 15. enteric |
| 2. c | 9. c | 16. neural crest |
| 3. e | 10. c | 17. sympathetic |
| 4. e | 11. adrenergic | 18. preganglionic, postganglionic |
| 5. a | 12. dual innervation | 19. baroreceptor |
| 6. e | 13. autonomic tone | 20. vasomotor tone |
| 7. d | 14. vagus | |

### True or False

(These items are false for the reasons given; all others are true.)

1. Normally both divisions are active simultaneously.
3. With biofeedback and other methods, some degree of voluntary control is possible.
4. It inhibits digestion.
6. These reflexes occur even without involvement of the brain but are less controllable.
7. All parasympathetic fibers are cholinergic.

### Figure Legend Questions

16.4    No; as explained in chapter 11, inspiration and expiration are achieved by skeletal muscles, which are not under autonomic control.
16.5    The sympathetic neuron arises from the lateral horn and the somatic neuron from the ventral horn of the spinal cord.
16.7    The vagus nerve
16.9    Dilated, because fear activates the sympathetic division, which stimulates the pupillary dilator

## Chapter 17

### Testing Your Recall

| | | |
|---|---|---|
| 1. a | 8. c | 15. outer hair cells |
| 2. a | 9. c | 16. stapes |
| 3. a | 10. a | 17. inferior colliculi |
| 4. d | 11. fovea centralis | 18. taste hairs |
| 5. b | 12. ganglion | 19. olfactory bulb |
| 6. e | 13. nociceptor | 20. referred pain |
| 7. d | 14. otoliths | |

### True or False

(These items are false for the reasons given; all others are true.)

2. Afferent touch fibers end in the spinal cord and medulla oblongata.
4. Pain signals are blocked after entering the spinal cord, before ascending to the brain.
8. Olfactory neurons are directly exposed to the external environment.
9. The tympanic membrane has sensory fibers of the vagus and trigeminal nerves.
10. The posterior chamber, between the iris and lens, is filled with aqueous humor.

### Figure Legend Questions

17.3    Postcentral gyrus; parietal lobe
17.5    The basal cell can divide, and one of its daughter cells can become a new taste cell.
17.14   High middle-ear pressure would interfere with inward movements of the tympanic membrane and therefore reduce the transfer of vibrations to the inner ear.
17.16   The macula sacculi is vertically oriented, so up or down movements in an elevator would cause the otolithic membrane to shift up or down across the hair cells and bend their stereocilia.
17.20   Watery eyes; tears would be unable to drain from the eye surface and would spill over the eyelid.
17.21   CN III, the oculomotor nerve. This nerve controls four muscles, whereas the others each control only one. CN III is indispensible to the ability to look up, down, and sideways.

## Chapter 18

### Testing Your Recall

| | | |
|---|---|---|
| 1. d | 8. a | 15. glucocorticoids |
| 2. d | 9. b | 16. anterior pituitary |
| 3. a | 10. c | 17. neuroendocrine |
| 4. c | 11. anterior pituitary | 18. interstitial |
| 5. d | 12. supraoptic nucleus | 19. zona fasciculata, ACTH |
| 6. d | 13. leptin | 20. enteric hormones |
| 7. a | 14. atrial natriuretic peptide | |

### True or False

(These items are false for the reasons given; all others are true.)

2. The heart, brain, stomach, and kidneys secrete hormones but are not usually thought of as endocrine glands.
4. The pineal gland and thymus shrink with age.
5. The center of the adrenal gland is the adrenal medulla.
8. The pituitary stalk is not a duct.
9. There are two pairs of parathyroids and one pair of gonads.

*Figure Legend Questions*

18.1   Heart, liver, stomach, placenta
18.2   Testosterone, estradiol
18.4   The posterior lobe, or neurohypophysis
18.8   To secrete calcitonin
18.11  To secrete digestive enzymes
18.15  The zona fasciculata of the adrenal cortex

## Chapter 19

*Testing Your Recall*

| | | |
|---|---|---|
| 1. b | 8. c | 15. serum |
| 2. c | 9. d | 16. hemostasis |
| 3. a | 10. b | 17. sickle-cell disease |
| 4. b | 11. hemopoiesis | 18. polycythemia |
| 5. e | 12. hematocrit | 19. vitamin $B_{12}$ |
| 6. d | 13. macrophages | 20. erythropoietin |
| 7. d | 14. leukopenia | |

*True or False*

(These items are false for the reasons given; all others are true.)

3.  Anemia is the cause, not the result, of low blood oxygen content.
4.  Neutrophils are the most actively antibacterial WBCs.
6.  Neutrophils are the most abundant WBCs.
9.  RBCs live longer than most WBCs.
10. WBC count is elevated in leukemia.

*Figure Legend Questions*

19.1   Nuclei
19.3   The developing erythrocyte sinks in at this point when its nucleus shrivels and is ejected from the cell.
19.4   To the $Fe^{2+}$ at the center of the heme group
19.8   It means "marrow" and refers to the fact that this process occurs in the red bone marrow.
19.10  Fibrin

## Chapter 20

*Testing Your Recall*

| | | |
|---|---|---|
| 1. d | 8. a | 15. gap junctions |
| 2. b | 9. b | 16. valvular prolapse |
| 3. a | 10. b | 17. vagus |
| 4. d | 11. systole, diastole | 18. myocardial infarction |
| 5. e | 12. systemic | 19. endocardium |
| 6. e | 13. coronary sulcus | 20. sinus venosus |
| 7. d | 14. Purkinje fibers | |

*True or False*

(These items are false for the reasons given; all others are true.)

1.  About 20% of the blood returns to the right atrium by way of thebesian veins.
5.  The heart does not require nervous stimulation to beat.
7.  It is anastomoses of the arteries, not veins, that serve this purpose.
8.  The primordial ventricle develops into the left ventricle only.
9.  There are no valves at the entrances to the right atrium.

*Figure Legend Questions*

20.1   Both. The pulmonary circuit delivers blood to the lungs for gas exchange. The systemic circuit delivers blood for nourishment of the pulmonary tissues.
20.2   To the left
20.9   They prevent the AV valves from prolapsing into the atria when the ventricles contract.
20.14  The gap junctions

## Chapter 21

*Testing Your Recall*

| | | |
|---|---|---|
| 1. c | 8. b | 15. chemoreceptors |
| 2. b | 9. b | 16. transcytosis |
| 3. a | 10. b | 17. superior vena cava, inferior venae cava |
| 4. e | 11. fenestrated | 18. carotid sinuses |
| 5. b | 12. continuous capillaries | 19. cerebral arterial circle |
| 6. b | 13. endothelium | 20. basilic, cephalic |
| 7. d | 14. common iliac | |

*True or False*

(These items are false for the reasons given; all others are true.)

2.  They receive blood from the celiac trunk.
4.  Blood sometimes passes through portal systems (two capillary beds) or anastomoses (bypassing capillaries).
5.  It is formed by the union of the two brachiocephalic veins.
7.  The tunica media is nourished mainly by capillaries of the vasa vasorum.
9.  One or more arteries of the circle are missing in 80% of people.

*Figure Legend Questions*

21.1   Arteries are subjected to greater blood pressure and must expand and recoil in phase with the heartbeat.
21.6   Endocrine glands, kidneys, small intestine (answers may vary)
21.10  Veins have thinner walls and less elastic tissue, and therefore expand more easily to accommodate a larger volume of blood.
21.12  Arterial anastomoses: the cerebral arterial circle, circumflex humeral arteries, and deep palmar arch. Venous anastomoses: union of the radial veins near the elbow, union of the left and right gastric veins, the dorsal venous arch of the foot joining the great and small saphenous veins. (Many other examples of both can be cited; answers may vary.)
21.25  Like the gonadal arteries, these veins are much shorter when the gonads begin their development high in the abdominal cavity, near the kidneys. The veins grow as the fetal gonads migrate downward.
21.27  Anastomoses allow for continued blood flow through alternate routes when joint movements temporarily compress an artery and shut off its flow.

## Chapter 22

*Testing Your Recall*

| | | |
|---|---|---|
| 1. b | 9. c | 15. cisterna chyli |
| 2. c | 10. d | 16. plasma |
| 3. e | 11. pathogen | 17. antigen-presenting cells |
| 4. a | 12. chyle | 18. red bone marrow |
| 5. c | 13. collecting vessels | 19. lymphatic nodules |
| 6. e | 14. right lymphatic duct, thoracic duct | 20. autoimmune |
| 7. a | | |
| 8. e | | |

*True or False*

(These items are false for the reasons given; all others are true.)

1.  B cells are involved in specific immunity only.
4.  Helper T cells also play a role in humoral immunity.
7.  Both B and T cells populate the lymph nodes.
8.  Lymphatic nodules are temporary and have no capsules.
9.  Tonsillectomy is now a much less common treatment than it used to be.

*Figure Legend Questions*

22.3   Gaps between the endothelial cells are much larger in lymphatic capillaries than they are in blood capillaries.
22.5   (1) It prevents the accumulation of excess tissue fluid (edema). (2) It enables immune cells in the lymph nodes to continually monitor the tissue fluids for foreign matter.
22.6   Cancer cells breaking free of a breast tumor enter the lymphatics and often lodge and seed the growth of secondary (metastatic) tumors in these nearby lymph nodes.

22.10  The reticular epithelial cells

22.14  Erythrocytes account for the color of red pulp; lymphocytes and macrophages account for the color of white pulp.

# Chapter 23

*Testing Your Recall*

| | | | |
|---|---|---|---|
| 1. c | 8. a | 15. obstructive |
| 2. c | 9. c | 16. dead space |
| 3. a | 10. c | 17. thyroid |
| 4. e | 11. laryngopharynx | 18. inspiratory center |
| 5. b | 12. bronchial tree | 19. hilum |
| 6. e | 13. alar | 20. alveolar macrophages |
| 7. d | 14. conchae | |

*True or False*

(These items are false for the reasons given; all others are true.)

1. The glottis is at the superior end of the larynx, not the inferior (tracheal) end.
3. The space between the parietal and visceral pleura contains only a thin film of pleural fluid.
4. Normal expiration is not produced by muscular contraction.
8. The aortic and carotid sinuses monitor blood pressure.
9. The respiratory system begins as a bud arising from the floor of the pharynx.

*Figure Legend Questions*

23.2  The line should be drawn between the larynx and trachea labels.

23.3  The septal cartilage

23.4  The epiglottic, corniculate, and arytenoid cartilages

23.8  To secrete mucus

23.10  By their lack of cartilage

# Chapter 24

*Testing Your Recall*

| | | | |
|---|---|---|---|
| 1. a | 8. a | 14. hepatic portal system |
| 2. b | 9. a | 15. vagus |
| 3. b | 10. c | 16. parietal |
| 4. d | 11. enteric nervous | 17. hepatic sinusoids |
| 5. e | system | 18. cardiac orifice |
| 6. c | 12. pyloric sphincter | 19. cementum |
| 7. a | 13. parotid | 20. lingual papillae |

*True or False*

(These items are false for the reasons given; all others are true.)

1. The pancreas is retroperitoneal, but the liver is not.
2. A tooth is composed mainly of dentine.
3. Bile is secreted into bile canaliculi, not into the sinusoids.
7. The greater omentum is not attached to the body wall.
9. The muscularis externa of the stomach has three layers.

*Figure Legend Questions*

24.6  The third molars

24.7  The enamel

24.11  The stomach wall has three layers of muscle; the esophagus has two.

24.16  The autonomic nervous system controls the internal anal sphincter, and the somatic nervous system controls the external anal sphincter. This can be deduced from the fact that the internal sphincter is smooth (involuntary) muscle and the external sphincter is skeletal (voluntary) muscle.

24.18  The hepatic portal vein and the right and left hepatic arteries

# Chapter 25

*Testing Your Recall*

| | | | |
|---|---|---|---|
| 1. c | 8. b | 15. podocytes |
| 2. d | 9. d | 16. proximal convoluted tubule |
| 3. a | 10. a | 17. thin segment |
| 4. c | 11. urea | 18. detrusor |
| 5. e | 12. ureteric bud | 19. minor calyx |
| 6. b | 13. trigone | 20. arcuate |
| 7. d | 14. macula densa | |

*True or False*

(These items are false for the reasons given; all others are true.)

1. The ureters open into the floor of the bladder.
2. ADH is secreted by the posterior lobe of the pituitary gland.
4. A substantial amount of fluid passes through the tight junctions.
6. The glomerulus is not located within the capsular space.
9. The kidneys are normally in the abdominal cavity.

*Figure Legend Questions*

25.1  The kidney itself cannot be palpated, but its position can be inferred by palpating ribs 11 and 12 and relating that to this figure.

25.2  It would have to be moved into the dark peritoneal cavity toward the upper left, where the spleen and colon are shown, anterior to the parietal peritoneum.

25.4  This is an anterior view, because the renal artery and vein lie anterior to the ureter. Compare the posterior view in figure 25.3b.

25.9  The afferent arteriole is larger than the efferent. This gives the glomerulus a large inlet, a small outlet, and consequently a high blood pressure, which is important for the filtration process.

25.11  An enlarged prostate gland compresses the prostatic urethra, the bladder's exit.

# Chapter 26

*Testing Your Recall*

| | | | |
|---|---|---|---|
| 1. a | 8. c | 15. endometrium |
| 2. a | 9. e | 16. seminal vesicles |
| 3. c | 10. d | 17. sustentacular |
| 4. b | 11. mesonephric | 18. prostate gland |
| 5. c | 12. fructose | 19. corpus luteum |
| 6. a | 13. pampiniform plexus | 20. infundibulum, fimbriae |
| 7. d | 14. follicle | |

*True or False*

(These items are false for the reasons given; all others are true.)

1. The follicle does not leave the ovary.
2. The uterine tubes develop from paramesonephric ducts.
4. The follicle that ovulates is the mature (graafian) follicle.
6. The female reproductive system develops as a result of a low androgen level.
8. The pampiniform plexus helps to keep the testes cool.

*Figure Legend Questions*

26.6  After meiosis, the resulting daughter cells will be genetically different from the rest of the body and would be subject to attack by blood-borne antibodies or immune cells if not protected from them.

26.10  If it were confined within a tunica albuginea, engorgement of the corpus spongiosum would probably compress the urethra and block ejaculation.

26.21  The paraurethral glands

26.22  They compress the acinus and expel milk into the lactiferous ducts.

26.25  The word root *vagin* means "sheath," which aptly describes the tunica vaginalis as a sheath or pouch of peritoneum.

This glossary defines terms likely to be most useful to the reader of this particular book, especially terms that are reintroduced most often and cannot be defined again at every introduction. Terms are defined only in the sense that they are used in this book. Some have broader meanings, even within biology and medicine, that are beyond its scope. Pronunciation guides are provided for words whose pronunciations may not be obvious. These guides should be quite intuitive, but a key at the end of the glossary indicates how to pronounce letter sequences within the guides if help is needed. Figures are cited where they will help convey the meaning of a term. Figure references such as A.3 and B.7 refer to figures in atlas A (p. 22) and atlas B (p. 360).

# A

**abdominal cavity**   The body cavity between the diaphragm and pelvic brim. (fig. A.7)

**abdominopelvic cavity**   Collective name for the abdominal and pelvic cavities, which constitute a continuous space between the diaphragm and pelvic floor. (fig. A.7)

**abduction**   Movement of a body part away from the median plane, as in raising the right arm away from the body to point to the right. (fig. 9.8)

**accessory organ**   A smaller organ associated with or embedded in another and performing a related function; for example, the hair, nails, and sweat glands are accessory organs of the skin.

**acetylcholine (ACh)**   (ASS-eh-till-CO-leen) A neurotransmitter released by somatic motor nerve fibers, parasympathetic nerve fibers, and some other neurons, composed of choline and an acetyl group.

**acetylcholinesterase (AChE)**   (ASS-eh-till-CO-lin-ESS-ter-ase) An enzyme found in synaptic clefts and on postsynaptic cells that breaks down acetylcholine and stops synaptic signal transmission.

**acidophil**   A cell that stains with acidic dyes, such as a pituitary acidophil. (fig. 18.5)

**acinar gland**   (ah-SEE-nur) A gland in which the secretory cells form a dilated sac or acinus. (fig. 3.29)

**acinus**   (ASS-in-nus) A sac of secretory cells at the inner end of a gland duct. (fig. 3.28)

**acromial region**   The apex of the shoulder.

**actin**   A filamentous intracellular protein that provides cytoskeletal support and interacts with other proteins, especially myosin, to cause cellular movement; important in muscle contraction and membrane actions such as phagocytosis, ameboid movement, and cytokinesis. *See also* microfilament.

**action**   The movement produced by the contraction of a muscle.

**action potential**   A rapid voltage change in which a plasma membrane briefly reverses electrical polarity; has a self-propagating effect that produces a traveling wave of excitation in nerve and muscle cells.

**acute**   Pertaining to a disorder with a sudden onset, severe effects, and brief duration. *Compare* chronic.

**adaptation**   **1.** An evolutionary process leading to the establishment of species characteristics that favor survival and reproduction. **2.** Any characteristic of anatomy, physiology, or behavior that promotes survival and reproduction. **3.** A sensory process in which a receptor adjusts its sensitivity or response to the prevailing level of stimulation, as in *dark adaptation* of the eye.

**adduction**   (ah-DUC-shun) Movement of a body part toward the median plane, such as bringing the feet together from a spread-legged position. (fig. 9.8)

**adenohypophysis**   The anterior two-thirds of the pituitary gland, consisting of the anterior lobe and pars tuberalis; synthesizes and secretes gonadotropins, thyrotropin, adrenocorticotropin, growth hormone, and prolactin. (fig. 18.4)

**adenosine triphosphate (ATP)**   A molecule composed of adenine, ribose, and three phosphate groups that functions as a universal energy-transfer molecule; briefly captures energy in its phosphate bonds and transfers it to other chemical reactions, yielding adenosine diphosphate and a free phosphate group upon hydrolysis.

**adipocyte**   A fat cell.

**adipose tissue**   A loose connective tissue composed predominantly of adipocytes; fat. (fig. 3.16)

**adrenal gland**   (ah-DREE-nul) An endocrine gland on the superior pole of each kidney; consists of an outer adrenal cortex and inner adrenal medulla, with separate functions and embryonic origins. (fig. 18.10)

**adult stem cell**   Any of several kinds of undifferentiated cells that populate the body's organs, where they multiply and differentiate to replace cells that are lost to damage or normal cellular turnover. Adult stem cells have more limited developmental potential than embryonic stem cells. *See also* embryonic stem cell.

**adventitia**   (AD-ven-TISH-uh) Loose connective tissue forming the outermost sheath around organs such as a blood vessel or the esophagus.

**afferent**   Carrying toward, as in *afferent neurons,* which carry signals toward the central nervous system, and *afferent arterioles,* which carry blood toward a tissue.

**afferent neuron**   *See* sensory neuron.

**aging**   Any changes in the body that occur with the passage of time, including growth, development, and senescence. *See also* senescence.

**agonist**   *See* prime mover.

**agranulocyte**   Either of the two leukocyte types (lymphocytes and monocytes) that lack specific cytoplasmic granules. (fig. 19.1)

**alveolus**   (AL-vee-OH-lus) **1.** A microscopic air sac of the lung. **2.** A gland acinus. **3.** A pit or socket in a bone, such as a tooth socket. **4.** Any small anatomical space.

**Alzheimer disease (AD)**   (ALTS-hy-mur) A degenerative disease of the senescent brain, typically beginning with memory lapses and progressing to severe losses of mental and motor functions and ultimately death.

**ameboid movement**   Ameba-like crawling of cells such as leukocytes by means of pseudopods.

**amnion**   A transparent membrane that surrounds the developing fetus and contains the amniotic fluid; the "bag of waters" that breaks during labor. (fig. 4.12)

**ampulla**   (AM-pyu-luh) A wide or saclike portion of a tubular organ such as a semicircular duct or uterine tube.

**anastomosis**   (ah-NASS-tih-MO-sis) An anatomical convergence, the opposite of a branch; a point where two blood vessels merge and combine their bloodstreams or where two nerves or ducts converge. (fig. 21.12)

**anatomical position**   A reference posture on which certain standardized anatomical terminology is based. A subject in anatomical position is standing with the feet flat on the floor, arms down to the sides, and the palms and eyes directed forward. (fig. A.1)

**anatomy**   **1.** Structure of the body. **2.** The study of structure. *See also* morphology.

**anemia**   A deficiency of erythrocytes or hemoglobin.

**aneurysm**   (AN-you-riz-um) A weak, bulging point in the wall of a heart chamber or blood vessel that presents a threat of hemorrhage. (fig. 21.3)

**angiogenesis**   The growth of new blood vessels, both prenatally and postnatally.

**angiography**   The process of visualizing blood vessels by injecting them with a radiopaque substance and photographing them with X-rays. (fig. 1.2)

**antagonist**   **1.** A muscle that opposes the prime mover at a joint. **2.** Any agent, such as a hormone or drug, that opposes another.

**antebrachium**   (AN-teh-BRAY-kee-um) The region from elbow to wrist; the forearm.

**anterior**   Pertaining to the front (facial–abdominal aspect) of the body; ventral.

**antibody**   A protein of the gamma globulin class that reacts with an antigen; found in the blood plasma, in other body fluids, and on the surfaces of certain leukocytes and their derivatives.

**antigen**   (AN-tih-jen) Any large molecule capable of binding to an antibody and triggering an immune response.

**antigen-presenting cell (APC)**   A cell that phagocytizes an antigen and displays fragments of it on its surface for recognition by other cells of the immune system; chiefly macrophages and B lymphocytes.

**antrum**   A saccular or pouchlike space, such as at the inferior end of the stomach or in an ovarian follicle.

**aorta**   A large artery that extends from the left ventricle to the lower abdominal cavity and gives rise to all other arteries of the systemic circulation. (fig. 21.16)

**aortic arch** **1.** In the embryo, any of six pairs of blood vessels that arise rostral to the heart and loop mainly through the pharyngeal arches; some of these later give rise to carotid and pulmonary arteries and the permanent aortic arch. (fig. 21.35) **2.** A segment of the adult aorta that arches over the heart like an inverted U; gives rise to the brachiocephalic trunk, left common carotid artery, and left subclavian artery; then continues posterior to the heart as the descending aorta. (fig. 21.16)

**apex** The summit or a pointed part of an organ or body region such as the heart, lung, or shoulder.

**apical surface** The uppermost surface of an epithelial cell, opposite from the basement membrane, usually exposed to the lumen of an organ. (fig. 2.5)

**apocrine** Pertaining to certain sweat glands with large lumens and relatively thick, aromatic secretions, and to similar glands such as the mammary gland; formerly thought to form secretions by pinching off bits of apical cytoplasm. (fig. 5.10)

**aponeurosis** A broad, flat tendon that attaches a muscle to a bone or to other soft tissues in such locations as the abdominal wall and deep to the scalp.

**apoptosis** The normal death of cells that have completed their function, usually in a process involving self-destruction of the cell's DNA, shrinkage of the cell, and its phagocytosis by a macrophage; also called *programmed cell death. Compare* necrosis.

**appendicular** (AP-en-DIC-you-lur) Pertaining to the limbs and their supporting skeletal girdles. (fig. 7.1)

**arcuate** (AR-cue-et) Making a sharp L- or U-shaped bend (arc), or forming an arch, as in *arcuate arteries* of the kidneys and uterus.

**areolar tissue** (AIR-ee-OH-lur) A fibrous connective tissue with loosely organized, widely spaced fibers and cells and an abundance of fluid-filled space; found under nearly every epithelium, among other places. (fig. 3.14)

**arrector pili** *See* piloerector.

**arteriole** A small artery that empties into a metarteriole or capillary.

**artery** Any blood vessel that conducts blood away from the heart, or in the case of coronary arteries, away from the aorta and into the heart wall.

**articular cartilage** A thin layer of hyaline cartilage covering the articular surface of a bone at a synovial joint, serving to reduce friction and ease joint movement. (fig. 9.4)

**articulation** A skeletal joint; any point at which two bones meet; may or may not be movable.

**aspect** A particular view of the body or one of its structures, or a surface that faces in a particular direction, such as the anterior aspect.

**association area** A region of the cerebral cortex that does not directly receive sensory input or control skeletal muscles, but serves to interpret sensory information, to plan motor responses, and for memory and cognition.

**atherosclerosis** A degenerative disease of the blood vessels characterized by the presence of plaques on the vessel wall composed of lipid, smooth muscle, and macrophages; can lead to arterial occlusion, loss of arterial elasticity, hypertension, heart attack, kidney failure, and stroke.

**ATP** *See* adenosine triphosphate.

**atrioventricular (AV) node** (AY-tree-oh-ven-TRIC-you-lur) A group of autorhythmic cells in the interatrial septum of the heart that relays excitation from the atria to the ventricles.

**atrioventricular (AV) valves** The bicuspid (right) and tricuspid (left) valves between the atria and ventricles of the heart.

**atrium** **1.** Either of the two superior chambers of the heart, which receive systemic and pulmonary blood. **2.** The central space of an alveolar sac into which individual pulmonary alveoli open.

**atrophy** Shrinkage of a tissue due to age, disuse, or disease.

**auditory ossicles** Three small middle-ear bones that transfer vibrations from the tympanic membrane to the inner ear; the malleus, incus, and stapes.

**Auerbach plexus** *See* myenteric plexus.

**auricle** **1.** The portion of the ear external to the cranium; the pinna. **2.** An ear-shaped structure, such as the auricles of the heart.

**autoantibody** An antibody that fails to distinguish the body's own molecules from foreign molecules and thus attacks host tissues, causing autoimmune diseases.

**autoimmune disease** Any disease in which antibodies fail to distinguish between foreign and self-antigens and attack the body's own tissues; for example, systemic lupus erythematosus and rheumatic fever.

**autolysis** (aw-TAHL-ih-sis) Digestion of cells by their own internal enzymes.

**autonomic nervous system (ANS)** A motor division of the nervous system that innervates glands, smooth muscle, and cardiac muscle; consists of sympathetic and parasympathetic divisions and functions largely without voluntary control. *Compare* somatic nervous system.

**autosome** Any chromosome except the sex chromosomes. Genes on the autosomes are inherited without regard to the sex of the individual.

**axial** Pertaining to the head, neck, and trunk; the part of the body excluding the appendicular portion. (fig. 7.1)

**axillary** (ACK-sih-LERR-ee) Pertaining to the armpit.

**axon** A process of a neuron that conducts action potentials away from the soma; also called a *nerve fiber.* There is only one axon to a neuron, and it is usually much longer and much less branched than the dendrites. (fig. 13.4)

**axoneme** The core of a cilium or flagellum, usually composed of a "9 + 2" array of microtubules that provide support and motility. (fig. 2.13)

# B

**baroreceptor** (BARE-oh-re-SEP-tur) Pressure sensor located in the heart, aortic arch, and carotid sinuses that triggers autonomic reflexes in response to fluctuations in blood pressure.

**basal lamina** A thin layer of collagen, proteoglycan, and glycoprotein that binds epithelial and other cells to adjacent connective tissue; forms part of the basement membrane of an epithelium, and surrounds some nonepithelial cells such as muscle fibers and Schwann cells. (fig. 13.8)

**basal nuclei** Masses of deep cerebral gray matter that play a role in the coordination of posture and movement and the performance of learned motor skills; also called *basal ganglia.* (fig. 15.15)

**base** The broadest part of a tapered organ such as the uterus, or the inferior aspect of an organ such as the brain.

**basement membrane** A thin layer of matter that underlies the deepest cells of an epithelium and binds them to the underlying connective tissue; consists of the basal lamina of the epithelial cells and fine reticular fibers of the connective tissue. (fig. 3.30)

**basophil** (BASE-oh-fill) **1.** A cell that stains with basic dyes, such as a pituitary basophil. (fig. 18.5) **2.** A leukocyte with coarse cytoplasmic granules that produces heparin, histamine, and other chemicals involved in inflammation. (fig. 19.1)

**belly** The thick part of a skeletal muscle between its origin and insertion. (fig. 10.4)

**bipedalism** The habit of walking on two legs; a defining characteristic of the family Hominidae that underlies many skeletal and other characteristics of humans.

**blastocyst** A hollow spheroidal stage of the conceptus that implants in the uterine wall; consists of an inner cell mass, or embryoblast, enclosed in a saclike outer cell mass, or trophoblast. (fig. 4.3)

**blood** A liquid connective tissue composed of plasma, erythrocytes, platelets, and five kinds of leukocytes.

**blood–brain barrier** A barrier between the bloodstream and nervous tissue of the brain that is impermeable to many blood solutes and thus prevents them from affecting the brain tissue; formed by the tight junctions between capillary endothelial cells, the basement membrane of the endothelium, and the perivascular feet of astrocytes.

**B lymphocyte** A lymphocyte that functions as an antigen-presenting cell and, in humoral immunity, differentiates into an antibody-producing plasma cell; also called a *B cell.*

**body** **1.** The entire organism. **2.** Part of a cell, such as a neuron, containing the nucleus and most other organelles. **3.** The largest or principal part of an organ such as the stomach or uterus; also called the *corpus.*

**bolus** A mass of matter, especially food or feces traveling through the digestive tract.

**bone** **1.** A calcified connective tissue; also called *osseous tissue.* **2.** An organ of the skeleton composed of osseous tissue, fibrous connective tissue, marrow, cartilage, and other tissues.

**Bowman capsule** *See* glomerular capsule.

**brachial** (BRAY-kee-ul) Pertaining to the brachium.

**brachium** The region between the shoulder and elbow; the arm proper.

**brainstem** The stalklike lower portion of the brain, composed of all of the brain except the cerebrum and cerebellum. (Many authorities exclude the diencephalon and regard only the medulla oblongata, pons, and midbrain as the brainstem.) (fig. 15.6)

**bronchiole** (BRON-kee-ole) A pulmonary air passage that is usually 1 mm or less in diameter and lacks cartilage, but has relatively abundant smooth muscle, elastic tissue, and a simple cuboidal, usually ciliated epithelium.

**bronchus** (BRON-kus) A relatively large pulmonary air passage with supportive cartilage in the wall; any passage beginning with the primary bronchus at the fork in the trachea and ending with tertiary bronchi, from which air continues into the bronchioles.

**brush border** A fringe of microvilli on the apical surface of an epithelial cell, serving to enhance surface area and promote absorption. (fig. 3.6)

**buccal** Pertaining to the cheek.

**bulb** A dilated terminal part of an organ such as the penis or hair, or the olfactory bulb at the beginning of the olfactory tract.

**bursa** A sac filled with synovial fluid at a synovial joint, serving to facilitate muscle or joint action. (fig. 9.5)

# C

**calcaneal tendon**   (cal-CAY-nee-ul) A thick tendon at the heel that attaches the triceps surae muscles to the calcaneus; also called the *Achilles tendon.* (fig. 12.18)

**calcification**   The hardening of a tissue due to the deposition of calcium salts; also called *mineralization.*

**calculus**   A calcified mass, especially a renal calculus (kidney stone) or biliary calculus (gallstone).

**calvaria**   (cal-VERR-ee-uh) The rounded bony dome that forms the roof of the cranium; the general portion of the skull superior to the eyes and ears; skullcap.

**calyx**   (CAY-lix) (plural, *calices*) A cuplike structure, as in the kidneys. (fig. 25.3)

**canal**   A tubular passage or tunnel such as the auditory, semicircular, or condylar canal.

**canaliculus**   (CAN-uh-LIC-you-lus) A microscopic canal, as in osseous tissue. (fig. 6.5)

**cancellous bone**   *See* spongy bone.

**capillary**   (CAP-ih-LERR-ee) The narrowest type of vessel in the cardiovascular and lymphatic systems; engages in fluid exchanges with surrounding tissues.

**capillary bed**   A network of blood capillaries that arise from a single metarteriole and converge on a thoroughfare channel or venule. (fig. 21.9)

**capsule**   The fibrous covering of a structure such as the spleen or a synovial joint.

**carbohydrate**   A hydrophilic organic compound composed of carbon and a 2:1 ratio of hydrogen to oxygen; includes sugars, starches, glycogen, and cellulose.

**cardiac center**   A nucleus in the medulla oblongata that regulates autonomic reflexes for controlling the rate and strength of the heartbeat.

**cardiac muscle**   Striated involuntary muscle of the heart. (fig. 20.14)

**cardiocyte**   A cardiac muscle cell.

**cardiopulmonary system**   Collective name for the heart and lungs, emphasizing their close spatial and physiological relationship.

**cardiovascular system**   An organ system consisting of the heart and blood vessels, serving for the transport of blood. *Compare* circulatory system.

**carotid body**   (ca-ROT-id) A small cellular mass near the branch in the common carotid artery, containing sensory cells that detect changes in the pH and the carbon dioxide and oxygen content of the blood. (fig. 21.4)

**carotid sinus**   A dilation at the base of the internal carotid artery; contains baroreceptors, which monitor changes in blood pressure. (fig. 21.4)

**carpal**   Pertaining to the wrist (carpus).

**carrier**   **1.** A protein that transports solutes through a cell membrane; also called a *transport protein.* **2.** A person who does not exhibit a particular hereditary disorder, but who has the gene for it and may pass it to the next generation.

**cartilage**   A connective tissue with a rubbery matrix, cells (chondrocytes) contained in lacunae, and no blood vessels; covers the joint surfaces of many bones and supports organs such as the ear and larynx.

**caudal**   (CAW-dul) **1.** Pertaining to a tail or narrow tail-like part of an organ. **2.** Pertaining to the inferior part of the trunk of the body, where the tail of other animals arises. *Compare* cranial. **3.** Relatively distant from the forehead, especially in reference to structures of the brain and spinal cord; for example, the medulla oblongata is caudal to the pons. *Compare* rostral.

**celiac**   Pertaining to the abdomen.

**celiac trunk**   An arterial trunk that arises from the abdominal aorta near the diaphragm, and quickly branches to give off arteries that supply the stomach, spleen, pancreas, liver, and other viscera of the upper abdominal cavity. (fig. 21.23)

**cell**   The smallest subdivision of a tissue considered to be alive; consists of a plasma membrane enclosing cytoplasm and, in most cases, a nucleus.

**cell body**   The main part of a cell, especially a neuron, where the nucleus is located; also called the *soma.*

**central**   Located relatively close to the median axis of the body, as in *central nervous system;* opposite of *peripheral.*

**central canal**   **1.** A canal that passes through the core of an osteon in bone, and contains blood vessels and nerves; also called a *haversian canal* or *osteonic canal.* **2.** A canal that passes through the center of the spinal cord, containing cerebrospinal fluid.

**central nervous system (CNS)**   The brain and spinal cord. *Compare* peripheral nervous system.

**central pattern generator**   A nucleus of neurons in the CNS that generates a repetitive motor output, producing rhythmic muscle contractions for such purposes as walking and breathing.

**centriole**   (SEN-tree-ole) An organelle composed of a short cylinder of nine triplets of microtubules, usually paired with another centriole perpendicular to it; origin of the mitotic spindle; identical to the basal body of a cilium or flagellum. (fig. 2.17)

**cephalic**   (seh-FAL-ic) Pertaining to the head.

**cerebellum**   (SERR-eh-BEL-um) A large portion of the brain posterior to the brainstem and inferior to the cerebrum, responsible for equilibrium, motor coordination, some timekeeping functions, and learning of motor skills. (fig. 15.9)

**cerebrospinal fluid (CSF)**   (SERR-eh-bro-SPY-nul, seh-REE-bro-SPY-nul) A liquid that fills the ventricles of the brain, the central canal of the spinal cord, and the space between the CNS and dura mater.

**cerebrum**   (SERR-eh-brum, seh-REE-brum) The largest and most superior part of the brain, divided into two convoluted cerebral hemispheres separated by a deep longitudinal fissure.

**cervical**   (SUR-vih-cul) Pertaining to the neck or any cervix.

**cervix**   (SUR-vix) **1.** The neck. **2.** A narrow or necklike part of an organ such as the uterus and gallbladder. (fig. 26.11)

**chemoreceptor**   An organ or cell specialized to detect chemicals, as in the carotid bodies and taste buds.

**chief cell**   The majority type of cell in an organ or tissue such as the parathyroid glands or gastric glands.

**choana**   (co-AN-ah) Opening of a nasal fossa into the pharynx; also called a *posterior naris.* (fig. 7.5)

**chondrocyte**   (CON-dro-site) A cartilage cell; a former chondroblast that has become enclosed in a lacuna in the cartilage matrix. (fig. 6.12)

**chordate**   Any animal, including humans, that has a notochord, pharyngeal pouches, a dorsal hollow nerve cord, and a tail extending beyond the anus, in at least some stage of prenatal development or postnatal life; any member of the phylum Chordata.

**chorion**   (CO-ree-on) A fetal membrane external to the amnion; forms part of the placenta and has diverse functions including fetal nutrition, waste removal, and hormone secretion. (fig. 4.9)

**chromatid**   (CRO-muh-tid) One of two genetically identical rodlike bodies of a metaphase chromosome, joined to its sister chromatid at the centromere. (fig. 2.21)

**chromatin**   (CRO-muh-tin) Filamentous material in the interphase nucleus, composed of DNA and protein; all of the chromosomes collectively.

**chromosome**   A strand of DNA and protein carrying the genetic material of a cell's nucleus, having a fine filamentous structure during interphase and a condensed rodlike structure during mitosis and meiosis. Normally there are 46 chromosomes in the nucleus of each cell except germ cells. (fig. 2.21)

**chronic**   Pertaining to a disorder with a gradual onset, slow progression, and long duration. *Compare* acute.

**chyme**   (kime) A slurry of partially digested food in the stomach and small intestine.

**cilium**   (SIL-ee-um) A hairlike process, with an axoneme, projecting from the surface of many or most cells; usually immobile, solitary, and serving a sensory or unknown role; found in large numbers on the apical surfaces of some epithelial cells (as in the respiratory tract and uterine tube), where they are motile and serve to propel matter across the surface of the epithelium. (fig. 2.13)

**circulatory system**   An organ system consisting of the heart, blood vessels, and blood. *Compare* cardiovascular system.

**circumduction**   A joint movement in which one end of an appendage remains relatively stationary and the other end moves in a circle. (fig. 9.11)

**cisterna**   (sis-TUR-nuh) A fluid-filled space or sac, such as the cisterna chyli of the lymphatic system and the cisternae of the endoplasmic reticulum and Golgi complex. (fig. 2.17)

**coelom**   A body cavity bounded on all sides by mesoderm and lined with peritoneum. The embryonic coelom becomes the thoracic and abdominopelvic cavities.

**collagen**   (COLL-uh-jen) The most abundant protein in the body, forming the fibers of many connective tissues in places such as the dermis, tendons, and bones.

**colony-forming unit (CFU)**   A bone marrow cell that differentiates from a pluripotent stem cell and gives rise to precursor cells, which, in turn, produce a specific class of formed elements. (fig. 19.8)

**commissure**   (COM-ih-shur) **1.** A bundle of nerve fibers that crosses from one side of the brain or spinal cord to the other. **2.** A corner or angle at which the eyelids, lips, or genital labia meet; in the eye, also called the *canthus.* (fig. 17.19)

**compact bone**   A form of osseous tissue found on bone surfaces and composed predominantly of osteons, with the tissue completely filled with mineralized matrix (other than lacunae and central canals) and leaving no room for bone marrow; also called *dense bone.* (fig. 6.5) *Compare* spongy bone.

**computed tomography (CT)**   A method of medical imaging that uses X-rays and a computer to create an image of a thin section of the body; the image is called a *CT scan.* (fig. 1.2)

**conception**   The fertilization of an egg, producing a zygote; the beginning of pregnancy.

**conceptus**   All products of conception, ranging from a fertilized egg to the full-term fetus with its fetal membranes, placenta, and umbilical cord. *Compare* embryo; fetus; preembryo.

**condyle**   (CON-dile) An articular surface on a bone, usually in the form of a knob (as on the mandible), but relatively flat on the proximal end of the tibia. (fig. 7.15)

**congenital** Present at birth; for example, an anatomical defect, a syphilis infection, or a hereditary disease.

**congenital anomaly** The abnormal structure or position of an organ at birth, resulting from a defect in prenatal development; a birth defect.

**connective tissue** A tissue usually composed of more extracellular than cellular volume and usually with a substantial amount of extracellular fiber; forms supportive frameworks and capsules for organs, binds structures together, holds them in place, stores energy (as in adipose tissue), or transports materials (as in blood).

**contralateral** On opposite sides of the body, as in reflex arcs where the stimulus comes from one side of the body and a response is given by muscles on the other side. *Compare* ipsilateral.

**convergent** Coming together, as in a *convergent muscle* and a converging neuronal circuit.

**cornified** Having a heavy surface deposit of keratin, as in the stratum corneum of the epidermis.

**corona** A halo- or crownlike structure, such as the corona radiata or coronal suture of the skull.

**coronal plane** *See* frontal plane.

**corona radiata** **1.** An array of nerve tracts in the brain that arise mainly from the thalamus and fan out to different regions of the cerebral cortex. **2.** The first layer of cuboidal cells immediately external to the zona pellucida around an egg cell.

**coronary** **1.** Crownlike; encircling. **2.** Pertaining to the heart.

**coronary artery** Either of two branching arteries that arise from the aorta near the heart and supply blood to the heart wall.

**coronary circulation** A system of blood vessels that serve the wall of the heart. (fig. 20.11)

**corpus** **1.** A body of tissue, such as the corpus cavernosum of the penis. **2.** The principal part (body) of an organ such as the uterus or stomach, as opposed to smaller regions of an organ such as its head, tail, fundus, or cervix.

**corpus callosum** (COR-pus ca-LO-sum) A prominent **C**-shaped band of nerve tracts that connect the right and left cerebral hemispheres to each other, seen superior to the third ventricle in a median section of the brain. (fig. 15.2)

**corpus luteum** A yellowish cellular mass that forms in the ovary from a follicle that has ovulated; secretes progesterone, hormonally regulates the second half of the menstrual cycle, and is essential to sustaining the first 7 weeks of pregnancy.

**cortex** (plural, *cortices*) The outer layer of some organs such as the adrenal gland, cerebrum, lymph node, and ovary; usually covers or encloses tissue called the medulla.

**corticospinal tract** A bundle of nerve fibers that descend through the brainstem and spinal cord and carry motor signals from the cerebral cortex to the neurons that innervate the skeletal muscles of the limbs; important in the fine control of limb movements. (fig. 14.5)

**costal** (COSS-tul) Pertaining to the ribs.

**costal cartilage** A bladelike plate of hyaline cartilage that attaches the distal end of a rib to the sternum; collectively the costal cartilages constitute much of the anterior part of the thoracic cage.

**coxal** Pertaining to the hip.

**cranial** **1.** Pertaining to the cranium. **2.** In a position relatively close to the head or a direction toward the head. *Compare* caudal.

**cranial nerve** Any of 12 pairs of nerves connected to the base of the brain and passing through foramina of the cranium.

**cranium** That portion of the skull that encloses the cranial cavity and protects the brain; also called the *braincase*. Comprises the frontal, parietal, temporal, occipital, sphenoid, and ethmoid bones.

**crest** A narrow ridge, such as the neural crest or the crest of the ilium.

**cricoid cartilage** The most inferior cartilage of the larynx, connecting the larynx to the trachea.

**crista** A crestlike structure, such as the crista galli of the ethmoid bone, crista ampullaris of the inner ear, or the crista of a mitochondrion.

**cross section (c.s.)** A cut perpendicular to the long axis of the body or of an organ. (fig. 3.2)

**crural** (CROO-rul) Pertaining to the leg proper or to the crus of a organ. *See also* crus.

**crus** (cruss) (plural, *crura*) **1.** The region from the knee to the ankle; the leg proper. **2.** A leglike extension of an organ such as the penis and clitoris. (fig. 26.9) *See also* crural.

**CT scan** An image of the body made by computed tomography. (fig. 1.2)

**cubital region** The anterior region at the bend of the elbow.

**cuboidal** (cue-BOY-dul) A shape that is roughly like a cube or in which the height and width are about equal.

**cuneiform** (cue-NEE-ih-form) Wedge-shaped, as in *cuneiform cartilages* and *cuneiform bone*.

**cusp** **1.** One of the flaps of a valve of the heart, veins, and lymphatic vessels. **2.** A conical projection on the occlusal surface of a premolar or molar tooth.

**cutaneous** Pertaining to the skin; integumentary.

**cuticle** **1.** The outermost layer of a hair, consisting of a single layer of overlapping squamous cells. **2.** A layer of dead epidermal cells that cover the proximal end of a nail; also called the *eponychium*.

**cytokinesis** (SY-toe-kih-NEE-sis) Division of the cytoplasm of a cell into two cells following nuclear division.

**cytology** The study of cell structure and function.

**cytoplasm** The contents of a cell between the plasma membrane and the nuclear envelope, consisting of cytosol, organelles, inclusions, and the cytoskeleton.

**cytoskeleton** A system of protein microfilaments, intermediate filaments, and microtubules in a cell, serving for physical support, cellular movement, and the routing of molecules and organelles to their destinations within the cell. (fig. 2.15)

**cytosol** A clear, featureless, gelatinous colloid in which the organelles and other internal structures of a cell are embedded.

**cytotoxic T cell** A T lymphocyte that directly attacks and destroys infected body cells, cancerous cells, and the cells of transplanted tissues.

# D

**darwinian medicine** *See* evolutionary medicine.

**daughter cells** Cells that arise from a parent cell by mitosis or meiosis.

**decussation** (DEE-cuh-SAY-shun) The crossing of nerve fibers from the right side of the central nervous system to the left, or vice versa, especially in the spinal cord, medulla oblongata, and optic chiasm. *Compare* hemidecussation.

**deep** Relatively far from the body surface; opposite of *superficial*. For example, the bones are deep to the skeletal muscles.

**dendrite** Process of a neuron that receives information from other cells or from environmental stimuli and conducts signals to the soma. Dendrites are usually shorter, more branched, and more numerous than the axon and are incapable of producing action potentials. (fig. 13.4)

**dendritic cell** An antigen-presenting cell of the epidermis, vaginal mucosa, and some other epithelia.

**denervation atrophy** The shrinkage of skeletal muscle that occurs when the motor neuron dies or is severed from the muscle.

**dense bone** *See* compact bone.

**dense connective tissue** A connective tissue with a high density of fiber, relatively little ground substance, and scanty cells; seen in tendons and the dermis, for example. Classified as *regular* if the extracellular fibers are more or less parallel and *irregular* if the fibers travel in highly varied directions. (figs. 3.17–3.18)

**depression** **1.** A sunken place on the surface of a bone. **2.** A joint movement that lowers a body part, as in dropping the shoulders or opening the mouth. (fig. 9.9)

**dermal papilla** **1.** A bump or ridge of dermis that extends upward to interdigitate with the epidermis, creating a wavy boundary that resists stress and slippage of the epidermis. (fig. 5.3) **2.** A projection of the dermis into the bulb of a hair, supplying blood to the hair. (fig. 5.6)

**dermatome** **1.** In the embryo, a group of mesodermal cells that arise from a somite and gives rise to the dermis on one side of one segment of the body. *Compare* myotome; sclerotome. **2.** In the adult, a region of skin on the neck, trunk, or limbs that is innervated by one spinal nerve. (fig. 14.18)

**dermis** The deeper of the two layers of the skin, underlying the epidermis and composed of fibrous connective tissue.

**desmosome** (DEZ-mo-some) A patchlike intercellular junction that mechanically links two cells together. (fig. 2.14)

**desquamation** *See* exfoliation.

**diaphragm** A muscular partition that separates the thoracic cavity from the abdominal cavity and plays a major role in respiration.

**diaphysis** (dy-AFF-ih-sis) The shaft of a long bone. (fig. 6.2)

**diarthrosis** *See* synovial joint.

**diencephalon** (DY-en-SEFF-uh-lon) A portion of the brain between the midbrain and corpus callosum; composed of the thalamus, epithalamus, and hypothalamus. (fig. 15.11)

**differentiation** Development of a relatively unspecialized cell or tissue into one with a more specific structure and function.

**digestive system** The organ system specialized for the intake and chemical breakdown of food, absorption of nutrients, and discharge of the indigestible residue.

**digit** A finger or toe.

**digital rays** The first ridgelike traces of fingers or toes to appear in the embryonic hand plate and foot plate.

**dilation** (dy-LAY-shun) Widening of an organ or passageway such as a blood vessel or the pupil of the eye.

**diploid (2n)** Pertaining to a cell or organism with chromosomes in homologous pairs. All nucleated cells of the human body are diploid except for germ cells beyond the meiosis I stage of cell division.

**distal** Relatively distant from a point of origin or attachment; for example, the wrist is distal to the elbow. *Compare* proximal.

**dizygotic (DZ) twins** Two individuals who developed simultaneously in one uterus but originated from separate fertilized eggs and therefore are not genetically identical.

**dorsal**    Toward the back (spinal) side of the body; also called *posterior.*

**dorsal root**    A branch of a spinal nerve that enters the spinal cord on its dorsal side, composed of sensory fibers; also called the *posterior root.* (fig. 14.10)

**dorsal root ganglion**    A swelling in the dorsal root of a spinal nerve, near the spinal cord, containing the somas of the afferent neurons of the nerve. (fig. 14.10)

**dorsiflexion**    (DOR-sih-FLEC-shun) A movement of the ankle that reduces the joint angle and raises the toes. (fig. 9.17)

**dorsum**    The dorsal surface of a body region, especially the hand or foot surface bearing the nails.

**Down syndrome**    *See* trisomy-21.

**duct**    An epithelium-lined, tubular passageway, such as a semicircular duct or a gland duct.

**duodenum**    (DEW-oh-DEE-num, dew-ODD-eh-num) The first portion of the small intestine extending for about 25 cm from the pyloric valve of the stomach to a sharp bend called the duodenojejunal flexure; receives chyme from the stomach and secretions from the liver and pancreas.

**dural sheath**    An extension of the dura mater into the vertebral canal, loosely enclosing the spinal cord.

**dura mater**    The thickest and most superficial of the three meninges around the brain and spinal cord.

**dynein**    (DINE-een) A motor protein involved in the beating of cilia and flagella and in the movement of molecules and organelles within cells.

**dyspnea**    Labored breathing.

# E

**ectoderm**    The outermost of the three primary germ layers of an embryo; gives rise to the nervous system and epidermis.

**ectopic**    (ec-TOP-ic) In an abnormal location; for example, ectopic pregnancy and ectopic pacemakers of the heart.

**edema**    Accumulation of excess tissue fluid, resulting in swelling of a tissue.

**effector**    A molecule, cell, or organ that carries out a response to a stimulus.

**efferent**    (EFF-ur-ent) Carrying away or out, such as a blood vessel that carries blood away from a tissue or a nerve fiber that conducts signals away from the central nervous system.

**efferent neuron**    *See* motor neuron.

**elastic cartilage**    A form of cartilage with an abundance of elastic fibers in its matrix, lending flexibility and resilience to the cartilage; found in the epiglottis and ear pinna. (fig. 3.20)

**elastic fiber**    A connective tissue fiber, composed of the protein elastin, that stretches under tension and returns to its original length when released; responsible for the resilience of organs such as the skin and lungs.

**elasticity**    The tendency of a stretched structure to return to its original dimensions when tension is released.

**elastin**    A fibrous protein with the ability to stretch and recoil; found in the skin, pulmonary airway, arteries, and elastic cartilage, among other locations.

**elevation**    A joint movement that raises a body part, as in hunching the shoulders or closing the mouth. (fig. 9.9)

**embryo**    In humans, a developing individual from the time the ectoderm, mesoderm, and endoderm have all formed at about 16 days, through the end of 8 weeks when all organ systems are represented; preceded by the *preembryo* and followed by the *fetus.* In other animals, any unborn stage of development beginning with the two-celled stage. *Compare* conceptus; fetus; preembryo.

**embryogenesis**    A process of prenatal development that occurs during implantation of the blastocyst and gives rise to the three primary germ layers; embryogenesis ends with the existence of an embryo.

**embryology**    The scientific study of prenatal development, from fertilization to birth.

**embryonic disc**    A flat plate of cells in early embryonic development, composed of initially two and then three cell layers.

**embryonic stage**    The stage of prenatal development from day 16 through the end of week 8. *See also* embryo; fetal stage.

**embryonic stem cell**    An undifferentiated cell from a preembryo of up to 150 cells, capable of developing into any type of embryonic or adult cell.

**encapsulated nerve ending**    Any sensory nerve ending that is surrounded by or associated with specialized connective tissues, which enhance its sensitivity or its mode of responding to stimulation.

**endocardium**    A tissue layer that lines the inside of the heart, composed of a simple squamous epithelium overlying a thin layer of areolar tissue.

**endochondral ossification**    A process of bone development in which the bone is preceded by a model of hyaline cartilage in roughly the shape of the bone to come, and the cartilage is then replaced by osseous tissue. *Compare* intramembranous ossification. (fig. 6.10)

**endocrine gland**    (EN-doe-crin) A ductless gland that secretes hormones into the bloodstream; for example, the thyroid and adrenal glands. *Compare* exocrine gland.

**endocrine system**    A system of internal chemical communication composed of all endocrine glands and the hormone-secreting cells found in other tissues and organs.

**endocytosis**    Any process of vesicular transport of materials from the extracellular material into a cell; includes pinocytosis, receptor-mediated endocytosis, and phagocytosis. (fig. 2.11)

**endoderm**    The innermost of the three primary germ layers of an embryo; gives rise to the mucosae of the digestive and respiratory tracts and to their associated glands.

**endogenous**    (en-DODJ-eh-nus) Originating internally, such as the endogenous cholesterol synthesized in the body in contrast to the exogenous cholesterol coming from the diet. *Compare* exogenous.

**endometrium**    (EN-doe-MEE-tree-um) The mucosa of the uterus; the site of implantation and source of menstrual discharge.

**endoplasmic reticulum (ER)**    (EN-doe-PLAZ-mic reh-TIC-you-lum) An extensive system of interconnected cytoplasmic tubules or channels; classified as *rough ER* or *smooth ER* depending on the presence or absence of ribosomes on its membrane. (fig. 2.17)

**endothelium**    (EN-doe-THEEL-ee-um) A simple squamous epithelium that lines the lumens of the blood vessels, heart, and lymphatic vessels.

**enteric**    (en-TERR-ic) Pertaining to the small intestine, as in *enteric hormones.*

**eosinophil**    (EE-oh-SIN-oh-fill) A leukocyte with a large, often bilobed nucleus and coarse cytoplasmic granules that stain with eosin; phagocytizes antigen–antibody complexes, allergens, and inflammatory chemicals and secretes enzymes that combat parasitic infections. (fig. 19.1)

**epiblast**    The layer of cells in the early embryonic disc facing the amniotic cavity. These cells migrate during gastrulation to replace the hypoblast with endoderm, then to form the mesoderm, after which the remaining surface epiblast cells are called the ectoderm.

**epicardium**    The outermost layer of the heart wall, composed of a simple squamous epithelium overlying a thin layer of areolar tissue, and in many areas, a much thicker layer of adipose tissue; also called the *visceral pericardium.*

**epicondyle**    A bony projection or ridge superior to a condyle, for example at the distal ends of the humerus and femur. (fig. 8.10)

**epidermis**    A stratified squamous epithelium that constitutes the superficial layer of the skin, overlying the dermis. (fig. 5.1)

**epigastric**    Pertaining to a medial region of the abdomen superior to the umbilical region, bordered inferiorly by the subcostal line and laterally by the midclavicular lines. (fig. A.6)

**epiglottis**    A flap of tissue in the pharynx that covers the glottis during swallowing, deflecting swallowed matter away from the airway and into the esophagus.

**epiphyseal plate**    (EP-ih-FIZZ-ee-ul) A plate of hyaline cartilage between the epiphysis and diaphysis of a long bone in a child or adolescent, serving as a growth zone for bone elongation. (fig. 6.10)

**epiphysis**    (eh-PIFF-ih-sis) 1. The head of a long bone. (fig. 6.2) 2. The pineal gland (epiphysis cerebri).

**epithelium**    A type of tissue consisting of one or more layers of closely adhering cells with little intercellular material and no blood vessels; forms the coverings and linings of many organs and the parenchyma of the glands.

**equilibrium**    1. The sense of balance. 2. A state in which opposing processes occur at comparable rates and balance each other so that there is little or no net change in the system, such as a chemical equilibrium.

**erectile tissue**    A tissue that functions by swelling with blood, as in the penis, clitoris, and inferior concha of the nasal cavity.

**erythrocyte**    (eh-RITH-ro-site) A red blood cell.

**erythropoiesis**    (eh-RITH-ro-poy-EE-sis) The production of erythrocytes.

**eversion**    A movement of the foot that turns the sole laterally. (fig. 9.17)

**evolution**    A change in the genetic composition of a population over a period of time; the mechanism that produces adaptations in human form and function. *See also* adaptation.

**evolutionary medicine**    A science that examines the evolutionary history of the human species for insights into human structure, function, and especially dysfunction; also called *darwinian medicine.*

**excitability**    The ability of a cell to respond to a stimulus, especially the ability of nerve and muscle cells to produce membrane voltage changes in response to stimuli; irritability.

**excretion**    The process of eliminating metabolic waste products from a cell or from the body. *Compare* secretion.

**excursion**    A side-to-side movement of the mandible, as in chewing. (fig. 9.15)

**exfoliation** The shedding of squamous cells from the surface of a stratified squamous epithelium. Also called *desquamation*. Sampling and examination of these cells, such as a Pap smear, is called *exfoliate cytology*. (fig. 3.12)

**exocrine gland** (EC-so-crin) A gland that secretes its products into another organ or onto the body surface, usually by way of a duct; for example, salivary and gastric glands. *Compare* endocrine gland.

**exocytosis** A mode of vesicular transport in which a secretory vesicle of a cell fuses with the plasma membrane and releases its contents from the cell; a mode of glandular secretion and discharge of cellular wastes. (fig. 2.11)

**exogenous** (ec-SODJ-eh-nus) Originating externally, such as exogenous (dietary) cholesterol; extrinsic. *Compare* endogenous.

**expiration** 1. Exhaling. 2. Dying.

**extension** Movement of a joint that increases the angle between articulating bones (straightens the joint). *Compare* flexion. (fig. 9.7)

**external acoustic meatus** A canal in the temporal bone that conveys sound waves to the eardrum; also called the *external auditory meatus*.

**exteroceptor** A sensory receptor that responds to stimuli originating outside the body, such as the eye or ear. *Compare* interoceptor.

**extracellular fluid (ECF)** Any body fluid that is not contained in the cells; for example, blood, lymph, and tissue fluid.

**extrinsic** (ec-STRIN-sic) 1. Originating externally, such as extrinsic blood-clotting factors; exogenous. 2. Not fully contained within an organ but acting on it, such as the *extrinsic muscles* of the hand and eye. *Compare* intrinsic.

# F

**facet** A smooth articular surface on a bone; may be flat, slightly concave, or slightly convex; for example, the articular facets of the vertebrae.

**facilitated diffusion** A process of solute transport through a cellular membrane, down its concentration gradient, with the aid of a carrier protein; the carrier does not consume ATP.

**fallopian tube** *See* uterine tube.

**fascia** (FASH-ee-uh) A layer of connective tissue between the muscles or between the muscles and the skin. (fig. 10.2)

**fascicle** (FASS-ih-cul) A bundle of muscle or nerve fibers ensheathed in connective tissue; multiple fascicles bound together constitute a muscle or nerve as a whole. Also called a *fasciculus*. (fig. 10.2)

**fat** 1. A triglyceride molecule. 2. Adipose tissue.

**female** In humans, any individual with no Y chromosome; normally, one possessing two X chromosomes in each somatic cell, and having reproductive organs that serve to produce eggs, receive sperm, provide sites of fertilization and prenatal development, expel the full-term fetus, and nourish the infant.

**femoral** Pertaining to the femur or the thigh.

**femoral region** The region between the hip and knee; the thigh.

**femoral triangle** A triangular region of the groin bounded by the sartorius muscle, adductor longus muscle, and inguinal ligament, and through which the femoral artery, femoral vein, and femoral nerve pass close to the body surface. (fig. 21.33)

**fenestrated** (FEN-eh-stray-ted) Perforated with holes or slits, as in certain blood capillaries and the elastic sheets of large arteries. (fig. 21.6)

**fetal stage** The period of prenatal development from the beginning of week 9 until birth; a period in which all organ systems are represented at the outset, and grow and differentiate until capable of supporting life outside the uterus. *See also* embryonic stage; fetus.

**fetus** In human development, an individual from the beginning of the ninth week when all of the organ systems are present, through the time of birth. *See also* conceptus; embryo.

**fiber** 1. In muscular histology, a skeletal muscle cell (*muscle fiber*). 2. In neurohistology, the axon of a neuron (*nerve fiber*). 3. Any long threadlike structure, such as a Purkinje fiber of the heart, a collagen or elastic fiber of the connective tissues, or cellulose and other digestion-resistant dietary fiber.

**fibrinogen** A protein synthesized by the liver and present in blood plasma, semen, and other body fluids; precursor of the sticky protein fibrin, which forms the matrix of a clot.

**fibroblast** A connective tissue cell that produces collagen fibers and ground substance; the only type of cell in tendons and ligaments.

**fibrocartilage** A form of cartilage with coarse bundles of collagen fibers in the matrix, found in the intervertebral discs, joint menisci, pubic symphysis, and some tendon–bone junctions. (fig. 3.21)

**fibrosis** Replacement of damaged tissue with fibrous scar tissue rather than by the original tissue type; scarring. *Compare* regeneration.

**fibrous connective tissue** Any connective tissue with a preponderance of fiber, such as areolar, reticular, dense regular, and dense irregular connective tissues.

**filament** A fine threadlike structure such as the myofilaments of muscle and the microfilaments and intermediate filaments of the cytoskeleton.

**filtration** A process in which a fluid is physically forced through a membrane that allows water and some solutes to pass, and holds back larger particles; especially important in the emission of fluid from blood capillaries.

**finger** Any of the five digits of the hand, including the thumb.

**first-order neuron** An afferent (sensory) neuron that carries signals from a receptor to a second-order neuron in the spinal cord or brain. (fig. 14.4) *See also* second-order neuron; third-order neuron.

**fissure** 1. A slit through a bone, such as the orbital fissure. 2. A deep groove, such as the longitudinal fissure between the cerebral hemispheres.

**fix** 1. To hold a structure in place, for example, by fixator muscles that prevent unwanted joint movements. 2. To preserve a tissue by means of a fixative.

**fixative** A chemical that prevents tissue decay, such as formalin or ethanol.

**fixator** A muscle that minimizes or prevents bone movement in certain joint actions, such as the rhomboideus major holding the scapula stationary while the biceps brachii flexes the elbow.

**flagellum** (fla-JEL-um) A long, motile, usually single hairlike extension of a cell; the tail of a sperm cell is the only functional flagellum in humans.

**flat bone** A bone with a platelike shape, such as the parietal bone or sternum.

**flexion** A joint movement that, in most cases, decreases the angle between two bones. (fig. 9.7) *Compare* extension.

**flexor** A muscle that flexes a joint.

**fMRI** *See* functional magnetic resonance imaging.

**follicle** (FOLL-ih-cul) A small space, such as a hair follicle, thyroid follicle, or ovarian follicle. (fig. 26.15) *See also* lymphatic nodule.

**foramen** (fo-RAY-men) A hole through a bone or other organ, in most cases providing passage for blood vessels and nerves.

**foramen magnum** The largest opening into the cranial cavity, at the point where the occipital bone articulates with the vertebral column; allows passage of the spinal cord and vertebral arteries into the cranial cavity.

**foramen ovale** 1. An ovoid foramen in the sphenoid bone that allows for passage of the mandibular division of the trigeminal nerve. 2. An opening in the fetal interatrial septum that allows blood to flow directly from the right atrium into the left atrium and bypass the pulmonary circulation.

**forebrain** The most rostral part of the brain, consisting of the cerebrum and diencephalon. (fig. 13.14)

**foregut** 1. The most rostral part of the embryonic digestive tract; all of the tract rostral to the initial attachment of the yolk sac. (fig. 4.5) 2. In adults, all of the digestive tract from the oral cavity to the major duodenal papilla, with a blood supply and innervation separate from those of the midgut and hindgut.

**formed element** An erythrocyte, leukocyte, or platelet; any normal component of blood or lymph that is a cell or cell fragment, as opposed to the extracellular fluid component.

**fossa** (FOSS-uh) A depression in an organ or tissue, such as the fossa ovalis of the heart or a cranial fossa of the skull.

**fovea** (FOE-vee-uh) A small pit, such as the fovea capitis of the femur or fovea centralis of the retina.

**free nerve ending** A bare sensory nerve ending, lacking associated connective tissue or specialized cells; includes receptors for heat, cold, and pain; also called an *unencapsulated nerve ending*.

**frontal plane** An anatomical plane that passes through the body or an organ from right to left and superior to inferior; also called a *coronal plane*. (fig. A.3)

**functional magnetic resonance imaging (fMRI)** A variation on MRI that enables the visualization of moment-to-moment changes in the metabolic activity of a tissue, rather than static images; used to study quickly changing patterns of brain activity, among other diagnostic and research purposes.

**fundus** The base or broadest part of certain organs such as the stomach and uterus.

**funiculus** (few-NICK-you-lus) Any of the three major divisions of the white matter of the spinal cord, composed of multiple fascicles, or tracts; also called a *column*. The three funiculi on each side of the cord are the dorsal, lateral, and ventral columns.

**fusiform** (FEW-zih-form) Spindle-shaped; elongated, thick in the middle, and tapered at both ends, such as the shape of a smooth muscle cell or a muscle spindle. (fig. 2.3)

# G

**gamete** (GAM-eet) An egg or sperm cell.

**gametogenesis** (GAM-eh-toe-JEN-eh-sis) The production of eggs or sperm.

**ganglion** (GANG-glee-un) A cluster of nerve cell bodies in the peripheral nervous system, often resembling a knot in a string.

**gangrene**   Tissue necrosis resulting from ischemia.

**gap junction**   A junction between two cells consisting of a pore surrounded by a ring of proteins in the plasma membrane of each cell, allowing solutes to diffuse from the cytoplasm of one cell to the next; functions include cell-to-cell nutrient transfer in the developing embryo and electrical communication between cells of cardiac and smooth muscle. (fig. 2.14)

**gastric**   Pertaining to the stomach.

**gastrointestinal (GI) system**   The part of the digestive tract composed of the stomach and intestines.

**gate**   A protein channel in a cellular membrane that can open or close in response to chemical, electrical, or mechanical stimuli, thus controlling when substances are allowed to pass through the membrane.

**general senses**   Senses such as touch, heat, cold, pain, vibration, and pressure, mediated by relatively simple sense organs that are distributed throughout the body. *See also* somesthetic; special senses.

**genitalia**   The pelvic reproductive organs including the *internal genitalia* in the pelvic cavity and *external genitalia* in the perineum; most of the external genitalia are externally visible, but some are subcutaneous, between the skin and the muscles of the pelvic floor.

**genitourinary (G-U) system**   *See* urogenital (U-G) system.

**germ cell**   A gamete or any precursor cell destined to become a gamete.

**germ layer**   Any of three tissue layers of an embryo: the ectoderm, mesoderm, or endoderm.

**gestation**   (jess-TAY-shun) Pregnancy.

**gland**   Any organ specialized for secretion or excretion; in some cases a single cell, such as a goblet cell.

**glial cell**   (GLEE-ul, GLY-ul) Any of the six types of supporting cells of the nervous system (oligodendrocytes, astrocytes, microglia, and ependyma in the CNS; Schwann cells and satellite cells in the PNS); constitute most of the bulk of the nervous system and perform various protective and supportive roles for the neurons. Also called *neuroglia*.

**glomerular capsule**   (glo-MERR-you-lur) A double-walled capsule around each glomerulus of the kidney; receives glomerular filtrate and empties into the proximal convoluted tubule. Also called the *Bowman capsule*. (fig. 25.8)

**glomerulus**   A spheroid mass of blood capillaries in the kidney that filters plasma and produces glomerular filtrate, which is further processed to form the urine. (fig. 25.9)

**glucose**   A monosaccharide ($C_6H_{12}O_6$) also known as blood sugar; glycogen, starch, cellulose, and maltose are made entirely of glucose, and glucose constitutes half of a sucrose or lactose molecule. The isomer involved in human physiology is also called *dextrose*.

**gluteal**   Pertaining to the buttocks.

**glycocalyx**   (GLY-co-CAY-licks) A layer of carbohydrate covalently bonded to the phospholipid and protein molecules of a plasma membrane; forms a surface coat on all human cells. (fig. 2.12)

**glycogen**   A glucose polymer synthesized by liver, muscle, uterine, and vaginal cells that serves as an energy-storage polysaccharide.

**glycolipid**   A phospholipid molecule with carbohydrate covalently bonded to it, found in the plasma membranes of cells.

**glycoprotein**   A protein–carbohydrate complex in which the protein is dominant; found in mucus and the glycocalyx of cells, for example.

**glycosaminoglycan (GAG)**   (GLY-cose-am-ih-no-GLY-can) A polysaccharide composed of modified sugars with amino groups; the major component of a proteoglycan. GAGs are largely responsible for the viscous consistency of tissue gel and the stiffness of cartilage.

**goblet cell**   A mucus-secreting gland cell, shaped somewhat like a wineglass, found in the epithelia of many mucous membranes. (fig. 3.7)

**Golgi complex**   (GOAL-jee) An organelle composed of several parallel cisternae, somewhat like a stack of saucers, that modifies and packages newly synthesized proteins and synthesizes carbohydrates. (fig. 2.17)

**Golgi vesicle**   A membrane-bounded vesicle pinched from the Golgi complex, containing its chemical product; may be retained in the cell as a lysosome or become a secretory vesicle that releases the product by exocytosis.

**gonad**   The ovary or testis.

**gonadal ridge**   The earliest trace of the embryonic gonad, a streak of tissue adjacent to the kidney, populated by the first germ cells arriving from the yolk sac at 5 to 6 weeks of gestation; also called a *genital ridge*.

**granulocyte**   (GRAN-you-lo-site) Any of three types of leukocytes (neutrophils, eosinophils, or basophils) with prominent cytoplasmic granules. (fig. 19.1)

**granulosa cells**   Cells that form a stratified cuboidal epithelium lining an ovarian follicle; source of steroid sex hormones. (fig. 26.15)

**gray matter**   A zone or layer of tissue in the central nervous system where the neuron cell bodies, dendrites, and synapses are found; forms the core of the spinal cord, nuclei of the brainstem, basal nuclei of the cerebrum, cerebral cortex, and cerebellar cortex. (fig. 15.4)

**great toe**   The large medial toe; also called the *hallux*.

**great vessels**   The largest of the blood vessels attached directly to the heart; the superior and inferior venae cavae, pulmonary trunk, and aorta.

**gross anatomy**   Bodily structure that can be observed without magnification.

**ground substance**   The clear, featureless material in which the fibers and cells of a connective tissue are embedded; includes the liquid plasma of the blood, tissue gel of areolar tissue, and calcified tissue of bone.

**guard hairs**   Coarse, stiff hairs that prevent insects, debris, or other foreign matter from entering the ear, nose, or eye; also called *vibrissae*.

**gustatory**   Pertaining to the sense of taste.

**gyrus**   (JY-rus) A wrinkle or fold in the cortex of the cerebrum or cerebellum. (fig. 15.1)

# H

**hair cell**   A sensory cell of the cochlea, semicircular ducts, utricle, and saccule, with a fringe of surface microvilli that respond to the relative motion of a gelatinous membrane at their tips; responsible for the senses of hearing and equilibrium. (fig. 17.13)

**hair follicle**   An oblique epithelial pit in the skin that contains a hair and extends into the dermis or hypodermis.

**hair receptor**   Free sensory nerve endings entwined around a hair follicle, responsive to movement of the hair.

**hallux**   The great toe; the medial digit of the foot.

**haploid (*n*)**   Having a single set of unpaired chromosomes. In humans, the only haploid cells are germ cells past the meiosis I stage of cell division, including the mature egg and sperm.

**haversian canal**   *See* central canal.

**head**   **1.** The uppermost part of the human body, above the neck. **2.** The expanded end of an organ such as a bone, the pancreas, or the epididymis.

**helper T cell**   A type of lymphocyte that performs a central coordinating role in humoral and cellular immunity; target of the human immunodeficiency virus (HIV).

**hematocrit**   (he-MAT-oh-crit) The percentage of blood volume that is composed of erythrocytes.

**hematoma**   (HE-muh-TOE-muh) A mass of clotted blood in the tissues; forms a bruise when visible through the skin.

**hemidecussation**   Crossing over of one half of the nerve fibers in a nerve or tract to the opposite side of the central nervous system, especially at the optic chiasm. *Compare* decussation.

**hemoglobin**   The red pigment of erythrocytes; binds and transports about 98.5% of the oxygen and 5% of the carbon dioxide carried in the blood.

**hemopoiesis**   (HE-mo-poy-EE-sis) Production of any of the formed elements of blood.

**hemopoietic tissue**   Any tissue in which hemopoiesis occurs, especially red bone marrow and lymphatic tissue.

**hemostasis**   The cessation of bleeding by the mechanisms of vascular spasm, a platelet plug, and blood clotting.

**hepatic**   Pertaining to the liver.

**hepatic macrophage**   A macrophage found in the sinusoids of the liver; also called a *Kupffer cell*.

**hepatic portal system**   A network of blood vessels that connect capillaries of the intestines to capillaries (sinusoids) of the liver, thus delivering newly absorbed nutrients directly to the liver.

**hepatocyte**   Any of the cuboidal gland cells that constitute the parenchyma of the liver.

**hiatus**   (hy-AY-tus) An opening or gap, such as the esophageal hiatus through the diaphragm.

**hilum**   (HY-lum) A point on the surface of an organ where blood vessels, lymphatic vessels, or nerves enter and leave, usually marked by a depression and slit; the midpoint of the concave surface of any organ that is roughly bean-shaped, such as the lymph nodes, kidneys, and lungs. Also called the *hilus*. (fig. 23.9)

**hindbrain**   The most caudal part of the brain, composed of the medulla oblongata, pons, and cerebellum. (fig. 13.14)

**hindgut**   **1.** The most caudal part of the embryonic digestive tract; all of the tract caudal to the initial attachment of the yolk sac. (fig. 4.5) **2.** In adults, all of the digestive tract from the end of the transverse colon through the anal canal, with a blood supply and innervation separate from those of the foregut and midgut.

**histological section**   A thin slice of tissue, usually mounted on a slide and artificially stained to make its microscopic structure more visible.

**histology**   **1.** The microscopic structure of tissues and organs. **2.** The study of such structure.

**holocrine gland**   An exocrine gland whose secretion is formed by the breakdown of entire gland cells; for example, a sebaceous gland.

**homeostasis**   (HO-me-oh-STAY-sis) The tendency of a living body to maintain relatively stable internal conditions in spite of greater changes in its external environment.

**homologous**   (ho-MOLL-oh-gus) **1.** Having the same embryonic or evolutionary origin but not necessarily the same function, such as the scrotum and labia majora. **2.** Pertaining to two chromosomes with identical structures and gene loci but not necessarily identical alleles; each member of the pair is inherited from a different parent.

**hormone** A chemical messenger that is secreted into the blood by an endocrine gland or isolated gland cell and triggers a physiological response in distant cells with receptors for it.

**human** Any species of primate classified in the family Hominidae, characterized by bipedal locomotion, relatively large brains, and usually articulate speech; currently represented only by *Homo sapiens* but including extinct species of *Homo* and *Australopithecus*.

**hyaline cartilage** (HY-uh-lin) A form of cartilage with a relatively clear matrix and fine collagen fibers but no conspicuous elastic fibers or collagen bundles as in other types of cartilage. (fig. 3.19)

**hyaluronic acid** (HY-uh-loo-RON-ic) A glycosaminoglycan that is particularly abundant in connective tissues, where it becomes hydrated and forms the tissue gel.

**hydrolysis** (hy-DRAHL-ih-sis) A chemical reaction in which water is broken down into hydrogen and hydroxide ions and these are used to split a covalent bond in an organic molecule, for example in digesting starch to glucose or protein to amino aicds, or breaking ATP down into ADP and phosphate.

**hyperextension** A joint movement that increases the angle between two bones beyond 180°. (fig. 9.7)

**hyperplasia** (HY-pur-PLAY-zhuh) The growth of a tissue through cellular multiplication, not cellular enlargement. *Compare* hypertrophy.

**hypertrophy** (hy-PUR-tro-fee) The growth of a tissue through cellular enlargement, not cellular multiplication; for example, the growth of muscle under the influence of exercise. *Compare* hyperplasia.

**hypoblast** The layer of cells in the early embryonic disc facing away from the amniotic cavity; forms the yolk sac and is then replaced during gastrulation by migrating epiblast cells.

**hypochondriac** Pertaining to an area on each side of the abdomen superior to the subcostal line and lateral to the midclavicular line. (fig. A.6)

**hypodermis** (HY-po-DUR-miss) A layer of connective tissue deep to the skin; also called *superficial fascia, subcutaneous tissue,* or when it is predominantly adipose, *subcutaneous fat.*

**hypogastric** Pertaining to a medial area of the lower abdomen inferior to the intertubercular line and medial to (between) the midclavicular lines; also called the *pubic region.* (fig. A.6)

**hypophyseal portal system** A circulatory pathway that connects a capillary plexus in the hypothalamus to a capillary plexus in the anterior pituitary; carries hypothalamic releasing and inhibiting hormones to the anterior pituitary. (fig. 18.4)

**hypophysis** The pituitary gland.

**hypothalamic thermostat** A nucleus of neurons in the hypothalamus responsible for the homeostatic regulation of body temperature.

**hypothalamo–hypophyseal tract** A bundle of nerve fibers that begin in nuclei in the hypothalamus, travel through the pituitary stalk, and terminate in the posterior lobe of the pituitary gland. They deliver the hormones oxytocin and antidiuretic hormone to the posterior pituitary for storage, and signal the pituitary when to release them into the blood. (fig. 18.4)

**hypothalamus** (HY-po-THAL-uh-mus) The inferior portion of the diencephalon of the brain, forming the walls and floor of the third ventricle and giving rise to the posterior pituitary gland; controls many fundamental physiological functions such as appetite, thirst, and body temperature. (fig. 15.2)

**hypothesis** An informed conjecture that is capable of being tested and potentially falsified by experimentation or data collection.

**hypoxemia** A deficiency of oxygen in the blood.

**hypoxia** A deficiency of oxygen in any tissue; may lead to tissue necrosis.

# I

**immune system** A population of cells, including leukocytes and macrophages, that occur in most organs of the body and protect against foreign organisms, some foreign chemicals, and cancerous or other aberrant host cells.

**immunity** The ability to ward off a specific infection or disease, usually as a result of prior exposure and the body's production of antibodies or lymphocytes against a pathogen.

**implantation** The process in which a conceptus attaches to the uterine endometrium and then becomes embedded in it.

**inclusion** Any visible object in the cytoplasm of a cell other than an organelle or cytoskeletal element; usually a foreign body or a stored cell product, such as a virus, dust particle, lipid droplet, glycogen granule, or pigment.

**infarction** **1.** The sudden death of tissue resulting from a loss of blood flow, often resulting from the occlusion of an artery; for example, cerebral infarction and myocardial infarction. **2.** A region of tissue that has died from lack of blood; also called an *infarct.*

**inferior** Lower than another structure or point of reference from the perspective of anatomical position; for example, the stomach is inferior to the diaphragm.

**infundibulum** (IN-fun-DIB-you-lum) Any funnel-shaped passage or structure, such as the distal portion of the uterine tube and the stalk that attaches the pituitary gland to the hypothalamus.

**inguinal** (IN-gwih-nul) Pertaining to the groin. (fig. A.6)

**innervation** (IN-ur-VAY-shun) The nerve supply to an organ.

**insertion** The point at which a muscle attaches to another tissue (usually a bone) and produces movement, opposite from its stationary origin. (fig. 10.4) *Compare* origin.

**inspiration** Inhaling.

**integument** The skin.

**integumentary system** An organ system consisting of the skin, cutaneous glands, hair, and nails.

**interatrial septum** The wall between the atria of the heart.

**intercalated disc** (in-TUR-kuh-LAY-ted) A complex of fascia adherens, gap junctions, and desmosomes that join two cardiac muscle cells end to end, microscopically visible as a dark line, which helps to histologically distinguish this muscle type; functions as a mechanical and electrical link between cells. (fig. 20.14)

**intercellular** Between cells.

**intercellular junction** A point at which two cells are joined together; includes desmosomes, tight junctions, and gap junctions. (fig. 2.14)

**intercostal** (IN-tur-COSS-tul) Between the ribs, as in the *intercostal* muscles, arteries, veins, and nerves.

**interdigitate** To fit together like the fingers of the folded hands; for example, at the dermal–epidermal boundary, podocytes of the kidney, and intercalated discs of the heart.

**interneuron** (IN-tur-NEW-ron) A neuron that is contained entirely in the central nervous system and, in the path of signal conduction, lies anywhere between an afferent pathway and an efferent pathway.

**interoceptor** A sensory receptor that responds to stimuli originating within the body. *Compare* exteroceptor.

**interosseous membrane** (IN-tur-OSS-ee-us) A fibrous membrane that connects the radius to the ulna and the tibia to the fibula along most of the shaft of each bone. (fig. 8.4)

**interstitial** (IN-tur-STISH-ul) **1.** Pertaining to the extracellular spaces in a tissue. **2.** Located between other structures, as in the *interstitial cells* of the testis.

**interstitial fluid** Fluid in the interstitial spaces of a tissue, also called *tissue fluid.*

**intervertebral disc** A cartilaginous pad between the bodies of two adjacent vertebrae.

**intracellular** Contained within a cell.

**intracellular fluid (ICF)** The fluid contained in the cells; one of the major fluid compartments.

**intramembranous ossification** A process of bone development in which there is no cartilage precursor; rather, the bone develops directly from a sheet of condensed mesenchyme. (fig. 6.8) *Compare* endochondral ossification.

**intraperitoneal** Within the peritoneal cavity. *Compare* retroperitoneal.

**intrinsic** **1.** Arising from within, such as intrinsic blood-clotting factors; endogenous. **2.** Fully contained within an organ, such as the intrinsic muscles of the hand and eye. *Compare* extrinsic.

**inversion** Movement of the foot that turns the sole medially. (fig. 9.17)

**involuntary** Not under conscious control, as in the case of the autonomic nervous system and cardiac and smooth muscle contraction.

**involution** Shrinkage of a tissue or organ by autolysis, such as shrinkage of the thymus after childhood and of the uterus after pregnancy.

**ipsilateral** (IP-sih-LAT-ur-ul) On the same side of the body, as in reflex arcs in which a muscular response occurs on the same side of the body as the stimulus. *Compare* contralateral.

**ischemia** A state in which the blood flow to a tissue is inadequate to meet its metabolic needs; may lead to tissue necrosis from hypoxia or waste accumulation.

**isthmus** A narrow zone of tissue connecting two larger masses; for example, at the front of the thyroid gland and connecting the uterine tube ampulla to the uterus.

# J

**joint** *See* articulation.

# K

**keratin** A tough protein formed by keratinocytes that constitutes the hair, nails, and stratum corneum of the epidermis.

**keratinized** Covered with keratin, such as the epidermis.

**keratinocyte** A cell of the epidermis that synthesizes keratin, then dies; most cells of the epidermis are keratinocytes, with dead ones constituting the stratum corneum.

**Kupffer cell** *See* hepatic macrophage.

**kyphosis** An exaggerated thoracic spinal curvature, often resulting from osteoporosis; also called *widow's hump* or *dowager's hump*.

# L

**labium** (LAY-bee-um) A lip, such as those of the mouth and the labia majora and minora of the vulva.

**lacrimal** Pertaining to the tears or tear glands.

**lacteal** A lymphatic capillary located in the core of an intestinal villus, serving to absorb dietary lipids.

**lacuna** (la-CUE-nuh) A small cavity or depression in a tissue such as bone, cartilage, and the erectile tissues.

**lamella** A little plate or sheet of tissue, such as a lamella of bone. (fig. 6.5)

**lamellated corpuscle** A bulbous sensory receptor with one or a few dendrites enclosed in onionlike layers of Schwann cells; found in the dermis, mesenteries, pancreas, and some other viscera, and responsive to deep pressure, stretch, and high-frequency vibration. Also called a *pacinian corpuscle*. (fig. 17.1)

**lamina** (LAM-ih-nuh) A thin layer, such as the lamina of a vertebra or the lamina propria of a mucous membrane. (fig. 7.25)

**lamina propria** (PRO-pree-uh) A thin layer of areolar tissue immediately deep to the epithelium of a mucous membrane. (fig. 3.30)

**laryngopharynx** (la-RIN-go-FAIR-inks) The portion of the pharynx formed by the union of the oropharynx and nasopharynx, beginning at the level of the hyoid bone and extending inferiorly to the opening of the esophagus. (fig. 23.2)

**larynx** (LAIR-inks) A cartilaginous chamber in the neck containing the vocal cords; the voicebox. (fig. 23.4)

**lateral** Away from the midline of an organ or median plane of the body; toward the side. *Compare* medial.

**leg** **1.** That part of the body between the knee and ankle; the crural region. **2.** A leglike extension of an organ. *See also* crus.

**lesion** A circumscribed zone of tissue injury, such as a skin abrasion or myocardial infarction.

**leukocyte** (LOO-co-site) Any nucleated blood cell; a neutrophil, eosinophil, basophil, lymphocyte, or monocyte. Also called a *white blood cell*. (fig. 19.1)

**leukopoiesis** The process of leukocyte development from hemopoietic stem cells.

**libido** The sex drive; a psychological desire for sex.

**ligament** A cord or band of tough collagenous tissue binding one organ to another, especially one bone to another, and serving to hold organs in place; for example, the cruciate ligaments of the knee and falciform ligament of the liver.

**light microscope (LM)** A microscope that produces images with visible light.

**limb** **1.** An appendage of the body arising from the shoulder or hip; *see also* lower limb; upper limb. **2.** An appendage or extension of another structure, such as the descending limb of the nephron loop.

**limb bud** An outgrowth of the embryo that develops into an upper or lower limb.

**limbic system** A ring of brain structures that encircle the corpus callosum and thalamus, including the cingulate gyrus, hippocampus, amygdala, and other structures; functions include learning and emotion. (fig. 15.16)

**line** **1.** Any long narrow mark. *See also* linea. **2.** An elongated, slightly raised ridge on a bone, such as the nuchal lines of the skull. (fig. 7.5)

**linea** (LIN-ee-uh) An anatomical line, such as the linea alba.

**lingual** (LING-wul) Pertaining to the tongue.

**lipid** A hydrophobic organic compound with a high ratio of hydrogen to oxygen; includes steroids, fatty acids, triglycerides (fats), phospholipids, and prostaglandins.

**LM** **1.** Light microscope. **2.** Light micrograph, a photograph made through the light microscope.

**load** **1.** To pick up oxygen or carbon dioxide for transport in the blood. **2.** The resistance acted upon by a muscle.

**lobe** **1.** A structural subdivision of an organ such as a gland, a lung, or the brain, bounded by a visible landmark such as a fissure or septum. **2.** The inferior, noncartilaginous, often pendant part of the ear pinna; the earlobe.

**lobule** (LOB-yool) A small subdivision of an organ or of a lobe of an organ, especially of a gland.

**long bone** A bone such as the femur or humerus that is markedly longer than wide and that generally serves as a lever.

**longitudinal section (l.s.)** A cut along the longest dimension of the body or of an organ. (fig. 3.2)

**loose connective tissue** Areolar, reticular, or adipose tissue; a connective tissue which, in the first two cases, has an abundance of ground substance and relatively widely spaced fibers and cells.

**lower limb** The appendage that arises from the hip, consisting of the thigh from hip to knee; the crural region from knee to ankle; the ankle; and the foot. Loosely called the leg, although that term properly refers only to the crural region.

**lumbar** Pertaining to the lower back and sides, between the thoracic cage and pelvis.

**lumen** The internal space of a hollow organ, such as a blood vessel or the esophagus, or a space surrounded by cells, as in a gland acinus.

**lymph** The fluid contained in lymphatic vessels and lymph nodes, produced by the absorption of tissue fluid.

**lymphatic nodule** A temporary, dense aggregation of lymphocytes in such places as mucous membranes and lymphatic organs; also called a *lymphatic follicle*. (fig. 22.8)

**lymphatic system** An organ system consisting of lymphatic vessels, lymph nodes, the tonsils, spleen, and thymus; functions include tissue fluid recovery and immunity.

**lymph node** A small organ found along the course of a lymphatic vessel; filters the lymph and contains lymphocytes and macrophages, which respond to antigens in the lymph. (fig. 22.11)

**lymphocyte** (LIM-foe-site) A relatively small leukocyte with numerous types and roles in nonspecific defense, humoral immunity, and cellular immunity. (fig. 19.1)

**lysosome** A membrane-bounded organelle containing a mixture of enzymes with a variety of intracellular and extracellular roles in digesting foreign matter, pathogens, and expired organelles. (fig. 2.17)

**lysozyme** An enzyme found in tears, milk, saliva, mucus, and other body fluids that destroys bacteria by digesting their cell walls; also called *muramidase*.

# M

**macrophage** (MAC-ro-faje) Any cell of the body, other than a leukocyte, that is specialized for phagocytosis; usually derived from blood monocytes and often functioning as antigen-presenting cells.

**macula** (MAC-you-luh) A patch or spot, such as the macula lutea of the retina and macula sacculi of the inner ear.

**magnetic resonance imaging (MRI)** A method of producing a computerized image of the interior of the body using a strong magnetic field and radio waves. (fig. 1.2)

**male** In humans, any individual with a Y chromosome; normally, one possessing one X and one Y chromosome in each somatic cell, and having reproductive organs that serve to produce and deliver sperm.

**mammary gland** The milk-secreting gland that develops within the breast in pregnancy and lactation; only minimally developed in the breast of a nonpregnant or nonlactating woman.

**mast cell** A connective tissue cell, similar to a basophil, that secretes histamine, heparin, and other chemicals involved in inflammation; often concentrated along the course of a blood capillary.

**matrix** **1.** The extracellular material of a tissue. **2.** The substance or framework within which other structures are embedded, such as the fibrous matrix of a blood clot. **3.** A mass of epidermal cells from which a hair root or nail root develops. **4.** The fluid within a mitochondrion containing enzymes of the citric acid cycle.

**meatus** (me-AY-tus) An opening into a canal, such as an acoustic meatus.

**mechanoreceptor** A sensory nerve ending or organ specialized to detect mechanical stimuli such as touch, pressure, stretch, or vibration.

**medial** Toward the midline of an organ or median plane of the body. *Compare* lateral.

**median plane** The sagittal plane that divides the body or an organ into equal right and left halves; also called the *midsagittal plane*. (fig. A.3) *Compare* sagittal plane.

**mediastinum** (ME-dee-ah-STY-num) The thick median partition of the thoracic cavity that separates one pleural cavity from the other and contains the heart, great blood vessels, and thymus. (fig. A.7)

**medical imaging** Any of several noninvasive or minimally invasive methods for producing images of the interior of the body, including X-rays, MRI, PET, CT, and sonography.

**medulla** (meh-DUE-luh, meh-DULL-uh) Tissue deep to the cortex of certain organs such as the adrenal glands, lymph nodes, hairs, and kidneys.

**medulla oblongata** (OB-long-GAH-ta) The most caudal part of the brainstem, immediately superior to the foramen magnum of the skull, connecting the spinal cord to the rest of the brain. (fig. 15.2)

**meiosis** (my-OH-sis) A form of cell division in which a diploid cell divides twice and produces four haploid daughter cells; occurs only in gametogenesis.

**Meissner plexus** *See* submucosal plexus.

**melanin** A brown or black pigment synthesized by melanocytes and some other cells; provides color to the skin, hair, eyes, and some other organs and tissues.

**melanocyte** A cell of the stratum basale of the epidermis that synthesizes melanin and transfers it to the keratinocytes.

**meninges** (meh-NIN-jeez) (singular, *meninx*) Three fibrous membranes between the central nervous system and surrounding bone: the dura mater, arachnoid mater, and pia mater. (fig. 15.3)

**merocrine** (MERR-oh-crin) Pertaining to gland cells that release their product by exocytosis; also called *eccrine*. (fig. 5.10)

**mesenchyme** (MEZ-en-kime) A gelatinous embryonic connective tissue derived from the mesoderm; differentiates into all permanent connective tissues and most muscle.

**mesentery** (MEZ-en-tare-ee) A serous membrane that binds the intestines together and suspends them from the abdominal wall; the visceral continuation of the peritoneum. (fig. 24.3)

**mesocolon** A dorsal mesentery that anchors parts of the colon to the abdominal wall. (fig. 24.3)

**mesoderm** (MEZ-oh-durm) The middle layer of the three primary germ layers of an embryo; gives rise to muscle and connective tissue.

**mesonephric ducts** A pair of embryonic ducts that form in association with the temporary mesonephric kidney; they degenerate in the female, but in the male, they develop into parts of the reproductive tract. (fig. 26.23)

**mesothelium** (MEZ-oh-THEEL-ee-um) A simple squamous epithelium that covers the serous membranes.

**metaphysis** A growth zone at the junction between the diaphysis and epiphysis of a long bone, where cartilage is replaced by osseous tissue and the bone grows in length. (fig. 6.10)

**metaplasia** Transformation of one mature tissue type into another; for example, a change from pseudostratified columnar to stratified squamous epithelium in an overventilated nasal cavity.

**metarteriole** A short blood vessel that links an arteriole to a bed of blood capillaries, with no tunica media except for a smooth muscle precapillary sphincter at the opening to each capillary. (fig. 21.9)

**metastasis** (meh-TASS-tuh-sis) The spread of cancer cells from the original tumor to a new location, where they seed the development of a new tumor.

**microfilament** A thin filament of actin in the cytoskeleton of a cell, involved especially in the supportive core of a microvillus, the membrane skeleton just deep to the plasma membrane, and in muscle contraction. *See also* actin.

**micrograph** A photograph made with a microscope.

**micrometer (μm)** One thousandth of a millimeter, or $10^{-6}$ meter; a convenient unit of length for expressing the sizes of cells.

**microtubule** An intracellular cylinder composed of the protein tubulin, forming centrioles, the axonemes of cilia and flagella, and part of the cytoskeleton.

**microvillus** An outgrowth of the plasma membrane that increases the surface area of a cell and functions in absorption and some sensory processes; distinguished from cilia and flagella by its smaller size and lack of an axoneme.

**midbrain** A short section of the brainstem between the pons and diencephalon. (fig. 15.2)

**midgut** **1.** The middle part of the embryonic digestive tract, located at the attachment of the yolk sac. (fig. 4.5) **2.** In adults, all of the digestive tract from the major duodenal papilla through the end of the transverse colon, with a blood supply and innervation separate from those of the foregut and hindgut.

**midsagittal plane** *See* median plane.

**mineralization** *See* calcification.

**mitochondrion** (MY-toe-CON-dree-un) An organelle specialized to synthesize ATP, enclosed in a double unit membrane with infoldings of the inner membrane called cristae.

**mitosis** A form of cell division in which a cell divides once and produces two genetically identical daughter cells; sometimes used to refer only to the division of the genetic material or nucleus and not to include cytokinesis, the subsequent division of the cytoplasm.

**mixed nerve** A nerve containing both afferent (sensory) and efferent (motor) nerve fibers.

**monocyte** A leukocyte specialized to migrate into the tissues and transform into a macrophage. (fig. 19.1)

**monozygotic (MZ) twins** Two individuals that develop from the same zygote and are therefore genetically identical.

**morphology** Anatomy, especially as interpreted from a functional perspective.

**morula** A preembryonic stage of development consisting of 16 or more identical-looking cells having a bumpy surface appearance reminiscent of a mulberry. The morula develops into a blastocyst and then implants on the uterine wall.

**motor neuron** A neuron that transmits signals from the central nervous system to any effector (muscle or gland cell); also called an *efferent neuron.* The axon of a motor neuron is an *efferent nerve fiber.*

**motor protein** Any protein that produces movements of a cell or its components owing to its ability to undergo quick repetitive changes in conformation and to bind reversibly to other molecules; for example, myosin, dynein, and kinesin.

**motor unit** One motor neuron and all the skeletal muscle fibers innervated by it.

**mouth** **1.** A narrow opening into any cavity or hollow organ. **2.** The oral (buccal) cavity, bordered by the lips, cheeks, and fauces.

**MRI** *See* magnetic resonance imaging.

**mucosa** (mew-CO-suh) A tissue layer that forms the inner lining of an anatomical tract that is open to the exterior (the respiratory, digestive, urinary, and reproductive tracts). Composed of epithelium, connective tissue (lamina propria), and often smooth muscle (muscularis mucosae). Also called a *mucous membrane.* (fig. 3.30)

**mucosa-associated lymphatic tissue (MALT)** Aggregations of lymphocytes, including lymphatic nodules, in the mucous membranes.

**mucous gland** A gland that secretes mucus, such as the glands of the large intestine and nasal cavity. *Compare* serous gland.

**mucous membrane** *See* mucosa.

**mucus** A viscous, slimy or sticky secretion produced by mucous cells and mucous membranes and consisting of a hydrated glycoprotein, mucin; serves to bind particles together, such as bits of masticated food, and to protect the mucous membranes from infection and abrasion.

**multipotent** Pertaining to a stem cell that is capable of differentiating into multiple, but not unlimited, adult cell types; for example, bone marrow colony-forming units that can produce multiple types of leukocytes.

**muscle fiber** One skeletal muscle cell. *Compare* myocyte.

**muscularis externa** The external muscular wall of certain viscera such as the esophagus and small intestine. (fig. 24.2)

**muscularis mucosae** (MUSS-cue-LERR-iss mew-CO-see) A layer of smooth muscle immediately deep to the lamina propria of a mucosa. (fig. 3.30)

**muscular system** An organ system composed of the skeletal muscles, specialized mainly for maintaining postural support and producing movements of the bones. Cardiac and smooth muscle are not regarded as part of the muscular system.

**muscular tissue** A tissue composed of elongated, electrically excitable cells specialized for contraction; the three types are skeletal, cardiac, and smooth muscle.

**mutagen** (MEW-tuh-jen) Any agent that causes a mutation, including viruses, chemicals, and ionizing radiation.

**mutation** Any change in the structure of a chromosome or a DNA molecule, often resulting in a change of organismal structure or function.

**myelin** (MY-eh-lin) A lipid sheath around a nerve fiber, formed from closely spaced spiral layers of the plasma membrane of an oligodendrocyte or Schwann cell. (fig. 13.7)

**myelination** The process in which an oligodendrocyte or Schwann cell deposits myelin around a nerve fiber.

**myeloid tissue** Bone marrow.

**myenteric plexus** A plexus of parasympathetic neurons located between the layers of the muscularis externa of the digestive tract; controls peristalsis. Also called the *Auerbach plexus.*

**myocardium** The middle, muscular layer of the heart.

**myocyte** A muscle cell, especially a cell of cardiac or smooth muscle. *Compare* muscle fiber.

**myoepithelial cell** An epithelial cell that has become specialized to contract like a muscle cell; important in dilation of the pupil and ejection of secretions from gland acini.

**myofibril** (MY-oh-FY-bril) A bundle of myofilaments forming an internal subdivision of a cardiac or skeletal muscle cell. (fig. 10.8)

**myofilament** A protein microfilament responsible for the contraction of a muscle cell, composed mainly of myosin or actin. (fig. 10.9)

**myosin** A motor protein that constitutes the thick myofilaments of muscle and has globular, mobile heads of ATPase that bind to actin molecules.

**myotome** A group of mesodermal cells that arise from a somite in the fourth week of development and give rise to body wall muscles in that region of the trunk of the body. *Compare* dermatome; sclerotome.

# N

**nasal concha** One of three curved or scroll-like plates of bone and mucous membrane that extends from the lateral wall toward the septum in each nasal fossa; serves to warm, cleanse, and humidify inhaled air. (fig. 23.2)

**nasal septum** A wall of bone and cartilage that separates the right and left nasal fossae.

**nasopharynx** That region of the pharynx that lies caudal to the nasal choanae and posterior or superior to the soft palate. (fig. 23.2)

**natural killer (NK) cell** A lymphocyte that attacks and destroys cancerous or infected cells of the body without requiring prior exposure or a specific immune response; one of the body's nonspecific defenses.

**necrosis** (neh-CRO-sis) Pathological tissue death due to such causes as infection, trauma, or hypoxia. *Compare* apoptosis.

**neonate**   An infant up to 6 weeks old.

**neoplasia**   (NEE-oh-PLAY-zee-uh) Abnormal growth of new tissue, such as a tumor, with no useful function.

**nephron**   One of approximately 1.2 million blood-filtering, urine-producing units in each kidney; consists of a glomerulus, glomerular capsule, proximal convoluted tubule, nephron loop, and distal convoluted tubule. (fig. 25.6) *Compare* renal tubule.

**nerve**   A cordlike organ of the peripheral nervous system composed of multiple nerve fibers ensheathed in connective tissue.

**nerve fiber**   The axon of a single neuron.

**nerve impulse**   A wave of self-propagating action potentials spreading along a nerve fiber; the nerve signal.

**nervous system**   An organ system composed of the brain, spinal cord, nerves, and ganglia, specialized for rapid communication of information.

**nervous tissue**   A tissue composed of neurons and neuroglia.

**neural circuit**   A group of interconnected neurons that conduct signals along defined pathways to produce a sustained, repetitive, convergent, or divergent output. (fig. 13.12)

**neural crest**   A mass of ectoderm that begins at the edges of the neural groove, then separates from the neural tube and gives rise primarily to nerves, ganglia, and the adrenal medulla. (fig. 13.13)

**neural groove**   A longitudinal depression in the ectoderm of the embryo that closes up to form the neural tube, forerunner of the central nervous system. (fig. 13.13)

**neural pool**   A group of interconnected neurons of the central nervous system that perform a single collective function; for example, the vasomotor center of the brainstem and speech centers of the cerebral cortex.

**neural tube**   A dorsal hollow ectodermal tube in the embryo that develops into the central nervous system. (fig. 13.13)

**neuroglia**   (noo-ROG-lee-uh) All cells of nervous tissue except neurons; cells that perform various supportive and protective roles for the neurons.

**neurohypophysis**   The posterior one-third of the pituitary gland, consisting of the posterior lobe, a stalk that attaches the pituitary to the hypothalamus, and the median eminence of the hypothalamic floor; stores and secretes antidiuretic hormone and oxytocin. (fig. 18.4)

**neuromuscular junction (NMJ)**   A synapse between a nerve fiber and a muscle cell. (fig. 10.11)

**neuron**   (NOOR-on) A nerve cell; an electrically excitable cell specialized for producing and transmitting action potentials and secreting chemicals that stimulate adjacent cells.

**neurotransmitter**   A chemical released at the distal end of an axon that stimulates an adjacent cell; for example, acetylcholine, norepinephrine, and serotonin.

**neutrophil**   (NOO-tro-fill) A leukocyte, usually with a multilobed nucleus, that serves especially to destroy bacteria by means of phagocytosis, intracellular digestion, and secretion of bactericidal chemicals. (fig. 19.1)

**nitrogenous waste**   Any nitrogen-containing substance produced as a metabolic waste and excreted in the urine; chiefly ammonia, urea, uric acid, and creatinine.

**nociceptor**   (NO-sih-SEP-tur) A nerve ending specialized to detect tissue damage and produce a sensation of pain; pain receptor.

**node of Ranvier**   A gap between adjacent segments of myelin in a myelinated nerve fiber; the point where action potentials are generated in a myelinated fiber.

**nonkeratinized**   Pertaining to a stratified squamous epithelium that lacks a surface layer of dead compacted keratinocytes; found in the oral cavity, pharynx, esophagus, anal canal, and vagina.

**notochord**   A middorsal supportive rod that develops in all chordate embryos, including humans; represented in the adult only by the nuclei of the intervertebral discs.

**nuchal**   Pertaining to the back of the neck.

**nuclear envelope**   (NEW-clee-ur) A pair of unit membranes enclosing the nucleus of a cell, with prominent pores allowing traffic of molecules between the nucleoplasm and cytoplasm. (fig. 2.17)

**nuclear medicine**   Any use of radioisotopes to treat disease or form diagnostic images of the body.

**nucleus**   (NEW-clee-us) 1. A cell organelle containing DNA and surrounded by a double unit membrane. 2. A mass of neurons (gray matter) surrounded by white matter of the brain, including the basal nuclei and brainstem nuclei. 3. A central structure, such as the nucleus pulposus of an intervertebral disc or nucleus of an atom.

**nucleus pulposus**   The gelatinous center of an intervertebral disc.

# O

**oblique section**   A cut through an elongated organ on a slant, between a longitudinal and a cross section. (fig. 3.2)

**occlusion**   1. Meeting of the surfaces of the teeth when one bites. 2. Obstruction of an anatomical passageway, such as blockage of an artery by a thrombus or atherosclerotic plaque.

**olfactory**   Pertaining to the sense of smell.

**omentum**   A ventral mesentery that extends from the stomach to the liver (*lesser omentum*) or is suspended from the greater curvature of the stomach and overhangs the intestines (*greater omentum*). (fig. 24.3)

**oocyte**   (OH-oh-site) In the development of an egg cell, a haploid stage between meiosis I and fertilization.

**oogenesis**   (OH-oh-JEN-eh-sis) The production of a fertilizable egg cell through a series of mitotic and meiotic cell divisions; female gametogenesis.

**ophthalmic**   (off-THAL-mic) Pertaining to the eye or vision; optic.

**opposition**   A movement of the thumb in which it approaches or touches any fingertip of the same hand. (fig. 9.16)

**optic**   Pertaining to the eye or vision.

**optic chiasm**   An X-shaped point at the base of the brain, immediately rostral to the hypothalamus, where the two optic nerves meet and continue as optic tracts.

**oral cavity**   The space enclosed by the lips anteriorly, the cheeks laterally, and the fauces posteriorly; also called the *buccal cavity*.

**orbit**   The eye socket of the skull.

**organ**   Any anatomical structure that is composed of at least two different tissue types, has recognizable structural boundaries, and has a discrete function different from the structures around it. Many organs are microscopic, and many organs contain smaller organs, such as the skin containing numerous microscopic sense organs.

**organelle**   Any structure within a cell that carries out one of its metabolic roles, such as mitochondria, centrioles, endoplasmic reticulum, and the nucleus; an intracellular structure other than the cytoskeleton and inclusions.

**organism**   Any living individual; the entire body of any living thing such as a bacterium, plant, or human.

**organogenesis**   The prenatal developmental process in which embryonic germ layers differentiate into specific organs and organ systems; the process that converts an embryo to a fetus, occurring between day 16 and the end of week 8 of gestation.

**organ system**   Any of 11 systems of interconnected or physiologically interrelated organs that perform one of the body's basic functions; for example, the digestive, urinary, and respiratory systems.

**origin**   The relatively stationary attachment of a skeletal muscle. (fig. 10.4) *Compare* insertion.

**oropharynx**   That part of the pharynx that is caudal to the fauces at the rear of the oral cavity, and anterior or inferior to the soft palate. (fig. 23.2)

**osmoreceptor**   (OZ-mo-re-SEP-tur) A neuron of the hypothalamus that responds to changes in the osmolarity of the extracellular fluid.

**osmosis**   The diffusion of water through a selectively permeable membrane from the side with less concentrated solutes to the side with more concentrated solutes.

**osseous**   (OSS-ee-us) Pertaining to bone.

**ossification**   (OSS-ih-fih-CAY-shun) Bone formation; also called *osteogenesis*. *See also* endochondral ossification; intramembranous ossification.

**osteoarthritis (OA)**   A chronic degenerative joint disease characterized by loss of articular cartilage, growth of bone spurs, and impaired movement; occurs to various degrees in almost all people with age.

**osteoblast**   A bone-forming cell that arises from an osteogenic cell, deposits bone matrix, and eventually becomes an osteocyte.

**osteoclast**   A macrophage of the bone surface that dissolves the matrix and returns minerals to the extracellular fluid.

**osteocyte**   A mature bone cell formed when an osteoblast becomes surrounded by its own matrix and entrapped in a lacuna.

**osteogenesis**   *See* ossification.

**osteon**   A structural unit of compact bone consisting of a central canal surrounded by concentric cylindrical lamellae of matrix. (fig. 6.5)

**osteoporosis**   (OSS-tee-oh-pore-OH-sis) A degenerative bone disease characterized by a loss of bone mass, increasing susceptibility to spontaneous fractures, and sometimes deformity of the vertebral column; causes include aging, estrogen hyposecretion, and insufficient resistance exercise.

**ovary**   The female gonad; produces eggs, estrogen, and progesterone.

**oviduct**   *See* uterine tube.

**ovulation**   The release of a mature oocyte by the bursting of an ovarian follicle.

**ovum**   Any stage of the female gamete from the conclusion of meiosis I until fertilization; a primary oocyte; an egg.

# P

**pacinian corpuscle**   *See* lamellated corpuscle.

**palate**   A horizontal partition between the oral and nasal cavities.

**palatine**   Pertaining to the palate, such as palatine bones and tonsils.

**palmar region**   The anterior surface (palm) of the hand.

**pancreas** A gland of the upper abdominal cavity, near the stomach, that secretes digestive enzymes and sodium bicarbonate into the duodenum and secretes hormones into the blood.

**pancreatic islets** (PAN-cree-AT-ic EYE-lets) Small clusters of endocrine cells in the pancreas that secrete insulin, glucagon, somatostatin, and other intercellular messengers; also called *islets of Langerhans.* (fig. 18.11)

**papilla** (pa-PILL-uh) A conical or nipplelike structure, such as a lingual papilla of the tongue or the papilla of a hair bulb.

**papillary** (PAP-ih-lerr-ee) 1. Pertaining to or shaped like a nipple, such as the papillary muscles of the heart. 2. Having papillae, such as the papillary layer of the dermis.

**paramesonephric ducts** A pair of embryonic ducts that form beside the mesonephric ducts; they degenerate in the male; in the female, they form the uterine tubes, uterus, and part of the vagina. (fig. 26.26)

**parasympathetic nervous system** (PERR-uh-SIM-pa-THET-ic) A division of the autonomic nervous system that issues efferent fibers through the cranial and sacral nerves and exerts cholinergic effects on its target organs. (fig. 16.7)

**parathyroid glands** (PERR-uh-THY-royd) Small endocrine glands, usually four in number, adhering to the posterior side of the thyroid gland. (fig. 18.9)

**parenchyma** (pa-REN-kih-muh) The tissue that performs the main physiological functions of an organ, especially a gland, as opposed to the tissues (stroma) that mainly provide structural support.

**parietal** (pa-RY-eh-tul) 1. Pertaining to a wall, as in the *parietal cells* of the gastric glands and *parietal bone* of the skull. 2. The outer or more superficial layer of a two-layered membrane such as the pleura, pericardium, or glomerular capsule. (fig. A.8) *Compare* visceral.

**pathogen** Any disease-causing chemical or organism.

**pectoral** Pertaining to the chest.

**pectoral girdle** The circle of bones that connect the upper limb to the axial skeleton; composed of the two scapulae and the two clavicles.

**pedal region** The foot.

**pedicel** *See* pedicle.

**pedicle** (PED-ih-cul) A small footlike process, as in the vertebrae and the renal podocytes; also called a *pedicel.* (fig. 7.22)

**pelvic cavity** The space enclosed by the true (lesser) pelvis, containing the urinary bladder, rectum, and internal reproductive organs. (fig. A.7)

**pelvic girdle** A ring of three bones—the two hip bones (ossa coxae) and the sacrum—which attach the lower limbs to the axial skeleton. *See also* pelvis.

**pelvis** 1. The basinlike cradle of bones that enclose the pelvic cavity and provide attachment for the lower limbs; includes the ossa coxae, sacrum, and coccyx. (fig. 8.6) 2. A basinlike structure such as the renal pelvis of the kidney. (fig. 25.3)

**perfusion** Loosely, blood flow to any tissue or organ. More specifically, the volume of blood received by a given mass of tissue in a given unit of time, such as milliliters per gram per minute.

**pericardial cavity** A narrow space between the parietal and visceral layers of the pericardium, containing pericardial fluid.

**pericardium** A two-layered serous membrane that folds around the heart. Its visceral layer forms the heart surface (*epicardium*), and its parietal layer forms a fibrous *pericardial sac* around the heart. (fig. 20.4)

**perichondrium** (PERR-ih-CON-dree-um) A layer of fibrous connective tissue covering the surface of hyaline or elastic cartilage. (fig. 3.19)

**perineum** (PERR-ih-NEE-um) The region between the thighs bordered by the coccyx, pubic symphysis, and ischial tuberosities; contains the orifices of the urinary, reproductive, and digestive systems. (figs. 26.1, 26.21)

**periosteum** (PERR-ee-OSS-tee-um) A layer of fibrous connective tissue covering the surface of a bone. (fig. 6.5)

**peripheral** Away from the center of the body or of an organ, as in *peripheral vision* and *peripheral blood vessels;* opposite of central.

**peripheral nervous system (PNS)** A subdivision of the nervous system composed of all nerves and ganglia; all of the nervous system except the central nervous system. *Compare* central nervous system.

**peristalsis** (PERR-ih-STAL-sis) A wave of constriction traveling along a tubular organ such as the esophagus or ureter, serving to propel its contents.

**peritoneum** (PERR-ih-toe-NEE-um) A serous membrane that lines the peritoneal cavity of the abdomen and covers the mesenteries and viscera.

**perivascular** (PERR-ih-VASS-cue-lur) Pertaining to the region surrounding a blood vessel.

**peroxisome** An organelle composed of a unit membrane enclosing a mixture of enzymes; serves to detoxify free radicals, alcohol, and other drugs, and to break down fatty acids; named for the hydrogen peroxide that it generates in the course of these activities.

**PET** *See* positron emission tomography.

**phagocytosis** (FAG-oh-sy-TOE-sis) A form of endocytosis in which a cell surrounds a foreign particle with pseudopods and engulfs it, enclosing it in a cytoplasmic vesicle called a phagosome. (fig. 2.11)

**pharyngeal arch** One of five pairs of bulbous swellings in the pharyngeal region of an embryo. (fig. 4.7)

**pharyngeal pouch** One of six pairs of outpocketings of the pharynx between and adjacent to the pharyngeal arches of an embryo; these form gill slits in fishes and amphibians but in humans give rise to such structures as the middle-ear cavities, palatine tonsils, thymus, parathyroid glands, and C cells of the thyroid gland. (fig. 4.7)

**pharynx** (FAIR-inks) A muscular passage in the throat at which the respiratory and digestive tracts cross. (fig. 23.2)

**phospholipid** A lipid composed of a hydrophilic head with a phosphate group and a nitrogenous group such as choline, and two hydrophobic fatty acid tails; especially important as the most numerous molecules of the plasma membrane and other unit membranes of a cell, but also involved in emulsification of dietary fat and as a component of pulmonary surfactant. (fig. 2.7)

**photoreceptor** Any cell or organ specialized to absorb light and generate a nerve signal; the eye and its rods, cones, and some of its ganglion cells.

**phrenic** (FREN-ic) 1. Pertaining to the diaphragm, as in *phrenic nerve.* 2. Pertaining to the mind, as in *schizophrenic.*

**physiology** 1. The functional processes of the body. 2. The study of such function.

**piloerector** A bundle of smooth muscle cells associated with a hair follicle, responsible for erection of the hair; also called *arrector pili.* (fig. 5.6)

**pineal gland** (PIN-ee-ul) A small conical endocrine gland arising from the roof of the third ventricle of the brain; produces melatonin and serotonin and may be involved in mood and timing the onset of puberty. (fig. 15.2)

**pinocytosis** A form of endocytosis in which the plasma membrane sinks in and internalizes a droplet of extracellular fluid in a pinocytotic vesicle. (fig. 2.11)

**pituitary gland** (pih-TOO-ih-terr-ee) An endocrine gland suspended from the hypothalamus and housed in the sella turcica of the sphenoid bone; secretes numerous hormones, most of which regulate the activities of other glands. (fig. 18.4)

**placenta** (pla-SEN-tuh) A thick discoid organ on the wall of the pregnant uterus, composed of a combination of maternal and fetal tissues, serving multiple functions in pregnancy including gas, nutrient, and waste exchange between mother and fetus. (fig. 4.11)

**plantar** (PLAN-tur) Pertaining to the sole of the foot.

**plantar flexion** A movement of the ankle that points the toes downward, as in pressing on the gas pedal of a car or standing on tiptoes. (fig. 9.17)

**plaque** A small scale or plate of matter, such as dental plaque, the fatty plaques of atherosclerosis, and the amyloid plaques of Alzheimer disease.

**plasma** The noncellular portion of the blood.

**plasma cell** A connective tissue cell that differentiates from a B lymphocyte and secretes antibodies. (fig. 22.16)

**plasma membrane** The unit membrane that encloses a cell and controls the traffic of molecules into and out of it. (fig. 2.6)

**platelet** A formed element of the blood derived from the peripheral cytoplasm of a megakaryocyte, known especially for its roles in stopping bleeding but also serves in dissolving blood clots, stimulating inflammation, and promoting tissue growth. (fig. 19.9)

**pleura** (PLOOR-uh) A two-layered serous membrane that folds around the lung. Its visceral layer forms the lung surface, and its parietal layer lines the inside of the rib cage. (fig. 23.12)

**pleural cavity** A narrow space between the parietal and visceral layers of the pleura, containing pleural fluid. (fig. 23.12)

**plexus** A network of blood vessels, lymphatic vessels, or nerves, such as a choroid plexus of the brain or the brachial plexus of nerves. (fig. 14.14)

**pluripotent** Pertaining to an embryonic stem cell from the morula that is capable of producing any type of embryonic or adult cell. More loosely, describing certain adult stem cells with an especially broad developmental potential, able to produce a wide variety of differentiated cell types. *See also* pluripotent stem cell.

**pluripotent stem cell (PPSC)** A stem cell of the bone marrow that can produce any of the formed elements of blood.

**pollex** The thumb.

**pons** The section of the brainstem between the midbrain and medulla oblongata.

**popliteal** (po-LIT-ee-ul) Pertaining to the posterior aspect of the knee.

**portal system** A circulatory pathway in which blood passes through two capillary beds in series in a single trip from the heart and back. (fig. 21.12)

**positron emission tomography (PET)** A method of producing a computerized image of the physiological state of a tissue using injected radioisotopes that emit positrons. (fig. 1.2)

**posterior** Near or pertaining to the back or spinal side of the body; dorsal.

**postganglionic**   Pertaining to a neuron that transmits signals from a ganglion to a more distal target organ. (fig. 16.2)

**postsynaptic**   Pertaining to a neuron or other cell that receives signals from the presynaptic neuron at a synapse. (fig. 13.10)

**potential space**   An anatomical space that is usually obliterated by contact between two membranes but opens up if air, fluid, or other matter comes between them. Examples include the pleural cavity and the lumen of the uterus.

**preembryo**   A developing human that has not yet formed ectoderm, mesoderm, and endoderm; when those germ layers have formed, the individual is regarded as an embryo. *Compare* conceptus; embryo.

**preembryonic stage**   Any stage of prenatal development from fertilization through 16 days, when the primary germ layers exist and the embryonic stage begins.

**preganglionic**   Pertaining to a neuron that transmits signals from the central nervous system to a ganglion. (fig. 16.2)

**prepuce**   A fold of tissue over the glans of the penis or clitoris; the penile foreskin or clitoral hood.

**presynaptic**   Pertaining to a neuron that transmits signals to a synapse. (fig. 13.10)

**prime mover**   The muscle primarily responsible for a given joint action; agonist.

**process**   An outgrowth of bone or other tissue, such as the mastoid process of the skull.

**programmed cell death (PCD)**   *See* apoptosis.

**projection pathway**   The route taken by nerve signals from their point of origin (such as a sense organ) to their point of termination (such as the primary sensory cortex). (fig. 17.15)

**pronation**   A rotational movement of the forearm that turns the palm downward or posteriorly. (fig. 9.13)

**prone**   A position in which the body is lying face down.

**proprioception**   (PRO-pree-oh-SEP-shun) The nonvisual perception, usually subconscious, of the position and movements of the body, resulting from input from proprioceptors and the vestibular apparatus of the inner ear.

**proprioceptor**   (PRO-pree-oh-SEP-tur) A sensory receptor of the muscles, tendons, and joint capsules that detects muscle contractions and joint movements.

**prostate gland**   (PROSS-tate) A male reproductive gland that encircles the urethra immediately inferior to the bladder and contributes to the semen. (fig. 26.9)

**protein**   A polypeptide of 50 amino acids or more.

**proteoglycan**   A protein–carbohydrate complex in which the carbohydrate is dominant; forms a gel that binds cells and tissues together, fills the umbilical cord and eye, lubricates the joints, and forms the rubbery texture of cartilage. Formerly called *mucopolysaccharide*.

**protraction**   Forward movement of a body part in the horizontal plane, such as moving the mandible forward in preparation to take a bite from an apple. (fig. 9.15)

**protuberance**   A bony outgrowth or protruding part, such as the mental protuberance of the mandible.

**proximal**   Relatively near a point of origin or attachment; for example, the shoulder is proximal to the elbow. *Compare* distal.

**pseudopod**   (SOO-doe-pod) A temporary cytoplasmic extension of a cell used for locomotion (ameboid movement) and phagocytosis.

**pseudostratified columnar epithelium**   An epithelium in which every cell contacts the basement membrane, but not all of them reach the free surface, thus giving an appearance of stratification. (fig. 3.7)

**pubic**   Concerning the region of the genitalia. *See also* hypogastric.

**pudendum**   *See* vulva.

**pulmonary**   Pertaining to the lungs.

**pulmonary circuit**   A route of blood flow that supplies blood to the pulmonary alveoli for gas exchange and then returns it to the heart; all blood vessels between the right ventricle and the left atrium of the heart. (fig. 21.13)

# R

**radiography**   The use of X-rays to form an image of the interior of the body. (fig. 1.2)

**radiology**   The branch of medicine concerned with producing images of the interior of the body, using such methods as X-rays, sonography, MRI, CT, and PET.

**ramus**   (RAY-mus) An anatomical branch, as in a nerve or in the pubis.

**receptive field**   An area of the environment or of an epithelial surface from which a given neuron receives sensory information. (fig. 17.2)

**receptor**   1. A cell or organ specialized to detect a stimulus, such as a taste cell or the eye. 2. A protein molecule that binds and responds to a chemical such as a hormone, neurotransmitter, or odor molecule.

**receptor-mediated endocytosis**   A mode of vesicular transport in which cell surface receptors bind a specific molecule in the extracellular fluid, then cluster together to be internalized by the cell. (fig. 2.11)

**rectus**   Straight; used in muscle names such as *rectus femoris* and *rectus abdominis*.

**reflected**   Folded back or away from something, often to expose another structure in anatomical demonstrations. (fig. 9.24)

**reflex**   A stereotyped, automatic, involuntary response to a stimulus; includes somatic reflexes, in which the effectors are skeletal muscles, and visceral (autonomic) reflexes, in which the effectors are usually visceral muscle, cardiac muscle, or glands.

**reflex arc**   A simple neural pathway that mediates a reflex; involves a receptor, an afferent nerve fiber, sometimes one or more interneurons, an efferent nerve fiber, and an effector. (fig. 14.19)

**regeneration**   Replacement of damaged tissue with new tissue of the original type. *Compare* fibrosis.

**renal**   (REE-nul) Pertaining to the kidney.

**renal tubule**   A urine-forming duct that converts glomerular filtrate to urine by processes of reabsorption and secretion of water and solutes. Consists of the proximal convoluted tubule, nephron loop, and distal convoluted tubule of an individual nephron, plus a collecting duct and papillary duct shared by multiple nephrons. (fig. 25.6) *Compare* nephron.

**renin**   An enzyme produced by the kidney that converts angiotensinogen to angiotensin I, the first step in producing the vasoconstrictor angiotensin II.

**reproductive system**   An organ system specialized for the production of offspring.

**resistance**   1. Opposition to the flow of fluid, such as blood in a vessel or air in a bronchiole. 2. Opposition to the movement of a joint; the load against which a muscle works. 3. A nonspecific ability to ward off an infection or disease, as opposed to the pathogen-specific defense provided by immunity.

**respiratory system**   An organ system specialized for the intake of air and exchange of gases with the blood, consisting of the lungs and the air passages from the nose to the bronchi.

**reticular cell**   (reh-TIC-you-lur) A delicate, branching cell in the reticular connective tissue of the lymphatic organs.

**reticular fiber**   A fine, branching collagen fiber coated with glycoprotein, found in the stroma of lymphatic organs and some other tissues and organs.

**reticular tissue**   A connective tissue composed of reticular cells and reticular fibers, found in bone marrow, lymphatic organs, and in lesser amounts elsewhere. (fig. 3.15)

**retraction**   Movement of a body part posteriorly on the horizontal plane; for example, retracting the mandible to grind food between the molars. (fig. 9.15)

**retroperitoneal**   Located between the peritoneum and body wall, rather than in the peritoneal cavity; descriptive of certain abdominal viscera such as the kidneys, ureters, and pancreas. (fig. A.9) *Compare* intraperitoneal.

**ribosome**   A granule found free in the cytoplasm or attached to the rough endoplasmic reticulum and nuclear envelope, composed of ribosomal RNA and enzymes; specialized to read the nucleotide sequence of messenger RNA and assemble a corresponding sequence of amino acids to make a protein.

**risk factor**   Any environmental factor or characteristic of an individual that increases one's chance of developing a particular disease; includes such intrinsic factors as age, sex, and race and such extrinsic factors as diet, smoking, and occupation.

**root**   1. Part of an organ that is embedded in other tissue and therefore not externally visible, such as the root of a tooth, a hair, or the penis. *Compare* shaft. 2. The proximal end of a spinal nerve, adjacent to the spinal cord.

**rostral**   Relatively close to the forehead, especially in reference to structures of the brain and spinal cord; for example, the frontal lobe is rostral to the parietal lobe. *Compare* caudal.

**rotation**   Movement of a body part such as the humerus or forearm around its longitudinal axis. (fig. 9.14)

**rough endoplasmic reticulum**   Regions of endoplasmic reticulum characterized by flattened, parallel cisternae externally studded with ribosomes; involved in making proteins for export from the cell, among other functions. *See also* endoplasmic reticulum; smooth endoplasmic reticulum.

**ruga**   (ROO-ga) 1. An internal fold or wrinkle in the mucosa of a hollow organ such as the stomach and urinary bladder; typically present when the organ is empty and relaxed but not when the organ is full and stretched. 2. Tissue ridges in such locations as the hard palate and vagina. (fig. 24.11)

# S

**sagittal plane**   (SADJ-ih-tul) Any plane that extends from anterior to posterior and cephalic to caudal, and divides the body into right and left portions. (fig. A.3) *Compare* median plane.

**sarcomere**   (SAR-co-meer) In skeletal and cardiac muscle, the portion of a myofibril from one Z disc to the next, constituting one contractile unit. (fig. 10.10)

**sarcoplasmic reticulum (SR)**   The smooth endoplasmic reticulum of a muscle cell, serving as a calcium reservoir. (fig. 10.8)

**satellite cell**   **1.** A type of glial cell found surrounding the somas of neurons in ganglia of the peripheral nervous system. **2.** Stem cells of skeletal muscle that can multiply in response to muscle injury and contribute to some extent to regeneration of muscle fibers.

**scanning electron microscope (SEM)**   A microscope that uses an electron beam in place of light to form high-resolution, three-dimensional images of the surfaces of objects; capable of much higher magnifications than a light microscope. *Compare* transmission electron microscope.

**Schwann cell**   A glial cell that forms the neurilemma around all peripheral nerve fibers and the myelin sheath around many of them; also encloses neuromuscular junctions. (fig. 13.4)

**sclerosis**   (scleh-RO-sis) Hardening or stiffening of a tissue, usually with scar tissue, as in *multiple sclerosis* of the central nervous system and *atherosclerosis* of the blood vessels.

**sclerotome**   A group of mesodermal cells that arise from a somite in the fourth week of development and give rise to a segment of the vertebral column. *Compare* dermatome; myotome.

**sebaceous gland**   A holocrine gland that is usually associated with a hair follicle and produces an oily secretion, sebum. (fig. 5.10)

**sebum**   (SEE-bum) An oily secretion of the sebaceous glands that keeps the skin and hair pliable.

**secondary sex characteristic**   Any feature that develops at puberty, further distinguishes the sexes from each other, and is not required for reproduction but promotes attraction between the sexes; examples include the distribution of subcutaneous fat, pitch of the voice, female breasts, male facial hair, and apocrine scent glands.

**secondary sex organ**   An organ other than the ovaries and testes that is essential to reproduction, such as the external genitalia, internal genital ducts, and accessory reproductive glands.

**second-order neuron**   An interneuron that receives sensory signals from a first-order neuron and relays them to a more rostral destination in the central nervous system (usually the thalamus). (fig. 14.4) *See also* first-order neuron; third-order neuron.

**secretion**   **1.** A chemical released by a cell to serve a physiological function, such as a hormone or digestive enzyme, as opposed to a waste product. **2.** The process of releasing such a chemical, usually by exocytosis. *Compare* excretion.

**secretory vesicle**   An organelle that arises from the Golgi complex and carries a secretion to the cell surface to be released by exocytosis.

**section**   *See* histological section.

**selection pressure**   A force of nature that favors the reproduction of some individuals over others and thus drives the evolutionary process; includes climate, predators, diseases, competition, and food supply. Human anatomy and physiology reflect adaptations to selection pressures encountered in the evolutionary history of the species.

**SEM**   **1.** Scanning electron microscope. **2.** Scanning electron micrograph, a photograph taken with the scanning electron microscope. *Compare* TEM.

**semen**   The fluid ejaculated by a male, including spermatozoa and the secretions of the prostate gland and seminal vesicles.

**semicircular duct**   A ring-shaped, fluid-filled tube of the inner ear that detects angular acceleration of the head; enclosed in a bony passage called the semicircular canal. There are three semicircular ducts in each ear. (fig. 17.11)

**semilunar valve**   A valve that consists of crescent-shaped cusps, including the aortic and pulmonary valves of the heart and valves of the veins and lymphatic vessels. (fig. 20.7)

**senescence**   Degenerative changes that occur with age. *See also* aging.

**sense organ**   Any organ that is specialized to respond to stimuli and generate a meaningful pattern of nerve signals; may be microscopic and simple, such as a tactile corpuscle, or macroscopic and complex, such as the eye or ear; may respond to stimuli arising within the body or from external sources.

**sensory neuron**   A nerve cell that responds to a stimulus and conducts signals to the central nervous system; also called an *afferent neuron*. The axon of a sensory neuron is an *afferent nerve fiber*.

**septum**   An anatomical wall between two structures or spaces, such as the nasal septum or the interventricular septum of the heart.

**serosa**   *See* serous membrane.

**serous fluid**   (SEER-us) A watery fluid similar to blood serum, formed as a filtrate of the blood or tissue fluid or as a secretion of serous gland cells; moistens the serous membranes.

**serous gland**   A gland that secretes a relatively nonviscous product, such as the pancreas or a tear gland. *Compare* mucous gland.

**serous membrane**   A membrane such as the peritoneum, pleura, or pericardium that lines a body cavity or covers the external surfaces of the viscera; composed of a simple squamous mesothelium and a thin layer of areolar connective tissue.

**Sertoli cell**   *See* sustentacular cell.

**serum**   **1.** The fluid that remains after blood has clotted and the solids have been removed; essentially the same as blood plasma except for a lack of fibrinogen. Used as a vehicle for vaccines. **2.** Serous fluid.

**sex chromosomes**   The X and Y chromosomes, which determine the sex of an individual.

**shaft**   **1.** The midpart, or diaphysis, of a long bone. **2.** The external, cylindrical part of an organ such as a hair or the penis. *Compare* root.

**short bone**   A bone that is not markedly longer than it is wide, such as the bones of the wrist and ankle.

**sign**   An objective indication of disease that can be verified by any observor, such as cyanosis or a skin lesion. *Compare* symptom.

**simple columnar epithelium**   An epithelium composed of a single layer of cells that are noticeably taller than they are wide. (fig. 3.6)

**simple cuboidal epithelium**   An epithelium composed of a single layer of cells that are about equal in height and width; often, but not always, the cells appear squarish in tissue sections. (fig. 3.5)

**simple diffusion**   Net movement of particles from a place of high concentration to a place of low concentration (down their concentration gradient), resulting from their own spontaneous motion; may or may not involve passage through a cell membrane or other membranes such as dialysis tubing.

**simple squamous epithelium**   An epithelium composed of a single layer of thin, flat cells. (fig. 3.4)

**sinoatrial (SA) node**   A mass of autorhythmic cells near the surface of the right atrium of the heart that serves as the pacemaker of the cardiac rhythm.

**sinus**   **1.** An air-filled space in the cranium. (fig. 7.8) **2.** A modified, relatively dilated vein that lacks smooth muscle and is incapable of vasomotion, such as the dural sinuses of the cerebral circulation and coronary sinus of the heart. **3.** A small fluid-filled space in an organ such as the lymph nodes. **4.** Pertaining to the sinoatrial node of the heart, as in *sinus rhythm*.

**sinusoid**   An irrregularly shaped, blood-filled space in a tissue, with wide gaps between the endothelial cells; found in the liver, bone marrow, spleen, and some other organs. (fig. 22.9)

**skeletal muscle**   Striated voluntary muscle, almost all of which is attached to the bones. (fig. 10.1)

**skeletal system**   An organ system consisting of the bones, ligaments, bone marrow, periosteum, articular cartilages, and other tissues associated with the bones.

**smear**   A tissue prepared for microscopic study by wiping it across a slide, rather than by sectioning; for example, blood, bone marrow, spinal cord, and Pap smears.

**smooth endoplasmic reticulum**   Regions of endoplasmic reticulum characterized by tubular, branching cisternae lacking ribosomes; involved in detoxification, steroid synthesis, and in muscle, storage of calcium ions. *See also* endoplasmic reticulum; rough endoplasmic reticulum.

**smooth muscle**   Nonstriated involuntary muscle found in the walls of the blood vessels, many of the viscera, and other places. (fig. 3.27)

**sodium–potassium pump**   An active transport protein, which, in each cycle of activity, pumps three sodium ions out of a cell and two potassium ions into the cell, with the expenditure of one ATP.

**soma**   *See* cell body.

**somatic**   **1.** Pertaining to the body as a whole. **2.** Pertaining to the skin, bones, and skeletal muscles as opposed to the viscera. **3.** Pertaining to all cells other than germ cells.

**somatic motor fiber**   A nerve fiber that innervates skeletal muscle and stimulates its contraction, as opposed to autonomic fibers.

**somatic nervous system**   A division of the nervous system that includes afferent fibers mainly from the skin, muscles, and skeleton and efferent fibers to the skeletal muscles. *Compare* autonomic nervous system.

**somatosensory**   *See* somesthetic.

**somatotopy**   A point-for-point correspondence between the locations where stimuli arise and the locations in the brain or spinal cord to which the sensory signals project, thus producing in the CNS a sensory "map" of part of the body. (fig. 15.18)

**somesthetic**   **1.** Pertaining to widely distributed *general senses* in the skin, muscles, tendons, joint capsules, and viscera, as opposed to the *special senses* found in the head only; also called *somatosensory*. **2.** Pertaining to the cerebral cortex of the postcentral gyrus, which receives input from such receptors. *See also* general senses; special senses.

**somite**   One of the segmental blocks of embryonic mesoderm that begin to appear around day 20 and eventually number up to 44 pairs; a somite subdivides into three tissue masses—dermatome, myotome, and sclerotome, which give rise to certain aspects of the skin, muscles, and vertebrae. *See also* dermatome; myotome; sclerotome. (fig. 4.8)

**sonography**   Production of an image of the interior of the body by means of ultrasound. (fig. 1.3)

**special senses**   The senses of taste, smell, hearing, equilibrium, and vision, mediated by sense organs that are confined to the head and in most cases are relatively complex in structure. *See also* general senses.

**sperm**   **1.** A spermatozoon. **2.** The fluid ejaculated by the male; semen. Contains spermatozoa and glandular secretions.

**spermatogenesis**   (SPUR-ma-toe-JEN-eh-sis) The production of sperm cells through a series of mitotic and meiotic cell divisions; male gametogenesis.

**spermatozoon**   (SPUR-ma-toe-ZOE-on) A sperm cell; the male gamete. (fig. 26.8)

**sphincter**   (SFINK-tur) A ring of muscle that opens or closes an opening or passageway; found, for example, in the eyelids, around the urinary orifice, and at the junction of the stomach and duodenum. (fig. 24.11)

**spinal column**   *See* vertebral column.

**spinal cord**   The nerve cord that passes through the vertebral column and constitutes all of the central nervous system except the brain.

**spinal nerve**   Any of the 31 pairs of nerves that arise from the spinal cord and pass through the intervertebral foramina. (fig. 14.10)

**spindle**   **1.** An elongated structure that is thick in the middle and tapered at the ends (fusiform). **2.** A football-shaped complex of microtubules that guide the movement of chromosomes in mitosis and meiosis. (fig. 2.20) **3.** A stretch receptor in the skeletal muscles. (fig. 17.1)

**spine**   **1.** The vertebral column. **2.** A pointed process or sharp ridge on a bone, such as the styloid process of the cranium and spine of the scapula. (fig. 8.2)

**spinothalamic tract**   A bundle of nerve fibers that ascend the spinal cord and brainstem and carry signals to the thalamus for light touch, tickle, itch, heat, cold, pain, and pressure. (fig. 14.4)

**splanchnic**   (SPLANK-nic) Pertaining to the digestive tract.

**spongy bone**   A form of osseous tissue found in the interiors of flat, irregular, and short bones and the epiphyses of long bones, with a matrix that forms a porous network of plates and bars, enclosing connected channels filled with bone marrow; also called *cancellous bone*. *Compare* compact bone. (fig. 6.5)

**squamous**   Flat, scalelike, as in the surface epithelial cells of the epidermis and serous membranes. (fig. 3.12)

**stain**   A pigment applied to tissues to color and enhance the contrast between their nuclei, cytoplasm, extracellular material, and other tissue components.

**stem cell**   Any undifferentiated cell that can divide and differentiate into more functionally specific cell types such as blood cells and germ cells.

**stenosis**   The pathological constriction or narrowing of a tubular passageway or orifice of the body, such as the esophagus, uterine tube, or a valve orifice of the heart.

**stereocilium**   An unusually long, sometimes branched microvillus lacking the axoneme and motility of a true cilium; serves such roles as absorption in the epididymis and sensory transduction in the inner ear.

**sternal**   Pertaining to the breastbone or sternum, or the overlying region of the chest.

**stimulus**   A chemical or physical agent in a cell's surroundings that is capable of creating a physiological response in the cell, especially agents detected by sensory cells, such as chemicals, light, and pressure.

**strain**   The extent to which a bone or other structure is deformed when subjected to stress. *Compare* stress.

**stratified**   **1.** Layered. **2.** A class of epithelia in which there are two or more cell layers, with some cells resting atop others rather than contacting the basement membrane.

**stratified cuboidal epithelium**   An epithelium composed of two or more layers of cells in which the cells at the surface are about equal in height and width. (fig. 3.10)

**stratified squamous epithelium**   An epithelium composed of two or more layers of cells in which the cells at the surface are flat and thin. (fig. 3.9)

**stratum**   Any layer of tissue, such as the stratum corneum of the skin or stratum basalis of the uterus.

**stratum corneum**   The surface layer of dead keratinocytes of the skin. (fig. 5.1)

**stress**   **1.** A mechanical force applied to any part of the body; important in stimulating bone growth, for example. *Compare* strain. **2.** A condition in which any environmental influence disturbs the homeostatic equilibrium of the body and stimulates a physiological response, especially involving the increased secretion of hormones of the pituitary–adrenal axis.

**striated muscle**   Muscular tissue in which the cells exhibit striations; skeletal and cardiac muscle. *See also* striations.

**striations**   Alternating light and dark bands in skeletal and cardiac muscle produced by the pattern of overlapping myofilaments. (fig. 10.1)

**stroma**   The connective tissue framework of a gland, lymphatic organ, or certain other viscera, as opposed to the tissue (parenchyma) that performs the physiological functions of the organ.

**subcutaneous**   Beneath the skin.

**submucosa**   A layer of loose connective tissue deep to the mucosa of an organ. (fig. 24.2)

**submucosal plexus**   A plexus of parasympathetic neurons in the submucosa of the digestive tract, responsible for controlling glandular secretion by the mucosa and movements of the muscularis mucosae; also called the *Meissner plexus*.

**sulcus**   A groove in the surface of an organ, as in the cerebrum, the heart, or a bone. (fig. 15.1)

**superficial**   Relatively close to the surface; opposite of *deep*. For example, the ribs are superficial to the lungs.

**superior**   Higher than another structure or point of reference from the perspective of anatomical position; for example, the lungs are superior to the diaphragm.

**supination**   (SOO-pih-NAY-shun) A rotational movement of the forearm that turns the palm so that it faces upward or forward. (fig. 9.13)

**supine**   A position in which the body is lying face up.

**suprarenal**   Pertaining to the adrenal (suprarenal) glands, as in *suprarenal artery*.

**surfactant**   A chemical that interferes with the formation of hydrogen bonds between water molecules, and thus reduces the cohesion of water; in the lung, a mixture of phospholipid and protein that prevents the alveoli from collapsing during expiration.

**sustentacular cell**   **1.** A cell in the wall of a seminiferous tubule of the testis that supports and protects the germ cells and secretes the hormone inhibin; also called a *Sertoli cell*. (fig. 26.6) **2.** In many epithelia, such as taste buds and olfactory mucosa, any cell that supports and spaces the primary functional cells of the tissue; also called a *supporting cell*. (fig. 17.5)

**suture**   A line along which any two bones of the skull are immovably joined, such as the coronal suture between the frontal and parietal bones. (fig. 7.6)

**sympathetic nervous system**   A division of the autonomic nervous system that issues efferent fibers through the thoracic and lumbar nerves and usually exerts adrenergic effects on its target organs; includes a chain of paravertebral ganglia adjacent to the vertebral column, and the adrenal medulla. (fig. 16.4)

**symphysis**   (SIM-fih-sis) A joint in which two bones are held together by fibrocartilage; for example, between bodies of the vertebrae and between the right and left pubic bones. (fig. 8.6)

**symptom**   A subjective indication of disease that can be felt by the person who is ill but not objectively observed by another person, such as nausea or headache. *Compare* sign.

**synapse**   (SIN-aps) **1.** A junction at the end of an axon where it stimulates another cell. (fig. 13.11) **2.** A gap junction between two cardiac or smooth muscle cells at which one cell electrically stimulates the other; called an *electrical synapse*. (fig. 10.17)

**synaptic cleft**   A narrow space between the synaptic knob of an axon and the adjacent cell, across which a neurotransmitter diffuses. (fig. 13.11)

**synaptic knob**   The swollen tip at the distal end of an axon; the site of synaptic vesicles and neurotransmitter release. (fig. 13.11)

**synaptic vesicle**   A spheroid organelle in a synaptic knob; contains neurotransmitter. (fig. 13.11)

**syndrome**   A group of signs and symptoms that occur together and characterize a particular disease.

**synergist**   (SIN-ur-jist) A muscle that works with the agonist to contribute to the same overall action at a joint.

**synovial fluid**   (sih-NO-vee-ul) A lubricating fluid similar to egg white in consistency, found in the synovial joint cavities and bursae.

**synovial joint**   A point where two bones are separated by a narrow, encapsulated space filled with lubricating synovial fluid; most such joints are relatively mobile. Also called a *diarthrosis*. (fig. 9.4)

**systemic**   Widespread or pertaining to the body as a whole, as in *systemic circulation*.

**systemic circuit**   All blood vessels that convey blood from the left ventricle to all organs of the body and back to the right atrium of the heart; all of the cardiovascular system except the heart and pulmonary circuit. (fig. 20.1)

# T

**tactile**   Pertaining to the sense of touch.

**tail**   **1.** A slender process at one end of an organ, such as the tail of the pancreas or epididymis. (fig. 24.19) **2.** In vertebrate animals, an appendage that extends beyond the anus and contains part of the vertebral column; in humans, limited to the embryo. (fig. 4.8)

**target cell**   A cell acted upon by a nerve fiber or by a chemical messenger such as a hormone.

**tarsal**   **1.** Pertaining to the ankle. **2.** Pertaining to the margin of the eyelid.

**T cell**   A type of lymphocyte involved in nonspecific defense, humoral immunity, and cellular immunity; occurs in several forms including helper, cytotoxic, and suppressor T cells.

**TEM** **1.** Transmission electron microscope. **2.** Transmission electron micrograph, a photograph taken with the transmission electron microscope. *Compare* SEM.

**temporal** **1.** Pertaining to time, as in *temporal summation* in neurons. **2.** Pertaining to the side of the head, as in *temporal bone.*

**tendinous cords** Fibers that extend from the papillary muscles to the atrioventricular valve cusps in each ventricle of the heart, and serve to keep the valves from prolapsing during ventricular systole; also called *chordae tendineae.* (fig. 20.7)

**tendon** A collagenous band or cord associated with a muscle, usually attaching it to a bone and transferring muscular tension to it. *See also* aponeurosis.

**teratogen** Any agent capable of causing birth defects, including chemicals, infectious microorganisms, and radiation.

**teres** (TERR-eez) Round, cylindrical; used in the names of muscles and ligaments such as *teres major* and *ligamentum teres.*

**Terminologia Anatomica** A code of standard anatomical terms developed by an international committee of anatomists, the Federative Committee on Anatomical Terminology, and published in 1998; provides a worldwide standard for naming human structures.

**testis** The male gonad; produces spermatozoa and testosterone.

**thalamus** (THAL-uh-muss) The largest part of the diencephalon, located immediately inferior to the corpus callosum and bulging into each lateral ventricle; a point of synaptic relay of nearly all signals passing from lower levels of the CNS to the cerebrum. (fig. 15.11)

**theory** An explanatory statement, or set of statements, that concisely summarizes the state of knowledge on a phenomenon and provides direction for further study; for example, the fluid mosaic theory of the plasma membrane and the sliding filament theory of muscle contraction.

**thermoreceptor** A neuron specialized to respond to heat or cold, found in the skin and mucous membranes, for example.

**third-order neuron** An interneuron of the brain that receives sensory signals from a second-order neuron (often at the thalamus) and usually relays them to their final destination in the primary sensory cortex of the brain; in a few cases, a fourth-order neuron completes the pathway. (fig. 14.4) *See also* first-order neuron; second-order neuron.

**thoracic** Pertaining to the chest.

**thorax** A region of the trunk between the neck and the diaphragm; the chest.

**thymus** A lymphatic organ in the mediastinum superior to the heart; the site where T lymphocytes differentiate and become immunocompetent. (fig. 18.7)

**thyroid cartilage** A large shieldlike cartilage that encloses the larynx anteriorly and laterally and provides an anterior anchorage for the vocal cords and insertion for the infrahyoid muscles. (fig. 23.4)

**thyroid gland** An endocrine gland in the neck, partially encircling the trachea immediately inferior to the larynx. (fig. 18.8)

**tight junction** A zipperlike junction between epithelial cells that limits the passage of substances between them. (fig. 2.14)

**tissue** An aggregation of cells and extracellular materials, usually forming part of an organ and performing some discrete function for it; the four primary classes are epithelial, connective, muscular, and nervous tissue.

**tissue gel** The viscous colloid that forms the ground substance of many tissues; gets its consistency from hyaluronic acid or other glycosaminoglycans.

**trabecula** (tra-BEC-you-la) A thin plate or sheet of tissue, such as the calcified trabeculae of spongy bone or the fibrous trabeculae that subdivide a gland. (fig. 6.5)

**trachea** (TRAY-kee-uh) A cartilage-supported tube from the inferior end of the larynx to the origin of the primary bronchi; conveys air to and from the lungs; the "windpipe."

**tract** **1.** In the central nervous system, a bundle of nerve fibers with a similar origin, destination, and function, such as the corticospinal tracts of the spinal cord and commissural tracts of the cerebrum. **2.** A continuous anatomical pathway such as the digestive tract.

**transitional epithelium** A stratified epithelium of the urinary tract that is capable of changing thickness and number of cell layers from relaxed to stretched states. (fig. 3.11)

**transmembrane protein** A protein of the plasma membrane that penetrates all the way through the membrane and contacts the intracellular and extracellular fluids. (fig. 2.8)

**transmission electron microscope (TEM)** A microscope that uses an electron beam in place of light to form high-resolution, two-dimensional images of ultrathin slices of cells or tissues; capable of extremely high magnification. *Compare* scanning electron microscope.

**transport protein** *See* carrier.

**transverse plane** A plane that cuts perpendicular to the long axis of an organ or passes horizontally through a human body in anatomical position. (fig. A.3)

**transverse section** *See* cross section.

**transverse (T) tubule** A tubular extension of the plasma membrane of a muscle cell that conducts action potentials into the sarcoplasm and excites the sarcoplasmic reticulum. (fig. 10.8)

**trauma** Physical injury caused by external forces such as falls, gunshot wounds, motor vehicle accidents, or burns.

**trisomy-21** The presence of three copies of chromosome 21 instead of the usual two; causes variable degrees of mental retardation, a shortened life expectancy, and structural anomalies of the face and hands. Also called *Down syndrome.*

**trochanter** Either of two massive processes serving for muscle attachment at the proximal end of the femur.

**trunk** **1.** That part of the body excluding the head, neck, and limbs. **2.** A major blood vessel, lymphatic vessel, or nerve that gives rise to smaller branches; for example, the pulmonary trunk and spinal nerve trunks. (fig. 14.14)

**T tubule** *See* transverse tubule.

**tubercle** A rounded process on a bone, such as the greater tubercle of the humerus.

**tuberosity** A rough area on a bone, such as the tibial or ischial tuberosity.

**tubuloacinar gland** A gland in which secretory cells are found in both the tubular and acinar portions. (fig. 3.29)

**tunic** A layer that encircles or encloses an organ, such as the tunics of a blood vessel or eyeball; also called a *tunica.* (fig. 21.1)

**tympanic membrane** The eardrum.

## U

**ultrastructure** Structure at or near the molecular level, made visible by the transmission electron microscope.

**umbilical** (um-BIL-ih-cul) **1.** Pertaining to the cord that connects a fetus to the placenta. **2.** Pertaining to the navel (umbilicus).

**undifferentiated** Pertaining to a cell or tissue that has not yet attained a mature functional form; capable of differentiating into one or more specialized functional cells or tissues; for example, stem cells and embryonic tissues.

**unencapsulated nerve ending** *See* free nerve ending.

**unipotent** Pertaining to a stem cell that is capable of differentiating into only one type of mature cell, such as a spermatogonium able to produce only sperm, or an epidermal basal cell able to produce only keratinocytes.

**unit membrane** Any cellular membrane composed of a bilayer of phospholipids and embedded proteins. A single unit membrane forms the plasma membrane and encloses many organelles of a cell, whereas double unit membranes enclose the nucleus and mitochondria. (fig. 2.6)

**unmyelinated** Lacking a myelin sheath. (fig. 13.7)

**upper limb** The appendage that arises from the shoulder, consisting of the brachium from shoulder to elbow, the antebrachium from elbow to wrist, the wrist, and the hand; loosely called the *arm,* but that term properly refers only to the brachium.

**urea** The most abundant nitrogenous waste in urine, formed in the liver by a reaction between ammonia and carbon dioxide.

**urethra** The passage that conveys urine from the urinary bladder to the outside of the body; in males, it also conveys semen and acts as part of both the urinary and reproductive tracts.

**urinary system** An organ system specialized to filter the blood plasma, excrete waste products from it, and regulate the body's water, acid–base, and electrolyte balance.

**urogenital (U-G) system** Collective term for the reproductive and urinary tracts; also called the *genitourinary (G-U) system.*

**uterine tube** A duct that extends from the ovary to the uterus and conveys an egg or conceptus to the uterus; also called the *fallopian tube* or *oviduct.*

## V

**varicose vein** A vein that has become permanently distended and convoluted due to a loss of competence of the venous valves; especially common in the lower limb, esophagus, and anal canal (where they are called *hemorrhoids*).

**vas** (vass) (plural, *vasa*) A vessel or duct.

**vascular** Possessing or pertaining to blood vessels.

**vasoconstriction** (VAY-zo-con-STRIC-shun) The narrowing of a blood vessel due to muscular constriction of its tunica media.

**vasodilation** (VAY-zo-dy-LAY-shun) The widening of a blood vessel due to relaxation of the muscle of its tunica media and the outward pressure of the blood exerted against the wall.

**vasomotion** Any constriction or dilation of a blood vessel.

**vein** Any blood vessel that carries blood toward either atrium of the heart.

**ventral** Pertaining to the front of the body, the regions of the chest and abdomen; also called *anterior.*

**ventral root**   The branch of a spinal nerve that emerges from the anterior side of the spinal cord and carries efferent (motor) nerve fibers; also called the *anterior root.* (fig. 14.10)

**ventricle**   A fluid-filled chamber of the brain or heart. (figs. 15.4, 20.7)

**venule**   (VEN-yool) The smallest type of vein, receiving drainage from capillaries.

**vertebra**   (VUR-teh-bra) One of the bones of the vertebral column.

**vertebral column**   (VUR-teh-brul) A posterior series of usually 33 vertebrae; encloses the spinal cord, supports the skull and thoracic cage, and provides attachment for the limbs and postural muscles. Also called the *spine* or *spinal column.*

**vesicle**   **1.** A fluid-filled tissue sac such as the seminal vesicle. **2.** A fluid-filled spheroidal organelle such as a synaptic or secretory vesicle.

**vestibular apparatus**   Structures of the inner ear concerned with equilibrium and the perception of the movements and orientation of the head, including the semicircular ducts, utricle, and saccule.

**vestibule**   An anatomical receiving chamber; for example, the vestibule between the teeth and cheek, the space immediately inside the nostril, the space enclosed by the female labia majora, and the chamber of the inner ear to which the cochlea and semicircular ducts are attached.

**viscera**   (VISS-er-uh) (singular, *viscus*) The organs contained in the body cavities, such as the brain, heart, lungs, stomach, intestines, and kidneys.

**visceral**   **1.** Pertaining to the viscera. **2.** The inner or deeper layer of a two-layered membrane such as the pleura, pericardium, or glomerular capsule. (fig. A.8) *Compare* parietal.

**visceral muscle**   Single-unit smooth muscle found in the walls of blood vessels and the digestive, respiratory, urinary, and reproductive tracts.

**volar**   Pertaining to the anterior surfaces of the fingers (the surfaces continuous with the palmar skin).

**voluntary**   Under conscious control, as in skeletal muscle.

**vulva**   The female external genitalia; the mons pubis, labia majora, and all superficial structures between the labia majora; also called the *pudendum.* (fig. 26.21)

# W

**white matter**   White myelinated nervous tissue deep to the cortex of the cerebrum and cerebellum and superficial to the gray matter of the spinal cord. (fig. 15.4)

# X

**X chromosome**   The larger of the two sex chromosomes; males have one X chromosome and females have two in each somatic cell.

**xiphoid process**   (ZIFF-oyd, ZYE-foyd) A small pointed cartilaginous or bony process at the inferior end of the sternum. (fig. 7.27)

**X-ray**   **1.** A high-energy, penetrating electromagnetic ray with wavelengths in the range of 0.1 to 10 nm; used in diagnosis and therapy. **2.** A photograph made with X-rays; radiograph.

# Y

**Y chromosome**   The smaller of the two sex chromosomes, found only in males and having little if any genetic function except development of the testis.

**yolk sac**   An embryonic membrane that encloses the yolk in vertebrates that lay eggs and serves in humans as the origin of the first blood and germ cells. (fig. 4.5)

# Z

**zygomatic arch**   An arch of bone anterior to the ear, formed by the zygomatic processes of the temporal, frontal, and zygomatic bones; origin of the masseter muscle. (fig. 7.5)

**zygote**   A single-celled, fertilized egg.

*Key to pronunciation guides.*

Pronounce letter sequences in the pronunciation guides as follows:

| | |
|---|---|
| ah | as in father |
| al | as in pal |
| ay | as in day |
| bry | as in bribe |
| byu | as in bureau |
| c | as in calculus |
| cue | as in ridiculous |
| cuh | as in cousin |
| cul | as in bicycle |
| cus | as in custard |
| dew | as in dual |
| eez | as in ease |
| eh | as in feather |
| err | as in merry |
| fal | as in fallacy |
| few | as in fuse |
| ih | as in fit |
| iss | as in sister |
| lerr | as in lair |
| lur | as in learn |
| ma | as in man |
| mah | as in mama |
| me | as in meat |
| merr | as in merry |
| mew | as in music |
| muh | as in mother |
| na | as in corona |
| nerr | as in nary |
| new | as in news |
| nuh | as in nothing |
| odj | as in dodger |
| oe | as in go |
| oh | as in home |
| ol | as in alcohol |
| oll | as in doll |
| ose | as in gross |
| oss | as in floss |
| perr | as in pair |
| pew | as in pewter |
| ruh | as in rugby |
| serr | as in serration |
| sterr | as in stereo |
| sy | as in siren |
| terr | as in terrain |
| thee | as in theme |
| tirr | as in tyranny |
| uh | as in mother |
| ul | as in bicycle |
| verr | as in very |
| y | as in why |
| zh | as in measure |
| zy | as in enzyme |

# CREDITS

## Photographs

### Chapter 1

**Opener:** © SPL/Photo Researchers, Inc.; **1.1:** National Library of Medicine/Peter Arnold, Inc.; **1.2a:** © U.H.B. Trust/Tony Stone Images/Getty Images; **1.2b:** Custom Medical Stock Photo, Inc.; **1.2c:** © CNR/Phototake; **1.2d:** © Monte S. Buchsbaum, Mt. Sinai School of Medicine, New York, NY; **1.2e:** © Tony Stone Images/Getty Images; **1.3:** © Alexander Tsiaras/Photo Researchers, Inc.; **1.3(inset):** © Scott Camazine/Sue Trainor/Photo Researchers, Inc.; **1.6:** Art Resource; **1.7:** © SPL/Photo Researchers, Inc.; **1.8a:** Courtesy of the Armed Forces Institute of Pathology; **1.8b:** © Corbis-Bettmann; **1.9:** © Dr. Landrum Shettles; **1.11:** © Tim Davis/Photo Researchers, Inc.

### Atlas A

**Opener:** © Jean Claude Rev-ISM/Phototake; **A.1, A.3, A.5:** © McGraw-Hill Companies; **A.17:** © McGraw-Hill Companies/Rebecca Gray, photographer/Don Kincaid, dissections; **A.18:** © McGraw-Hill Companies; **A.19, A.20, A.21:** © McGraw-Hill Companies, Inc./Rebecca Gray, photographer/Don Kincaid, dissections; **A.22a:** © McGraw-Hill Companies, Inc./Dennis Strete, photographer; **A.22b:** © McGraw-Hill Companies, Inc./Rebecca Gray, photographer/Don Kincaid, dissections

### Chapter 2

**Opener:** © Dr. Donald Fawcett & Dr. Porter/Visuals Unlimited; **2.1a, b:** From Cell Ultrastructure by William A. Jensen and Roderick B. Park. © 1967 Wadsworth Publishing Co. Inc. Reprinted by permission of the publisher; **2.2a:** © Ed Reschke; **2.2b, c:** David Phillips/Photo Researchers, Inc.; **2.6a:** © Don Fawcett/Photo Researchers, Inc.; **2.12a:** © Ed Reschke; **2.12b:** Biophoto Associates/Photo Researchers, Inc.; **2.13a:** Custom Medical Stock Photo, Inc.; **2.13c:** © Biophoto Associates/Photo Researchers, Inc.; **2.15b(both):** © K.G. Murti/Visuals Unlimited; **2.15c:** © Biology Media/Photo Researchers, Inc.; **2.20(1-4):** © Ed Reschke; **2.21b:** © Biophoto Associates/Science Source/Photo Researchers, Inc.

### Chapter 3

**Opener:** © Dr. Andrejs Liepins/Photo Researchers, Inc.; **3.4a, 3.5a:** © The McGraw-Hill Companies, Inc./Dennis Strete, photographer; **3.6a:** © Lester V. Bergman/Corbis; **3.7a:** © The McGraw-Hill Companies, Inc./Dennis Strete, photographer; **3.9a:** © The McGraw-Hill Companies, Inc./Joe DeGrandis, photographer; **3.10a:** © Ed Reschke; **3.11a, b:** © The McGraw-Hill Companies, Inc./Dennis Strete, photographer ; **3.13:** The McGraw-Hill Companies, Inc./Rebecca Gray, photographer/Don Kincaid, dissections; **3.14a, 3.15a, 3.16a, 3.17a, 3.18a, 3.19a, 3.20a:** © The McGraw-Hill Companies, Inc./Dennis Strete, photographer; **3.21a:** © Ed Reschke/Peter Arnold, Inc.; **3.22a:** © The McGraw-Hill Companies, Inc./Dennis Strete, photographer; **3.23a, 3.24a, 3.25a, 3.26a:** © Ed Reschke; **3.27a:** © The McGraw-Hill Companies, Inc./Dennis Strete, photographer

### Chapter 4

**Opener:** Photo Researchers, Inc.; **4.8a:** © Landrum B. Shettles, MD; **4.8b, c:** Anatomical Travelogue/Photo Researchers, Inc.; **4.11a, b:** Dr. Kurt Benirschke; **4.12a:** © Martin Rotker/Phototake, Inc.; **4.12b:** Photo Researchers, Inc.; **4.12c:** © Landrum B. Shettles, MD; **4.14a:** Photo Researchers, Inc.; **4.14b:** Courtesy Mihalay Bartalos, from Bartalos 1967: Medical Cytogenetics, fig 10.2 pg. 154, Waverly, a division of Williams & Wilkins; **4.15:** Thalidomide UK

### Chapter 5

**Opener:** © Petit Format/Nestle/Photo Researchers, Inc.; **5.2(left):** © Tom McHugh/Photo Researchers, Inc.; **5.2(right):** © The McGraw-Hill Companies, Inc./Joe DeGrandis, photographer; **5.3b, 5.4a:** © The McGraw-Hill Companies, Inc./Dennis Strete, photographer; **5.5a(top):** © Tom & Dee Ann McCarthy/Corbis; **5.5a(bottom):** © The McGraw-Hill Companies, Inc./Dennis Strete, photographer; **5.5b(top):** © Creatas / PunchStock; **5.5b(bottom):** © The McGraw-Hill Companies, Inc./Dennis Strete, photographer; **5.6b:** © CBS/Phototake; **5.6c:** © P.M. Motta/SPL/Custom Medical Stock Photo, Inc.; **5.7(all) & 5.10a-c:** © The McGraw-Hill Companies, Inc./Joe DeGrandis, photographer; **5.13a:** © NMSB/Custom Medical Stock Photo, Inc.; **5.13b:** © Biophoto Associates/Photo Researchers, Inc.; **5.13c:** © James Stevenson/SPL/Photo Researchers, Inc.; **5.14a:** © SPL/Custom Medical Stock Photo, Inc.; **5.14b, c:** © John Radcliffe/Photo Researchers, Inc.

### Chapter 6

**Opener:** © The McGraw-Hill Companies, Inc./Joe DeGrandis, photographer; **6.5a, 6.5c:** © D.W. Fawcett/Visuals Unlimited; **6.5d:** Visuals Unlimited; **6.6:** © Robert Calentine/Visuals Unlimited; **6.9:** © Ken Saladin; **6.11:** Courtesy of Utah Valley Regional Medical Center, Department of Radiology; **6.12:** Victor Eroschenko; **6.13:** © The McGraw-Hill Companies, Inc./Joe DeGrandis, photographer; **6.15a:** © Doug Sizemore/Visuals Unlimited; **6.15b:** © SIU/Visuals Unlimited; **6.17a:** © Michael Klein/Peter Arnold, Inc.; **6.17b:** © Dr. P. Marzzi/Photo Researchers, Inc.; **6.17c:** © Yoav Levy/Phototake

### Chapter 7

**Opener:** Mehau Kulyk/Science Photo Library/Photo Researchers, Inc.; **7.30:** © Biophoto Associates/Photo Researchers, Inc.; **7.34:** © The McGraw-Hill Companies, Inc./Bob Coyle, photographer

### Chapter 8

**Opener:** © NHS Trust/Tony Stone Images/Getty Images; **8.16b:** © Walter Reiter/Phototake; **8.18a:** © SPL/Photo Researchers, Inc.; **8.18b:** Jim Stevenson/Science Photo Library/Photo Researchers, Inc.

### Chapter 9

**Opener:** CNRI/Science Photo Library/Photo Researchers, Inc.; **9.7a-9.22a:** © The McGraw-Hill Companies, Inc./Timothy L. Vacula, photographer; **9.24:** © The McGraw-Hill Companies, Inc./Rebecca Gray, photographer/Don Kincaid, dissections; **9.26b:** © L. Bassett/Visuals Unlimited; **9.27:** © Richard Anderson; **9.28a:** © SIU/Visuals Unlimited; **9.28b:** © Ron Mensching/Phototake; **9.29c:** © SIU/Peter Arnold, Inc.; **9.29d:** © Mehau Kulyk/SPL/Photo Researchers, Inc.

### Chapter 10

**Opener:** © Don W. Fawcett/Photo Researchers, Inc.; **10.1:** © Ed Reschke; **10.2c:** Victor Eroschenko; **10.10a:** Visuals Unlimited; **10.11a:** Victor B. Eichler; **10.16a:** University of Kansas Medical Center Research Institute Inc.; **10.16b:** © The McGraw-Hill Companies, Inc./Dennis Strete, photographer; **10.20:** Shady Awwad, MD

### Chapter 11

**Opener:** © Simon Fraser/Photo Researchers, Inc.; **11.2:** © The McGraw-Hill Companies, Inc./Rebecca Gray, photographer/Don Kincaid, dissections; **11.4(all):** © The McGraw-Hill Companies, Inc./Joe DeGrandis, photographer; **11.8:** © The McGraw-Hill Companies, Inc./Joe DeGrandis, photographer; **11.9:** © The McGraw-Hill Companies, Inc./Rebecca Gray, photographer/Don Kincaid, dissections; **11.12:** © imagingbody.com; **11.16:**

© The McGraw-Hill Companies, Inc./Rebecca Gray, photographer/Don Kincaid, dissections

## Chapter 12

**Opener:** Custom Medical Stock Photo Inc.; **12.4a, b:** © The McGraw-Hill Companies, Inc./Rebecca Gray, photographer/Don Kincaid, dissections; **12.13:** © The McGraw-Hill Companies, Inc./Rebecca Gray, photographer/Don Kincaid, dissections; **12.16a, b:** © The McGraw-Hill Companies, Inc./Photo and Dissection by Christine Eckel

## Atlas B

**Opener:** Scala/Art Resource, NY; **B.1 - B.15:** © The McGraw-Hill Companies, Inc./Joe DeGrandis, photographer

## Chapter 13

**Opener:** © SPL/Photo Researchers, Inc.; **13.7c:** © The McGraw-Hill Companies, Inc./Dr. Dennis Emery, Dept. of Zoology and Genetics, Iowa State University, photographer; **13.9:** © Omikron/Science Source/Photo Researchers, Inc.; **13.15:** Biophoto Associates/Photo Researchers, Inc.

## Chapter 14

**Opener:** © Ed Reschke; **14.6:** MMP/Campix; **14.11:** From: A Stereoscopic Atlas of Anatomy by David L. Bassett. Courtesy of Dr. Robert A. Chase, MD; **14.15:** © The McGraw-Hill Companies, Inc./Photo and Dissection by Christine Eckel

## Chapter 15

**Opener:** © CNRI/Photo Researchers, Inc.; **15.1c:** © The McGraw-Hill Companies, Inc./Rebecca Gray, photographer/Don Kincaid, dissections; **15.2b:** © The McGraw-Hill Companies, Inc./Dennis Strete, photographer; **15.4c:** © The McGraw-Hill Companies, Inc./Rebecca Gray, photographer/Don Kincaid, dissections; **15.20:** © Marcus E. Raichle, MD, Washington University School of Medicine, St. Louis, Missouri; **15.23a:** Photo Researchers, Inc.; **15.23b:** Custom Medical Stock Photo; **15.24:** © The McGraw-Hill Companies, Inc./Rebecca Gray, pho-

tographer/Don Kincaid, dissections; **15.31c:** © The McGraw-Hill Companies, Inc./Joe DeGrandis, photographer; **15.37a:** Custom Medical Stock Photo, Inc.; **15.37b:** © Simon Fraser / Photo Researchers, Inc.

## Chapter 16

**Opener & 16.3:** © From: A Stereoscopic Atlas of Anatomy by David L. Basett. Courtesy of Dr. Robert A. Chase, MD

## Chapter 17

**Opener:** Photo Researchers, Inc.; **17.5c:** © Ed Reschke; **17.9:** © The McGraw-Hill Companies, Inc./Joe DeGrandis, photographer; **17.13:** Quest/Science Photo Library/Photo Researchers, Inc.; **17.19:** © The McGraw-Hill Companies, Inc./Joe DeGrandis, photographer; **17.24:** © Ralph C. Eagle/MD/Photo Researchers, Inc.; **17.25a, b:** © Lisa Klancher; **17.27a:** © The McGraw-Hill Companies, Inc. /Joe DeGrandis, photographer; **17.28a:** Courtesy of Beckman Vision Center at UCSF School of Medicine/D. Copenhagen, S. Miltman, and M. Maglio

## Chapter 18

**Opener:** © P. Bagavandoss/Photo Researchers, Inc.; **18.5a:** © Dr. John D. Cunningham/Visuals Unlimited; **18.5b:** © Science VU/Visuals Unlimited; **18.8b:** © Robert Calentine/Visuals Unlimited; **18.9b:** © John Cunningham/Visuals Unlimited; **18.11c:** © Ed Reschke; **18.12a:** © Manfred Kage/Peter Arnold, Inc.; **18.12b:** © Ed Reschke; **18.15a, b:** From: Atlas of Pediatric Physical Diagnosis, 3/e by Zitelli & Davis, fig 9-17 1997, with permission from Elsevier; **18.16:** Courtesy Mihaly Bartalos, from M. Bartalos and T.A. Baramki, 1967 Medical Cytogenetics, Williams & Wilkins

## Chapter 19

**Opener:** © Juergen Berger, Max-Planck Institute/Photo Researchers, Inc.; **19.3b:** © Richard J. Poole/Polaroid International Photomicrography Competition; **19.3c:** © Don W. Fawcett/Visuals Unlimited; **19.7:** © SIU/Photo Researchers,

Inc.; **Table 19.4** (neutrophil): © Ed Reschke; (Eosinophil): © Ed Reschke; (Basophil): © Ed Reschke; (Monocyte): Michael Ross/Photo Researchers, Inc.; (Lymphocyte): Michael Ross/Photo Researchers, Inc.; **19.9a:** NIBSC/Science Photo Library/Photo Researchers, Inc.; **19.10:** © P. Motta/SPL/Photo Researchers, Inc.; **19.11:** © Meckes/Ottawa/Photo Researchers, Inc.

## Chapter 20

**Opener:** Gondelon/Photo Researchers, Inc; **20.5a, b:** © The McGraw-Hill Companies, Inc.; **20.6:** © imagingbody.com; **20.8b:** © The McGraw-Hill Companies, Inc.; **20.12a, b:** © Ed Reschke; **20.12c:** Custom Medical Stock Photo, Inc.; **20.14a:** © Ed Reschke

## Chapter 21

**Opener:** © Biophoto Associates/Photo Researchers, Inc.; **21.2a:** © The McGraw-Hill Companies, Inc./Dennis Strete, photographer; **21.2b:** © Wolf H. Fahrenbach/Visuals Unlimited; **21.3:** © Photo Researchers, Inc.; **21.6b:** Courtesy of S. McNutt

## Chapter 22

**Opener:** © Eye of Science/Photo Researchers, Inc.; **22.2:** © SPL/Custom Medical Stock Photo, Inc.; **22.4a:** © The McGraw-Hill Companies, Inc./Dennis Strete, photographer; **22.7:** Peter Arnold, Inc.; **22.8:** Custom Medical Stock Photo; **22.10b:** © The McGraw-Hill Companies/Dennis Strete, photographer; **22.11c:** Francis Leroy, Biocosmos/Photo Researchers, Inc.; **22.12b:** © The McGraw-Hill Companies/Rebecca Gray, photographer/Don Kincaid, dissections; **22.13b:** © Biophoto Associates/Photo Researchers, Inc.; **22.14a:** © The McGraw-Hill Companies, Inc./Dennis Strete, photographer **22.14c:** © The McGraw-Hill Companies, Inc./Photo by Dr. Alvin Telser; **22.16a, b:** © Dr. Don W. Fawcett/Visuals Unlimited

## Chapter 23

**Opener:** Peter Arnold, Inc.; **23.2a:** © The McGraw-Hill Companies, Inc./

Rebecca Gray, photographer/Don Kincaid, dissections; **23.3a, b:** © The McGraw-Hill Companies, Inc./Joe DeGrandis, photographer; **23.5a:** © Phototake; **23.5b:** © J Siebert/Custom Medical Stock Photo; **23.8:** Custom Medical Stock Photo, Inc.; **23.10a:** © imagingbody.com; **23.10b:** Visuals Unlimited; **23.12:** © imagingbody.com

## Chapter 24

**Opener:** © SPL/Photo Researchers, Inc.; **24.8:** © The McGraw-Hill Companies, Inc./Rebecca Gray, photographer/Don Kincaid, dissections; **24.10b** © The McGraw-Hill Companies, Inc./Dennis Strete, photographer ; **24.11b:** © The McGraw-Hill Companies, Inc./Rebecca Gray, photographer/Don Kincaid, dissections; **24.12d:** Visuals Unlimited; **24.13a, b:** CNRL/SPL/Photo Researchers, Inc.; **24.15a:** © Meckes/Ottawa/Photo Researchers, Inc.; **24.15b, 24.18b & 24.20b:** © The McGraw-Hill Companies, Inc./Dennis Strete, photographer

## Chapter 25

**Opener:** ©Science Photo Library/Photo Researchers, Inc.; **25.3a:** ©imagingbody.com; **25.8b:** Peter Arnold, Inc.; **25.9b:** © Don Fawcett/Photo Researchers, Inc.; **25.9c:** © Barry F. King/Biological Photo Service

## Chapter 26

**Opener:** © Simon Fraser/Photo Researchers, Inc.; **26.3a:** © The McGraw-Hill Companies, Inc./Dennis Strete, photographer; **26.4b:** © Ed Reschke; **26.8a:** Visuals Unlimited; **26.13c:** © The McGraw-Hill Companies, Inc./Rebecca Gray, photographer/Don Kincaid, dissections; **26.15a:** © Ed Reschke; **26.15b:** Manfred Kage/Peter Arnold, Inc.; **26.16:** Dr. Landrum Shettles; **26.17:** Photo Researchers, Inc.; **26.18:** © Ed Reschke; **26.22b:** From Anatomy & Physiology Revealed, © The McGraw-Hill Companies, Inc./The University of Toledo, photography and dissection; **26.22d:** Courtesy Tochikazu Nagato, from Cell and Tissue Research, 209: 1-10, 3, pg. 6, Springer-Verlag, 1980; **26.26a,b:** © SPL / Photo Researchers, Inc.

# N

# O

# P

# Lexicon of Biomedical Word Elements

**a-** no, not, without (atom, agranulocyte)
**ab-** away (abducens, abduction)
**acetabulo-** small cup (acetabulum)
**acro-** tip, extremity, peak (acromion, acromegaly, acrosome)
**ad-** to, toward, near (adsorption, adrenal)
**adeno-** gland (lymphadenitis, adenohypophysis, adenoids)
**aero-** air, oxygen (aerobic, anaerobe, aerophagy)
**af-** toward (afferent)
**ag-** together (agglutination)
**-al** pertaining to (parietal, pharyngeal, temporal)
**ala-** wing (ala nasi)
**albi-** white (albicans, linea alba, albino)
**algi-** pain (analgesic, myalgia)
**aliment-** nourishment (alimentary, hyperalimentation)
**allo-** other, different (allele, allosteric)
**amphi-** both, either (amphiphilic, amphiarthrosis)
**an-** without (anaerobic, anemic)
**ana-** 1. up, build up (anabolic, anaphylaxis). 2. apart (anaphase, anatomy). 3. back (anastomosis)
**andro-** male (androgen)
**angi-** vessel (angiogram, angioplasty, hemangioma)
**ante-** before, in front (antebrachium)
**antero-** forward (anterior, anterograde)
**anti-** against (antidiuretic, antibody, antagonist)
**apo-** from, off, away, above (apocrine, aponeurosis)
**arbor-** tree (arboreal, arborization)
**artic-** 1. joint (articulation). 2. speech (articulate)
**-ary** pertaining to (axillary, coronary)
**-ase** enzyme (polymerase, kinase, amylase)
**ast-, astro-** star (aster, astrocyte)
**-ata, -ate 1.** possessing (Chordata, corniculate).
   2. plural of -a (stomata, carcinomata)
**athero-** fat (atheroma, atherosclerosis)
**atrio-** entryway (atrium, atrioventricular)
**auri-** ear (auricle, auricular)
**auto-** self (autolysis, autoimmune)
**axi-** axis, straight line (axial, axoneme, axon)
**baro-** pressure (baroreceptor, hyperbaric)
**bene-** good, well (benign, beneficial)
**bi-** two (bipedal, biceps, bifid)
**bili-** bile (biliary, bilirubin)
**bio-** life, living (biology, biopsy, microbial)
**blasto-** precursor, bud, producer (fibroblast, osteoblast, blastomere)
**brachi-** arm (brachium, brachialis, antebrachium)
**brady-** slow (bradycardia, bradypnea)
**bucco-** cheek (buccal, buccinator)
**burso-** purse (bursa, bursitis)
**calc-** calcium, stone (calcified, calcaneus, hypocalcemia)
**callo-** thick (callus, callosum)
**calori-** heat (calorie, calorimetry, calorigenic)
**calv-, calvari-** bald, skull (calvaria)
**calyx** cup, vessel, chalice (glycocalyx, renal calyx)
**capito-** head (capitis, capitate, capitulum)
**capni-** smoke, carbon dioxide (hypocapnia)
**carcino-** cancer (carcinogen, carcinoma)
**cardi-** heart (cardiac, cardiology, pericardium)
**carot-** 1. carrot (carotene). 2. stupor (carotid)
**carpo-** wrist, seize (carpus, metacarpal)
**case-** cheese (caseosa, casein)
**cata-** down, break down (catabolism)
**cauda-** tail (cauda equina, caudate nucleus)
**-cel** little (pedicel)
**celi-** belly, abdomen (celiac)
**centri-** center, middle (centromere, centriole)
**cephalo-** head (cephalic, encephalitis)
**cervi-** neck, narrow part (cervix, cervical)
**chiasm-** cross, X (optic chiasm)
**choano-** funnel (choana)
**chole-** bile (cholecystokinin, cholelithotripsy)

**chondro-** 1. grain (mitochondria). 2. cartilage, gristle (chondrocyte, perichondrium)
**chromo-** color (dichromat, chromatin, cytochrome)
**chrono-** time (chronotropic, chronic)
**cili-** eyelash (cilium, supraciliary)
**circ-** about, around (circadian, circumduction)
**cis-** cut (incision, incisor)
**cisterna-** reservoir (cisterna chyli)
**clast-** break down, destroy (osteoclast)
**clavi-** hammer, club (clavicle, supraclavicular)
**-cle** little (tubercle, corpuscle)
**cleido-** clavicle (sternocleidomastoid)
**cnemo-** lower leg (gastrocnemius)
**co-** together (coenzyme, cotransport)
**collo-** 1. hill (colliculus). 2. glue (colloid, collagen)
**contra-** opposite (contralateral)
**corni-** horn (cornified, corniculate, cornu)
**corono-** crown (coronary, corona, coronal)
**corpo-** body (corpus luteum, corpora quadrigemina)
**corti-** bark, rind (cortex, cortical)
**costa-** rib (intercostal, subcostal)
**coxa-** hip (os coxae, coxal)
**crani-** helmet (cranium, epicranius)
**cribri-** sieve, strainer (cribriform, area cribrosa)
**crino-** separate, secrete (holocrine, endocrinology)
**crista-** crest (crista ampullaris, mitochondrial crista)
**crito-** to separate (hematocrit)
**cruci-** cross (cruciate ligament)
**-cule, -culus** small (canaliculus, trabecula, auricular)
**cune-** wedge (cuneiform, cuneatus)
**cutane-, cuti-** skin (subcutaneous, cuticle)
**cysto-** bladder (cystitis, cholecystectomy)
**cyto-** cell (cytology, cytokinesis, monocyte)
**de-** down (defecate, deglutition, dehydration)
**demi-** half (demifacet, demilune)
**den-, denti-** tooth (dentition, dens, dental)
**dendro-** tree, branch (dendrite, oligodendrocyte)
**derma-, dermato-** skin (ectoderm, dermatology, hypodermic)
**desmo-** band, bond, ligament (desmosome, syndesmosis)
**dia-** 1. across, through, separate (diaphragm, dialysis).
   2. day (circadian)
**dis-** 1. apart (dissect, dissociate). 2. opposite, absence (disinfect, disability)
**diure-** pass through, urinate (diuretic, diuresis)
**dorsi-** back (dorsal, dorsum, latissimus dorsi)
**duc-** to carry (duct, adduction, abducens)
**dys-** bad, abnormal, painful (dyspnea, dystrophy)
**e-** out (ejaculate, eversion)
**-eal** pertaining to (hypophyseal, arboreal)
**ec-, ecto-** outside, out of, external (ectopic, ectoderm, splenectomy)
**ef-** out of (efferent, effusion)
**-el, -elle** small (fontanel, organelle, micelle)
**electro-** electricity (electrocardiogram, electrolyte)
**em-** in, within (embolism, embedded)
**emesi-, emeti-** vomiting (emetic, hyperemesis)
**-emia** blood condition (anemia, hypoxemia, hypovolemia)
**en-** in, into (enzyme, parenchyma)
**encephalo-** brain (encephalitis, telencephalon)
**enchymo-** poured in (mesenchyme, parenchyma)
**endo-** within, into, internal (endocrine, endocytosis)
**entero-** gut, intestine (mesentery, myenteric)
**epi-** upon, above (epidermis, epiphysis, epididymis)
**ergo-** work, energy, action (allergy, adrenergic)
**eryth-, erythro-** red (erythema, erythrocyte)
**esthesio-** sensation, feeling (anesthesia, somesthetic)
**eu-** good, true, normal, easy (eukaryote, eupnea, aneuploidy)
**exo-** out (exopeptidase, exocytosis, exocrine)
**facili-** easy (facilitated)
**fasci-** band, bundle (fascia, fascicle)

**fenestr-** window (fenestrated, fenestra vestibuli)
**fer-** to carry (efferent, uriniferous)
**ferri-** iron (ferritin, transferrin)
**fibro-** fiber (fibroblast, fibrosis)
**fili-** thread (myofilament, filiform)
**flagello-** whip (flagellum)
**foli-** leaf (folic acid, folia)
**-form** shape (cuneiform, fusiform)
**fove-** pit, depression (fovea)
**funiculo-** little rope, cord (funiculus)
**fusi-** 1. spindle (fusiform). 2. pour out (perfusion)
**gamo-** marriage, union (monogamy, gamete)
**gastro-** belly, stomach (digastric, gastrointestinal)
**-gen, -genic, -genesis** producing, giving rise to (pathogen, carcinogenic, glycogenesis)
**genio-** chin (geniohyoid, genioglossus)
**germi-** 1. sprout, bud (germinal, germinativum).
   2. microbe (germicide)
**gero-** old age (progeria, geriatrics, gerontology)
**gesto-** 1. to bear, carry (ingest). 2. pregnancy (gestation, progesterone)
**glia-** glue (neuroglia, microglia)
**globu-** ball, sphere (globulin, hemoglobin)
**glom-** ball (glomerulus)
**glosso-** tongue (hypoglossal, glossopharyngeal)
**glyco-** sugar (glycogen, glycolysis, hypoglycemia)
**gono-** 1. angle, corner (trigone). 2. seed, sex cell, generation (gonad, oogonium, gonorrhea)
**gradi-** walk, step (retrograde, gradient)
**-gram** recording of (sonogram, electrocardiogram)
**-graph** recording instrument (sonograph, electrocardiograph)
**-graphy** recording process (sonography, radiography)
**gravi-** severe, heavy (gravid, myasthenia gravis)
**gyro-** turn, twist (gyrus)
**hallu-** great toe (hallux, hallucis)
**hemi-** half (hemidesmosome, hemisphere, hemizygos)
**-hemia** blood condition (polycythemia)
**hemo-** blood (hemophilia, hemoglobin, hematology)
**hetero-** different, other, various (heterotrophic, heterozygous)
**histo-** tissue, web (histology, histone)
**holo-** whole, entire (holistic, holocrine)
**homeo-** constant, unchanging, uniform (homeostasis, homeothermic)
**homo-** same, alike (homologous, homozygous)
**hyalo-** clear, glassy (hyaline, hyaluronic acid)
**hydro-** water (dehydration, hydrolysis, hydrophobic)
**hyper-** above, above normal, excessive (hyperkalemia, hypertonic)
**hypo-** below, below normal, deficient (hypogastric, hyponatremia, hypophysis)
**-ia** condition (anemia, hypocalcemia, osteomalacia)
**-ic** pertaining to (isotonic, hemolytic, antigenic)
**-icle, -icul** small (ossicle, canaliculus, reticular)
**ilia-** flank, loin (ilium, iliac)
**-illa, -illus** little (bacillus)
**-in** protein (trypsin, fibrin, globulin)
**infra-** below (infraspinous, infrared)
**ino-** fiber (inotropic, inositol)
**insulo-** island (insula, insulin)
**inter-** between (intercellular, intercalated, intervertebral)
**intra-** within (intracellular, intraocular)
**iono-** ion (ionotropic, cationic)
**ischi-** to hold back (ischium, ischemia)
**-ism** 1. process, state, condition (metabolism, rheumatism). 2. doctrine, belief, theory (holism, reductionism, naturalism)
**iso-** same, equal (isometric, isotonic, isomer)
**-issimus** most, greatest (latissimus, longissimus)
**-ite** little (dendrite, somite)
**-itis** inflammation (dermatitis, gingivitis)

**jug-** to join (conjugated, jugular)
**juxta-** next to (juxtamedullary, juxtaglomerular)
**kali-** potassium (hypokalemia)
**karyo-** seed, nucleus (megakaryocyte, karyotype, eukaryote)
**kerato-** horn (keratin, keratinocyte)
**kine-** motion, action (kinetic, kinase, cytokinesis)
**labi-** lip (labium, levator labii)
**lacera-** torn, cut (foramen lacerum, laceration)
**lacrimo-** tear, cry (lacrimal gland, puncta lacrimalia)
**lacto-** milk (lactose, lactation, prolactin)
**lamina-** layer (lamina propria, laminar flow)
**latero-** side (bilateral, ipsilateral)
**lati-** broad (fascia lata, latissimus dorsi)
**-lemma** husk (sarcolemma, neurilemma)
**lenti-** lens (lentiform)
**-let** small (platelet)
**leuko-** white (leukocyte, leukemia)
**levato-** to raise (levator labii, elevation)
**ligo-** to bind (ligand, ligament)
**line-** line (linea alba, linea nigra)
**litho-** stone (otolith, lithotripsy)
**-logy** study of (histology, physiology, hematology)
**lucid-** light, clear (stratum lucidum, zona pellucida)
**lun-** moon, crescent (lunate, lunule, semilunar)
**lute-** yellow (macula lutea, corpus luteum)
**lyso-, lyto-** split apart, break down (lysosome, hydrolysis, electrolyte, hemolytic)
**macro-** large (macromolecule, macrophage)
**macula-** spot (macula lutea, macula sacculi, macula densa)
**mali-** bad (malignant, malocclusion, malformed)
**malle-** hammer (malleus, malleolus)
**mammo-** breast (mammary, Mammalia)
**mano-** hand (manus, manipulate)
**manubri-** handle (manubrium)
**masto-** breast (mastoid, gynecomastia)
**medi-** middle (medial, mediastinum, intermediate)
**medullo-** marrow, pith (medulla)
**mega-** large (megakaryocyte, hepatomegaly)
**melano-** black (melanin, melanocyte, melancholy)
**meno-** month (menstruation, menopause)
**mento-** chin (mental, mentalis)
**mero-** part, segment (isomer, centromere, merocrine)
**meso-** in the middle (mesoderm, mesenchyme, mesentery)
**meta-** beyond, next in a series (metaphase, metacarpal, metopic)
**metabolo-** change (metabolism, metabolite)
**-meter** measuring device (hemocytometer, spirometer)
**metri-** 1. length, measure (isometric, emmetropic). 2. uterus (endometrium)
**micro-** small (microscopic, microcytic, microglia)
**mito-** thread, filament (mitochondria, mitosis)
**mono-** one (monocyte, monogamy, mononucleosis)
**morpho-** form, shape, structure (morphology, amorphous)
**muta-** change (mutagen, mutation)
**myelo-** 1. spinal cord (poliomyelitis, myelin). 2. bone marrow (myeloid, myelocytic)
**myo-, mysi-** muscle (myoglobin, myosin, epimysium)
**natri-** sodium (hyponatremia, natriuretic)
**neo-** new (neonatal, gluconeogenesis)
**nephro-** kidney (nephron, hydronephrosis, mesonephros)
**neuro-** nerve (aponeurosis, neurosoma, neurology)
**nucleo-** nucleus, kernel (nucleolus, nucleic acid)
**oo-** egg (oogenesis, oocyte)
**ob-** 1. life (aerobic, microbe). 2. against, toward, before (obstetrics, obturator, obstruction)
**oculo-** eye (oculi, oculomotor)
**odonto-** tooth (odontoblast, periodontal, heterodonty)
**-oid** like, resembling (colloid, sigmoid, ameboid)
**-ole** small (arteriole, bronchiole, nucleolus)
**oligo-** few, a little, scanty (oligopeptide, oligodendrocyte, oliguria)
**-oma** tumor, mass (carcinoma, hematoma)
**omo-** shoulder (omohyoid, acromion)

**onycho-** nail, claw (hyponychium, onychomycosis)
**op-** vision (optics, myopia, photopic)
**-opsy** viewing, to see (biopsy, rhodopsin)
**or-** mouth (oral, orbicularis oris)
**orbi-** circle (orbicularis, orbit)
**organo-** tool, instrument (organ, organelle)
**ortho-** straight (orthopnea, orthodontics, orthopedics)
**-ose** 1. full of (adipose). 2. sugar (sucrose, glucose)
**-osis** 1. process (osmosis, exocytosis). 2. condition, disease (cyanosis, thrombosis). 3. increase (leukocytosis)
**osmo-** push (osmosis, chemiosmotic)
**osse-, oste-** bone (osseous, osteoporosis)
**oto-** ear (otolith, otitis, parotid)
**-ous** 1. full of (nitrogenous, edematous). 2. pertaining to (mucous, nervous). 3. like, characterized by (squamous, filamentous)
**ovo-** egg (ovum, ovary, ovulation)
**oxy-** 1. oxygen (hypoxia, oxyhemoglobin). 2. sharp, quick (oxytocin)
**palli-** pale (pallor, globus pallidus)
**palpebro-** eyelid (palpebrae)
**pan-** all (panhypopituitarism, pancreas)
**panni-** cloth, rag (pannus, panniculus)
**papillo-** nipple (papilla, papillary)
**par-** birth (postpartum, parturition, multiparous)
**para-** next to (parathyroid, parotid)
**parieto-** wall (parietal)
**patho-** 1. disease (pathology, pathogen). 2. feeling (sympathetic)
**pecto-** 1. chest (pectoral, pectoralis). 2. comblike (pectineus)
**pedi-** 1. foot (bipedal, pedicle). 2. child (pediatrics)
**pelvi-** basin (pelvis, pelvic)
**-penia** deficiency (leukopenia, thrombocytopenia)
**penna-** feather (unipennate, bipennate)
**peri-** around (periosteum, peritoneum, periodontal)
**perone-** fibula (peroneus tertius, peroneal nerve)
**phago-** eat (phagocytosis, macrophage)
**philo-** loving, attracted to (hydrophilic, amphiphilic)
**phobo-** fearing, repelled by (hydrophobic)
**phor-** to carry, bear (diaphoresis, electrophoresis)
**phragm-** partition (diaphragm)
**phreno-** diaphragm (phrenic nerve)
**physio-** nature, natural cause (physiology, physician, physics)
**-physis** growth (diaphysis, hypophysis)
**pilo-** hair (piloerection)
**pino-** drink, imbibe (pinocytosis)
**planto-** sole of foot (plantaris, plantar wart)
**plasi-** growth (hyperplasia)
**plasm-** shaped, molded (cytoplasm, endoplasmic)
**plasti-** form (thromboplastin)
**platy-** flat (platysma)
**pnea-** breath, breathing (eupnea, dyspnea)
**pneumo-** air, breath, lung (pneumonia, pneumothorax)
**podo-** foot (pseudopod, podocyte)
**poies-** forming (hemopoiesis, erythropoietin)
**poly-** many, much, excessive (polypeptide, polyuria)
**primi-** first (primary, primipara, primitive)
**pro-** 1. before, in front, first (prokaryote, prophase, prostate). 2. promote, favor (progesterone, prolactin)
**pseudo-** false (pseudopod)
**psycho-** mind (psychosis, psychosomatic)
**ptero-, pterygo-** wing (pterygoid)
**-ptosis** dropping, falling, sagging (apoptosis, nephroptosis)
**puncto-** point (puncta)
**pyro-** fire (pyrogen)
**quadri-** four (quadriceps, quadratus)
**quater-** fourth (quaternary)
**radiat-** radiating (corona radiata)
**rami-** branch (ramus)
**recto-** straight (rectus abdominis, rectum)
**reno-** kidney (renal, renin)
**reti-** network (reticular, rete testis)
**retinac-** retainer, bracelet (retinaculum)

**retro-** behind, backward (retroperitoneal, retrovirus)
**rhombo-** rhombus (rhomboideus, rhombencephalon)
**rubo-, rubro-** red (bilirubin, rubrospinal)
**rugo-** fold, wrinkle (ruga, corrugator)
**sacculo-** little sac (saccule)
**sarco-** flesh, muscle (sarcoplasm, sarcomere)
**scala-** staircase (scala tympani)
**sclero-** hard, tough (sclera, sclerosis)
**scopo-** see (microscope, endoscopy)
**secto-** cut (section, dissection)
**semi-** half (semilunar)
**sepsi-** infection (asepsis, septicemia)
**-sis** process (diapedesis, amniocentesis)
**sole-** sandal, sole of foot, flatfish (sole, soleus)
**soma-, somato-** body (somatic, somatotropin)
**spheno-** wedge (sphenoid)
**spiro-** breathing (inspiration, spirometry)
**splanchno-** viscera (splanchnic)
**spleno-** 1. bandage (splenius capitis). 2. spleen (splenic artery)
**squamo-** scale, flat (squamous, desquamation)
**stasi-, stati-** put, remain, stay the same (hemostasis, homeostatic)
**steno-** narrow (stenosis)
**ster-, stereo-** solid, three-dimensional (steroid, stereoscopic)
**sterno-** breast, chest (sternum, sternocleidomastoid)
**stria-** stripe (striated, corpus striatum)
**sub-** below (subcutaneous, subclavicular)
**sulc-** furrow, groove (sulcus)
**supra-** above (supraspinous, supraclavicular)
**sura-** calf of leg (triceps surae)
**sym-** together (sympathetic, symphysis)
**syn-** together (synostosis, syncytium)
**tachy-** fast (tachycardia, tachypnea)
**tarsi-** ankle (tarsus, metatarsal)
**tecto-** roof, cover (tectorial membrane, tectum)
**telo-** last, end (telophase, telencephalon, telodendria)
**tempo-** time (temporal)
**terti-** third (tertiary)
**theli-** nipple, female, tender (epithelium, polythelia)
**thermo-** heat (thermogenesis, endothermic)
**thrombo-** blood clot (thrombosis, thrombin)
**thyro-** shield (thyroid, thyrohyoid)
**-tion** process (circulation, pronation)
**toci-** birth (oxytocin)
**tomo-** 1. cut (tomography, atom, anatomy). 2. segment (dermatome, myotome, sclerotome)
**tono-** force, tension (isotonic, tonus, myotonia)
**topo-** place, position (isotope, ectopic)
**trabo-** plate (trabecula)
**trans-** across (transpiration, transdermal)
**trapezi-** 1. table, grinding surface (trapezium). 2. trapezoid (trapezius)
**tri-** three (triceps, triglyceride)
**tricho-** hair (peritrichial)
**trocho-** wheel, pulley (trochlea)
**troph-** 1. food, nourishment (heterotrophic, trophoblast). 2. growth (dystrophy, hypertrophy)
**tropo-** to turn, change (metabotropic, gonadotropin)
**tunica-** coat (tunica intima, tunica vaginalis)
**tympano-** drum, eardrum (tympanic, tensor tympani)
**-ul** small (trabecula, tubule, capitulum, glomerulus)
**-uncle, -unculus** small (homunculus, caruncle)
**uni-** one (unipennate, unipolar)
**uri-** urine (glycosuria, urinalysis, diuretic)
**utriculo-** little bag (utriculus)
**vagino-** sheath (invaginate, tunica vaginalis)
**vago-** wander (vagus)
**vaso-** vessel (vascular, vas deferens, vasa recta)
**ventro-** belly, lower part (ventral, ventricle)
**vermi-** worm (vermis)
**vertebro-** spine (vertebrae, Vertebrata)
**vesico-** bladder, blister (vesical, vesicular)
**villo-** hair, hairy (microvillus)
**vitre-** glass (in vitro, vitreous humor)
**vivi-** life, alive (in vivo, revive)
**zygo-** union, join, mate (zygomatic, zygote, azygos)

Anatomy & Physiology | REVEALED® is a unique multimedia study aid designed to help you learn and review human anatomy using cadaver specimens. Key features that will maximize your study time and improve your grade are detailed below!

**Capture and save any image.**

## Dissection

Detailed photographs of prosected cadavers are blended together with a state-of-the-art layering technique to provide a uniquely interactive dissection experience.

**Use the layer controls to peel away structures of the human body. Adjust the layers to see relationships between structures.**

**Every structure includes detailed information and an audio pronunciation.**

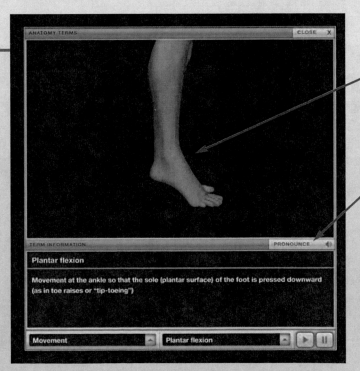

**Structures can be pinned and labeled, just like in a real dissection lab.**

## Anatomy Terms

This audiovisual glossary makes learning the language of anatomy easy. Use this feature to review:

- Directional terms
- Regional terms
- Planes of section
- Terms of movement
- System-specific terms

**Each term is demonstrated with an illustration or animation.**

**Audio pronunciations help you learn the correct way to say each word.**

# The Ultimate Digital Study Tool

McGraw Hill

## Self-Test ✓

A comprehensive quizzing section lets you test your ability to identify anatomical structures in a simulated practical exam. Additional quizzes provide review of physiology concepts and the functions or features of specific structures.

**Diagnostics displayed throughout the test track your progress.**

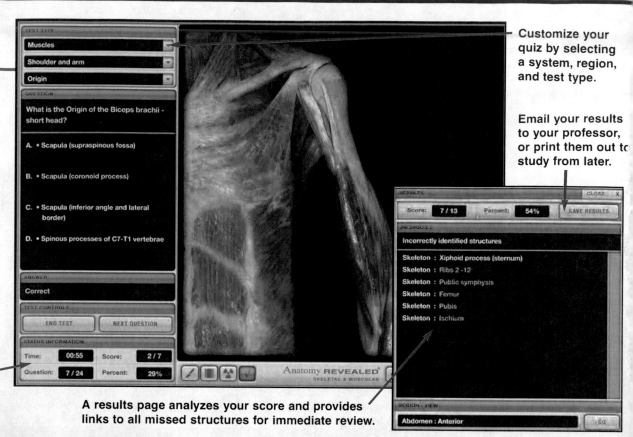

**Customize your quiz by selecting a system, region, and test type.**

**Email your results to your professor, or print them out to study from later.**

**A results page analyzes your score and provides links to all missed structures for immediate review.**

## Animation

Compelling animations help clarify anatomical relationships or explain difficult physiological concepts.

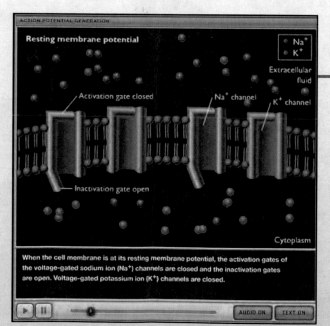

**Pin and label important structures.**

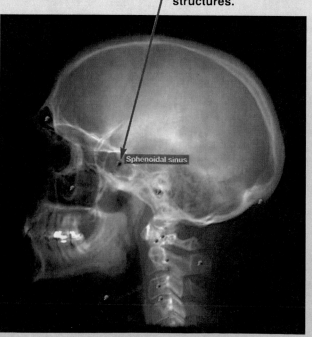

## Imaging ☢

Labeled X-ray, MRI, and CT images help you learn to recognize key anatomical structures as seen through various medical imaging techniques.